Alternating-Current Circuits

INTRODUCTORY ELECTRICAL ENGINEERING
By George F. Corcoran and Henry R. Reed

ALTERNATING-CURRENT CIRCUITS
By Russell M. Kerchner and George F. Corcoran
Fourth Edition

ELECTRICAL ENGINEERING EXPERIMENTS
By Henry R. Reed and George F. Corcoran

ELECTRONICS
By George F. Corcoran and Henry W. Price

JOHN WILEY & SONS, INC., NEW YORK · LONDON

Alternating-Current Circuits

4th edition

RUSSELL M. KERCHNER

Professor and Head of Electrical Engineering Department, Kansas State University

GEORGE F. CORCORAN

Professor and Chairman of Electrical Engineering Department, University of Maryland

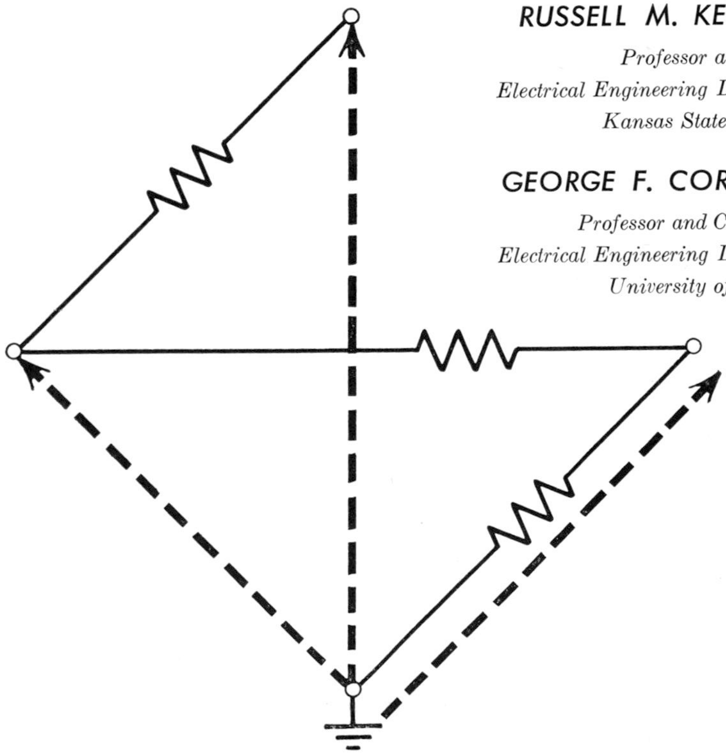

FOURTH EDITION

Second Printing, November, 1962

Library of Congress Catalog Card Number: 60-11724

Printed in the United States of America

Preface

The approach to alternating-current circuits which has been employed in previous editions has been found to be reasonably satisfactory in introducing the subject to students of electrical engineering and physics and has therefore been retained in this edition. Numerous additions and modifications have been made throughout the book where experience has shown the need for improvement. The changes have been made with a view toward making the book more understandable to the student. An introductory chapter on network concepts has been added in order to give the student a deeper insight into the general methods of network analysis. Network variables, topology, and duality are considered. For those students who have a knowledge of Kirchhoff's laws and some experience with solving networks employing direct currents it is possible to begin study of this edition with Chapter II. However most students will likely find Chapter I a good review and many will find in it a considerable amount of material which is new and of value in a study of more advanced network theory.

Because of the great advances in electronics and the consequent need for additional circuit theory, nearly all students now follow the first course in alternating-current-circuit theory with a rather intensive course in network theory and in many instances with some network synthesis. For courses of this kind some knowledge of complex frequency and poles and zeros is highly desirable. These subjects have been introduced in this edition, first in Chapter V where steady-state analysis is considered and again in Chapter XIV where the transient analysis of the *RLC* series circuit is treated.

In order not to interfere with the vector terminology of electromagnetic theory the term *phasor* has been adopted for a time-varying quantity which is handled by vector methods. The change from vector to phasor diagram is made in Chapter IV although as used in this book the distinction is unnecessary. To many electrical engineers a vector diagram will always be a vector diagram.

By certain reductions and eliminations, the book has been held to approximately the same size even though a considerable amount of material has been added. Some new kinds of problems have also been included at the end of some of the chapters.

Russell M. Kerchner
George F. Corcoran

June, 1960

Preface to First Edition

This book is primarily written as a textbook for courses in alternating-current circuits as offered to junior electrical engineering students by most engineering colleges. It is assumed that the student has finished the usual courses in differential and integral calculus, or at least has some knowledge of differentiation and integration. An endeavor has been made to arrange the materials in a logical sequence so as to lead the student gradually from the simple to the more complex analyses in alternating-current circuits.

The method of presentation is an outgrowth of the teaching experience which the authors have had at several institutions, and an effort has been made to produce a teachable book. In carrying out this idea, free use has been made of illustrative examples and line drawings. Also a number of illustrative oscillograms of actual circuit performance have been included. In order that many of these oscillograms may be made the basis of further study, rather complete legends have been given.

Problems for which answers are given have been included in many places in the text material immediately following the presentation of certain principles. These problems are primarily intended as exercises which will help the student determine for himself whether he has a workable knowledge of the principles involved. The sequence of the problems at the end of the chapters corresponds to the order in which the text material is presented. The end-of-chapter problems, therefore, form a suitable list from which regular assignments may be made.

To make the book more useful to the student, and to the practicing engineer, it was deemed desirable to include a greater amount of material than can be covered in the average college course as now given, provided such subject matter could be omitted without loss in continuity and without affecting the students' preparation for studying succeeding chapters.

With the exception of the fundamentals of symmetrical components in Chapter XII which are necessary to understand Chapter XIII, any part or all of any chapter after Chapter IX can be omitted without affecting the students' preparation for studying succeeding chapters.

Beginning with Chapter X the remainder of the text is, for the most part, made up of extensions and applications of the principles studied in the first nine chapters. In consequence, selected parts of the last five chapters may be studied to the extent of the time available. Chapter VIII will also be found to contain a rather large amount of material that is of interest to students and desired by a number of teachers but may be omitted without affecting the reader's preparation for understanding subsequent chapters.

We acknowledge our indebtedness to the earlier writers in this field and to our many colleagues who have assisted and encouraged us in the production of this book. In particular we wish to thank Mr. J. L. Potter for his advice and assistance.

R. M. K.
G. F. C.

MANHATTAN, KANSAS
IOWA CITY, IOWA
April, 1938

Contents

I	*Network Concepts*	1
II	*Instantaneous Current, Voltage and Power*	45
III	*Effective Current and Voltage — Average Power*	85
IV	*Phasor Algebra (As Applied to A-C Circuit Analysis)*	107
V	*Sinusoidal Single-Phase Circuit Analysis*	142
VI	*Non-Sinusoidal Waves*	223
VII	*Coupled Circuits*	273
VIII	*Balanced Polyphase Circuits*	325
IX	*Unbalanced Polyphase Circuits*	373
X	*Transmission Line Calculations*	409
XI	*Electric Wave Filters*	435
XII	*Symmetrical Components*	489

XIII *Power System Short-Circuit Calculations* 522

XIV *Transient Conditions* 549

Index 591

chapter I Network Concepts

Most of this textbook will be devoted to the analysis of networks which are energized with sine-wave voltages or currents. Before considering these time-varying sources, however, it will be advantageous to review some basic network concepts: concepts which are equally applicable to time-varying sources or non-time-varying sources.

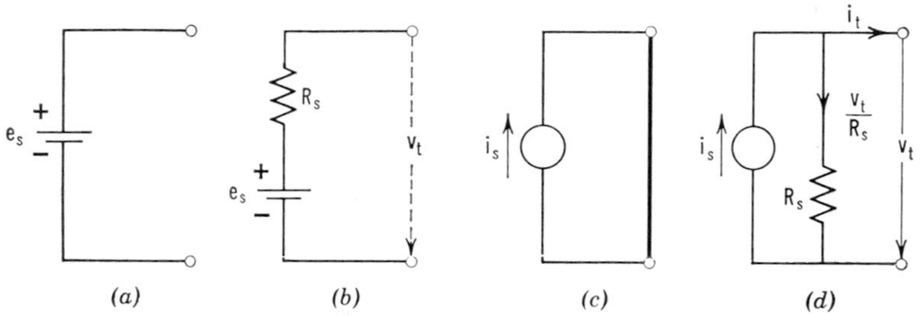

FIG. 1. Voltage and current sources.

Sources. The common non-time-varying voltage sources are batteries and direct-current generators. Since the reader undoubtedly has an intuitive understanding of how these sources are employed to energize electric circuits, we start with them. In later chapters, sources which develop time-varying voltages and currents will be employed almost exclusively. For the present, only the sources indicated in Fig. 1 will be used, and the battery symbol will indicate a non-time-varying voltage source regardless of the exact nature of the voltage source. Unless specifically noted, this voltage source is assumed to possess zero internal resistance. Where it is desirable to simulate the internal loss of a voltage source, a resistance will be placed in series with the ideal voltage source as indicated in Fig. 1*b*.

Where a voltage source, e_s, is specified, it will be understood that a potential difference of e_s volts is maintained between (or across) the terminals of the ideal source regardless of the current that may pass through this ideal source. The actual terminal voltage of a voltage source having internal resistance R_s which is *delivering* current to a network is

$$v_t = e_s - R_s i \tag{1}$$

where i is the current flowing in the $-$ to $+$ direction. See Fig. 2a where $i = i_t$.

A voltage source is idle when it is operating open-circuited; $i = 0$. Otherwise it is delivering or absorbing power to the extent of

$$P_s = e_s i \quad \text{watts} \tag{2}$$

depending upon the direction of i relative to the polarity of e_s. The power delivered by a voltage source possessing internal resistance is

$$P_t = v_t i = (e_s - R_s i)i = e_s i - R_s i^2 \tag{3}$$

$R_s i^2$ is the heat power developed internally and as such is not available for distribution to the rest of the network.

Where a current source, i_s, is specified in circuit theory, it will be understood that the source delivers this specified current regardless of the resistance which is placed across the terminals of the source. It is, of course, unrealistic to ask that a current source look into an open circuit (or infinite resistance) since this situation results in infinite power (Ri^2) being delivered to the open circuit. This example, however, illustrates an important point: if a current source of i_s amperes is specified, then by definition this number of amperes is delivered to the network regardless of the resistance placed across the generator terminals. (A contradiction of definitions, of course, occurs when current generators of different specified currents are connected in series.)

A current source is idle when it is short-circuited as indicated in Fig. 1c. In this case the power delivered is zero owing to the fact that the specified current circulates through zero external resistance. When a finite resistance, R, appears across the terminals, the ideal current source delivers

$$P_s = R i_s^2 \quad \text{watts} \tag{4}$$

A practical current source can be simulated by incorporating an internal resistance, R_s, across the terminals as illustrated in Fig. 1d. Under these conditions the terminal current is

$$i_t = i_s - \frac{v_t}{R_s} \tag{5}$$

where v_t is the terminal voltage developed when the current source is connected to a load resistance. This generator develops a terminal voltage of $R_s i_s$ when $i_t = 0$, that is, when the current source is operating open-circuited. If R_L is placed across the current source, the terminal voltage is

$$v_t = R_L i_t = R_L i_s - \frac{R_L}{R_s} v_t \tag{6}$$

and the power delivered to R_L is

$$R_L i_t^2 = (R_L i_t) i_s - \frac{R_L}{R_s} v_t i_t \tag{7}$$

The total power generated is $(R_L i_t) i_s = v_t i_s$ of which $\frac{R_L}{R_s} v_t i_t = \frac{v_t^2}{R_s}$ watts are dissipated in the internal resistance, R_s.

Although sources have been designated as voltage sources and current sources, it is evident that either one energizes the network with both

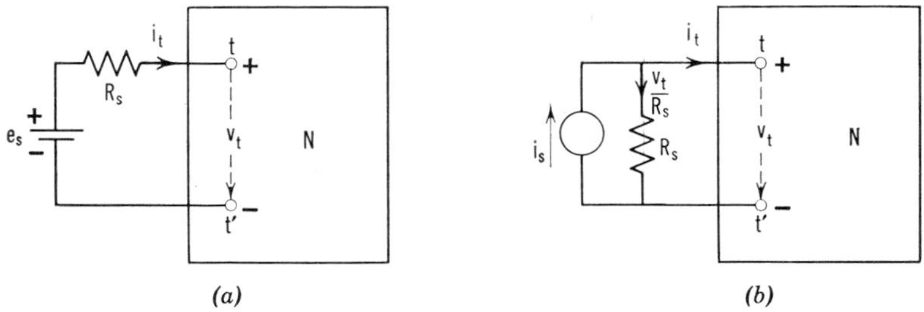

FIG. 2. Equivalent sources.

current and voltage. Indeed the two sources are entirely interchangeable when a finite internal resistance is present. The voltage source depicted in Fig. 2*a*, for example, supplies the network N with i_t amperes and v_t volts. The current, i_t, may be expressed as

$$\frac{e_s - v_t}{R_s} = i_t \tag{8}$$

which may be rearranged as

$$\frac{e_s}{R_s} - \frac{v_t}{R_s} = i_t \tag{8a}$$

Thus a specified e_s in series with a specified resistance R_s results in a specific current source

$$i_s = \frac{e_s}{R_s}$$

The conditions imposed by equation (8*a*) are satisfied by the circuit configuration shown in Fig. 2*b* where a current source i_s delivers i_t amperes to the network at v_t volts. Substitution of i_s permits equation (8*a*) to be written as

$$i_s = \frac{v_t}{R_s} + i_t \tag{8b}$$

where v_t/R_s is the current which is *lost* to the network as a result of the internal resistance R_s and the terminal voltage v_t.

Reference to Fig. 2 and to equations (8), (8*a*), and (8*b*) shows that a voltage source having an internal resistance of R_s ohms may be replaced with an ideal current source of e_s/R_s amperes in parallel with a resistive path of R_s ohms or that a current source i_s in parallel with R_s may be replaced with a voltage source ($e_s = R_s i_s$) in series with a resistance of R_s ohms. The rest of the network, that is, the portion of the network to the right of terminals tt' in Fig. 2, cannot tell whether it is energized with e_s in series with R_s as in Fig. 2*a* or with $i_s = e_s/R_s$ in parallel with R_s as in Fig. 2*b*. Where a source having internal resistance is specified, there exists a choice of using either e_s in series with R_s or of using i_s in parallel with R_s. Other more elaborate combinations of series-parallel resistances could conceivably be employed.

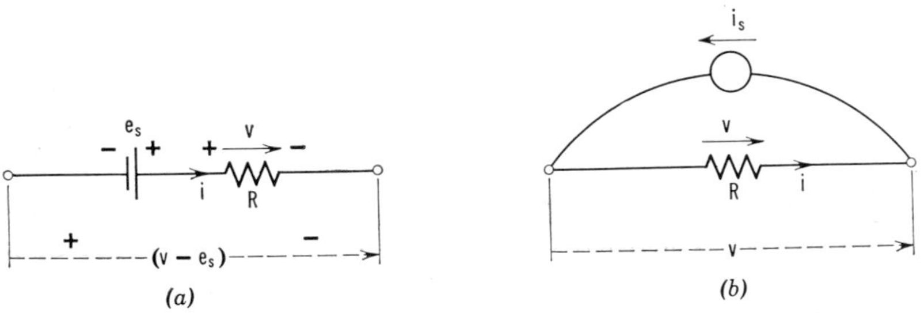

FIG. 3. Branch voltages in the presence of sources.

Where an ideal voltage source, e_s, is specified ($R_s = 0$), this source constrains the potential difference between its terminals to be e_s volts regardless of the current. If e_s is placed in series with a resistive branch, the terminal voltage of the branch including the known e_s is $(v - e_s)$ and is considered as a voltage drop as indicated in Fig. 3*a*. The inclusion of e_s does not increase the number of unknowns since e_s is specified. Where an ideal current source is placed across a resistive branch as illustrated in Fig. 3*b*, it can either be associated with R to form a series branch equivalent to that shown in Fig. 3*a* or be left as a fixed or specified current between the two terminals.

An ideal voltage source has zero internal series resistance. An ideal current source possesses infinite internal series resistance. This conclusion may be deduced from the definition of an ideal current source, namely, a source which delivers i_s regardless of the finite load resistance, R_L, which is placed across the terminals of the source. To satisfy this definition, it is evident that the internal voltage, say e_s, as well as the internal series resistance R_{int} must approach infinity. The specified current may be considered to be

$$i_s = \frac{k_1 e_s}{k_2 R_{\text{int}} + R_L} = \frac{k_1}{k_2} \tag{9}$$

as both e_s and R_{int} approach infinity, R_L remaining finite.

Superposition. A linear circuit element is one in which the current through the element is directly proportional to the voltage across the terminals of the element. Linear networks consist of linear elements and fixed (or specified) voltage and current sources.

One reason for the rapid strides which have been made in the analysis of linear networks is that the principle of superposition can be applied to these networks. With the aid of this principle, the voltage or current response in any part of a linear network resulting from two or more sources may be determined by:

(1) Finding the component response developed by each individual source.

(2) Adding (algebraically) the component responses to obtain the actual response.

The truth of the principle of superposition is almost self-evident since effects are proportional to causes in linear systems where the principle applies. In any event, a general proof will be left for the reader *after* the subjects of determinants and general network solutions have been considered.

A simple application of superposition is illustrated in Fig. 4 where the current in the resistance $R = 2$ ohms is found as the sum of the current in R due to e_s, namely, I_{R1}, and the current due to i_s, namely, I_{R2}. In determining I_{R1} (Fig. 4*b*), i_s is de-energized either by opening the i_s branch[1] (for purposes of analysis) or by letting $i_s = 0$ and recognizing that a current source possesses infinite internal resistance. The value of the current in resistance R due to $e_s = 23$ volts is

$$I_{R1} = \frac{e_s}{R} = \frac{23}{1+2} = \frac{23}{3} \quad \text{amperes}$$

In determining I_{R2}, the current in R due to i_s (Fig. 4*c*), e_s, is replaced by a short circuit since an ideal voltage source has zero internal resistance. Application of Kirchhoff's voltage law to the two parallel branches in Fig. 4*c* shows that

$$2I_{R2} = 1(4 - I_{R2})$$

[1] A branch is a conducting path terminated at either end by one of the network junctions or nodes.

or

$$I_{R2} = \tfrac{4}{3} \text{ amperes}$$

The actual current in resistance R is

$$I_R = I_{R1} + I_{R2} = \frac{23}{3} + \frac{4}{3} = 9 \text{ amperes}$$

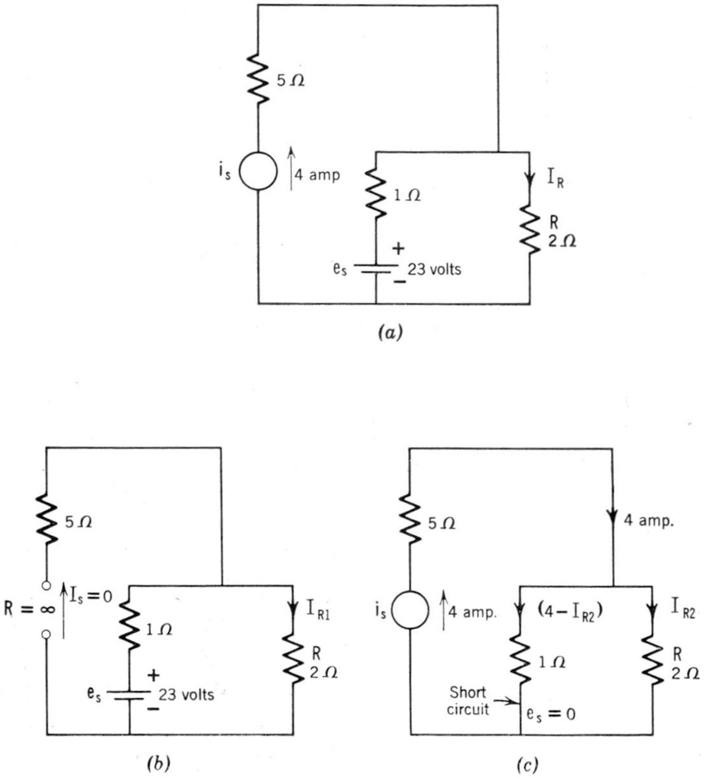

FIG. 4. An example of superposition: $I_R = I_{R1} + I_{R2}$.

The principle of superposition will be employed later in developing certain general methods of analysis where component responses due to the independent variables as well as those due to the sources are combined to establish general equilibrium equations for the network.

Network Variables. In a network consisting of b branches, there are in general $2b$ unknowns: b unknown branch currents, i_b, and b unknown branch voltages, v_b. A direct relationship exists, however, between each branch current and the associated branch voltage. Where the branches are resistive in character for example,

$$v_b = R_b i_b \qquad \text{or} \qquad i_b = G_b v_b \tag{10}$$

where R_b is the branch resistance and G_b is the branch conductance.

After the application of either of the volt-ampere relationships [given in equation (10)] to each of the branches there remain only b unknowns. Evaluation of these unknowns requires that b independent relationships be established. If the network has a total of n_t nodes or junctions, Kirchhoff's current law may be applied independently

$$(n_t - 1) = n \tag{11}$$

times. These n relationships together with $(b - n)$ relationships established by the application of the voltage law are sufficient in number to effect solutions for the b unknowns.

Systematized methods of network analysis ordinarily employ either linear combinations of branch currents or of branch voltages rather than the branch quantities themselves because we can write the reduced number of equations directly from the network map. Network variables which are linearly related to branch currents and branch voltages are respectively *loop currents* and *node-pair voltages*, the subjects of the following two articles.

Loop Currents. A loop current as the name implies traverses a closed path. Ordinarily the closed path is so selected that the associated loop current is a *measurable* current of the network, that is, a current which could be measured physically with the aid of an ammeter. It is not, however, essential to analysis that loop currents be measurable currents, nor is the closed path necessarily restricted to a single passage through any branch. Simple closed paths are usually easier to handle and are therefore to be preferred. The direction of the fictitious loop currents is arbitrary provided that the sense is taken care of algebraically in the summation.

In Fig. 5 are illustrated three loop currents, i_1, i_2, and i_3, together with the six branch currents i_{b1}, i_{b2}, i_{b3}, i_{b4}, i_{b5}, and i_{b6}. The linear relationship can most easily be visualized from

$$i_b = \sum i_{\text{loop}} \tag{12}$$

Any particular branch current, i_b, is the algebraic sum of the loop currents traversing this branch. Thus in Fig. 5

$$i_{b1} = i_1 \qquad i_{b5} = i_2 \qquad i_{b6} = i_3$$

$$i_{b2} = i_1 - i_3 \quad i_{b3} = i_1 - i_2 \quad i_{b4} = i_2 - i_3$$

In effect, the six branch currents have been replaced with three loop currents for the purpose of analysis. This reduction in the number of variables is accomplished at the expense of the current-law relationships. The manner in which loop currents automatically satisfy $\sum i = 0$ at the junctions is illustrated below. As applied to Fig. 5, we note that

$$\text{At node ①: } i_{b1} - i_{b2} - i_{b6} = i_1 - (i_1 - i_3) - i_3 = 0 \quad (13)$$

$$\text{At node ②: } i_{b2} - i_{b3} - i_{b4} = (i_1 - i_3) - (i_1 - i_2) - (i_2 - i_3) = 0 \quad (14)$$

$$\text{At node ③: } i_{b4} - i_{b5} + i_{b6} = (i_2 - i_3) - i_2 + i_3 = 0 \quad (15)$$

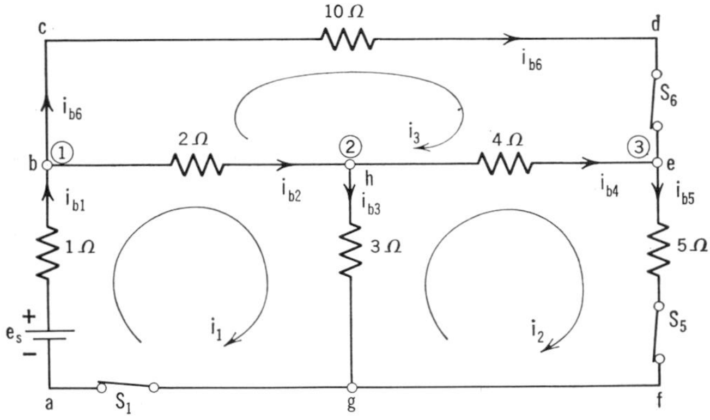

FIG. 5. Loop currents employed to replace branch currents.

In a four-junction network, $n_t = 4$, the current law can be applied independently only three times, and it will be observed from equations (13) through (15) that the loop currents automatically establish three independent relationships between the branch currents.

That loop currents can always be selected as " measurable " currents will be evident after network topology has been considered. In Fig. 5, for example, ammeters placed at the S_1, S_5, and S_6 positions would measure respectively loop currents i_1, i_2, and i_3.

Since the current-law relationships are satisfied with loop currents, the voltage-law relationships ($\sum v = 0$) must be applied $(b - n_t + 1)$ times. Obviously these $(b - n_t + 1) = (b - n)$ voltage equations must be independent relationships. One method of establishing independent voltage equations is to think of opening all loops except one and then establish the voltage law for this particular loop invoking the principle of superposition with the loop currents considered as independent variables. In other words, the sum of the voltage drops around any loop will be obtained employing one loop current at a time and then all of these voltage drops will be summed to equal zero in accordance with Kirchhoff's voltage law. As applied to the loop traversed by i_1 of Fig. 5, we think of opening switches S_5 and S_6 and sum the voltage drops occasioned by i_1 (and e_s if a source is specified). Thus

$$(1 + 2 + 3)i_1 - e_s = 0 \qquad \text{or} \qquad 6i_1 = e_s \tag{16}$$

The resistance of loop 1 through which i_1 flows is 6 ohms. This resistance is called the self-resistance of loop 1 to distinguish it from the mutual resistances or the resistances of loop 1 which are common to loops 2 and 3.

The voltage equation given in equation (16) does not include the voltages developed in loop 1 by loop currents i_2 and i_3. To account for the effect of i_2, we think of closing switch S_5 and observe that loop current i_2 circulates through a portion of loop 1, that is, through the 3-ohm resistance. The direction of i_2 through the 3-ohm resistance is such as to establish a voltage *rise* in loop 1 as seen from the tracing direction employed for loop 1. Taking into account the voltage rise established in loop 1 by loop current i_2, we expand equation (16) to read

$$6i_1 - 3i_2 = e_s \tag{17}$$

Next, switch S_6 is closed and the effect of loop current i_3 on the voltage equilibrium of loop 1 is observed. The current i_3 circulates through the 2-ohm resistor of loop 1 in such a direction as to produce a voltage rise in the tracing direction of loop 1. The final voltage equation for loop 1 in terms of loop currents i_1, i_2, and i_3 takes the form

$$6i_1 - 3i_2 - 2i_3 = e_s \tag{18}$$

An important aspect of equation (18) is that it can be brought into being with the aid of superposition employing elementary physical concepts. Exactly the same method may be employed to show that the voltage equation for loop 2 is

$$-3i_1 + 12i_2 - 4i_3 = 0 \tag{19}$$

and for loop 3

$$-2i_1 - 4i_2 + 16i_3 = 0 \tag{20}$$

In using superposition to establish the voltage equations, we have taken i_1, i_2, and i_3 as *independent* variables and considered their effects one at a time. Although the establishment of voltage equations with loop currents soon becomes a routine procedure, we should realize that this procedure is in effect based upon the superposition principle.

Equations (18), (19), and (20) may be solved simultaneously for i_1, i_2, and i_3. Then any particular branch current can be found from the algebraic sum of the loop currents flowing through the particular branch. That is

$$i_{\text{branch}} = \sum i_{\text{loop}}$$

Or equations (13), (14), and (15) may be employed to find i_{branch} in terms of i_{loop}, but this procedure is unnecessarily laborious.

Ordinarily, the closed paths employed in establishing the voltage-law equations coincide in contour and direction with the paths selected for the loop currents. This is a matter of convenience but not of necessity since any three independent closed paths may be employed to obtain three independent voltage equations. Independent closed paths can always be obtained by including successively a branch *not previously traversed*. Assume, for example, that paths 1 and 2 of Fig. 5 follow i_1 and i_2 respectively. A third voltage equation may be obtained by summing the voltage drops around the path *abhefga*. Thus

$$3i_1 + 9i_2 - 6i_3 = e_s \tag{21}$$

which is the sum of equations (18) and (19) and hence not independent of these equations. A third independent voltage equation may be obtained [in place of equation (20)] by summing around a closed path which includes the *cd* path or branch. If the *abcdefga* path is selected, there is obtained

$$1i_1 + 5i_2 + 10i_3 = e_s \tag{22}$$

This equation [which is the sum of equations (18), (19), and (20)] may be used in conjunction with equations (18) and (19) to find the values of i_1, i_2, and i_3.

The coefficients of the independent variables of equations (18), (19), and (20) may be arranged in an orderly fashion as shown below:

$$\begin{bmatrix} 6 & -3 & -2 \\ -3 & 12 & -4 \\ -2 & -4 & 16 \end{bmatrix} \tag{23}$$

Except for the sources, this ordered array of numbers completely characterizes the network to which it is applicable. In this type of characterization, the first column represents the coefficients of i_1; the second column represents the coefficients of i_2, and so on. An ordered array (or arrangement) of numbers or symbols is called a *matrix*. In general a matrix consists of m rows and n columns as, for example,

$$A = A_{(m,n)} = \begin{bmatrix} a_{11} & a_{12} & a_{13} & \cdots & a_{1n} \\ a_{21} & a_{22} & a_{23} & \cdots & a_{2n} \\ \cdot & \cdot & \cdot & \cdots & \cdot \\ a_{m1} & a_{m2} & a_{m3} & \cdots & a_{mn} \end{bmatrix}$$

A rather complete algebra involving matrices has been developed, but here we are concerned only with the orderly arrangement of $n \times m$ symbols or numbers which characterize a network, also with the evaluation of the determinant of the matrix. Brackets will be employed to designate matrices, whereas straight bars will be used to designate the determinant. (It is expected that the reader understands the elementary algebra of determinants including the application of Cramer's rule which is widely used in solving simultaneous equations.)

The matrix representing the coefficients of the i's in equations (18), (19), and (20) is written as indicated above in matrix (23). The determinant of this matrix is written as

$$\begin{vmatrix} 6 & -3 & -2 \\ -3 & 12 & -4 \\ -2 & -4 & 16 \end{vmatrix} = 816 \text{ ohms}^3 \tag{23a}$$

In this case the matrix is called the resistance system matrix and the determinant of this matrix has a numerical value of 816 ohms^3. If equations (18), (19), and (22) were employed, the resistance matrix would take the form

$$\begin{bmatrix} 6 & -3 & -2 \\ -3 & 12 & -4 \\ 1 & 5 & 10 \end{bmatrix} \quad \text{and} \quad \begin{vmatrix} 6 & -3 & -2 \\ -3 & 12 & -4 \\ 1 & 5 & 10 \end{vmatrix} = 816 \text{ ohms}^3 \tag{24}$$

If measurable currents are selected as the loop currents and the paths traversed in writing the voltage equations coincide with the current paths, the determinant of the resistance matrix of a network has the same numerical value regardless of the paths traversed by the loop currents. Only by selecting involved multiple loops will the network determinant differ from its base value. (For an example of what is meant here, see Problem 10 and Fig. 26*b* at the end of the chapter.)

If the numerical value of i_2 per unit e_s in Fig. 5 were required, it could be obtained with the aid of Cramer's rule and equations (18), (19), and (20) as

$$i_2 = \frac{\begin{vmatrix} 6 & 1 & -2 \\ -3 & 0 & -4 \\ -2 & 0 & 16 \end{vmatrix}}{816} = \frac{56}{816} = \frac{7}{102} \text{ ampere}$$

or, if equations (18), (19), and (22) are employed, as

$$i_2 = \frac{\begin{vmatrix} 6 & 1 & -2 \\ -3 & 0 & -4 \\ 1 & 1 & 10 \end{vmatrix}}{816} = \frac{56}{816} = \frac{7}{102} \text{ ampere}$$

If a network has l independent loop currents, the resistance matrix will have l columns; one column for each loop current. Since l equations are required to obtain a unique solution, the matrix must also have l rows. Thus $l \times l$ matrices are involved in network solutions where (as previously considered) $l = b - n$. The matrix may be written down from an inspection of the network if proper physical interpretation is given to each of the elements in the general matrix

$$\begin{bmatrix} R_{11} & R_{12} & R_{13} & \cdots & R_{1l} \\ R_{21} & R_{22} & R_{23} & \cdots & R_{2l} \\ \cdot & \cdot & \cdot & \cdots & \cdot \\ R_{l1} & R_{l2} & R_{l3} & \cdots & R_{ll} \end{bmatrix} \tag{25}$$

The use of brackets in matrix (25) implies that *only the ordered arrangement of the coefficients* of the general voltage equations is being portrayed. The *determinant of the matrix* is indicated with straight side bars and implies that the actual value of this array is being considered.

If reasonably simple paths are selected for the loop currents, the elements of the matrix may be given such physical meanings that the numerical values of these elements can be read directly from the diagram of the network. R_{11} is the self-resistance of loop 1 through which loop current 1 flows, and in general R_{jj} is the self-resistance of loop j through which loop current j flows, and in general R_{jk} is that part of the resistance of loop j through which loop current k flows. If the closed paths selected for the establishment of the voltage relationships coincide with the paths traversed by the loop currents and if j and k are integers from 1 to l inclusive,

$$R_{jk} = R_{kj} \qquad (\text{for } j \neq k) \tag{26}$$

A situation where $R_{jk} = R_{kj}$ is given in equation (23*a*), and a situation where $R_{jk} \neq R_{kj}$ is given in equation (24). Ordinarily the closed paths employed to establish the voltage equations are the same as the paths traversed by measurable loop currents. Under these conditions the system matrix is symmetrical about the main diagonal. The main diagonal consists of R_{11}, R_{22}, R_{33}, $\cdots$, R_{ll}.

Example. Let it be required to find the form of the resistance matrix of the network given in Fig. 6*a* when the voltage relationships are established by following the closed paths mapped out by the designated loop currents.

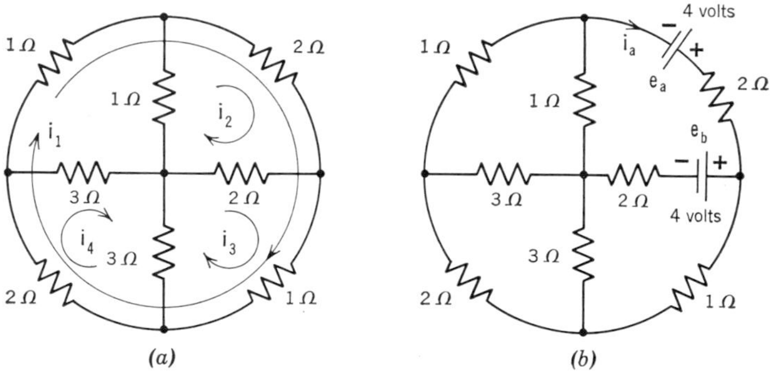

FIG. 6. Example of network analysis employing loop currents.

From an inspection of the network resistance and remembering that the sign of a resistance must be considered negative when the loop currents in the resistance are in opposite directions, we find directly that

$$R_{11} = 6 \text{ ohms} \qquad R_{12} = R_{21} = 2 \text{ ohms}$$
$$R_{22} = 5 \qquad R_{13} = R_{31} = 1$$
$$R_{33} = 6 \qquad R_{14} = R_{41} = 2$$
$$R_{44} = 8 \qquad R_{23} = R_{32} = -2$$
$$R_{24} = R_{42} = 0$$
$$R_{34} = R_{43} = -3$$

The system determinant is

$$\Delta = \begin{vmatrix} 6 & 2 & 1 & 2 \\ 2 & 5 & -2 & 0 \\ 1 & -2 & 6 & -3 \\ 2 & 0 & -3 & 8 \end{vmatrix} = 506 \text{ ohms}^4$$

The system determinant expressed in matrix form is simply a shorthand way of expressing the voltage relationships

$$6i_1 + 2i_2 + 1i_3 + 2i_4 = 0 \qquad \text{(loop 1)}$$
$$2i_1 + 5i_2 - 2i_3 + 0i_4 = 0 \qquad \text{(loop 2)}$$
$$1i_1 - 2i_2 + 6i_3 - 3i_4 = 0 \qquad \text{(loop 3)}$$
$$2i_1 + 0i_2 - 3i_3 + 8i_4 = 0 \qquad \text{(loop 4)}$$

The right-hand members of these equations are zero because no voltage sources were specified in Fig. 6*a*. If two 4-volt sources are employed to energize the network as indicated in Fig. 6*b*,

$$e_{s1} = 4, \quad e_{s2} = 4 - 4 = 0, \quad e_{s3} = 4, \quad e_{s4} = 0 \text{ volts}$$

where the subscript s indicates a source voltage and the numerical subscript refers to the number of the loop to which the driving voltage is applicable. After we incorporate these driving voltages into the voltage equations given above, any or all of the loop currents may be found. Loop current i_1, for example, may be found with the aid of Cramer's rule as indicated below:

$$i_1 = \frac{\begin{vmatrix} 4 & 2 & 1 & 2 \\ 0 & 5 & -2 & 0 \\ 4 & -2 & 6 & -3 \\ 0 & 0 & -3 & 8 \end{vmatrix}}{506} = \frac{244}{506} = 0.482 \text{ ampere}$$

If the analysis requires the power delivered to the network by the source e_a, the actual branch current, i_a, flowing through e_a will have to be evaluated as

$$i_a = \sum i_{\text{loop}} = i_1 + i_2$$

$$i_2 = \frac{\begin{vmatrix} 6 & 4 & 1 & 2 \\ 2 & 0 & -2 & 0 \\ 1 & 4 & 6 & -3 \\ 2 & 0 & -3 & 8 \end{vmatrix}}{506} = \frac{40}{506} \text{ ampere}$$

$$i_a = \frac{244}{506} + \frac{40}{506} = \frac{284}{506} = 0.561 \text{ ampere}$$

The power delivered to the network by the e_a source is

$$P_a = e_a i_a = 4 \times 0.561 = 2.244 \text{ watts}$$

The voltage equations used to effect a network solution are not restricted to the equations obtained by traversing the paths mapped out by the loop currents. If in Fig. 6*a*, for example, we should choose to write voltage equations around the four *inside* meshes, the voltage equations (in terms of i_1, i_2, i_3, and i_4 of Fig. 6*a*) take the form

$$1i_1 - 1i_2 + 0i_3 - 3i_4 = 0$$

$$2i_1 + 5i_2 - 2i_3 + 0i_4 = 0$$

$$1i_1 - 2i_2 + 6i_3 - 3i_4 = 0$$

$$2i_1 + 0i_2 - 3i_3 + 8i_4 = 0$$

The resistance matrix under these conditions takes the unsymmetrical form

$$R = \begin{bmatrix} 1 & -1 & 0 & -3 \\ 2 & 5 & -2 & 0 \\ 1 & -2 & 6 & -3 \\ 2 & 0 & -3 & 8 \end{bmatrix}$$

The determinant of this matrix, however, has the same numerical value (506 ohms^4) as the system determinant previously employed.

Node-Pair Voltages. The potential difference between any two nodes or junctions of a network is called a node-pair voltage. If properly selected, node-pair voltages may be used as the independent variables in network analysis in place of loop currents. This procedure is sometimes referred to as nodal analysis. In certain network configurations, the use of node-pair voltages has distinct advantages over the use of loop currents. The concept of node-pair voltages as network variables will be first illustrated in a particular case before any attempt is made at generalizations. To this end, we propose to determine branch voltage v_a in Fig. 7*a*, employing node-pair voltages as the independent network variables.

In nodal analysis, it is convenient to relate branch currents and branch voltages by way of branch conductance; that is

$$i_b = G_b v_b \tag{27}$$

where $G_b = 1/R_b$. Before proceeding with any analysis it is desirable to combine the simple series and parallel combinations of resistances to form a single branch conductance between nodes. The two 1-ohm resistances which are in series between nodes ① and ③ of Fig. 7*a*, for example, are combined to form a 2-ohm resistance and converted to a 0.5-mho conductance in Fig. 7*b*. It is also desirable to transform voltage sources associated with series resistance to equivalent current sources since the network solution is to be based upon current-law equations. Thus $e_{s2} = 2$ volts in series with 0.5 ohm in Fig. 7*a* is replaced with 4-ampere current generator in parallel with a 2-mho conductance as indicated in Fig. 7*b*. (See page 3.)

The correct number of node-pair voltages to employ in nodal analysis is equal to the total number of network nodes less one or

$$(n_t - 1) = n$$

The justification for this statement will become evident when it is recognized that a nodal analysis involves the establishment of current-law equations only. It will be remembered that, in a network having

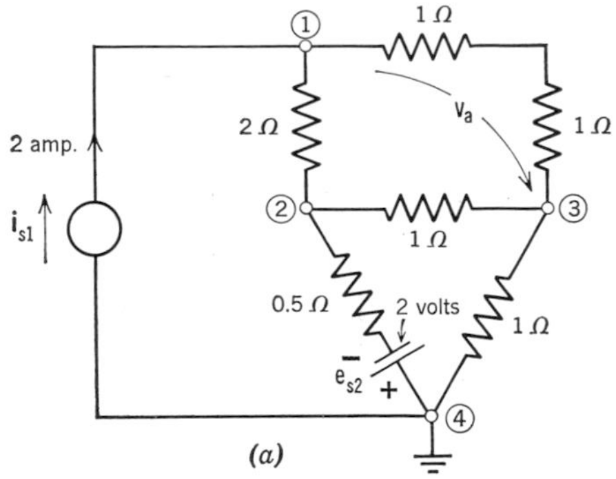

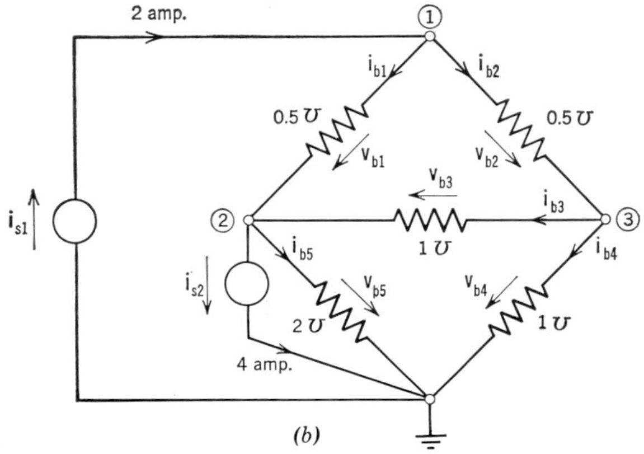

FIG. 7. Equivalent networks.

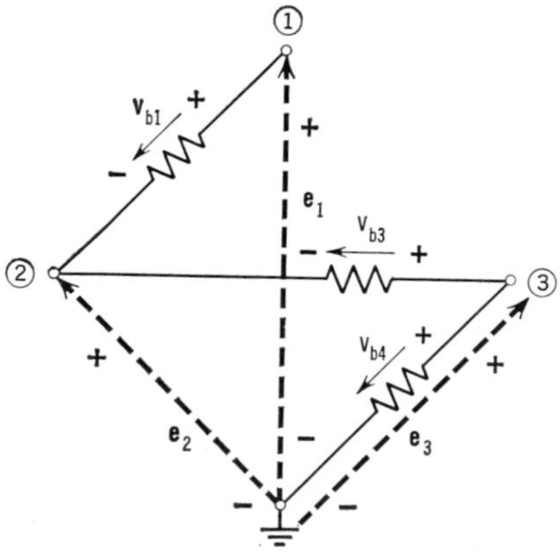

FIG. 8. Node-pair voltages e_1, e_2, and e_3 employed in the analysis of the network given in Fig. 7.

$n_t = (n + 1)$ junctions or nodes, only n independent current equations can be established. Therefore n independent node-pair voltages must be employed in the analysis.

The network of Fig. 7 has four nodes. Hence three node-pair voltages (e_1, e_2, and e_3 of Fig. 8) are selected as the independent variables upon which to base the analysis. The node-pair voltages selected must not of themselves form a closed path because in this case $(e_1 + e_2 + e_3)$ would equal zero, thus exhibiting a dependency. In Fig. 8, e_1, e_2, and e_3 are so selected that they have only one node in common. This particular selection yields independent node-pair voltages and results in certain simplifications as will become evident presently.

It will be observed from Figs. 7 and 8 that all the branch voltages can be expressed as linear combinations of e_1, e_2, and e_3. The equations will be established by setting the voltage drops, represented by the v's, equal to the sum of the voltage rises, designated by the e's, when tracing from a node in the direction of the voltage drop, thence through the voltage rises back to the starting point. Thus

$$\begin{aligned} v_{b1} &= e_1 - e_2 \qquad & v_{b4} &= e_3 \\ v_{b2} &= e_1 - e_3 \qquad & v_{b5} &= e_2 \\ v_{b3} &= e_3 - e_2 \end{aligned} \tag{28}$$

Following a closed path, for example, $v_{b1} - v_{b3} - v_{b2} = (e_1 - e_2) - (e_3 - e_2) - (e_1 - e_3) = 0$. The result of using the e's as independent network variables is that the voltage-law relationships of the network have in effect been used and there remains only three current-law relationships to be established. These latter relationships may be obtained by applying Kirchhoff's current law at nodes ①, ②, and ③ of Fig. 7b. We observe first, however, that the branch currents are related to the e's as follows:

$$\begin{aligned} i_{b1} &= 0.5v_{b1} = 0.5e_1 - 0.5e_2 \\ i_{b2} &= 0.5v_{b2} = 0.5e_1 - 0.5e_3 \\ i_{b3} &= 1v_{b3} = 1e_3 - 1e_2 \\ i_{b4} &= 1v_{b4} = 1e_3 \\ i_{b5} &= 2v_{b5} = 2e_2 \end{aligned} \tag{29}$$

The current-law relationships are

At node ①: $i_{b1} + i_{b2} = 1e_1 - 0.5e_2 - 0.5e_3 = i_{s1}$ (30)

At node ②: $-i_{b1} - i_{b3} + i_{b5} = -0.5e_1 + 3.5e_2 - 1e_3 = -i_{s2}$ (31)

At node ③: $-i_{b2} + i_{b3} + i_{b4} = -0.5e_1 - 1e_2 + 2.5e_3 = 0$ (32)

Since i_{s1} and i_{s2} are known quantities, the numerical values of the e's may be obtained straightforwardly, and, from the e's, the branch voltages follow directly. In the present example, we set out to determine the numerical value of $v_a = v_{b2}$ in Fig. 7.

$$v_{b2} = e_1 - e_3 = \frac{\begin{vmatrix} 2 & -0.5 & -0.5 \\ -4 & 3.5 & -1 \\ 0 & -1 & 2.5 \end{vmatrix} - \begin{vmatrix} 1 & -0.5 & 2 \\ -0.5 & 3.5 & -4 \\ -0.5 & -1 & 0 \end{vmatrix}}{\begin{vmatrix} 1 & -0.5 & -0.5 \\ -0.5 & 3.5 & -1 \\ -0.5 & -1 & 2.5 \end{vmatrix}}$$

$$v_a = v_{b2} = e_1 - e_3 = \frac{8.5 - (-0.5)}{5.75} = 1.566 \text{ volts}$$

The method outlined above is elegant in its simplicity, but, with more general choices of the e's, the physical phenomena involved may become obscured. It will prove instructive to solve the problem outlined above making use of the principle of superposition. This principle has already been employed in the establishment of the voltage equations of the loop-current method of analysis. There, all loops but the pertinent one were open-circuited, and the component voltage drops around each loop were evaluated using one loop current at a time. A similar method of attack will be employed here in establishing the required number of current equations, but in this case we shall let all of the e's but the pertinent one equal zero in finding the current directed away from nodes ①, ②, and ③. In this way we shall be able to interpret the elements of the conductance matrix of a network in light of measurable conductances.

When we apply Kirchhoff's current law at each of the three marked nodes of Fig. 7*b*, it will be convenient to think of placing an ammeter at the pertinent node as indicated in Fig. 9. In Fig. 9*a*, the current directed away from node ① for a 1-volt rise of e_1 (and for $e_2 = e_3 = 0$) may be determined

$$I_{11} = 0.5e_1 + 0.5e_1 = 1e_1$$

Insofar as e_1 and i_{s1} are concerned, the current equation at node ① reads

$$\underset{\text{(away)}}{I_{11}} = 1e_1 = \underset{\text{(toward node 1)}}{i_{s1}} \tag{33}$$

This relationship, of course, does not account for the effect upon the current at node ① caused by e_2, e_3, or i_{s2}. To find the effect of e_2 upon the current at node ①, we short-circuit e_1 and e_3 as indicated in Fig. 9*b* and note that

$$I_{12} = -0.5e_2 \tag{34}$$

The minus sign is required since an increase in e_2 produces $0.5e_2$ ampere directed *toward* node ① and current *away from* that node has been taken as positive. (See Fig. 9*a* and equation 33.) Next, the effect of e_3 upon the current at node ① is observed. In making this observation, we short-circuit e_1 and e_2 as indicated in Fig. 9*c* and find

$$I_{13} = -0.5e_3 \tag{35}$$

The component currents of equations (33), (34), and (35) may be combined in accordance with the principle of superposition to obtain the current-law relationship which exists at node ①.

$$1e_1 - 0.5e_2 - 0.5e_3 = i_{s1} \tag{36}$$

i_{s1} is the source current directed *toward* node ① with $e_1 = e_2 = e_3 = i_{s2} = 0$. With a more general choice of the *e*'s, the effect of i_{s2} might make a contribution to the current at node ①. Since i_{s2} is connected directly across the terminal points of e_2 in this instance and since e_2 is replaced by a short circuit for this particular evaluation, i_{s2} produces a zero component current at node ① or at the I_1 position. (It will, of course, be recognized that the ammeter connected to node ① is merely an artifice for helping us keep track of the various component currents established at this node by e_1, e_2, e_3, i_{s1}, and i_{s2}.)

In establishing the current-law relationship which exists at node ② of Fig. 7*b*, we make use of Figs. 9*d*, 9*e*, and 9*f* to obtain

$$-0.5e_1 + 3.5e_2 - 1e_3 = -i_{s2} \tag{37}$$

In a similar manner, we find that the current law applied to node ③ yields

$$-0.5e_1 - 1e_2 + 2.5e_3 = 0 \tag{38}$$

The coefficients of equations (36), (37), and (38) indicate that $G_{11} = 1$ mho, $G_{22} = 3.5$ mhos, and $G_{33} = 2.5$ mhos. Reference to Fig. 7*b* will show that these conductances are precisely the conductances connected to nodes ①, ②, and ③ respectively. Further examination will show that the mutual conductances like G_{12}, G_{13}, G_{21}, G_{23}, etc., are the negatives of the connecting conductances. This method of finding the *G*'s is widely used in cases where the *e*'s have a common terminal as in Figs. 7 and 8.

Equations (36), (37), and (38) have resulted from the application of the principle of superposition and in this particular case are identical in

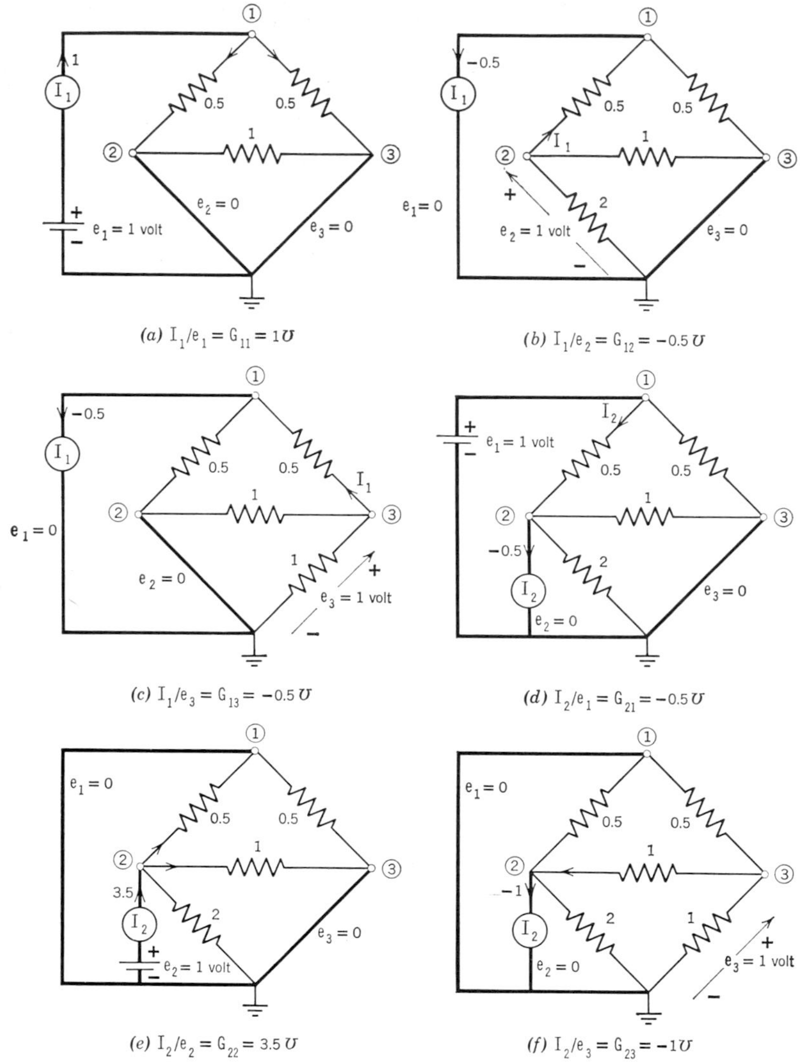

FIG. 9. Component currents at nodes ①, ②, and ③ produced by unit steps of the node pair voltages e_1, e_2, and e_3. Numbers on resistances are mhos.

form to equations (30), (31), and (32). (For a more general choice of the e's, the two sets of equations might differ in numerical form.) One advantage which accrues from the use of superposition is that the elements of the conductance matrix have values which can be measured

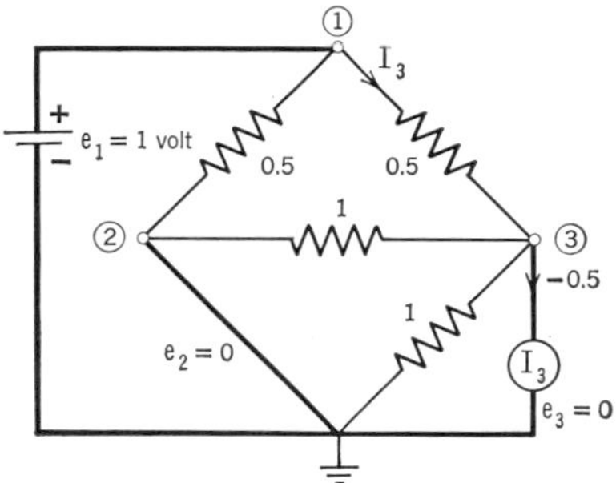

(g) $I_3/e_1 = G_{31} = -0.5$ ℧

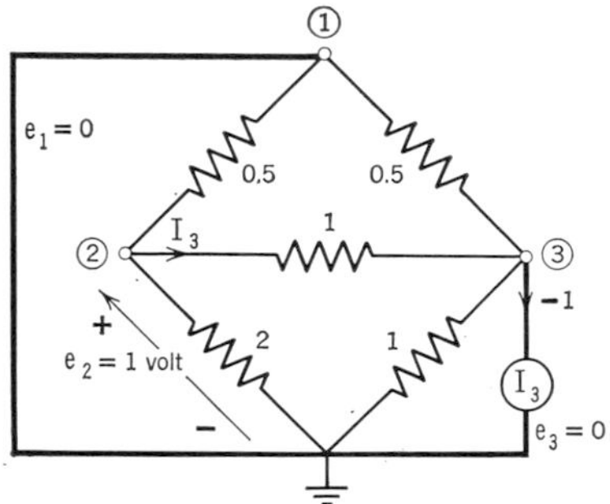

(h) $I_3/e_2 = G_{32} = -1$ ℧

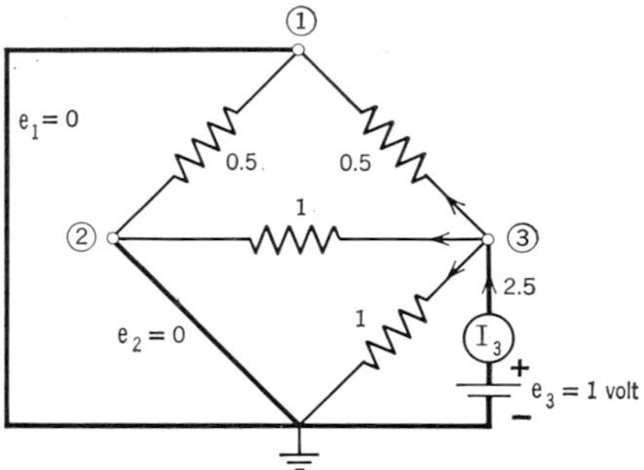

(i) $I_3/e_3 = G_{33} = 2.5$ ℧

FIG. 9 *(Continued)*

with the aid of an ideal ammeter and a 1-volt source. In general, this matrix takes the form

$$\begin{bmatrix} G_{11} & G_{12} & G_{13} & \cdots & G_{1n} \\ G_{21} & G_{22} & G_{23} & \cdots & G_{2n} \\ \cdot & \cdot & \cdot & \cdots & \cdot \\ G_{n1} & G_{n2} & G_{n3} & \cdots & G_{nn} \end{bmatrix} \tag{39}$$

If the scheme outlined in Fig. 9 is followed, the meanings of the G's are clear. For j equal to any number from 1 to n inclusive, G_{jj} is the current flowing from node j into the network per unit voltage increase in e_j. (e_j is the node-pair voltage, the arrow end of which terminates at node j.) In Fig. 9*a* ammeter I_1 is employed to measure G_{11}, in Fig. 9*e* ammeter I_2 is employed to measure G_{22}, and so on. All node-pair voltages except e_j are set equal to zero during this measurement since the scheme employed here makes use of the principle of superposition. G_{jk} is the current flowing into the network from node j per unit voltage increase in e_k; $j \neq k$. (e_k is the node-pair voltage, the arrow end of which terminates at node k.) In Fig. 9*b*, for example, ammeter I_1 is employed to measure G_{12}, the current flowing into the network per unit voltage increase in e_2 with all other independent node-pair voltages (e_1 and e_3) set equal to zero.

After the conductance matrix has been established and the source currents properly accounted for, the nodal solution is complete except for routine manipulations.

A deeper insight into the nodal method will be obtained, however, if the independent node-pair voltages selected do not have a common node. This subject will be pursued after the meaning of a *topological tree* has been established.

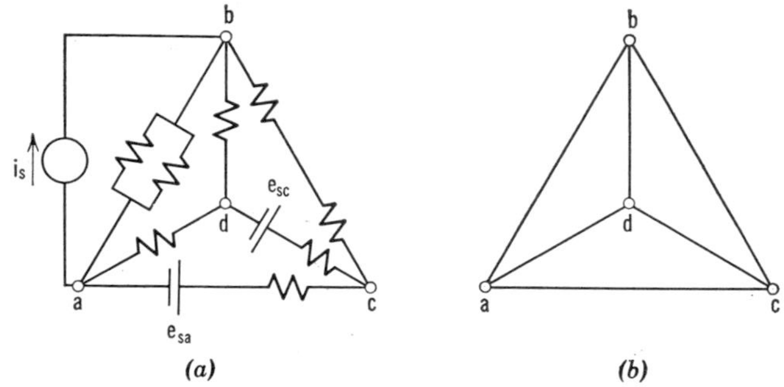

FIG. 10. (*b*) is a topological representation of the *unknown* branches of (*a*).

Network Topology.[2] Certain aspects of network behavior are brought into better perspective if the network is considered as a graph. In constructing this graph, we replace each branch of the network by a line, without regard to the circuit elements that go to make up this branch. Simple parallel elements may also be combined. The graph of the network given in Fig. 10*a*, for example, is illustrated in Fig. 10*b*. Where a branch consists solely of a current source, this branch may be omitted from the graph because it represents neither an unknown voltage nor an unknown current. For purposes of analysis, the b unknown branch voltages or the b unknown branch currents are of im-

[2] Topology, generally, is concerned with the form or structure of a geometrical entity, not with the precise size or shape of this entity. Network topology is concerned with the line graph formed by the interconnected network branches and not with the size, shape, or operating characteristics of the network elements that go to form the branches. In this sense, network topology is network geometry.

mediate importance. The known sources may be incorporated into the equilibrium equations at any appropriate stage of the analysis.

The network graph illustrated in Fig. 10*b* has four nodes, six branches, and three *inside loops* or *meshes* and is mappable on a plane. The graph may be considered as separating the entire area of the plane into four bounded areas, the three *inside* meshes and the *outside* area or *outside* mesh. In this connection, any undivided area having a boundary composed of branch lines is called a mesh. Since the outside area has such a boundary, it can be classed as a mesh. When the graph is mapped on a sphere, any one of the inside meshes of a plane graph like Fig. 10*b* can become the *outside* mesh. The process whereby this is accomplished is called topological warping.

A network solution based on loop currents requires that the correct number of *independent voltage equations* be employed. If based on node-pair voltages, the solution requires that the correct number of *independent current equations* be employed. In simple networks, *independent* equations can be obtained readily by inspection or by methods previously considered. Certain general aspects of this problem can be brought to light by the use of a topological *tree*.

A *tree* is a set of branches such that each node (or terminal) has connected to it at least one branch, the set contains no closed loops, and a single (unique) path can be found which joins any two nodes of the graph to which the tree is applicable.

Four open-ended graphs based on the circuit configuration of Fig. 10 are presented in Fig. 11. Since each of these open-ended graphs satisfies all the requirements of a tree, each graph is a tree corresponding to the network of Fig. 10.

In forming a tree (corresponding to a particular network) certain branches are of necessity opened. The branches thus opened are called links or link branches. The *links* of Fig. 11*a*, for example, are branches *ab, bc,* and *ca* and of Fig. 11*b* are *ab*, *dc*, and *da*. Obviously, the link branches and the tree branches combine to form the graph of the entire network.

The identification of the link currents with the loop currents leads directly to *measurable* loop currents. In cases where interest centers around particular currents, as, for example, around the input and output currents of the network, the input and output branches may be selected as links, the reason being that only one loop current traverses a link branch. Only one loop current is then required to obtain the current in this branch. Thus the tree may actually be selected with ulterior motives of this kind in mind.

Once a topological tree has been formed for a particular network, the determination of *independent* loop currents is a straightforward procedure. Simply close one link as, for example, link *ab* of Fig. 11*a*, and employ the loop thus formed as the path for loop current number 1. In this case

$$I_{\text{loop}} = I_{\text{link}} = I_{abda} = I_1$$

Then *open this link* and close another link to obtain the path of a second loop current and repeat this process until each link-branch current has been identified with a loop current. Thus we obtain loops for which

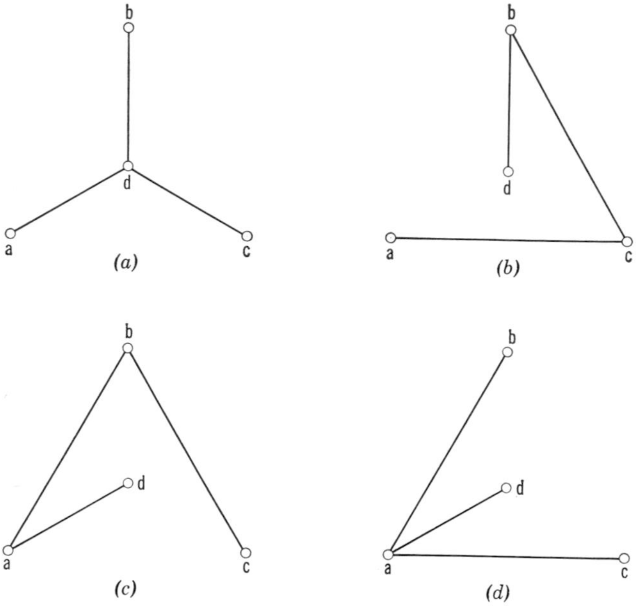

FIG. 11. Four topological trees corresponding to the network of Fig. 10.

independent voltage equations can be written. The loop currents are independent inasmuch as each can be measured with an ammeter in a different link branch. The correct number of independent loop currents is obtained since all the loop currents thus selected are required to obtain a network solution, and more than this number of loop currents will lead to voltage equations which are not independent of those already established.

The independent node-pair voltages required to effect a nodal solution can also be found readily from a topological tree. In elementary nodal analysis we ordinarily select one node of the network to be common to each of the node-pair voltages employed. In Fig. 11*a*, for example, we might select node *d* as common and use

$$e_1 = v_{ad}, \quad e_2 = v_{bd}, \quad \text{and} \quad e_3 = v_{cd}$$

as the three independent node-pair voltages required to effect a solution. Or we might select node *c* as common and use

$$e_1 = v_{ac}, \quad e_2 = v_{bc}, \quad \text{and} \quad e_3 = v_{dc}$$

as the required node-pair voltages. It should be noted that this method of selecting node-pair voltages automatically leads to $(n_t - 1)$ or n voltages, the correct number required to obtain a network solution. The *independence* of the node-pair voltages thus selected follows from:

1. One path only exists between the common node and any other node by way of tree branches.
2. The nodes are separated in potential one from the other by at least the potential difference of one tree branch.

One advantage of the topological approach to circuit analysis is that it opens up avenues of attack that might otherwise be overlooked. For example, the tree-branch voltages themselves form an independent set of node-pair voltages that can be used in a nodal analysis to effect a network solution. There are n_t nodes and, except for the first tree

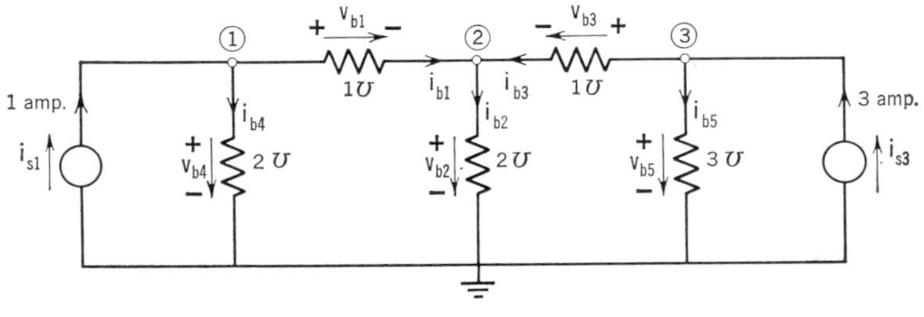

FIG. 12. For illustrative example.

branch (which will be considered to have two nodes incident upon it), every other tree branch utilizes one additional node in its specification. Thus n tree branches exist in a given tree, and hence n independent node-pair voltages can be obtained directly from the tree-branch voltages. The one requirement in selecting a set of node-pair voltages with which to carry out a network analysis is that these node-pair voltages correspond to the node-pair voltages of a topological tree.

In order to further illustrate the nodal method, the network given in Fig. 12 will be analyzed in three different ways employing node-pair voltages. First the e's of the tree shown in Fig. 13a will be taken as the independent node-pair voltages. Where a common node is employed, the self-conductances and mutual conductances may be obtained directly from an inspection of the network. Thus in mhos

$$\begin{array}{lll} G_{11} = 3 & G_{12} = -1 & G_{13} = 0 \\ G_{21} = -1 & G_{22} = 4 & G_{23} = -1 \\ G_{31} = 0 & G_{23} = -1 & G_{33} = 4 \quad \text{mhos} \end{array}$$

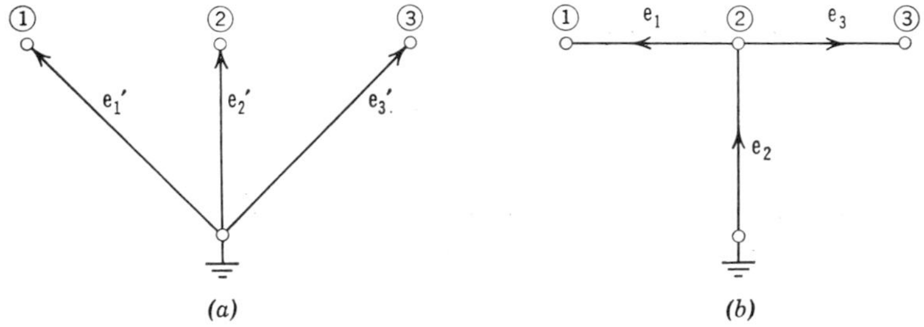

FIG. 13. Two trees corresponding to the network of Fig. 12.

Let it be required to find the voltages of nodes ① and ② relative to ground.

$$\text{Potential of node ①} = e_1' = \frac{\begin{vmatrix} 1 & -1 & 0 \\ 0 & 4 & -1 \\ 3 & -1 & 4 \end{vmatrix}}{\begin{vmatrix} 3 & -1 & 0 \\ -1 & 4 & -1 \\ 0 & -1 & 4 \end{vmatrix}} = \frac{18}{41} \quad \text{volt}$$

$$\text{Potential of node ②} = e_2' = \frac{\begin{vmatrix} 3 & 1 & 0 \\ -1 & 0 & -1 \\ 0 & 3 & 4 \end{vmatrix}}{41} = \frac{13}{41} \quad \text{volt}$$

If the tree given in Fig. 13b is used in the analysis, it is found that

$$\left.\begin{aligned} v_{b1} &= e_1 & i_{b1} &= 1e_1 \\ v_{b2} &= e_2 & i_{b2} &= 2e_2 \\ v_{b3} &= e_3 & i_{b3} &= 1e_3 \\ v_{b4} &= e_1 + e_2 & i_{b4} &= 2e_1 + 2e_2 \\ v_{b5} &= e_2 + e_3 & i_{b5} &= 3e_2 + 3e_3 \end{aligned}\right\} \tag{40}$$

At node ①: $i_{b1} + i_{b4} = 3e_1 + 2e_2 + 0e_3 = 1$ (41)

At node ②: $-i_{b1} + i_{b2} - i_{b3} = -1e_1 + 2e_2 - 1e_3 = 0$ (42)

At node ③: $i_{b3} + i_{b5} = 0e_1 + 3e_2 + 4e_3 = 3$ (43)

Solving for e_1 and e_2

$$e_1 = \frac{\begin{vmatrix} 1 & 2 & 0 \\ 0 & 2 & -1 \\ 3 & 3 & 4 \end{vmatrix}}{\begin{vmatrix} 3 & 2 & 0 \\ -1 & 2 & -1 \\ 0 & 3 & 4 \end{vmatrix}} = \frac{5}{41} \text{ volt}$$

$$e_2 = \frac{\begin{vmatrix} 3 & 1 & 0 \\ -1 & 0 & -1 \\ 0 & 3 & 4 \end{vmatrix}}{41} = \frac{13}{41} \text{ volt}$$

The potential of node ① of Fig. 12 relative to ground is

$$v_{b4} = e_1 + e_2 = \frac{18}{41} \text{ volt}$$

If the node-pair voltages e_1, e_2, and e_3 of Fig. 13b are employed in conjuuction with the principle of superposition, the self-conductances and mutual conductances are determined from the physical considerations outlined in Fig. 14. If it is recognized that $G_{21} = G_{12}$, $G_{31} = G_{13}$, $G_{32} = G_{23}$, and $G_{33} = 4$ mhos, the conductance matrix becomes

$$\begin{bmatrix} G_{11} & G_{12} & G_{13} \\ G_{21} & G_{22} & G_{23} \\ G_{31} & G_{32} & G_{33} \end{bmatrix} = \begin{bmatrix} 3 & 2 & 0 \\ 2 & 7 & 3 \\ 0 & 3 & 4 \end{bmatrix} \tag{44}$$

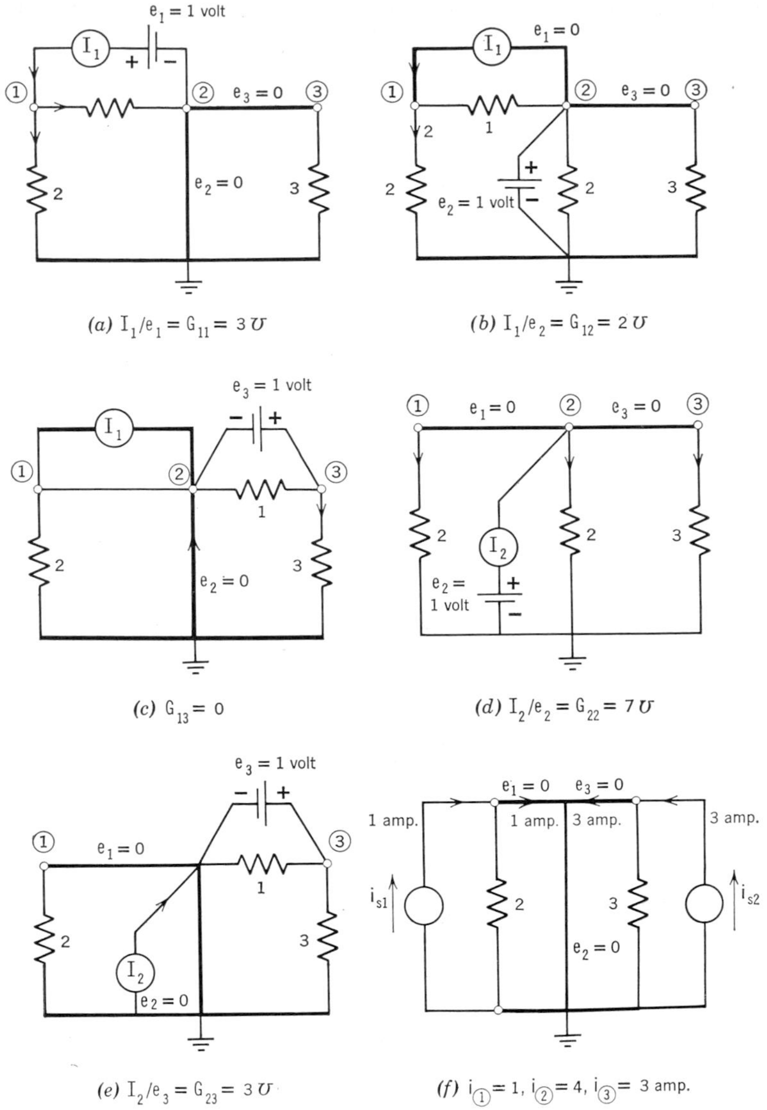

Fig. 14. Evaluation of self-conductance and mutual conductance of the network of Fig. 12 employing the node-pair voltages e_1, e_2, and e_3 of Fig. 13*b*.

Since the law of superposition is being employed in the establishment of the current equations at nodes ①, ②, and ③, it is necessary to include the currents directed toward these nodes from all the current sources with $e_1 = e_2 = e_3 = 0$. From Fig. 14*f*, we find that 1 ampere is directed toward node ① from the sources, 4 amperes are directed toward node ② from the sources, and 3 amperes toward node ③. Since the component currents resulting from e_1, e_2, and e_3 have been taken as positive away from the nodes, the three current equations may be written as follows:

$$3e_1 + 2e_2 + 0e_3 = 1 \tag{45}$$

$$2e_1 + 7e_2 + 3e_3 = 4 \tag{46}$$

$$0e_1 + 3e_2 + 4e_3 = 3 \tag{47}$$

Solving for e_1 and e_2

$$e_1 = \frac{\begin{vmatrix} 1 & 2 & 0 \\ 4 & 7 & 3 \\ 3 & 3 & 4 \end{vmatrix}}{\begin{vmatrix} 3 & 2 & 0 \\ 2 & 7 & 3 \\ 0 & 3 & 4 \end{vmatrix}} = \frac{5}{41} \text{ volt}$$

$$e_2 = \frac{\begin{vmatrix} 3 & 1 & 0 \\ 2 & 4 & 3 \\ 0 & 3 & 4 \end{vmatrix}}{41} = \frac{13}{41} \text{ volt}$$

From the three examples outlined above (and from others that can be developed) it is evident that node-pair voltages may be used in a variety of ways to effect network solutions. The same may be said for the use of loop currents. Ingenious combinations of node-pair voltages and loop currents as well as ingenious network theorems are often employed to obtain desired solutions. One of the fascinating aspects of network analysis is the variety of attack available to the analyst.

Duality. Where circuit elements are in series as in Fig. 15*a*, the natural choice for independent variable is current since it is common to each element. For the case considered

$$R_1 i_b + R_2 i_b + R_3 i_b = v_b \tag{48}$$

or

$$R_b = (R_1 + R_2 + R_3) = \frac{v_b}{i_b} \tag{48a}$$

Where elements are in parallel as in Fig. 15*b*, the natural choice for independent variable is the voltage which is common to (or across) each of the elements. In Fig. 15*b*

$$G_1 v_b + G_2 v_b + G_3 v_b = i_b \qquad (49)$$

or

$$G_b = (G_1 + G_2 + G_3) = \frac{i_b}{v_b} \qquad (49a)$$

The similarity in form of equations (48) and (49) is evident. In one, the voltage law is used to establish the basic relationship between i_b and v_b; in the other, the current law is employed. In one, resistances are used; in the other, conductances.

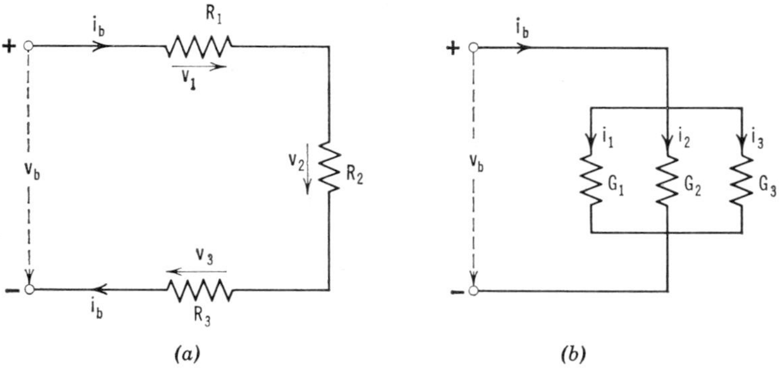

FIG. 15. $v_b = v_1 + v_2 + v_3$ and $i_b = i_1 + i_2 + i_3$.

This dualism extends throughout the two fundamental methods of network analysis. One method utilizes loop currents, resistances, voltage equations, and voltage sources. The other utilizes node-pair voltages, conductances, current equations, and current sources. Measurable independent loop currents may be identified with the current flowing in the link branches of the network whereas measurable independent node-pair voltages may be identified with the tree-branch voltages. The equilibrium equations in one method of analysis are based upon

$$\sum v_{\text{around a closed loop}} = 0$$

The equilibrium equations of the other are based upon

$$\sum i_{\text{directed toward a node}} = 0$$

Wherever all the elements of one system can be put into a one-to-one correspondence with the elements of another system, the correspondence is referred to as *duality*. Duality can therefore exist between the loop-current and node-pair-voltage methods of analysis, one method being the dual of the other. From an algebraic point of view, two networks are *duals* if the nodal equations of the one are of the same form as the loop equations of the other. The equations of equilibrium for the network of Fig. 16*a* which has two independent loop currents are, for example,

$$\begin{aligned} R_{11}i_1 + R_{12}i_2 &= e_{s1} \\ R_{21}i_1 + R_{22}i_2 &= e_{s2} \end{aligned} \tag{50}$$

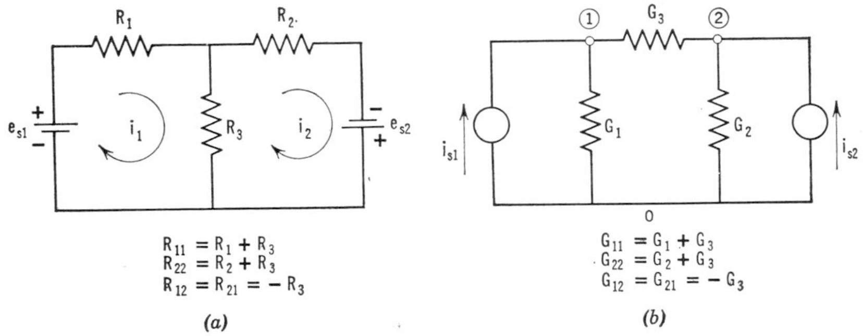

FIG. 16. Dual networks.

The equations of equilibrium for the network of Fig. 16*b* which has two independent node-pair voltages are of the form

$$\begin{aligned} G_{11}e_1 + G_{12}e_2 &= i_{s1} \\ G_{21}e_1 + G_{22}e_2 &= i_{s2} \end{aligned} \tag{51}$$

Except for the interpretations given to the symbols in equations (50) and (51), these equations are identical. The fact that the forms of the equations are identical makes them duals. Obviously, duality is a mutual relationship. Equations (50) are as much the dual of equations (51) as equations (51) are the dual of equations (50).

From a graphical point of view, two networks are duals when meshes (around which $\sum v = 0$) in one network are in a one-to-one correspondence with the nodes (at which $\sum i = 0$) in the other network. In this connection a mesh is regarded as a region or area bounded by network branches or voltage drops. With this interpretation of the term mesh, *a network branch divides exactly two meshes* (or regions) provided that the network graph can be mapped on a plane or sphere (without cross-overs). Correspondingly, *a network branch joins exactly two nodes.* It will be remembered that a network possesses $(n_t - 1) = n$

nodes at which independent current relationships can be established. The dual of this network will possess $(m_t - 1) = l$ meshes or loops around which independent voltage relationships can be established. (m_t symbolizes the total number of meshes or regions of a particular graph.) The graph of Fig. 16*a*, for example, is composed of three meshes, *two inside meshes* around which i_1 and i_2 circulate and *one outside mesh* (or region) bounded by the $e_{s1} - R_1$ and $R_2 - e_{s2}$ branches. The outside region is, of course, as much a mesh as either of the inside regions since it is bounded by network branches. Furthermore, if Fig. 16*a* were mapped on a sphere and topologically warped (by stretching), either of the present inside meshes could be made to be the "outside" mesh.

Some of the major correspondences which exist between the loop-current and node-pair-voltage solutions are listed in Table I. Others

TABLE I

Element Involved	Solution	
	Loop Current	Node-Pair Voltage
Equilibrium equations	voltage $\sum v = 0$	current $\sum i = 0$
Number of independent equations	$b - n = l$	$(b - l) = n$
Basic constituent	branch voltage	branch current
Energizing element	voltage source	current source
Network variable	loop current	node-pair voltage
Independent-network variables	link-branch currents	tree-branch voltages
Circuit parameter	resistance	conductance
Parameters add	in series	in parallel
Infinite parameter	$R = \infty$ (open circuit)	$G = \infty$ (short circuit)
Zero parameter	$R = 0$ (short circuit)	$G = 0$ (open circuit)
Topographical entity	mesh	node
Any topological branch	*divides* exactly two regions (or meshes) providing the graph will map on a plane (or sphere)	*joins* exactly two nodes

will become evident as we proceed. It should be noted that, whereas $l = n$ in dual networks, l is not necessarily equal to n in a particular network.

Graphical Construction of Dual Networks. In constructing a network which is to be the dual of a specified network, all of the voltage drops encountered on the contour of a mesh of one network are transformed into current paths emanating from the corresponding node of the other, or vice versa. A simple graphical scheme for developing the correspondence between $\sum v = 0$ in one network with $\sum i = 0$ in the other is depicted in Fig. 17*c*. The original network in this case is Fig. 17*a*

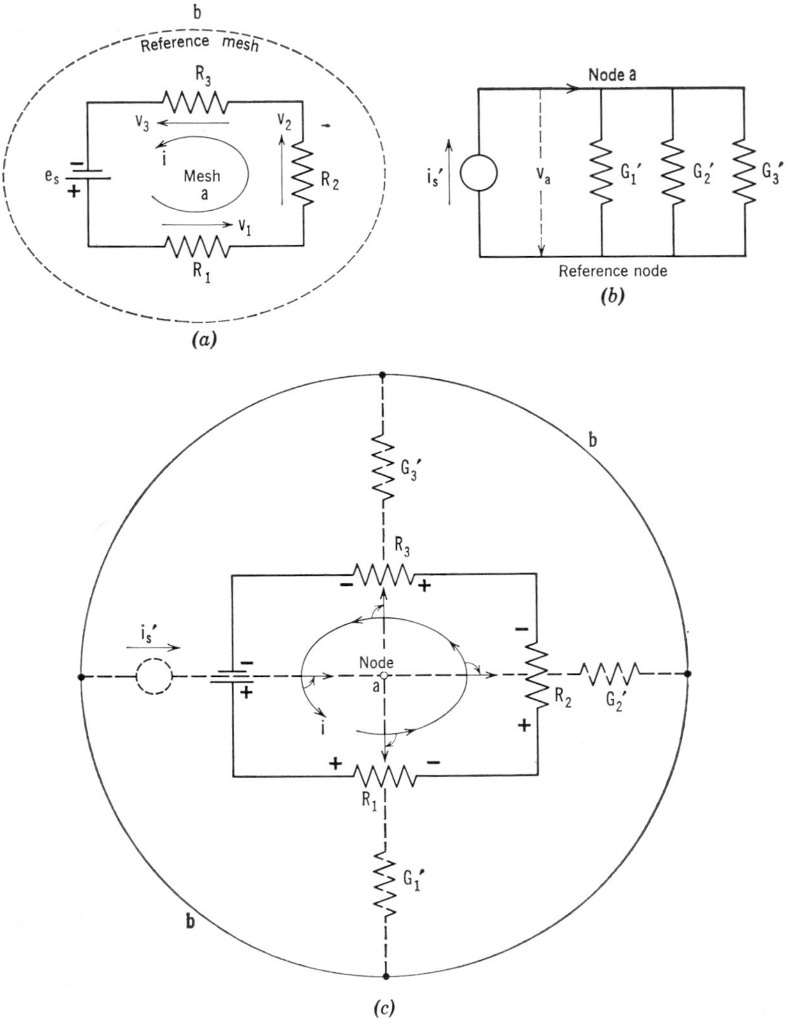

FIG. 17. (*a*) and (*b*) are duals; (*c*) indicates how (*b*) is obtained from (*a*).

which consists of a single loop (or one branch) and two meshes, say, mesh *a* (inside the current loop) and mesh *b* (outside the current loop). Node *a* of the proposed dual corresponds to mesh *a* of the original circuit and similarly for node *b* and mesh *b*.

The details involved in the graphical construction of a dual are illustrated in Fig. 17*c*. From node *a* in Fig. 17*c*, for example, a line is so drawn that it connects node *a* and the reference node as it passes through one element (or voltage drop) of the original loop. This process is repeated for each voltage drop involved in $\sum v = 0$ with due regard for positive direction. Some orderly convention must be adopted for correlating positive directions in the dual with those which have been selected for analysis of the original. The simple scheme illustrated in Fig. 17*c* consists of turning the arrow direction of the loop current (as it crosses the line connecting node *a* and the reference node) in the direction we select for positive current flow in the branch of the dual which is being generated. For the case considered, the positive direction of current flow is selected as being *from* node *a to* the reference node. Thus the loop-current direction in being turned clockwise for each of the three voltage drops (v_1, v_2, and v_3 of Fig. 17*a*) determines the positive direction of the current flow in the three corresponding paths of the dual as being *from node a to the reference node.* In applying this scheme to the voltage source e_s, we note that the loop-current direction coincides with a voltage rise as it passes through e_s. The positive direction of the current source, i_s, in the dual which replaces e_s of the original network is therefore obtained by turning the loop-current direction in the counter*clockwise* direction. The positive direction of i_s' is thus determined to be *from* the reference node *to* node *a* as indicated in Fig. 17*b* or Fig. 17*c*. (Any other scheme for determining positive circuit directions in the dual is as good provided that it is used consistently.)

The numerical values of the mhos in the dual network are related to the ohmic values in the original network by the normalizing factor g_n^2. Thus

$$G_j' = g_n^2 R_j \tag{52}$$

where g_n is arbitrarily selected.

A current source, i_s', of the dual network is made to correspond to a voltage source of the original network by a normalizing factor g_n if the power delivered by i_s' is to be equal to the power delivered by e_s. Thus for P_{es} to equal P_{is}

$$P_{es} = \frac{e_s^2}{R} = \frac{i_s'^2}{G'} = P_{is}' \tag{53}$$

from which

$$\frac{i_s'}{e_s} = \sqrt{\frac{G'}{R}} = g_n \tag{54}$$

If, for example, in Fig. 17, $R_1 = 2$, $R_2 = 1$, and $R_3 = 3$ ohms and $e_s = 12$ volts, the equation for equilibrium is

$$2i + 1i + 3i = 12 \text{ volts} \qquad (i = 2 \text{ amperes})$$

If a normalizing factor, g_n^2, of 4 is arbitrarily selected,

$$G_1' = 8, \quad G_2' = 4, \quad \text{and} \quad G_3' = 12 \text{ mhos}$$

Also $i_s' = (2 \times 12)$ amperes and the equation for equilibrium of the dual network is

$$8v_a + 4v_a + 12v_a = 24 \text{ amperes} \qquad (v_a = 1 \text{ volt})$$

In Fig. 17*a*

$$P_{es} = 12 \times 2 = 24 \text{ watts}$$

In Fig. 17*b*

$$P_{is}' = 1 \times 24 = 24 \text{ watts}$$

The graphical process illustrated in Fig. 17 is extended to a four-mesh network in Fig. 18. It will be observed that all of the elements common to loop 1 of Fig. 18*a* appear as elements which are common to node ① of the dual network; similarly for the other loops and corresponding nodes. The dual network contains the same number of branches as the original network if the three parallel paths which connect to node ① (and which are derived from a single series branch of the original network) are counted as a single branch. It is, of course, evident that for algebraic duality l (the number of independent loop currents) of one network must equal n (the number of independent nodes) of the other. For $l = n$

$$m_t = l + 1 = n + 1 = n_t$$

where m_t is the total number of meshes and n_t is the total number of nodes.

The manner in which the graphical process described above may be reversed is illustrated in Fig. 19. Here the dual of a dual is constructed to obtain the original network. (See Fig. 18.) Since duality is a mutual relationship, the construction of a dual goes *from* meshes *to* nodes (if the original network is viewed as consisting of meshes) or *from* nodes *to* meshes (if the original network is viewed in light of nodes as the topological entities). An example of the latter situation is given in Fig. 19*a*. Each current directed away from node ① corresponds to a voltage drop in mesh 1 of Fig. 19*b*; similarly for the other corresponding nodes and meshes.

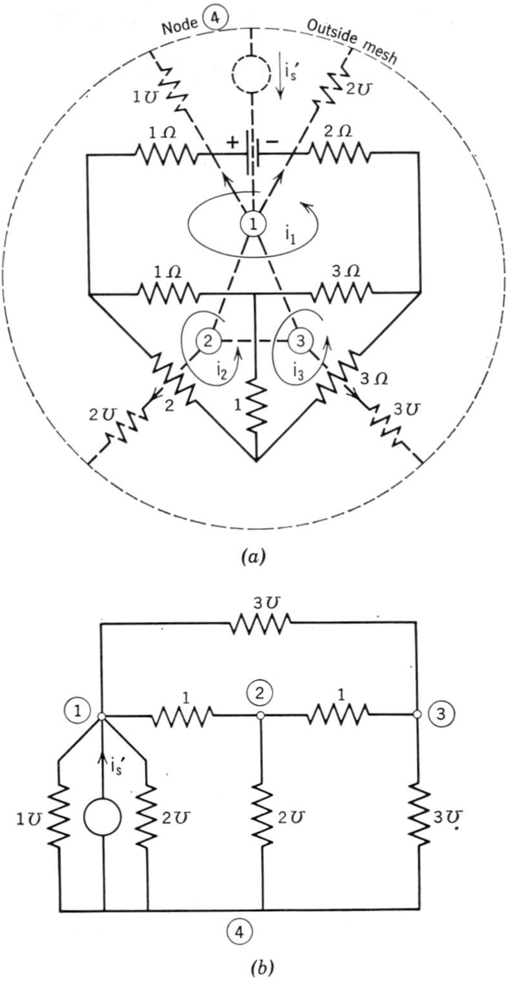

FIG. 18. (a) Original network. (b) Dual network, $g_n = 1$.

A qualification has previously been made that, if a geometrical dual of a network is to be constructed, the graph of the original network must be mappable on a plane or sphere. The reason for this qualification is that the construction requires the network branches to be so oriented

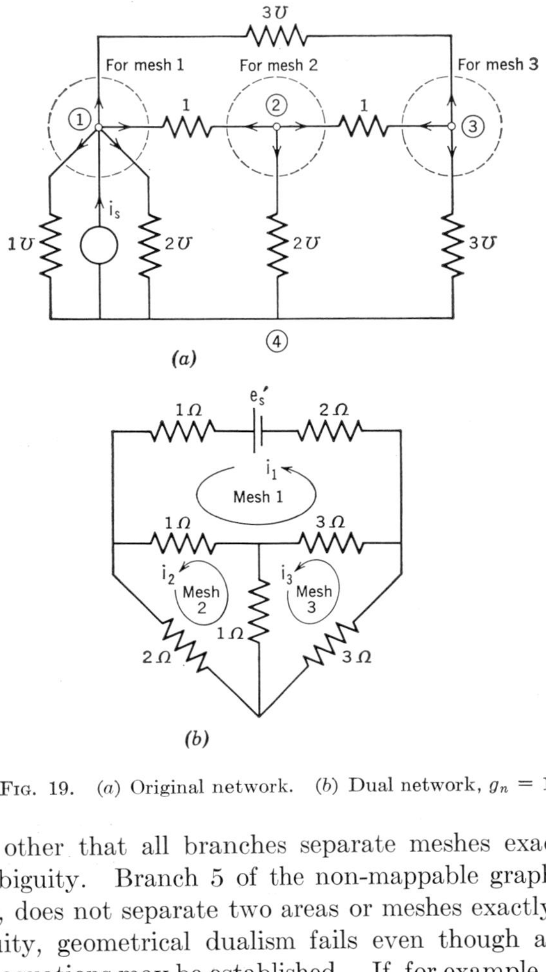

FIG. 19. (a) Original network. (b) Dual network, $g_n = 1$.

one to the other that all branches separate meshes exactly, that is, without ambiguity. Branch 5 of the non-mappable graph of Fig. 20b, for example, does not separate two areas or meshes exactly. Owing to this ambiguity, geometrical dualism fails even though a dual set of equilibrium equations may be established. If, for example, the numbers on the graphs of Fig. 20 refer to ohms resistance, the three equilibrium equations for either network are

$$\begin{aligned} 7i_1 - 2i_2 - 3i_3 &= 0 \\ -2i_1 + 11i_2 - 5i_3 &= 0 \\ -3i_1 - 5i_2 + 14i_3 &= 0 \end{aligned} \tag{55}$$

A dual set of equations may be written as

$$
\begin{aligned}
7e_1 - 2e_2 - 3e_3 &= 0 \\
-2e_1 + 11e_2 - 5e_3 &= 0 \\
-3e_1 - 5e_2 + 14e_3 &= 0
\end{aligned}
\tag{56}
$$

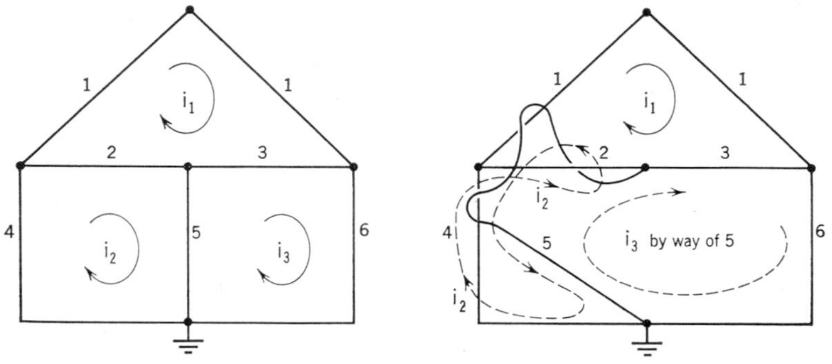

(a) (b)

FIG. 20. (a) A mappable graph. (b) A non-mappable graph.

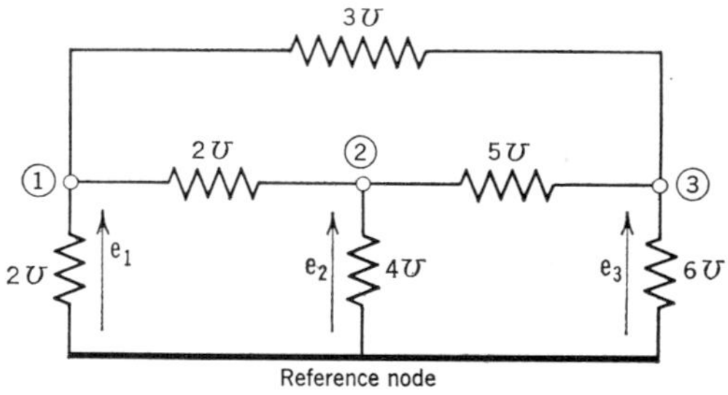

FIG. 21. Dual of Fig. 20a. (Prob. 19.)

A network to which equations (56) are applicable is given in Fig. 21, where the node-pair voltages e_1, e_2, and e_3 are the voltages of nodes ①, ②, and ③ relative to the reference node.

PROBLEMS

1. A three-branch network is given in Fig. 22 where the branch voltages are

$$v_{b1} = (-2 + 3i_{b1}) \qquad v_{b2} = (-4 + 2i_{b2}) \qquad v_{b3} = 2i_{b3}$$

(a) Write the required number of current and voltage equations (to effect a network solution) employing i_{b1}, i_{b2}, and i_{b3} as independent variables, and evaluate i_{b2} therefrom.

(b) Write two voltage equations employing loop currents i_1 and i_2 as independent

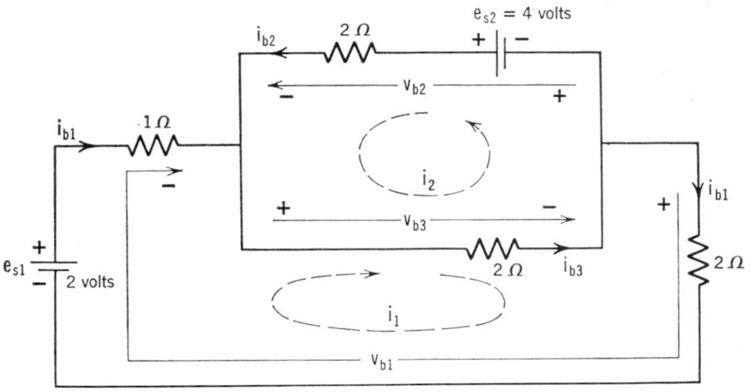

FIG. 22. Prob. 1.

variables starting with

$$3i_{b1} + 2i_{b3} = 2 \qquad 2i_{b2} + 2i_{b3} = 4$$

Evaluate i_{b3} as $(i_1 + i_2)$.

2. In Fig. 20*a*, page 38, is given a six-branch network where the numbers alongside the branches indicate ohms of resistance as well as the designations of the branches. Thus

$$R_{b1} = 2, \quad R_{b2} = 2, \quad R_{b3} = 3, \quad R_{b4} = 4, \quad R_{b5} = 5, \quad R_{b6} = 6 \text{ ohms}$$

The energizing sources are not shown in Fig. 20, the assumption being that any one or all of the branches may have voltage sources in series with the branch resistances.

Write three voltage equations employing the loop currents i_1, i_2, and i_3 as the independent variables. Let the source voltages in loop 1 be $E_1 = e_{s1} + e_{s2} + e_{s3}$; the source voltages in loop 2 be $E_2 = e_{s4} + e_{s5} - e_{s2}$; and the source voltages in loop 3 be $E_3 = e_{s6} - e_{s5} - e_{s3}$.

Note: With only a very little practice, voltage equations of this kind can be written down directly from an inspection of the network by mental applications of the principle of superposition.

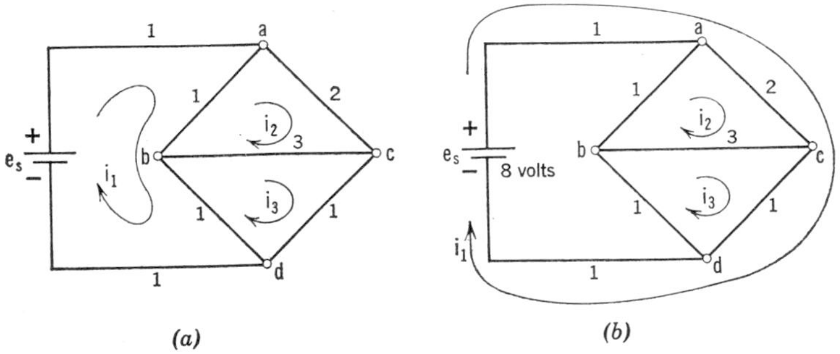

FIG. 23. The numerical values placed alongside the branches (or parts of branches) refer to ohms resistance.

3. Refer to Fig. 23*a*.

(*a*) Determine by inspection the numerical values of b and n_t, and specify n and l numerically.

(*b*) Write the voltage equilibrium equations employing numerical coefficients and the loop currents indicated in Fig. 23*a*.

(*c*) Evaluate the current i_1 per volt of e_s.

(*d*) Determine the current in the 3-ohm resistance, namely, $(i_2 - i_3)$ if $e_s = 8$ volts.

4. Refer to Fig. 23*b*.

(*a*) Write the voltage equilibrium equations employing numerical coefficients and the loop currents indicated there.

(*b*) Determine the power delivered to the network by $e_s = 8$ volts.

(*c*) Evaluate the current in the 3-ohm resistance, namely, $(i_2 - i_3)$.

5. (*a*) Determine by inspection the numerical values of b and n_t of Fig. 24 and specify the numerical values of n and l.

(*b*) What physical restrictions are imposed by the loop currents shown in Fig. 24 which render them insufficient (in number) to effect a network solution?

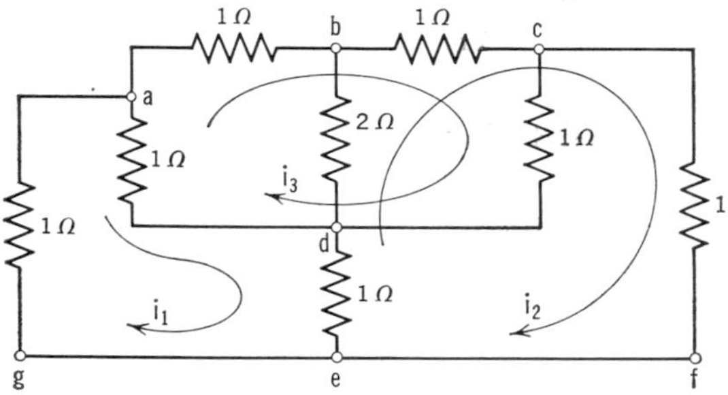

FIG. 24. Problems 5, 6, and 18.

(*c*) What is the correct numerical value of the resistance determinant of the network employing measurable currents as loop currents? By *resistance determinant* is meant the determinant of the resistance matrix which characterizes the network.

6. (*a*) Construct a topological tree corresponding to the network shown in Fig. 24 such that

1. Loop current i_1 is identified with link-branch current i_{ega}.
2. Loop current i_2 is identified with link-branch current i_{cfe}.
3. Loop current i_3 is identified with link-branch current i_{ab}.
4. Loop current i_4 is identified with link-branch current i_{bc}.

(*b*) Repeat part (*a*) above for

$$i_1 = i_{ega}, \quad i_2 = i_{cfe}, \quad i_3 = i_{bd}, \quad i_4 = i_{bc}$$

7. (*a*) Construct four topological trees corresponding to Fig. 23*a*. Draw the tree in solid lines (oriented with respect to the nodes *a*, *b*, *c*, *d*) and the remainder of the circuit, the link branches, in dotted lines.

(*b*) On each of the above diagrams, show the three independent loop currents that are obtained by identifying loop currents with link-branch currents.

8. Given the network illustrated in Fig. 25.

(*a*) Calculate the current through the branch *ab* which contains the 1-volt battery using the loop currents shown in Fig. 25*a*.

(*b*) Again calculate the current through branch *ab* employing the loop currents shown in Fig. 25*b*. All resistance values remain at 1 ohm as indicated in Fig. 25*a*.

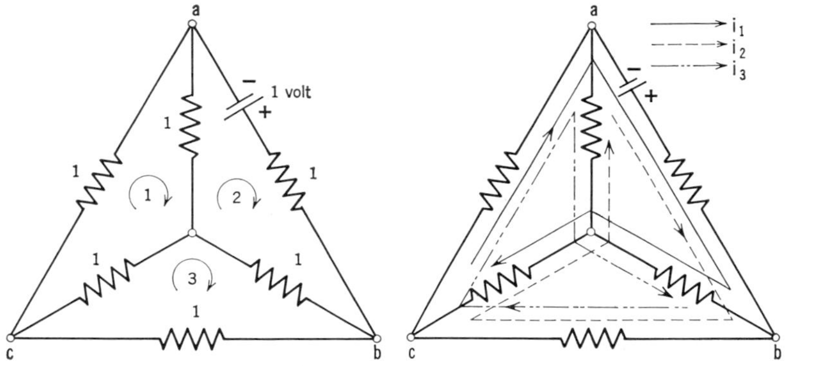

(a) (b)

FIG. 25. Prob. 8. (Resistance values refer to ohms.)

9. (a) Write the voltage equilibrium equations for the network illustrated in Fig. 26a for the loop currents indicated.

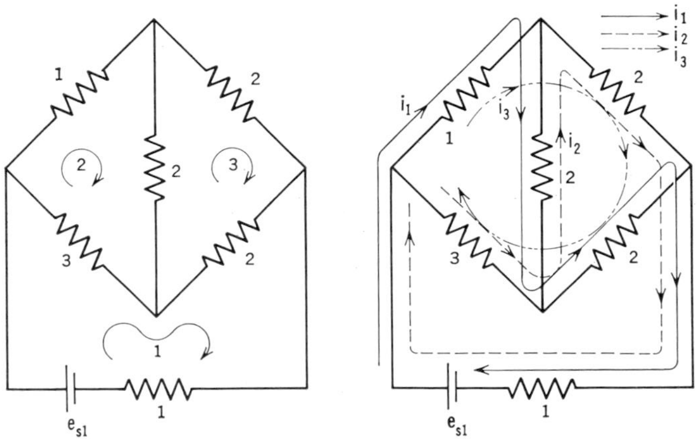

(a) (b)

FIG. 26. Problems 9 and 10. (Resistance values refer to ohms.)

(b) What is the numerical value of the resistance determinant of the network, that is, the determinant of the resistance matrix which characterizes the network?

10. (a) Write the voltage equilibrium equations for the network given in Fig. 26b for the loop currents indicated.

(b) What is the numerical value of the determinant of the resistance matrix which characterizes the network?

11. (a) In Fig. 27, a resistance matrix is formed which corresponds to the loop currents shown there. What is the numerical value of the determinant of this matrix?

(b) What is the correct value of the resistance determinant of the network?

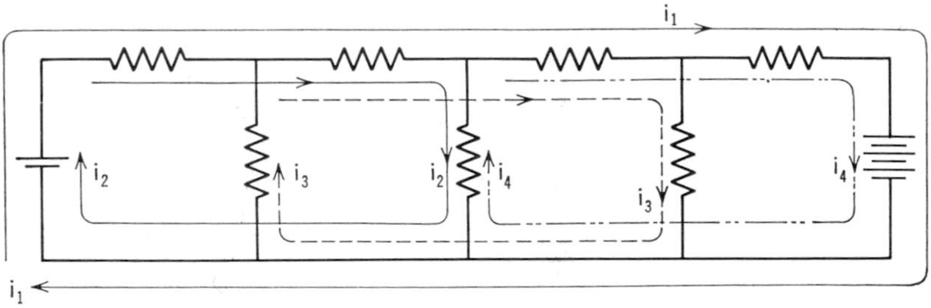

FIG. 27. Prob. 11. (All resistance values are 1 ohm.)

12. Refer to Fig. 28.
(a) Find the potential of node x relative to ground.
(b) Find the potential of point y relative to ground.

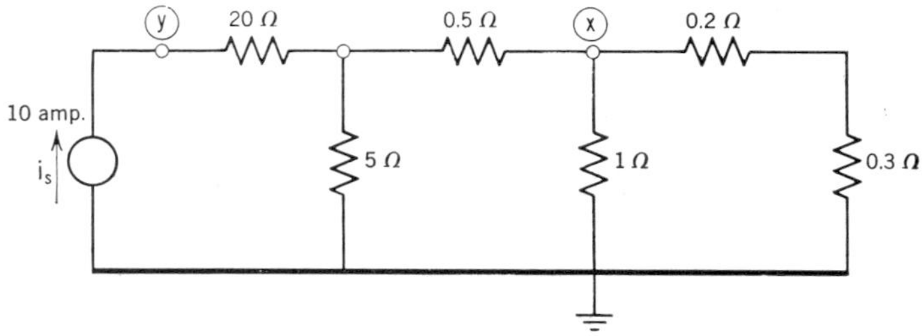

FIG. 28. Prob. 12.

13. (a) Determine by inspection the numerical values of b and n_t of the network illustrated in Fig. 29 and specify the numerical values of n (the number of independent nodes) and l (the number of independent loops).

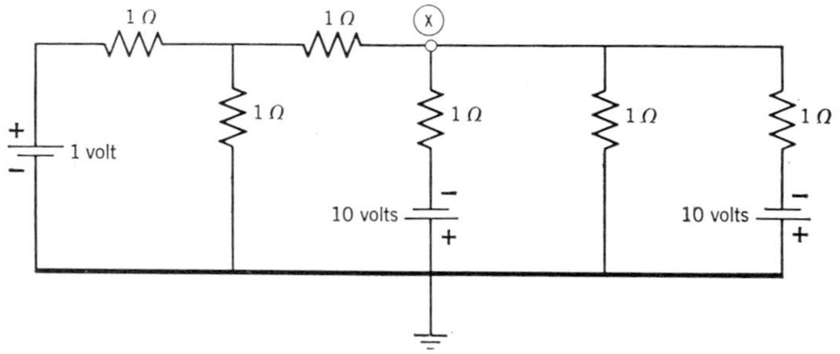

FIG. 29. Problems 13 and 14.

(b) Transform the three voltage sources and associated series resistances to equivalent current sources with due regard for positive directions, and draw the equivalent network incorporating the three current sources.

14. Find the voltage of node x relative to ground in the network given in Fig. 29.

15. Find the potentials of nodes ① and ② of Fig. 30 relative to ground, employing v_1 and v_2 as independent node-pair voltages.

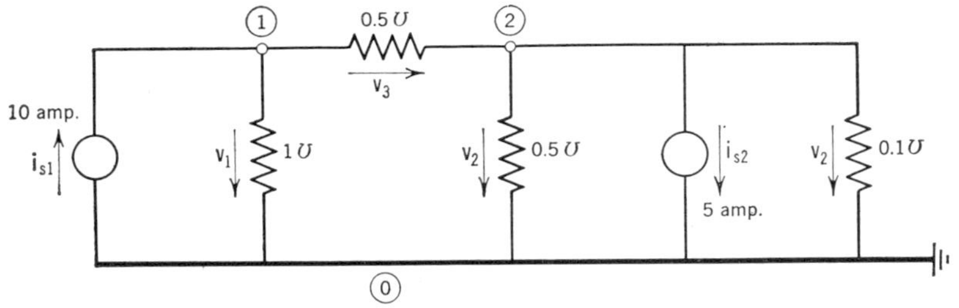

Fig. 30. Problems 15 and 16.

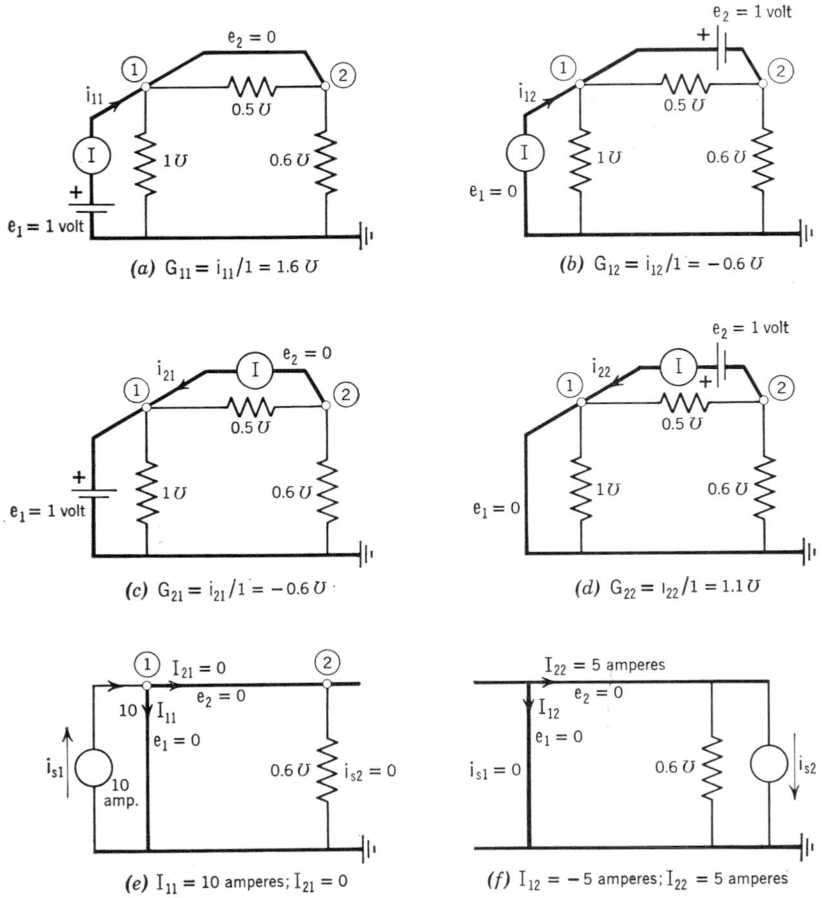

Fig. 31. Prob. 17. For use in solving a problem by superposition.

16. Repeat Problem 15 employing v_1 and v_3 as independent node-pair voltages.

17. Determine the potentials of nodes ① and ② in Fig. 30 employing the principle of superposition as it applies to

$$e_1 = v_1 \quad e_2 = v_3 \quad i_{s1} \quad i_{s2}$$

Sketches showing G_{11}, G_{12}, G_{21}, G_{22} and the component currents at nodes ① and ② are given in Fig. 31. This exercise in superposition is designed to show how the effects of e_1, e_2, i_{s1}, and i_{s2} may be considered separately in the analysis of the circuit. When all effects are combined it will be found that

$$1.6e_1 - 0.6e_2 = I_{11} + I_{12} = 5 \text{ amperes}$$

$$-0.6e_1 + 1.1e_2 = I_{22} + I_{21} = 5 \text{ amperes}$$

18. Construct the dual of the network given in Fig. 24, page 40, without regard to sources with the construction going *from* meshes *to* nodes. Employ a normalizing factor (g_n^2) of 4.

19. Construct the dual of the network illustrated in Fig. 21, page 38, with the construction going *from* nodes *to* meshes. Let g_n^2, the normalizing factor, equal unity.

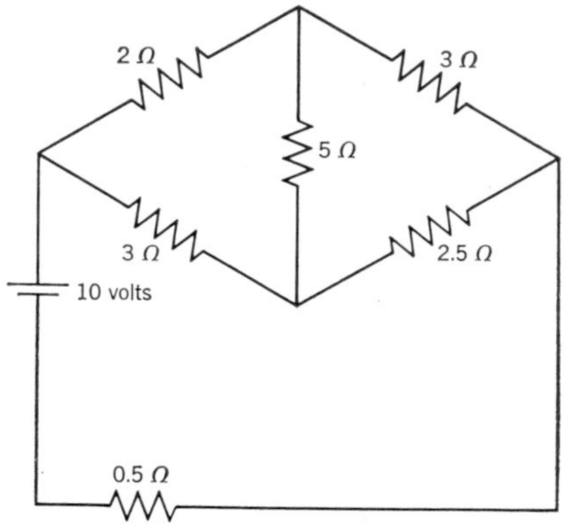

FIG. 32. Prob. 20.

20. Construct the dual of the network shown in Fig. 32 with the construction going *from* meshes *to* nodes. $g_n^2 = 2$.

21. Evaluate v_a in Fig. 7, page 16, employing one known loop current and two unknown loop currents.

chapter **II**

Instantaneous Current, Voltage, and Power

Large segments of circuit analysis are devoted to the steady-state responses of circuits which are energized with alternating currents or voltages having approximate sinusoidal time variations. Several definitions or conventions involving alternating quantities of this kind must be learned and several concepts must be mastered before alternating currents and voltages can be handled with facility.

Early History. The first successful electrical power system in the United States was probably Edison's direct-current installation in New York City. This station was performing creditably in 1885. Alternating-current power systems began commercially with the Great Barrington (Massachusetts) installation in 1886.

During the decade 1907–1917, which followed the invention of the three-electrode vacuum tube, sustained oscillatory currents at high frequencies became a reality. These high-frequency oscillatory or alternating currents are essential to all modern radio, television, and radar forms of communication.

The outstanding advantage of a-c systems (as contrasted with d-c systems) is the relative ease with which alternating potential differences can be generated, amplified, and otherwise transformed in magnitude. The result is that, at the present time, approximately 95 per cent of the electrical energy consumed in the United States is generated, transmitted, and actually utilized in the form of alternating current. In the power field the annual energy consumption amounts to about 600 billion kilowatthours. In the communication field several thousand broadcast stations (of the AM, FM, and television variety) employ alternating potential differences to generate their carrier waves.

Generation of Alternating Potential Differences. When magnets are moved relative to electrical conductors as shown in Fig. 1, there is induced in the conductors a potential difference or emf. In accordance with Faraday's law, $e = -N\frac{d\phi}{dt}$ or its equivalent $e = N'Blv$ and the emf varies with time. For the instant depicted in Fig. 1, the application of one of the rules for finding the magnitude and direction of an induced emf will show that the emf induced in the armature conductors is zero, since at that instant no flux is being cut by these conductors. One-eighth revolution later, however, the induced emf is of maximum magnitude and of such a direction as to establish a voltage rise *from* terminal *a to* terminal *d*. One-quarter of a revolution after the position shown in Fig. 1 the induced emf will again be zero. Three-eighths of

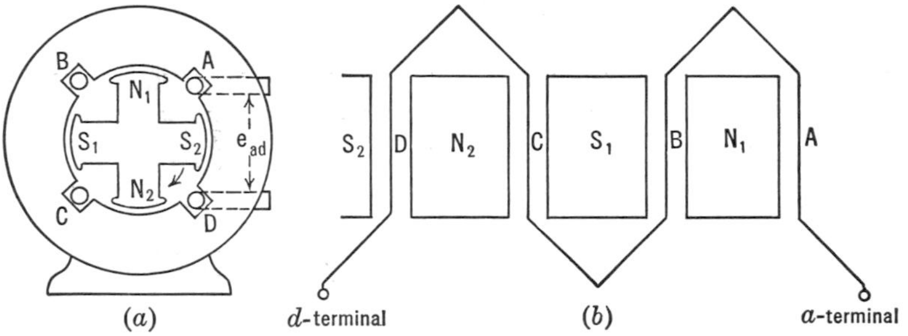

FIG. 1. (*a*) A four-pole, four-conductor a-c generator of the revolving field type. (*b*) Developed diagram showing method of connecting conductors *A*, *B*, *C*, and *D*. Pole faces are toward the reader.

a revolution from the reference position the emf will again be of maximum magnitude but so directed as to establish a voltage rise *from* terminal *d to* terminal *a*.

Thus the terminals *a* and *d* of the generator become alternately positive and negative relative to each other, and a time-varying potential difference of the general nature shown in Oscillogram 1 (page 51) is developed.

In communication systems, vacuum tubes or transistors (working in conjunction with suitable electrical circuits) produce alternating currents of higher frequencies than those obtainable with rotating equipment. A common triode oscillator circuit is shown schematically in Fig. 2. The a-c energy developed across the output terminals is actually derived from the d-c supply voltage labeled E_{bb}, but it is not expected that the reader will understand the conversion from direct current to alternating current which takes place in Fig. 2 until after he has studied the subject of electrical resonance. The only purpose in mentioning the triode oscillator at this stage is to acquaint the reader with the fact that high-frequency alternating currents can be produced with very simple circuit configurations. Many simple circuit configurations other than that shown in Fig. 2 may be used for this purpose.

Definition of Alternating Current. An alternating current, as the name implies, goes through a series of different values both positive

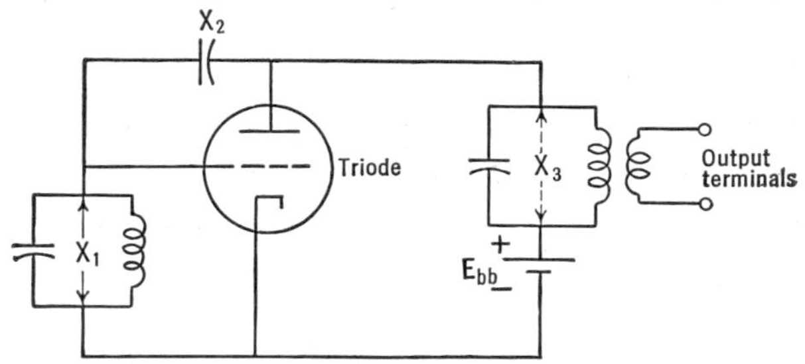

FIG. 2. Circuit arrangement of a simple triode oscillator.

and negative in a period of time T, after which it continuously repeats this same series of values in a cyclic manner as indicated in Fig. 3*c*.

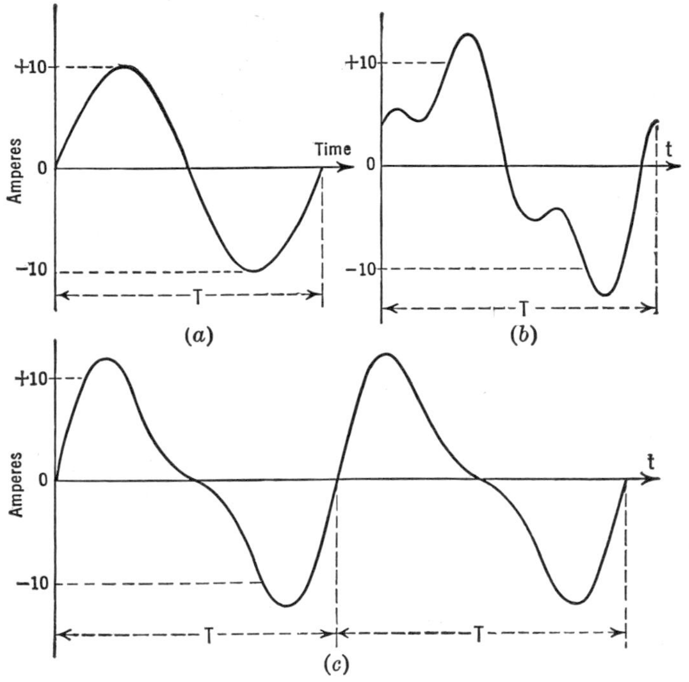

FIG. 3. Wave forms of three a-c variations. T is the period (or duration) of one cycle.

In the current A.I.E.E. "Definitions of Electrical Terms," an *alternating current* is defined in terms of a periodic current, and the latter in terms of an oscillating current.

" An *oscillating current* is a current which alternately increases and decreases in magnitude with respect to time according to some definite law.

" A *periodic current* is an oscillating current the values of which recur at equal intervals of time. Thus

$$i = I_0 + I_1 \sin(\omega t + \alpha_1) + I_2 \sin(2\omega t + \alpha_2) + \cdots \tag{1}$$

where i = the instantaneous value of a periodic current at time t

$I_0, I_1, I_2, \alpha_1, \alpha_2$ = constants (positive, negative, or zero)

$$\omega = \frac{2\pi}{T} \qquad (T \text{ being the period})$$

" An *alternating current* is a periodic current, the average value of which over a period is zero. The equation for an alternating current is the same as that for a periodic current except that $I_0 = 0$."

Examples. In Fig. 3*a*, $i = 10 \sin \omega t$ amperes; in Fig. 3*b*, $i = 10 \sin \omega t + 4 \sin (3\omega t + 90°)$ amperes; and, in Fig. 3*c*, $i = 10 \sin \omega t + 4 \sin 2\omega t$ amperes.

Period and Cycle. The *period* of an alternating current or voltage is the smallest value of time which separates recurring values[1] of the alternating quantity. The period of time which separates these recurring values is shown in Fig. 3 as T, the symbol normally employed to designate the *period* of one cycle of an alternating quantity.

One complete set of positive and negative values of an alternating quantity is called a *cycle*. Thus Figs. 3*a* and 3*b* each depict one cycle. A cycle is sometimes specified in terms of angular measure since, as will be shown presently, ω in equation (1) actually represents angular velocity. One complete cycle is then said to extend over 360° or 2π radians of angular measure.

Frequency. Frequency is the number of cycles per second. Unless otherwise stated, the term " cycles " implies " cycles per second."

In the rotating machine of Fig. 1, it is apparent that a complete cycle is produced in the armature conductors when these conductors are cut by the flux from a pair of poles or, in this case, one-half revolution of the rotating field. Each conductor will be cut by two pairs of poles in one revolution of the field structure, and two complete cycles of emf will be developed in the armature winding per revolution.

In general, for a p-pole machine the number of cycles per revolution is $p/2$, and, if the speed of rotation in revolutions per second is repre-

[1] The mathematical meaning of " recurring values " is implied in this definition, namely, that at least one complete *set* of values intervenes between two recurring values.

sented by rps, the equation for frequency is

$$f = \frac{p\ (\text{rps})}{2} \quad \text{cycles per second} \tag{2}$$

Since T is the time (or duration) of one cycle, it is plain that

$$f = \frac{1}{T} \quad \text{cycles per second} \tag{3}$$

if T is expressed in seconds.

Example. Let it be required to find the *frequency* and the *period* of the emf generated in the armature winding of Fig. 1 if the speed of rotation is 1800 rpm.

$$f = \frac{4}{2} \times \frac{1800}{60} = 60 \text{ cycles per second}$$

$$T = \frac{1}{f} = \frac{1}{60} \quad \text{second}$$

The common power plant frequencies in use today are 60, 50, and 25 cycles, the first mentioned being by far the most prevalent in this country. Abroad 50 cycles is very common, and some foreign railways use frequencies considerably less than 25 cycles. A 25-cycle variation causes a noticeable flicker in incandescent lamps; hence it is undesirable for lighting. Formerly 25 cycles was used for power work but, with the advent of a better understanding of the laws governing a-c power transmission and the design of machinery, this frequency is rapidly being superseded. In general, 60-cycle apparatus is lighter and costs less than 25-cycle equipment. The difference is similar to that between high- and low-speed d-c machines.

Audio frequencies range from approximately 16 cycles to approximately 20,000 cycles, voice frequencies occupying the range from about 200 to 2500 cycles. Carefully engineered audio systems, like some theater installations, are designed to accommodate frequencies from 30 to 12,000 cycles.

Radio frequencies range from about 50,000 cycles to 10^{10} cycles, the AM program broadcast band being from 540 to 1600 kilocycles, and the FM and television broadcast bands being from about 50 to 200 megacycles. Radar systems often operate with a carrier frequency of 3000 or 10,000 megacycles.

At the 1947 Atlantic City Conference it was agreed to express frequencies as employed by radio engineers in kilocycles per second at and below 30,000 kilocycles per second and in megacycles per second above this frequency. The present FCC standard band designations follow.

VLF	(very low frequency)	less than 30	kilocycles per second
LF	(low frequency)	30–300	kilocycles per second
MF	(medium frequency)	300–3000	kilocycles per second
HF	(high frequency)	3000–30,000	kilocycles per second
VHF	(very high frequency)	30,000	kilocycles per second–
		300	megacycles per second
UHF	(ultra high frequency)	300–3000	megacycles per second
SHF	(super high frequency)	3000–30,000	megacycles per second
EHF	(extremely high frequency)	30,000–	
		300,000	megacycles per second

Wave Form. The shape of the curve resulting from a plot of instantaneous values of voltage or current as ordinate against time as abscissa is its *wave form* or *wave shape.* It has been shown that the passage of a pair of poles past a given reference point on the stator of Fig. 1 produced a complete cycle of generated or induced emf. This corresponded to 2π electrical radians, or 360 electrical degrees. In other words, one cycle occurs in or occupies 2π radians, or 360°. The abscissa, instead of being expressed in terms of time in seconds, can be and is quite frequently expressed in terms of radians or degrees. Thus one cycle occurs in 2π radians, or 360°.

Angular Velocity or Angular Frequency. In the preceding article a complete cycle was seen to correspond to 2π radians. The time for a complete cycle was defined as the period T. Hence the angular velocity ω in radians per second is $2\pi/T$. Therefore

$$\omega = \frac{2\pi}{T} = 2\pi f \tag{4}$$

Equation (4) specifies angular velocity in terms of frequency, and this velocity is called electrical[2] angular velocity or *angular frequency.*

If equations (2) and (4) are combined,

$$\omega = 2\pi f = 2\pi \frac{p}{2} \text{ (rps)} = \frac{p}{2} [2\pi \text{ (rps)}] \tag{5}$$

Equation (5) shows that electrical angular velocity equals (pairs of poles) times (mechanical angular velocity) in generators of the type shown in Fig. 1.

Alternating Voltages and Currents Represented by Sine Waves. Whereas the foregoing has referred to waves of any shape, the usual

[2] Mechanical angular velocity, 2π(rps) radians per second, is not to be confused with electrical angular velocity. In Fig. 1 the two are related by the factor $p/2$, but in vacuum tube oscillators of the type shown in Fig. 2 the electrical angular velocity or angular frequency is defined almost solely by the inductance and capacitance employed at the X_1 and X_3 positions in the circuit.

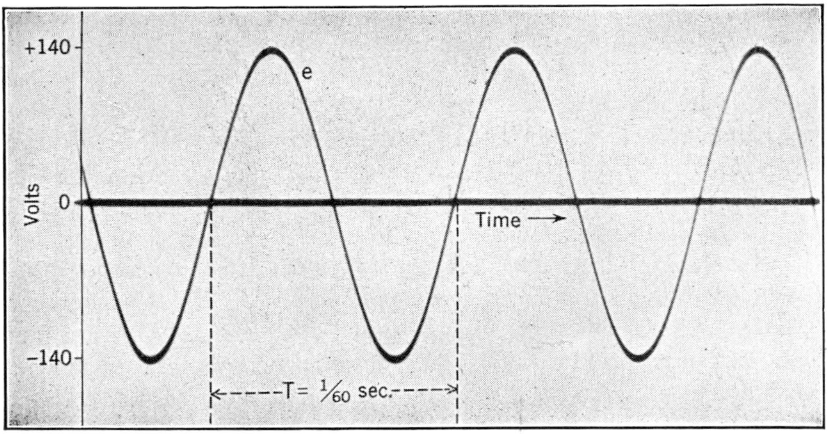

OSCILLOGRAM 1. Emf of a sine-wave generator.

attempt is to secure a sine wave. Oscillogram 1 is a photographic record of the potential difference produced by a so-called sine-wave generator.

Many of the alternating waves met with in practice approximate a sine wave very closely. Alternating-voltage and -current calculations are therefore based on sine waves. (The method whereby non-sinusoidal waves are expressed so as to be calculated according to the laws of sine waves is explained in Chapter VI.) A true sine wave is shown in Fig. 4. The equation for it is

$$i = I_m \sin \omega t \tag{6}$$

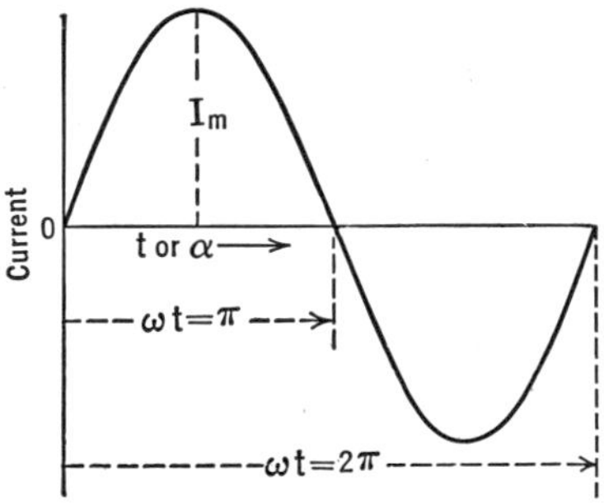

FIG. 4. Sine wave may be expressed as $I_m \sin \alpha$ or as $I_m \sin \omega t$.

where ωt is expressed in radians and is called the time angle, i is the instantaneous value of current, and I_m is the maximum value of the sinusoidal variation. Since ωt represents an angle, equation (6) may be expressed in terms of radians or degrees. Thus

$$i = I_m \sin \alpha \tag{7}$$

where α is in degrees or radians. Equation (6) expresses the current as a sinusoidal variation with respect to time, whereas equation (7) expresses it as a function of angular measure.

Alternating Potential Difference. Alternating voltage or potential difference may take the form of a generated (or induced) emf or the form of a potential drop, sometimes abbreviated p.d. In the interest of clear thinking these two forms of voltage should be distinguished from one another. Instantaneous values of generated or induced emf's will be designated by e, and instantaneous values of potential drops by the symbol v. Similarly E_m and V_m will be used to distinguish a maximum value of induced voltage from a maximum value of potential drop. Corresponding distinctions will be made between other particular values of induced voltages and voltage drops.

Phase. Phase (as the term is defined by the A.I.E.E.) is the fractional part of a period through which time or the associated time angle ωt has advanced from an arbitrary reference. In the case of a simple sinusoidal variation, the origin is usually taken as the last previous passage through zero from the negative to the positive direction. Thus one phase of a sine wave is $\frac{1}{12}$ of a period (or 30° from the origin) where the ordinate is one-half the maximum ordinate; another phase is $\frac{1}{4}$ of a period (or 90° from the origin) where the ordinate has its maximum positive value; and so on for any other fractional part of T (or of $\omega T = 2\pi$).

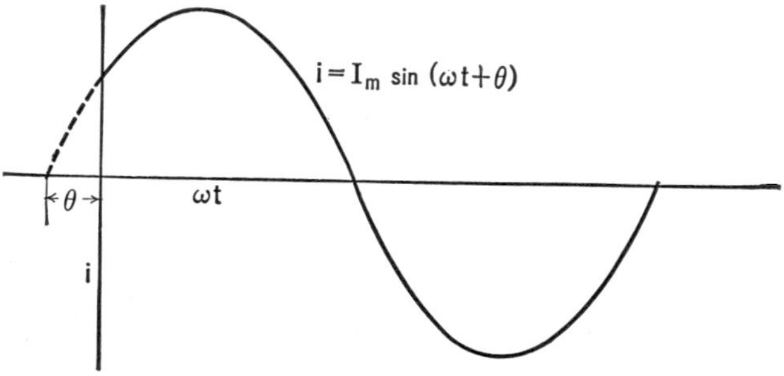

FIG. 5. Phase angle θ of a sine wave.

In accordance with the above definition, the phase angle of a single wave is the angle from the zero point on the wave to the value at the point from which time is reckoned. Thus $i = I_m \sin(\omega t + \theta)$ represents a sine wave of current with a phase angle θ. The phase of the wave from which time is reckoned (i.e., when $t = 0$) is $i = I_m \sin\theta$. The angle θ is the phase angle of the current with respect to the point where $i = 0$ as a reference. These principles are illustrated in Fig. 5.

The phase angle when used in connection with a single alternating quantity merely provides a simple analytical method of starting the variation in question at any point along the wave. As such it is of little importance in steady-state analysis in contrast with its great usefulness in the analysis of transient conditions.

Phase Difference. The phase angle is a very important device for properly locating different alternating quantities with respect to one another. For example, if the applied voltage is

$$v = V_m \sin \omega t \tag{8}$$

and it is known from the nature and magnitude of the circuit parameters that the current comes to a corresponding point on its wave before the voltage wave by θ degrees, the current can be expressed as

$$i = I_m \sin (\omega t + \theta) \tag{9}$$

Figure 6 illustrates the phase positions of v and i for $\theta = 45°$. The current in this case is said to lead the voltage by 45°, or the voltage is said to lag the current by 45°. A given alternating quantity lags

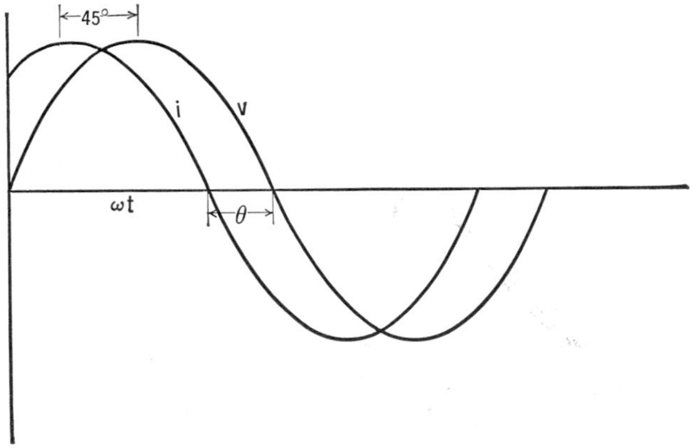

FIG. 6. Illustrating a case where the i wave leads the v wave by $\theta = 45°$.

another if it comes to a certain point on its wave later than the other one comes to the corresponding point on its wave. Another way of saying the same thing is that the positive maximum of the leading quantity occurs before the positive maximum of the lagging quantity. Thus it is said that there is a phase difference of 45° between the two waves. The angle of phase difference is the difference of the phase angles of the two waves. Thus, if $e = 100 \sin (\omega t + 45°)$ and $i = 10 \sin (\omega t - 15°)$, the angle of phase difference is $45° - (-15°) = 60°$.

Oscillogram 2 illustrates the actual phase relation between an applied sinusoidal voltage and the resulting current that flows in a particular

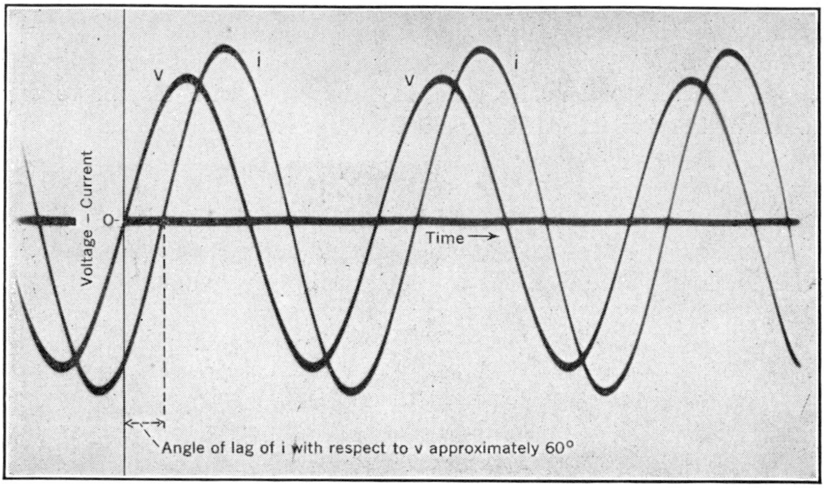

OSCILLOGRAM 2. Photographic record of voltage and current for a circuit containing resistance and inductance.

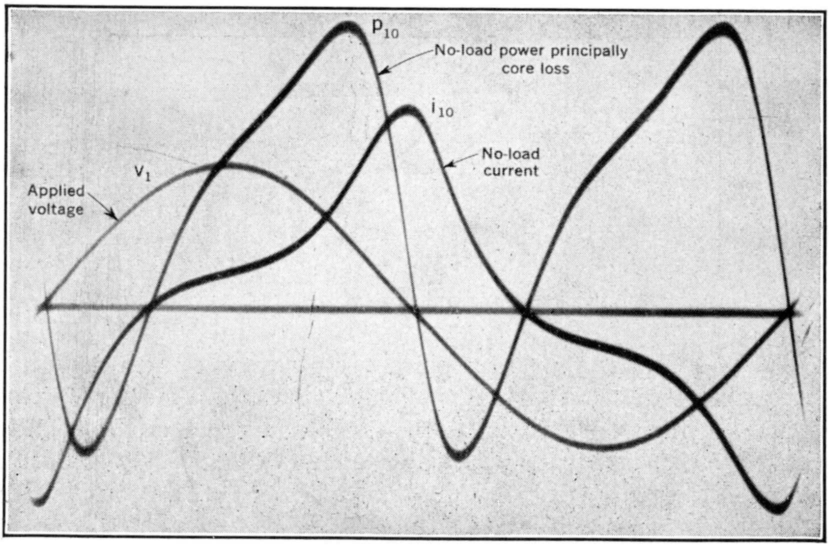

OSCILLOGRAM 3. Oscillographic records of the no-load current and no-load power taken by the primary of an iron-core transformer. The applied voltage variation, v_1, is also shown.

circuit. Inspection of the oscillogram will show that the current lags the voltage in this particular case by approximately 60°. Oscillogram 3 illustrates a case where the current and power waves are distinctly non-sinusoidal.

Examples. If a voltage is described as having sinusoidal wave form, a maximum value of 200 volts, and an angular frequency of 377 radians per second (60 cycles per second), and it is desired to reckon time from the point of zero voltage where dv/dt

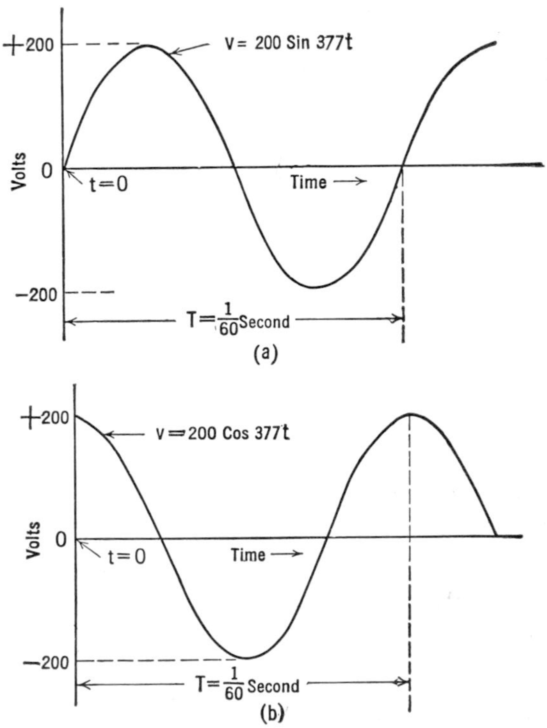

FIG. 7. Graphical representations of equations (10) and (11).

is positive, as illustrated in Fig. 7a, the mathematical expression for the alternating voltage as a function of time, t, is

$$v = 200 \sin 377t \text{ volts} \tag{10}$$

If it is desired to reckon time from some other point along the voltage wave, it is simply necessary to add to the angle $377t$ in the above equation an angle equal to the angular displacement between $v = 0$ (dv/dt positive) and the point on the voltage wave from which it is desired to reckon time. If it is assumed that time is to be reckoned from the point of positive maximum voltage, the angular displacement referred to above is +90°, and the expression for voltage becomes

$$v = 200 \sin (377t + 90°) = 200 \cos 377t \text{ volts} \tag{11}$$

This type of variation is shown in Fig. 7*b*.

Equations (10) and (11) describe exactly the same type of voltage variation except for the $t = 0$ reference.

The current that flows in a circuit as a result of applying a sinusoidal voltage is governed in magnitude and phase by the circuit parameters (resistance R, self-inductance L, capacitance C, and mutual inductance M) and the angular velocity or frequency of the applied voltage. In one sense of the word the angular frequency is an a-c circuit parameter. If the circuit parameters are constant, the current that flows will be of sinusoidal wave form but will, in general, differ in phase from the sinusoidal applied voltage.

Mathematically a particular type of function is required to relate voltage and current in an a-c circuit. The one generally employed is called the impedance function or simply the impedance of the circuit. The impedance function must tell two important facts: (1) the ratio of V_m to I_m,[3] and (2) the phase angle between the waves of voltage and current. A special type of notation is required to signify the two properties of the impedance function in abbreviated form. One such type of notation is

$$Z\underline{/\text{angle}}$$

The above expression does not signify the multiplication of Z and $\underline{/\text{angle}}$. Z is the magnitude of the impedance and in a particular case is represented by a certain number of ohms. It defines the ratio of V_m to I_m. The angle associated with Z, if it is positive, defines the *lead* of the voltage with respect to the current. In accordance with the convention thus adopted a positive angle specifies the number of degrees or radians by which the current lags the voltage.

The determination of the complete impedance function for various combinations of R, L, and C is the first step in a-c circuit analysis. The combinations considered in the present chapter are shown in diagrammatic fashion in Fig. 8.

The *R* Branch. The consideration of a circuit element which possesses only ohmic resistance is, of course, a hypothetical venture because some self-inductance is inevitably associated with any circuit configuration. However, the case may be approached in practice to a degree comparable to the accuracy of ordinary measurements. It is well known that

[3] It will be shown in Chapter III that the magnitude of the impedance Z defines the ratio of $V_{\text{effective}}$ to $I_{\text{effective}}$ as well as the ratio V_m to I_m.

resistance impedes the motion of electricity and causes an irreversible transformation of electrical energy into heat energy in accordance with Joule's law.

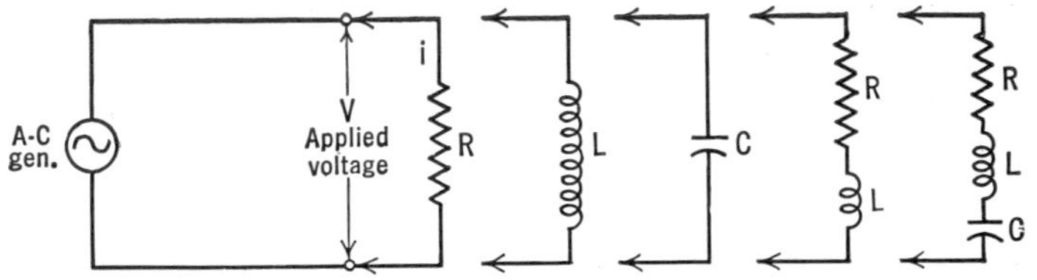

FIG. 8. Elementary circuit arrangements of R, L, and C.

Impedance. The impedance of a simple R branch may be expressed as

$$R\underline{/0^\circ} \text{ ohms}$$

The reason follows directly from Kirchhoff's emf law. If a voltage, $v = V_m \sin \omega t$, is applied to a branch of R resistance, Fig. 9, the equation for dynamic equilibrium is

$$v = Ri = V_m \sin \omega t \quad (12)$$

from which

$$i = \frac{V_m}{R} \sin \omega t = I_m \sin \omega t \quad (13)$$

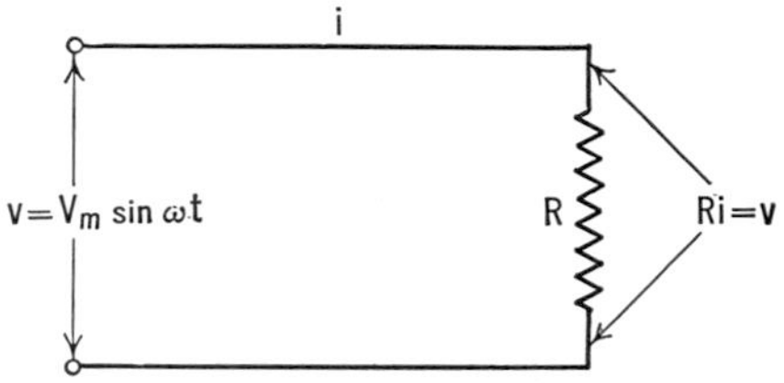

FIG. 9. The R branch.

From the above equation it is evident that $V_m/I_m = R$ and that the current wave is in time phase with the voltage wave. It is possible to express these facts in the single statement

$$\mathbf{Z}_R = R\underline{/0^\circ}$$

In general, R is expressed directly in ohms, in which case $\mathbf{Z}_R$ is in ohms.

Power. The determination of the rate at which electrical energy is generated or absorbed is, in general, an important problem. Instantaneous power is symbolized by the lower-case letter p.

$$p = ei \quad \text{(generated power)}$$

$$p = vi \quad \text{(absorbed power)}$$

The present discussion confines itself to the determination of instantaneous absorbed power wherein positive values of p indicate that the circuit under consideration is receiving energy from the supplying source.

Negative values of p indicate that the reactive elements of the circuit, if such are present, are actually releasing energy at a rate which is greater than the rate at which energy is being received.

In the present case, that of the simple R branch, all the energy produced by the instantaneous power absorbed is converted into heat. Presumably no reactive elements, inductance coils or condensers, are present. The instantaneous power is given by the product of equations (12) and (13).

$$p = vi = V_m I_m \sin^2 \omega t \tag{14}$$

Since $\sin^2 \omega t = \frac{1}{2} - \frac{1}{2} \cos 2\omega t$, it follows that

$$p = \frac{V_m I_m}{2} - \frac{V_m I_m}{2} \cos 2\omega t \tag{15}$$

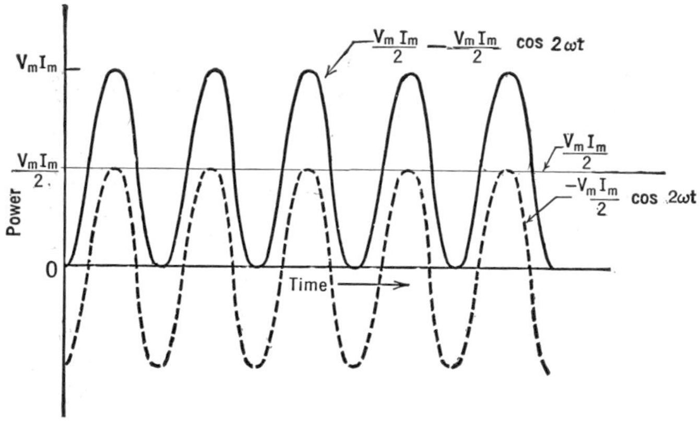

FIG. 10. Graphical representation of equation (15).

Figure 10 illustrates the component parts of equation (15). It will be observed from the above equation that the instantaneous power wave is a double-frequency variation, with respect to the frequency of the current or the voltage, which has an average positive value of $\frac{V_m I_m}{2}$. The cos $2\omega t$ term causes the instantaneous power to acquire periodically zero and $V_m I_m$ values. At no time does the power reach instantaneous negative values.

Photographic records of v, i, and p in a branch which approximates the purely resistive case are shown in Oscillogram 4. The oscillogram illustrates in a graphical manner the relations which have been derived for the R branch and substantiates the physical fact that voltage and current are in time phase in a resistive circuit.

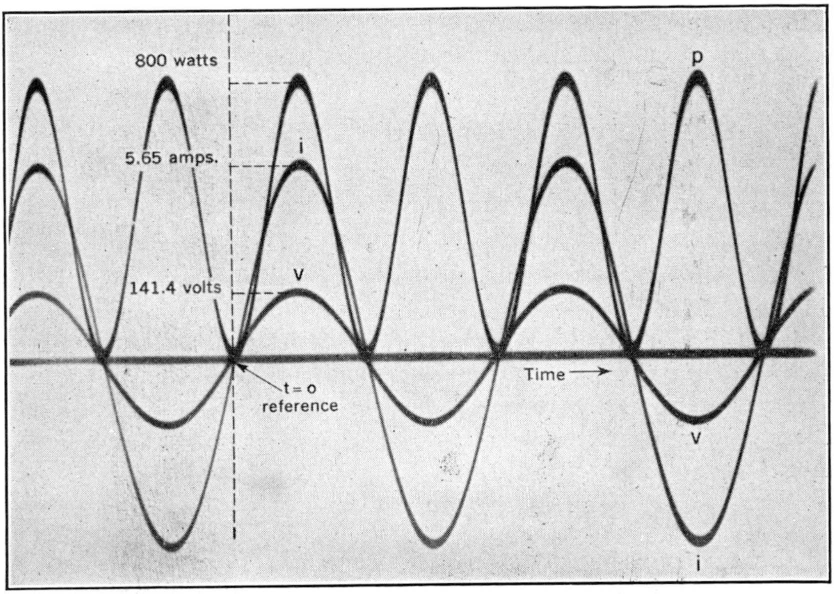

OSCILLOGRAM 4. Voltage, current, and power variations in a resistive circuit element. $R = 25$ ohms. If time is reckoned from the point of zero voltage (dv/dt positive): $V = 141.4 \sin 377t$ volts, $i = 5.65 \sin 377t$ amperes, $p = 400 - 400 \cos 754t$ watts, average power = 400 watts.

The L Branch. If a circuit element of pure inductance, Fig. 11, is considered, the equation for dynamic equilibrium is

$$v = L\frac{di}{dt} = V_m \sin \omega t \tag{16}$$

$$di = \frac{V_m}{L} \sin \omega t \, dt \tag{17}$$

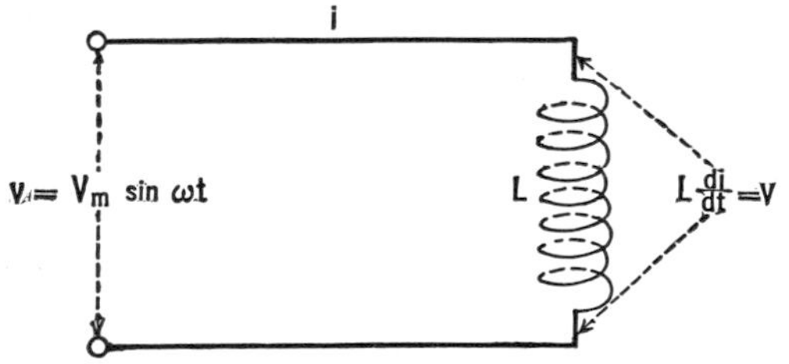

FIG. 11. The L branch.

After both sides of the above equation are integrated it follows that

$$i = -\frac{V_m}{\omega L} \cos \omega t + c_1 \tag{18}$$

The constant of integration c_1 will be considered to be equal to zero since only the steady-state current symmetrical about the zero axis is to be considered.[4]

Under the above conditions equation (18) reduces to

$$i = \frac{V_m}{\omega L} \sin (\omega t - 90°) = I_m \sin (\omega t - 90°) \tag{19}$$

Impedance. Inductance opposes the *rate of change* of current, and for this reason it is sometimes called *electrical inertia.* Since the inductance, L, limits the rate at which the current can change, it follows logically that L actually governs the maximum value of the current in an a-c circuit which is energized by a voltage of specified angular velocity.

It will be observed from equation (19) that $V_m/I_m = \omega L$ and that i lags v by one-quarter of a cycle or 90°. The impedance of a pure L branch is according to the convention previously adopted

$$\mathbf{Z}_L = \omega L \underline{/90°}$$

The reason for using the positive angle in connection with impedances that cause lagging currents will become more evident when the rules of vector algebra and the conventions pertaining to vector diagrams are considered.

The magnitude of the above impedance, ωL, is called *inductive reactance.* Inasmuch as the inductive reactance is directly proportional to the angular velocity of the driving voltage, $2\pi f$, it is obvious that the magnitude of the impedance offered to the flow of alternating current by a coil of fixed self-inductance, L, is directly proportional to frequency. When ω is expressed in radians per second and L is expressed in henrys, the inductive reactance, X_L, is in ohms.

$$X_L = \omega L = 2\pi f L \tag{20}$$

Example. The inductive reactance of a 10-millihenry inductance coil in a 60-cycle circuit is

$$X_L = 2\pi \times 60 \times 0.010 = 3.77 \text{ ohms}$$

and

$$\mathbf{Z} = 3.77 \underline{/90°} \text{ ohms}$$

The inductive reactance of the same coil in a 60,000-cycle circuit is

$$X_L = 2\pi \times 60{,}000 \times 0.010 = 3770 \text{ ohms}$$

If a 60-cycle sinusoidal voltage of maximum value equal to 100 volts is applied to

[4] In a general analysis, c_1 would be evaluated in terms of the boundary conditions under which the circuit is initially closed. Determined in this manner, c_1 would define the transient component of the current. c_1 is neglected here because transient components of the current are not to be considered at this time. In a physically realizable circuit the transient component is of short duration.

the 10-millihenry inductance coil,

$$v = 100 \sin 377t \text{ volts}$$

and

$$i = \frac{100}{3.77} \sin (377t - 90°) \text{ amperes}$$

Power and Energy. The instantaneous power delivered to the pure inductance branch as obtained by multiplying equation (16) by equation (19) is

$$p = vi = [V_m \sin \omega t][I_m \sin (\omega t - 90°)] \tag{21}$$

from which

$$p = V_m I_m(-\sin \omega t \cos \omega t) \tag{22}$$

or

$$p = -\frac{V_m I_m}{2} \sin 2\omega t \tag{23}$$

Figure 12 illustrates the v, i, and p variations in a purely inductive branch. It will be observed that the power variation is again a double-

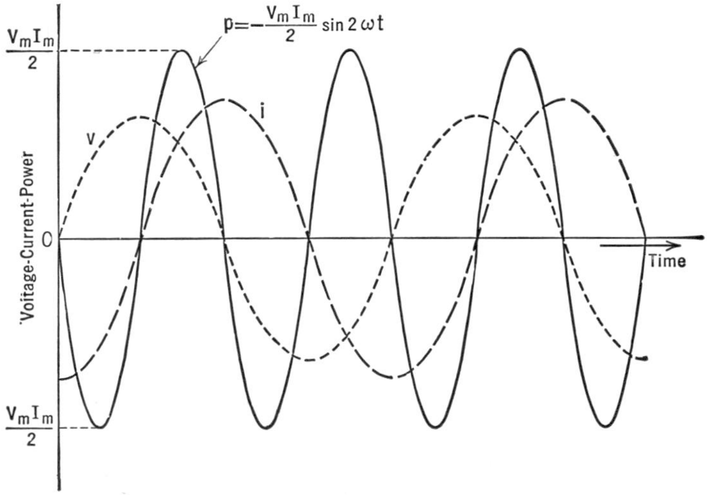

FIG. 12. Voltage, current, and power variations in a purely inductive branch.

frequency variation with respect to the frequency of the driving voltage. The fact that equation (23) indicates negative power during the first one-quarter of a cycle of the driving voltage, that is, from $t = 0$ to $t = T/4$, is the direct result of the choice of the time reference.[5]

[5] The assumption of sinusoidal driving voltage, $v = V_m \sin \omega t$, automatically imposes the condition of $t = 0$ at the point of $v = 0$ (dv/dt positive). The beginner should not confuse the $t = 0$ reference of a steady-state variation with the time at which the circuit is initially energized.

Since steady-state conditions have been assumed, the circuit has presumably adjusted itself to the relative phase relations indicated by equations (16), (19), and (23).

Under the conditions which have been assumed, namely, a steady-state sinusoidal driving voltage and a purely inductive circuit, the power variation is symmetrical about the zero power axis. The average power absorbed is equal to zero. The implication is that the inductive element receives energy from the source during one-quarter of a cycle of the applied voltage and returns exactly the same amount of energy to the driving source during the next one-quarter of a cycle. The exact amount of energy delivered to the circuit during a quarter of a cycle may be obtained by integrating any positive loop of the power wave, for example, integrating p between the limits of $t = T/4$ and $t = T/2$.

$$W_L = \int_{T/4}^{T/2} -\frac{V_m I_m}{2} \sin 2\omega t \, dt$$

$$= \frac{V_m I_m}{2\left(\frac{4\pi}{T}\right)} \left[\cos \frac{4\pi}{T} t\right]_{T/4}^{T/2}$$

$$= \frac{V_m I_m}{2\omega}$$

Since $V_m = \omega L I_m$,

$$W_L = \frac{(\omega L I_m) I_m}{2\omega} = \frac{L I_m^2}{2} \tag{24}$$

If L is expressed in abhenrys and I_m in abamperes, the above energy is in ergs. If L and I_m are expressed in henrys and amperes respectively, W_L is given in joules.

Oscillogram 5 illustrates the relative phase relations in a circuit which approaches, to a fair degree of accuracy, the purely inductive arrangement that has been described mathematically.

The *C* Branch. If it assumed that a sinusoidal voltage, $V_m \sin \omega t$, is applied to an ideal capacitor as indicated in Fig. 13, the expression for steady-state equilibrium is

$$v = \frac{q}{C} = V_m \sin \omega t \tag{25}$$

When the above equation is differentiated with respect to time, it follows that

$$\frac{dq}{dt} = V_m \omega C \cos \omega t \tag{26}$$

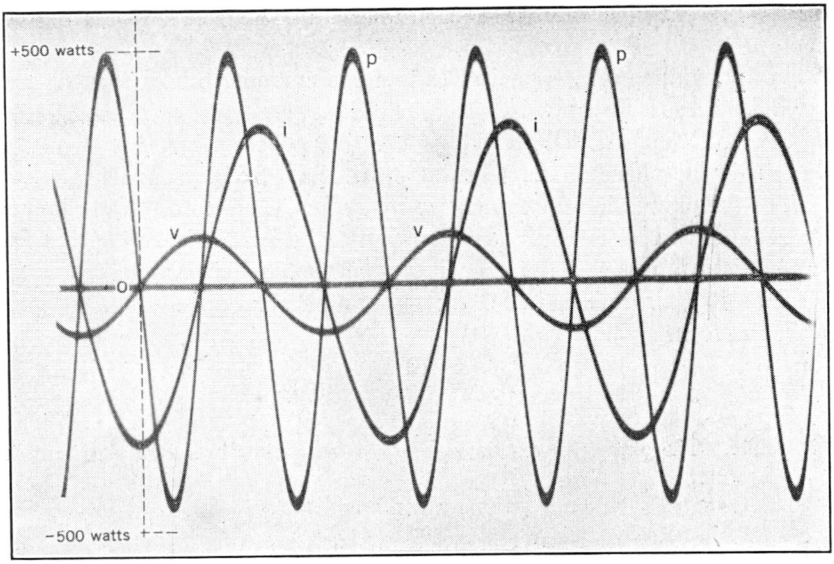

OSCILLOGRAM 5. Voltage, current, and power variations in a highly inductive circuit element. $L = 0.056$ henry, $f = 60$ cycles, $X_L = 21.2$ ohms, $R = 1.0$ ohm, $V_{max} = 141.4$ volts, $I_{max} = 6.66$ amperes, $P_{av} = 25$ watts approximately. Note the lag of the i wave with respect to the v wave; also the large negative power loops. Positive power peaks of approximately 500 watts are present even though the average power dissipated in the circuit element is only about 25 watts.

or

$$i = \frac{V_m}{\dfrac{1}{\omega C}} \sin(\omega t + 90°) = I_m \sin(\omega t + 90°) \tag{27}$$

Impedance. The ratio of V_m to I_m in the pure C branch is $1/\omega C$, and the current leads the applied voltage by one-quarter of a cycle or 90°. In accordance with the convention which has been adopted, the impedance of the C branch is

$$\mathbf{Z}_C = \frac{1}{\omega C} \underline{/-90°}$$

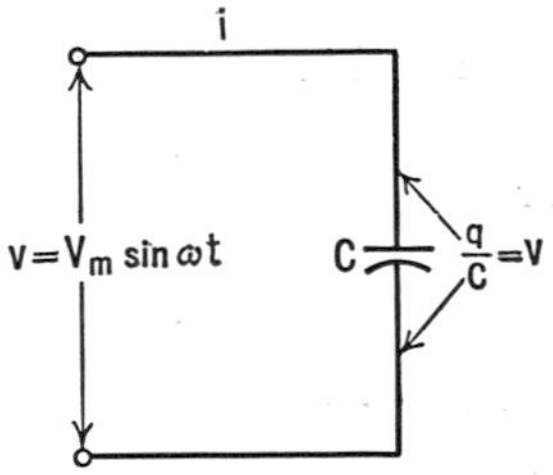

FIG. 13. The C branch.

The magnitude of the impedance, $1/\omega C$, is called *capacitive reactance*, and it is evident from the nature of the expression that capacitive reactance is inversely proportional to the frequency of the driving voltage and also inversely proportional to the capacitance of the capacitor, C. A series circuit in which no capacitor is present has infinite capacitance and, hence, zero capacitive reactance.

The impedance of a capacitor causes the current to lead the voltage by 90°, whereas the impedance of an inductance causes the current to lag the voltage 90°. The effects of the two types of reactive elements as regards the phase of the resulting current are exactly opposite.

If, in the expression for capacitive reactance, ω is expressed in radians per second and C is expressed in farads, the resulting capacitive reactance is in ohms. If the capacitance of the capacitor is expressed in microfarads (abbreviated μf), the expression for capacitive reactance takes the form

$$X_C = \frac{10^6}{\omega C_{\mu f}} \quad \text{ohms}$$

Example. The capacitive reactance of a 15-μf capacitor in a 25-cycle circuit is

$$X_C = \frac{10^6}{2\pi \times 25 \times 15} = 425 \text{ ohms}$$

and

$$\mathbf{Z}_C = 425 \underline{/-90°} \text{ ohms}$$

The capacitive reactance of the same capacitor to a 250-cycle driving voltage is

$$X_C = \frac{10^6}{2\pi \times 250 \times 15} = 42.5 \text{ ohms}$$

If a 25-cycle sinusoidal voltage of maximum value equal to 200 volts is applied to the 15-μf capacitor

$$v = 200 \sin (157t) \text{ volts}$$

and

$$i = \frac{200}{425} \sin (157t + 90°) \text{ amperes}$$

Power and Energy. The instantaneous power delivered to the C branch is

$$p = vi = [V_m \sin \omega t][I_m \sin (\omega t + 90°)] \tag{28}$$

from which

$$p = V_m I_m (\sin \omega t \cos \omega t) \tag{29}$$

or

$$p = \frac{V_m I_m}{2} \sin 2\omega t \tag{30}$$

The phase relations of v, i, and p in a purely capacitive branch are shown in Fig. 14. The double-frequency power variation is, as in the pure L branch, symmetrical about the zero power axis. In the present case the capacitor receives energy from the source during the first quarter of a cycle of the voltage variation and returns the same amount

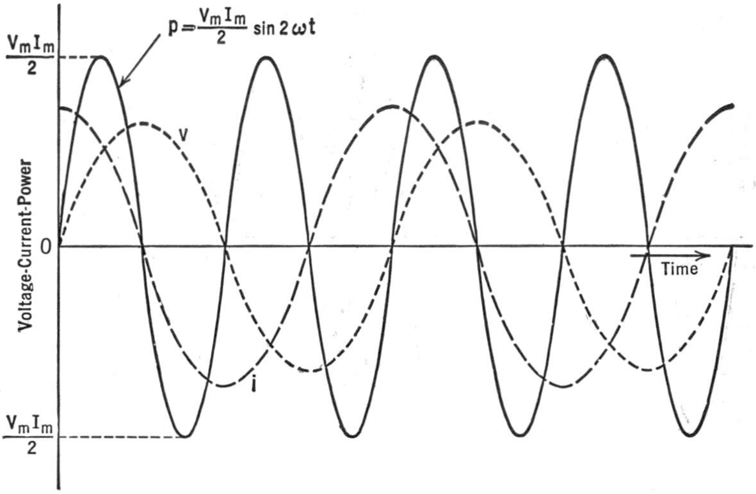

FIG. 14. Voltage, current, and power in a purely capacitive branch.

during the second quarter cycle, etc. The average power absorbed over an integral number of half cycles is, obviously, equal to zero.

The amount of energy received by the capacitor during a quarter cycle may be determined by integrating the power wave over any positive loop; for example, integrating equation (30) between the limits of $t = 0$ and $t = T/4$.

$$W_C = \int_0^{T/4} \frac{V_m I_m}{2} \sin 2\omega t \, dt$$

$$= \frac{V_m I_m}{2\left(\frac{4\pi}{T}\right)} \left[-\cos \frac{4\pi}{T} t \right]_0^{T/4}$$

$$= \frac{V_m I_m}{\left(\frac{4\pi}{T}\right)} = \frac{V_m I_m}{2\omega}$$

Since $I_m = \omega C V_m$,

$$W_C = \frac{V_m(\omega C V_m)}{2\omega} = \frac{V_m^2 C}{2} \tag{31}$$

If V_m and C are expressed in volts and farads respectively, the above expression for energy is in joules. W_C is the maximum amount of energy stored in the electric field of the capacitor at any one time.

Comparison of equations (30) and (23) will show that the capacitive

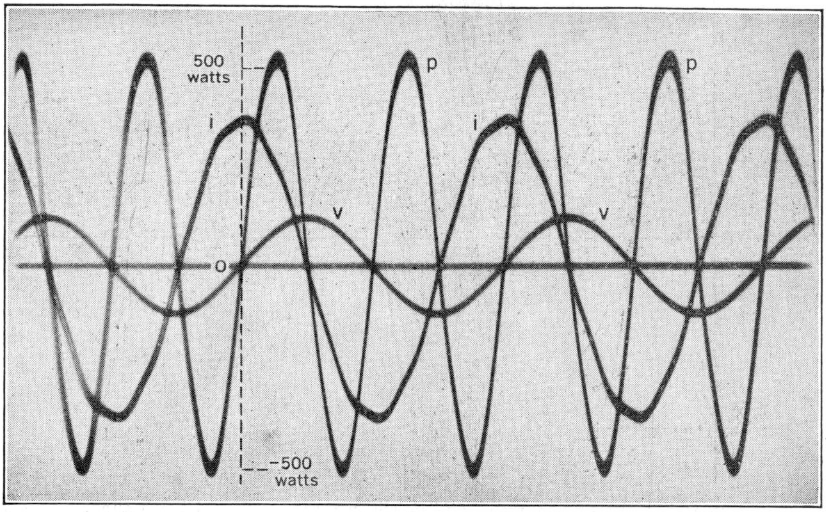

OSCILLOGRAM 6. Voltage, current, and power variations in a highly capacitive circuit element. $C = 144\ \mu f$, $f = 60$ cycles, $X_C = 18.4$ ohms, $R = 1.0$ ohm approx., $V_{max} = 141.4$, $I_{max} = 7.6$ amperes, $P_{av} = 25$ watts, approx. Note the lead of the i wave with respect to the v wave.

element receives energy from the supplying source during the periods in which the inductive element returns energy to the source, and vice versa. When capacitive elements and inductive elements are both present in a given circuit, there is, in general, a natural tendency for the elements to exchange energy. In certain circuit arrangements relatively large amounts of energy oscillate between the electromagnetic fields of the inductances and the electric fields of the capacitors.

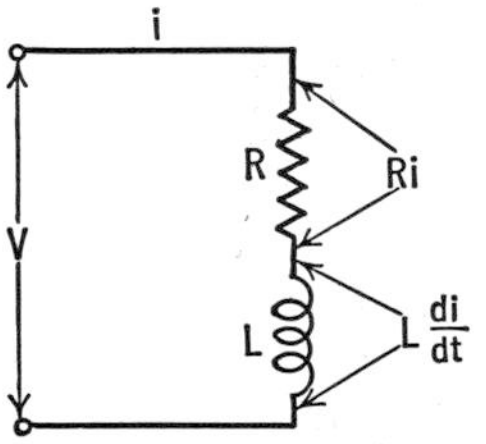

FIG. 15. The RL branch.

Oscillogram 6 illustrates the v, i, and p variations in a branch which approaches, to a close degree of accuracy, a purely capacitive circuit element.

The *RL* Branch. If it is assumed that a sinusoidal driving voltage, $V_m \sin \omega t$, is applied to a series combination of a resistive element and an inductive element, Fig. 15, the equation for voltage balance is

$$v = Ri + L\frac{di}{dt} = V_m \sin \omega t \tag{32}$$

This is one form of Kirchhoff's emf law applied to instantaneous voltages. It states that the instantaneous voltage drop across the resistive element plus the instantaneous voltage drop across the inductive element equals the instantaneous voltage drop across the RL branch.

A straightforward solution of equation (32) for i in terms of the applied voltage and circuit parameters requires a certain knowledge of differential equations on the part of the reader which is not essential to the problem at hand. The problem in which we are particularly

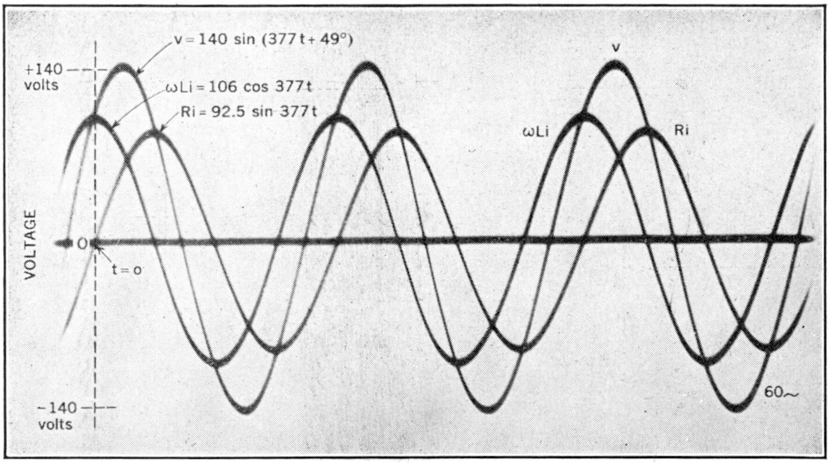

OSCILLOGRAM 7. Illustrating the manner in which the voltage drop Ri across the resistance and the voltage drop ωLi across an inductance coil combine to equal the applied voltage v. $R = 18.5$ ohms connected in series with $X_L = 21.1$ ohms. $RI_{\max} = 92.5$ volts, $\omega LI_{\max} = 106$ volts, $V_{\max} = 140$ volts.

interested at this point is the evaluation of the ratio V_m/I_m together with the time-phase difference between the voltage and current in an RL branch. Provided that R and L are constant, a current of sinusoidal wave form will flow in the branch if a sinusoidal voltage is applied. A critical inspection of equation (32) will help to establish the mathematical reasons for this physical fact.

If it is assumed that a sinusoidal current, $i = I_m \sin \omega t$, flows through a series branch consisting of a resistive element, R, and an inductive element, L, then

$$Ri + L\frac{di}{dt} = \text{voltage applied, } v \tag{33}$$

or

$$RI_m \sin \omega t + \omega LI_m \cos \omega t = v \tag{34}$$

Equations (33) and (34) state that the instantaneous component voltage drops, Ri and $L\,di/dt$, add together to form the combined voltage drop across the RL branch. Oscillogram 7 illustrates the manner in which the Ri component ($RI_m \sin \omega t$) and the $L\,di/dt$ component ($\omega LI_m \cos \omega t$) combine to equal the applied voltage (v) in a particular RL branch.

Since sine and cosine waves are 90° out of time phase with respect to one another, the RI_m and the ωLI_m components may be related as shown in Fig. 16*a*, that is, as the two right-angle sides of a right triangle.

If both sides of the equation are divided by $\sqrt{R^2 + (\omega L)^2}$, equation (34) takes the following form:[6]

$$I_m\left[\sin \omega t \frac{R}{\sqrt{R^2 + (\omega L)^2}} + \cos \omega t \frac{\omega L}{\sqrt{R^2 + (\omega L)^2}}\right] = \frac{v}{\sqrt{R^2 + (\omega L)^2}} \tag{35}$$

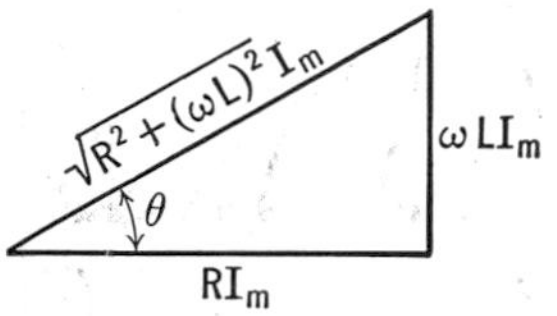

FIG. 16*a*. The addition of RI_m and ωLI_m.

From Fig. 16*a*,

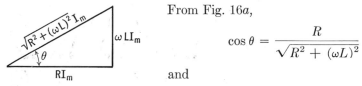

$$\cos \theta = \frac{R}{\sqrt{R^2 + (\omega L)^2}} \tag{36}$$

and

$$\sin \theta = \frac{\omega L}{\sqrt{R^2 + (\omega L)^2}} \tag{37}$$

Then

$$I_m[\sin \omega t \cos \theta + \cos \omega t \sin \theta] = \frac{v}{\sqrt{R^2 + (\omega L)^2}} \tag{38}$$

from which

$$v = I_m\sqrt{R^2 + (\omega L)^2} \sin (\omega t + \theta)$$

or

$$v = I_m Z \sin (\omega t + \theta) = V_m \sin (\omega t + \theta) \tag{39}$$

[6] The method of combination here employed requires only a knowledge of trigonometry. Since the combination of

$$(A \sin x + B \cos x)$$

occurs frequently in a-c circuit analysis, a simpler method of combination is often used. This scheme consists of representing the sines and cosines by revolving vectors

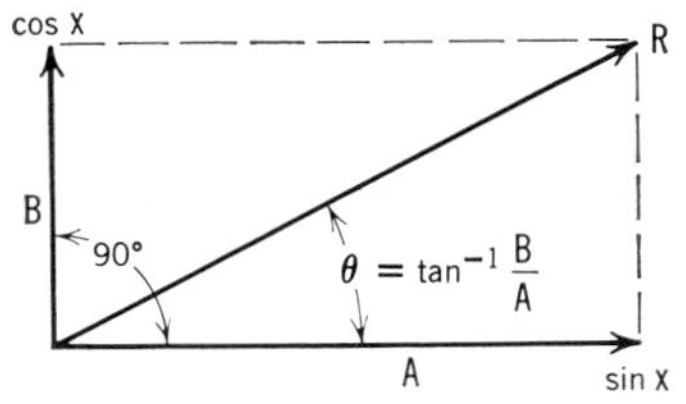

FIG. 16*b*. Vector representation of sine and cosine functions.

or phasors as explained on pages 90 and 91 which most students will remember was done in physics when sine waves were used to represent simple harmonic motion.

It is thus shown that (1) $Z = \sqrt{R^2 + (\omega L)^2} = V_m/I_m$, (2) $\theta = \tan^{-1} \omega L/R$, and (3) v leads i in the RL branch by $\theta°$.

Impedance.

$$\mathbf{Z}_{RL} = \sqrt{R^2 + (\omega L)^2} \underline{/ \tan^{-1} \frac{\omega L}{R}} \tag{40}$$

The above expression for $\mathbf{Z}_{RL}$ implies that the numerical ratio of V_m to I_m in the RL branch is $\sqrt{R^2 + (\omega L)^2}$ and that the current lags the applied voltage by the angle whose tangent is $\omega L/R$. In general, R is expressed in ohms, ω in radians per second, and L in henrys, in which case $\sqrt{R^2 + (\omega L)^2}$ is given in ohms. In determining the phase angle it is, of course, only necessary that ωL and R be expressed in similar units.

The expression for the impedance of a pure R branch is at once obtainable from $\mathbf{Z}_{RL}$ by assuming that $L = 0$, in which case $\mathbf{Z}_{RL}$ reduces to $R\underline{/0°}$. If the assumption is made that $R = 0$, $\mathbf{Z}_{RL}$ reduces immediately to the expression which has previously been derived for the impedance of a pure L branch, namely, $\omega L\underline{/90°}$.

An examination of the two factors which combine to form $\mathbf{Z}_{RL}$ will show that R is the factor which directly impedes or opposes the flow of current, whereas ωL is the factor which impedes or opposes any change in current. For a resulting sinusoidal current these two factors act in time quadrature with respect to one another. For example, when the current is zero the R factor has zero effect and the L factor has its greatest effect because it is when $i = 0$ that $[di/dt]$ for a sine wave is at its maximum value. When the current is at its maximum value, I_m, the R factor has its greatest effect and the L factor has zero effect because $[di/dt]$ for a sine wave is zero at the point of maximum current. It is the time quadrature nature (90° time-phase displacement) of the individual impedance effects that makes possible a simple vector algebra method of analyzing a-c circuits.[7]

Example. If $R = 20$ ohms and $L = 0.056$ henry, the 60-cycle impedance of the RL branch which is formed by placing R in series with L is

$$\mathbf{Z} = \sqrt{20^2 + (377 \times 0.056)^2} \underline{/ \tan^{-1} \frac{21.1}{20}}$$

$$= 29.1 \underline{/46.5°} \text{ ohms}$$

Through employing such methods, the $\sin x$ component may be represented by a horizontal vector of magnitude A. Since counterclockwise is the standard direction for positive or forward rotation, the $\cos x$ component (which leads the $\sin x$ component by 90°) will then be drawn to a magnitude of B vertically upward. Thus Fig. 16*b* is obtained and the resultant R is readily seen to be $\sqrt{A^2 + B^2} \sin (x + \theta)$.

[7] The vector or phasor method of analysis is considered in Chapter IV.

If

$$v = 200 \sin (377t) \text{ volts}$$

$$i = \frac{200}{29.1} \sin (377t - 46.5°)$$

$$= 6.87 \sin (377t - 46.5°) \text{ amperes}$$

It will be observed that the instantaneous current is obtained from the instantaneous voltage ($200 \sin 377t$) and the impedance function ($29.1 \underline{/46.5°}$) by *two distinct operations* which are performed in a single step. These are:

(*a*) The maximum magnitude of the voltage (200) is divided by the magnitude of the impedance (29.1) to obtain the maximum magnitude of the current, 6.87 amperes.

(*b*) The correct angular displacement of the current wave with respect to the voltage wave is obtained by subtracting the impedance angle (46.5°) from the time angle of the voltage wave, namely, $377t$.

Note: In evaluating the correct angular displacement between the instantaneous current and voltage waves in terms of the impedance angle, it is better to combine the angles in such a way as to yield the relation between current and voltage waves which are known to exist from a knowledge of the physical characteristics of the circuit. This process should not be obscured by any elaborate mathematical conventions.

Power. The instantaneous power or, as it is sometimes called, the instantaneous volt-amperes, delivered to the RL branch may be obtained from

$$p = vi = [V_m \sin (\omega t + \theta)][I_m \sin \omega t] \tag{41}$$

After the $\sin (\omega t + \theta)$ term is expanded, the above equation can be written in the following forms:

$$\begin{aligned} p &= V_m I_m \sin \omega t \,[\sin \omega t \cos \theta + \cos \omega t \sin \theta] \\ &= V_m I_m \sin^2 \omega t \cos \theta + V_m I_m (\sin \omega t \cos \omega t) \sin \theta \\ &= \frac{V_m I_m}{2} \cos \theta - \frac{V_m I_m}{2} [\cos 2\omega t] \cos \theta + \frac{V_m I_m}{2} [\sin 2\omega t] \sin \theta \end{aligned} \tag{42}$$

Figure 17 is a graphical representation of the component parts of equation (42) together with the resultant graph of instantaneous power. It should be plain that the average value with respect to time of either the $[\cos 2\omega t]$ or the $[\sin 2\omega t]$ term is equal to zero when considered over a time interval equal to an integral number of cycles. The average value with respect to time of the power when considered over an integral number of cycles is, therefore, equal to

$$P_{\text{av}} = \frac{V_m I_m}{2} \cos \theta$$

The above expression for average power may also be obtained by finding

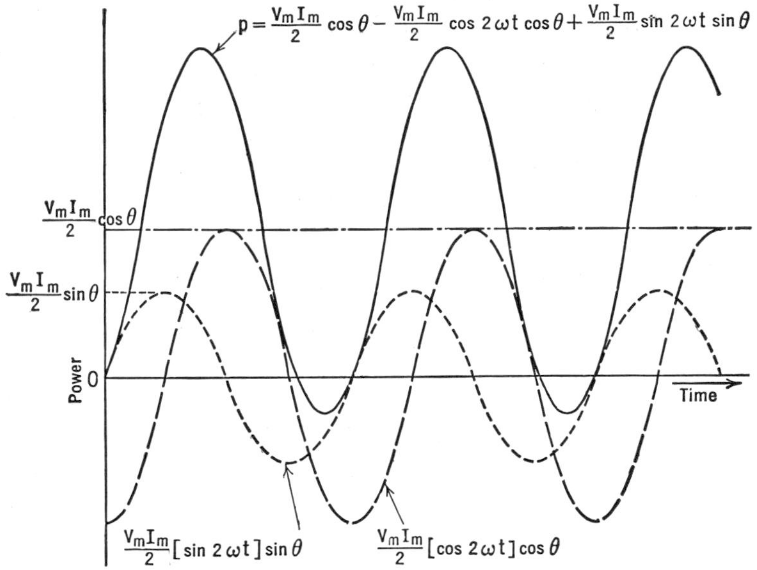

FIG. 17. Graphical representation of equation (42) for the particular case of $\theta = 30°$.

the average value of the right-hand member of equation (41) as follows:

$$P_{av} = \frac{1}{T}\int_0^T V_m \sin(\omega t + \theta) I_m \sin \omega t \, dt$$

$$= \frac{V_m I_m}{2} \cos \theta \qquad (43)$$

Real Power and Reactive Power or Reactive Volt-Amperes. A detailed analysis of the component parts of equation (42) will aid in understanding why electrical power is treated in terms of real and reactive components and why these two components are sometimes represented as the legs of a right triangle.

Real Power. Instantaneous real power refers to $\left[\frac{V_m I_m}{2} \cos \theta - \frac{V_m I_m}{2} (\cos 2\omega t) \cos \theta\right]$, the first two terms on the right-hand side of equation (42). Reference to Fig. 17 will show that these two terms combine to form an instantaneous power variation which contains no negative values; hence this portion of equation (42) is called the *instantaneous real power.*

Unless qualified to mean *instantaneous* real power, the expression *real power* refers only to $\frac{V_m I_m}{2} \cos \theta$, the average value of the total instantaneous power with respect to time. [See equations (42) and (43).]

Reactive Power or Reactive Volt-Amperes. The third term on the right-hand side of equation (42), $\left[\frac{V_m I_m}{2} (\sin 2\omega t) \sin \theta\right]$, is variously called *instantaneous reactive power, instantaneous quadrature power, instantaneous reactive volt-amperes,* etc., for the reason that the area under the $\left[\frac{V_m I_m}{2} (\sin 2\omega t) \sin \theta\right]$ curve represents the energy which oscillates between the driving source and the reactive (either inductive or capacitive) elements of the receiving circuit. It will be observed from Fig. 17 that the *instantaneous reactive power* is that portion of the total instantaneous power variation which has equal positive and negative loops, and which contains the sine of the phase angle between v and i as a factor.

Unless qualified to mean *instantaneous* reactive power or *instantaneous* reactive volt-amperes, the expressions *reactive power* and *reactive volt-amperes* refer simply to $\frac{V_m I_m}{2} \sin \theta$, the maximum instantaneous value of the third term on the right-hand side of equation (42).

Units of reactive volt-amperes in the practical system of units are called *vars.* (See pages 98 and 99.)

Volt-Amperes. Both the real power, $\frac{V_m I_m}{2} \cos \theta$, and the reactive volt-amperes, $\frac{V_m I_m}{2} \sin \theta$, are important quantities, and they are often measured independently, a wattmeter being used to measure $\frac{V_m I_m}{2} \cos \theta$ and a reactive volt-ampere meter, called a varmeter, being used to measure $\frac{V_m I_m}{2} \sin \theta$.

The real power and the reactive power may be combined to yield the volt-amperes of the circuit, namely, $\frac{V_m I_m}{2}$

$$\sqrt{\left[\frac{V_m I_m}{2} \cos \theta\right]^2 + \left[\frac{V_m I_m}{2} \sin \theta\right]^2} = \frac{V_m I_m}{2}$$

The above relationship is illustrated graphically in Fig. 18 and will be encountered in later chapters in a more universally used form.

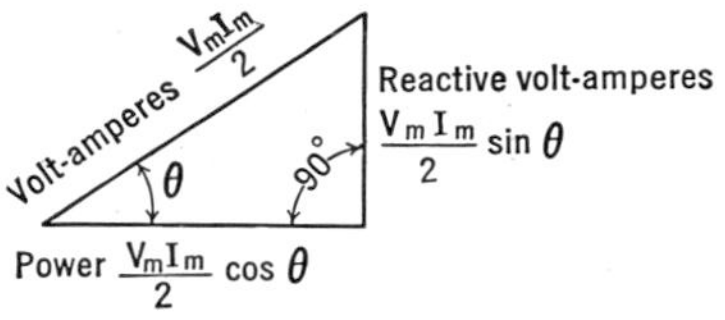

FIG. 18. Relation of power, reactive volt-amperes, and volt-amperes.

Example. Consider the RL circuit whose voltage, current, and power variations are depicted in Oscillogram 8. $R = 19.7$ ohms, $\omega L = 21.1$ ohms, and $v = 141.4 \sin 377t$ volts.

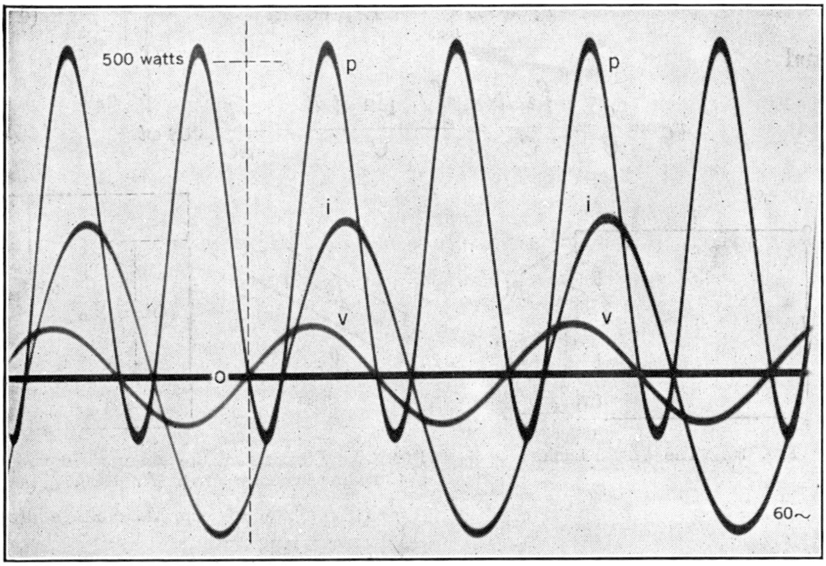

OSCILLOGRAM 8. Voltage, current, and power variations in an RL circuit. $R = 19.7$ ohms connected in series with $L = 0.056$ henry, $X_L = 21.1$ ohms, $V_{max} = 141.4$ volts, $I_{max} = 4.90$ amperes, $P_{av} = 236$ watts.

Let it be required to evaluate the expressions for the instantaneous current and the instantaneous power from the above data.

$$\mathbf{Z} = \sqrt{19.7^2 + 21.1^2} \,\Big/ \tan^{-1} \frac{21.1}{19.7} = 28.85 \underline{/47°} \text{ ohms}$$

The instantaneous current is

$$i = \frac{141.4}{28.85} \sin (377t - 47°) = 4.9 \sin (377t - 47°) \text{ amperes}$$

The expression for the instantaneous power is, by equation (42),

$$p = 236 - 236 \cos 754t + 253 \sin 754t \text{ watts}$$

In this expression,

> $[236 - 236 \cos 754t]$ is called the *instantaneous* real power
> $253 \sin 754t$ is the *instantaneous* reactive volt-amperes
> 236 watts is the real power
> 253 vars is the reactive power or reactive volt-amperes.

The *RLC* Branch. If a current of sinusoidal wave form, $i = I_m \sin \omega t$, is assumed to flow through the RLC branch shown in Fig. 19, it is plain that

$$v_R = Ri = RI_m \sin \omega t \tag{44}$$

$$v_L = L\frac{di}{dt} = \omega L I_m \cos \omega t \tag{45}$$

and

$$v_C = \frac{q}{C} = \frac{\int i\,dt}{C} = \frac{\int I_m \sin \omega t\,dt}{C} = \frac{-I_m}{\omega C}\cos \omega t \qquad (46)^8$$

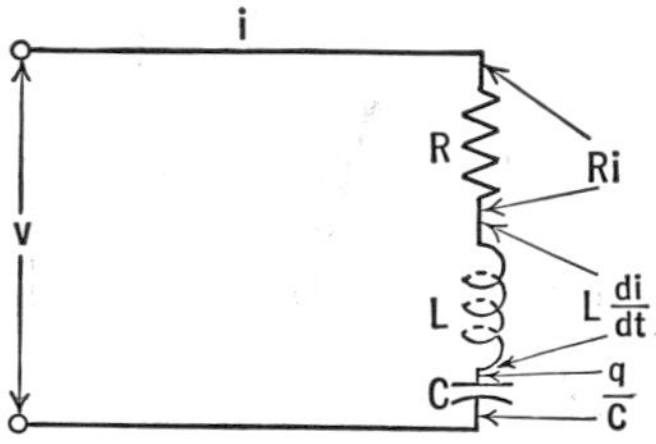

FIG. 19. The RLC branch.

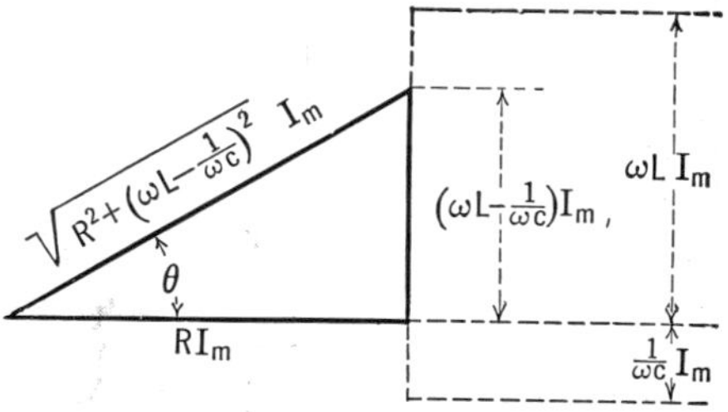

FIG. 20. Illustrating the manner in which the three voltage drops RI_m, $\omega L I_m$, and $\frac{1}{\omega C} I_m$ combine to form the voltage drop $\sqrt{R^2 + (\omega L - 1/\omega C)^2}\, I_m$.

The voltage applied to the branch is, physically, the sum of the three component voltages. In the form of an equation

$$RI_m \sin \omega t + \omega L I_m \cos \omega t - \frac{1}{\omega C} I_m \cos \omega t = v \tag{47}$$

or

$$RI_m \sin \omega t + \left(\omega L - \frac{1}{\omega C}\right) I_m \cos \omega t = v \tag{48}$$

The combination of the sine and cosine terms of the above equation may be effected in the same manner as previously outlined for the sine and cosine components. In the present case RI_m and $\left(\omega L - \frac{1}{\omega C}\right) I_m$ are considered as the two legs of the right triangle shown in Fig. 20.

[8] The reason for neglecting the constant of integration is similar to that given in the footnote on page 60.

It will be remembered from the discussion of the purely inductive and the purely capacitive branches that these two reactive elements cause exactly opposite phase displacements of the current with respect to the voltage. Since ωL has arbitrarily been considered to be a positive quantity, it becomes necessary to consider $1/\omega C$ a negative quantity. It should be recognized that, of and by itself, there is nothing inherently negative about the quantity $1/\omega C$. The fact that it acts oppositely to the quantity ωL in governing current flow requires that $1/\omega C$ be treated negatively if ωL is treated positively.

Impedance. If equation (48) is manipulated as indicated on page 68, the impedance of the RLC branch is found to be

$$\mathbf{Z}_{(RLC)} = \sqrt{R^2 + \left(\omega L - \frac{1}{\omega C}\right)^2} \bigg/ \underline{\tan^{-1} \frac{\left(\omega L - \frac{1}{\omega C}\right)}{R}} \tag{49}$$

If R is in ohms, L in henrys, C in farads, and ω in radians per second, $\mathbf{Z}$ is in ohms. Given R, L, C, and ω, the complete impedance function can be evaluated. The general expression for $\mathbf{Z}_{(RLC)}$ is of considerable importance in a-c circuit theory because all the impedance functions which have thus far been treated are directly deducible from this expression.

In a branch where ωL is negligibly small as compared with R and $1/\omega C$, the ωL term may be considered to be equal to zero, in which case the branch reduces to a resistance and capacitance branch.

$$\mathbf{Z}_{(RC)} = \sqrt{R^2 + \left(-\frac{1}{\omega C}\right)^2} \bigg/ \underline{\tan^{-1} \frac{\left(-\frac{1}{\omega C}\right)}{R}} \tag{50}$$

The negative angle implies that the current wave lags the voltage wave by a *negative* angle. The correct physical interpretation is that the current wave leads the voltage wave by the angle whose tangent is $\left(\frac{1}{\omega C}\right) \big/ R$.

With respect to its terminals the RLC branch will, in general, simulate the behavior of either the RL or the RC branch. If $\omega L > 1/\omega C$, the RLC branch responds to an impressed voltage at its terminals exactly as would an equivalent RL branch, the inductive reactance of which is $(\omega L - 1/\omega C)$. Similarly, if $1/\omega C > \omega L$, the RLC branch will respond to an impressed voltage at its terminals exactly as would an equivalent RC branch, the capacitive reactance of which is $(1/\omega C - \omega L)$. In either of the cases referred to, there will be interchanges of energy taking place between the two reactive elements.

The singular case, wherein $\omega L = 1/\omega C$, is of particular interest because the impedance here reduces to $R\underline{/0^\circ}$. With respect to its terminals the RLC branch, under the condition of $\omega L = 1/\omega C$, responds as would a purely resistive branch. If R is assumed to be a fixed quantity, the above condition may be obtained by the proper adjustment of L, C, or ω, and when $\omega L = 1/\omega C$ the impedance of the branch will be a minimum.

Example. If $R = 10$ ohms, $L = 0.056$ henry, and $C = 50\ \mu$f, the impedance of the RLC branch at 60 cycles is

$$\mathbf{Z} = \sqrt{10^2 + \left(377 \times 0.056 - \frac{10^6}{377 \times 50}\right)^2} \Big/ \underline{\tan^{-1} \frac{(21.1 - 53.0)}{10}}$$

$$= 33.4 \underline{/\tan^{-1}(-3.19)}$$

$$= 33.4 \underline{/-72.6^\circ} \text{ ohms}$$

If

$$v = 200 \sin 377t \text{ volts}$$

$$i = \frac{200}{33.4} \sin (377t + 72.6^\circ) \text{ amperes}$$

Power. Since $i = I_m \sin \omega t$ and $v = V_m \sin (\omega t + \theta)$, the expression for the instantaneous power delivered to the RLC branch takes the same form as equation (42), namely,

$$p = \frac{V_m I_m}{2} \cos \theta - \frac{V_m I_m}{2} [\cos 2\omega t] \cos \theta + \frac{V_m I_m}{2} [\sin 2\omega t] \sin \theta \quad (51)$$

In the present case θ may presumably take any value between $+90^\circ$ and -90°. The average power delivered to the RLC branch is in any case $\frac{V_m I_m}{2} \cos \theta$. [See equation (43).] The maximum value of the instantaneous reactive volt-amperes, $\left[\frac{V_m I_m}{2} \sin 2\omega t \sin \theta\right]$, is directly proportional to $\sin \theta$. Since the $\sin 2\omega t$ factor causes the instantaneous reactive volt-amperes to be alternately positive and negative, the absolute meaning of the sign of the reactive power term is not highly significant.

According to the convention of signs which has been employed in the present discussion, positive reactive volt-amperes — that is, a positive coefficient of $[\sin 2\omega t]$ in equation (51) — indicate inductive reactive volt-amperes, whereas negative reactive power indicates capacitive reactive volt-amperes. These signs are merely the result of choosing ωL positive and $1/\omega C$ negative. Further consideration of signs of reactive power will be given in the next chapter.

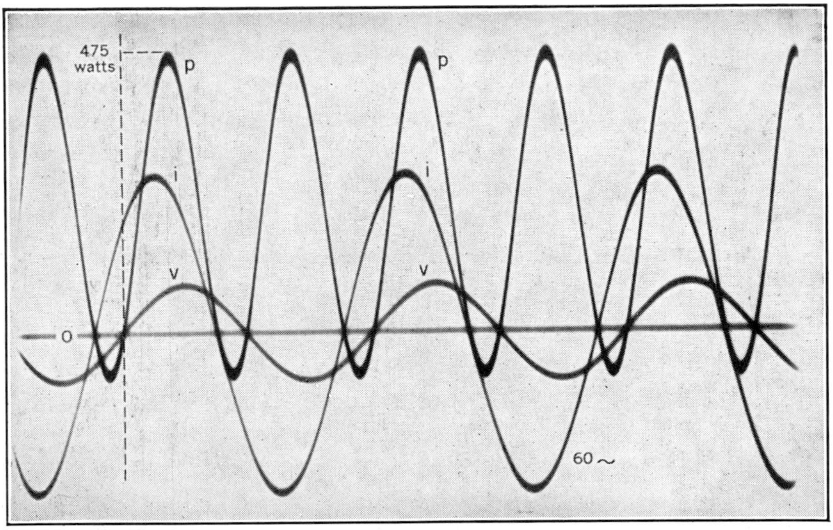

OSCILLOGRAM 9. Voltage, current, and power variations in an RLC circuit. $R = 20$ ohms, $L = 0.042$ henry, $C = 78\ \mu$f, $X_L = 15.8$ ohms, $X_C = 34$ ohms, $V_{max} = 141.4$ volts, $I_{max} = 5.23$ amperes, $P_{av} = 275$ watts.

The term $\left[\frac{V_m I_m}{2} \sin 2\omega t \sin \theta\right]$ is equal to zero at all times when $\theta = 0$, that is, when $\omega L = 1/\omega C$. In this case the reactive volt-amperes required by the inductive element are furnished by the capacitive element, and vice versa. Relatively large amounts of energy may oscillate between the reactive elements even though the RLC branch simulates a purely resistive branch at its terminals.

Oscillogram 9 illustrates the variations of v, i, and p in a particular RLC circuit. In the case shown $\omega L < 1/\omega C$ and the lead of the current with respect to the voltage is clearly indicated.

Impedance Functions. It should be understood from the foregoing analyses that impedance functions for any combinations of R, L, and C are independent of the point on the wave from which time is reckoned. In addition, the functions are entirely independent of whether the voltage or current wave is made the dependent wave. Thus in the RL branch a current wave $i = I_m \sin \omega t$ was assumed and the voltage wave $v = V_m \sin(\omega t + \theta)$ was found to lead the current by $\theta = \tan^{-1}(\omega L/R)$. If a voltage $v = V_m \sin \omega t$ is assumed impressed upon the circuit, the impedance function is the same, and it states that the voltage wave must lead the current by $\tan^{-1}(\omega L/R)$. Hence the current wave may be written as $i = I_m \sin(\omega t - \theta)$. Similar interpretations apply to any combination of R, L, and C. When the impedance function is found,

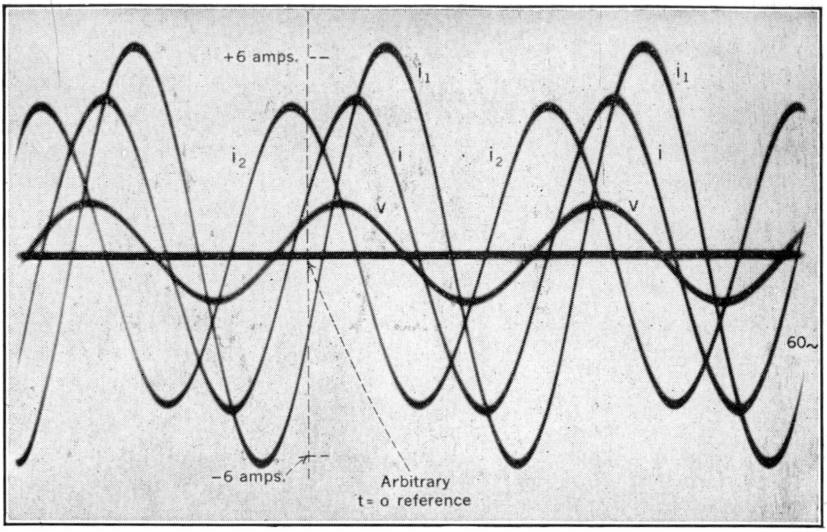

Oscillogram 10. Photographic records of the applied voltage and the three branch currents of the circuit arrangement shown in Fig. 22.

the *relation* between the voltage drop and the current is thereby determined. If one is assumed, the other may be determined from the impedance function as illustrated by the examples in the preceding articles.

Instantaneous Currents Combine Algebraically. The concept of adding instantaneous voltage drops across series elements to obtain the total voltage applied to a series circuit has been considered. Kirchhoff's emf law applies to a-c circuits if instantaneous values of voltage or their equivalents are considered. Likewise Kirchhoff's current law applies to a-c circuits provided instantaneous values of current or their equivalents[9] are employed. Figure 21 illustrates the principle in a simple case. Kirchhoff's current law states that the current flowing toward a junction, which in the present case is i, is equal to the current flowing away from the junction, namely, $i_1 + i_2$.

In general

$$\sum i_{\text{toward a junction}} = \sum i_{\text{away from the junction}} \tag{52}$$

or, if current *away* from the junction is considered as *negative* current *toward* the junction,

$$\sum i_{\text{toward a junction}} = 0 \tag{53}$$

[9] The equivalents referred to are the vector forms that are employed to replace instantaneous values. See Chapters III and IV.

If the currents are measured by devices which do not respond to instantaneous values, the combined measurements, in general, will not satisfy the above current law, for the simple reason that the devices employed fail to account for the relative phase positions of the currents involved.

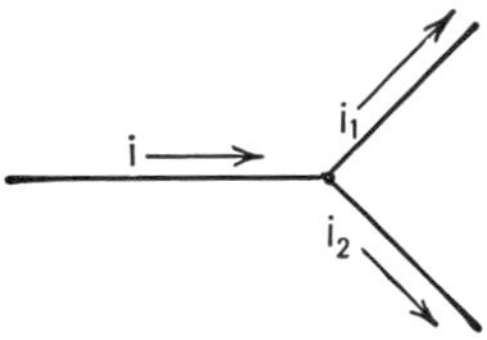

FIG. 21. Instantaneous current toward a junction is equal to the instantaneous current away from the junction.

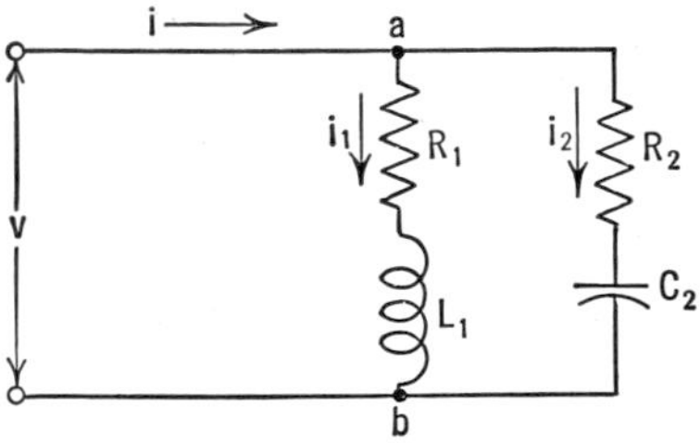

FIG. 22. R_1L_1 branch in parallel with R_2C_2 branch.

Oscillogram 10 shows how the instantaneous currents i_1 and i_2 of Fig. 22 add algebraically to yield the resultant current i. The analytical method of finding the expression for i from i_1 and i_2 will be explained in Chapter VI.

PROBLEMS

1. (*a*) What is the frequency of a 10-pole alternator when running at 360 rpm? (*b*) At what speeds should a 6-pole alternator run to yield 25, 30, 50, and 60 cycles per second?

2. How many poles are required on an alternator which runs at 300 rpm to develop 50 cycles per second?

3. What is the mechanical angular velocity of the machine in Problem 2? What is the electrical angular velocity or the angular frequency?

4. Write the expression for a sine-wave current having a maximum value of 1.732 amperes and a frequency of 1591 kilocycles. The $t = 0$ reference is to be selected at a point where di/dt is positive and $i = +1.5$ amperes.

5. Express as a sine function of time a 50-cycle alternating current which has a maximum value of 10 amperes. What is the angular velocity of this current wave?

6. Express an alternating current of 10 amperes maximum value which has an angular velocity of 377 radians per second as a cosine function of time. What is the frequency of this wave?

7. Express the equation of the current wave of Problem 5 if time is reckoned from the positive maximum value of the wave. Also express it for each possibility when time is reckoned from the negative 5-ampere value of the wave.

8. The time variation of a voltage wave is given by $e = 100 \sin 157t$ volts, where t is expressed in seconds.

(*a*) What is the maximum value of the voltage?

(*b*) What is the frequency of the voltage variation?

(*c*) If $e = 100 \sin (157t + 30°)$, what is the maximum value of the voltage? the frequency?

9. What are the maximum and minimum rates of change of the voltage depicted in Oscillogram 1, page 51, if the maximum voltage is 140 volts? Express results in volts per second.

10. At what instantaneous value of current is the 60-cycle current wave $i = 10 \sin (\omega t - 30°)$ amperes changing at the rate of 3265 amperes per second? (*b*) at 2260 amperes per second?

11. Find the maximum value of a 50-cycle current wave that is changing at 2000 amperes per second at an instantaneous value 30° from the maximum value of the wave.

12. If $v = 100 \sin (\omega t - 30°)$ and $i = 10 \sin (\omega t - 60°)$, what is the angle of phase difference between the current and voltage waves? Which wave leads?

13. Find the angle of phase difference between $v = 100 \cos (\omega t - 30°)$ and $i = -10 \sin (\omega t - 60°)$. Which wave lags?

14. A voltage has for its equation $v = 100 \cos \omega t$. Write the equation of a current wave of 10 amperes maximum which leads the specified voltage wave by $\frac{1}{6}$ of a cycle. Let angular measure be expressed in radians in this particular case.

15. (*a*) Given a sine-wave signal, the analytical expression of which is $[k \sin (2\pi ft)]$. If this wave is sampled (or tested) at $t = 0$ and at equal time intervals thereafter of $\Delta t = 1/f_s = 3/(2f)$, what is the nature of the sampled signal? (f_s represents the sampling frequency.)

(*b*) Make a rough plot of 6 or 8 cycles of a sine-wave voltage. Let this signal be sampled first at 135° after $v = 0$ (dv/dt positive) and thereafter at equal intervals of 315° of the signal voltage. If the sampled data is interpreted as representing points of a sine wave, what is the sampled frequency relative to the frequency of the actual signal?

16. (*a*) Find the instantaneous value of a sinusoidal alternating current having a maximum value of 90 amperes, 60° after the current passes through its zero value going positive; 225° after the current passes through its zero value going positive.

(*b*) Find the difference in time between the 60° value of current and the 225° value of current if the frequency is 50 cycles.

17. The current through a particular filter choke may be represented approximately by the equation

$$i = 1.0 + 0.50 \sin 1885t - 0.10 \cos 3770t \text{ amperes}$$

or

$$i = 1.0 + 0.50 \sin \alpha - 0.10 \cos 2\alpha \text{ amperes}$$

where $\alpha = 1885t$ radians if t is expressed in seconds.

(*a*) What is the frequency of the sine term? of the cosine term?

(*b*) What are the maximum and minimum values of current?

(*c*) Graph the current i with respect to time t or with respect to angular measure α.

18. A voltage $v = 150 \cos 314t$ volts is applied to a purely resistive branch of $R = 30$ ohms.

(*a*) Write the expression for i as a function of time, employing numerical coefficients.

Ans.: $i = 5 \cos 314t$ amperes.

(*b*) What is the frequency of the voltage and current variations?

Ans.: 50 cycles.

(*c*) Write the expression for p as a function of time, employing numerical coefficients.

Ans.: $p = 750 \cos^2 314t = 375 + 375 \cos 628t$ watts.

(*d*) What is the frequency of the power variation?

Ans.: 100 cycles.

19. A current $i = 5 \sin (110t + 30°)$ amperes flows in a purely resistive branch of 20 ohms.

(*a*) Write the expression for v as a function of time employing numerical coefficients.

(*b*) What is the frequency of the voltage variation?

(*c*) Write the expression for p as a function of time, employing numerical coefficients.

(*d*) What is the frequency of the power variation?

20. A voltage $v = 100 \cos (\omega t + 60°)$ volts is impressed upon a pure resistance circuit of 10 ohms.

(*a*) Write the equation with respect to time of the current wave and employ numerical coefficients.

(*b*) Find the equation with respect to time of the power wave.

(*c*) What is the maximum instantaneous power?

(*d*) What is the minimum instantaneous power?

(*e*) What is the average value of the power wave?

21. (*a*) What is the maximum time rate of change of a 60-cycle alternating current of sine form, the maximum value of which is 10 amperes?

(*b*) If this current flows through a pure inductance of 100 millihenrys, find the maximum value of the voltage across the terminals of the inductance.

22. A voltage $v = -150 \sin 377t$ volts is applied to a particular ciruit element, and it is found, by oscillographic analysis, that $i = 10 \cos 377t$ amperes. Make a sketch of the v and i waves. Find the nature and magnitude of the circuit parameter.

Ans.: $L = 0.0398$ henry.

23. A voltage drop $v = 100 \sin (377t + 30°)$ volts is across a pure inductance of 0.02654 henry.

(*a*) Use numerical coefficients and express the current through the coil as a function of time.

(*b*) Find the equation with respect to time of the power wave. Express the result as a single sine function.

(*c*) What is the average power?

(*d*) What is the first value of time at which maximum energy is stored in the inductance?

(*e*) What is the maximum amount of energy stored in the inductance during a cycle? State units.

24. A current of $5 \sin 300t$ amperes flows through a pure inductive branch of 0.2 henry.

(*a*) Find the impedance function and express numerically.

(*b*) How many joules are stored in the magnetic field about the inductance when $t = 0.05$ second?

(*c*) Write the expression for v as a function of time employing numerical coefficients.

25. A voltage $v = 200 \cos (157t + 30°)$ volts is applied to a particular circuit element, and it is found, by oscillographic analysis, that $i = 5 \sin (157t - 150°)$ amperes. Sketch the v and i waves. Find the nature and magnitude of the circuit parameter.

26. A voltage $v = 100 \sin 377t$ volts is impressed on a pure capacitance of 530.5 μf.

(*a*) Write the expression for i as a function of time employing numerical coefficients.

(*b*) Find the expression for the power wave as a function of time, employing numerical coefficients.

(*c*) How many joules are stored in the condenser when the current is zero? when the current is a maximum?

27. A voltage $v = 200 \sin 377t$ volts is applied to an inductive branch, and the maximum current is found, by oscillographic analysis, to be 10 amperes.

(*a*) Find the value of L in millihenrys.

Ans.: 53.1 millihenrys.

(*b*) If it is known that this inductance coil actually possesses 1.0 ohm resistance, what is the true value of L, assuming that $V_m = 200$ volts and $I_m = 10$ amperes?

Ans.: $L_{\text{true}} = \sqrt{20^2 - 1^2}/377 = 53.04$ millihenrys.

28. $R = 10$ ohms and $L = 0.05$ henry are connected in series and energized by a 25-cycle sinusoidal voltage, the maximum value of which is 150 volts.

(*a*) Find the complete impedance expression for the RL branch.

(*b*) Write the expression for the supply voltage as a function of time, making $v = 0$ (dv/dt positive) at $t = 0$.

(*c*) Write the expression for current as a function of time, assuming that the voltage in (*b*) is applied to the branch. Employ numerical coefficients.

(*d*) Write the expression for the instantaneous power delivered to the branch as a function of time. Express the result in three terms — a constant term, a single cosine term, and a single sine term. What is the average power?

(*e*) What are the reactive volt-amperes or vars?

(*f*) Sketch the v, i, and p variations in rectangular coordinates.

29. $R = 10$ ohms and $L = 0.05$ henry are connected in series and energized by a 25-cycle sinusoidal voltage, the maximum value of which is 150 volts.

(*a*) Find the complete impedance expression for the RL branch.

Ans.: $12.7 \underline{/38.2^\circ}$ ohms.

(*b*) Write the expression for the supply voltage as a function of time, making $v = 75$ (dv/dt positive) at $t = 0$.

Ans.: $v = 150 \sin (157t + 30^\circ)$ volts.

(*c*) Write the expression for current as a function of time, assuming that the voltage in (*b*) is applied to the branch. Employ numerical coefficients.

Ans.: $i = 11.8 \sin (157t - 8.2^\circ)$ amperes.

(*d*) Write the expression for the instantaneous power delivered to the branch as a function of time. Express the result in three terms — a number, one cosine, and one sine term. What is the average power delivered?

Ans.: $p = 695 - 820 \cos 314t + 328 \sin 314t$ watts.
$P_{\text{av}} = 695$ watts.

30. A resistive element of 30 ohms is connected in series with an inductance coil, the self-inductance of which is 50 millihenrys and the ohmic resistance of which is 4.5 ohms. A voltage $v = 100 \cos 377t$ volts is connected to the series branch.

(*a*) Evaluate the expression for i.

(*b*) Evaluate the expression for p.

(*c*) Write the expression for the real power as a function of time, employing numerical coefficients. What is the average value of the instantaneous real power?

(*d*) Write the expression for the reactive volt-amperes as a function of time, employing numerical coefficients. What is the average value of the instantaneous reactive power?

(*e*) What is the inductive reactance of the branch in ohms?

31. A current $i = 10 \cos 157t$ amperes flows in an RL circuit containing $R = 15$ ohms and $L = 0.0637$ henry.

(*a*) Write the equation of v as a function of time, employing numerical coefficients.

(*b*) Write the expression for the power wave as a function of time.

32. (*a*) What is the capacitive reactance of an 8-μf capacitor at 60 cycles?

(*b*) What is the capacitive reactance of an 800-$\mu\mu$f capacitor at 6 megacycles?

33. A resistive element of 151 ohms is connected in series with a capacitor of 4 μf capacitance. A 500-cycle sinusoidal voltage, the maximum value of which is 15 volts, energizes the RC branch.

(*a*) Write the expression for the supply voltage, choosing the $t = 0$ reference at the point of maximum positive voltage.

(*b*) Evaluate $\mathbf{Z}_{RC}$ completely.

(*c*) Evaluate the expression for i.

(*d*) Evaluate the expression for p which corresponds to the product of voltage and current employed here, and express all trigonometric terms with exponents no higher than unity.

34. Assume that the current $i = I_m \sin \omega t$ flows through a given RC branch. Show that the voltage across the branch is

$$v = I_m Z \sin(\omega t + \theta) = V_m \sin(\omega t + \theta)$$

where

$$Z = \frac{V_m}{I_m} = \sqrt{R^2 + \left(\frac{-1}{\omega C}\right)^2}$$

and

$$\theta = \tan^{-1}\frac{\left(\frac{-1}{\omega C}\right)}{R} \qquad \textit{Hint: } \frac{q}{C} = \frac{\int i\,dt}{C}$$

35. A resistance of 10 ohms is in series with a 303-μf capacitor. If the voltage drop across the capacitor is $150 \sin(220t - 60^\circ)$ volts, find the equation with respect to time of the voltage drop across the entire series circuit. Find also the expression for the current at any time t.

36. A 2000-cycle alternating voltage of sine form when impressed across the terminals of a condenser establishes a current of 0.01 ampere (maximum value). If the maximum value of the voltage is 20 volts, find the capacitance of the condenser in microfarads.

37. Consider a series RLC branch wherein $R = 10$ ohms, $L = 0.10$ henry, and C is 200 μf. Assume that the current $i = 10 \sin(157t)$ amperes flows through the RLC branch.

(*a*) Write the expression for the voltage drop across R, namely, Ri, employing numerical coefficients.

(*b*) Write the expression for the voltage drop across L, namely, $L\,di/dt$, employing numerical coefficients.

(*c*) Write the expression for the voltage drop across C, namely, q/C, employing numerical coefficients.

(*d*) Add (*a*), (*b*), and (*c*) to find the voltage drop across the RLC branch. Express the result as a single sine function of time.

(*e*) What is the numerical value of the impedance of the series RLC branch?

38. Assume that the current $i = I_m \cos \omega t$ flows through a given RLC branch.

Show that the voltage across the branch is

$$v = I_m Z \cos(\omega t + \theta) = V_m \cos(\omega t + \theta)$$

where

$$Z = \sqrt{R^2 + \left(\omega L - \frac{1}{\omega C}\right)^2}$$

and

$$\theta = \tan^{-1} \frac{\left(\omega L - \dfrac{1}{\omega C}\right)}{R}$$

39. In the following exercise, it is assumed that a coil having L henrys of inductance and R ohms of series resistance is placed in series with a condenser of C farads of capacitance. A current of $i = I_m \sin(t\sqrt{LC})$ amperes flows in the circuit. Show that the energy $w_L + w_C =$ constant, and evaluate this constant.

40. A resistive element of 20 ohms, an inductance coil of $L = 300$ millihenrys and $R_L = 10$ ohms, and a condenser of 50 μf capacitance are connected in series to form an RLC branch. A voltage $v = 100 \sin 157t$ volts is applied to the RLC branch.

(*a*) What is the numerical value of Z_{RLC}?

(*b*) Write the expression for i, employing numerical coefficients.

(*c*) Write the expression for p, employing numerical coefficients, and express all trigonometric functions with exponents no higher than unity.

(*d*) What is the average value of the power delivered to the branch?

(*e*) What is the maximum value of the reactive volt-amperes?

(*f*) Write the expression for the voltage drop across the 20-ohm resistive element as a function of time, employing numerical coefficients.

(*g*) Write the expression for the instantaneous power delivered to the 20-ohm resistor as a function of time, employing numerical coefficients.

41. A voltage $v = 282.8 \sin 500t$ volts is applied to a series circuit, and the resulting current is found to be $i = 5.656 \sin(500t - 36.87°)$ amperes. One element of this series combination is known to be a capacitor which has a capacitance of 100 μf. Determine the magnitudes of the other series elements present.

chapter **III**

Effective Current and Voltage—Average Power

Except for the maximum values of sinusoidal wave variations attention has been given only to general instantaneous values of current and voltage. The only practicable method of measuring instantaneous values of current, voltage, and power is by means of an oscillograph, a very useful instrument in many respects but one which is relatively inaccurate, cumbersome, and costly. It was shown in the previous chapter that instantaneous values are inconvenient to manipulate analytically, and in general they fail to specify concisely the magnitudes of the quantities involved. In this chapter the values of currents and voltages usually dealt with will be considered.

Ampere Value of Alternating Current. Alternating currents are defined so as to make applicable to them essentially the same laws that govern heating and transfer of power by direct current. An alternating current which produces heat in a given resistance at the same average rate as I amperes of direct current is said to have a value of I amperes. The average rate of heating produced by an alternating current during one cycle is $\frac{1}{T}\int_0^T Ri^2\,dt$. The average rate of producing heat by I amperes of direct current in the same resistance is RI^2. Hence by definition

$$RI^2 = \frac{1}{T}\int_0^T Ri^2\,dt$$

and

$$I = \sqrt{\frac{1}{T}\int_0^T i^2\,dt} = \sqrt{\text{average } i^2} \tag{1}$$

The current given in equation (1) which defines the alternating current in terms of its average rate of producing heat in a resistance is called the root mean square (abbreviated rms) value. It is also called the effective or virtual value. The graphical evaluation of the rms value of an alternating current is illustrated in Fig. 1. When the equation of the wave is not known or when it is inconvenient to determine it, the graphical means, suggested by Fig. 1, of evaluating equation (1) becomes a useful method to employ.

Problem 1. Find the effective value of a current that starts at zero, rises instantaneously, then remains at a value of 20 amperes for 10 seconds, then decreases instantaneously, remaining at a value of 10 amperes for 20 seconds, and then repeats this cycle. *Ans.:* 14.14 amperes.

The rms value of an alternating current may be measured with the ordinary dynamometer type of meter. This meter consists of two coils in series, one of them being movable. The force tending to turn

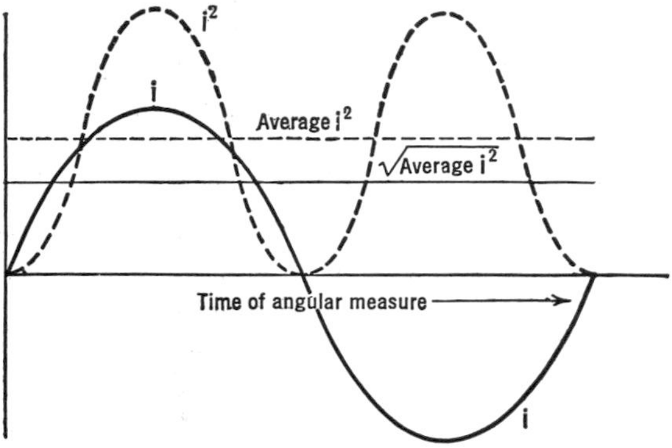

FIG. 1. Graphical evaluation of rms value.

the movable coil from any fixed position is proportional to the product of the currents in the two coils. Since the coils are in series and the same current flows in each, the force for any given position of the coils is proportional to i^2. Since the coil has a relatively high inertia, it cannot follow the variation in the force produced, and therefore takes a position corresponding to the average force or average i^2. If a suitable square root scale is placed under the pointer, the pointer will indicate the square root of the average square, or the rms value. Other types of a-c ammeters are also used to indicate effective values of current. (See Chapter X.)

Alternating Volt. An alternating volt is the value of a wave of alternating potential which maintains an alternating current of 1 rms ampere through a non-inductive resistance of 1 ohm. It therefore follows that the volt value of a wave is measured by the square root of the average square of the instantaneous values of the voltage wave.

Average Values. The average value of any a-c wave which is symmetrical about the zero axis is zero. However, when average value is applied to alternating quantities, it usually means the average of either the positive or negative loop of the wave. This value represents the d-c equivalent for electrolytic action of the alternating wave *abcde*, Fig. 2, if the wave were commutated (or rectified) and made the same as the wave *abcfe*. Since the average ordinate multiplied by the base is equal to the area under the curve, it follows directly that

$$\text{Average value} = \frac{2}{T}\int_0^{T/2} i\,dt \tag{2}$$

Equation (2) is applicable only when the wave passes through zero at the time $t = 0$. For any other condition the time t_1 at which the instantaneous value of the wave is zero must be determined and the average value found from

$$\text{Average value} = \frac{2}{T}\int_{t_1}^{(t_1+T/2)} i\,dt \tag{3}$$

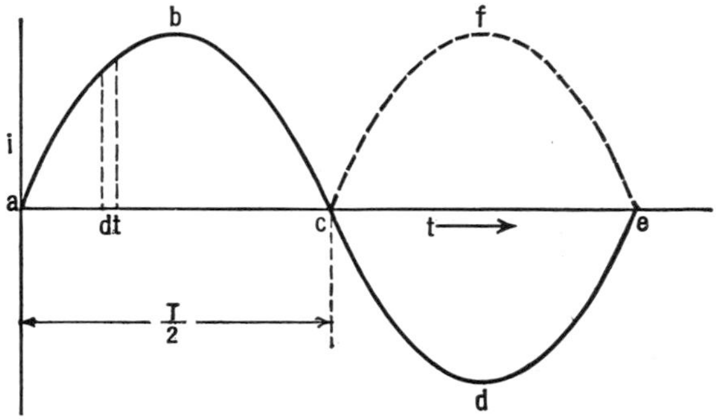

FIG. 2. Rectified a-c wave shown dotted.

If the average values of the positive and negative loops are different, the actual average value taken over a complete cycle represents the value of a d-c component in the wave. For example, the average

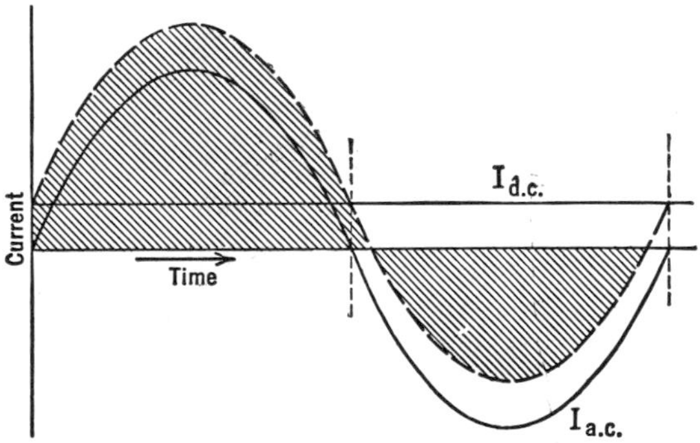

FIG. 3. Displaced a-c wave is equivalent to a symmetrical a-c wave and a d-c component.

value of the cross-hatched wave in Fig. 3 is I_{dc}. Inspection will show that the dotted wave is the sum of the alternating wave I_{ac} and the direct current I_{dc}.

Effective and Average Values of a Sinusoid. Through the use of equation (1) the effective value of any wave may be found. If the equation of the wave is not known, the integration must be performed graphically. When the equation is known, the analytical solution is generally to be preferred. Consider the sinusoid,

$$i = I_m \sin \omega t$$

$$I^2_{(\mathrm{rms})} = \frac{1}{T}\int_0^T i^2\,dt = \frac{1}{T}\int_0^T I_m{}^2 \sin^2 \omega t\,dt = \frac{I_m{}^2}{T}\int_0^T \left(\tfrac{1}{2} - \tfrac{1}{2}\cos 2\omega t\right) dt$$

$$= \frac{I_m{}^2}{T}\left[\frac{t}{2} - \frac{1}{4\omega}\sin 2\left(\frac{2\pi}{T}\right)t\right]_0^T = \frac{I_m{}^2}{2}$$

$$I_{(\mathrm{rms})} = \frac{I_m}{\sqrt{2}} = 0.707 I_m \tag{4}$$

For a *sine wave,* therefore, the rms value is 0.707 times the maximum. In general, $I_{(\mathrm{rms})}$ is written simply as I, and unless otherwise specified the symbol I refers to the effective or rms value of an alternating current.

The average value of a sinusoid over one-half cycle is

$$I_{\mathrm{av}} = \frac{2}{T}\int_0^{T/2} I_m \sin \omega t\,dt = \frac{2}{\pi} I_m = 0.636 I_m \tag{5}$$

Problem 2. A resultant current wave is made up of two components, a 5-ampere, d-c component and a 60-cycle, a-c component which is of sinusoidal wave form and which has a maximum value of 4 amperes.

(*a*) Draw a sketch of the resultant current wave.

(*b*) Write the analytical expression for the resultant current wave, choosing the $t = 0$ reference at a point where the a-c component is at zero value and where di/dt is positive.

Ans.: $i = [5 + 4 \sin (377t)]$ amperes.

(*c*) What is the average value with respect to time of the resultant current over a complete cycle?

Ans.: $I_{\mathrm{av}} = 5$ amperes.

(*d*) What is the effective value of the resultant current?

Ans.: $I_{\mathrm{eff}} = 5.75$ amperes.

Form Factor. Form factor is the ratio of the effective to the average value of a wave. Hence, for a voltage wave, e, which has equal positive and negative loops:

$$\text{Form factor} = \frac{\sqrt{\dfrac{1}{T}\displaystyle\int_0^T e^2\,dt}}{\dfrac{2}{T}\displaystyle\int_0^{T/2} e\,dt} \tag{6}$$

Equation (6) is subject to the same limitations as those explained for equation (2). Form factor has very little physical significance. It gives no certain indication of wave shape or wave form. Although a peaked wave will usually have a higher form factor than a flat-topped wave, it cannot be conclusively stated that one wave is more peaked than another because it has a higher form factor. That form factor tells nothing of the shape of a wave is evident from the fact that a sine wave and the wave $e = E_m \sin \omega t + (5/12)E_m \sin 5\omega t$, shown in Fig. 4, have the

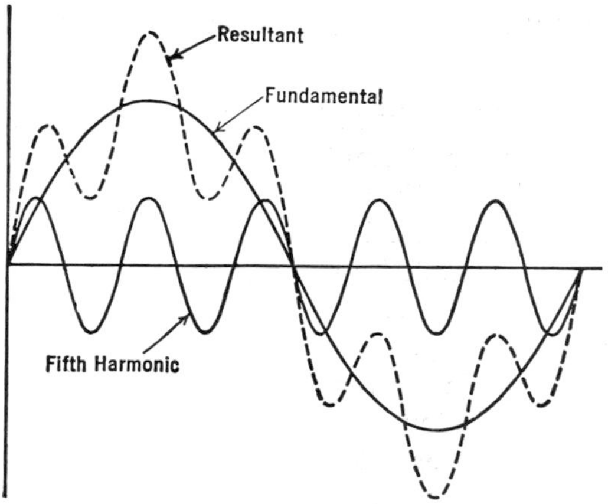

Fig. 4. Form factor of dotted wave is the same as that of a sine wave.

same form factor, namely, 1.11. However, form factor does give some indication of the relative hysteresis loss that will exist when a voltage is impressed on a coil wound on an iron core. Also some use is made of form factor in determining effective voltages induced in such coils when a known non-sinusoidal flux wave is present in the iron core.

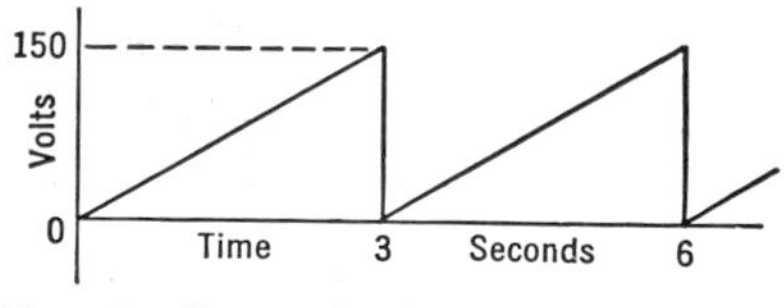

Fig. 5. Sawtooth wave form of voltage for Problems 3 and 4.

Problem 3. Find the form factor of the sawtooth wave form shown in Fig. 5. *Hint:* Between the limits of $t = 0$ and $t = T = 3$ seconds, the analytical expression for the voltage is $e = 50t$ volts. In a case of this kind,

$$E_{av} = \frac{1}{T}\int_0^T e\,dt$$

Ans.: 1.155.

Crest or Peak Factor. The crest, peak, or amplitude factor is the ratio of the maximum value of a voltage wave to the effective value. For the dotted wave shown in Fig. 4 the crest factor is 1.85. A knowledge of this factor is necessary when using an ordinary voltmeter to measure a voltage employed in insulation testing. The dielectric stress to which insulation is subjected depends upon the maximum value of the voltage attained. Since waves of the same effective value may have different maximum values, it is obvious that a knowledge of crest factor is required when making dielectric tests. The crest factor of a *sine wave* is

$$\frac{E_m}{0.707E_m} = \sqrt{2}$$

Problem 4. Find the crest factor of the sawtooth wave form shown in Fig. 5.
Ans.: 1.732.

Representation of Sine Waves by Vectors or Phasors. It has previously been stated that an attempt is made to secure sine waves of alternating currents and potentials. Alternating-current computations are often based upon the assumption of sine waves of voltage and current. When non-sinusoidal quantities are encountered, they are expressed in terms of a number of sine components of different magnitudes and frequencies, and these components are then handled according to the methods applicable to sine waves. In general, it would be cumbersome continually to handle instantaneous values in the form of equations of the waves. A more convenient means is to employ a vector method of representing these sine waves. The directed lines or vectors that are employed to represent sinusoidally time-varying quantities in a coplanar system are called phasors. Actually for the purposes in this book there is no difference between considering these representations as vectors or phasors. This distinction is made to avoid confusion in some of the more advanced work involving vector analysis as defined in mathematics. Since in elementary circuit analysis a vector diagram and phasor diagram mean the same thing, the terms will be used interchangeably. The phasor or vector representations of sine functions may be manipulated instead of the sine functions themselves to secure the desired result.

The sine wave of current $i = I_m \sin \omega t$ is shown in Fig. 6*a*. All the ordinates of this wave at the various times t may be represented by the projection of the revolving vector OA on the vertical axis of Fig. 6*b*. This projection is $I_m \sin \omega t$ if OA has a magnitude of I_m. This is the equation of the wave shown in Fig. 6*a*.

If two sine waves are related as shown in Fig. 7, each may be represented by the projections of counterclockwise[1] revolving vectors on the

[1] Counterclockwise is assumed the positive direction of rotation of vectors. The counterclockwise direction of rotation has been arbitrarily used by engineers in the United States and many foreign countries. Some foreign countries have used clock-

vertical. A little study will show that the angle of phase difference for the two waves must also be the angular displacement between the two vectors OA and OB representing them. If OA and OB are added vec-

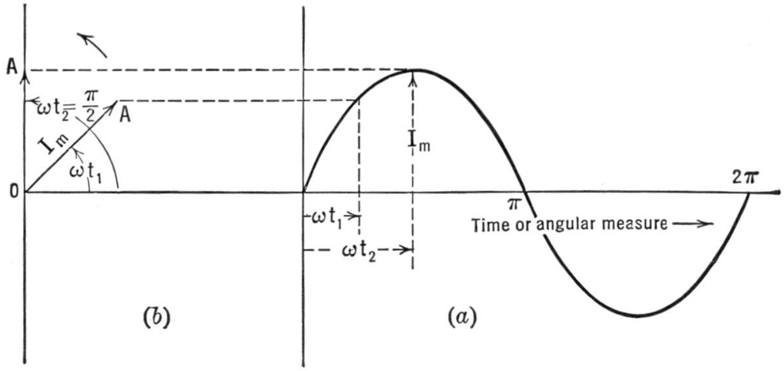

FIG. 6. Projection of a revolving vector represents a sine wave.

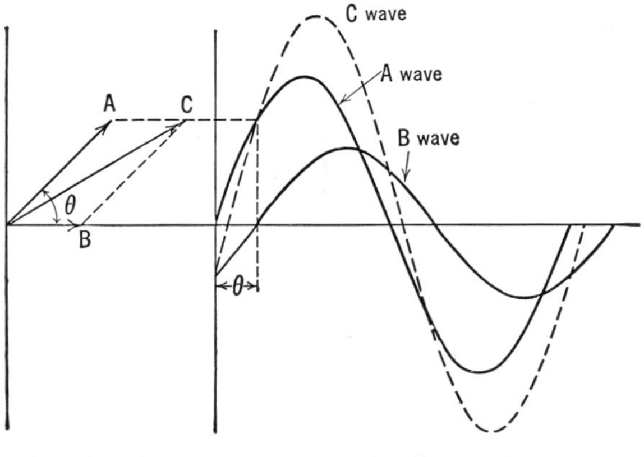

FIG. 7. Addition of sine waves by the use of vectors.

torially, a resultant OC is obtained whose projection on the vertical will represent the instantaneous values of the algebraic sum of the sine waves A and B.

Example 1. Add the following currents as waves and as vectors:

$$i_1 = 5 \sin \omega t$$
$$i_2 = 10 \sin (\omega t + 60°)$$

---

wise as positive. To avoid errors the student must always consider counterclockwise as the positive direction of rotation of all vectors in this book. One vector is said to be ahead or leading another when it is farther advanced counterclockwise than the other.

As waves:

$$\text{Sum} = i_0 = i_1 + i_2 = 5 \sin \omega t + 10 \sin (\omega t + 60°)$$
$$= 5 \sin \omega t + 10 \sin \omega t \cos 60° + 10 \cos \omega t \sin 60°$$
$$= 10 \sin \omega t + 8.66 \cos \omega t$$

Refer to the right triangle shown in Fig. 8*a*. If the previous equation is multiplied and divided by 13.23, there results

$$i_0 = 13.23 \left[\frac{10}{13.23} \sin \omega t + \frac{8.66}{13.23} \cos \omega t \right]$$
$$= 13.23 [\cos \alpha \sin \omega t + \sin \alpha \cos \omega t]$$
$$= 13.23 \sin (\omega t + \alpha)$$
$$= 13.23 \sin (\omega t + 40.9°)$$

As vectors: A wave of relative phase represented by $\sin \omega t$ will be represented by a vector along the reference axis. Positive angles will be assumed to be measured

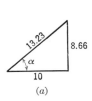

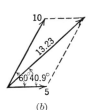

FIG. 8.

counterclockwise. The two waves are then represented by vectors, as shown in Fig. 8*b*. The sum will be found by adding x and y components.

$$\textstyle\sum x = 5 + 10 \cos 60° = 10$$
$$\textstyle\sum y = 10 \sin 60° = 8.66$$
$$\text{Sum} = \sqrt{\textstyle\sum x^2 + \sum y^2} = \sqrt{10^2 + 8.66^2} = 13.23$$
$$\alpha = \tan^{-1} \frac{\sum y}{\sum x} = \tan^{-1} \frac{8.66}{10} = 40.9°$$

Since the resultant is counterclockwise (positive) from the reference, the equation may be written as

$$i_0 = 13.23 \sin (\omega t + 40.9°)$$

Problem 5. Subtract i_2 from i_1 in example 1 by both methods shown above.
Ans.: $8.66 \sin (\omega t - 90°)$.

It is apparent that these coplanar vectors are merely convenient representations of sine waves, the independent variable of which is time. As such, they are time vectors and do not have any meaning so far as space relations are concerned. When the lengths of the two vectors represent maximum values of the waves respectively, the resultant vector will represent the maximum value of the resultant of the two waves.

Effective or rms values of voltages and currents are ordinarily used.

For sine waves these have been shown to be equal to the maximum value divided by $\sqrt{2}$. Thus maximum values of the vectors could be handled vectorially and the resultant divided by $\sqrt{2}$ to obtain the effective value. Instead, all the initial vectors could have their maximum values multiplied by 0.707 and the resultant of these would then be the resultant maximum divided by $\sqrt{2}$. If the latter procedure is followed, the vectors can be considered to represent effective values. Vectorial representation of effective values is customary, in which case the results are given directly in terms of effective values, the ones usually desired.

In drawing vector diagrams certain conventions must be observed. First, a convenient reference axis should be established. The vectors have their relations to one another fixed but they may be represented with respect to any axis. In Fig. 7, the vectors OA and OB were considered to revolve in order to represent the waves. The resultant OC was obtained by adding the two vectors when OB was along the axis of reference. Obviously, the same result would have been obtained had OA and OB been added when stopped in any other position with respect to the reference axis, provided that their magnitudes and the angle θ between them were not changed. Second, it must be observed that *counterclockwise is considered the positive direction of rotation of vectors* and that a vector rotated through an angle of lead or ahead of another vector must be rotated counterclockwise. It then follows that an angle of lag from a given axis must be in the clockwise direction. A vector thus rotated is said to be behind the axis in question.

Fig. 9. Resistance branch and vector diagram.

To illustrate the use of these conventions, the vector diagrams of voltage and current for a pure resistance, a pure inductance, and a pure capacitance circuit will be drawn. The waves shown on Oscillogram 4, page 59, for a pure resistance circuit, indicate that the applied voltage is in phase with the current. With current taken as, or along, the reference axis the vector diagram is shown in Fig. 9.

It was shown in Chapter II and experimentally illustrated in Oscillogram 5, page 63, that the wave of voltage drop across a circuit containing only inductance leads the current by 90°. This relation is illustrated vectorially with the current as the reference in Fig. 10 of the present chapter.

Reference to Oscillogram 6, page 66, will show that Fig. 11 of the present chapter represents vectorially the relations previously explained for the purely capacitive circuit.

Current was taken as the reference in the three previous diagrams. This was not necessary. The current could just as well have been drawn at any angle with respect to the reference axis, but for any partic-

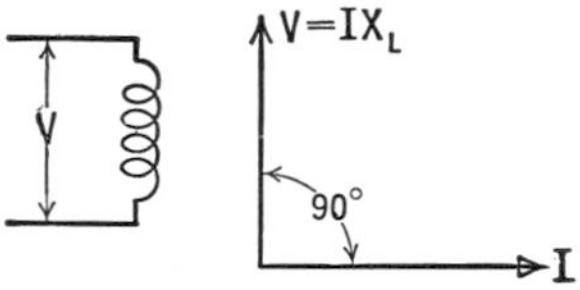

FIG. 10. Inductance branch and vector diagram.

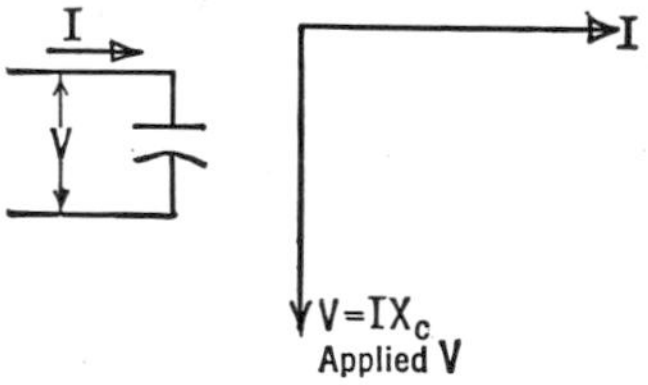

FIG. 11. Capacitance branch and vector diagram.

ular case the relation between current and voltage must remain the same, that is, the resistance drop must always be in phase with the current, the drop across the inductance must always lead the current by exactly 90°, and the drop across the capacitance must always lag the current by exactly 90°. The reference axis that appears to be the most convenient for the particular problem at hand should be chosen.

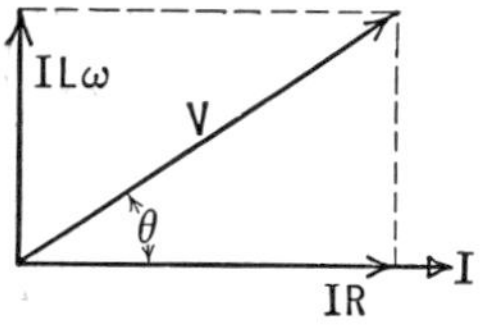

FIG. 12. Addition of voltage drops across L and R.

Vector Diagrams as Determined by Resistance and Reactance Drops and Impedance Functions. If a current $i = I_m \sin \omega t$ is assumed to flow in a circuit containing R and L, Kirchhoff's emf law states that $v = Ri + L\, di/dt$. Therefore $v = RI_m \sin \omega t + I_m L\omega \cos \omega t$. Since $RI_m \sin \omega t$ is of the same phase as $I_m \sin \omega t$, the resistance drop is shown in phase with the current in the vector diagram of Fig. 12. It will also be noted that $I_m L\omega \cos \omega t$ is 90° ahead of $I_m \sin \omega t$. Hence it is so drawn on the vector diagram. The vector sum of these two components is the resultant applied voltage **V**. The angle between **V** and **I** is $\theta = \tan^{-1} \omega L/R$. The same relation between **V** and **I** is obtained from the impedance function $Z\underline{/\theta}$. As explained in Chapter II, a positive angle θ means that the applied voltage leads the current or that the current lags the applied voltage by the phase angle θ. Thus the relation of **V** and **I** shown in the vector diagram could have been shown directly from the impedance function where the angle tells the phase and V/Z gives the magnitude of **I**. It should be noted that effective values were used exclusively in Fig. 12. Through the same procedure the student can show that Fig. 13 represents the vector diagram for an R and C circuit. The vector diagram of the R, L, and C circuit combines the vector diagrams in Figs. 12 and 13 the results of which appear in Fig. 14.

Problem 6. A 60-cycle current of 15 amperes flows in a circuit of 5 ohms resistance, 10/377 henry inductance, and 1/(377 × 15) farad capacitance. Draw the vector diagram, and calculate the applied voltage and the phase angle between it and the current. *Ans.:* 106 volts; angle 45°.

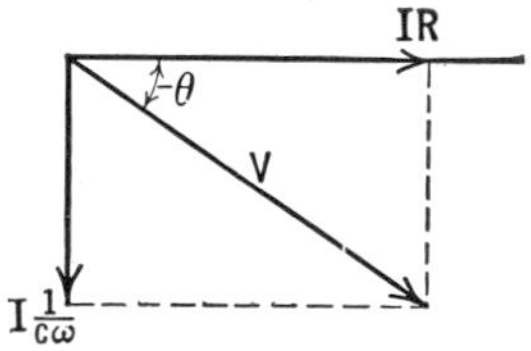

FIG. 13. Addition of voltage drops across *C* and *R*.

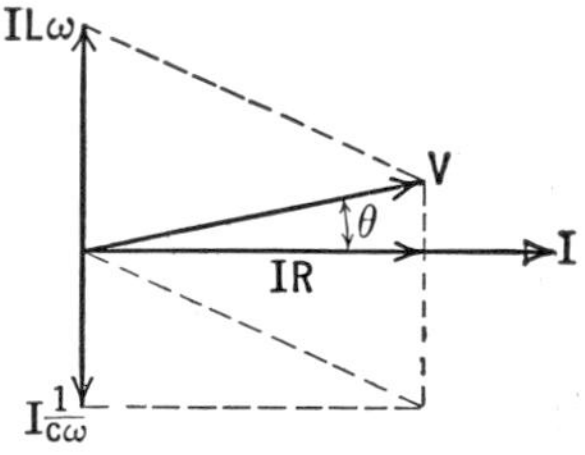

FIG. 14. Addition of voltage drops across *L*, *C*, and *R*.

Significance of Currents Flowing in the Direction of Voltage Rises and Drops. If the potential becomes greater in the direction of tracing a circuit, a voltage rise is being encountered. For example, assume the polarities of a circuit at some instant to be as indicated in Fig. 15. When tracing from *a* to *b* through the generator, the tracing is in the direction of increasing potential (from minus to plus) or in the direction of a voltage rise. In a similar way, when tracing through the load from *c* to *d*, the tracing is in the direction of a fall of potential or a voltage drop. Since the generator is the " pump," the current will flow from minus to plus through the generator, whereas in the external circuit it flows from plus to minus. It is evident, then, that a current flowing in the general direction of a potential rise represents electrical power generated or delivered. Also, when the current flows in the direction of a potential fall or drop, as it does through a load, power is being consumed or taken. If, then, a voltage rise is assumed positive, the generated power would be positive. A voltage drop is then negative and, since the same current flows in the direction of the voltage drop through the load, the power determined would be negative. These are the usual conventions employed when power generated and power consumed are simultaneously considered. If a voltage drop is assumed positive, then positive current in conjunction with the positive drop would yield positive power and

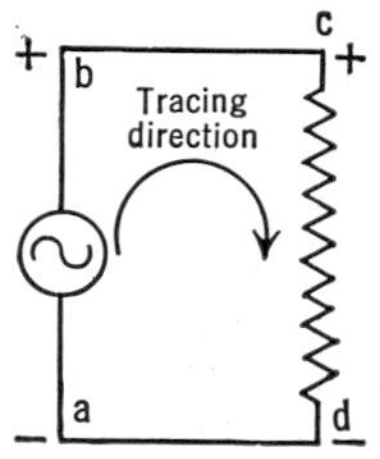

FIG. 15. Polarities of an a-c generator and load at some instant.

under such conditions power absorbed is positive. It is immaterial which conventions are used; that which is the most expedient is the one to choose. Physically, the same results are obtained. Although the above conventions are the most common, it is possible to establish other systems.

If a voltage rise is assumed positive, the question sometimes arises: Will generated power still be positive if the tracing direction is reversed? The answer is yes, as may be shown by the following considerations. Assume the tracing direction in Fig. 15 is *badc*. Then a voltage drop is encountered in the tracing direction through the generator. Since a voltage rise was considered positive, this drop through the generator will be negative. Since current flows through a generator in the general direction of increasing potential, the current will be in a direction opposite to that of the tracing direction. Hence it must be called a negative current. The product of the voltage drop through the generator, which was negative, by the negative current (opposite to the tracing direction) is positive. The sign of power generated is therefore unchanged. Similarly, it may be shown that the sign of the power dissipated by the load is unchanged. Hence the choice of the tracing direction does not affect the signs of generated and dissipated power. These are fixed by the signs assumed for voltage rises and drops in conjunction with the current.

Power, Real and Reactive. In Chapter II it was shown that the general expression for average power, when waves of voltage and current are sinusoidal, is $\frac{V_mI_m}{2}\cos\theta$. Since the maximum value of a sine wave divided by the square root of 2 is the effective value, the equation for average power may be written

$$P = \frac{V_m}{\sqrt{2}}\frac{I_m}{\sqrt{2}}\cos\theta = VI\cos\theta \tag{7}$$

When V is in volts and I is in amperes, the power is expressed in watts. As previously shown, the power in a single-phase circuit is not constant. The instantaneous power from equation (42), Chapter II, is

$$p = \left[\frac{V_mI_m}{2}\cos\theta - \frac{V_mI_m}{2}\cos\theta\cos 2\omega t\right] + \frac{V_mI_m}{2}\sin\theta\sin 2\omega t \tag{8}$$

The first two terms of the right side of equation (8) represent instantaneous real power. When $2\omega t$ is an odd multiple of π, the value of the real power is

$$\frac{2V_mI_m}{2}\cos\theta = 2VI\cos\theta$$

When $2\omega t$ is a multiple of 2π, real power is 0. Hence real power in a single-phase circuit fluctuates between 0 and $2VI \cos \theta$ and has an average value of $VI \cos \theta$ (shown in Chapter II). The third term of the right-hand member of equation (8) represents what has been called instantaneous reactive power, or, preferably, instantaneous reactive volt-amperes. Its equation is

$$p_X = \left(\frac{V_m I_m}{2} \sin \theta\right) \sin 2\omega t \tag{9}$$

Thus instantaneous reactive volt-amperes fluctuate between $+\frac{V_m I_m}{2} \sin \theta$ and $-\frac{V_m I_m}{2} \sin \theta$. Whereas the average value of the instantaneous reactive volt-amperes is zero, the maximum value is $\frac{V_m I_m}{2} \sin \theta$. This is the value referred to when reactive volt-amperes are considered.[2] Hence

$$P_X = \frac{V_m}{\sqrt{2}} \frac{I_m}{\sqrt{2}} \sin \theta = VI \sin \theta \tag{10}$$

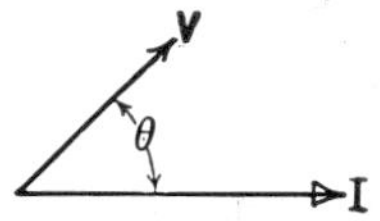

FIG. 16. Angle θ is positive when voltage leads current if current is along the reference axis.

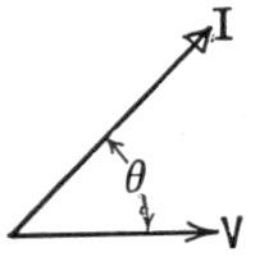

FIG. 17. Angle θ is positive when current leads voltage if voltage is along the reference axis.

It is plain that reactive volt-amperes as determined from equation (10) will be positive when θ is positive. As interpreted from vector diagrams when current is taken as a reference, Fig. 16, θ is positive when the voltage leads the current or for inductive loads. If voltage is taken along the reference, Fig. 17, θ is positive when the current leads the generated voltage. In the former case reactive volt-amperes are positive for inductive loads or lagging currents, whereas in the second case positive reactive volt-amperes are obtained when the load is capacitive or where the current leads the voltage. Another basis for determining the sign of reactive power was given in Chapter II. It is apparent that inductive reactive power or volt-amperes can be defined as positive or

[2] It should be recognized that this discussion refers to components of the resultant power wave. These components do not exist as separate entities but they are convenient components to consider for purposes of analysis. Actually a single wave, as shown in Chapter II, is the only power wave which has a physical existence.

negative depending upon the basis employed. Which of these signs to adopt has been a subject of discussion for many years, and each sign has been employed at various times. At the 1934 Paris meeting of the Committee on Electrical Units, reactive power caused by a current lagging the voltage was defined as negative reactive power. However this definition encountered several inconsistencies and after a great deal of discussion a committee of the American Institute of Electrical Engineers as reported in the January 1948 issue of *Electrical Engineering* recommended that inductive reactive volt-amperes be defined as positive reactive power. This convention is consistent with the sign obtained if the sign of the angle in the impedance function is employed in the formula for reactive volt-amperes. This convention is also consistent with the sign obtained by calculating I^2X where the sign of X for an inductive reactance is positive. This is the standard sign employed for inductive reactance. It will be seen in the next chapter that, when counterclockwise is considered as the direction for measuring positive angles of rotation, the use of complex numbers requires the adoption of the positive sign for inductive reactance. As a result of these and other considerations the present standard in the United States is to call inductive reactive volt-amperes positive. This is the sign which has been recommended to the International Committee on Electrical and Magnetic Units for adoption although no official action by that body has yet been taken. In any event it is desirable to label the reactive volt-amperes as inductive or capacitive. In combining the two in analytical work the important requirement is to consider one positive and the other negative regardless of the convention employed.

Reactive volt-amperes are expressed in vars, a term coined from the first letters of the words "volt amperes reactive." Reactive volt-amperes considered over a period of time represent oscillations of energy between the source and the load. Their function is to supply the energy for magnetic fields and charging capacitors, and to transfer this energy back to the source when the magnetic field collapses or when the capacitor discharges. Although reactive volt-amperes, as such, require no average energy input to the generators, they do necessitate a certain amount of generator volt-ampere capacity and thereby limit the available power output of the generators. Reactive volt-amperes cannot be transferred without incurring a copper loss. Although this i^2r loss is caused by the transfer of the reactive volt-amperes, it is not a part of the reactive volt-amperes. Reactive volt-amperes are due to quadrature components of voltage and current and as such represent zero average power. These additional losses must be supplied by an average energy input to the alternators.

From equation (42), Chapter II, instantaneous real power was found to be $V_m I_m \cos\theta \sin^2 \omega t$. This may be considered to consist of a voltage $V_m \sin \omega t$ and a current $(I_m \cos\theta) \sin \omega t$, which is in phase with the voltage. The current $I_m \cos\theta$ is called the in-phase component, power component, active component, or energy component of current with respect to voltage. In terms of root mean square values the power is due to a voltage V and a component of current $I \cos\theta$ in phase with V, as shown in Fig. 18. Since the product of the voltage V and energy component of current $I \cos\theta$ is $VI \cos\theta$, the same expression as equation (7) for power, it is evident that power may be determined in this

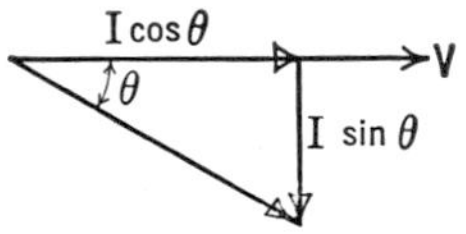

FIG. 18. In-phase and quadrature components of current with respect to voltage.

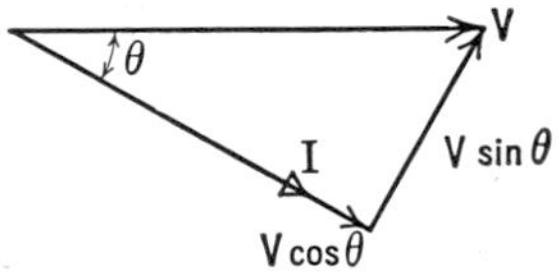

FIG. 19. In-phase and quadrature components of voltage with respect to current.

manner. If $\cos\theta$ is grouped with V, then $V \cos\theta$ may be viewed as the in-phase component, active component, energy component, or power component of voltage with respect to current, as shown in Fig. 19. Obviously, power may also be obtained by multiplying the in-phase component of voltage with respect to current by the current. Similarly, $I \sin\theta$ in Fig. 18 is the "out-of-phase component," quadrature component, or reactive component of current with respect to voltage. This component multiplied by the voltage gives reactive volt-amperes, as may be seen by comparison with equation (10). Also, $V \sin\theta$ is the quadrature, reactive, or wattless component of voltage with respect to current. This component of voltage multiplied by current also yields the reactive volt-amperes, or vars.

Volt-Amperes. The product of effective voltage by effective current in an a-c circuit is called volt-amperes. A larger unit is kilovolt-amperes, abbreviated kva. Obviously, a given number of volt-amperes may represent any number of different values of power, depending upon the value of $\cos\theta$ in equation (7). Cosine θ is therefore a factor by which volt-amperes are multiplied to give power. Hence cosine θ is called power factor. As an equation

$$\text{Power factor} = \cos\theta = \frac{\text{power}}{\text{volt-amperes}} \tag{11}$$

Reference to equation (10) will show that $\sin\theta$ is the factor by which volt-amperes are multiplied to yield reactive volt-amperes or vars.

Hence sin θ is called the reactive factor:

$$\text{Reactive factor} = \sin\theta = \frac{\text{reactive volt-amperes}}{\text{volt-amperes}} \tag{12}$$

Since $\sin^2\theta + \cos^2\theta = 1$, reactive factor $= \sqrt{1 - (\text{p.f.})^2}$ and power factor $= \sqrt{1 - (\text{r.f.})^2}$.

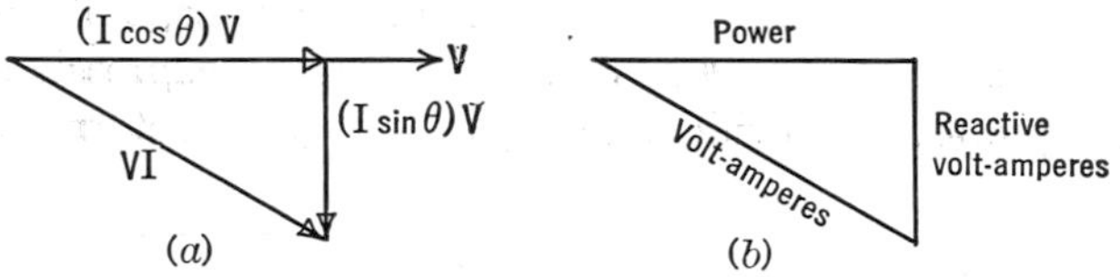

FIG. 20. Relation of power, reactive volt-amperes, and resultant volt-amperes.

If the current and each of its two components in Fig. 18 are multiplied by V, a relationship between power, reactive volt-amperes, and volt-amperes is obtained, as shown in Figs. 20*a* and *b*. Hence

$$\text{Volt-amperes} = \sqrt{(\text{power})^2 + (\text{reactive va})^2}$$

This relation is very useful in problems involving correction of power factor.

Example 2. One hundred and ten volts are applied to a series circuit consisting of 8 ohms resistance, 0.0531 henry inductance, and 189.7 μf capacitance. When

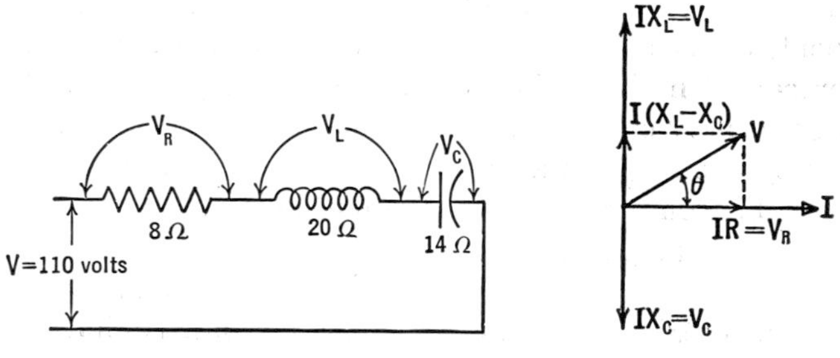

FIG. 21. *R*, *L*, and *C* in series and the corresponding vector diagram.

the frequency is 60 cycles, calculate current, power, power factor, vars, reactive factor, and volt-amperes. Also calculate the voltage drop across each circuit element. The circuit and vector diagrams are shown in Fig. 21.

$$X_L = 2\pi fL = 2\pi\, 60 \times 0.0531 = 20 \text{ ohms}$$

$$X_C = \frac{1}{2\pi fC} = \frac{1}{2\pi\, 60 \times 189.7 \times 10^{-6}} = 14 \text{ ohms}$$

$$X = X_L - X_C = 20 - 14 = 6 \text{ ohms}$$

$$R = 8 \text{ ohms}$$

$$Z = \sqrt{R^2 + X^2} = \sqrt{8^2 + 6^2} = 10 \text{ ohms}$$

$$I = \frac{110}{10} = 11 \text{ amperes}$$

$$\text{P.f.} = \cos\theta = \frac{IR}{V} = \frac{IR}{IZ} = \frac{R}{Z} = \frac{8}{10} = 0.8$$

$$P = VI\cos\theta = 110 \times 11 \times 0.8 = 968 \text{ watts}$$

Also $$P = I^2R = 11^2 \times 8 = 968 \text{ watts}$$

$$\text{Reactive va} = VI\sin\theta = 110 \times 11 \times \frac{XI}{ZI} = 110 \times 11 \times \frac{6}{10} = 726 \text{ vars}$$

$$\text{va} = VI = 110 \times 11 = 1210 = \sqrt{968^2 + 726^2}$$

$$V_R = IR = 11 \times 8 = 88 \text{ volts}$$

$$V_L = IX_L = 11 \times 20 = 220 \text{ volts}$$

$$V_C = IX_C = 11 \times 14 = 154 \text{ volts}$$

It will be noted that the arithmetic sum of these three voltages is much greater than the applied voltage. Alternating voltages of the same frequency can be added but they *must* be added *vectorially* with due regard for phase relation. Thus

$$220 - 154 = 66 \text{ volts in quadrature with } \mathbf{I}$$

$$V_R = 88 \text{ volts in phase with } \mathbf{I}$$

Therefore

$$V = \sqrt{88^2 + 66^2} = 110 \text{ volts, which checks the applied voltage.}$$

Example 3. Given the parallel circuit shown in Fig. 22, find I, I_1, I_2, and total power consumed.

Solution. The impedance functions of branches 1 and 2 are

$$\mathbf{Z}_1 = \sqrt{6^2 + 8^2}\,\angle\tan^{-1}\frac{8}{6} = 10\,\angle 53.17° \text{ ohms}$$

$$\mathbf{Z}_2 = \sqrt{5^2 + 5^2}\,\angle\tan^{-1}\left(\frac{-5}{5}\right) = 7.07\,\angle -45° \text{ ohms}$$

$$I_2 = \frac{100}{7.07} = 14.14 \text{ amperes}$$

$$I_1 = \frac{100}{10} = 10 \text{ amperes}$$

$$\mathbf{I} = \mathbf{I}_2 + \mathbf{I}_1$$

The vector diagram is drawn as shown in Fig. 23.

The currents may be added by using $\sum x$ and $\sum y$ components or by the cosine law. The former will be used and a tabulation of results made. The x-axis will be taken along V. This is arbitrary. Any other position may be used.

Current	x components	y components
I_2	$I_2 \cos 45 = 10$	$I_2 \sin 45 = 10$
I_1	$I_1 \cos(-53.17°) = 6$	$I_1 \sin(-53.17°) = -8$

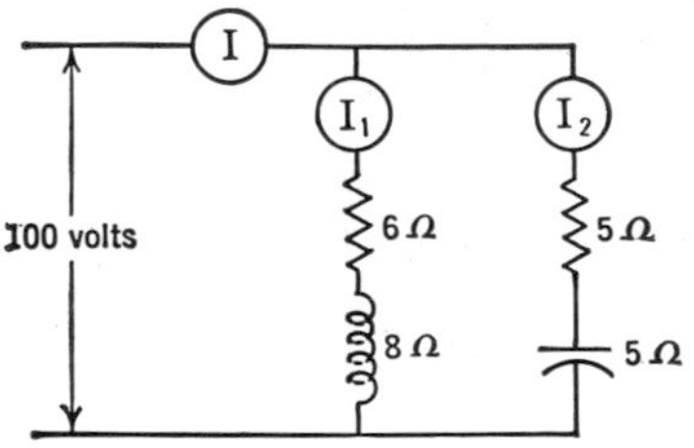

FIG. 22. Parallel branches.

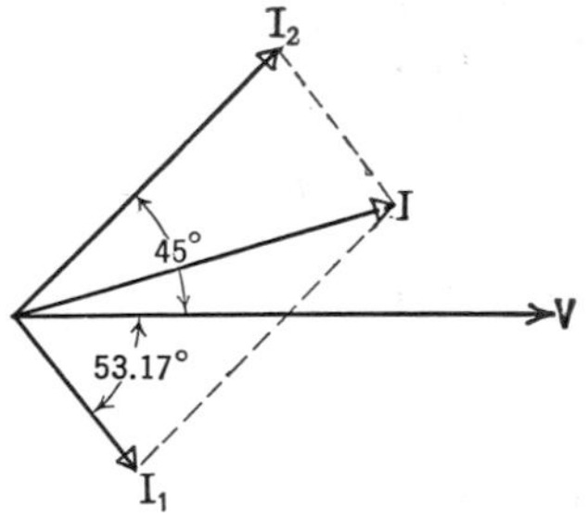

FIG. 23. Vector diagram of Fig. 22.

$$\sum x = 16 \qquad \sum y = 2$$
$$I = \sqrt{16^2 + 2^2} = 16.13 \text{ amperes}$$
$$P = VI_{\text{in-phase}} = 100 \times \sum x = 100 \times 16 = 1600 \text{ watts}$$

An alternative is

$$P = I_1{}^2R_1 + I_2{}^2R_2 = 10^2 \times 6 + 14.14^2 \times 5$$
$$= 600 + 1000 = 1600 \text{ watts}$$

Vector Combination of Voltages. Thus far, only currents have been added and subtracted vectorially. Since vector combinations are based upon the assumption of sine waves, it is apparent that sinusoidal voltage waves can be added and subtracted vectorially. For example,

FIG. 24. Coils in which a-c voltages are induced.

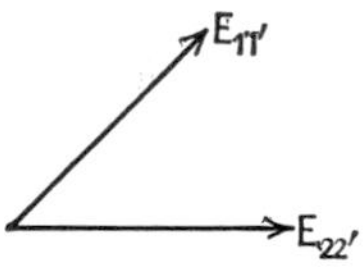

FIG. 25. Voltages induced in coils of Fig. 24.

the coils shown in Fig. 24 are assumed to have induced voltages which are phase-displaced by 45°, as shown in Fig. 25. The voltage $E_{12'}$ is desired when 1′ and 2 of Fig. 24 are connected. In general, the difference of potential between two points of a winding or circuit is found by adding all the potential drops (rises are negative drops) encountered in *tracing through* the winding from one point in question to the other. This statement follows from the definition of potential difference. The voltages are denoted by subscripts, and the order in which the subscripts are written must be the same as the order in which they are encountered as the circuit is being traced. Thus for Fig. 24, when 1′ and 2 are connected, $\mathbf{E}_{12'} = \mathbf{E}_{11'} + \mathbf{E}_{22'}$. This vector addition is shown in Fig. 26

If 1′ were connected to 2′ in Fig. 24, the emf $\mathbf{E}_{12}$ would be $\mathbf{E}_{12} = \mathbf{E}_{11'} + \mathbf{E}_{2'2}$. This result is obtained by adding the voltage vectors, $\mathbf{E}_{11'}$ and $\mathbf{E}_{2'2}$, as shown in Fig. 27.

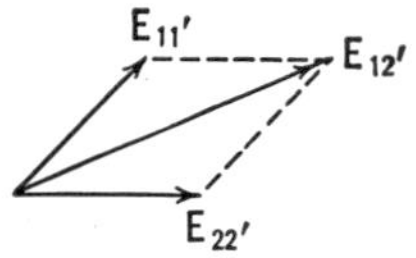

FIG. 26. $E_{12'}$ for Fig. 24 when 1 and 2 are connected.

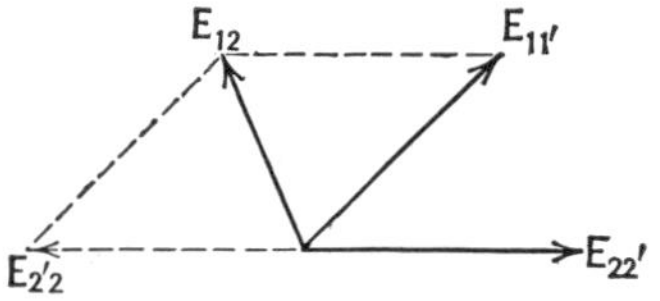

FIG. 27. E_{12} for Fig. 24 when 1′ and 2′ are connected.

Problem 7. Two coils on the armature of an alternator are displaced 60 electrical degrees. The emf of each coil is 100 volts. What is the resultant emf of the two coils when connected series adding and also when series subtracting?

Ans.: 173.2 volts, 100 volts.

PROBLEMS

8. An elevator motor takes 20 amperes for 15 seconds. Power is then cut off for 45 seconds, after which the cycle is repeated. If rated full-load current of the motor is 12 amperes, will it overheat on a continuation of this cycle? What is the equivalent continuous current which will yield the same average rate of heating?

9. A motor takes 50 amperes for 10 seconds, after which power is off for 20 seconds. It then takes 60 amperes for 5 seconds, after which power is cut off for 1 minute. What will the continuous rated current have to be so that the motor will not overheat?

10. (*a*) What is the average value of the pulsating current shown in Fig. 28?

(*b*) What is the effective value?

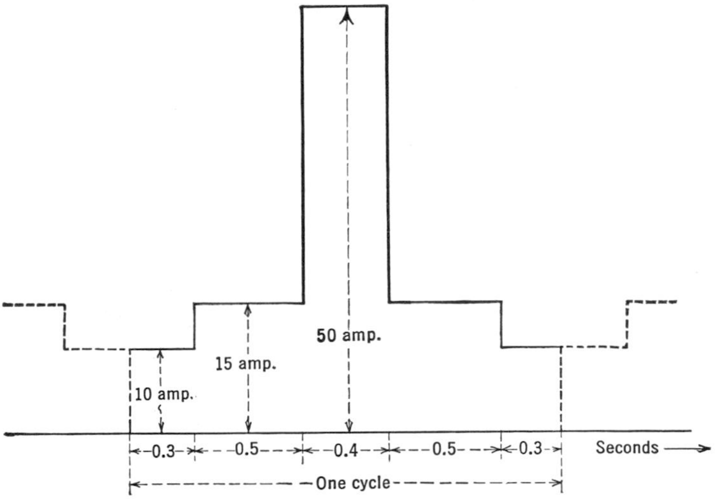

FIG. 28. See Problems 10, 11, 12, and 25.

11. (*a*) If the current shown in Fig. 28 flows through a d-c ammeter in series with an effective reading a-c ammeter, what will be the reading of each instrument, assuming perfect calibration of the instruments?

(*b*) If the resistance of the circuit is constant (the pulsating current being produced by a pulsating voltage), which of the above readings should be employed in finding the power by the I^2R formula?

12. (*a*) If the current shown in Fig. 28 flows through a 5-ohm resistance, what number of joules of heat energy is produced each cycle? what number of gram calories?

(*b*) What power is dissipated in the above resistance over any integral number of cycles?

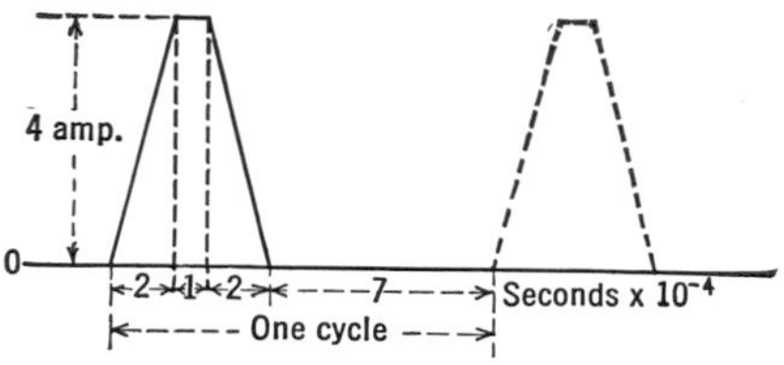

FIG. 29. See Problem 13.

13. The plate current of a triode operating as an oscillator takes the general form shown in Fig. 29.

(*a*) What is the frequency of oscillation depicted in Fig. 29?

(*b*) What is the average value of the pulsating current?

(*c*) What is the effective value of the pulsating current?

Note: The current during the first 2×10^{-4} second shown in Fig. 29 may be represented by the equation $i = 2 \times 10^4 t$ amperes. Utilize symmetry.

14. A current in a circuit starts at zero and increases linearly until a value of 12 amperes is attained. It then drops to zero in negligible time and repeats the cycle. What will an effective reading a-c ammeter in this circuit read?

15. A current starts abruptly at 10 amperes and decreases linearly to zero and then repeats this cycle. Find the rms value without changing the orientation of the wave from that given.

16. Find the rms value of a current in terms of radius ρ whose instantaneous values make semicircles of radius ρ above and below the x-axis.

17. A current has a positive loop which follows a semicircle of radius 1 ampere and the diameter of this semicircle lies on the x-axis. If through the addition of a constant current of 1 ampere the resultant current is represented by the semicircle with its diameter raised 1 ampere above the x-axis, find the rms value of the resultant current.

18. Calculate the form factor of the current wave in Problem 14.

19. Find the rms value of $e = 100 \sin \omega t + 60 \sin (5\omega t + 30°)$ volts by integration.

20. Calculate the form factor of $e = 100 \sin \omega t + 60 \cos 3\omega t$.

21. Find the rms value of $e = 100 \sin \omega t - 40 \sin 3\omega t$ volts.

22. Calculate the form factor of the voltage wave in Problem 21.

23. Find a wave other than that given in the text which is not a sine wave but which has the same form factor as a sine wave.

24. Calculate the peak factor of (*a*) a sine wave, (*b*) a rectangular wave, (*c*) a symmetrical triangular wave whose positive and negative halves are symmetrical about their respective midordinates if the angle at the peak is 60°, and (*d*) a triangular wave whose angle at the peak is 90°.

25. Calculate the crest factor for the wave shown in Fig. 28.

26. Calculate the crest factor and form factor of a wave whose positive and negative loops are semicircles.

27. The respective branch currents flowing toward a junction of two parallel branches of a circuit are $i_1 = 30 \sin(\omega t + 60°)$ amperes and $i_2 = 20 \sin(\omega t - 20°)$ amperes. Find the resultant current leaving the junction in terms of a single sine wave. Find also the effective value of the current.

28. One branch current of $i_1 = 40 \sin(\omega t - 40°)$ amperes combines with a second branch current to yield a resultant of $50 \sin(\omega t + 80°)$ amperes. Find the equation of the second branch current. Find also the effective value.

29. A motor requires 25 amperes and 220 volts at a lagging power factor of 0.88. Find the power, vars, reactive factor, and the volt-amperes taken.

30. A motor requires 10 amperes and 220 volts at a power factor of 0.8 lag. Find the power, reactive volt-amperes, reactive factor, and the volt-amperes required.

31. The voltage of a circuit is $v = 200 \sin(\omega t + 30°)$, and the current is $i = 50 \sin(\omega t + 60°)$. What are the average power, volt-amperes, and power factor?

32. A motor takes 15 amperes and 220 volts at a lagging power-factor angle of 72° when running at no load. Find the number of watts, vars, and volt-amperes it is taking.

33. How many resultant volt-amperes will be taken from the line when the two motors in Problems 29 and 32 are operating simultaneously as stated from the same line? What is the resultant line current and power supplied?

34. One motor takes 250 amperes at 0.8 power factor lag while another motor takes 50 kw at 0.5 leading power factor from a line of 220 volts. What is the resultant line current for these two motors? What is the power factor of the combined loads? Is it leading or lagging?

35. The voltage of a circuit is $v = 200 \sin \omega t$ volts, and the current is $i = 50 \cos(\omega t - 30°)$ amperes. What are the average power, vars, and power factor?

36. A varmeter in a circuit indicates 600 vars, and a wattmeter in the same circuit shows 800 watts. Find the volt-amperes, power factor, and reactive factor of the circuit.

37. A series circuit has 8 ohms resistance and 20 millihenrys inductance. If 110 volts at 60 cycles are impressed, calculate the current and power.

38. One branch of a parallel circuit consists of 6 ohms resistance, 48 ohms inductive reactance, and 40 ohms capacitive reactance, while the other branch consists of a resistance of 7 ohms and a capacitive reactance of 2 ohms. Find the current delivered to the combination when 100 volts are impressed across the entire circuit. Calculate the total power and that consumed by each branch.

39. (*a*) Find the readings of ammeters I_1, I_2, and I, and of wattmeter W of Fig. 30. Compare the reading of W with $I_1^2R_1 + I_2^2R_2$.

(*b*) Draw the vector diagram of $\mathbf{V}$, $\mathbf{I}_1$, $\mathbf{I}_2$, $\mathbf{I}$, $\mathbf{I}_1\mathbf{R}_1$, $\mathbf{I}_1\mathbf{X}_{L1}$, $\mathbf{I}_2\mathbf{R}_2$, and $\mathbf{I}_2\mathbf{X}_{C2}$.

(*c*) Assuming that $\mathbf{V}$ represents a potential drop from a to b through the circuit branches, find the potential drop from d to c, or $\mathbf{V}_{dc}$.

(*d*) Assuming that $\mathbf{V}$ represents a potential drop from b to a through the circuit branches, find the potential drop from d to c, or $\mathbf{V}_{dc}$.

40. Work Problem 39 if the parameters are changed to $R_1 = 8$ ohms, $L_1 = 0.025$ henry, $R_2 = 10$ ohms, and $C_2 = 120$ μf.

41. Find the readings of the ammeter I and of the wattmeter W in Fig. 30 if an

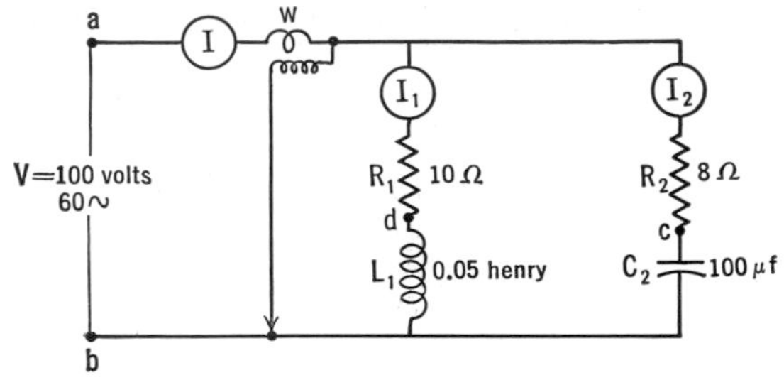

FIG. 30. See Problems 39, 40, and 41.

additional branch R_3L_3 is placed in parallel with the R_1L_1 and R_2C_2 branches. $R_3 = 15$ ohms and $L_3 = 0.12$ henry.

42. Find the readings of the ammeter I and of the wattmeter W in Fig. 31 for the parameters specified.

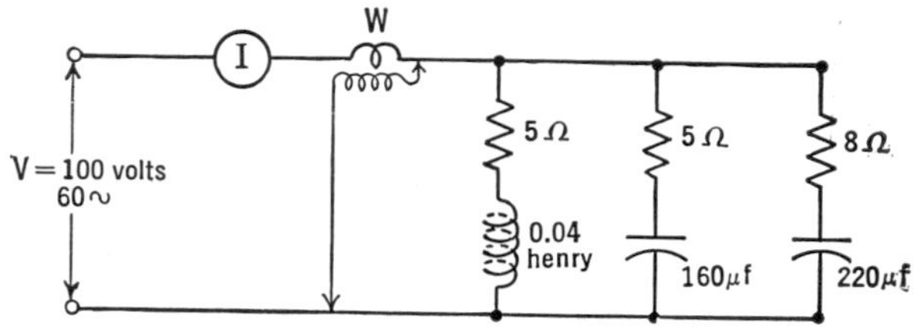

FIG. 31. See Problem 42.

43. A type of alternator much used in laboratories has six coils spaced about the armature at intervals of 30 electrical degrees. The two leads of each coil are brought out to a terminal board, making available six voltages. Because of the 30 electrical

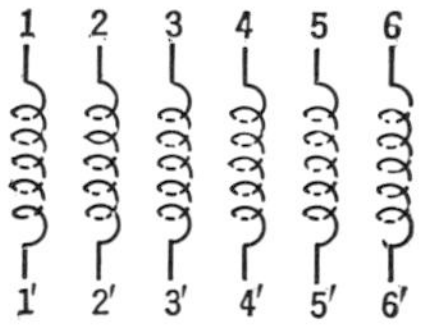

FIG. 32. Six coils of an a-c generator. Adjacent coils are displaced 30 electrical degrees.

degrees of space displacement of the coils on the armature, the individual coil voltages have phase differences of 30°. Let Fig. 32 represent the six coils, and assume that adjacent coils in the figure are electrically adjacent coils on the alternator armature. Assume also that the coil voltages are sinusoidal and that leads 1, 2, 3, 4, 5, and 6 are corresponding ends of the coils, and that $\mathbf{E}_{1'1}$ is 30° behind $\mathbf{E}_{2'2}$, $\mathbf{E}_{2'2}$ is 30° behind $\mathbf{E}_{3'3}$, and so on.

(*a*) Draw the vector diagram of $\mathbf{E}_{1'1}$, $\mathbf{E}_{2'2}$, $\mathbf{E}_{3'3}$, $\mathbf{E}_{4'4}$, $\mathbf{E}_{5'5}$, and $\mathbf{E}_{6'6}$ when $\mathbf{E}_{1'1}$ is laid off along the $+x$-axis. Each coil has an effective emf of 50 volts.

(*b*) Find $\mathbf{E}_{13'}$ when $1'$ is connected to 3.

(*c*) Find $\mathbf{E}_{13}$ when $1'$ is connected to $3'$.

(*d*) Find the greatest voltage that can be obtained by connecting all coils in series.

(*e*) Draw the vector diagram that represents the three voltages, $\mathbf{E}_{12'}$, $\mathbf{E}_{34'}$, and $\mathbf{E}_{56'}$, assuming that $1'$ is connected to 2, $3'$ to 4, and $5'$ to 6.

chapter IV Phasor Algebra (as Applied to A-C Circuit Analysis)

The Operator j. Since the complex quantities normally employed in a-c circuit analysis to simplify calculations are added and subtracted like coplanar vectors, they are often referred to as vectors. However such coplanar vectors which represent sinusoidally time-varying quantities are now more properly called phasors.

It is well known that a plane vector can be specified in magnitude and direction in terms of its x-axis projection and its y-axis projection. For example, if the x-axis projection of the phasor or vector **A**[1] in Fig. 1 is known as x_A and the y-axis projection is known as y_A then the magnitude of the phasor **A** is

$$A = \sqrt{x_A{}^2 + y_A{}^2} \tag{1}$$

From the geometry of Fig. 1 it is plain that the angle, θ_A, between the direction of phasor **A** and the direction of the positive x-axis is

$$\theta_A = \tan^{-1} \frac{y_A}{x_A} \tag{2}$$

In order to specify a phasor in terms of its x and y components, some means must be employed to distinguish between the x-axis projection and the y-axis projection. Inasmuch as the $+y$-axis projection is $+90°$ from the $+x$-axis, a convenient operator for the purpose at hand is one which will, when applied to a phasor, rotate it 90° counterclockwise without changing the magnitude of the phasor.

Let j be an operator which produces 90° counterclockwise rotation of any phasor to which it is applied as a multiplying factor. The physical significance of the operator j can best be appreciated by first considering that it operates on a given phasor **A**, the direction of which is along the $+x$-axis. Then, by definition, when the phasor **A** of Fig. 2 is multiplied by j a new phasor, j**A**, 90° counterclockwise from **A**, will be obtained. If the operator j is applied to the phasor j**A** it will, by definition, rotate j**A** 90° in the counterclockwise direction. The result

[1] Bold-face type is used to represent a phasor in both magnitude and phase, whereas light-face italics represent the magnitude only.

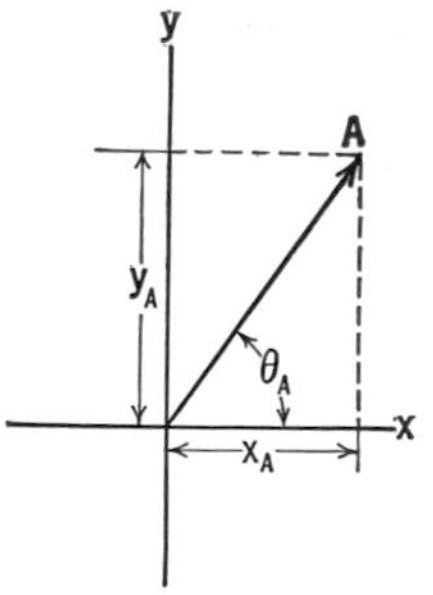

FIG. 1. Resolution of phasor **A** into its x-axis and y-axis components.

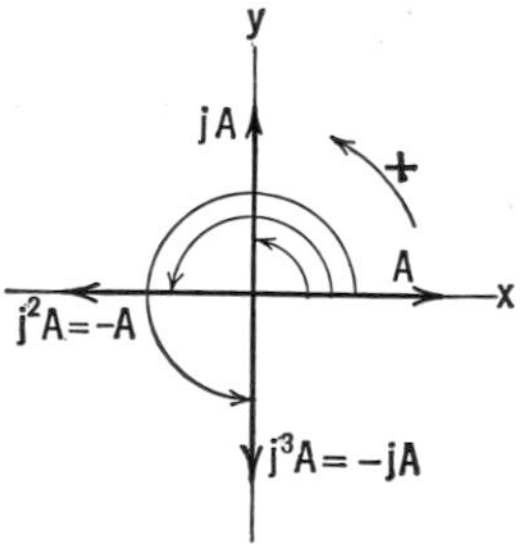

FIG. 2. Effects produced by successive applications of the operator j upon a phasor **A**, the original position of which is along the $+x$-axis.

is $jj\mathbf{A} = j^2\mathbf{A}$ as shown in Fig. 2. Also from Fig. 2

$$j^2\mathbf{A} = -\mathbf{A}$$

Hence:

$$j^2 = -1$$

and

$$j = \sqrt{-1} \tag{3}$$

If the operator j is applied to the phasor $j^2\mathbf{A}$ the result is $j^3\mathbf{A} = -jA$. The phasor $j^3\mathbf{A}$ is 270° counterclockwise from the reference axis, directly opposite the phasor $j\mathbf{A}$ in Fig. 2. If the phasor $j^3\mathbf{A}$, in turn, is operated on by j, the result is $j^4\mathbf{A} = j^2j^2\mathbf{A} = \mathbf{A}$. It will be observed that successive applications of the operator j to the phasor **A** produce successive 90° steps of rotation of the phasor in the counterclockwise direction without affecting the magnitude of the phasor.

From Fig. 2 it is apparent that multiplying **A** by $-j$ yields $-j\mathbf{A}$, a phasor of identical magnitude rotated clockwise 90° from **A**. Hence $-j$ is an operator which produces clockwise rotation of 90°.

The Cartesian Form of Notation. A phasor in any quadrant can be completely specified in a cartesian or rectangular form of notation, as shown below.

$$\mathbf{A} = \pm a \pm ja' \tag{4}$$

where a is the x-axis projection and a' is the y-axis projection of the phasor. In any case the magnitude of the phasor **A** is

$$A = \sqrt{a^2 + a'^2} \tag{5}$$

The phase position of a first-quadrant vector is conveniently described in terms of the positive acute angle measured in a ccw direction from the $+x$-axis to the position of the phasor. In equation form

$$\theta_{1st} = \tan^{-1}\frac{(+a')}{(+a)} \tag{6}$$

The phase position of a fourth-quadrant phasor is conveniently described in terms of the negative acute angle measured in a cw direction from the $+x$-axis to the position of the phasor.

$$\theta_{4th} = \tan^{-1}\frac{(-a')}{(+a)} \tag{7}$$

A fourth-quadrant phasor can, of course, be specified in terms of the positive angle $(360° - \theta_{4th})$, where θ_{4th} is the magnitude of the angle measured in a negative or clockwise direction from the $+x$-axis to the position of the phasor.

Phase positions of second- and third-quadrant phasors are easily located in terms of the a and a' components by first finding the acute angle, the tangent of which is a'/a, without regard to sign, and then subtracting this angle from or adding it to 180°, depending upon whether the a' component is positive or negative.

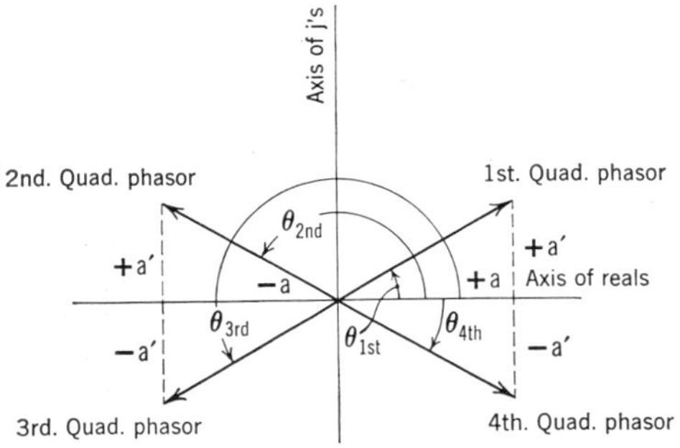

FIG. 3. Phasors in any quadrant can be specified in terms of their real (x-axis) and j (y-axis) components.

Figure 3 illustrates how phasors in any quadrant can be specified in magnitude and phase position in terms of real and j components. In determining the phase angle it is necessary to know the individual signs of the a and a' components in order to locate the angle θ correctly.

The Operator ($\cos\theta \pm j\sin\theta$). Reference to Fig. 3 will show that the x-axis projection of a phasor in any quadrant is $A\cos\theta$. The angle θ may be measured either positively or negatively from the $+x$-axis in determining the x-axis projection, since $\cos\theta = \cos(-\theta)$.

The y-axis projection of the phasor in any quadrant is $A\sin\theta$ if θ

is measured in the ccw direction from the $+x$-axis. The y-axis projection is $-A \sin \theta$ if θ is measured in the cw direction from the $+x$-axis to the position of the phasor. Therefore,

$$\mathbf{A} = A\ (\cos \theta \pm j \sin \theta) \tag{8}$$

is equivalent to the form shown in equation (4). The plus sign is used if θ is measured counterclockwise from the reference axis, the minus sign if θ is measured clockwise.

Equation (8) shows that $(\cos \theta + j \sin \theta)$ operating on a real magnitude A, that is a phasor of A units magnitude along the $+x$-axis, rotates this phasor through a $+\theta$-angle from its initial position. Similarly the operator $(\cos \theta - j \sin \theta)$ rotates the original phasor through a $-\theta$-angle.

It may be shown that the operator $(\cos \theta \pm j \sin \theta)$ rotates any phasor to which it is attached as a multiplying factor through $+\theta$ or $-\theta$ degrees, depending whether the plus or minus sign is employed. Consider a phasor in an initial position such that $a = A \cos \alpha$ and $a' = A \sin \alpha$.

$$\mathbf{A}\ \text{(initially)} = a + ja' = A\ (\cos \alpha + j \sin \alpha) \tag{9}$$

Let $\mathbf{A}' = \mathbf{A}$ [operated on by $(\cos \theta + j \sin \theta)$].

$$\mathbf{A}' = A\ (\cos \alpha + j \sin \alpha)\ (\cos \theta + j \sin \theta) \tag{10}$$

$$\begin{aligned} \mathbf{A}' &= A\ (\cos \alpha \cos \theta + j \cos \alpha \sin \theta + j \sin \alpha \cos \theta + j^2 \sin \alpha \sin \theta) \\ &= A\ [(\cos \alpha \cos \theta - \sin \alpha \sin \theta) + j\ (\sin \alpha \cos \theta + \cos \alpha \sin \theta)] \\ &= A\ [\cos\ (\alpha + \theta) + j \sin\ (\alpha + \theta)] \end{aligned} \tag{11}$$

Equation (11) shows that $\mathbf{A}'$ is a phasor equal in magnitude to the phasor $\mathbf{A}$ but advanced θ degrees from the $\mathbf{A}$ position since it now makes an angle of $(\alpha + \theta)$ with the reference axis.

In similar manner it may be shown that the operator $(\cos \theta - j \sin \theta)$ rotates any phasor to which it is attached through $-\theta$ degrees.

Exponential Form of the Operator ($\cos \theta \pm j \sin \theta$). An important relationship is contained in the following equation:

$$(\cos \theta \pm j \sin \theta) = \epsilon^{\pm j\theta} \tag{12}$$

Equation (12), known as Euler's equation, follows directly from an inspection of the Maclaurin series expansions[2] of $\cos \theta$, $\sin \theta$, and $\epsilon^{j\theta}$.

[2] Certain functions, among which are $\cos(\theta)$, $\sin(\theta)$, and $\epsilon^{\pm j\theta}$, can be expanded into series form by means of Maclaurin's theorem. The theorem states that

$$f(\theta) = f(0) + \frac{f'(0)\theta}{1} + \frac{f''(0)\theta^2}{\underline{/2}} + \frac{f'''(0)\theta^3}{\underline{/3}} + \cdots \text{etc.}$$

where $f(\theta)$ is the particular function of θ that is to be expanded, $f(0)$ is the value of

Expanded into series form

$$\cos\theta = 1 - \frac{\theta^2}{\underline{/2}} + \frac{\theta^4}{\underline{/4}} - \frac{\theta^6}{\underline{/6}} + \cdots \tag{13}$$

$$\sin\theta = \theta - \frac{\theta^3}{\underline{/3}} + \frac{\theta^5}{\underline{/5}} - \frac{\theta^7}{\underline{/7}} + \cdots \tag{14}$$

$$\epsilon^{j\theta} = 1 + j\theta + \frac{(j\theta)^2}{\underline{/2}} + \frac{(j\theta)^3}{\underline{/3}} + \frac{(j\theta)^4}{\underline{/4}} + \frac{(j\theta)^5}{\underline{/5}} + \frac{(j\theta)^6}{\underline{/6}} + \cdots \tag{15}$$

All quantities involving even powers of j reduce to real numbers since $j^2 = -1$, $j^4 = 1$, $j^6 = -1$, etc. All quantities involving odd powers of j reduce to first-degree j terms because $j^3 = -j$, $j^5 = j$, etc. If the j terms are properly evaluated, equation (15) may be arranged as follows:

$$\epsilon^{+j\theta} = \left(1 - \frac{\theta^2}{\underline{/2}} + \frac{\theta^4}{\underline{/4}} - \frac{\theta^6}{\underline{/6}} + \cdots\right) + j\left(\theta - \frac{\theta^3}{\underline{/3}} + \frac{\theta^5}{\underline{/5}} - \frac{\theta^7}{\underline{/7}} + \cdots\right) \tag{16}$$

Therefore $$\epsilon^{j\theta} = \cos\theta + j\sin\theta \tag{17}$$

and $$A\epsilon^{j\theta} = A\ (\cos\theta + j\sin\theta) \tag{18}$$

In a similar manner it may be shown that

$$\epsilon^{-j\theta} = \cos\theta - j\sin\theta \tag{19}$$

Polar Form of the Operator (cos $\theta \pm j$ sin θ). The exponential form of the operator $(\cos\theta \pm j\sin\theta)$ is very often written in a simplified form. It has been shown that

$$\epsilon^{\pm j\theta} = (\cos\theta \pm j\sin\theta) \tag{20}$$

Therefore

$$A\epsilon^{\pm j\theta} = A\ (\cos\theta \pm j\sin\theta) \tag{21}$$

By definition

$$\epsilon^{\pm j\theta} = 1\ \underline{/\pm\theta} \tag{22}$$

and

$$A\epsilon^{\pm j\theta} = A\ \underline{/\pm\theta} \tag{23}$$

Therefore

$$\epsilon^{j\theta} = \underline{/\theta} = (\cos\theta + j\sin\theta) \tag{24}$$

$$\epsilon^{-j\theta} = \underline{/-\theta} = (\cos\theta - j\sin\theta) \tag{25}$$

---

this particular function when θ is set equal to zero, $f'(0)$ is the value of the first derivative of the function when θ is set equal to zero, f'' is the value of the second derivative of the function when θ is set equal to zero, etc.

and

$$A\epsilon^{j\theta} = A\,\underline{/\theta} = A\,(\cos\theta + j\sin\theta) \tag{26}$$

$$A\epsilon^{-j\theta} = A\,\underline{/-\theta} = A\,(\cos\theta - j\sin\theta) \tag{27}$$

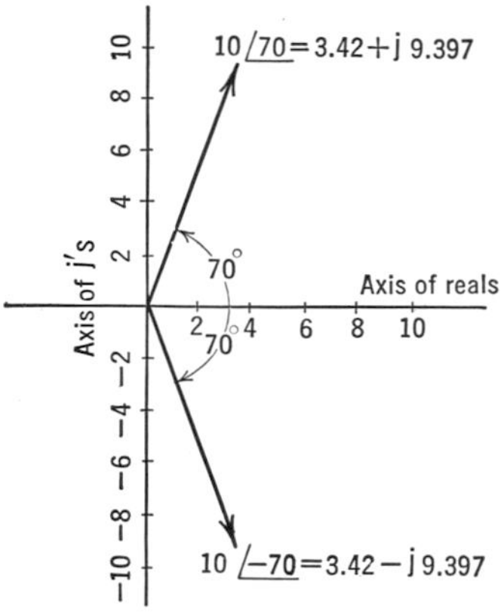

FIG. 4. Phasor representation of equations (26) and (27) for the case of $A = 10$ units and $\theta = 70°$.

Equations (26) and (27) state the equivalence of the three forms of notation that are commonly employed to define a given phasor in magnitude and phase position. Graphical representations of equations (26) and (27) for particular values of A and θ are shown in Fig. 4. The exponential and polar forms are identical by definition and find their greatest use in the processes of multiplication, division, extraction of roots, and raising phasors to given powers. Both these forms express a phasor in terms of polar coordinates. $A\,\underline{/\theta}$ is simply a shorthand or symbolic style of writing $A\epsilon^{j\theta}$. Common usage distinguishes between the two forms by calling $A\epsilon^{j\theta}$ the exponential form and $A\,\underline{/\theta}$ the polar form.

The rectangular or cartesian form, $A\,(\cos\theta \pm j\sin\theta)$, is indispensable in the processes of addition or subtraction of phasors if the j form of phasor algebra is employed.

Problem 1. Write the equivalent polar form of the phasor $3 + j4$ where the numbers refer to unit lengths. Illustrate the phasor by means of a diagram.

Ans.: $5\epsilon^{j53.1°} = 5\,\underline{/53.1°}$.

Problem 2. A phasor is given in the form of $10\epsilon^{-j120°}$. Write the symbolic polar and cartesian forms of the phasor, and illustrate, by means of a phasor diagram, the magnitude and phase position of the phasor.

Ans.: $10\,\underline{/-120°} = -5 - j8.66$.

Addition of Phasors. The phasor sum of two phasors **A** and **B** is a third phasor which is defined in magnitude and phase position by the diagonal of the parallelogram which has for two of its sides the phasors **A** and **B**. The particular diagonal of the parallelogram thus formed, which represents the phasor sum, **A** + **B**, is indicated in Fig. 5.

Each phasor may be considered as having a tail and a head. If the arrow heads in Fig. 5 indicate the heads of the phasors, then the phasor sum of two phasors is the line which joins the tail of the first phasor and the head of the second phasor after the second phasor has been placed so that its tail coincides with the head of the first phasor.

The fact that

$$\mathbf{A} + \mathbf{B} = \mathbf{B} + \mathbf{A} \tag{28}$$

is obvious from the definition that has been given for the phasor sum of two phasors.

The process of adding two phasors may be extended to include any number of phasors simply by first adding any two of the phasors involved and then adding to this phasor sum, which is in itself a phasor, the third phasor, etc. The order in which the addition is carried out is immaterial. For example

$$\mathbf{A} + \mathbf{B} + \mathbf{C} = \mathbf{B} + \mathbf{C} + \mathbf{A} = \mathbf{C} + \mathbf{A} + \mathbf{B} \tag{29}$$

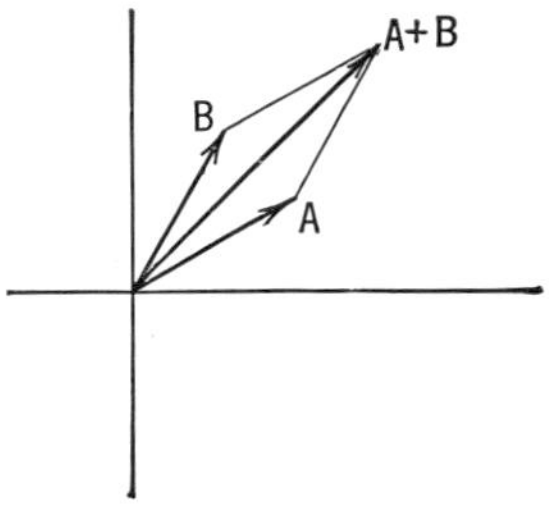

FIG. 5. Addition of the phasors **A** and **B**.

Phasors are written in the rectangular $(a + ja')$ form when addition is to be performed, since the exponential or polar forms do not lend themselves to the addition process. If $\mathbf{A} = a + ja'$, $\mathbf{B} = b + jb'$, and $\mathbf{C} = c + jc'$,

$$\mathbf{A} + \mathbf{B} + \mathbf{C} = (a + b + c) + j\,(a' + b' + c') \tag{30}$$

The magnitude of the resultant phasor is

$$D = \sqrt{(a + b + c)^2 + (a' + b' + c')^2} \tag{31}$$

The phase position of the resultant phasor is

$$\theta_D = \tan^{-1}\frac{(a' + b' + c')}{(a + b + c)} \tag{32}$$

Any or all of the component parts of the phasors **A**, **B**, and **C** in the above example may be negative. The process that has been given for the addition of three phasors can, of course, be extended.

Example. Let it be required to add

$$\mathbf{A} = 10\,\underline{/36.9^\circ} = 8 + j6 \quad \text{and} \quad \mathbf{B} = 6\,\underline{/120^\circ} = -3 + j5.20$$

$$\mathbf{A} + \mathbf{B} = \mathbf{C} = (8 - 3) + j\,(6 + 5.2)$$

$$\mathbf{C} = 5 + j11.2$$

The magnitude of the **C** phasor is

$$C = \sqrt{5^2 + 11.2^2} = 12.27 \text{ units}$$

The position of the phasor **C** with respect to the $+x$-axis is

$$\theta_C = \tan^{-1}\frac{11.2}{5} = \tan^{-1} 2.24 = 65.95^\circ$$

Figure 6 illustrates the phasor addition of **A** and **B** for the particular values that have been employed in this example.

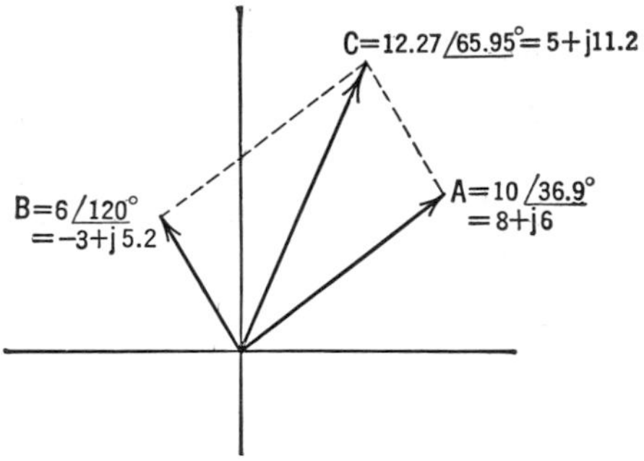

FIG. 6. Phasor addition in a particular numerical case.

Problem 3. Add the phasors $14\underline{/60^\circ}$ and $20\underline{/15^\circ}$. State the result in both rectangular and polar forms, and illustrate, by means of a phasor diagram, the operation that has been performed.

Ans.: $26.3 + j17.3 = 31.5\underline{/33.35^\circ}$.

Problem 4. Given the following three phasors:

$$\mathbf{A} = 40\epsilon^{j120^\circ},\ \mathbf{B} = 20\underline{/-40^\circ},\ \mathbf{C} = 26.46 + j0$$

find **A** + **B** + **C** and illustrate the three phasors, together with their phasor sum, by means of a phasor diagram.

Ans.: $21.78 + j21.78 = 30.8\underline{/45^\circ}$.

Subtraction of Phasors. In ordinary algebra the operation or process of subtraction is accomplished by changing the sign of the quantity to be subtracted and proceeding as in addition. In phasor algebra the phasor which is to be subtracted is rotated through 180° and then added. To rotate a phasor through 180° the operator $j^2 = -1$ may be applied or 180° may be added or subtracted from the original phase angle of the phasor. Thus a phasor $\mathbf{A} = A\underline{/\theta}$ rotated through 180° becomes

$$\mathbf{A}' = j^2A\underline{/\theta} = -A\underline{/\theta} = A\underline{/\theta \pm 180^\circ}$$

and a phasor $\mathbf{B} = b + jb'$ rotated through 180° becomes

$$\mathbf{B}' = j^2(b + jb') = -b - jb'$$

Figure 7*a* illustrates the subtraction of phasor **D** from phasor **C**. Symbolically, the operation may be indicated as: **C** − **D** = **E**. After the phasor which is to be subtracted has been rotated through 180°, the phasor thus resulting is added to the phasor from which the subtraction is being made.

Figure 7*b* illustrates the subtraction of phasor **C** from phasor **D**. It will be observed that (**D** − **C**) is of equal magnitude and 180° removed from (**C** − **D**). In general

$$(\mathbf{C} - \mathbf{D}) = -(\mathbf{D} - \mathbf{C}) \tag{33}$$

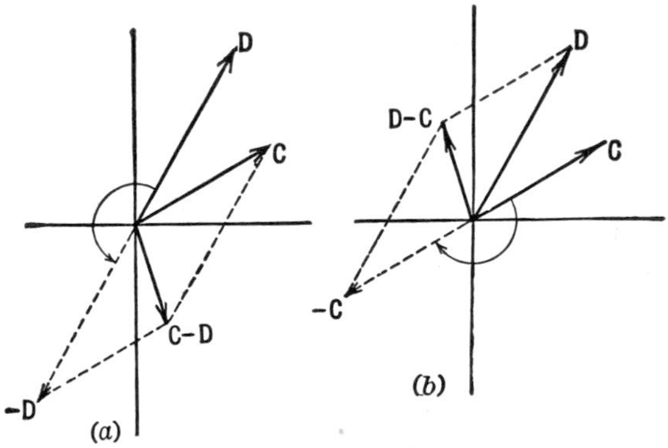

Fig. 7. Illustrating phasor subtraction.

The difference of two phasors might have been defined in terms of one of the diagonals of the parallelogram formed by the two phasors.

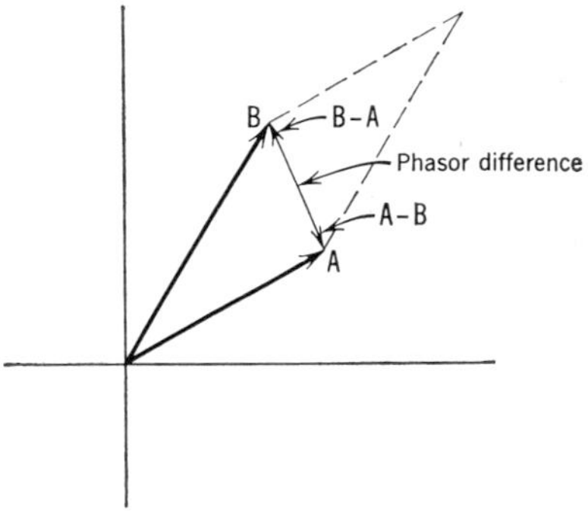

Fig. 8. The diagonal which defines the difference between two phasors. (The sense or direction of the diagonal is dependent upon the particular phasor difference in question.)

Figure 8 illustrates the particular diagonal which represents the difference between phasors **B** and **A**. The diagonal concept is useful in certain types of phasor diagrams, but for general calculations the method which has previously been described is to be preferred.

Examples. Given the phasors

$$\mathbf{A} = 30\underline{/60^\circ}$$

and

$$\mathbf{B} = 21\ (\cos 160° - j \sin 160°)$$

let it be required to subtract phasor **B** from phasor **A**. The first step is to write the phasors in cartesian form.

$$\mathbf{A} = 30\underline{/60°} = 30\ (\cos 60° + j \sin 60°) = 15 + j26$$

$$\mathbf{B} = 21\ (\cos 160° - j \sin 160°) = -19.75 - j7.18$$

$$\mathbf{A} - \mathbf{B} = (15 + j26) - (-19.75 - j7.18)$$

$$= 34.75 + j33.18 = 48\underline{/43.6°}$$

For the particular case considered, the difference (**A** − **B**) is somewhat greater in magnitude than either of the original phasors. This condition is in general true if the original phasors are separated by more than 90°.

Let it be required to subtract phasor **A** from phasor **B**.

$$(\mathbf{B} - \mathbf{A}) = (-19.75 - j7.18) - (15 + j26) = -34.75 - j33.18 = 48\underline{/223.6°}$$

Problem 5. Draw a phasor diagram showing the phasors **A** and **B** of the above illustrative example, together with the phasors (**A** − **B**) and (**B** − **A**).

Problem 6. Given the following three phasors:

$$\mathbf{A} = 42\epsilon^{j200°}$$

$$\mathbf{B} = 20\underline{/-40°}$$

$$\mathbf{C} = 24.25 + j14$$

find (**A** + **C**) − **B** analytically and draw the phasor diagram.

Ans.: $32.95\underline{/157.7°}$.

Multiplication of Phasors and Complex Quantities. In a-c circuit analysis it is often desirable to operate on a phasor current with an impedance function so that the resulting voltage may be obtained. Similarly, it is sometimes desirable to operate on a phasor voltage with an admittance function, i.e., the reciprocal of the impedance function, to obtain the resulting current. The process of operating on a current (or voltage) phasor with a complex impedance (or admittance) function is called complex or phasor multiplication.

The complex product of two phasors, **A** and **B**, in so far as a-c circuit analysis is concerned, is a third phasor which has a magnitude equal to AB and a phase position with respect to the reference axis which is equal to the sum of the individual phase angles of **A** and **B**, namely, $(\alpha_A + \alpha_B)$. It will be shown presently why this particular definition of a complex product is especially suited to the phasor manipulations that are universally employed in a-c circuit theory. A graphical interpretation of the definition is given in Fig. 9 for the particular case of $\mathbf{A} = 2\underline{/40°}$ and $\mathbf{B} = 3\underline{/100°}$.

Analytically, the product of two phasors can be formed most conveniently when the phasors are expressed in exponential or polar form.

For example, the product of the **A** and **B** phasors shown in Fig. 9 is simply

$$\mathbf{AB} = 2\epsilon^{j40°} \cdot 3\epsilon^{j100°} = 6\epsilon^{j(40°+100°)} = 6\epsilon^{j140°}$$

or

$$\mathbf{AB} = 2 \times 3\underline{/40° + 100°} = 6\underline{/140°}$$

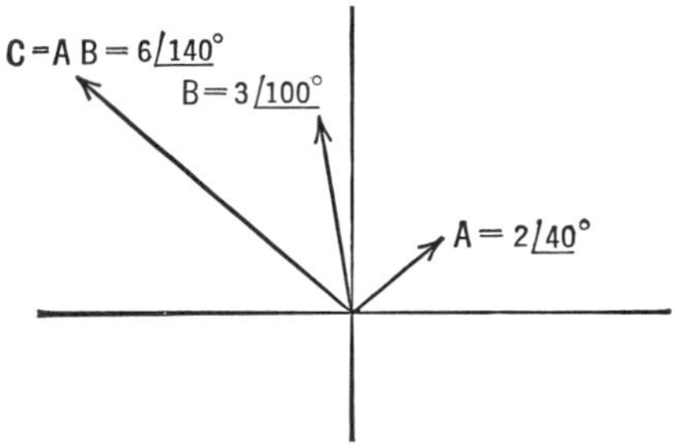

FIG. 9. Illustrating phasor multiplication.

From the definition which has been given for the complex product it is evident that the order in which the multiplication is carried out is immaterial. That is

$$\mathbf{AB} = \mathbf{BA} \tag{34}$$

Furthermore, the definition which has been given is capable of extension to any number of phasors or complex quantities. For example,

$$\mathbf{ABC} = ABC\underline{/\alpha_A + \alpha_B + \alpha_C} \tag{35}$$

and

$$\mathbf{ABC} = \mathbf{BCA} = \mathbf{CAB}, \text{ etc.} \tag{36}$$

The product of two phasors expressed in rectangular style can be formed by taking the cross-products of the component parts as in ordinary algebra. The proper interpretation must, of course, be given to the terms which involve j. If the phasors are given as $\mathbf{A} = a + ja'$ and $\mathbf{B} = b + jb'$, the product is formed exactly in accordance with the rules of ordinary algebra.

$$\mathbf{F} = \mathbf{AB} = (a + ja')\,(b + jb') = (ab - a'b') + j\,(a'b + ab') \tag{37}$$

The magnitude of the resulting phasor is

$$\begin{aligned} F &= \sqrt{(ab - a'b')^2 + (a'b + ab')^2} \\ &= \sqrt{a^2b^2 - 2aba'b' + a'^2b'^2 + a'^2b^2 + 2a'bab' + a^2b'^2} \\ &= \sqrt{(a^2 + a'^2)\,(b^2 + b'^2)} = \sqrt{A^2B^2} = AB \end{aligned} \tag{38}$$

The magnitude of **F** is thus shown to be equal to the product of the magnitudes of the phasors whose product is being formed. It remains to be shown that the phase angle of **F** as defined by the real and j components of equation (37) agrees with the definition that has been given for the product of two phasors. From equation (37) the phase angle of **F** takes the following form:

$$\alpha_F = \tan^{-1}\frac{(a'b + ab')}{(ab - a'b')} = \tan^{-1}\frac{\dfrac{a'b + ab'}{AB}}{\dfrac{ab - a'b'}{AB}}$$

It is evident from the definitions that have been given to a, a', b, and b' that

$$\frac{a'}{A} = \sin\alpha_A, \quad \frac{a}{A} = \cos\alpha_A, \quad \frac{b'}{B} = \sin\alpha_B, \quad \text{and} \quad \frac{b}{B} = \cos\alpha_B$$

Therefore

$$\alpha_F = \tan^{-1}\frac{\sin\alpha_A\cos\alpha_B + \cos\alpha_A\sin\alpha_B}{\cos\alpha_A\cos\alpha_B - \sin\alpha_A\sin\alpha_B}$$

$$\alpha_F = \tan^{-1}\frac{\sin(\alpha_A + \alpha_B)}{\cos(\alpha_A + \alpha_B)} = \tan^{-1}\tan(\alpha_A + \alpha_B)$$

$$\alpha_F = \alpha_A + \alpha_B \tag{39}$$

Equations (38) and (39) show that the product of two phasors may be formed by ordinary algebraic multiplication when the factors are expressed in cartesian form.

Example. Given the phasors:

$$\mathbf{A} = 2(\cos 40° + j\sin 40°) = 1.532 + j1.286$$
$$\mathbf{B} = 3(\cos 100° + j\sin 100°) = -0.521 + j2.954$$

let it be required to find the product of **A** and **B** by the algebraic multiplication of the cartesian forms.

$$\mathbf{F} = \mathbf{AB} = (1.532 + j1.286)(-0.521 + j2.954)$$
$$= -0.799 + j4.525 - j0.670 + j^2 3.798$$
$$= (-0.799 - 3.798) + j(-0.670 + 4.525)$$
$$= -4.597 + j3.855$$
$$\mathbf{F} = \sqrt{-4.597^2 + 3.855^2}\,\Big/\tan^{-1}\frac{3.855}{-4.597}$$
$$= 6.0\,\underline{/180° - 40°} = 6\,\underline{/140°}$$

The graphical representations of the phasors **A**, **B**, and **F** are given in Fig. 9.

Problem 7. Find the complex product of

$$\mathbf{A} = 5 - j4 \quad \text{and} \quad \mathbf{B} = 2 + j3$$

by algebraic multiplication of the cartesian forms and draw the phasor diagram. Change **A** and **B** to polar form and perform the multiplication process, **BA**.

Ans.: $22 + j7 = 23.09\underline{/17.65^\circ}$.

Problem 8. Given the following three phasors:

$$\mathbf{A} = 20 + j20,\ \mathbf{B} = 30\underline{/-120^\circ},\ \mathbf{C} = 5 + j0$$

perform the following indicated operations:

$$(a)\ \ \mathbf{A} + \mathbf{B} + \mathbf{C}, \qquad (b)\ \ (\mathbf{A} + \mathbf{B})\mathbf{C}, \qquad (c)\ \ \mathbf{ABC}.$$

Draw a phasor diagram of **A**, **B**, and **C**, together with the phasors which represent the results of the above indicated operations.

Ans.: (*a*) $11.67\underline{/-31^\circ}$, (*b*) $39.05\underline{/-50.2^\circ}$, (*c*) $4242\underline{/-75^\circ}$.

Division of Complex Quantities (or Phasors). For the purposes of a-c circuit theory the division of one complex quantity by another is carried out algebraically, as shown below, when the quantities are expressed in exponential form.

$$\frac{\mathbf{A}}{\mathbf{B}} = \frac{A\epsilon^{j\alpha_A}}{B\epsilon^{j\alpha_B}} = \frac{A}{B}\epsilon^{j\alpha_A}\epsilon^{-j\alpha_B} = \frac{A}{B}\epsilon^{j(\alpha_A - \alpha_B)} \tag{40}$$

That is, the process of dividing one phasor, **A**, by a second phasor, **B**, results in a third phasor, the magnitude of which is the quotient of the magnitudes of the phasors **A** and **B**, namely A/B. The phase position of the resulting phasor with respect to the reference axis is the algebraic difference between the individual phase angles of the phasors **A** and **B** with respect to the reference axis, namely, $\alpha_A - \alpha_B$. It should be noted that the angle of the phasor in the denominator is always subtracted from the angle of the phasor in the numerator. Due regard is taken for the inherent signs of the individual phase angles, α_A and α_B, during the process of forming the algebraic difference. In symbolic polar form division is carried out as shown below:

$$\frac{\mathbf{A}}{\mathbf{B}} = \frac{A\underline{/\alpha_A}}{B\underline{/\alpha_B}} = \frac{A}{B}\underline{/\alpha_A - \alpha_B} \tag{40a}$$

Examples. The processes of division in two particular cases are shown below:

$$\mathbf{F} = \frac{\mathbf{A}}{\mathbf{B}} = \frac{20\underline{/60^\circ}}{5\underline{/30^\circ}} = 4\ \underline{/30^\circ}$$

$$\mathbf{G} = \frac{\mathbf{C}}{\mathbf{D}} = \frac{12\epsilon^{j90^\circ}}{4\epsilon^{-j30^\circ}} = 3\epsilon^{j120^\circ}$$

The graphical interpretations of the above operations are contained in Fig. 10*a* and Fig. 10*b*.

The process of division can be carried out very conveniently when the phasors are expressed in exponential or polar form. However, it is entirely possible and in some cases desirable to perform the operation with the phasors expressed in rectangular form. If $\mathbf{A} = a + ja'$ and $\mathbf{B} = b + jb'$, then

$$\frac{\mathbf{A}}{\mathbf{B}} = \frac{a + ja'}{b + jb'} = \frac{(a + ja')\,(b - jb')}{(b + jb')\,(b - jb')} \tag{41}$$

Both numerator and denominator of the above expression are multiplied by $(b - jb')$, the conjugate of $(b + jb')$. The conjugate of a given phasor is a second phasor, the real component of which is identical with the real component of the given phasor and the j part of which is equal in magnitude but reversed in sign from the j component of the given phasor.

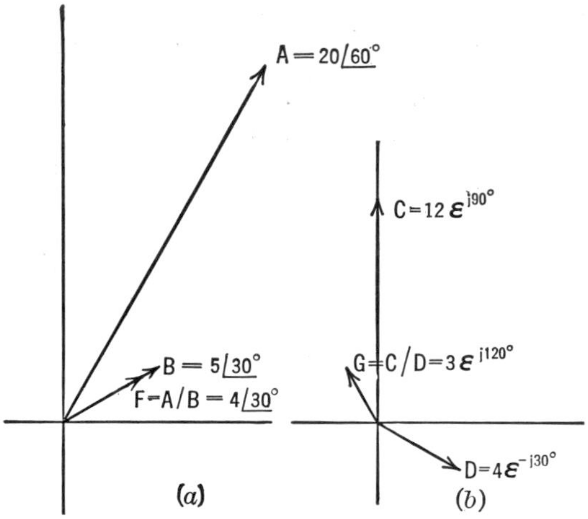

FIG. 10. Phasor division in two particular numerical cases.

The purpose of multiplying both numerator and denominator of equation (41) by the conjugate of the denominator is to clear the denominator of its j component. This rationalization process reduces the quotient $\mathbf{A}/\mathbf{B}$ to a more intelligible form. If the operations indicated in equation (41) are performed, the equation reduces to

$$\frac{\mathbf{A}}{\mathbf{B}} = \frac{(ab + a'b') + j(a'b - ab')}{(b^2 + b'^2)} \tag{42}$$

By a process which is somewhat similar to that employed on pages 117–118 it may be shown that

$$\frac{\mathbf{A}}{\mathbf{B}} = \frac{A}{B}\Big/\underline{\tan^{-1}\left[\frac{\sin\,(\alpha_A - \alpha_B)}{\cos\,(\alpha_A - \alpha_B)}\right]} = \frac{A}{B}\Big/\underline{\alpha_A - \alpha_B} \tag{43}$$

Example. If $\mathbf{A} = 10 + j17.3$ and $\mathbf{B} = 4.33 + j2.5$, let it be required to find $\mathbf{A}/\mathbf{B}$ by the method given in equations (41) and (42).

$$\frac{\mathbf{A}}{\mathbf{B}} = \frac{10 + j17.3}{4.33 + j2.5} = \frac{(10 + j17.3)\,(4.33 - j2.5)}{(4.33 + j2.5)\,(4.33 - j2.5)}$$

$$\frac{\mathbf{A}}{\mathbf{B}} = \frac{(43.3 + 43.3) + j(75 - 25)}{4.33^2 + 2.5^2}$$

Reduced to polar form

$$\frac{\mathbf{A}}{\mathbf{B}} = \sqrt{3.465^2 + 2.0^2} \,\Big/ \tan^{-1}\frac{2.0}{3.465} = 4.0\,/30°$$

Problem 9. Given $\mathbf{A} = 40\,/105°$ and $\mathbf{B} = 5 + j8.66$, find $\mathbf{A}/\mathbf{B}$, and draw a phasor diagram illustrating **A**, **B**, and **A/B**.

Ans.: $4\,/45°$.

Problem 10. Given the following three phasors:

$$\mathbf{A} = 20 + j20, \quad \mathbf{B} = 30\,/-120°, \quad \mathbf{C} = 5 + j0$$

perform the following indicated operations:

$$(a)\ \frac{\mathbf{A} + \mathbf{B}}{\mathbf{C}} \qquad\qquad (b)\ \frac{\mathbf{BC}}{\mathbf{A}}$$

Draw a phasor diagram of **A**, **B**, and **C**, together with the phasors which represent the results of the above indicated operations.

Ans.: (*a*) $1.56\,/-50.2°$. (*b*) $5.3\,/-165°$.

Raising a Phasor to a Given Power. A phasor or preferably a complex quantity may be raised to a given power n, where n is an integer, by multiplying the phasor by itself n times. For example, if $\mathbf{A} = A\,/\alpha_A$,

$$\mathbf{A}^n = A^n\,/n\alpha_A \tag{44}$$

The nth power of **A** is a phasor whose magnitude is A^n and whose phase position with respect to the reference is $n\alpha_A$. The concept of successive applications of a given operator follows directly from the successive multiplication of the operator by itself. Obviously the process involved is accomplished most easily with the phasor or operator in exponential or polar form.

From the rules which have been given for multiplication it is evident that

$$\mathbf{A}^n\mathbf{B}^n = A^nB^n\,/n\alpha_A + n\alpha_B \tag{45}$$

Example. An operator which is commonly used successively is the one which rotates a given phasor through +120°. This operator is

$$\mathbf{a} = 1\,(\cos 120° + j \sin 120°) = -0.50 + j0.866$$

In polar form

$$\mathbf{a} = 1\,/120°$$

$$\mathbf{a}^2 = 1\,/240°$$

$$\mathbf{a}^3 = 1\,/360° = 1\,/0°$$

$$\mathbf{a}^4 = 1\,/480° = 1\,/120°$$

The above operators are widely used in three-phase circuit problems because, under balanced conditions, the individual phase voltages (and currents) are displaced from one another by 120°. Figure 11 illustrates **a**, $\mathbf{a}^2$, and $\mathbf{a}^3$ diagrammatically. Incidentally, the three values indicated in Fig. 11, $\left(-\frac{1}{2}+j\frac{\sqrt{3}}{2}\right)$, $\left(-\frac{1}{2}-j\frac{\sqrt{3}}{2}\right)$, and $(1 + j0)$, are the three roots of $\sqrt[3]{1}$ because each of these roots cubed equals unity.

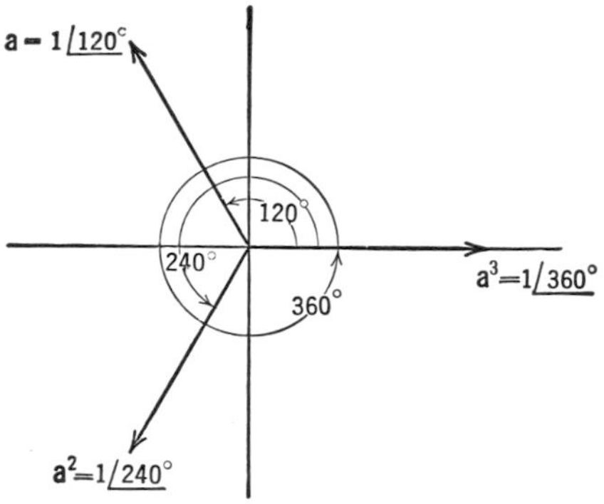

FIG. 11. Illustrating the operator $\mathbf{a} = (-0.50 + j0.866)$, together with $\mathbf{a}^2$ and $\mathbf{a}^3$.

Problem 11. Raise the phasor $(8.66 + j5.0)$ to the second power; to the fifth power. *Ans.:* $100 \angle 60°$; $100{,}000 \angle 150°$.

Extracting the Roots of a Phasor. The inverse of the process of raising a phasor to a given power is employed in the extraction of the roots of a particular phasor. If $\mathbf{A} = A \angle \alpha_A$ it follows that one of the n roots of $\sqrt[n]{\mathbf{A}}$ is $\sqrt[n]{A} \angle \frac{\alpha_A}{n}$ because the latter value multiplied by itself n times will equal **A**. The remaining $(n - 1)$ roots are found by adding $2\pi q$ radians or $360q$ degrees to α_A before the division by n is performed. q is any integer and is used as 1, 2, 3, $\cdots$, and $(n - 1)$ to obtain the remaining roots. It should be noted that the addition of any multiple of 360° to the angle of the phasor does not change the phasor although it does provide a systematic method of evaluating the $(n - 1)$ remaining roots. In this method only positive magnitudes are employed, as

$$\sqrt[n]{\mathbf{A}} = \sqrt[n]{A} \angle \frac{\alpha_A + 2\pi q}{n} \qquad [q = 0, 1, 2, \cdots (n - 1)] \tag{46}$$

The cartesian form of the above equation is

$$\sqrt[n]{\mathbf{A}} = \sqrt[n]{A}\left[\cos\left(\frac{\alpha_A + 2\pi q}{n}\right) + j \sin\left(\frac{\alpha_A + 2\pi q}{n}\right)\right] \tag{47}$$

Example. Let it be required to find the square roots of **A** where $\mathbf{A} = 3.08 + j8.455$.

For convenience the phasor is first transformed into polar form.

$$\mathbf{A} = \sqrt{3.08^2 + 8.455^2} \Big/ \tan^{-1}\frac{8.455}{3.08} = 9.0\underline{/70^\circ}$$

The first root is $\sqrt{9.0}\Big/\frac{70^\circ}{2} = 3\underline{/35^\circ}$.

The second root is $\sqrt{9.0}\Big/\frac{70^\circ + 360^\circ}{2} = 3\underline{/215^\circ}$.

Figure 12 illustrates the phasor **A** together with its two roots. It will be noted that either root multiplied by itself yields the phasor **A**.

Problem 12. Find the cube roots of the phasor $(8 + j0)$, and draw a complete phasor diagram of the phasor and its three roots.

Ans.: $2\underline{/0^\circ}$, $2\underline{/120^\circ}$, $2\underline{/240^\circ}$.

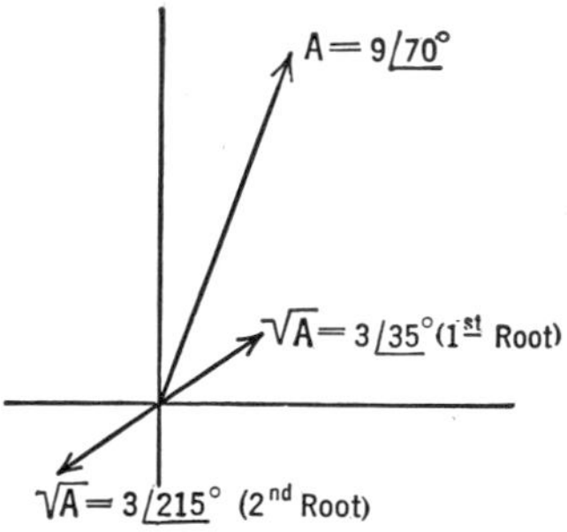

FIG. 12. Phasor $9\underline{/70^\circ}$ and its two roots.

The Logarithm of a Phasor. Certain definitions in long-line and recurrent network theory utilize logarithms of phasor quantities. The general concept of the logarithm of a phasor is similar to that of the logarithm of an ordinary number. The logarithm of a phasor **A** is the inverse of the exponential of **A**. In other words, the logarithm of the phasor $\mathbf{A} = A\epsilon^{j\theta}$ to the base ϵ is defined as the power to which ϵ must be raised to equal $A\epsilon^{j\theta}$. By definition

$$\log_\epsilon A\epsilon^{j\theta} = \log_\epsilon A + \log_\epsilon \epsilon^{j\theta} = \log_\epsilon A + j\theta \log_\epsilon \epsilon = \log_\epsilon A + j\theta \quad (48)$$

It will be noted that the logarithm of the phasor $\mathbf{A} = A\underline{/\theta}$ is itself a phasor. In rectangular form, when the logarithm is taken to the base ϵ, the real component is $\log_\epsilon A$; that is, the logarithm to the base ϵ of the magnitude of the phasor **A** and the j component is θ (radians) in magnitude. In this connection, θ, the phase angle of the phasor **A**, *must be considered in radians.*

Example. If $\mathbf{A} = 52\underline{/70^\circ}$, let it be required to find $\log_\epsilon \mathbf{A}$.

$$\log_\epsilon 52\underline{/70^\circ} = \log_\epsilon 52 + j\frac{70^\circ}{57.3^\circ} = 3.95 + j1.22$$

Problem 13. Perform the following indicated operations:

$$\frac{15\underline{/70^\circ}}{(3 - j4)} + \log_\epsilon (8 + j5)$$

Draw a phasor diagram including each of the three original phasors together with the $\log_\epsilon (8 + j5)$ and the phasor which represents the result of the indicated operations.

Ans.: $0.60 + j3.07$.

Impedance Expressed in Polar Form. It was shown in Chapter III that the currents and voltages in an a-c circuit can be conveniently represented by phasors. With the aid of phasor algebra it is a simple matter to represent these currents and voltages analytically. However, the great benefit to be derived from the use of phasor or complex algebra is the simple algebraic relations that can be established between the voltages and currents by using the impedance function as a complex quantity. Although the impedance function may take the form of a phasor or vector, it is not a phasor in the same sense that alternating voltages or currents are phasors. From an algebraic point of view the impedance function is merely a complex quantity which properly relates phasor voltages and phasor currents one to the other. As such it is a most important operator in circuit analysis.

The physical considerations concerning the impedance function have been explained in Chapters II and III. If the polar form of the impedance function which was used throughout Chapter II is manipulated in accordance with the rules of phasor algebra, the results obtained will agree with physical facts. For example, it has been shown that the impedance function of a series RLC branch is

$$\mathbf{Z} = \sqrt{R^2 + \left(\omega L - \frac{1}{\omega C}\right)^2} \Bigg/ \underline{\tan^{-1} \frac{\left(\omega L - \frac{1}{\omega C}\right)}{R}} \tag{49}$$

The abbreviated form is

$$\mathbf{Z} = Z/\underline{\theta} \tag{50}$$

where $+\theta$ represents a lead of the voltage with respect to the current or a lag of the current with respect to the voltage. If a phasor voltage $\mathbf{V} = V/\underline{\alpha}$ is applied to the above branch the resulting current is

$$\mathbf{I} = \frac{\mathbf{V}}{\mathbf{Z}} = \frac{V/\underline{\alpha}}{Z/\underline{\theta}} = \left[\frac{V}{Z}\right]/\underline{(\alpha - \theta)} \tag{51}$$

The phasor quotient $\mathbf{V}/\mathbf{Z}$ results in a phasor current which is V/Z in magnitude and θ degrees behind $\mathbf{V}$ regardless of the position that $\mathbf{V}$ has with respect to the reference axis. Thus $\mathbf{I}$ is correctly defined in magnitude and phase position.

In a similar manner it may be shown that $\mathbf{IZ} = \mathbf{V}$. If it be assumed that a current $\mathbf{I} = I/\underline{\beta}$ flows through an RLC branch, the impedance of which is $\mathbf{Z} = Z/\underline{\theta}$,

$$\mathbf{IZ} = (I/\underline{\beta})\,(Z/\underline{\theta}) = [IZ]/\underline{(\beta + \theta)} = \mathbf{V} \tag{52}$$

The product of the phasors $\mathbf{IZ}$ yields a phasor voltage $\mathbf{V}$, which is (IZ) in magnitude and θ degrees in advance of the current $\mathbf{I}$. It will be remembered that θ has been defined as

$$\tan^{-1} \frac{\left(\omega L - \dfrac{1}{\omega C}\right)}{R}$$

If $\omega L < 1/\omega C$, θ is a negative angle, in which case **V** actually lags **I**.

Example. A given RL branch has $R = 3.5$ ohms and $L = 0.092$ henry. Find the complex expression for the current which flows through the branch if a 60-cycle voltage, $\mathbf{V} = 110\underline{/30°}$ volts, is applied to the RL branch. (The phase angle which is associated with V is wholly arbitrary in a simple series circuit. For simplicity it might have been taken as zero degrees.)

$$\mathbf{Z} = \sqrt{R^2 + (\omega L)^2}\ \underline{/\tan^{-1} \frac{(\omega L)}{R}}$$

$$\mathbf{Z} = \sqrt{3.5^2 + (377 \times 0.092)^2}\ \underline{/\tan^{-1} \frac{(377 \times 0.092)}{3.5}}$$

$$\mathbf{Z} = 34.8\underline{/84.25°} \text{ ohms}$$

$$\mathbf{I} = \frac{\mathbf{V}}{\mathbf{Z}} = \frac{110\underline{/30°}}{34.8\underline{/84.25°}} = 3.16\underline{/-54.25°} \text{ amperes}$$

Figure 13 is a phasor diagram of **V** and **I** for the particular RL branch that has been considered.

Problem 14. An RLC series branch consists of $R = 12.9$ ohms, $L = 0.056$ henry, and $C = 78\ \mu$f. (*a*) What is the complex impedance of the RLC branch at 60 cycles? (*b*) If a 60-cycle current, $\mathbf{I} = 10\underline{/30°}$ amperes, flows through the branch, find the voltage phasor **V** across the terminals of the series branch. Draw a phasor diagram illustrating the phasor positions of **I** and **V** and the magnitude of the phase angle of **V** with respect to **I**.

Ans.: (*a*) $12.9 + j(21.1 - 34) = 12.9 - j12.9 = 18.24\underline{/-45°}$ ohms.
(*b*) $182.4\underline{/-15°}$ volts.

Impedance Expressed in Cartesian Form. The cartesian form of the impedance function of a given branch or circuit is, in general,

$$\mathbf{Z} = R + j(X_L - X_C) \tag{53}$$

where R is the equivalent resistance of the branch or circuit with respect to the terminals considered and $(X_L - X_C)$ is the equivalent reactance of the branch or circuit with respect to the terminals considered.

In accordance with previous definitions, $X_L = 2\pi fL$ and $X_C = \dfrac{1}{2\pi fC}$. A simple method of showing the validity of equation (53) is to employ a phasor diagram in which are represented the RI, X_LI, and X_CI voltage drops which combine vectorially to equal the applied voltage **V**.

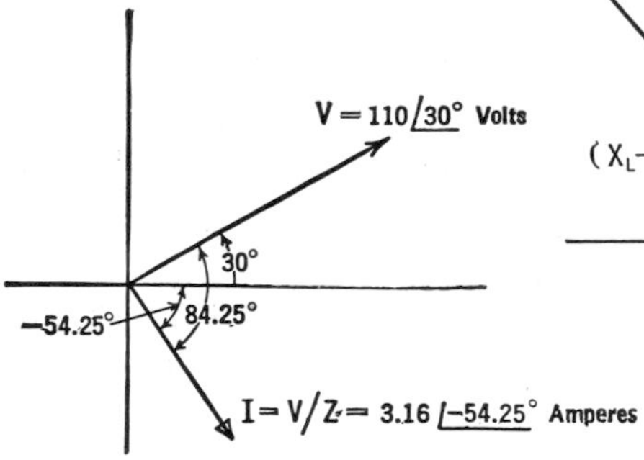

FIG. 13. Phasor diagram of **V** and **I**, in a particular RL series circuit.

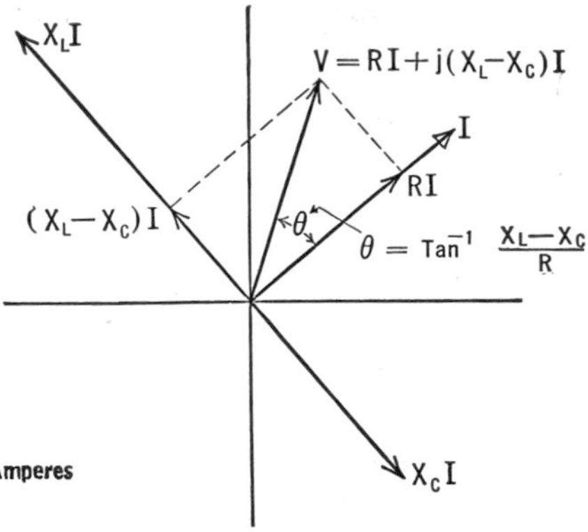

FIG. 14. Phasor addition of drops equals applied voltage.

In order to agree with physical facts: (1) the RI drop must be in phase with **I**; (2) the X_LI drop must be 90° in advance of **I**; (3) the X_CI drop must be 90° behind **I**.

Reference to Fig. 14 will show that the voltage

$$\mathbf{V} = RI + (X_L - X_C)I \quad \text{as phasors} \tag{54}$$

or

$$\mathbf{V} = R\mathbf{I} + j(X_L - X_C)\mathbf{I} \tag{55}$$

from which the complex impedance function is

$$\mathbf{Z} = \frac{\mathbf{V}}{\mathbf{I}} = R + j(X_L - X_C) \tag{56}$$

Obviously the relations stated in equations (54), (55), and (56) are independent of the phasor diagram position of **I**.

The cartesian or rectangular form of the complex expression for **Z** can be transformed to the polar form of **Z** by the method of complex algebra, and the transformation is, of course, reversible.

$$R + j(X_L - X_C) = \sqrt{R^2 + (X_L - X_C)^2} \Big/ \tan^{-1} \frac{(X_L - X_C)}{R} \tag{57}$$

The rectangular form of the impedance function is, in general, essential in combining impedances because impedances cannot be added or subtracted in polar form.

Example. The terminals of an a-c generator which has an internal resistance of 2 ohms and an equivalent internal inductive reactance of 6 ohms are connected to a particular RLC series branch, the R of which is 10 ohms, the ωL of which is 20 ohms, and the $1/\omega C$ of which is 40 ohms. If the magnitude of the internally generated emf is 500 volts, find the current that flows in the series circuit and the terminal voltage of the generator.

The internal impedance of the generator is

$$\mathbf{Z}_g = 2 + j6 = 6.32\underline{/71.6^\circ} \text{ ohms}$$

The total impedance of the series circuit is

$$\begin{aligned}\mathbf{Z}_t &= \mathbf{Z}_g + \mathbf{Z}_{RLC} \\ &= (2 + j6) + [10 + j(20 - 40)] \\ &= 12 - j14 = 18.44\underline{/-49.4^\circ} \text{ ohms}\end{aligned}$$

The generated emf, $\mathbf{E}_g$, is arbitrarily chosen to coincide with the reference axis. Therefore

$$\mathbf{E}_g = 500 + j0 = 500\underline{/0^\circ} \text{ volts}$$

The current that flows in the series circuit is

$$\mathbf{I} = \frac{\mathbf{E}_g}{\mathbf{Z}_t} = \frac{500\underline{/0^\circ}}{18.44\underline{/-49.4^\circ}} = 27.1\underline{/49.4^\circ} \text{ amperes}$$

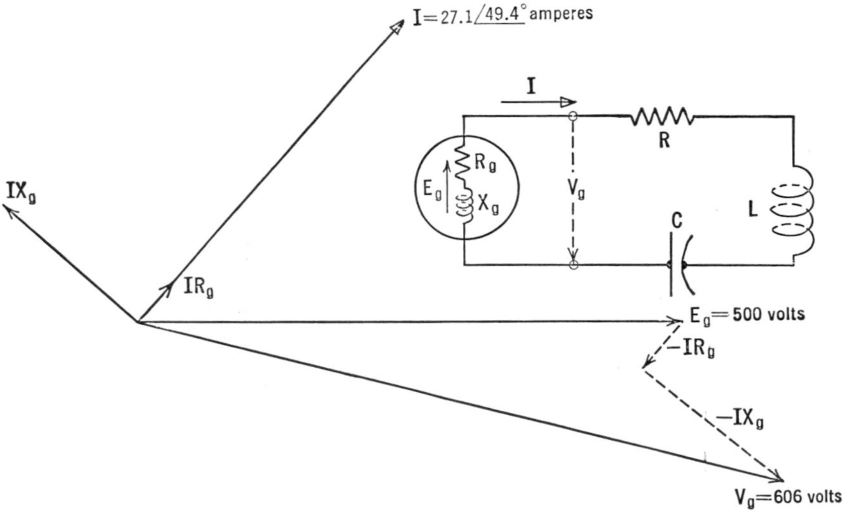

FIG. 15. Voltage relations for a generator supplying a leading power-factor load.

The terminal voltage of the generator considered as a voltage drop across the external circuit is

$$(1)\quad \mathbf{V}_g = \mathbf{E}_g - \mathbf{I}\mathbf{Z}_g \quad \text{or} \quad (2)\quad \mathbf{V}_g = \mathbf{I}\mathbf{Z}_{RLC}$$

$$\begin{aligned}\mathbf{V}_g &= (500\underline{/0^\circ}) - (27.1\underline{/49.4^\circ})(6.32\underline{/71.6^\circ}) \\ &= 500\underline{/0^\circ} - 171.3\underline{/121^\circ} \\ &= (500 + j0) - (-88.3 + j147) \\ &= 588.3 - j147 = 606\underline{/-14^\circ} \text{ volts}\end{aligned}$$

$$\mathbf{V}_g = (27.1\underline{/49.4^\circ})(22.36\underline{/-63.4^\circ}) = 606\underline{/-14^\circ} \text{ volts}$$

A phasor diagram illustrating $\mathbf{E}_g$, $\mathbf{I}$, $\mathbf{I}R_g$, $\mathbf{I}X_g$, and $\mathbf{V}_g$ is given in Fig. 15. It will be observed that the terminal voltage of the generator ($\mathbf{V}_g$) is greater in magnitude than the internally generated emf (E_g) owing to the manner in which the voltage phasor $\mathbf{I}X_g$ subtracts from $(\mathbf{E}_g - \mathbf{I}R_g)$ to form phasor $\mathbf{V}_g$.

Problem 15. (*a*) Draw a phasor diagram illustrating $\mathbf{E}_g$, $\mathbf{I}$, $\mathbf{IR}$, $\mathbf{IX}_L$, $\mathbf{IX}_C$, and $\mathbf{V}_g$ of the above numerical example and show how $\mathbf{IR}$, $\mathbf{IX}_L$, and $\mathbf{IX}_C$ combine vectorially to form $\mathbf{V}_g$.

(*b*) Calculate the total power generated and the total power absorbed by the external *RLC* branch. Compare $V_gI \cos \theta \Big]_{\mathbf{I}}^{\mathbf{V}_g}$ plus I^2R_g with $E_gI \cos \theta \Big]_{\mathbf{I}}^{\mathbf{E}_g}$.

Ans.: Total power = 8810 watts; branch power = 7345 watts.

Addition and Subtraction of Voltages and Currents. Correctly written, the complex expressions for voltages and currents specify both the magnitudes and relative phase positions of these quantities. Therefore, in complex form:

1. Voltage drops in series may be added to obtain the combined voltage drop of the series elements considered. If the combined voltage drop and one component are known, the remaining voltage drop may be determined by subtracting the component in question from the combined voltage drop.
2. Generated emf's connected in additive or subtractive series may be added or subtracted, depending upon the relative polarities of the terminals which are joined together to form the series connection. Series connections of generated emf's will be considered in more detail when polyphase systems are studied.
3. Two or more currents flowing away from a junction may be added to find the current flowing toward the junction, or vice versa.

Circuit Directions of Voltages and Currents. It has been shown that the average power absorbed by a branch or circuit is

$$P = VI \cos \theta \Big]_{\mathbf{I}}^{\mathbf{V}} \tag{58}$$

where V is the magnitude of the voltage drop across the branch or circuit,

I is the magnitude of the current flowing through the branch or circuit in the same circuit direction as that which has been taken for the $+V$ direction.

$\theta \Big]_{\mathbf{I}}^{\mathbf{V}}$ is the angle of lag (or lead) of $\mathbf{I}$ with respect to $\mathbf{V}$. In a normal dissipative type of branch or circuit, θ will not be as great as $\pm 90°$.

Similarly, the average power generated by a generating device is

$$P = EI \cos \theta \Big]_{\mathbf{I}}^{\mathbf{E}} \tag{59}$$

where E is the magnitude of the generated voltage,

I is the magnitude of the current flowing in the same circuit direction as that which has been taken for the $+E$ direction.

$\theta\Big]_{\mathrm{I}}^{\mathrm{E}}$ is the angle of lag (or lead) of $\mathbf{I}$ with respect to $\mathbf{E}$. In case the generating device is actually delivering power, $\theta\Big]_{\mathrm{I}}^{\mathrm{E}}$ will be less than 90° in magnitude. This, in general, is the condition that exists when only one generator is present. Average negative generated power indicates that the generating device in question is actually absorbing power from some other generator.

A single generator connected to a dissipative branch is shown in Fig. 16. If the $+E$ circuit direction is assumed to be from b to a *through* the generator, the positive circuit direction of the current is from b to a *through* the generator, and from a to b *through* the dissipative branch. The positive circuit direction of a voltage drop through a dissipative branch defines the positive circuit direction of the current through the branch, or vice versa. In Fig. 16, therefore, the $+V$ direction is from a to b through the external branch. With the aid of these elementary concepts, the correct phase relations of all quantities involved may be conveniently determined. If E_g is taken as reference,

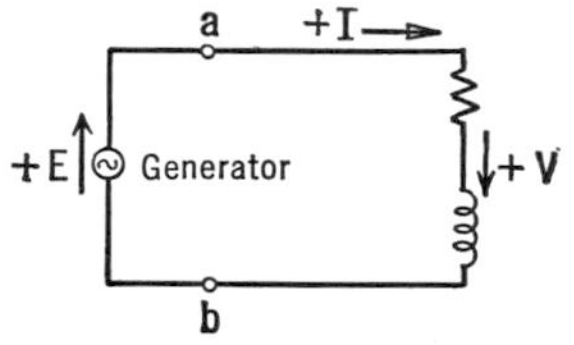

FIG. 16. Illustrating an arbitrarily assigned positive circuit direction of the generated voltage, E, together with the resulting positive circuit directions of I and V.

$$\mathbf{I} = \frac{E_g\underline{/0^\circ}}{\mathbf{Z}_{\text{gen}} + \mathbf{Z}_{\text{load}}} = I\underline{/\alpha} \tag{60}$$

$$\mathbf{V} = E_g\underline{/0^\circ} - \mathbf{I}\mathbf{Z}_{\text{gen}} = V\underline{/\beta} \tag{61}$$

$$\text{Average generated power} = E_g I \cos \alpha \tag{62}$$

$$\text{Average power absorbed by the external branch} = VI \cos (\beta - \alpha) \tag{63}$$

Thus it will be seen that the current in a series loop may be associated with the generated voltage to obtain the generated power and with a particular voltage drop across a given part of the circuit to obtain the power absorbed by this particular part of the circuit. Unless otherwise specified, the current in a series loop having only one generator is assumed to flow in the positive direction of voltage rise through the generator and in the positive direction of voltage drop through the load portion of the circuit.

Example of Two Generators. Figure 17 illustrates two a-c generators which are connected in parallel with respect to the load terminals but are connected in subtractive series with respect to the series loop joining the two generators. If no load

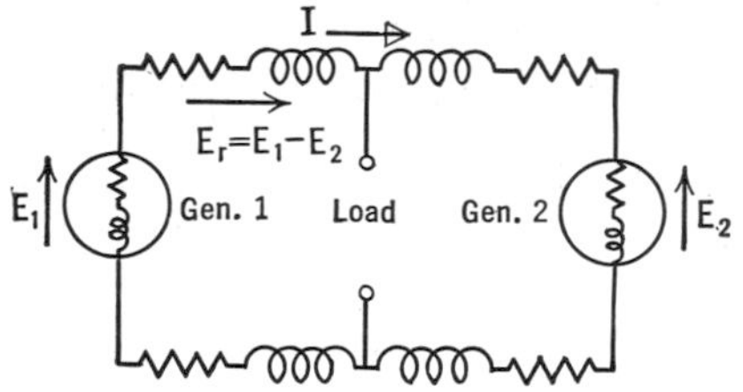

FIG. 17. Two generated emf's connected in parallel with respect to the load terminals. $\mathbf{E}_1$ and $\mathbf{E}_2$ are in subtractive series with respect to the series loop which joins the two generators.

is placed across the load terminals, the series loop is the only path in which current flows. If it is assumed that the generators are driven by separate prime movers and controlled by separate voltage regulators, it is entirely possible for the voltages to differ in magnitude and phase position.

Let $E_1 = 1350\underline{/0°}$ volts and $E_2 = 1300\underline{/-10°}$ with respect to the load terminals. The impedance of each generator is $(1 + j3)$ ohms and each of the series loop connecting lines has $(2 + j1)$ ohms impedance. Find the magnitude and phase position of the current which circulates in the series loop under the above conditions.

The resultant generated emf which acts to send current through the series loop in the $+E_1$ direction is

$$\mathbf{E}_r = \mathbf{E}_1 - \mathbf{E}_2 = (1350 + j0) - (1280 - j226) = 70 + j226 \text{ volts}$$

The positive circuit direction of E_r is the same as that which has been arbitrarily assigned to $\mathbf{E}_1$, since the phasor difference $\mathbf{E}_1 - \mathbf{E}_2$ has been employed in defining $\mathbf{E}_r$. The current that flows in the direction of $\mathbf{E}_r$ is

$$\begin{aligned} \mathbf{I} &= \frac{\mathbf{E}_r}{\mathbf{Z}_{\text{loop}}} = \frac{70 + j226}{6 + j8} \\ &= \frac{(70 + j226)\,(6 - j8)}{(6 + j8)\,(6 - j8)} \\ &= (22.28 + j7.96) = 23.65\underline{/19.65°} \text{ amperes} \end{aligned}$$

The power generated by the $\mathbf{E}_1$ generator is

$$P_{g1} = 1350 \times 23.65 \cos 19.65° = 30{,}110 \text{ watts}$$

The power generated by the $\mathbf{E}_2$ is

$$\begin{aligned} P_{g2} &= 1300 \times 23.65 \cos [180° - (10° + 19.65°)] \\ &= -26{,}750 \text{ watts} \end{aligned}$$

In calculating the power generated by the $\mathbf{E}_2$ machine, either the voltage or the current is reversed in phase position so that the $\mathbf{E}_2$ and $\mathbf{I}$ circuit directions coincide. The physical interpretation of the negative generated power found for machine 2 is that machine 2 is actually receiving power from machine 1. A phasor diagram of $\mathbf{E}_1$, $\mathbf{E}_2$, $\mathbf{E}_r$, and $\mathbf{I}$ is shown in Fig. 18.

In general, a circulating current between the two generators may exist as a result of difference in the *magnitude* of the two generated voltages, or a difference in *phase*, or *both*.

A further insight into the power relations of the circuit arrangement shown in Fig. 17 may be obtained by adding to the power absorbed by machine 2 the total I^2R loss of the series loop and comparing the result with the total power generated by machine 1.

$$(23.65^2 \times 6) + 26{,}750 = 30{,}110 \text{ watts}$$

The physical interpretation of the above equation is that machine 1 generates 30,110 watts, of which 3360 are dissipated in the form of heat in the resistance of the series loop and 26,750 watts are absorbed by machine 2 in the form of electromagnetic motor power.

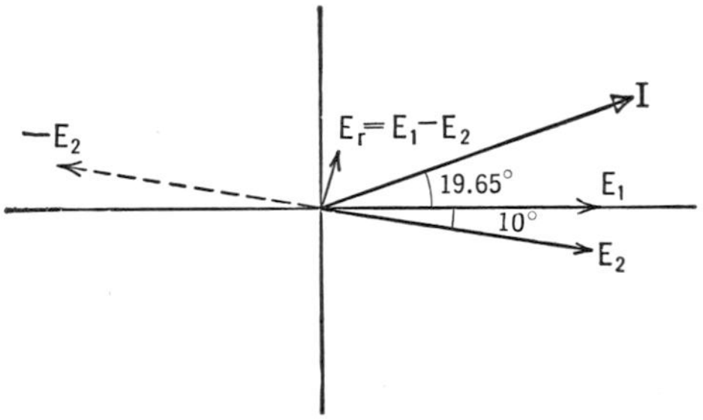

FIG. 18. Phasor diagram of two-generator problem.

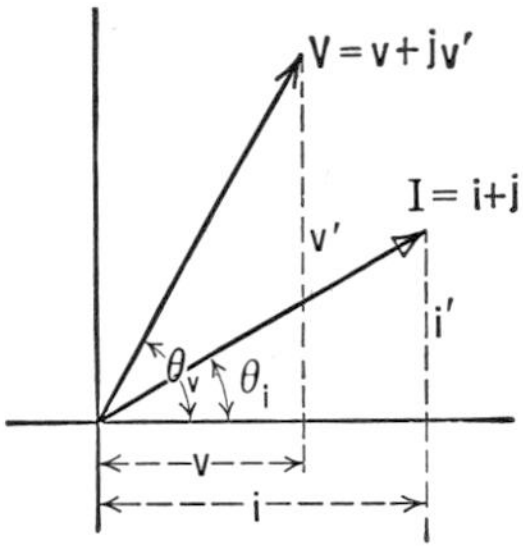

FIG. 19.

Power Calculations Employing Complex Forms. If voltage and current are expressed in rectangular complex form, the average absorbed or generated power may be calculated in terms of the components of the voltage and current which are involved. Reference to Fig. 19 will show that

$$P = VI \cos \theta \Big]_{\mathbf{I}}^{\mathbf{V}} \tag{64}$$

or

$$\begin{aligned} P &= VI \cos (\theta_v - \theta_i) = VI \cos (\theta_i - \theta_v) \\ &= VI [\cos \theta_v \cos \theta_i + \sin \theta_v \sin \theta_i] \\ &= (V \cos \theta_v)(I \cos \theta_i) + (V \sin \theta_v)(I \sin \theta_i) \end{aligned} \tag{65}$$

In rectangular form

$$\mathbf{V} = V \cos \theta_v + jV \sin \theta_v = v + jv' \tag{66}$$

$$\mathbf{I} = I \cos \theta_i + jI \sin \theta_i = i + ji' \tag{67}$$

If the above components of $\mathbf{V}$ and $\mathbf{I}$ in equation (65) are employed, it follows that

$$P = vi + v'i' \text{ (absorbed power)} \tag{68}$$

If the voltage in question is a generated voltage,

$$P = ei + e'i' \text{ (generated power)} \tag{69}$$

Due regard must be taken for the sign of each component in equations (68) and (69) when these power equations are employed.

Example. If, at a certain stage in the solution of a problem, it is found that $\mathbf{E} = (200 + j40)$ volts and that the current flowing in the positive circuit direction of $\mathbf{E}$ is $\mathbf{I} = (30 - j10)$ amperes, the power generated is

$$P = ei + e'i' = (200)\,(30) + (40)\,(-10)$$
$$= 6000 - 400 = 5600 \text{ watts}$$

The same result could, of course, be obtained by first evaluating the magnitudes of E, I, and $\theta\Big]_{\mathbf{I}}^{\mathbf{E}}$ and then making use of the more familiar relation

$$P = EI\cos\theta\Big]_{\mathbf{I}}^{\mathbf{E}}$$

Reactive Volt-Ampere Calculations Employing Complex Forms. Reactive volt-amperes or reactive power, P_X, may also be calculated in terms of the rectangular components of the voltage and current involved. If the voltage phasor and the current phasor shown in Fig. 19 are considered,

$$\mathbf{V} = v + jv'$$
$$\mathbf{I} = i + ji'$$

As defined in Chapters II and III,

$$P_X = VI\sin\theta\Big]_{\mathbf{I}}^{\mathbf{V}} \tag{70}$$

In accordance with a convention which is in common use, θ is the angle of *lead* of the voltage with respect to the current. If this convention of signs is employed, reactive power is a positive quantity for lagging currents and a negative quantity for leading currents. (See Chapter III, page 98.) If the angle θ in equation (70) is considered as the angle of lead of the voltage with respect to the current, then

$$P_X = VI\sin(\theta_v - \theta_i)$$
$$= VI(\sin\theta_v\cos\theta_i - \cos\theta_v\sin\theta_i)$$
$$= (V\sin\theta_v)(I\cos\theta_i) - (V\cos\theta_v)(I\sin\theta_i) \tag{71}$$

From the definitions which have been attached to v, v', i, and i', equation (71) reduces directly to

$$P_X = v'i - vi' \tag{72}$$

Example. If $\mathbf{V} = 200\underline{/30°} = (173.2 + j100)$ volts and $\mathbf{I} = 10\underline{/60°} = (5 + j8.66)$ amperes, find the real power, the reactive volt-amperes, and the total volt-amperes involved.

$$P = vi + v'i' = 866 + 866 = 1732 \text{ watts}$$

$$P_X = v'i - vi' = 500 - 1500 = -1000 \text{ vars}$$

The minus sign in connection with P_X merely indicates that the reactive power in question is the result of a leading current.

The volt-amperes associated with **V** and **I** can be obtained directly from the product of V and I, or as follows:

$$Va = \sqrt{P^2 + P_X{}^2} = \sqrt{1732^2 + (-1000)^2}$$
$$= 2000 \text{ volt-amperes}$$

The Conjugate Method of Calculating Real and Reactive Power. The question naturally arises as to the significance of the product of phasor voltage and phasor current. The answer is to be found in the definition that has been given to the product of two complex numbers. The magnitude of the product of voltage and current, even in complex form, represents the volt-amperes which are associated with **V** and **I**. The component parts of the cartesian expression for **VI** are, however, meaningless. For this reason, phasor voltage times phasor current cannot be used directly to calculate real power or reactive volt-amperes.

A method of conjugates is sometimes employed in the determination of real power and reactive volt-amperes. It affords a convenient means of calculating these quantities when both the voltage and current are expressed in cartesian form.

If the conjugate of the current, that is, the cartesian expression of the current with the sign of the j component reversed, is multiplied by the voltage in cartesian form, the result is a complex quantity the real part of which is the real power and the j part of which is the reactive volt-amperes.

Let $\mathbf{V} = v + jv'$ and $\mathbf{I} = i + ji'$

The conjugate of **I** is $(i - ji')$ and

$$(v + jv')(i - ji') = (vi + v'i') + j(v'i - vi') \tag{73}$$

or

$$(v + jv')\,(i - ji') = P + jP_X \tag{74}$$

If the conjugate of **V** is multiplied by **I** in complex form, the result is

$$(v - jv')\,(i + ji') = (vi + v'i') - j(v'i - vi') \tag{75}$$

or

$$(v - jv')\,(i + ji') = P - jP_X \tag{76}$$

The real power, as obtained by the method of conjugates, is the same regardless of whether **V** or **I** is conjugated. The sign of the reactive volt-amperes, however, is dependent upon the choice of the **V** or **I** conjugate as shown by equations (74) and (76). To be consistent with convention of signs employed in equation (70), the conjugate of the *current* must be employed. Also to be in accord with the discussion in the previous chapter (page 98) and the recommendation to the International Committee on Electrical and Magnetic Units the conjugate of current must be employed. In any event $P_X = v'i - vi'$ or $vi' - v'i$ with the sign being a matter of definition. The present situation indicates that the current should be conjugated or that $P_X = v'i - vi'$ should be used and that inductive vars should be called positive.

Example. Given $\mathbf{V} = 173.2 + j100$ volts and $\mathbf{I} = 5.0 + j8.66$ amperes, find the real power and the reactive volt-amperes by the method of conjugates. Employing the conjugate of the current,

$$\begin{aligned} P_{\text{va}} &= (173.2 + j100)\ (5.0 - j8.66) \\ &= 866 - j1500 + j500 + 866 \\ &= 1732 - j1000 \end{aligned}$$

This above result may be interpreted, in light of equations (73) and (74), to mean that $P = 1732$ watts and that $P_X = -1000$ vars. The negative sign indicates capacitive vars when the conjugate of the current is used.

Transmission Expressed as a Complex Number. The term " transmission " will be used here as a general designation of the effect (say the current or power) in a receiver station produced by a generator at the sending station. (See Fig. 20.[3]) In low-power communication networks, particular attention centers on the *change* in magnitude (and the phase shift) of the receiver current *relative* to the receiver current which could be obtained under optimum conditions of operation. These relative changes are due to two causes, namely:

(1) R_2 in Fig. 20 not being equal to the generator resistance R_1, the latter being fixed by the generator characteristics.

(2) The network intervening between the sending-station generator E_1 and the receiver-station resistance R_2.

The intervening network will usually take the form of a transmission line, transformer, selective filter, attenuator, or amplifier. Various combinations of these basic four-terminal networks may be employed between the generator terminals (11′ in Fig. 20) and the receiver terminals 22′, but until the detailed operation of these devices has been studied we shall represent them simply as a box having four terminals as shown in the figure.

[3] If any series or shunt reactance is associated with either the generator or load, it may be placed within the four-terminal network for the purposes of analysis, thus making Fig. 20 a more general case than is apparent from the diagram.

It will be accepted here, subject to later proof, that the most efficient possible transmission between E_1 and R_2 will occur when the impedance looking to right of terminals 11′ is equal to R_1, that is, when $V_1/I_1 = R_1$. (Amplifiers are excluded from the foregoing statement because these

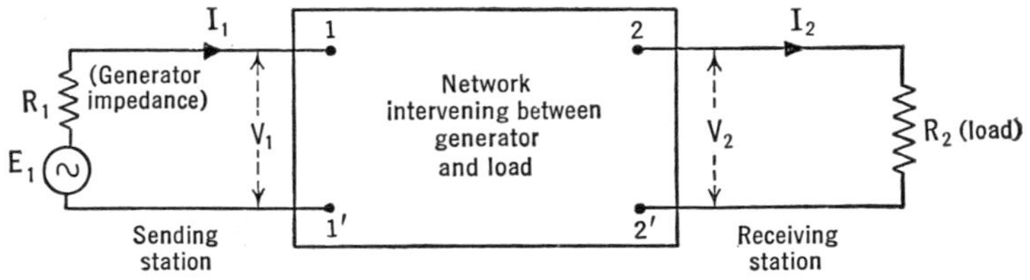

FIG. 20. Four-terminal network intervening between a generator and a resistive load.

devices draw power from sources other than the E_1 generator.) Under this condition of operation the generator resistance is said to match the impedance looking to the right of terminals 11′ and

$$I_{1(\text{matched})} = \frac{E_1}{2R_1}$$

The ratio of the powers entering and leaving the network under the condition that $\mathbf{V}_1/\mathbf{I}_1 = R_1$ is

$$\frac{\text{Power entering terminals } 11'}{\text{Power leaving terminals } 22'} = \frac{V_1 I_1}{V_2 I_2} = \frac{(E_1/2)(E_1/2R_1)}{(R_2 I_2)(I_2)} \tag{77}$$

If now we define the *transfer impedance* from E_1 to R_2 under any condition of operation as

$$\mathbf{Z}_T = \frac{\mathbf{E}_1}{\mathbf{I}_2} \tag{78}$$

we note that the value of $\mathbf{Z}_T$ which will make the power ratio of equation (77) unity is

$$\mathbf{Z}_{T(\text{opt})} = 2\sqrt{R_1 R_2} \tag{79}$$

In other words, for fixed values of R_1 and R_2, all the power entering terminals 11′ in Fig. 20 will leave terminals 22′ if the intervening network is such that $\mathbf{E}_1/\mathbf{I}_2 = 2\sqrt{R_1 R_2}$.

In describing the transmission characteristics of an arbitrary four-terminal network of the kind shown in Fig. 20, it is desirable that the receiver current, $\mathbf{I}_2$, be measured relative to its optimum value, $\mathbf{E}_1/2\sqrt{R_1 R_2}$. Both the magnitude and phase of $\mathbf{I}_2$ relative to this base can be measured in terms of the real and j components of the transmission constant, $\boldsymbol{\gamma}$, if the latter is defined as

$$\boldsymbol{\gamma} = \alpha + j\beta = \log_\epsilon \frac{\mathbf{Z}_T}{2\sqrt{R_1R_2}} = \log_\epsilon \frac{\mathbf{E}_1/2\sqrt{R_1R_2}}{\mathbf{I}_{2(\text{general})}} = \log_\epsilon \frac{\mathbf{I}_{2(\text{opt})}}{\mathbf{I}_{2(\text{general})}} \quad (80)$$

where $\mathbf{Z}_T = \mathbf{E}_1/\mathbf{I}_2$ for any arbitrary intervening network.

α is the attenuation (to be described in more detail later).
β is the phase shift (also to be described in detail later).

The transmission constant is thus defined as a logarithmic measure of $\mathbf{Z}_T$ relative to $\mathbf{Z}_{T(\text{opt})}$. Since $E_1/2\sqrt{R_1R_2}$ in Fig. 20 is considered to be a constant, it is plain that α is a logarithmic measure of $I_{2(\text{opt})}/I_{2(\text{general})}$ and that β is the phase angle difference between $\mathbf{I}_{2(\text{general})}$ and $\mathbf{I}_{2(\text{opt})}$. The phase angle of $\mathbf{I}_{2(\text{opt})}$ would normally be zero, since the reference would normally be $\mathbf{E}_1 = E_1\underline{/0^\circ}$ and $\mathbf{I}_{2(\text{opt})}$ is in phase with $\mathbf{E}_1$, being equal to $\mathbf{E}_1/2\sqrt{R_1R_2}$.

Attenuation, α. It will be noted from equation (80) that the attenuation can be written as

$$\alpha = \log_\epsilon \frac{\sqrt{I^2_{(\text{opt})}}}{\sqrt{I^2_{(\text{general})}}} = \frac{1}{2} \log_\epsilon \frac{I_2{}^2_{(\text{opt})}R_2}{I_2{}^2_{(\text{general})}R_2} \quad \text{nepers} \quad (81)$$

Attenuation in this case is an inverse logarithmic measure of the power received by R_2 under general conditions of operation to that which is received by R_2 under optimum conditions of operation. The fact that logarithmic measure is employed in the definition of $\boldsymbol{\gamma}$ makes $\alpha = 0$ if $I_2{}^2_{(\text{general})}R_2$ is equal to $I_2{}^2_{(\text{opt})}R_2$, and as the former decreases in value owing to losses in the intervening network α grows larger logarithmically. If $\log_\epsilon$ is employed as in equation (81), the units of α are called nepers.

Another common definition of attenuation as it applies to general transmission characteristics is

$$\alpha_{\text{db}} = 10 \log_{10} \frac{I_2{}^2_{(\text{opt})}R_2}{I_2{}^2_{(\text{general})}R_2} \quad \text{decibels} \quad (82)$$

Plainly

$$\frac{(\text{No. of})\alpha_{\text{db}}}{\alpha_{\text{nepers}}} = \frac{10 \log_{10} K}{\frac{1}{2} \log_\epsilon K} = \frac{20 \log_{10} K}{2.303 \log_{10} K} = 8.686$$

where K is any power ratio. The above relationship indicates that the number of decibels per neper is 8.686. It is a matter of indifference which unit of attenuation is used, since engineers generally understand that the decibel is by definition a unit of attenuation which is 8.686 times smaller in magnitude than the neper, there being 8.686 decibels of attenuation for each neper of attenuation in any particular specification of attenuation.

Phase Shift, β. In taking the logarithm indicated in equation (80) it will be noted that

$$\boldsymbol{\gamma} = \alpha + j\beta = \log_\epsilon \frac{\mathbf{I}_{2(\text{opt})}}{\mathbf{I}_{2(\text{general})}} = \log_\epsilon \frac{I_{2(\text{opt})}}{I_{2(\text{general})}} + j[\theta_{(\text{opt})} - \theta_{(\text{general})}] \quad (83)$$

Thus, if $\mathbf{E}_1$ is selected as a reference, $\theta_{(\text{opt})} = 0$ and $\beta = -\theta_{(\text{general})}$. Regardless of the reference selected, β specifies the phase difference between $\mathbf{I}_2$ under optimum conditions and $\mathbf{I}_2$ under general operating conditions.

If the evaluation of $\alpha + j\beta$ is to be carried no further than that shown in equation (83), it is a matter of choice whether β is stated in radians or degrees. If $\boldsymbol{\gamma}$ is to be expressed in polar form, however, β must be expressed in radians.

Examples. In Fig. 20, let $R_1 = 100$ ohms, $R_2 = 25$ ohms, and assume that terminal 1 is connected directly to terminal 2 and terminal 1′ directly to 2′. Let it be required to find the attenuation and phase shift relative to the optimum operating conditions.

If equation (80) is to be employed, we note that

$$\mathbf{I}_{2(\text{opt})} = \frac{\mathbf{E}_1}{2\sqrt{100 \times 25}} = \frac{\mathbf{E}_1}{100}$$

$$\mathbf{I}_{2(\text{actual})} = \frac{\mathbf{E}_1}{125}$$

$$\alpha + j\beta = \log_\epsilon \frac{\mathbf{E}_1/100}{\mathbf{E}_1/125} = 0.223 + j0$$

Thus $\alpha = 0.223$ neper or 1.938 decibels. This attenuation results from R_2 not being equal to R_1.

$\beta = 0$ since no phase difference exists between the two conditions of operation.

As a check on the arithmetic we might employ equation (82) as

$$\alpha_{\text{db}} = 20 \log_{10} \frac{\mathbf{I}_{2(\text{opt})}}{\mathbf{I}_{2(\text{actual})}} = 20 \log_{10} \frac{E_1/100}{E_1/125}$$

$$\alpha_{\text{db}} = 20 \log_{10} \frac{125}{100} = 20 \times 0.0969 = 1.938 \text{ decibels}$$

As a second example of the use of equation (80) let it be assumed that $R_1 = 25$ ohms, $R_2 = 100$ ohms, and that, for $\mathbf{E}_1 = 10\underline{/0°}$ volts, $\mathbf{V}_2 = 3.53\underline{/-45°}$ volts.

It is required that the transmission constant, $\boldsymbol{\gamma}$, be found from the above data.

$$\mathbf{I}_{2(\text{opt})} = \frac{\mathbf{E}_1}{2\sqrt{R_1R_2}} = \frac{10\underline{/0°}}{2\sqrt{2500}} = 0.1\underline{/0°} \text{ ampere}$$

$$\mathbf{I}_{2(\text{actual})} = \frac{\mathbf{V}_2}{R_2} = \frac{3.53\underline{/-45°}}{100} = 0.0353\underline{/-45°} \text{ ampere}$$

$$\mathbf{Z}_T = \frac{\mathbf{E}_1}{\mathbf{I}_2} = \frac{10\underline{/0^\circ}}{0.0353\underline{/-45^\circ}} = 283\underline{/45^\circ} \text{ ohms}$$

$$\boldsymbol{\gamma} = \alpha + j\beta = \log_\epsilon \frac{Z_T}{2\sqrt{R_1R_2}} = \log_\epsilon \frac{283\underline{/45^\circ}}{100} = 1.04 + j45^\circ$$

or

$$\boldsymbol{\gamma} = \alpha + j\beta = \log_\epsilon \frac{\mathbf{I}_{2(\mathrm{opt})}}{\mathbf{I}_{2(\mathrm{actual})}} = \log_\epsilon \frac{0.1\underline{/0^\circ}}{0.0353\underline{/-45^\circ}} = 1.04 + j0.785 \text{ radians}$$

Thus

$$\boldsymbol{\gamma} = 1.304\underline{/0.647 \text{ (radians)}} = 1.304\underline{/37.05^\circ}$$

If $\boldsymbol{\gamma}$ is specified in polar form as above, we obtain α and β as the real and j terms directly by changing the polar form of $\boldsymbol{\gamma}$ to rectangular form.

A significant point which should not be overlooked in the foregoing discussion of *attenuation* and *phase shift* is that, as applied to the four-terminal network shown in Fig. 20, these quantities were obtained from

$$\alpha + j\beta = \log_\epsilon \frac{\mathbf{Z}_{T(\mathrm{general})}}{\mathbf{Z}_{T(\mathrm{opt})}} = \frac{1}{2}\log_\epsilon \frac{I_{2\,(\mathrm{opt})}^{2}R_2}{I_{2\,(\mathrm{general})}^{2}R_2} + j[\theta_{Z_{T(\mathrm{general})}}]$$

where $\mathbf{Z}_{T(\mathrm{opt})}$ was an *arbitrarily selected* base which yielded maximum power delivered to the load resistance, R_2. (It was assumed that R_1 was fixed by the characteristics of the E_1 generator and that R_2 was fixed by the characteristics of the receiving device.) The base selected here is that which is normally employed when we wish to take account of the possible mismatch between R_1 and R_2 as well as the loss and phase shift introduced by the intervening four-terminal network. It also permits the possible mismatch between R_1 and R_2 to be rectified by the intervening network if the latter is designed for this purpose.

In general circuit analysis, *attenuation* and *phase shift* are used in a wide variety of different ways to describe loss (or gain) and phase difference relative to other *arbitrarily selected* bases. Attenuation and phase shift are meaningful quantities only when the base is clearly understood, since attenuation and phase shift are measures of power loss (or gain) and phase relative to the base which is selected as being most appropriate for the problem at hand.

PROBLEMS

16. Perform the following indicated operations: (*a*) $(5 + j8) + (-2 - j4)$; (*b*) $(-12 + j6) - (30 - j20)$; (*c*) $(16 - j12)(-5 + j8)$; (*d*) $(-5 + j8.66) \div (5 - j8.66)$; (*e*) $(2 - j3) \div (-1 + j2)$.

17. Two impedances, $Z_1 = 2 + j3$ ohms and $Z_2 = 3 - j7$ ohms, are connected in a circuit so that they are additive. Find the equivalent impedance of the two in polar form.

18. Write the cartesian and polar expressions for a phasor, the magnitude of which is 100 units and the phase position of which is:

(*a*) 30° behind the reference axis.
(*b*) 45° behind the reference axis.
(*c*) 120° behind the reference axis.
(*d*) 180° behind the reference axis.
(*e*) 60° ahead of the reference axis.
(*f*) 120° ahead of the reference axis.
(*g*) 210° ahead of the reference axis.

19. Find the magnitude and angular position with respect to the reference axis of the phasors which are represented by:

(*a*) $8.0 + j6.0$.
(*b*) $-10 + j10.0$.
(*c*) $38.3 - j31.14$.
(*d*) $-57.36 + j81.92$.
(*e*) $-76.6 - j64.3$.
(*f*) $-50.0 - j86.6$.

20. (*a*) Rotate the phasor $(8.66 + j5.0)$ through $+40°$ by multiplying it by the correct operator.

(*b*) Rotate the phasor $(-5.0 - j8.66)$ through $-30°$.

(*c*) Express the results of (*a*) and (*b*) in both cartesian and polar forms.

21. Perform the following indicated operations:

(*a*) $(8 + j6)(10\underline{/-120°})(\cos 36.87° - j \sin 36.87°)(0.1\epsilon^{+j60°})$.

(*b*) $$\frac{[34.2 + j94][10\epsilon^{-j30°}][30(\cos 60° + j \sin 60°)]}{[20\underline{/40°}][50(\cos 30° + j \sin 30°)]}.$$

22. Express each of the following as a single complex number in cartesian and polar forms:

(*a*) $[\sqrt{4.5 - j7.79} + \log_\epsilon 10\underline{/172°}]$.

(*b*) $$\sqrt{\frac{(940 + j342)}{10\epsilon^{j10°}}}.$$

(*c*) $$\frac{(-8.66 + j5.0)(50\underline{/-100°})(2\epsilon^{j70°})}{j5}.$$

(*d*) $50\epsilon^{-j\omega t}$ at $t = \dfrac{1}{480}$ second if $\omega = 377$ radians per second.

(*e*) $$\frac{30 + j10}{6 - j3} \cdot \sqrt{4.5 - j7.794}.$$

23. Find all possible roots of

$$\sqrt[3]{\frac{10\underline{/45°}5\epsilon^{j60°}(-4.047 - j2.94)}{1 - j1.732}}$$

24. The series impedance of a transmission line is $Z_a = 10\underline{/68°}$ ohms, and the shunt impedance of the line is $Z_b = 25{,}000\underline{/-90°}$ ohms.

(*a*) Find the characteristic impedance of the line which is defined as $Z_0 = \sqrt{Z_a Z_b}$.

(*b*) Find the propagation constant of the line which is defined as $\gamma = \sqrt{Z_a/Z_b}$.

25. A voltage of $125\underline{/40°}$ volts is impressed across a series combination of 2.0 ohms resistance and 8.0 ohms inductive reactance. Find the magnitude and phase position of the current with respect to the reference axis employed in stating the voltage phasor.

26. Two impedances, $\mathbf{Z}_1 = (1 - j3)$ ohms and $\mathbf{Z}_2 = (3 + j6)$ ohms, are connected in parallel. The magnitude of the current through $\mathbf{Z}_1$ is known to be 10 amperes.

(*a*) Find the complex polar expression for the current through $\mathbf{Z}_2$ with respect to $\mathbf{I}_1 = 10\underline{/0^\circ}$ as a reference.

(*b*) Find $\mathbf{I}_0 = \mathbf{I}_1 + \mathbf{I}_2$ in cartesian form.

(*c*) Draw a phasor diagram of $\mathbf{V}$, $\mathbf{I}_1$, $\mathbf{I}_2$, and $\mathbf{I}_0$, employing $\mathbf{I}_1$ as reference.

27. The characteristic impedance of a T-section filter is $\mathbf{Z}_{0T} = \sqrt{\mathbf{Z}_1\mathbf{Z}_2 + \dfrac{\mathbf{Z}_1^2}{4}}$, where $\mathbf{Z}_1$ is the full series arm impedance and $\mathbf{Z}_2$ is the shunt impedance of the filter section. If $\mathbf{Z}_1 = 30\underline{/86.0^\circ}$ ohms and $\mathbf{Z}_2 = 10.0\underline{/-90^\circ}$ ohms, find $\mathbf{Z}_{0T}$ from the above definition of $\mathbf{Z}_{0T}$.

28. Express $\log_\epsilon \sqrt{\dfrac{125\underline{/-90^\circ}}{5\underline{/90^\circ}}}$ in rectangular form.

Ans.: $1.61 \mp j\pi/2$.

29. An equation which is useful in filter circuit analysis is

$$\alpha + j\beta = 2\log_\epsilon\left(\sqrt{1 + \frac{\mathbf{Z}_1}{4\mathbf{Z}_2}} + \sqrt{\frac{\mathbf{Z}_1}{4\mathbf{Z}_2}}\right)$$

If $\mathbf{Z}_1 = 25.14\underline{/-90^\circ}$ ohms and $4\mathbf{Z}_2 = 795\underline{/+90^\circ}$, evaluate α and β.

30. Find α and β in Problem 29 if

$$\mathbf{Z}_1 = 4 \times 10^3\underline{/-90^\circ} \quad \text{ohms}$$

$$4\mathbf{Z}_2 = 1000\underline{/90^\circ} \quad \text{ohms}$$

31. Given the equation

$$\mathbf{V}_m = \mathbf{V} - \mathbf{ZI}$$

where $\mathbf{V} = 100\underline{/0^\circ}$ volts, $\mathbf{Z} = 15\underline{/80^\circ}$ ohms, $\mathbf{I} = 10\underline{/-3^\circ}$ amperes. Express $\mathbf{V}_m$ in polar form.

32. (*a*) Solve the following equation for a and for b:

$$(12 + a) + jb = 20 + j10$$

(*b*) Solve the following equation for a and for β:

$$(a + 10) + j50 = 100(\cos\beta + j\sin\beta)$$

(*c*) Given: $(100 + j0) + 5R\underline{/-45^\circ} = 200\underline{/-\theta^\circ}$; find R and θ.

33. (*a*) Plot $A\epsilon^{+j\omega t}$ and $A\epsilon^{-j\omega t}$ in polar coordinates for $\omega = 157$ radians per second at $t = 0.005$, $t = 0.010$, $t = 0.015$, $t = 0.020$, and $t = 0.04$ second.

(*b*) Plot $\dfrac{A\epsilon^{j\omega t} + A\epsilon^{-j\omega t}}{2}$ in polar coordinates and also in rectangular coordinates versus ωt for one complete cycle.

(*c*) Show that a simple harmonic oscillating variation, such as $A\cos\omega t$, can be represented by two oppositely rotating phasors, each of which has the same angular velocity as the oscillating phasor and each of which has a magnitude equal to one-half the magnitude of the oscillating phasor.

34. (*a*) A voltage $\mathbf{V} = 100 - j50$ volts across a circuit causes a current $\mathbf{I} = -2 - j8$ amperes to flow. Calculate the power absorbed by the circuit, employing equation (68).

(*b*) Calculate power if $\mathbf{V} = -50 + j100$ volts and $\mathbf{I} = -6 - j2$ amperes.
(*c*) Calculate power if $\mathbf{V} = -50 + j100$ volts and $\mathbf{I} = -8 + j3$ amperes.

35. Calculate the vars for each of the parts of Problem 34, employing equation (72).

36. Calculate the power and vars by the method of conjugates for each part of Problem 34.

37. The voltage applied to two parallel branches is $40\underline{/80^\circ}$ volts. The current through branch 1 is $5\underline{/30^\circ}$ amperes, and the current through branch 2 is $(-6 + j8)$ amperes. Find the real power, P, and the reactive volt-amperes, P_x, supplied to the parallel combination by the method of conjugates. *Note:* Check results against $VI = 40 \times 10.62 = \sqrt{P^2 + P_x^2}$.

38. In Fig. 20, page 135, $R_1 = 200$ ohms, $R_2 = 20{,}000$ ohms, and $V_2 = (0.1\underline{/114.6^\circ})\mathbf{E}_1$. Find the attenuation and phase shift which are produced by the combination of the mismatch of R_1 and R_2 and the intervening network.

39. In Fig. 20, $R_1 = 200$ ohms, $R_2 = 20{,}000$ ohms, and $\mathbf{I}_2 = \mathbf{E}_1/4000$ amperes. Find the attenuation and phase shift which are produced by the combination of the mismatch of R_1 and R_2 and the intervening network.

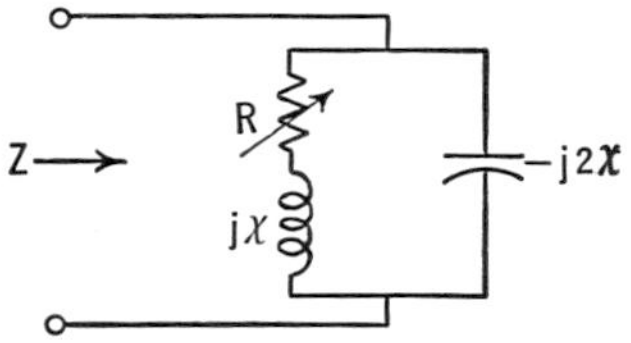

FIG. 21. See Problem **40.**

40. For the circuit shown in Fig. 21,

$$\mathbf{Z} = \frac{(R + jX)(-j2X)}{R + jX - j2X}$$

Plot Z and θ of $\mathbf{Z} = Z\underline{/\theta}$ versus R, employing $R = 0$, $R = X/2$, $R = X$, $R = 2X$, $R = 5X$, $R = 10X$, and $R = \infty$.

chapter V

Sinusoidal Single-Phase Circuit Analysis

Impedances in Series. A series circuit of three impedances is shown in Fig. 1. In a circuit of this kind it is evident that only a single current

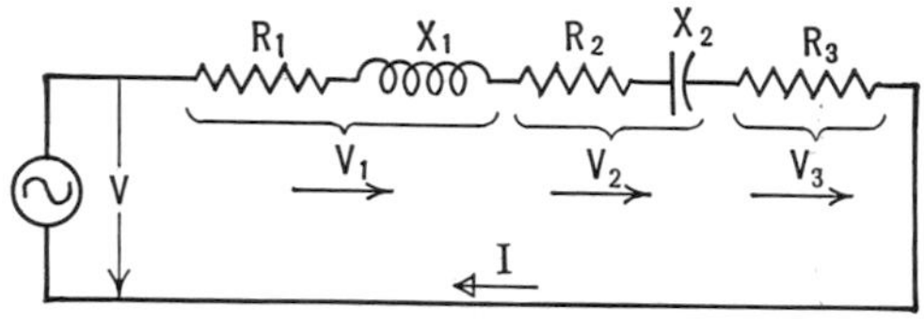

FIG. 1. Impedances in series.

can exist at any instant and that the current throughout all impedances is the same.[1] Kirchhoff's emf law states that

$$\mathbf{V} = \mathbf{V}_1 + \mathbf{V}_2 + \mathbf{V}_3 \tag{1}$$

or

$$\mathbf{V} = \mathbf{IZ}_1 + \mathbf{IZ}_2 + \mathbf{IZ}_3 \tag{2}$$

and

$$\mathbf{V} = \mathbf{I}(\mathbf{Z}_1 + \mathbf{Z}_2 + \mathbf{Z}_3) = \mathbf{IZ} \tag{3}$$

Equation (3) shows that series impedances are added in complex form to obtain the equivalent impedance. Thus

$$\mathbf{Z} = \mathbf{Z}_1 + \mathbf{Z}_2 + \mathbf{Z}_3 = (R_1 + jX_1) + (R_2 + jX_2) + (R_3 + j0)$$

or

$$\mathbf{Z} = (R_1 + R_2 + R_3) + j(X_1 + X_2) = R + jX \tag{4}$$

Equation (4) shows that the resultant resistance R of a simple series circuit is obtained by arithmetically adding the separate resistances. When it is remembered that inductive reactances are considered positive and capacitive reactances are negative, equation (4) also shows that the resultant reactance X of a series circuit is the algebraic sum of the separate reactances.

If current is taken as the reference, the vector diagram of the circuit of Fig. 1 appears as shown in Fig. 2. Such a vector diagram is called a funicular or string diagram. Another type of vector diagram which

[1] The assumption is made that the current is confined to the series circuit. Maxwellian space displacement currents are neglected.

represents the same circuit is shown in Fig. 3. This is called a polar diagram. The distinguishing characteristic of a string vector diagram is that certain component vectors are combined head-to-tail to form a resultant vector as, for example, the component voltages $\mathbf{IR}_1$, $\mathbf{IX}_1$, $\mathbf{IR}_2$,

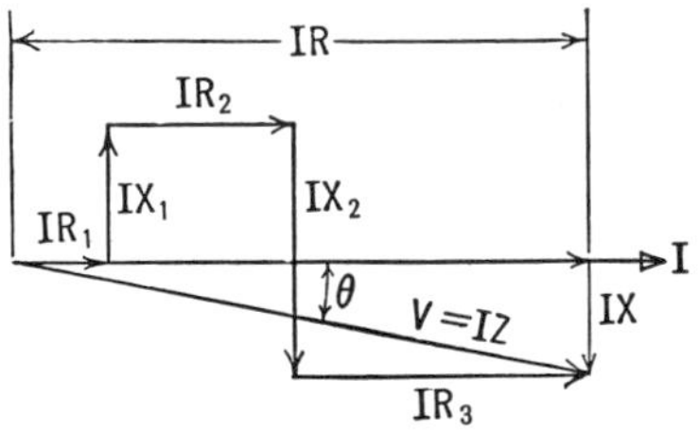

FIG. 2. Funicular or string vector diagram of circuit in Fig. 1.

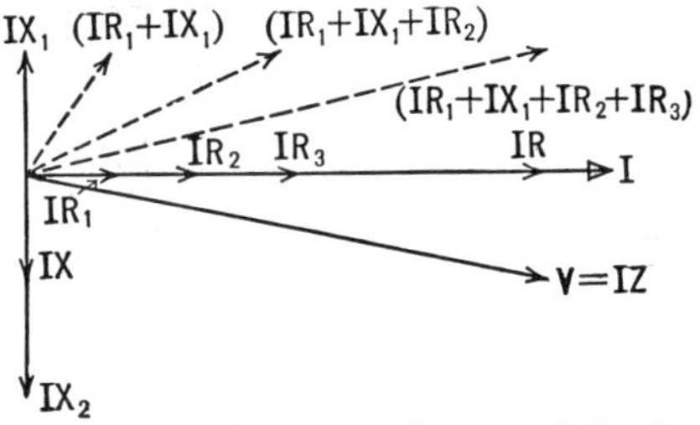

FIG. 3. Polar vector diagram of circuit in Fig. 1.

$\mathbf{IX}_2$, and $\mathbf{IR}_3$ are combined head-to-tail to form the resultant voltage vector $\mathbf{V}$. In a polar vector diagram, all vectors are started from a common origin as shown in Fig. 3.

Either type of diagram may be used since they represent the same thing. The one which appears to be the simpler in any particular case should be used. In certain cases the funicular diagram shows the quantities to better advantage, whereas for others the polar diagram is more suggestive of the relationships and more convenient to use.

In general, for a series circuit of n impedances

$$\mathbf{V} = \mathbf{I}(\mathbf{Z}_1 + \mathbf{Z}_2 + \mathbf{Z}_3 + \cdots + \mathbf{Z}_n) \tag{5}$$

and
$$\mathbf{Z} = (R_1 + R_2 + R_3 + \cdots + R_n) + j(X_1 + X_2 + X_3 + \cdots + X_n) \tag{6}$$

$$\mathbf{Z} = \sqrt{(R_1 + R_2 + R_3 + \cdots + R_n)^2 + (X_1 + X_2 + X_3 + \cdots + X_n)^2} \Big/ \tan^{-1} \frac{X_1 + X_2 + X_3 + \cdots + X_n}{R_1 + R_2 + R_3 + \cdots + R_n} \tag{7}$$

In Chapter II the impedance angle was shown to be the phase angle between the current and the voltage. In Chapter III power factor was shown to be the cosine of this angle. Hence, for a series circuit, Fig. 2 shows

$$\text{Power factor} = \cos\theta = \frac{IR}{IZ} = \frac{R}{Z}$$

$$= \frac{R_1 + R_2 + R_3 + \cdots + R_n}{\sqrt{(R_1 + R_2 + R_3 + \cdots + R_n)^2 + (X_1 + X_2 + X_3 + \cdots + X_n)^2}} \tag{8}$$

Example 1. Calculate the current, voltage drops V_1, V_2, and V_3, power consumed by each impedance, and the total power taken by the circuit with the constants shown in Fig. 4. The impressed voltage will be taken along the reference axis.

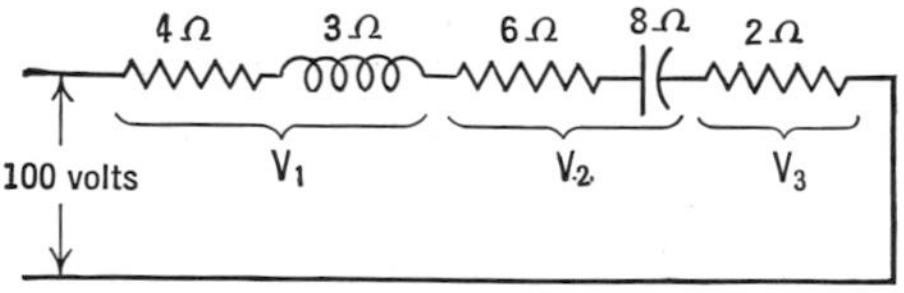

FIG. 4. Circuit for example 1.

$$\mathbf{I} = \frac{\mathbf{V}}{\mathbf{Z}} = \frac{100 + j0}{4 + j3 + 6 - j8 + 2} = \frac{100\,(12 + j5)}{(12 - j5)\,(12 + j5)} = 7.1 + j2.96 \text{ amperes}$$

$$\mathbf{V}_1 = \mathbf{IZ}_1 = (7.1 + j2.96)\,(4 + j3) = 19.53 + j33.14 \text{ volts}$$

$$\mathbf{V}_2 = \mathbf{IZ}_2 = (7.1 + j2.96)\,(6 - j8) = 66.27 - j39.06 \text{ volts}$$

$$\mathbf{V}_3 = \mathbf{IZ}_3 = (7.1 + j2.96)\,(2 + j0) = 14.2 + j5.92 \text{ volts}$$

Check: $\mathbf{V} = 100 + j0$ volts

Note that the drops are added *vectorially* to check the impressed voltage.

$$P_1 = RI^2 = 4(\sqrt{7.1^2 + 2.96^2})^2 = 4 \times 7.69^2 = 237 \text{ watts}$$

$$P_2 = 6 \times 7.69^2 = 355 \text{ watts}$$

$$P_3 = 2 \times 7.69^2 = 118 \text{ watts}$$

$$\text{Total power} = 710 \text{ watts}$$

The total power is also $(vi + v'i') = 100 \times 7.1 = 710$ watts.

Problem 1. (*a*) Find the current through the circuit in Fig. 5 and the voltage drops $\mathbf{V}_{ab}$, $\mathbf{V}_{bc}$, and $\mathbf{V}_{cd}$.

Ans.: $\mathbf{I} = 10 \angle 0°$ amperes, $\mathbf{V}_{ab} = 20 - j40 = 44.7 \angle -63.45°$ volts.
$\mathbf{V}_{bc} = 30 + j110 = 114 \angle 74.75°$ volts.
$\mathbf{V}_{cd} = 20 + j0 = 20 \angle 0°$ volts.

(*b*) Draw a string vector diagram of $\mathbf{V}_{ab}$, $\mathbf{V}_{bc}$, and $\mathbf{V}_{cd}$, including both $\mathbf{V}$ and $\mathbf{I}$ on the diagram.

(*c*) Draw a polar vector diagram of $\mathbf{V}_{ab}$, $\mathbf{V}_{bc}$, $\mathbf{V}_{cd}$, $\mathbf{V}$, and $\mathbf{I}$.

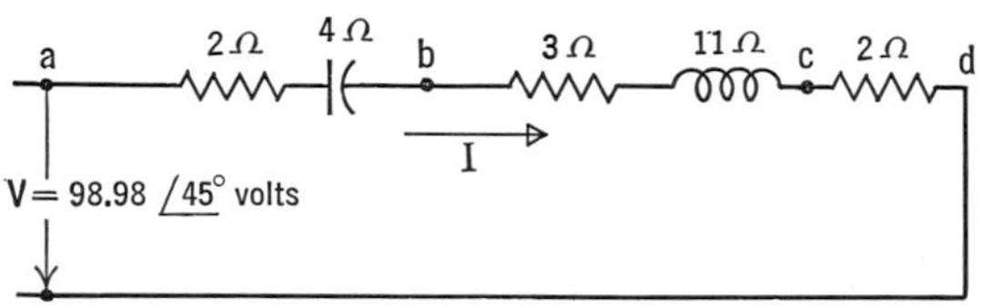

FIG 5. See Problems 1 and 2.

Problem 2. Calculate the total power dissipated in Fig. 5 from (I^2R), from (VI cos θ), and from $(vi + v'i')$. *Ans.:* $P = 700$ watts.

Series Resonance. A series circuit containing R, L, and C is in resonance when the resultant reactance is zero. Since the drop across the inductance leads the current by 90° whereas that across the condenser lags the current by 90°, the two drops are opposite. If they are made equal as in Fig. 6, the reactive voltage drops neutralize and the impressed voltage is equal only to the resistance drop. This condition is called series resonance. Inspection of the vector diagram of Fig. 6 shows that the applied voltage is in phase with the current. The power factor is unity, and the circuit is in resonance. Thus for series resonance

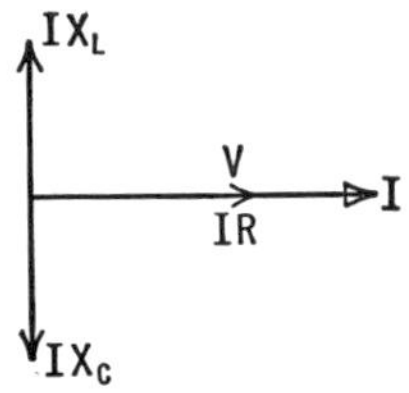

FIG. 6. Vector diagram of series circuit in resonance.

$$IX_L = IX_C \quad \text{or} \quad X_L = X_C \tag{9}$$

Since $2\pi fL = 1/2\pi fC$ at the point of series resonance, the series resonant frequency is

$$f_m = \frac{1}{2\pi\sqrt{LC}} \tag{10}$$

where f_m is in cycles per second when L is expressed in henrys and C in farads. It is apparent that series resonance can be produced in a series circuit by varying either L, C, or f. The current is always given by

$$I = \frac{V}{Z} = \frac{V}{\sqrt{R^2 + (X_L - X_C)^2}} = \frac{V}{\sqrt{R^2 + \left(2\pi fL - \dfrac{1}{2\pi fC}\right)^2}} \tag{11}$$

For any value of current the drop across the resistance is

$$V_R = IR = \frac{VR}{\sqrt{R^2 + \left(2\pi fL - \dfrac{1}{2\pi fC}\right)^2}} \tag{12}$$

Similarly, the drops across the inductance and capacitance are respectively

$$V_L = IX_L = \frac{VX_L}{\sqrt{R^2 + \left(2\pi fL - \dfrac{1}{2\pi fC}\right)^2}} \tag{13}$$

and

$$V_C = IX_C = \frac{VX_C}{\sqrt{R^2 + \left(2\pi fL - \dfrac{1}{2\pi fC}\right)^2}} \tag{14}$$

The general characteristics of a circuit in resonance are the same regardless of which parameter is varied to produce resonance. For instance, in all cases the power factor at resonance is 1. The power is simply the impressed voltage times the current. The current is V/R, the maximum possible value for the resistance which is in the circuit. The general shape of the current curve before, at, and after resonance is shown in Fig. 7. Resonance occurs at the point C. Limited as it is only by the resistance of the circuit, the current at the resonant point C will be large if the resistance is small. When the resultant reactance is large as it is at point A there will be only a small current flowing. Hence

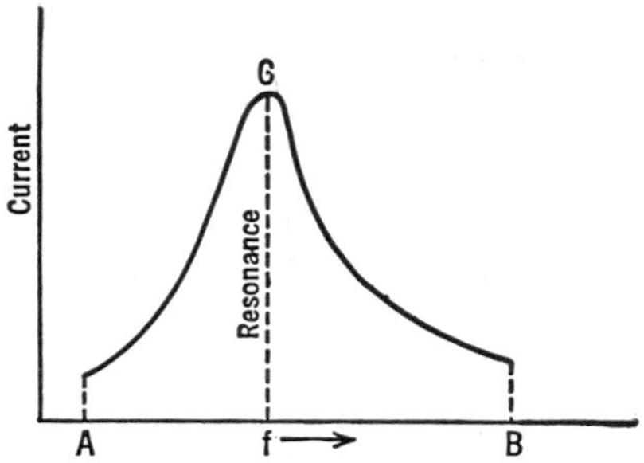

FIG. 7. Variation of current with frequency in the range series resonance.

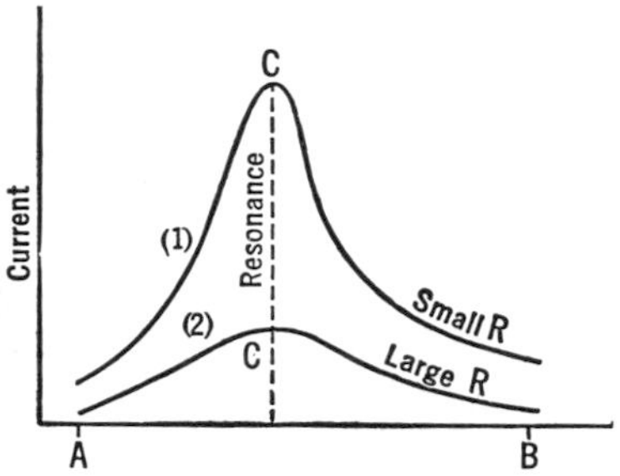

FIG. 8. Effect of resistance on current variation in the range of series resonance.

there is a rapid rise in current from point A to point C. Conversely, when the resistance is large, the amount of the change in current from point A to C will be small. In the former case the current peak will be sharper than in the latter, as illustrated in Fig. 8. Hence the small resistance is said to give sharp tuning and the large resistance broad tuning. More accurately, the ratio of L to R governs the sharpness of tuning. This is shown later. The preceding statements are true for all methods of securing resonance. The various ways of securing resonance will now be considered in somewhat more detail.

Varying Inductance. When L is varied to produce resonance, a series of curves shown in Fig. 9 is obtained. Equations (11), (12), (13), and (14) are the equations of the current and potential drop curves shown. It will be noted that V_C becomes a maximum at resonance whereas *the maximum value of V_L occurs after resonance.* This result is expected. Since $V_C = IX_C$ and X_C is constant, the maximum drop across the condenser will occur when the current is a maximum. In the case of $V_L = IX_L$, both I and X_L are increasing before resonance and the product must be increasing. At resonance, I is not changing but X_L is increasing, and hence the drop is increasing. The drop continues to increase until the reduction in the current offsets the increase in X_L. This point can be determined from $dV_L/dX_L = 0$. Differentiating equation (13) and setting the result equal to zero yield

$$\frac{dV_L}{dX_L} = \frac{[R^2+(X_L-X_C)^2]^{\frac{1}{2}}V - VX_L\frac{1}{2}[R^2+(X_L-X_C)^2]^{-\frac{1}{2}}2(X_L-X_C)}{R^2+(X_L-X_C)^2} = 0$$

and
$$X_L = \frac{R^2 + X_C^2}{X_C}$$

or
$$L = \frac{1}{2\pi f}\left(\frac{R^2 + X_C^2}{X_C}\right) = C(R^2 + X_C^2) \quad (15)$$

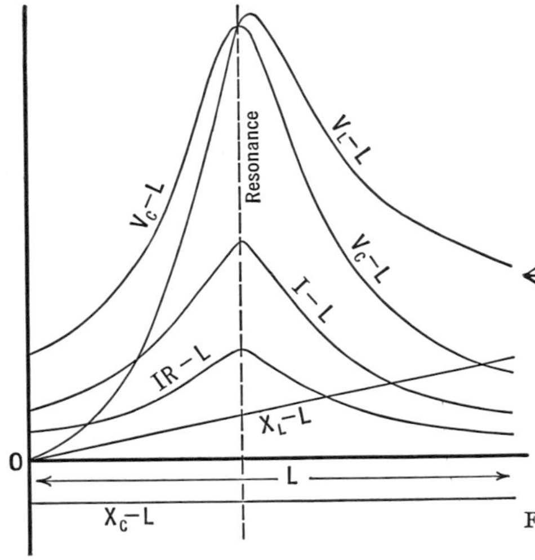

FIG. 9. Series reasonance by varying L.

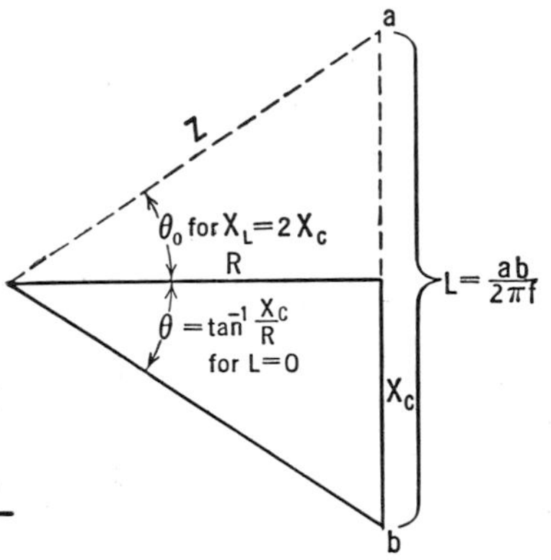

FIG. 10. Impedance diagram showing the power factor angle θ as L is varied in an RLC series circuit.

Example 2. As L is varied to produce resonance in a series circuit containing $R = 100$ ohms, $X_C = 200$ ohms, and $f = 60$ cycles, find the voltage drop across L at resonance and also when the drop across L is a maximum if 1000 volts are impressed.

For resonance $X_L = X_C = 200$. $\mathbf{Z} = 100 + j200 - j200 = 100 + j0$ ohms.

$$I = \frac{1000}{100} = 10 \text{ amperes.}$$

V_L (at resonance) $= IX_L = 10 \times 200 = 2000$ volts.

For maximum V_L $\quad 2\pi fL = \dfrac{R^2 + X_C^2}{X_C} = \dfrac{100^2 + 200^2}{200} = 250$ ohms.

$$I \text{ (for maximum } V_L) = \frac{1000}{\sqrt{100^2 + (250 - 200)^2}} = 8.94 \text{ amperes.}$$

Maximum $V_L = 8.94 \times 250 = 2235$ volts.

The variation in phase angle between **V** and **I** as L is varied is easily obtained from the impedance diagram in Fig. 10. The angle can be seen to vary from $\tan^{-1}\dfrac{X_C}{R}$

(a negative angle) when L is zero to $+90°$ when L becomes ∞. Hence the power factor varies from $\frac{R}{\sqrt{R^2 + X_C^2}}$ (when L is 0) to 0 (when L becomes infinite).

Problem 3. (*a*) Find the value of inductive reactance and the value of inductance which will make the power factor of the above series circuit equal to 0.866, current leading.

Hint: Problems of this type are most easily solved when it is recognized that $\frac{\sum X}{\sum R} = \pm \tan \theta$. *Ans.:* $X_L = 142.3$ ohms, $L = 0.377$ henry.

(*b*) Find the value of inductive reactance which will make the p.f. equal to 0.866, current lagging.

Ans.: $X_L = 257.7$ ohms.

Varying Capacitance. When C is varied to produce resonance, curves as shown in Fig. 11 are obtained. As before, the equations of these curves are equations (11), (12), (13), and (14). Here the drop across the inductance is a maximum when the current is a maximum, since X_L is constant. The maximum drop across the condenser occurs before resonance. At resonance, X_C is decreasing whereas the current is not changing (slope being zero). The drop IX_C must, therefore, be decreasing. Consequently, the drop must have been a maximum before resonance. At resonance the drops across the inductance and the capacitance are equal and opposite. The conditions for maximum V_C may be determined analytically by setting the first derivative of equation (14) with respect to C or X_C equal to zero, similarly to the procedure illustrated when L was varied. This derivation is left to the student.

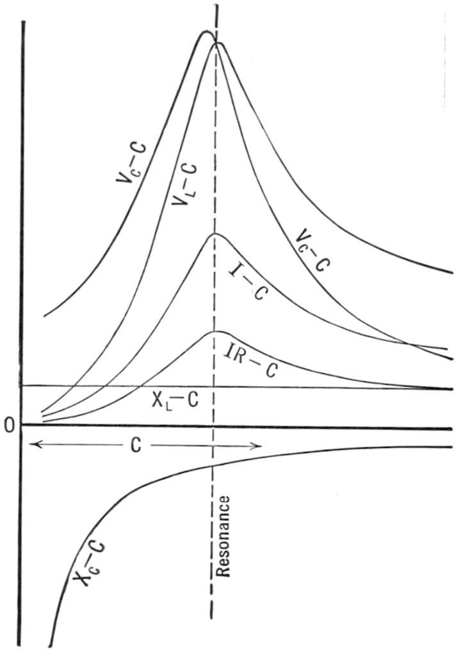

FIG. 11. Series resonance by varying capacitance.

The impressed voltage equals the IR drop, the power factor is unity, and the current is a maximum at resonance. For zero capacitance the capacity reactance is infinite and the current is therefore zero. For infinite capacitance the capacity reactance is zero and the current is $\frac{V}{\sqrt{R^2 + X_L{}^2}}$. The phase angle between the current and the applied voltage varies between the limits indicated in Fig. 12. The power factor varies from $\frac{R}{\sqrt{R^2 + X_L{}^2}}$, when C is infinite, to zero when C is zero.

Resonance is usually obtained by varying capacitance since it is only necessary to make alternate plates of a condenser movable to secure variable capacitance. This is easily and simply accomplished, and the variation of capacitance can be made extremely smooth and gradual.

Problem 4. When varying C to produce resonance in a circuit containing 100 ohms resistance and 200 ohms inductive reactance at 60 cycles, find the maximum drop across the capacitance if the impressed voltage on the circuit is 100 volts.

Ans.: 223.5 volts.

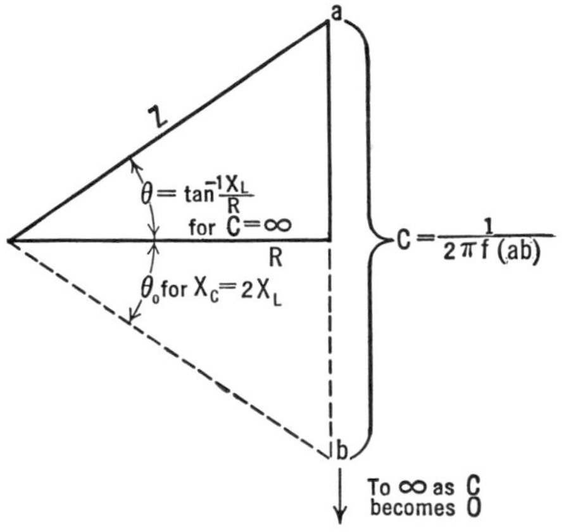

FIG. 12. Impedance diagram indicating range of power factor angle θ as C is varied in an *RLC* series circuit.

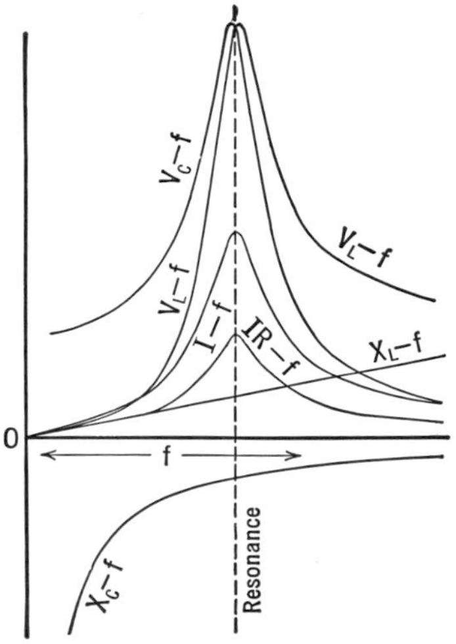

FIG. 13. Series resonance by varying frequency.

Varying Frequency. When frequency is varied to produce resonance, the curves shown in Fig. 13 are obtained. Here neither the inductance nor the capacitance has the maximum drop across it at resonance. Inspection of Figs. 9, 11, and 13 will show that this method of securing resonance partakes of both the methods previously discussed. The student can explain these curves by considering the principles previously presented. The current is zero for both zero frequency and infinite frequency. The phase angle between current and voltage varies between $-90°$ to $+90°$, as may be seen by studying the impedance triangles portrayed in Fig. 14. It will be observed that, for all methods of producing resonance, the current is a maximum and dependent only upon the impressed voltage and the resistance of the circuit, that the power factor is 1, and that the power is a maximum and equal to the volt-amperes at the point of resonance.

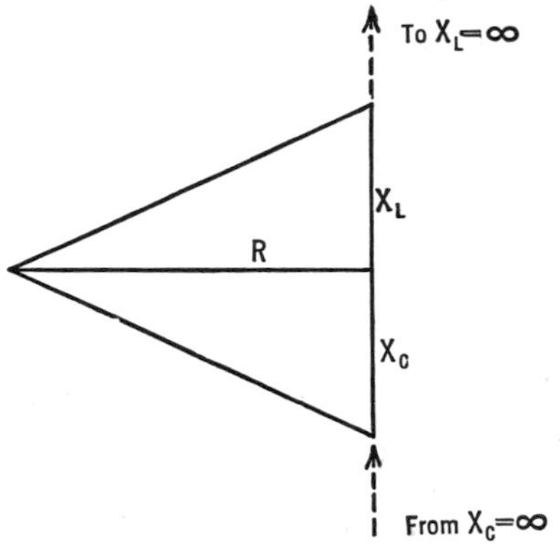

FIG. 14. Impedance triangle indicating variation of phase angle from $-90°$ to $+90°$ as frequency is varied in an *RLC* series circuit.

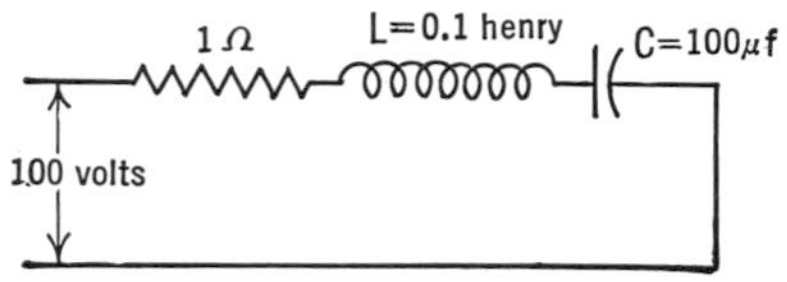

FIG. 15. Circuit for example 3.

Example 3. For the circuit arrangement and constants shown in Fig. 15 calculate the frequency, power, power factor, and voltage drop across each part of the circuit at resonance.

$$f_m = \frac{1}{2\pi}\sqrt{\frac{1}{LC}} = \frac{1}{2\pi}\sqrt{\frac{1}{0.1 \times 0.000100}} = 50.4 \text{ cycles}$$

Check:

$$\begin{cases} X_L = 2\pi\, 50.4 \times 0.1 = 31.6 \text{ ohms} \\ X_C = \dfrac{1}{2\pi\, 50.4 \times 0.0001} = 31.6 \text{ ohms} \end{cases}$$

$$I = \frac{100}{\sqrt{1^2 + (31.6 - 31.6)^2}} = 100 \text{ amperes}$$

$$P = 100 \times 100 = 10{,}000 \text{ watts}$$

$$\text{P.f.} = \frac{\text{watts}}{\text{va}} = \frac{10{,}000}{100 \times 100} = 1$$

$$V_R = 100 \times 1 = 100 \text{ volts}$$

$$V_L = 100 \times 31.6 = 3160 \text{ volts}$$

$$V_C = 100 \times 31.6 = 3160 \text{ volts}$$

Problem 5. (*a*) What is the resonant frequency of a series circuit consisting of 2 ohms resistance, 150 microhenrys, and 200 μμf capacitance? (*b*) What is the resonant frequency if $R = 3$ ohms, $L = 300$ microhenrys, and $C = 100$ μμf? (*c*) What is the impedance of each of the combinations at 1000 kilocycles?

Ans.: (*a*) 920 kilocycles, (*b*) 920 kilocycles, (*c*) 147 ohms and 294 ohms.

The Series *RLC* Circuit as a Selector. Even though the *RLC* circuit passes all waves of finite frequency to some extent, it has been shown to have the lowest impedance for the resonant frequency. As Fig. 7 shows, the *RLC* circuit passes frequencies near the resonant frequency more readily than other frequencies. The circuit thus has selective properties. The band of frequencies which is passed quite readily is called

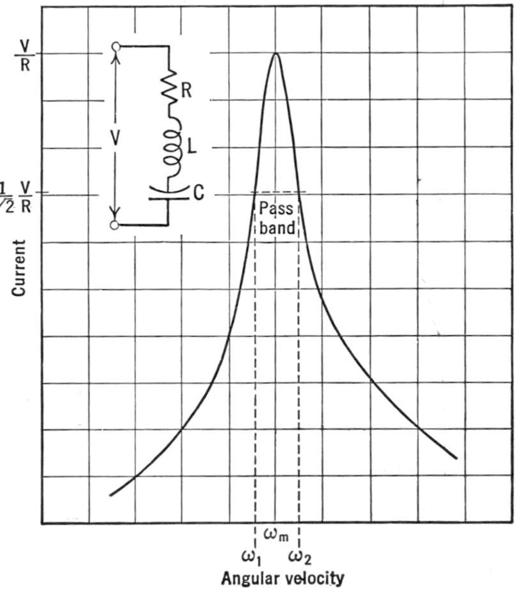

FIG. 16. The *RLC* series branch, as a band selector, graphed for $R = 10$ ohms, $L = 0.01$ henry, and $C = 4.0$ μf.

the pass band. The pass band is sometimes arbitrarily considered to be the range of frequency over which the current is equal to or greater than $V/\sqrt{2}R$, as indicated in Fig. 16. Within this range, the power (I^2R) is equal to or greater than $V^2/2R$. This range will now be determined. From equation (11)

$$I = \frac{V}{\sqrt{R^2 + (\omega L - 1/\omega C)^2}} \tag{16}$$

The maximum current (V/R) and the maximum power V^2/R occur at the resonant frequency or when

$$\omega_m = \frac{1}{\sqrt{LC}} \tag{17}$$

where ω_m is 2π times the resonant frequency f_m. Let ω_x be the angular velocities at which

$$I = \frac{V}{\sqrt{2}R}$$

Since at these points the power is exactly one-half the maximum power which occurs at resonance, they are called the half-power points. Substituting the above current in equation (16) gives

$$\frac{V}{\sqrt{2}R} = \frac{V}{\sqrt{R^2 + (\omega_x L - 1/\omega_x C)^2}} \tag{18}$$

From which $R = \pm(\omega_x L - 1/\omega_x C)$.

Note that at these points the resistance of the circuit equals the resultant reactance, the phase angle between the applied voltage and current is 45°, and the power factor 0.707.

When solved for ω_x the above equation yields

$$\omega_x = \pm \frac{R}{2L} \pm \sqrt{\frac{R^2}{4L^2} + \frac{1}{LC}} \tag{19}$$

In a selective RLC branch, $(R/2L)^2$ is usually much smaller than $1/LC$. Hence, neglecting this term, equation (19) becomes

$$\omega_x \approx \pm R/2L \pm \sqrt{1/LC} \tag{20}$$

But $\sqrt{1/LC}$ is the angular velocity ω_m corresponding to the resonant frequency. Therefore

$$\omega_x \approx \pm \frac{R}{2L} \pm \omega_m \tag{21}$$

and, if only positive values of ω_m are considered,

$$\omega_x = \omega_m \pm \frac{R}{2L} \tag{22}$$

Let

$$\omega_1 = \omega_m - \frac{R}{2L} \tag{23}$$

and

$$\omega_2 = \omega_m + \frac{R}{2L} \tag{24}$$

The width of the pass band as shown on Fig. 16 is

$$\Delta\omega = \omega_2 - \omega_1 = \frac{R}{L} \text{ radians per second} \tag{25}$$

The frequency range for the pass band, as here defined, is $\Delta f = f_2 - f_1 = R/2\pi L$. The per unit band width is defined as $\Delta f/f_m$. If we arbitrarily select a band width other than that shown in Fig. 16, as we shall have occasion to do later, we make appropriate changes in our definition of Δf.

Example 4. Let it be required to find the decibel (db) current response at the half-power points of Fig. 16 (relative to the response at ω_m) if by definition we take

$$\text{db} = 20 \log \frac{I}{\dfrac{V}{R}}$$

where I is the current response at any point on the graph shown in the figure.

Since $I = V/\sqrt{2}R$ at the points in question,

$$\text{db} = 20 \log \frac{\dfrac{V}{\sqrt{2}R}}{\dfrac{V}{R}} = -20 \log 1.414 = -3$$

The above arithmetic shows why the half-power points are sometimes referred to in the literature as the -3 db points.

The Q of a Series Circuit. The degree of selectivity of a circuit, that is, the narrowness of the band width shown in Fig. 16, is usually expressed in terms of the symbol Q. Although several different forms of the definition of Q appear in the literature, they are all intended to convey the same meaning. We shall employ the following definition since it ties in closely with experimental procedures:

$$Q = \frac{\omega_m}{\omega_2 - \omega_1} = \frac{\omega_m}{\Delta\omega} = \frac{f_m}{\Delta f} \tag{26}$$

See Fig. 16 for the meanings of ω_1, ω_2, and ω_m.

In the case of the series RLC circuit

$$Q_s = \frac{\omega_m}{\Delta\omega} = \frac{\omega_m}{\dfrac{R_s}{L}} = \frac{\omega_m L}{R_s} = \frac{1}{\omega_m C R_s} = \frac{1}{\dfrac{1}{\sqrt{LC}} C R_s} = \frac{1}{R_s}\sqrt{\frac{L}{C}} \tag{27}$$

where R_s is the total equivalent series resistance of the circuit. Since the equivalent series circuit resistance of the capacitor is usually negligibly small in comparison with the series circuit resistance of the coil, it is customary to speak of the Q of the coil alone, the assumption being that the coil will be resonated at some specified frequency with a capacitor of suitable size.

From equation (27) $Q_s = \dfrac{\omega_m L}{R_s}$. If the numerator and denominator of the right member of this equation are each multiplied by the current at resonance, I_{res}

$$Q_s = \frac{\omega_m L I_{\text{res}}}{R_s I_{\text{res}}} = \frac{\text{voltage drop across } L}{\text{applied voltage}} \tag{28}$$

Thus Q_s is a multiple of the applied circuit voltage that will exist across each of the reactive elements at resonance.

Example 5. The per unit band width between the half-power (or -3 db) points in Fig. 16 is to be 0.02. Find the Q of the coil required.

$$\text{Per unit band width} = \frac{\Delta\omega}{\omega_m} = \frac{1}{Q}$$

$$Q = \frac{1}{0.02} = 50$$

If the coil to be employed has an inductance of 10 millihenrys and the resonant frequency is 20 kc, find the values of R_s and C.

$$R_s = \frac{\omega_m L}{Q_s} = \frac{2\pi \times 20{,}000 \times 0.01}{50} = 8\pi = 25.1 \text{ ohms}$$

$$C = \frac{1}{\omega_m{}^2 L} = \frac{1}{4\pi^2 (20{,}000)^2 \times 0.01} = 0.00633 \times 10^{-6} \text{ farad}$$

The use of Q (or the reciprocal of Q) in circuit analysis will take on more importance and significance in radio-frequency circuits where Q_s is essentially constant than in low-frequency circuits where R_s is essentially constant. [It should be noted that R_s has been tacitly assumed constant in equation (27) as well as in Fig. 16.] In analyzing tuned radio-frequency circuits near resonant frequency, $\omega_m = 1/\sqrt{LC}$, we obtain greater accuracy by writing

$$Z = R_s + j\left(\omega L - \frac{1}{\omega C}\right)$$

as

$$Z = \omega_m L\left[\frac{R_s}{\omega_m L} + j\left(\frac{\omega}{\omega_m} - \frac{\omega_m}{\omega}\right)\right]$$

or

$$Z = \omega_m L\left(\frac{1}{Q} + jF\right) = \sqrt{\frac{L}{C}}\left(\frac{1}{Q} + jF\right) \tag{28}$$

since Q is considerably more constant over a reasonable frequency range centered on ω_m than is R_s. It is plain that $F = (\omega/\omega_m - \omega_m/\omega)$.

If L, C, and Q in equation (28) are essentially constant, then $F = (\omega/\omega_m - \omega_m/\omega)$ is the only variable involved, and it should be plain that the current response versus ω will take the same shape as that shown in Fig. 16 since in one case the response is based upon

$$I = \frac{V}{\sqrt{R_s^2 + \left(\omega L - \frac{1}{\omega C}\right)^2}}$$

and the other upon

$$I = \frac{V}{\sqrt{\frac{L}{CQ^2} + \left(\omega L - \frac{1}{\omega C}\right)^2}}$$

which is obtained by substitution for R_s its value obtained from equation (27). In the low-frequency case we assume that R_s is constant, which is essentially true, and in the high-frequency case we assume that L/CQ^2 is essentially constant. Cases arise where neither assumption is justified, but cases of this kind are reserved for more advanced courses.

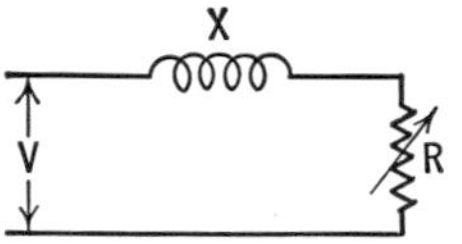

FIG. 17. Series circuit with variable R.

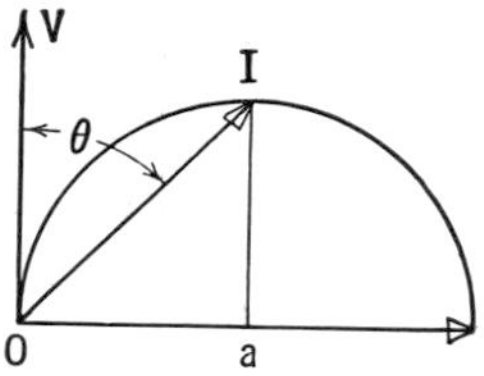

FIG. 18. Circle diagram of Fig. 17 for constant V and X but with variable R.

Circle Diagram of Series Circuit. Circle diagrams are often employed as an aid in analyzing the operating characteristics of circuits which under some conditions are used in representing transmission lines and some types of a-c machinery. The basis of representing a series circuit by means of a circle diagram will be derived with reference to Fig. 17.

The resistance R of the circuit in Fig. 17 will be considered a variable, whereas the applied voltage and reactance will be assumed constant. The power-factor angle is designated by θ. If R is zero, I is obviously equal to V/X, and this value of I will lag $\mathbf{V}$ by 90° if X is inductive. (See Fig. 18.) As R is increased from its zero value, the magnitude of $\mathbf{I}$ becomes less than V/X and θ becomes less than 90° and finally, when R equals ∞, I equals zero and θ equals zero. The fact that the locus of the vector $\mathbf{I}$ traces out a semicircle, as indicated in Fig. 18, may be seen from the following derivation.

In general,

$$I = \frac{V}{Z} \tag{29}$$

and

$$\sin\theta = \frac{X}{Z} \tag{30}$$

or

$$Z = \frac{X}{\sin\theta} \tag{31}$$

Substituting (31) in (29),

$$I = \frac{V}{X}\sin\theta \tag{32}$$

For constant V and X, equation (32) is the polar equation of a circle of diameter V/X. Figure 18 shows a plot of equation (32) with respect to V as a reference and for positive angles θ, representing inductive loads, measured clockwise. These conventions are employed because they are the ones most commonly used for such circle diagrams in a-c machinery. Since Ia in Fig. 18 is $OI \cos\theta$, it is apparent that Ia is proportional to the power consumed by the circuit. If the diagram is drawn to a certain current scale as, for example, I amperes per inch, the watt scale will be VI watts per inch.

A simple transmission line circuit in which the capacitance and leakance are assumed negligible may be represented by Fig. 19, where

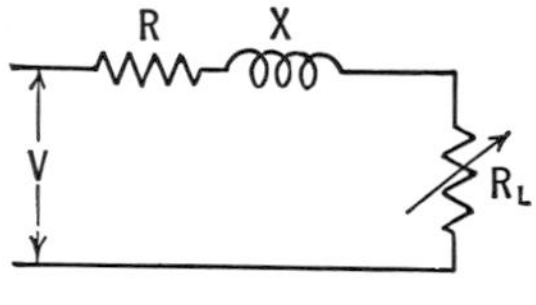

FIG. 19. Series circuit, R and X assumed constant, R_L variable.

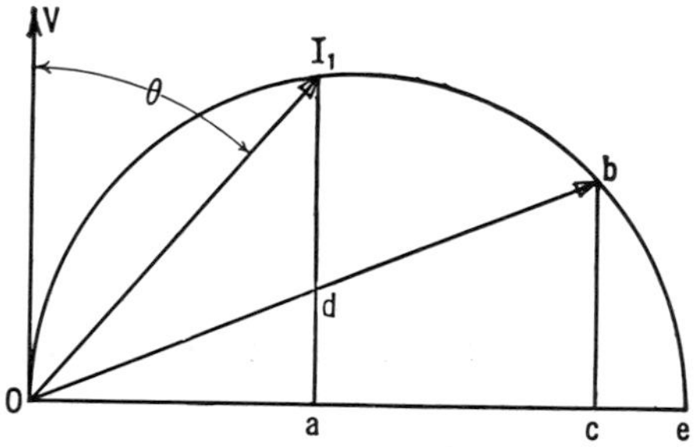

FIG. 20. Circle diagram of Fig. 19 for constant V, R, and X and variable R_L.

R and X are, respectively, the series resistance and reactance of the line and R_L is the load resistance. If R is constant and R_L is varied, the current follows the equation $I = (V/X) \sin\theta$ as in the previous case. The distance Ia in Fig. 18 again represents the total power consumed by the circuit, but the total power dissipated is consumed in both R and R_L. The power dissipated by each resistance can easily be represented on the diagram.

If the resistance R_L is assumed to be zero, all power must be dissipated in the resistance R. For this condition the power is represented by bc in Fig. 20 and Ob represents the corresponding current. For some finite value of R_L other than zero, the current is OI_1 and the total power consumed is proportional to I_1a. Of this total, da is the amount consumed in R and I_1d is dissipated by R_L. To prove that da represents the power dissipated in R, it is only required to show that da and bc are proportional to the respective squares of the currents OI_1 and Ob for the two conditions.

From similar triangles
$$\frac{da}{bc} = \frac{Oa}{Oc}$$

Since
$$Oa = OI_1 \cos aOI_1$$
$$= OI_1 \frac{OI_1}{Oe} = \frac{(OI_1)^2}{Oe}$$

and
$$Oc = Ob \cos cOb = Ob \frac{Ob}{Oe} = \frac{(Ob)^2}{Oe}$$

$$\frac{da}{bc} = \frac{\dfrac{(OI_1)^2}{Oe}}{\dfrac{(Ob)^2}{Oe}} = \frac{(OI_1)^2}{(Ob)^2}$$

Therefore, for any current such as OI_1, I_1d represents the power consumed in R_L, da shows the watts lost in R, and the total power input to the circuit is given by I_1a. If I^2R_L is considered as the output of the circuit (the power transmitted by the line), the efficiency must be

$$\text{Efficiency} = \frac{\text{output}}{\text{input}} = \frac{I_1d}{I_1a}$$

The power factor at the input end is $\cos\theta$. It is also I_1a/OI_1.

The maximum power that can be transmitted by a circuit like Fig. 19 under conditions of constant R and X occurs when the extremity of OI_1 in Fig. 20 coincides with the point of tangency to the circle of a line drawn parallel to Ob. It is a matter of simple geometry to show that V times I_1d under these conditions yields the result for maximum power as given by equation (59) if $X_r = 0$ [which requires that k in equation (79) be zero]. Since I_1d may be employed as a quantitative measure of the power delivered to the load resistance R_L, it is plain from Fig. 20 that this load power varies from zero (when $R_L = 0$) to a maximum and back to zero again (when $R_L = \infty$).

The details of circle diagram constructions which apply to circuits of the kind shown in Fig. 19 may be readily comprehended from a numerical problem like the following.

Problem 6. Refer to Fig. 19. R and X are constant at the values $R = 2$ ohms and $X = 3.464$ ohms. V is constant at 346.4 volts.

(*a*) Lay off $OV = V$ graphically in a vertical position to any convenient voltage scale as, for example, 100 volts per inch.

(*b*) Lay off Oe (of Fig. 20) equal to V/X in a horizontal position to a scale of not more than 20 amperes per inch. (A scale of 10 amperes per inch will give more accurate results.)

(*c*) Lay off Ob (of Fig. 20) equal to I when $R_L = 0$.

Ans.: $I = 346.4/4 = 86.6$ amperes, 60° behind **V**.

(*d*) Draw a tangent to the semicircle which is parallel to Ob and construct OI_1 from O to this point of tangency. What is the magnitude of the current and what is the p.f. at this point of operation? *Ans.:* $I = 50$ amperes, p.f. $= 0.86$.

(*e*) What is the maximum power that can be delivered to R_L?

Ans.: $P_{\text{max}} = V \times I_1 d_{\text{max}} = 10{,}000$ watts.

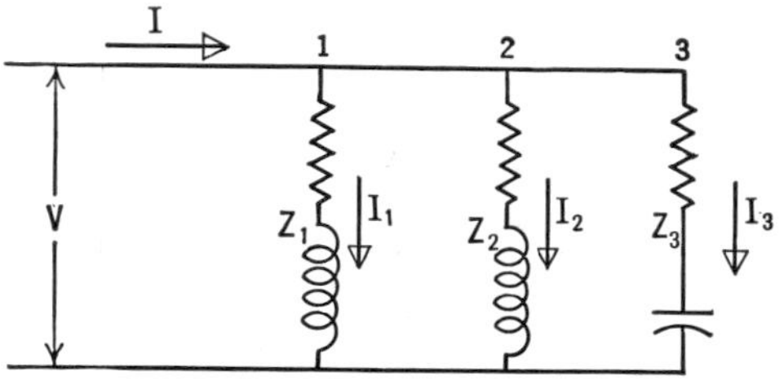

FIG. 21. Impedances in parallel.

Parallel Branches. When impedances are connected in parallel, as in Fig. 21, the same voltage V is impressed across each impedance. The current in each impedance is therefore

$$\mathbf{I}_1 = \frac{\mathbf{V}}{\mathbf{Z}_1}, \quad \mathbf{I}_2 = \frac{\mathbf{V}}{\mathbf{Z}_2}, \quad \text{and} \quad \mathbf{I}_3 = \frac{\mathbf{V}}{\mathbf{Z}_3}$$

From Kirchhoff's current law,

$$\begin{aligned} \mathbf{I} &= \mathbf{I}_1 + \mathbf{I}_2 + \mathbf{I}_3 \\ &= \frac{\mathbf{V}}{\mathbf{Z}_1} + \frac{\mathbf{V}}{\mathbf{Z}_2} + \frac{\mathbf{V}}{\mathbf{Z}_3} = \mathbf{V}\left(\frac{1}{\mathbf{Z}_1} + \frac{1}{\mathbf{Z}_2} + \frac{1}{\mathbf{Z}_3}\right) \\ &= \mathbf{V}(\mathbf{Y}_1 + \mathbf{Y}_2 + \mathbf{Y}_3) = \mathbf{V}\mathbf{Y}_0 \end{aligned} \tag{33}$$

where the symbol **Y** represents the reciprocal of impedance and is called admittance. Equation (33) shows that the resultant current flowing through several impedances in parallel is the product of the voltage and the sum of the reciprocals of the several branch impedances. In other words, the voltage is multiplied by the sum of the admittances of the several branches. Equation (33) shows that *admittances* are *added* for *parallel* branches. For branches in series it will be remembered that *impedances* are added. Since both admittance and impedance are complex quantities, all additions involving either of them *must* be made in *complex* form. Arithmetic addition should not be attempted. In only one case is arithmetic addition correct, and in this case the addition in complex form will give the same result. If equation (33) is solved for impedance $\mathbf{Z}_0$ by obtaining the ratio of $\mathbf{V}$ to $\mathbf{I}$, we obtain

$$\mathbf{Z}_0 = \frac{\mathbf{V}}{\mathbf{I}} = \frac{1}{\mathbf{Y}_1 + \mathbf{Y}_2 + \mathbf{Y}_3} = \frac{1}{\mathbf{Y}_0} \tag{34}$$

Equation (34) shows that the resultant impedance of several parallel branches is the reciprocal of the resultant admittance. Since the unit of impedance is the ohm and admittance is the reciprocal of impedance, the unit of admittance is the reciprocal ohm or mho (ohm spelled backwards).

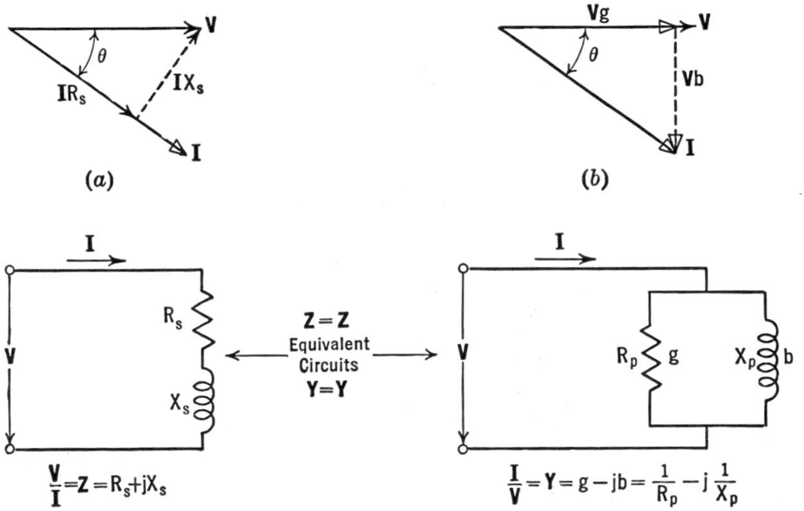

FIG. 22. The parallel equivalent of a series impedance, $R_s + jX_s$.

The Parallel Equivalent of a Series Impedance. Cases arise where it becomes desirable to change a series branch impedance as shown in Fig. 22*a* to its parallel equivalent (shown in Fig. 22*b*). For equivalence, $\mathbf{Y}$ of Fig. 22*a* must equal $\mathbf{Y}$ of Fig. 22*b*. Therefore

$$\mathbf{Y} = \frac{1}{R_s + jX_s} = \frac{1}{R_p} + \frac{1}{jX_p}$$

or, upon rationalizing,

$$\frac{R_s}{R_s^2 + X_s^2} - j\frac{X_s}{R_s^2 + X_s^2} = \frac{1}{R_p} - j\frac{1}{X_p} \tag{35}$$

$R_s/(R_s^2 + X_s^2)$ is called the conductance of the series impedance Z_s and is denoted by the symbol g. $X_s/(R_s^2 + X_s^2)$ is called the susceptance of the series impedance Z_s and is denoted by the symbol b. Employing the symbols g and b, we have

$$\mathbf{Y} = g - jb = \frac{1}{R_p} - j\frac{1}{X_p} \tag{36}$$

The physical significance of g and b may be interpreted as follows. If equation (36) is multiplied by **V** to obtain the current **I**, we have:

$$\mathbf{I} = \mathbf{V}g - j\mathbf{V}b = \frac{\mathbf{V}}{R_p} - j\frac{\mathbf{V}}{X_p}$$

It will be seen that $\mathbf{V}g$ shown on the vector diagram, Fig. 22*b*, is the component of current in phase with the voltage and is the current $\mathbf{V}/R_p$ in the resistive branch of the parallel equivalent of $\mathbf{Z}_s$. Also $\mathbf{V}b$ shown on the vector diagram is the component of current in quadrature with the voltage and is the component $\mathbf{V}/X_p$ in the inductive branch of the parallel equivalent of $\mathbf{Z}_s$. Hence the conductance $1/R_p$ of the resistive branch of the equivalent parallel circuit is the conductance g of the admittance $\mathbf{Y} = g - jb = 1/\mathbf{Z}_s$, and the susceptance $1/X_p$ of the inductive branch is the susceptance b of the admittance $\mathbf{Y} = 1/\mathbf{Z}_s$. It is important to observe that conductance g in the circuits of Fig. 22 is the reciprocal of R_p but *not* of R_s. Similarly susceptance is the reciprocal of X_p but *not* of X_s.

Since g and b are components of admittance and either g, b, or Y multiplied by voltage yields a current, they are all expressed in the same units, namely, mhos.

If the admittances in equation (33) are expressed in terms of their conductances and susceptances, we have

$$\begin{aligned} \mathbf{I} &= \mathbf{V}(g_1 - jb_1 + g_2 - jb_2 + g_3 - jb_3) \\ &= \mathbf{V}[(g_1 + g_2 + g_3) - j(b_1 + b_2 + b_3)] = \mathbf{V}(g_0 - jb_0) \end{aligned} \tag{37}$$

Equation (37) shows that conductances may be added arithmetically to obtain the resultant conductance while susceptance must be added algebraically to obtain the resultant susceptance. That algebraic addition of susceptances is required is evident from the expression $X/(R^2 + X^2)$ for susceptance when it is remembered that X may be positive or negative depending upon whether it is inductive or capacitive, respectively.

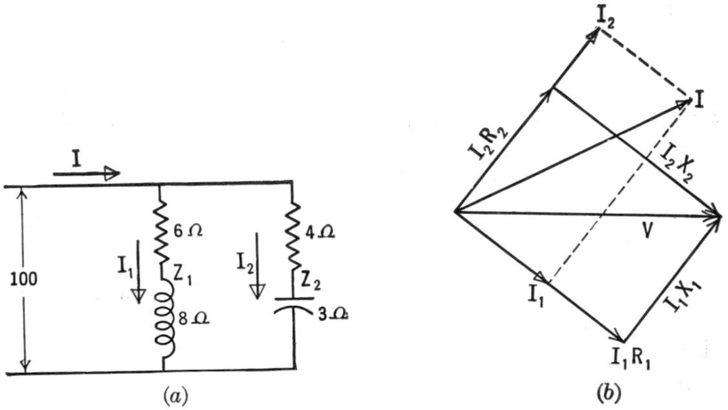

FIG. 23. (a) Circuit for example 6. (b) Phasor diagram of (a).

Example 6. For the circuit of Fig. 23*a* with the parameters shown, the following are desired: (*a*) conductance and susceptance of each branch; (*b*) the resultant conductance and susceptance; (*c*) the vector or phasor diagram.

$$\mathbf{I}_1 = \frac{100 + j0}{6 + j8} = 6 - j8 = 10\underline{/-53.2°} \text{ amperes}$$

$$\mathbf{I}_2 = \frac{100 + j0}{4 - j3} = 16 + j12 = 20\underline{/36.9°} \text{ amperes}$$

$$\mathbf{I} = \mathbf{I}_1 + \mathbf{I}_2 = 22 + j4 = 22.35\underline{/10.3°} \text{ amperes}$$

$$\mathbf{Y}_1 = \frac{1}{\mathbf{Z}_1} = \frac{1}{(6 + j8)} \frac{(6 - j8)}{(6 - j8)} = 0.06 - j0.08 \text{ mho}$$

from which

$$g_1 = 0.06 \text{ mho}, \quad b_1 = 0.08 \text{ mho}$$

or, as an alternative method,

$$g_1 = \frac{R_1}{Z_1^2} = \frac{6}{100}, \quad b_1 = \frac{X_1}{Z_1^2} = \frac{8}{100}$$

$$\mathbf{Y}_2 = \frac{1}{Z_2} = \frac{1}{(4 - j3)} \frac{4 + j3}{(4 + j3)} = 0.16 + j0.12 \text{ mho}$$

from which

$$g_2 = 0.16 \text{ mho}, \quad b_2 = -0.12 \text{ mho}$$

or, as an alternative method,

$$g_2 = \frac{R_2}{Z_2^2} = \frac{4}{25}, \quad b_2 = \frac{X_2}{Z_2^2} = \frac{-3}{25}$$

The vector or phasor diagram is shown in Fig. 23*b*.

Another way to obtain the resultant current is shown below:

$$g = g_1 + g_2 = 0.06 + 0.16 = 0.22 \text{ mho}$$
$$b = b_1 + b_2 = 0.08 - 0.12 = -0.04 \text{ mho}$$

$$\mathbf{Y} = g - jb = 0.22 - j(-0.04) = 0.22 + j0.04 \text{ mho}$$

$$\mathbf{I} = \mathbf{VY} = 100\ (0.22 + j0.04) = 22 + j4 = 22.35\underline{/10.3°} \text{ amperes}$$

Or admittances may be added as follows:

$$\mathbf{Y} = \mathbf{Y}_1 + \mathbf{Y}_2 = 0.06 - j0.08 + 0.16 + j0.12 = 0.22 + j0.04$$

and

$$I = \mathbf{VY} = 22 + j4 \text{ amperes}$$

The calculation of admittances from the reciprocals of impedances and their addition in complex form is generally the most direct procedure. Experience has shown that students make fewer errors in signs when following this procedure.

Instead of representing admittance in general as $g - jb$ and then using $g = R/Z^2$ and $b = X/Z^2$, many prefer to call it $g + jb$ and then to use $g = R/Z^2$ and b as $-X/Z^2$. Both give the same result for admittance. In either case, X is substituted as a positive value for inductance and negative for capacitance. In a dissipative circuit conductance is always positive. To *avoid confusion* in signs it is *best* to obtain admittance from $1/(R + jX)$ rather than from calculations of conductance and susceptance. Knowing how to calculate and use conductances and susceptances expedites the solution of some types of problems, although they may be solved by other means. The special case of two parallel impedances $\mathbf{Z}_1$ and $\mathbf{Z}_2$ occurs often in electrical engineering. For this case, $\mathbf{Y}_1 = 1/\mathbf{Z}_1$ and $\mathbf{Y}_2 = 1/\mathbf{Z}_2$. Hence

$$\mathbf{Y} = \frac{1}{\mathbf{Z}_1} + \frac{1}{\mathbf{Z}_2} \quad \text{and} \quad \mathbf{Z} = \frac{1}{\mathbf{Y}} = \frac{\mathbf{Z}_1\mathbf{Z}_2}{\mathbf{Z}_1 + \mathbf{Z}_2}$$

This expression, which is analogous to the much used expression for the resultant of two parallel resistances in direct currents, is very useful in alternating currents. When all reactances are zero, the expression reduces to the d-c case of $R_1R_2/(R_1 + R_2)$.

Problem 7. Three impedances $\mathbf{Z}_1$, $\mathbf{Z}_2$, and $\mathbf{Z}_3$ are connected in parallel across a 60-cycle voltage the magnitude of which is 40 volts.

$$\mathbf{Z}_1 = 10 + j0, \quad \mathbf{Z}_2 = 20 + j20, \quad \mathbf{Z}_3 = 30 - j40 \text{ ohms}$$

(*a*) Find g_1, b_1, g_2, b_2, g_3, and b_3.

(*b*) Find the resultant g and the resultant b of the three parallel branches.

Ans.: $g = 0.137$, $b = 0.009$ mho.

(*c*) What is the in-phase component of the resultant current; the quadrature component of the resultant current?

Ans.: $Vg = 5.48$ amperes, $Vb = 0.36$ amperes.

Resonance in Parallel Branches. Parallel branches containing inductance and capacitance are in resonance when the reactive current in the inductive branch is equal to the reactive current in the capacitive branch. The resultant reactive current for the circuit as a whole is therefore zero. For resonance

$$Vb_L = Vb_C$$

$$b_L = b_C \tag{38}$$

Hence the resultant current flowing is in phase with the applied voltage, and the power factor of the whole circuit is 1. This is sometimes called unity-power-factor resonance. Figure 24 shows a circuit and the corresponding vector diagram for this condition. From an inspection of the vector diagram it will be noted that the reactive components of current

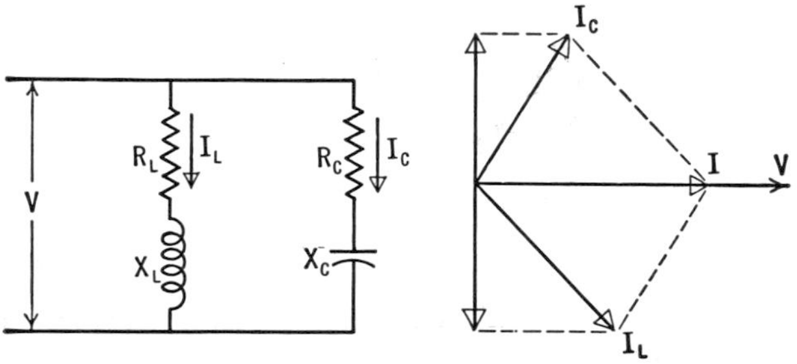

FIG. 24. Circuit and corresponding vector diagram for parallel resonance.

contribute nothing to the total current. Only the components of current in phase with the voltage exist in the resultant current. It might be inferred from this that the resultant current is a minimum at resonance. This is true if the *conductances* are *constant.* It is approximately true if the conductances are negligibly small, as they usually are in selective circuits as used in radio. An example will be considered later wherein minimum current does not occur at resonance.

The parameters possible of variation to make equation (38) true may be seen when the susceptances are replaced by their equivalent values, as shown in equation (39).

$$\frac{2\pi fL}{R_L{}^2 + (2\pi fL)^2} = \frac{\dfrac{1}{2\pi fC}}{R_C{}^2 + \left(\dfrac{1}{2\pi fC}\right)^2} \tag{39}$$

The quantities that may be varied are L, C, f, R_L, or R_C.

Resonance by Varying L. In the following discussion L will be varied by a means which will not change the resistance of the inductive circuit. Let OV, Fig. 25, be the voltage impressed on a circuit like the one shown in Fig. 24. A current, I_C, will then flow in the condenser branch whose parameters are held constant. When L is zero, the current through the inductive branch is V/R_L and it is in phase with the applied voltage. The applied voltage is equal to $I_L R_L$ under these conditions. When L is increased from zero, the current through the

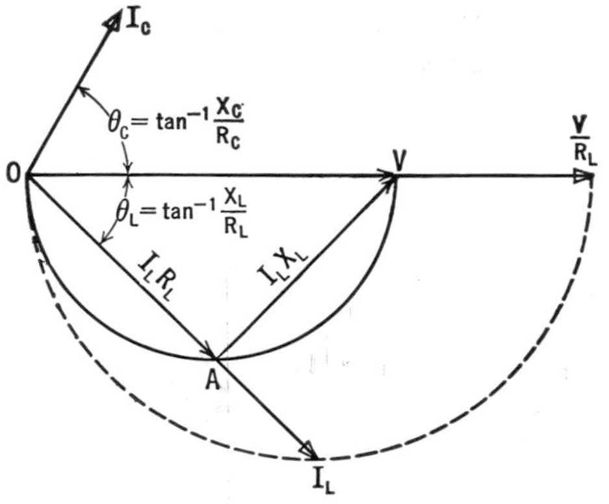

FIG. 25. Locus of I as L is varied in the circuit shown in Fig. 24.

inductive branch lags V by the $\tan^{-1}(X_L/R_L)$, as illustrated in Fig. 25 by OI_L. For any value of I_L, the $I_L R_L$ drop and the $I_L X_L$ drop must add at right angles to give the applied voltage. These component drops are OA and AV, respectively. Since they are always at right angles and their sum must be OV, the locus of the $I_L R_L$ drop must be a semicircle OAV. Since I_L is proportional to the $I_L R_L$ drop and in phase with it, the locus of I_L must also be a semicircle.

When the $I_L R_L$ drop coincides with the diameter of its circle, the current I_L must also coincide with the diameter of its own circle. The diameter of the latter must, therefore, be V/R_L. Hence the dotted circle drawn with V/R_L as a diameter must be the locus of I_L. Since the resultant current is $I_C + I_L$, this addition is performed by drawing the semicircle OI_LB with the left extremity of its diameter starting at I_C as shown in Fig. 26. For example, a particular sum of I_C and I_L is represented by OC. As L is varied, the locus of the resultant current is, therefore, the circle $I_C Cb$. Hence, as L is increased from 0 to ∞, the resultant current varies from Ob to Oe, which is one point of resonance; thence to Od, which is a second resonant point; and then to OI_C. Neither of the resonant points gives either a maximum or minimum current, but they do yield unity power factor. The minimum current is OI_m, the value where the resultant current is normal to the circle

I_CCb. For any particular problem the values of I_C, θ_C, and I_Cb, which is equal to V/R_L, can be calculated directly from the parameters. Any other values of current can then be calculated trigonometrically from the geometry of the figure. A few facts should be observed. First, if $V/2R_L$ (the radius of the circle I_CCb) is less than $I_C \sin \theta_C$, parallel resonance cannot be obtained regardless of the value of L. This is in contrast to the series circuit, where some value of L will yield resonance for any value of R or C. Second, if $V/2R_L = I_C \sin \theta_C$,

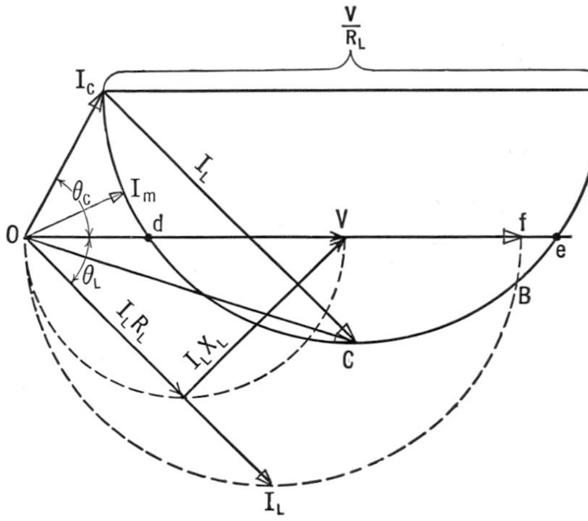

FIG. 26. Locus of OC, the resultant current to the circuit of Fig. 24 as L is varied.

there will be only one resonant point. Third, if $V/2R_L > I_C \sin \theta_C$, there will be two resonant points. Fourth, if the resistance of the inductance were zero, minimum current would occur at resonance. Note that for this condition the conductances would be constant for the two branches.

Resonance by Varying C. Through a similar procedure to that outlined above, the student can develop the graphical representation for the case where resonance is produced by varying C while R_L, L, R_C, and f are held constant. The graphical representation is shown in Fig. 27. The locus of the resultant current is the circle *adce*. Again it will be noted that resonance which occurs at d and e is not the condition for minimum current. Minimum current occurs at I_m, where the resultant current is normal to the circle *adce*. If R_C is zero, the radius of the circle *adce* becomes infinite, or, what is the same thing, the current I_C is in quadrature with the voltage V. Under this condition there is but one point of resonance and it corresponds to minimum current. The conductance of the capacitor circuit is zero, whereas that of the inductive branch is constant. This constant conductance makes the current at resonance a minimum, and hence the impedance a maximum. Since most selective circuits employ constant inductance and variable capacitance and the resistances of the capacitive branches are very small, maximum impedance or minimum current at resonance is practically realized in these circuits. Since at resonance the current is

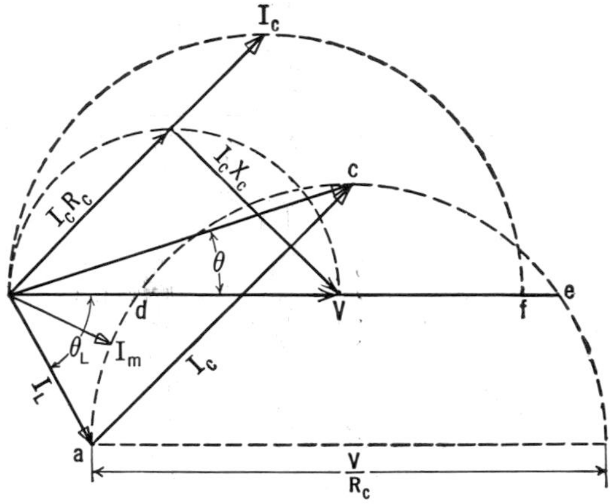

FIG. 27. Locus of resultant current to the circuit of Fig. 24 is the circle *adce* as C is varied.

simply the conductance times the voltage impressed, it is evident that the power factor is 1. An inspection of Fig. 27 will reveal the manner in which the phase angle θ between the resultant current and the applied voltage varies as the resultant current follows the circle *adce*. Between points d and e, leading power factor obtains.

Resonance by Varying Frequency. From equation (39) the frequency for parallel resonance is found to be

$$f_m = \frac{1}{2\pi\sqrt{LC}}\left[\frac{R_L^2C - L}{R_C^2C - L}\right]^{1/2} \tag{40}$$

When $R_L^2C > L$ and $R_C^2C < L$, the quantity $\left[\frac{R_L^2C - L}{R_C^2C - L}\right]^{1/2}$ is imaginary and therefore no real frequency will yield resonance. The same situation results if both inequality signs are reversed. If R_L and R_C are equal, equation (40) for resonance becomes

$$f_m = \frac{1}{2\pi\sqrt{LC}}$$

which is the same as that for series resonance. This equation is also correct when $R_L = R_C = 0$ and may therefore be used as a close approximation when R_L and R_C are very small. It should be apparent that there are values of R_L, C, R_C, and L in a parallel circuit for which parallel resonance is impossible, regardless of frequency. This is in contrast to the series circuit containing R, L, and C where there is

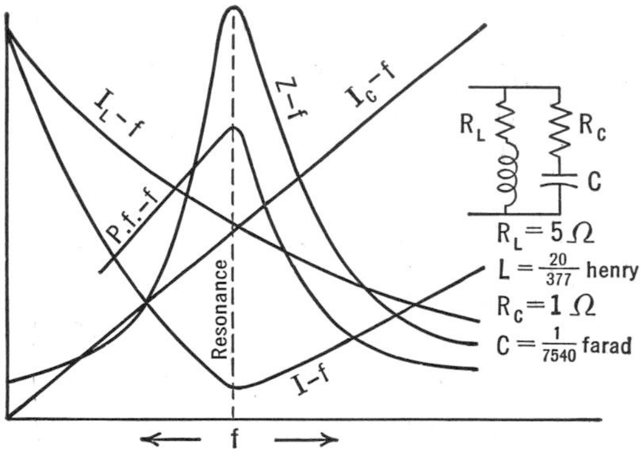

FIG. 28. Parallel resonance by varying frequency.

always some real resonant frequency for any values of the three parameters. The trends of various quantities as frequency is varied from a value too small to produce resonance to a value higher than that required for resonance are shown in Fig. 28 for a condition where resonance is obtainable.

Resonance by Varying R_L or R_C. When equation (40) is solved for R_L, the following equations result:

$$R_L = \sqrt{\frac{LC\omega^2\,(R_C{}^2C - L) + L}{C}} \tag{41}$$

$$R_L = \sqrt{LC\omega^2R_C{}^2 - L^2\omega^2 + \frac{L}{C}} \tag{42}$$

$$R_L = \sqrt{\frac{X_L}{X_C}\,R_C{}^2 - X_L{}^2 + \frac{L}{C}} \tag{43}$$

When the parameters are such as to make the expressions under the above radical positive, R_L takes on definite positive values. It is thus shown that within limits there are definite values of R_L which will bring the circuit to resonance at some particular values of frequency, L, C, and R_C. Also, for resonance,

$$R_C = \sqrt{\frac{R_L^2}{\omega^2 LC} - \frac{1}{\omega^2 C^2} + \frac{L}{C}} \tag{44}$$

Equation (44) shows that, for those values of parameters which make the quantity under the radical positive, resonance may be produced by choosing the proper value of R_C.

In contrast to the series circuit, where resistances have no part in determining the frequency of resonance, the resistances of a parallel circuit are of signal importance in determining the frequency of resonance, even to the extent of making resonance either possible or impossible to attain. Physically this can be understood when it is remembered that, with a certain quadrature component of current in the capacitive branch, some sufficiently large value of R_L will prevent a resultant current in the inductive branch from flowing, which is as much as the quadrature current in the capacitive circuit even when the inductance is zero. Under such conditions it is apparent that inserting inductance will do nothing but make the current in the inductive branch still smaller and hence contribute nothing toward making resonance possible. Such a case was discussed with reference to Fig. 26 when $I_C \sin \theta_C$ was greater than $V/2R_L$. Figure 26, which is simply a phasor diagram, shows that $I_L \sin \theta_L$ can never be made as large as $I_C \sin \theta_C$ if $V/2R_L$ is less than $I_C \sin \theta_C$. A similar situation obtains for the capacitive branch.

Problem 8. Draw the phasor diagram and show the locus of I_L as X_L is varied, when $R_C = 1$ ohm, $X_C = 10$ ohms, $R_L = 6$ ohms, and the impressed voltage 100 volts for a circuit as shown in Fig. 24. Repeat the problem when R_L is changed to 4 ohms. What is the largest possible quadrature component of current in the inductive branch as X_L is varied in each case? In which case can resonance be produced? Why?

Ans.: 8.33 amperes, 12.5 amperes, resonance for 4-ohm case only.

Duality. The principle of duality (pages 29–38) may be extended to series and parallel resonance as shown below:

Series Resonance	Parallel Resonance
a. Reactive components of voltage combine to equal zero.	*a.* Reactive components of current combine to equal zero.
b. Voltage source constant in maximum magnitude.	*b.* Current source constant in maximum magnitude.
c. Current maximum for constant resistance.	*c.* Voltage maximum for constant conductance.
d. Impedance at minimum value.	*d.* Admittance at minimum value.
e. Inductive and capacitive reactances equal in magnitude.	*e.* Inductive and capacitive susceptances equal in magnitude.

From the above tabulation it will be noted that the dual elements are

Series	Parallel
a. Reactive voltage	*a.* Reactive current
b. Voltage	*b.* Current
c. Current	*c.* Voltage
d. Impedance	*d.* Admittance
e. Resistance	*e.* Conductance
f. Reactance	*f.* Susceptance

Recognition of duality will often yield a deeper understanding of circuit behavior than would otherwise be the case. It may also help to reduce the time required for an understanding of the physical operation of circuits. If, for example, series resonance is thoroughly understood, it is a simple matter to extend this knowledge to parallel resonance by way of the duality principle.

A Simple Form of Wave Trap. Resonance phenomena as presented in the foregoing articles form the basis upon which many circuits used in both wire and wireless communication operate. They are especially adapted to selective circuits such as those for filters and oscillators. A parallel combination of capacitance and inductance, along with its incidental resistance, can be made into an effective band eliminator, suppressor, or wave trap. The impedance of such a circuit (from *a* to *b* in Fig. 29), where the resistance of the capacitance is negligibly small and R_L is very small compared to ωL, is most easily found by taking the reciprocal of the resultant admittance. Since the branches are tuned for parallel resonance, the resultant admittance is conductance only. Thus

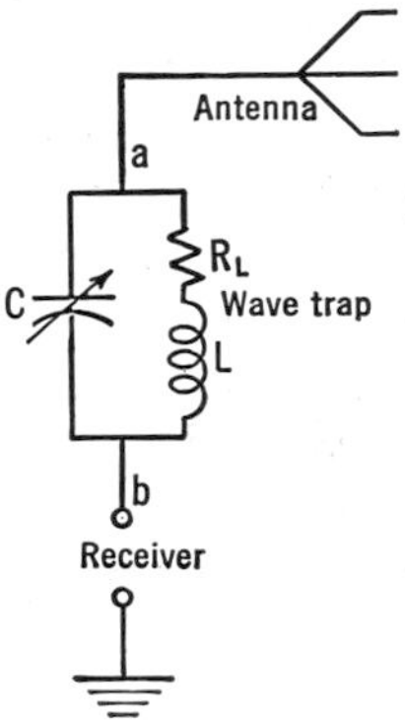

FIG. 29. Simple form of wave trap.

$$Y_m = \frac{R_L}{Z_L^2} \tag{45}$$

and

$$Z_m = \frac{1}{Y_m} = \frac{Z_L^2}{R_L} \tag{46}$$

Since $R_L^2 \ll \omega^2 L^2$,

$$Z_m = \frac{\omega^2 L^2}{R_L} \tag{47}$$

In a previous article it was shown that when $R_L = R_C = 0$ the resonant frequency is practically

$$f_m = \frac{1}{2\pi\sqrt{LC}} \quad \text{or} \quad \omega = \omega_m = 2\pi f_m = \frac{1}{\sqrt{LC}} \tag{48}$$

Substituting (48) in (47) gives the impedance at resonance

$$Z_m = \frac{L}{CR_L} \tag{49}$$

When used as a wave trap, the parallel combination of inductance and capacitance is placed in series with the antenna lead as shown in Fig. 29. At the resonant frequency the dynamic resistance of the wave trap is very nearly equal to L/CR_L [equation (49)]. Experience has shown that within the standard broadcast band the dynamic resistance at the frequency f_m can be made about 10 times the impedance at frequencies ± 20 kc from f_m. Thus the wave trap acts as a band suppressor or eliminator.

Problem 9. A typical coil used in the broadcast band for a wave trap like that in Fig. 29 has $L = 250 \times 10^{-6}$ henry and a ratio of reactance to resistance at 10^6 cycles of 170. Assuming the resistance of the condenser to be zero, calculate the following:

(*a*) C to produce resonance at 1000 kc from equation (39).
(*b*) C to produce resonance at 1000 kc from equation (48).
(*c*) Impedance of the wave trap from a to b when adjusted for parallel resonance at 1000 kc.
(*d*) Impedance of the wave trap to 990 kc when in resonance for 1000 kc.
(*e*) The ratio of the impedances for (*c*) to (*d*).

Ans.: 101.3 $\mu\mu$f, 101.3 $\mu\mu$f, 267,000 ohms, 75,100 ohms, 3.56.

A Singular Case of Parallel Resonance. For some values of the parameters R_L, R_C, L, and C connected as in Fig. 24, the circuit is in resonance for all frequencies. This may be shown as follows. From equation (39) the condition for parallel resonance is

$$\frac{\omega L}{R_L{}^2 + \omega^2 L^2} = \frac{\dfrac{1}{\omega C}}{R_C{}^2 + \dfrac{1}{\omega^2 C^2}}$$

$$= \frac{1}{\omega C} \frac{\omega^2 C^2}{R_C{}^2 \omega^2 C^2 + 1} = \frac{\omega C}{1 + \omega^2 C^2 R_C{}^2}$$

or

$$\frac{1}{\dfrac{R_L{}^2}{L} + \omega^2 L} = \frac{1}{\dfrac{1}{C} + \omega^2 C R_C{}^2} \tag{50}$$

To be independent of frequency, an inspection of equation (50) will show that the following two conditions must be imposed simultaneously.

Condition 1 $$\frac{R_L{}^2}{L} = \frac{1}{C} \quad \text{or} \quad R_L = \sqrt{\frac{L}{C}}$$

Condition 2 $$CR_C{}^2 = L \quad \text{or} \quad R_C = \sqrt{\frac{L}{C}}$$

Hence for resonance at all frequencies

$$R_L = R_C = \sqrt{\frac{L}{C}} \tag{51}$$

Since the circuit is in resonance (resultant susceptance = 0), its admittance must be the resultant conductance. Therefore

$$Y_m = g_m = \frac{R_L}{Z_L{}^2} + \frac{R_C}{Z_C{}^2} = \frac{\sqrt{\frac{L}{C}}}{\frac{L}{C} + \omega^2 L^2} + \frac{\sqrt{\frac{L}{C}}}{\frac{L}{C} + \frac{1}{\omega^2 C^2}} = \sqrt{\frac{C}{L}}$$

and

$$Z_m = \sqrt{\frac{L}{C}} \tag{52}$$

Equation (52) shows that the impedance of the circuit is also independent of frequency. The preceding demonstration has shown that, when $R_L = R_C = \sqrt{L/C}$, a circuit arrangement like that in Fig. 24 is in resonance for all frequencies and offers the same impedance $\sqrt{L/C}$ to all frequencies.

It has been shown that under certain conditions the network of Fig. 24 is equivalent to a single series resistance of value $\sqrt{L/C}$ at all frequencies. For general information it may be stated that it is possible to find networks that are equivalent to a given network at all frequencies although in contrast with the one discussed the impedances of the different networks, while being the same for any given frequency, will not remain constant at the various frequencies. A detailed study of such circuits is left for courses covering the theory of networks.

The Q of Parallel Circuits. In vacuum tube circuit analysis one frequently encounters the circuit arrangement which reduces essentially to that shown in Fig. 30*a*, namely, a coil and capacitor connected in parallel and energized with a current source. In the practical cases which will be encountered, the resistance of the coil, R_s, is very small compared to ωL; therefore

$$R_s{}^2 \ll \omega^2 L^2$$

Under these conditions the transformation of the series R_s and L to a parallel combination of g and b_L as suggested in Fig. 22 transforms Fig. 30*a* to that shown in Fig. 30*b*, where

$$g = \frac{1}{R_p} \approx \frac{R_s}{\omega^2 L^2}$$

$$b_L \approx \frac{1}{\omega L} \quad \text{and} \quad b_C = \omega C$$

It should be noted that b_L and b_C are magnitudes of the inductive and capacitive susceptances, respectively. Where purely reactive

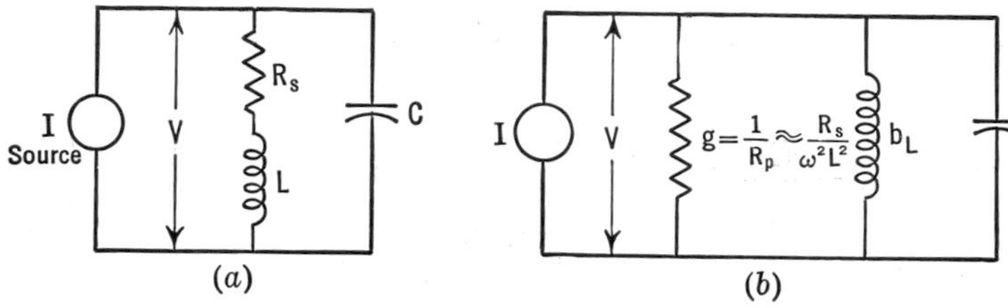

FIG. 30. Circuit shown in (*b*) is the equivalent of that shown in (*a*).

branches are placed in parallel, as in Fig. 30*b*, it is convenient to write $\mathbf{Y} = g + j(b_C - b_L)$ and thereby obtain an expression which is directly analogous to $\mathbf{Z} = R + j(X_L - X_C)$. In Fig. 30*b* we find

$$V = \frac{I}{\sqrt{g^2 + (b_C - b_L)^2}} = \frac{I}{\sqrt{g^2 + \left(\omega C - \dfrac{1}{\omega L}\right)^2}} \tag{53}$$

Comparing the above equation with equation (16), we observe a correspondence which allows us to interpret Fig. 16 as the voltage response versus ω. This response has a maximum value of I/g, and the analysis following equation (16) can with a few obvious changes in notation be employed to determine the band width of the selective circuit shown in Fig. 30.

Since g in equation (53) corresponds to R in equation (16), and C to L, and L to C, we may write for the parallel circuit

$$\Delta\omega = \omega_2 - \omega_1 = \frac{g}{C} \tag{54}$$

either by analogy with equation (25) or by direct computation.

Employing the same definition of Q as given on page 153 (namely, $Q = \omega_m/\Delta\omega$) and remembering that $\omega_m \approx 1/\sqrt{LC}$ when the resistances of the parallel branches are small relative to the reactances, we find that for the parallel circuit

$$Q_p = \frac{\omega_m}{\Delta\omega} = \frac{\omega_m C}{g} = \frac{1}{g\omega_m L} = \frac{1}{g}\sqrt{\frac{C}{L}} \tag{55}$$

In elementary analytical calculations, it is quite customary to treat both R_s of equation (27) and g of equation (55) as constants, that is, independent of frequency. Neither of these approximations, however, agrees with the physical facts as accurately as treating Q as constant over a reasonable frequency range centered on the resonant frequency, f_m, since R_s increases with increases in ω. Over certain ranges of the radio-frequency band, R_s varies almost linearly with respect to ω, and under these conditions we may set $R_s = k\omega$ with the following results:

$$Q_s = \frac{\omega L}{R_s} = \frac{\omega L}{k\omega} = \text{constant}$$

$$Q_p = \frac{1}{g\omega L} = \frac{\omega^2 L^2}{R_s \omega L} = \text{constant}$$

Example 7. In Fig. 30*a* it will be assumed that the coil has a series resistance, R_s, of 25.1 ohms and a self-inductance of 10 millihenrys. This coil is to be resonated at 20 kc with the capacitor C.

Let it be required to find the equivalent parallel circuit resistance, $1/g$, the tuning capacitance, the Q of the parallel circuit, and maximum voltage response per milliampere of current I.

$$g \approx \frac{R_s}{\omega_m{}^2 L^2} = \frac{25.1}{(2\pi \times 20{,}000)^2 \times (0.01)^2} = 1.59 \times 10^{-5} \text{ mho}$$

$$R_p = \frac{1}{g} \approx 62{,}900 \text{ ohms}$$

$$C \approx \frac{1}{L\omega_m{}^2} = \frac{1}{0.01\,(2\pi \times 20{,}000)^2} = 0.00633 \times 10^{-6} \text{ farad}$$

$$Q = \frac{\omega_m C}{g} = \frac{\omega_m \omega_m{}^2 L^2}{R_s \omega_m{}^2 L} = \frac{\omega_m L}{R_s} = 50$$

$$\text{Maximum voltage response} = \frac{0.001}{g} = 62.9 \text{ volts per milliampere}$$

A certain class of vacuum tube, namely, the pentode, can under certain operating conditions be made to function as current source supplying up to several milliamperes of alternating current simply by energizing one of its electrodes (the control grid) with a small a-c voltage. Since this small a-c voltage is often considerably less than 1 volt in magnitude, it is plain that large voltage amplifications may be obtained from the circuit configuration shown in Fig. 30*b* if the current source takes the form of a pentode. Moreover this circuit has a reasonable degree of selectivity since the band width between the $0.707V_{max}$ points on the response curve is

$$\Delta\omega = \frac{g}{C} = \frac{1.59 \times 10^{-5}}{0.00633 \times 10^{-6}} = 2510 \text{ radians per second}$$

On this basis of reckoning, the per unit band width is

$$\frac{\Delta\omega}{\omega_m} = \frac{2510}{2\pi \times 20{,}000} = 0.02$$

Series-Parallel Circuits. The series-parallel circuit illustrated in Fig. 31 is a combination of the series and parallel circuits which have been discussed previously. The principles previously considered apply to the analysis of series-parallel circuits. These are (1) impedances in series are added in complex form and (2) admittances of those branches which are in parallel must be added in complex form. To illustrate, consider Fig. 31. The admittances of impedances Z_4 and Z_5 are added in complex form, and the reciprocal of the resultant admittance is then the equivalent impedance of section B. An alternative method of finding the impedance of section B, as was previously shown, is to use $\mathbf{Z}_B = \mathbf{Z}_4\mathbf{Z}_5/(\mathbf{Z}_4 + \mathbf{Z}_5)$. Through a similar procedure the impedance of section A is determined. The impedances of section A, section B, and Z_1 are in series and are, therefore, added in complex form. This procedure yields the equivalent or resultant impedance $\mathbf{Z}_e$ of the series-parallel circuit. The current $\mathbf{I}$ may then be found from $\mathbf{V}/\mathbf{Z}_e$.

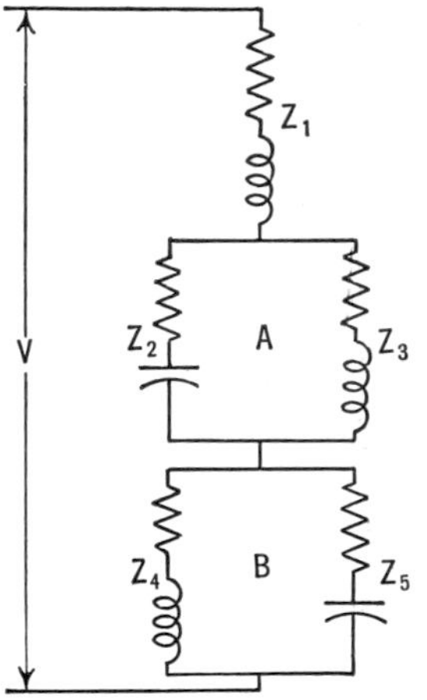

FIG. 31. Impedances in series-parallel.

Determination of Branch Currents and Voltages. After the resultant current is determined, the process is reversed to determine branch voltages and currents. The general procedure is to subtract the voltage drop calculated for the known current and the impedance through which it flows from the applied voltage to obtain the voltage drop across the remainder of the circuit, or to calculate the drops across various sections from the resultant current and the equivalent impedance of the branch through which the current flows. For example, in Fig. 31, the drop across section A is the product of equivalent impedance $\mathbf{Z}_A$ of that section and the current $\mathbf{I}$. The current through each of the parallel impedances is then determined by dividing this drop by the impedance of the particular branch or, if the admittances have been determined, by multiplying the voltage drop across the branch by the particular branch admittance. A similar procedure can be followed for section B, and so on.

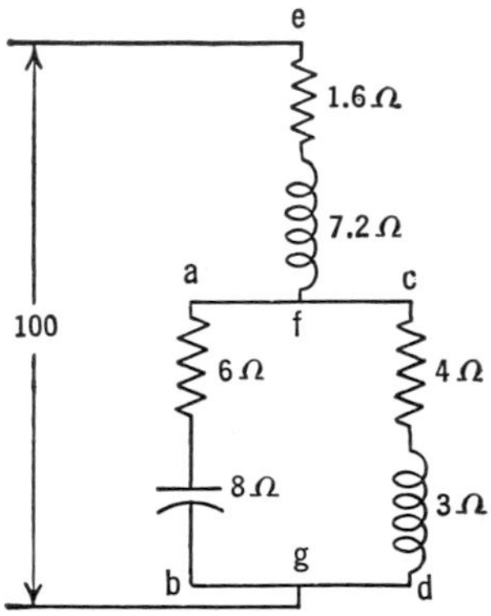

FIG. 32. Circuit for example 8.

Example 8. Calculate current, power, and power factor for each impedance shown in Fig. 32, and the total current and power and the power factor of the whole combination.

$$\mathbf{Y}_{ab} = \frac{1}{6 - j8} = 0.06 + j0.08 \text{ mho}$$

$$\mathbf{Y}_{cd} = \frac{1}{4 + j3} = 0.16 - j0.12 \text{ mho}$$

$$\mathbf{Y}_{fg} = \mathbf{Y}_{ab} + \mathbf{Y}_{cd} = 0.22 - j0.04 \text{ mho}$$

$$\mathbf{Z}_{fg} = \frac{1}{\mathbf{Y}_{fg}} = \frac{1}{(0.22 - j0.04)} \frac{(0.22 + j0.04)}{(0.22 + j0.04)} = 4.4 + j0.8 \text{ ohms}$$

An alternative method is

$$\mathbf{Z}_{fg} = \frac{\mathbf{Z}_{ab}\mathbf{Z}_{cd}}{\mathbf{Z}_{ab} + \mathbf{Z}_{cd}} = \frac{(6 - j8)\ (4 + j3)}{6 - j8 + 4 + j3} = 4.4 + j0.8 \text{ ohms}$$

$$\mathbf{Z}_{eg} = \mathbf{Z}_{ef} + \mathbf{Z}_{fg} = 1.6 + j7.2 + 4.4 + j0.8 = 6 + j8 \text{ ohms}$$

$$\mathbf{I} = \frac{100\,\underline{/0^\circ}}{6 + j8} = 6 - j8 = 10\,\underline{/-53.2^\circ} \text{ amperes}$$

$$P = vi + v'i' = 6 \times 100 + 0 \times 8 = 600 \text{ watts}$$

$$\text{P.f.} = \frac{600}{100 \times 10} = 0.6 \quad \text{or} \quad \frac{R}{Z} = \frac{6}{10} = 0.6 \text{ lag}$$

$$\mathbf{V}_{ef} = \mathbf{I}_{ef}\mathbf{Z}_{ef} = (6 - j8)(1.6 + j7.2) = 67.2 + j30.4$$
$$= 73.8\,/24.4^\circ \text{ volts}$$

$$\mathbf{V}_{fg} = \mathbf{V} - \mathbf{I}_{ef}\mathbf{Z}_{ef} = 100 - 67.2 - j30.4 = 32.8 - j30.4$$
$$= 44.7\,/-42.8^\circ \text{ volts}$$

Or, more directly,

$$\mathbf{V}_{fg} = \mathbf{I}\mathbf{Z}_{fg} = (6 - j8)(4.4 + j0.8) = 32.8 - j30.4$$
$$= 44.7\,/-42.8^\circ \text{ volts}$$

$$\mathbf{I}_{ab} = \mathbf{V}_{fg}\mathbf{Y}_{ab} = (32.8 - j30.4)(0.06 + j0.08)$$
$$= 4.4 + j0.8 = 4.48\,/10.3^\circ \text{ amperes}$$

$$\mathbf{I}_{cd} = \mathbf{V}_{fg}\mathbf{Y}_{cd} = (32.8 - j30.4)(0.16 - j0.12)$$
$$= 1.6 - j8.8 = 8.95\,/-79.7^\circ \text{ amperes}$$

or

$$\mathbf{I}_{cd} = \mathbf{I} - \mathbf{I}_{ab} = 6 - j8 - 4.4 - j0.8 = 1.6 - j8.8$$
$$= 8.95\,/-79.7^\circ \text{ amperes}$$

The powers in the various branches may now be determined in terms of principles previously considered.

$$P_{ab} = vi + v'i' = (32.8)(4.4) + (-30.4)(0.8)$$
$$= 144.32 - 24.32 = 120 \text{ watts}$$

$$P_{cd} = (32.8)(1.6) + (-30.4)(-8.8)$$
$$= 52.48 + 267.52 = 320 \text{ watts}$$

$$P_{ef} = (67.2)(6) + (30.4)(-8) = 403.2 - 243.2 = 160 \text{ watts}$$

or

$$P_{ef} = I^2r = (6^2 + 8^2)(1.6) = 160 \text{ watts}$$

$$P_{eg} = 100 \times 6 = 600 \text{ watts}$$

Check:

$$P = P_{ab} + P_{cd} + P_{ef} = 120 + 320 + 160 = 600 \text{ watts}$$

$$Pf_{ab} = \frac{R_{ab}}{Z_{ab}} = \frac{6}{\sqrt{6^2 + 8^2}} = 0.6 \text{ lead}$$

$$Pf_{cd} = \frac{R_{cd}}{Z_{cd}} = \frac{4}{\sqrt{4^2 + 3^2}} = 0.8 \text{ lag}$$

Problem 10. Study through the details of the above example and draw a vector diagram of **V**, **I**, $\mathbf{V}_{ef}$, $\mathbf{I}_{ab}$, $\mathbf{I}_{cd}$, and $\mathbf{V}_{fg}$. Employ a voltage scale of 25 volts per inch and a current scale of 2 amperes per inch.

Series-Parallel Tuning. It has been shown that for certain conditions parallel resonance yields maximum impedance and that series resonance gives minimum impedance. These facts suggest that a combination of these two phenomena may be used to exaggerate the effect of some certain frequency and minimize the effect of another. An arrangement that does this is shown in Fig. 33. This procedure is known as series-parallel tuning. To illustrate, assume that two waves, one of 10,000 cycles and the other of 20,000 cycles, are impressed at *ab* and that it is desired to detect the 10,000-cycle wave at *D*. Obviously as much 10,000-cycle current through *D* as can be obtained is desired, and as little as possible of the 20,000-cycle wave is to be tolerated. Hence the parallel branches of capacitance and inductance are adjusted for parallel resonance at 20,000 cycles. Then the 20,000-cycle wave encounters a high impedance, and little current due to it will flow through *D*. For the 10,000-cycle wave a little thought will show that the parallel circuit acts as an inductance. If a capacitance is placed in series with the parallel circuit *de* and its reactance for the 10,000-cycle frequency is made equal to the equivalent inductive reactance of the parallel circuit *de* for this same frequency, the circuit from *a* to *b* will be in series resonance for the 10,000-cycle wave. The current through *D* for the 10,000-cycle wave, therefore, will be large, whereas parallel resonance from *d* to *e* for the 20,000-cycle frequency will allow only a small 20,000-cycle current to flow through *D*.

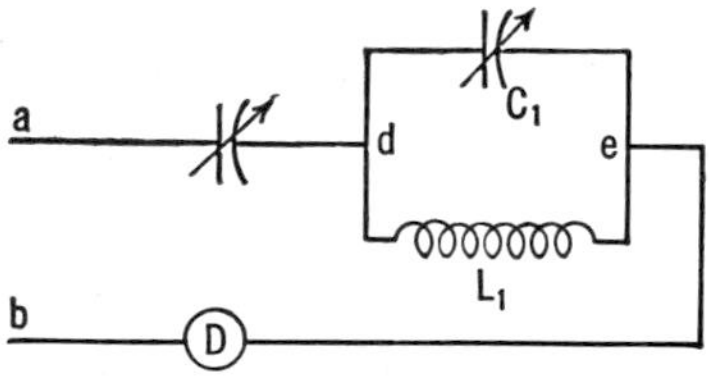

FIG. 33. Series-parallel tuning circuit.

Example 9. Assume L_1 to have 0.005 henry inductance and 50 ohms resistance. Neglect resistance of the condensers. Parallel resonance for 20,000 cycles obtains when

$$b_L = b_C$$

$$\frac{\omega 0.005}{50^2 + \omega^2(0.005)^2} = \omega C_1$$

where

$$\omega = 2\pi\, 20{,}000 = 12.57 \times 10^4 \text{ radians per second}$$

$$C_1 = \frac{0.005}{50^2 + 0.005^2\omega^2} = 1.257 \times 10^{-8} \text{ farad}$$

$$\mathbf{Y}_{de} = g = \frac{50}{50^2 + 0.005^2\omega^2} = \frac{50}{397{,}300} \text{ mho}$$

$$\mathbf{Z}_{de} = \frac{397{,}300}{50} = 7946 \text{ ohms}$$

For 10,000 cycles,

$$\mathbf{Y}_{C1} = j2\pi\, 10{,}000 \times 1.257\; 10^{-8} = j79 \times 10^{-5} \text{ mho}$$

$$\mathbf{Y}_{L1} = \frac{1}{50 + j0.005 \times 2\pi\, 10{,}000} = 49.3 \times 10^{-5} - j310 \times 10^{-5} \text{ mho}$$

$$\mathbf{Y}_{de} = \mathbf{Y}_{C1} + \mathbf{Y}_{L1} = 49.3 \times 10^{-5} - j231 \times 10^{-5} \text{ mho}$$

$$\mathbf{Z}_{de} = \frac{10^5}{49.2 - j231} = 88.1 + j413 \text{ ohms}$$

Since 413 ohms is the equivalent reactance of the divided circuit, a capacitive reactance of 413 ohms is required to produce series resonance. Then $\mathbf{Z}_{ab} = 88.1$ ohms for 10,000 cycles.

For 20,000 cycles,

$$\mathbf{Z}_{ad} = -\frac{j413}{2} = -j206.5 \text{ ohms}$$

$$\mathbf{Z}_{ab} = 7946 - j206.5 \quad \text{or} \quad 7946 \text{ ohms approximately}$$

$$\frac{Z_{ab20,000}}{Z_{ab10,000}} = \frac{7946}{88.1} = 90.2$$

Hence for equal impressed voltages across *ab*, the value of the 20,000-cycle current will be about $\frac{1}{90}$ of the value of the 10,000-cycle current.

The student should devise the explanation to show that if the 10,000-cycle wave is to be suppressed and the 20,000-cycle wave detected, an inductance would have to be substituted for the capacitance between *a* and *d*.

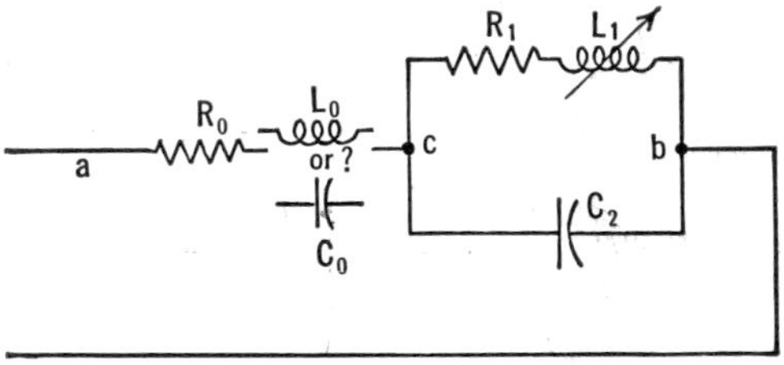

FIG. 34. See Problem 11.

Problem 11. The circuit *ab* of Fig. 34 is to pass a 45,000-cycle current with minimum impedance and is to block a 15,000-cycle current as effectively as possible. $R_0 = 20$ ohms, $R_1 = 40$ ohms, and $C_2 = 0.05$ μf are fixed. R_2, the resistance of the C_2 branch, is assumed to be negligibly small. L_1 is capable of being varied over the required range, it being assumed that the resistance of branch 1 is 40 ohms when L_1 is set at the desired value. Either a fixed C_0 *or* a fixed L_0 (of negligibly small resistance presumably) is to be placed in series with R_0 to accomplish the above-stated tuning effect.

(*a*) Solve for L_1, which will put the parallel circuit *bc* into parallel resonance at 15,000 cycles.

(*b*) Calculate the equivalent impedance from *b* to *c* at 45,000 cycles with L_1 set at its 15,000-cycle resonant value. Is *bc* predominantly capacitive or predominantly inductive at 45,000 cycles?

(*c*) What type of reactance (inductive or capacitive) must be placed in series with R_0 to put the branch *ab* into series resonance? Calculate the value of L_0 or C_0 which is required to put the branch *ab* into series resonance at 45,000 cycles.

(*d*) Assuming that the branch *ab* has been put into series resonance at 45,000 cycles, what is the actual impedance from *a* to *b* at 45,000 cycles? at 15,000 cycles?

Outline the above procedure for the reverse tuning effect, that is, for circuit *ab* to pass 15,000 cycles and block 45,000 cycles.

Ans.: (*a*) $L_1 = 2.17$ or 0.0835 millihenry. Use 2.17 for lower conductance.
(*b*) $\mathbf{Z}_{bc} = 0.69 - j79.9$ ohms, predominantly capacitive.
(*c*) $L = 0.283$ millihenry.
(*d*) $Z_{ab45,000} = 20.69$ ohms. $Z_{ab15,000} = 1103$ ohms.

Complex Frequency. As applied to sinusoidal wave forms of current or voltage, $i = I_m \sin(\omega t + \theta)$ or $v = V_m \sin(\omega t + \theta)$, we might define complex angular frequency as

$$j\omega = \frac{di/dt}{i} = \frac{dv/dt}{v} = \frac{\omega \cos(\omega t + \theta)}{\sin(\omega t + \theta)} \tag{56}$$

all of which has the requisite dimension, namely a number per second. In this connection, we recognize j as an operator which advances the real quantity $[\sin(\omega t + \theta)]$ through 90° to yield $\cos(\omega t + \theta)$. That is

$$\omega[j \sin(\omega t + \theta)] = \omega \cos(\omega t + \theta)$$

An extension of the above definition to complex exponential currents and voltages provides us with the general concept of *complex frequency.* A complex exponential may be represented in any one of several different ways; for example:

$$\mathbf{i} = I\epsilon^{(st+j\theta)} = \mathbf{I}\epsilon^{st} = \mathbf{I}\epsilon^{\alpha t}(\cos \omega t + j \sin \omega t) \tag{57}$$

where $\mathbf{I} = I\epsilon^{j\theta}$ and $\mathbf{s} = \alpha + j\omega$. Depending upon the manner in which it is used, I may be expressed either as the maximum or rms value of the sinusoidal component of the complex exponential.

It will be observed that the complex exponential is capable of representing any of the four wave forms shown in Fig. 35 with either the real part, $\mathcal{R}$, or imaginary part, $\mathcal{I}$, of $\mathbf{i}$. In this connection

$$\mathcal{R}(\mathbf{i}) = I\epsilon^{\alpha t} \cos(\omega t + \theta) \tag{58}$$

and

$$\mathcal{I}(\mathbf{i}) = I\epsilon^{\alpha t} \sin(\omega t + \theta) \tag{59}$$

In later courses, analyses will often be carried through in terms of complex exponentials. Then either the real or imaginary portion of the final result will be used. The interesting aspect of this approach is that the analysis, in terms of complex exponentials, is usually simpler to write than is the analysis of either the real or imaginary component alone. Consider, for example, the *LRC* series branch shown in Fig. 19, page 74. If the steady-state branch current, i, is to be represented as a complex exponential it will be expressed as: $\mathbf{i} = \mathbf{I}\epsilon^{st}$. Since in linear circuits, current is directly proportional to voltage the voltage drop

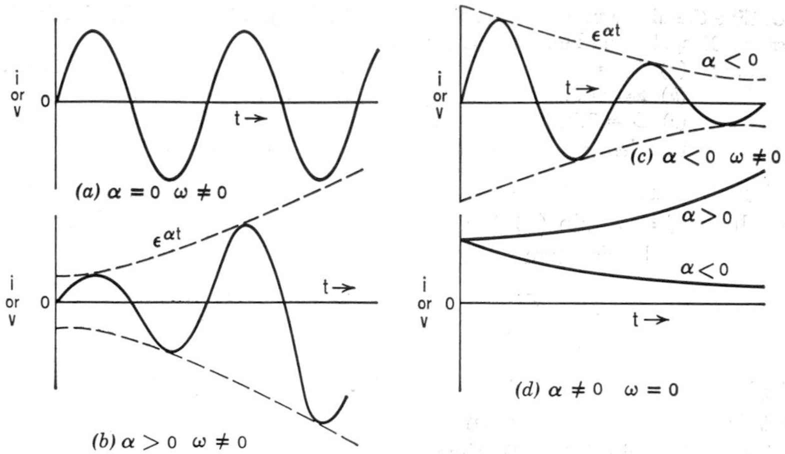

FIG. 35. Wave forms which can be represented by complex exponentials.

across the branch will be $\mathbf{V}\epsilon^{st}$ as is evident from a detailed study of the voltage equation

$$L\frac{d\mathbf{i}}{dt} + R\mathbf{i} + \frac{\int \mathbf{i}\,dt}{C} = \mathbf{V}\epsilon^{st} \tag{60}$$

Substitution of $\mathbf{i} = \mathbf{I}\epsilon^{st}$ into the left-hand side of this equation will show that

$$\left(L\mathbf{s} + R + \frac{1}{C\mathbf{s}}\right)\mathbf{I} = \mathbf{V} \tag{61}$$

The impedance of the LRC series circuit ($\mathbf{V}/\mathbf{I}$) in terms of the complex frequency $\mathbf{s}$ is usually written as $\mathbf{Z}(\mathbf{s})$, meaning $\mathbf{Z}$ expressed as a function of $\mathbf{s}$. Thus

$$\mathbf{Z}(\mathbf{s}) = \frac{\mathbf{V}}{\mathbf{I}} = \left(L\mathbf{s} + R + \frac{1}{C\mathbf{s}}\right) \tag{62}$$

Where the circuit parameters L, R, and C are constants, it is evident that complex exponentials satisfy Kirchhoff's laws in rather elegant fashion. The associated complex frequency is

$$\mathbf{s} = \frac{d\mathbf{i}/dt}{\mathbf{i}} = \frac{d\mathbf{v}/dt}{\mathbf{v}} = \alpha + j\omega \tag{63}$$

which may be verified as follows. From $\mathbf{i} = \mathbf{I}\epsilon^{st}$, $d\mathbf{i}/dt = \mathbf{s}\mathbf{I}\epsilon^{st} = \mathbf{s}\mathbf{i}$. Therefore $\mathbf{s} = \dfrac{d\mathbf{i}/dt}{\mathbf{i}}$. A similar procedure using $\mathbf{v} = \mathbf{V}\epsilon^{st}$ will also yield $\mathbf{s}$. The real part of $\mathbf{s}$, namely α, accounts for an exponential increase or decrease of the current or voltage whereas the imaginary part, ω, defines or specifies the angular frequency of the current or voltage.

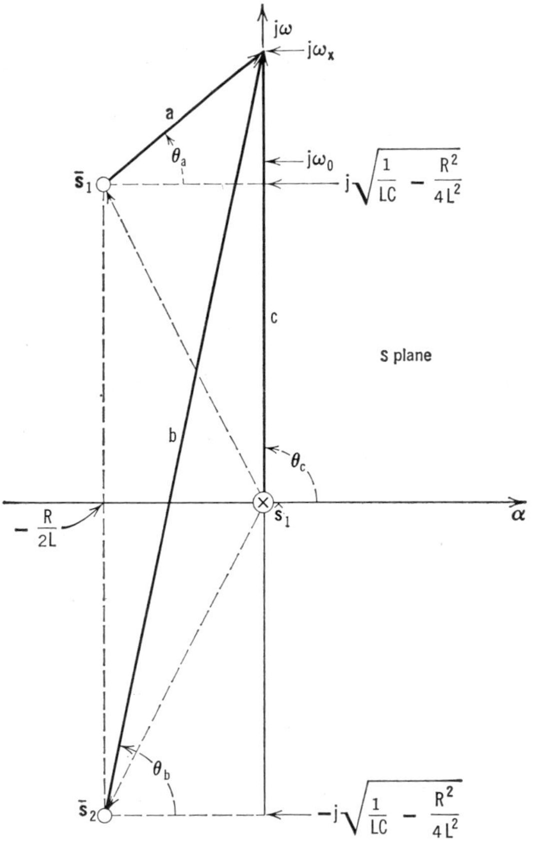

FIG. 36. Illustrating the pole and zeros of $\mathbf{Z}(\mathrm{s}) = L \dfrac{(\mathrm{s} - \bar{\mathrm{s}}_1)(\mathrm{s} - \bar{\mathrm{s}}_2)}{(\mathrm{s} - \hat{\mathrm{s}}_1)}$.

Since s is a complex number, it is natural to employ an s plane in circuit analysis with α measured along the axis of reals and ω measured along the axis of imaginaries. In terms of this convention, real angular frequency ω is plotted along the j axis of the complex s plane as indicated in Fig. 36.

Poles and Zeros. Network behavior is sometimes characterized by the poles and zeros of the impedance function $\mathbf{Z}(\mathrm{s})$ of the network.[2]

[2] More generally, the transfer characteristics of the network, $\mathbf{V}_{out}/\mathbf{V}_{in}$, $\mathbf{V}_{out}/\mathbf{I}_{in}$, $\mathbf{I}_{out}/\mathbf{I}_{in}$, and $\mathbf{I}_{out}/\mathbf{V}_{in}$, are characterized by the poles and zeros of these transfer functions, all of which are ratios of polynomials in s.

A *pole* of $\mathbf{Z}(\mathrm{s})$ is defined as the value of complex frequency at which $\mathbf{Z}(\mathrm{s})$ becomes infinite and a zero of $\mathbf{Z}(\mathrm{s})$ is defined as the value of s at which $\mathbf{Z}(\mathrm{s})$ equals zero. For example, the impedance of the *LRC* series circuit derived in the previous article may be expressed as:

$$\mathbf{Z}(\mathrm{s}) = L\mathrm{s} + R + \frac{1}{C\mathrm{s}} = \frac{L\left(\mathrm{s}^2 + \frac{R}{L}\mathrm{s} + \frac{1}{LC}\right)}{\mathrm{s}}$$

or

$$\mathbf{Z}(\mathrm{s}) = \frac{L(\mathrm{s} - \bar{\mathrm{s}}_1)(\mathrm{s} - \bar{\mathrm{s}}_2)}{(\mathrm{s} - \hat{\mathrm{s}}_1)} \tag{64}$$

$\hat{\mathrm{s}}_1 = 0$ is the single pole of $\mathbf{Z}(\mathrm{s})$

$\bar{\mathrm{s}}_{1,2} = -\dfrac{R}{2L} \pm j\sqrt{\dfrac{1}{LC} - \dfrac{R^2}{4L^2}}$ are the two zeros of $\mathbf{Z}(\mathrm{s})$.

If the pole and zeros of $\mathbf{Z}(\mathrm{s})$ are plotted on the s plane as in Fig. 36, it is evident just how the magnitude and phase angle of $\mathbf{Z}(\mathrm{s})$ could be evaluated for any value of s with the aid of a scale and a protractor. Ordinarily, interest lies only in values of s which are on the real frequency axis, that is, the $j\omega$ axis of the s plane. At any value of $\mathrm{s} = j\omega_x$, for example,

$$\mathbf{Z}(\mathrm{s}) = \mathbf{Z}(j\omega_x) = L\frac{(j\omega_x - \bar{\mathrm{s}}_1)(j\omega_x - \bar{\mathrm{s}}_2)}{j\omega_x}$$

or

$$\mathbf{Z}(j\omega_x) = L\frac{ab}{c}\underline{/\theta_a + \theta_b - \theta_c} \tag{65}$$

where $a = |j\omega_x - \bar{\mathrm{s}}_1|$, $b = |j\omega_x - \bar{\mathrm{s}}_2|$, and $c = \omega_x$, all of which may be measured with the aid of a suitable scale. θ_a, θ_b, and θ_c are the angles of the three phasors $(j\omega_x - \bar{\mathrm{s}}_1)$, $(j\omega_x - \bar{\mathrm{s}}_2)$, and $j\omega_x$ respectively measured from the $+\alpha$-axis direction.

In order to illustrate the pole-zero method of analysis (as well as to point out some of its shortcomings), we shall evaluate $\mathbf{Z}(\mathrm{s})$ at $\mathrm{s} = j\omega_0 = j\dfrac{1}{\sqrt{LC}}$ from the location of the zeros and pole in Fig. 36.

At $\mathrm{s} = j\omega_0 = j\dfrac{1}{\sqrt{LC}}$

$$a = \sqrt{\left(\frac{R}{2L}\right)^2 + \left[\frac{1}{\sqrt{LC}} - \sqrt{\frac{1}{LC} - \left(\frac{R}{2L}\right)^2}\right]^2}$$

$$\text{a} = \sqrt{\frac{2}{LC} - 2\sqrt{\frac{1}{L^2C^2} - \frac{R^2}{4L^3C}}}$$

$$\text{b} = \sqrt{\frac{2}{LC} + 2\sqrt{\frac{1}{L^2C^2} - \frac{R^2}{4L^3C}}}$$

$$\text{c} = \frac{1}{\sqrt{LC}}, \quad \theta_c = \pi/2 \text{ radians}$$

$$\theta_a = \tan^{-1}\frac{\dfrac{1}{\sqrt{LC}} - \sqrt{\dfrac{1}{LC} - \dfrac{R^2}{4L^2}}}{R/2L}, \quad \theta_b = \tan^{-1}\frac{\dfrac{1}{\sqrt{LC}} + \sqrt{\dfrac{1}{LC} - \dfrac{R^2}{4L^2}}}{R/2L}$$

$$\mathbf{Z}(\text{s}) = L\frac{ab}{c}\underline{/\Sigma\theta} = L\frac{\sqrt{\dfrac{4}{L^2C^2} - 4\left(\dfrac{1}{L^2C^2} - \dfrac{R^2}{4L^3C}\right)}}{1/\sqrt{LC}}\underline{/0^\circ}$$

$$= R\underline{/0^\circ} \text{ ohms} \tag{66}$$

In arriving at $\Sigma\theta = 0$, we make use of the well-known and easily derived relationship: $\tan^{-1} x + \tan^{-1} y = \tan^{-1}\dfrac{x+y}{1-xy}$. Obviously, no advantage accrues from the use of poles and zeros in this simple case.

In complicated filter circuits, the phase characteristics ($\Sigma\theta$ versus ω) are often evaluated by the graphical method (or with the aid of an electronic computer) since the analytical expressions for the phase characteristics can become extremely cumbersome.

Example. Let it be required to find the frequency response of the so-called stagger-tuned amplifier circuit shown in Fig. 37. By frequency response in this case we mean the manner in which $\mathbf{E}_{out}/\mathbf{E}_{in} = \mathbf{E}_3/\mathbf{E}_1$ varies with angular frequency, ω. If we let

$$\frac{\mathbf{E}_{out}}{\mathbf{E}_{in}} = \frac{\mathbf{E}_3}{\mathbf{E}_1} = A\underline{/\theta}$$

we might plot A versus ω to show how the magnitude of $\mathbf{E}_3/\mathbf{E}_1$ varies with ω and plot θ versus ω to show how the phase of $\mathbf{E}_3$ (relative to $\mathbf{E}_1$) varies with ω. The latter plot is sometimes referred to as the phase characteristic.

In the circuit of Fig. 37 $g_{m1}\mathbf{E}_1$ and $g_{m2}\mathbf{E}_2$ are the current-generator representations of the two tubes. The details of how these current generators represent the amplifying properties of the tubes are incidental to the present problem.

If the impedance of L is represented by $L\mathbf{s}$ and the impedance of C is represented by $1/C\mathbf{s}$ as derived on page 180, the application of Kirchhoff's voltage law to the $\mathbf{I}_1$ loop shows that

$$\left(L_1\mathbf{s} + R_1 + \frac{1}{C_1\mathbf{s}}\right)\mathbf{I}_1 = \frac{-g_{m1}\mathbf{E}_1}{C_1\mathbf{s}}$$

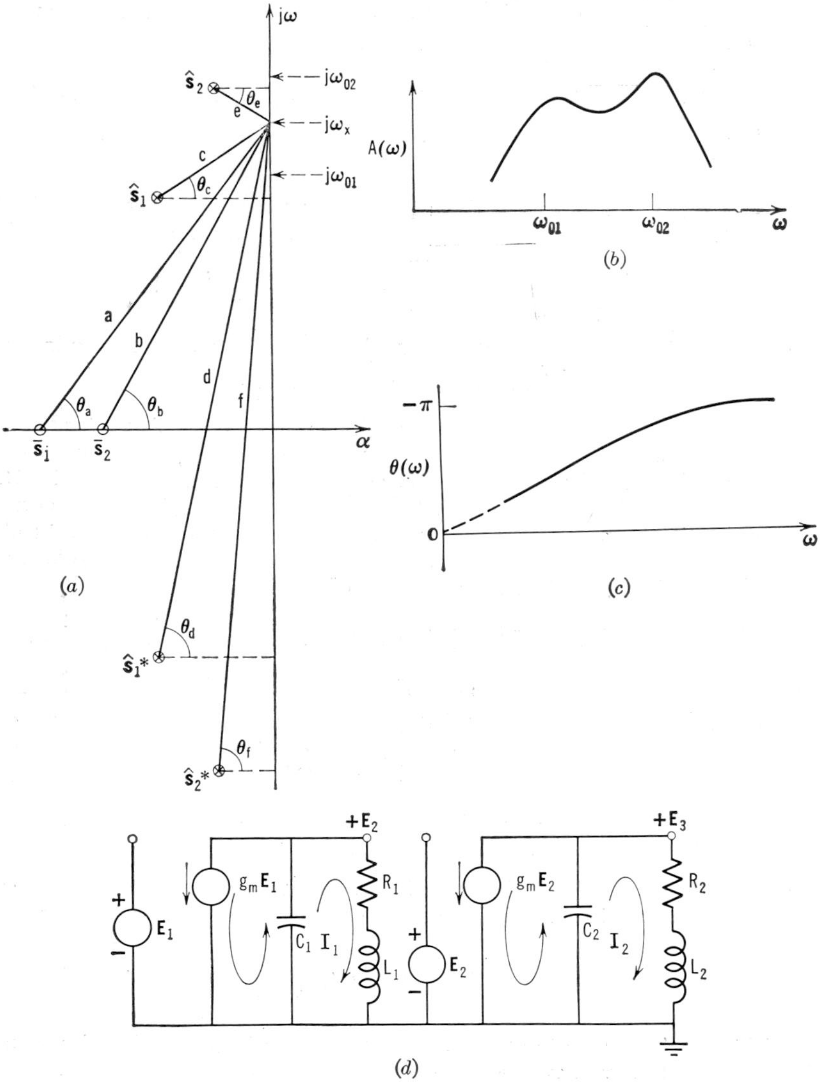

FIG. 37. Illustrating the pole-zero method of circuit analysis.

$$\frac{\mathbf{E}_3(\mathbf{s})}{\mathbf{E}_1(\mathbf{s})} = k\,\frac{(\mathbf{s}-\bar{\mathbf{s}}_1)(\mathbf{s}-\bar{\mathbf{s}}_2)}{(\mathbf{s}-\hat{\mathbf{s}}_1)(\mathbf{s}-\hat{\mathbf{s}}_1^*)(\mathbf{s}-\hat{\mathbf{s}}_2)(\mathbf{s}-\hat{\mathbf{s}}_2^*)}$$

From which

$$\mathbf{E}_2 = (L_1\mathbf{s} + R_1)\mathbf{I}_1 = \frac{-(L_1\mathbf{s} + R_1)g_{m1}\mathbf{E}_1}{C_1\mathbf{s}\left(L_1\mathbf{s} + R_1 + \dfrac{1}{C_1\mathbf{s}}\right)}$$

and

$$\frac{\mathbf{E}_2}{\mathbf{E}_1} = \frac{-g_{m1}}{C_1} \times \frac{L_1\left(\mathbf{s} + \frac{R_1}{L_1}\right)}{L_1\left(\mathbf{s}^2 + \frac{R_1}{L_1}\mathbf{s} + \frac{1}{L_1C_1}\right)} = \frac{-g_{m1}}{C_1} \times \frac{(\mathbf{s} - \bar{\mathbf{s}}_1)}{(\mathbf{s} - \hat{\mathbf{s}}_1)(\mathbf{s} - \hat{\mathbf{s}}_1{}^*)}$$

where $\bar{\mathbf{s}}_1 = -R_1/L_1$ is a zero on the negative α axis of the **s** plane.

$$\hat{\mathbf{s}}_1 = -\frac{R_1}{2L_1} + j\sqrt{\frac{1}{L_1C_1} - \frac{R_1^2}{4L_1^2}}, \text{ a second-quadrant pole.}$$

$$\hat{\mathbf{s}}_1{}^* = -\frac{R_1}{2L_1} - j\sqrt{\frac{1}{L_1C_1} - \frac{R_1^2}{4L_1^2}}, \text{ the conjugate of } \hat{\mathbf{s}}_1.$$

In a similar manner

$$\frac{\mathbf{E}_3}{\mathbf{E}_2} = \frac{-g_{m2}}{C_2} \times \frac{(\mathbf{s} - \bar{\mathbf{s}}_2)}{(\mathbf{s} - \hat{\mathbf{s}}_2)(\mathbf{s} - \hat{\mathbf{s}}_2{}^*)}$$

where $\bar{\mathbf{s}}_2 = -R_2/L_2$ is a zero on the negative α axis of the **s** plane.

$$\hat{\mathbf{s}}_2 = -\frac{R_2}{2L_2} + j\sqrt{\frac{1}{L_2C_2} - \frac{R_2^2}{4L_2^2}}, \text{ a second-quadrant pole.}$$

$$\hat{\mathbf{s}}_2{}^* = -\frac{R_2}{2L_2} - j\sqrt{\frac{1}{L_2C_2} - \frac{R_2^2}{4L_2^2}}, \text{ the conjugate of } \hat{\mathbf{s}}_2.$$

It follows directly that

$$\frac{\mathbf{E}_3}{\mathbf{E}_1} = \frac{g_{m1}g_{m2}}{C_1C_2} \times \frac{(\mathbf{s} - \bar{\mathbf{s}}_1)(\mathbf{s} - \bar{\mathbf{s}}_2)}{(\mathbf{s} - \hat{\mathbf{s}}_1)(\mathbf{s} - \hat{\mathbf{s}}_1{}^*)(\mathbf{s} - \hat{\mathbf{s}}_2)(\mathbf{s} - \hat{\mathbf{s}}_2{}^*)} = A\underline{/\theta}$$

Let ω_x be *any* value of ω. Then $\mathbf{s} = \mathbf{s}_x = j\omega_x$ and the following quantities may be measured from the pole and zero plot:

$$|j\omega_x - \bar{\mathbf{s}}_1| = a \qquad |j\omega_x - \bar{\mathbf{s}}_2| = b$$

$$|j\omega_x - \hat{\mathbf{s}}_1| = c \qquad |j\omega_x - \hat{\mathbf{s}}_1{}^*| = d$$

$$|j\omega_x - \hat{\mathbf{s}}_2| = e \qquad |j\omega_x - \hat{\mathbf{s}}_2{}^*| = f$$

θ_a = angle associated with $(j\omega_x - \bar{\mathbf{s}}_1) = \mathbf{a}$

θ_b = angle associated with $(j\omega_x - \bar{\mathbf{s}}_2) = \mathbf{b}$

θ_c = angle associated with $(j\omega_x - \hat{\mathbf{s}}_1) = \mathbf{c}$

θ_d = angle associated with $(j\omega_x - \hat{\mathbf{s}}_1{}^*) = \mathbf{d}$

θ_e = angle associated with $(j\omega_x - \hat{\mathbf{s}}_2) = \mathbf{e}$

θ_f = angle associated with $(j\omega_x - \hat{\mathbf{s}}_2{}^*) = \mathbf{f}$

Then

$$A(\omega) = \frac{g_{m1}g_{m2}}{C_1C_2} \times \frac{ab}{cdef}$$

where a, b, c, d, e, and f depend upon ω for their values:

$$\theta(\omega) = \underline{/\theta_a + \theta_b - \theta_c - \theta_d - \theta_e - \theta_f}$$

If the coils are of the high-Q variety

$$\omega_{01} \gg \frac{R_1}{L_1} \quad \text{and} \quad \omega_{02} \gg \frac{R_2}{L_2}$$

Under these conditions a/d and b/f are each approximately equal to 1/2, and ab/df of the $A(\omega)$ expression reduces to 1/4. Then

$$A(\omega) \doteq \frac{g_{m1}g_{m2}}{4C_1C_2} \times \frac{1}{ce}$$

It is also evident from Fig. 37*a* that $(\theta_a + \theta_b - \theta_d - \theta_f) \doteq 0$ so that

$$\theta(\omega) \doteq -(\theta_c + \theta_e)$$

The results are indicated schematically in Fig. 37.

The great advantage of the pole-zero method of circuit analysis is that the general behavior of the circuit is displayed without detailed and laborious calculations. The method is generally more suitable for advanced courses than it is for a first course in circuit analysis. On pages 572–575, the use of complex frequency, poles, and zeros in finding both the steady-state and transient responses of a circuit is given.

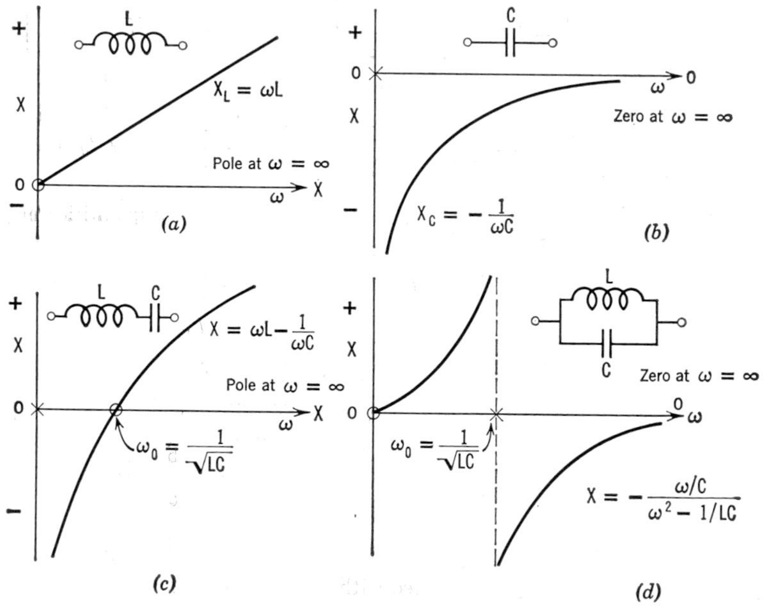

FIG. 38. Reactance of four elementary circuits plotted against ω as the independent variable.

Pure Reactance Circuits. Four characteristics of pure reactance circuits are illustrated in Fig. 38:

(1) Either a pole or zero exists at $\omega = 0$.
(2) Either a pole or zero exists at $\omega = \infty$.
(3) Poles and zeros alternate along the real frequency axis.
(4) The slope of the reactance curves is always positive, that is, $dX/d\omega > 0$ for all finite ω.

It will prove instructive to investigate these properties of reactance circuits employing the s-plane method of attack.

The poles and zeros of a reactance network are confined to the $j\omega$-axis of the s plane since there are no dissipative elements like R and G present to give the critical frequencies a real component. In Fig. 38*c*, series resonance occurs at $\omega L = 1/\omega C$ or at a zero of $\mathbf{Z}(\mathsf{s}) = L\mathsf{s} + 1/C\mathsf{s}$. Parallel resonance occurs in Fig. 38*d* at a pole of

$$\mathbf{Z}(\mathsf{s}) = \frac{1}{\mathbf{Y}(\mathsf{s})} = \frac{1}{1/L\mathsf{s} + C\mathsf{s}} = \frac{\mathsf{s}/C}{\mathsf{s}^2 + 1/LC} \tag{67}$$

The latter expression has a zero at $\mathsf{s} = 0$ (or at $j\omega = 0$) and poles at $\hat{\mathsf{s}} = \pm j\dfrac{1}{\sqrt{LC}}$. The poles and zeros of functions which are plotted against real ω are often indicated by crosses and circles respectively as in Fig. 38.

An illustration of multiple resonance is given in Fig. 39 where

$$\mathbf{Z}(\omega) = \frac{1}{\mathbf{Y}_1} + \mathbf{Z}_2 = \frac{1}{j\left(\omega C_1 - \dfrac{1}{\omega L_1}\right)} + j\left(\omega L_2 - \frac{1}{\omega C_2}\right)$$

or

$$\mathbf{Z}(\omega) = \frac{j\omega L_2\left[\omega^4 - \left(\dfrac{1}{L_1C_1} + \dfrac{1}{L_2C_2} + \dfrac{1}{L_2C_1}\right)\omega^2 + \dfrac{1}{L_1L_2C_1C_2}\right]}{\omega^2\left(\omega^2 - \dfrac{1}{L_1C_1}\right)} \tag{68}$$

It will be observed that $\mathbf{Z}(\omega)$ is a pure reactance that has a pole at $\omega = 0\left(\text{equal to } -j\dfrac{1}{\omega C_2}\right)$ and a pole at $\omega = \infty$ (equal to $j\omega L_2$) as well as internal poles at $\omega_2 = \pm\sqrt{\dfrac{1}{L_1C_1}}$. Poles and zeros at $\omega = 0$ and at $\omega = \infty$ are referred to as *external* poles and zeros, whereas those between these limits are called *internal* poles and zeros. The bracket term in the numerator of equation (68) contains four zeros: two between $\omega = 0$ and $\omega = \infty$ (designated in Fig. 39) and their negatives (not shown) which, of course, lie between $\omega = 0$ and $\omega = -\infty$. It will be observed that the poles and zeros alternate along the ω-axis which is equivalent to their alternating along the $j\omega$-axis of the s plane. It will prove instructive to investigate this property in more general terms.

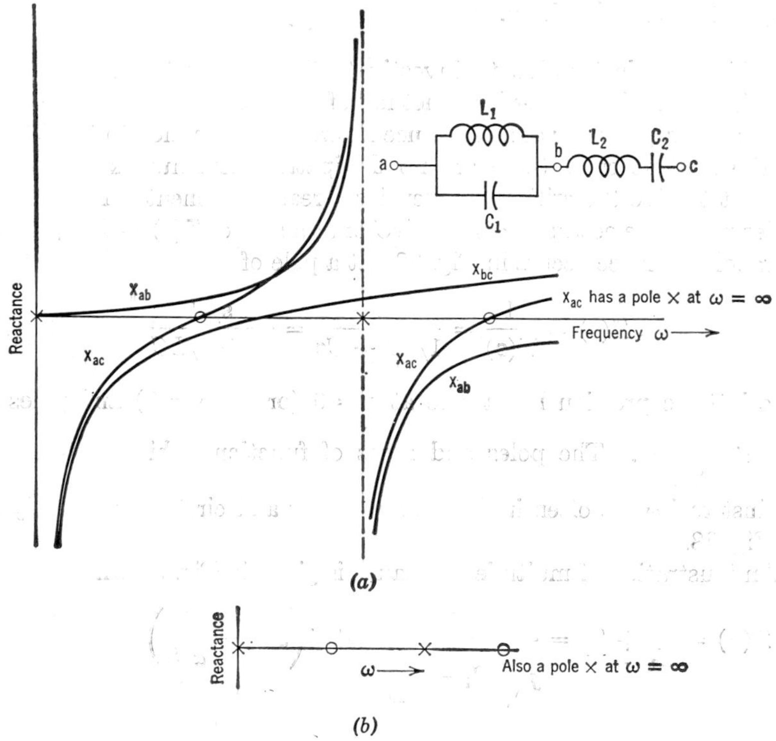

FIG. 39. Poles and zeros of the reactance function for the circuit shown. Multiple resonance is illustrated when *bc* resonates at a lower frequency than *ab*.

A theorem due to R. M. Foster[3] states that the impedance seen looking into any network of pure reactances is given by

$$\mathbf{Z}(\omega) = \mathbf{K}\frac{(\omega^2 - \bar{\omega}_1{}^2)(\omega^2 - \bar{\omega}_2{}^2)\cdots(\omega^2 - \bar{\omega}_n{}^2)}{(\omega^2 - \hat{\omega}_1{}^2)(\omega^2 - \hat{\omega}_2{}^2)\cdots(\omega^2 - \hat{\omega}_m{}^2)} \tag{69}$$

where $\mathbf{K}$ is equal to $j\omega H$ or to $\dfrac{H}{j\omega}$. H is a real number which depends upon the values of certain L's and C's in the network. In effect, this theorem states that the shape of the curve for a given impedance function is entirely determined by the poles and zeros. In other words, through

[3] " A Reactance Theorem " by R. M. Foster, B.S.T.J., April 1924, pp. 259–267.

the same poles and zeros only curves of the same shape can be drawn. These curves differ only by the scale factor H.

$\bar{\omega}_1, \bar{\omega}_2, \cdots, \bar{\omega}_n$ are the internal zeros or the values of ω at which $\mathbf{Z}(\omega) = 0$, not counting the possibility of a zero at $\omega = 0$ or at $\omega = \infty$.

$\hat{\omega}_1, \hat{\omega}_2, \cdots, \hat{\omega}_m$ are the internal poles or the values of ω at which $\mathbf{Z}(\omega) = \infty$, not counting the possibility of a pole at $\omega = 0$ or $\omega = \infty$. It will be observed that m and n represent the numbers of internal poles and zeros respectively.

In manipulating equation (69), four cases each of which is defined and illustrated by the sketches shown in Fig. 40 must be allowed for, namely:

LL circuits which have an external zero at $\omega = 0$ and an external pole at $\omega = \infty$,
CC circuits which have an external pole at $\omega = 0$ and an external zero at $\omega = \infty$,
LC circuits which have external zeros at $\omega = 0$ and at $\omega = \infty$,
CL circuits which have external poles at $\omega = 0$ and at $\omega = \infty$.

Case I: $\mathbf{K} = j\omega H$ and $n = m$. The LL circuit where

$$\mathbf{Z}(\omega) = j\omega H \frac{(\omega^2 - \bar{\omega}_1^{\,2}) \cdots (\omega^2 - \bar{\omega}_n^{\,2})}{(\omega^2 - \hat{\omega}_1^{\,2}) \cdots (\omega^2 - \hat{\omega}_m^{\,2})} \tag{70}$$

The reactance versus ω graph is given in Fig. 40*a*.

Case II: $\mathbf{K} = \dfrac{H}{j\omega}$ and $n = m$. The CC circuit where

$$\mathbf{Z}(\omega) = \frac{H}{j\omega} \frac{(\omega^2 - \bar{\omega}_1^{\,2}) \cdots (\omega^2 - \bar{\omega}_n^{\,2})}{(\omega^2 - \hat{\omega}_1^{\,2}) \cdots (\omega^2 - \hat{\omega}_m^{\,2})} \tag{71}$$

See Fig. 40*b*.

Case III: $\mathbf{K} = j\omega H$ and $m = n + 1$. The LC circuit where

$$\mathbf{Z}(\omega) = j\omega H \frac{(\omega^2 - \bar{\omega}_1^{\,2}) \cdots (\omega^2 - \bar{\omega}_n^{\,2})}{(\omega^2 - \hat{\omega}_1^{\,2}) \cdots (\omega^2 - \hat{\omega}_{n+1}^{\,2})} \tag{72}$$

See Fig. 40*c*.

Case IV: $\mathbf{K} = \dfrac{H}{j\omega}$ and $m = n - 1$. The CL circuit where

$$\mathbf{Z}(\omega) = \frac{H}{j\omega} \frac{(\omega^2 - \bar{\omega}_1^{\,2}) \cdots (\omega^2 - \bar{\omega}_n^{\,2})}{(\omega^2 - \hat{\omega}_1^{\,2}) \cdots (\omega^2 - \hat{\omega}_{n-1}^{\,2})} \tag{73}$$

See Fig. 40*d*.

In order to show that, in general, the poles and zeros alternate along

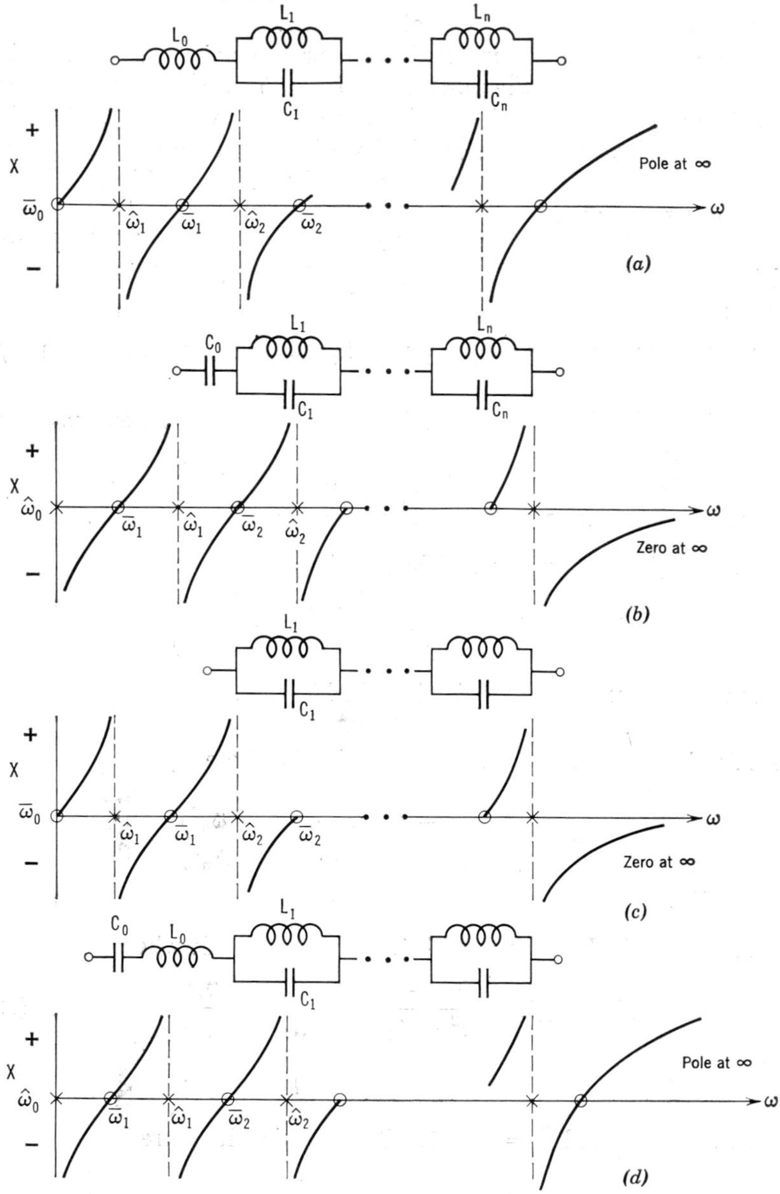

FIG. 40. Reactance graphs of *LL*, *CC*, *LC*, and *CL* networks. (Of the many possible circuit configurations which might be employed to obtain the reactance graphs, one simple configuration is indicated for each of the four cases.)

the $j\omega$-axis of the $\mathbf{s}$ plane, we should first investigate the behavior of the reactance in the *immediate* vicinity of a zero and in the *immediate* vicinity of a pole. Reference to Fig. 41*a* will show that just below the zero $\bar{\mathbf{s}}_1$ where $\omega_- < \bar{\omega}_1$ the reactance is governed essentially by $(\mathbf{s} - \bar{\mathbf{s}}_1)$ regardless of the other zeros and poles. For $\mathbf{s} = j\omega_-$ (just short of the zero $\bar{\mathbf{s}}_1$) the reactance of the network is negative.

$$k(\mathbf{s} - \bar{\mathbf{s}}_1) = j(\omega_- - \bar{\omega}_1)k = -jX$$

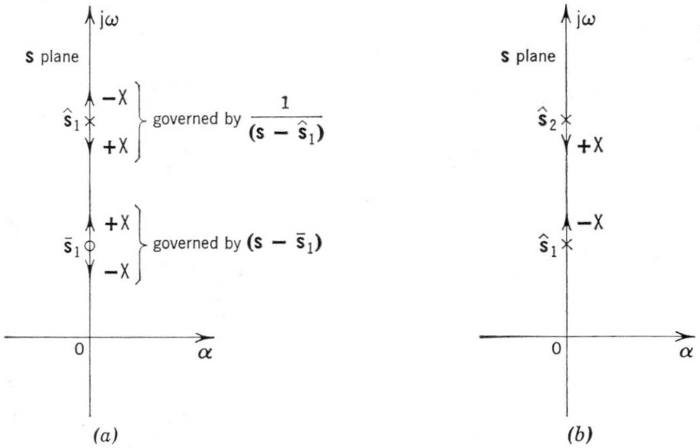

FIG. 41. For use in proving that the poles and zeros alternate along the $j\omega$ axis.

where k is a positive real number for zeros on the positive $j\omega$-axis $(\bar{\omega}_1 > 0)$.

Just above $\bar{\mathbf{s}}_1$ where $\omega_+ > \bar{\omega}_1$ the reactance of the network is positive since the governing factor is $(\mathbf{s} - \bar{\mathbf{s}}_1)$. That is

$$k(\mathbf{s} - \bar{\mathbf{s}}_1) = j(\omega - \bar{\omega}_1)k = +jX$$

The effects of the other poles and zeros do not affect these results because the zero *very* near $\mathbf{s} = j\omega$ dominates completely the behavior of $\mathbf{Z}(j\omega)$ in this neighborhood.

Reference to Fig. 41*a* will also show that just below a pole, say $\hat{\mathbf{s}}_1$,

$$\mathbf{Z}(j\omega) \to \frac{k}{(\mathbf{s} - \hat{\mathbf{s}}_1)} = \frac{k}{j(\omega_- - \hat{\omega}_1)} = +jX \tag{74}$$

At $j\omega = j\hat{\omega}_1$, $\mathbf{Z}(j\omega) = \pm j\infty$
Just above $\hat{\mathbf{s}}_1$ in Fig. 41*a*

$$\mathbf{Z}(j\omega) \to \frac{k}{(\mathbf{s} - \hat{\mathbf{s}}_1)} = \frac{k}{j(\omega_+ - \hat{\omega}_1)} = -jX \tag{75}$$

In passing through a pole in the direction of increasing ($j\omega$), **Z** changes from an infinitely large positive reactance to an infinitely large negative reactance. Suppose now that two poles, $\hat{\mathbf{s}}_1$ and $\hat{\mathbf{s}}_2$, appeared consecutively along the $j\omega$-axis as illustrated in Fig. 41*b*. Since $\mathbf{s} = j\omega$ is allowed to vary *from* $\hat{\mathbf{s}}_1$ *to* $\hat{\mathbf{s}}_2$, the reactance would have to change continuously from $-\infty$ to $+\infty$. As applied to a physical circuit arrangement, this change in reactance (from $-\infty$ to $+\infty$) requires that the reactance, X, be zero somewhere between $\hat{\mathbf{s}}_1$ and $\hat{\mathbf{s}}_2$ or that the poles be separated from one another by zeros. A natural consequence of the alternation of the poles and zeros along the $j\omega$-axis is that $dX/d\omega$ is always positive except *at* the poles where $dX/d\omega$ is not defined.

Impedance Matching and Maximum Power Transfer. A common problem in impedance matching is to determine the load impedance which will allow the maximum power to be transferred to the load from some generating device having a constant generated voltage, E_g. Let Fig. 42 represent such an arrangement and consider R_1 to represent the sum of the internal resistance of the generating device and the resistance of the connecting lines. Also assume X_1 to be the combined reactance of the line and internal reactance of the generating device. The solution is obtained by expressing the power at the receiver algebraically and then finding the maximum value of the expression. Let the receiver impedance be represented by R_r and X_r. If the receiver is a two-terminal network, R_r and X_r are its equivalent series parameters. Thus

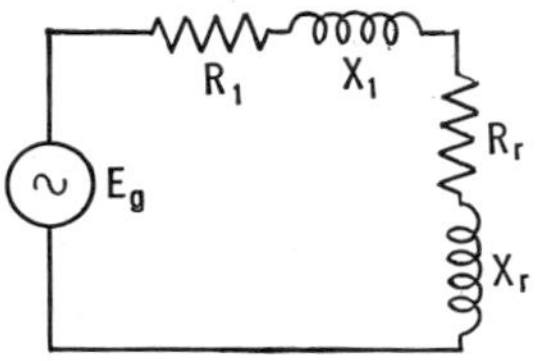

FIG. 42. Generator connected to a load through line impedance.

$$I = \frac{E_g}{\sqrt{(R_1 + R_r)^2 + (X_1 + X_r)^2}}$$

$$P_r = I^2 R_r = \frac{E_g^{\,2} R_r}{(R_1 + R_r)^2 + (X_1 + X_r)^2} \tag{76}$$

In order to make the derivation easily applicable to all conditions, the ratio of X_r/R_r will be represented by k. Then

$$X_r = kR_r$$

and

$$P_r = \frac{E_g^{\,2} R_r}{(R_1 + R_r)^2 + (X_1 + kR_r)^2} \tag{77}$$

Setting $dP_r/dR_r = 0$ and solving for R_r give

$$R_r = \frac{Z_1}{\sqrt{1 + k^2}} \tag{78}$$

where $Z_1 = \sqrt{R_1^2 + X_1^2}$. Substituting equation (78) in equation (77), expanding the terms in the denominator, and simplifying give

$$P_{\max} = \frac{E_g^2}{2Z_1 \sqrt{1 + k^2} + 2(R_1 + kX_1)} \tag{79}$$

Equation (79) gives the maximum power for any value of k, the ratio of X_r/R_r. To find the value of k that yields the greatest maximum power, it is necessary simply to set $dP_{\max}/dk = 0$ and solve for k. Then

$$k = \pm \frac{X_1}{R_1} \tag{80}$$

Substituting equation (80) in equation (79) yields

$$P_{\max\max} = \frac{E_g^2}{4R_1 + \dfrac{2}{R_1}(X_1^2 \pm X_1^2)} \tag{81}$$

It is obvious from equation (81) that the greatest maximum power will occur when the minus sign is used or when $k = -X_1/R_1$. For this case

$$P_{\max\max} = \frac{E_g^2}{4R_1} \tag{82}$$

Since R_r cannot be negative in a dissipative network, X_r must be minus to make k negative. Hence X_r is capacitive if X_1 is inductive, and vice versa. Also for this condition, from equation (78),

$$R_r = \frac{\sqrt{R_1^2 + X_1^2}}{\sqrt{1 + X_1^2/R_1^2}} = \frac{R_1\sqrt{R_1^2 + X_1^2}}{\sqrt{R_1^2 + X_1^2}} = R_1$$

Also for the greatest maximum power $X_r = kR_r = -(X_1/R_1)\,R_r = -(X_1/R_1)\,R_1 = -X_1$. Hence the receiver impedance must equal the generator plus line impedance, and the reactances must be of opposite signs. In short, the receiver impedance must be the conjugate of the combined generator and line impedance. As would be expected, the circuit is tuned for series resonance. Since R_1 and R_r are equal and the current is the same in both, one-half the power input is dissipated in the generator and line, and one-half is given to the receiver. The efficiency of transmission for the greatest maximum power is, therefore, 50 per cent.

Constant potential power systems are not designed to operate on the basis of maximum power transfer, but most low-current circuits are so designed. Impedance matching is, therefore, of considerable importance in all communication networks, and much attention has been given to this phase of circuit analysis by communication engineers.

Problem 12. A generating device has an impedance of $0.5 + j1$ ohms and is connected to a load by a line of $1.5 + j4$ ohms. At what load will maximum power transfer be realized? If the generated voltage is 20 volts, what is the power received by the load when adjusted for maximum power transfer? Find the line loss and loss in the generating device.

Ans.: $Z_{\text{load}} = 2 - j5$ ohms. $P_{\text{max max}} = 50$ watts at receiver.
$P_{\text{line loss}} = 37.5$ watts. $P_{\text{gen loss}} = 12.5$ watts.

Problem 13. If a load impedance having a ratio of $X/R = 5$ is used at the end of the line in Problem 12, find the load impedance for maximum power transfer. What is the maximum power the load can receive?

Ans.: For positive k, $P = 3.675$ watts. $\mathbf{Z}_L = 1.056 + j5.28$ ohms.
For negative k, $P = 45.2$ watts. $\mathbf{Z}_L = 1.056 - j5.28$ ohms.

Networks. Resistors, inductors, capacitors, vacuum tubes, and sources of emf may be linked together in all conceivable forms. Most of the combinations, and almost all of those which contain emf's in more than one branch, cannot be solved by simple series-parallel circuit theory alone, as previously outlined in this chapter Such combinations may be classed as networks. Networks that contain sources of emf or power are sometimes called active, whereas those that do not contain any internal emf's or sources of power are called passive networks. Networks are said to be linear when the current in all branches is directly proportional to the driving voltage or emf impressed. Thus a network containing iron-core inductance coils and resistances that vary with current strength are non-linear. Networks may be composed of bilateral or unilateral elements. *Bilateral* elements are those circuit elements like inductance, resistance, and capacitance which transmit current equally well in either direction. *Unilateral* elements are those circuit elements like rectifiers and vacuum tubes which transmit effectively in only one direction.

Through the application of a few simple network theorems, certain combinations of circuit elements which are not solvable by ordinary series-parallel circuit theory directly may be solved quite readily.

The Superposition Theorem. The current which flows at any point or the voltage between any two points in a linear network, as a result of the simultaneous action of a number of emf's distributed throughout the network, is the sum of the currents or voltages at these points which would exist if each source of emf were considered separately, each of the other sources being replaced at that time by their internal impedances. This theorem states that each emf in a network may be treated as acting independently and the current in any branch of a network due to the simultaneous action of all emf's is the vector sum of the currents in the particular branch produced by each emf acting separately. It is important to keep all circuit elements closed or connected as they are in the network. All the emf's except the one for which currents are being calculated are assumed to be zero. Any impedances associated with the source of emf must be left connected in the network whether the emf is assumed to be zero or whether it is the one considered as an independent driving voltage.

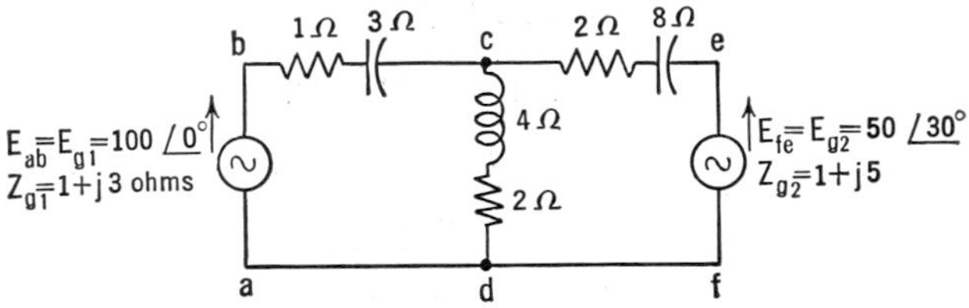

FIG. 43. See example 10.

Example 10. Calculate the current in branch *bc* for the network of Fig. 43.
Solution: Assume

$$E_{g2} = 0$$

$$\mathbf{Z}_{cf} = \frac{\mathbf{Z}_{cef}\mathbf{Z}_{cd}}{\mathbf{Z}_{cef} + \mathbf{Z}_{cd}} = \frac{(3 - j3)\ (2 + j4)}{(3 - j3 + 2 + j4)} = 3.69 + j0.462 \text{ ohms}$$

$$\mathbf{Z}_{bf} = \mathbf{Z}_{abc} + \mathbf{Z}_{cf} = 1 + j3 + 1 - j3 + 3.69 + j0.462$$
$$= 5.69 + j0.462 \text{ ohms}$$

$$\mathbf{I}_{bc1} = \frac{100 + j0}{5.69 + j0.462} = 17.43 - j1.417 \text{ amperes}$$

Now assume

$$E_{g1} = 0$$

$$\mathbf{Z}_{ca} = \frac{\mathbf{Z}_{cba}\mathbf{Z}_{cd}}{\mathbf{Z}_{cba} + \mathbf{Z}_{cd}} = \frac{(1 - j3 + 1 + j3)\ (2 + j4)}{2 + 2 + j4} = 1.5 + j0.5 \text{ ohms}$$

$$\mathbf{Z}_{ea} = \mathbf{Z}_{fec} + \mathbf{Z}_{ca} = 1 + j5 + 2 - j8 + 1.5 + j0.5 = 4.5 - j2.5 \text{ ohms}$$

$$\mathbf{I}_{ec} = \frac{50 \underline{/30°}}{4.5 - j2.5} = 5 + j8.34 \text{ amperes}$$

$$\mathbf{I}_{cb2} = \frac{\mathbf{I}_{ec}\mathbf{Z}_{ca}}{\mathbf{Z}_{cba}} = \frac{(5 + j8.34)\ (1.5 + j0.5)}{2} = 1.66 + j7.50 \text{ amperes}$$

$$\mathbf{I}_{bc} = \mathbf{I}_{bc1} + \mathbf{I}_{bc2} = \mathbf{I}_{bc1} - \mathbf{I}_{cb2} = 17.43 - j1.417 - 1.66 - j7.50$$
$$= 15.77 - j8.917 \text{ amperes}$$

Problem 14. Calculate the current in branch *ac* of Fig. 44.

Ans.: $\mathbf{I}_{ac} = 1.76 - j3.14$ amperes.

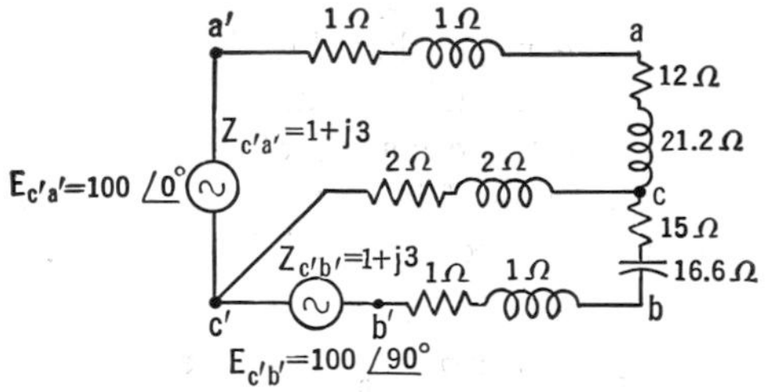

FIG. 44. See Problem 14.

Reciprocity Theorem. If any source of emf, **E**, located at one point in a network composed of linear bilateral circuit elements, produces a current **I** at a second point in the network, the same source of emf, **E**, acting at the second point will produce the same current **I** at the first point.

Example 11. The application of the above theorem may be illustrated as follows. Given the network shown in Fig. 45. The reciprocity theorem states that, if 100 volts are inserted in *bc* and branch *ef* is left closed, the current flowing in *ef* will

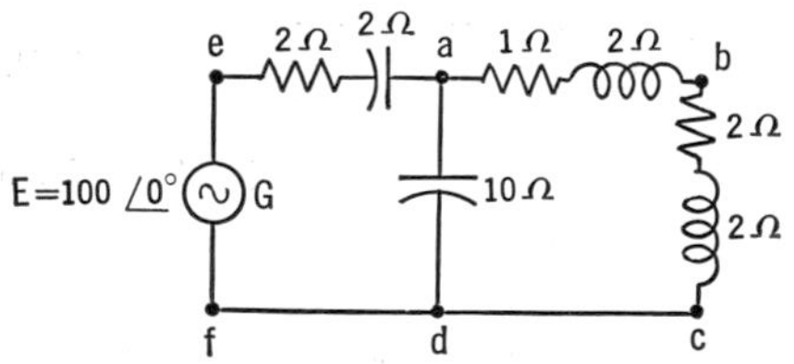

FIG. 45. See example 11.

then be exactly the same as the current that flowed in *bc* when this same voltage was applied at *ef*. To verify this theorem the current in *bc* will be calculated for the 100 volts at *ef*.

$$\mathbf{Z}_{ac} = \frac{\mathbf{Z}_{abc}\mathbf{Z}_{ad}}{\mathbf{Z}_{abc} + \mathbf{Z}_{ad}} = \frac{(3 + j4)\,(-j10)}{3 + j4 - j10} = 6.67 + j3.33 \text{ ohms}$$

$$\mathbf{Z}_{ec} = \mathbf{Z}_{ea} + \mathbf{Z}_{ac} = 2 - j2 + 6.67 + j3.33 = 8.67 + j1.33 \text{ ohms}$$

$$\mathbf{I}_{ec} = \frac{\mathbf{V}_{fe}}{\mathbf{Z}_{ec}} = \frac{100 + j0}{8.67 + j1.33} = 11.27 - j1.732 \text{ amperes}$$

$$\mathbf{V}_{ac} = \mathbf{I}_{ec}\mathbf{Z}_{ac} = (11.27 - j1.732)\,(6.67 + j3.33) = 81 + j26 \text{ volts}$$

$$\mathbf{I}_{bc} = \frac{\mathbf{V}_{ac}}{\mathbf{Z}_{abc}} = \frac{81 + j26}{3 + j4} = 13.88 - j9.84 \text{ amperes}$$

Now assume that 100 volts are inserted in branch *cb* and that *ef* remains closed. The current in *ef* will be calculated by a procedure similar to that shown above.

$$\mathbf{Z}_{af} = \frac{(2 - j2)\,(-j10)}{(2 - j2 - j10)} = 1.352 - j1.892 \text{ ohms}$$

$$\mathbf{Z}_{caf} = 3 + j4 + 1.352 - j1.892 = 4.352 + j2.108 \text{ ohms}$$

$$\mathbf{I}_{caf} = \frac{100 + j0}{4.352 + j2.108} = 18.6 - j9.02 \text{ amperes}$$

$$\mathbf{V}_{af} = (18.6 - j9.02)\,(1.352 - j1.892) = 8.07 - j47.4 \text{ volts}$$

$$\mathbf{I}_{ef} = \frac{8.07 - j47.4}{2 - j2} = 13.88 - j9.84 \text{ amperes}$$

which is the same as the current $\mathbf{I}_{bc}$ above.

From the reciprocity theorem it follows that the ratio of the emf in branch 1 of a linear bilateral network to the current it causes in branch 2 is the same as the ratio of a voltage placed in branch 2 to the current it would cause in branch 1. This ratio of voltage in one branch to the current in another branch is called the *transfer impedance.*

Problem 15. Make use of the first set of calculations for Fig. 45 when the emf is inserted in *fe* and with the aid of the reciprocity theorem find the current in *fe* if 100 volts are inserted in branch *ad*. Verify your result by actually calculating the current in *fe* when 100 volts are inserted in branch *ad*.

Ans.: $-2.6 + j8.1$ amperes.

Thévenin's Theorem. If an impedance **Z** is connected between any two points of an energized network, the resulting current **I** through this impedance is the potential difference **V** between these points, prior to connection, divided by the sum of the connected impedance **Z** and the impedance $\mathbf{Z}_0$, where $\mathbf{Z}_0$ is the impedance of the rest of the network looking back into the network from the points across which impedance **Z** is connected. In evaluating $\mathbf{Z}_0$ all sources of emf must be assumed to be zero and replaced by their internal impedances.

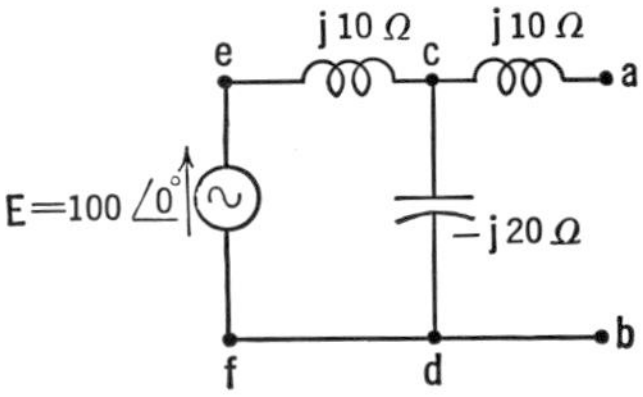

Fig. 46. See example 12.

Example 12. For the network shown in Fig. 46 the voltage drop at *ab* is found as follows:

$$\mathbf{I}_{fecd} = \frac{100\,\underline{/0^\circ}}{10\,\underline{/-90^\circ}} = 10\,\underline{/90^\circ} \text{ amperes}$$

$$\mathbf{V}_{cd} = \mathbf{V}_{ab} = (10\,\underline{/90^\circ})(20\,\underline{/-90^\circ}) = 200\,\underline{/0^\circ} \text{ volts}$$

Now suppose that the current through a load impedance $\mathbf{Z}_L = 30\,\underline{/0^\circ}$ ohms connected across ab is desired. According to Thévenin's theorem, the current is $\mathbf{V}_{ab}$ divided by the sum of the load impedance and the impedance looking into the network at ab. Thus the impedance looking into the network at ab (designated by $\mathbf{Z}_0$) when the emf in the branch ef is assumed zero is:

$$\mathbf{Z}_0 = j10 + \frac{(j10)(-j20)}{j10 - j20} = j30 \text{ ohms}$$

According to Thévenin's theorem

$$\mathbf{I}_{\text{load}} = \frac{\mathbf{V}_{ab}}{\mathbf{Z}_0 + \mathbf{Z}_L} = \frac{200\,\underline{/0^\circ}}{j30 + 30\,\underline{/0^\circ}} = 4.72\,\underline{/-45^\circ} \text{ amperes}$$

This result may be checked by the usual series-parallel circuit theory as follows:

$$\mathbf{Z}_{cb} = \frac{(30 + j10)(-j20)}{30 + j10 - j20} = 12 - j16 \text{ ohms}$$

$$\mathbf{Z}_{eb} = j10 + 12 - j16 = 12 - j6 \text{ ohms}$$

$$\mathbf{I}_{ec} = \frac{100 + j0}{12 - j6} = 6.667 + j3.333 \text{ amperes}$$

$$\mathbf{V}_{cb} = (6.667 + j3.333)(12 - j16) = 133.3 - j66.67 \text{ volts}$$

$$\mathbf{I}_{ab} = \frac{133.3 - j66.67}{30 + j10} = 3.333 - j3.333 = 4.72\,\underline{/-45^\circ} \text{ amperes}$$

which is the same as that obtained by Thévenin's theorem.

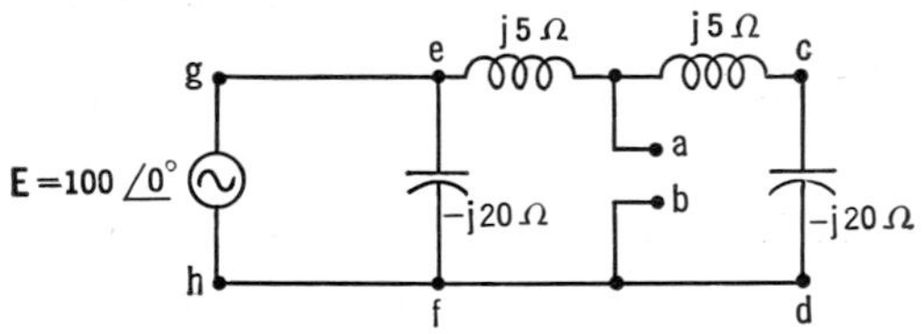

FIG. 47. See Problem 16.

Problem 16. In the circuit of Fig. 47, the impedance of the generator is assumed low enough so that it may be considered to be zero. Find the impedance $\mathbf{Z}_0$ looking into the terminals ab as employed in applying Thévenin's theorem. As may be easily shown, the drop across ab is $150\,\underline{/0^\circ}$ volts. Calculate the current in a load impedance $\mathbf{Z}_L = 10 - j7.5$ ohms connected across ab.

Ans.: $\mathbf{Z}_0 = j7.5$ ohms, $\mathbf{I}_L = 15\,\underline{/0^\circ}$ amperes.

The Nodal Method. The method ordinarily employed in analyzing circuits consists in establishing the necessary number of *voltage equilibrium equations* and solving for the currents. In many cases, particularly in vacuum tube circuits, it is desirable to employ *current equilibrium equations* and solve for the voltages. The latter method, known as the nodal method, consists essentially in writing Kirchhoff's current law at the nodes or junctions of the network the required number of times to effect a solution for various voltages in which we might be interested. See Chapter I.

In its simplest sense, a *node* of a network is any accessible terminal which is at a significant potential difference with respect to the other terminals. In this sense, the network shown in Fig. 48 *might be* considered a four-node network having nodes *a*, *b*, *c*, and *d*. Only the junction points (*c* and *d*) of the network, however, *need be* considered nodes, since the number of independent nodes is the number of junctions minus one. This will become more evident as we proceed.

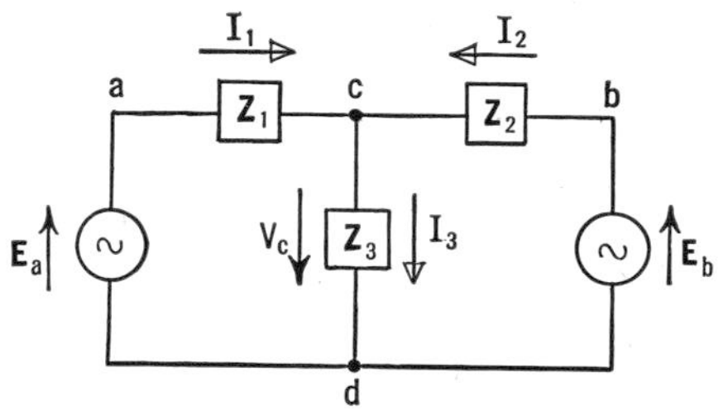

FIG. 48. Voltage sources may be transformed to equivalent current sources shown in Figs. 49 and 50.

Before the nodal method of analysis can be applied to voltage sources having internal impedance, these voltage sources must be transformed to equivalent current sources in accordance with the following principles. (If a specified voltage source is assumed to have zero impedance, it follows that the potential difference between the terminals of the generator is specified and hence does not enter the analysis as an unknown potential difference.)

In order to illustrate the transformation of a voltage source having internal impedance to an equivalent current source, let us suppose that $\mathbf{Z}_1$ of Fig. 48 is actually the internal impedance of the E_a voltage generator, thus eliminating point *a* as a node. Let V_c be the potential of node *c* relative to node *d*. Applying Kirchhoff's voltage law we have

$$\mathbf{I}_1\mathbf{Z}_1 + \mathbf{V}_c = \mathbf{E}_a \tag{83}$$

or

$$\mathbf{I}_1 = \frac{\mathbf{E}_a}{\mathbf{Z}_1} - \frac{\mathbf{V}_c}{\mathbf{Z}_1} \tag{84}$$

It will be observed in equation (83) that the inclusion of the potential of node *d* (V_d) is unnecessary and in general any node may be selected as a reference node from which to reckon all other nodal potentials.

If $\mathbf{E}_a$ and $\mathbf{Z}_1$ are specified quantities, equation (84) states that the current flowing into node *c* (I_1) is equal to a specified current ($\mathbf{E}_a/\mathbf{Z}_1$) minus a current ($\mathbf{V}_c/\mathbf{Z}_1$). The specified current ($\mathbf{E}_a/\mathbf{Z}_1$) may be considered as a current source across nodes *c* and *d*, provided that a $\mathbf{Z}_1$ path is placed in parallel with this source to account for the $(\mathbf{V}_c/\mathbf{Z}_1)$ current in equation (84). Thus the voltage source $\mathbf{E}_a$ in series with $\mathbf{Z}_1$ shown in Fig. 48 may be replaced with the circuit configuration shown in Fig. 49. In a similar manner the $\mathbf{E}_b$ source and the impedance $\mathbf{Z}_2$ may be replaced with the configuration shown in Fig. 50.

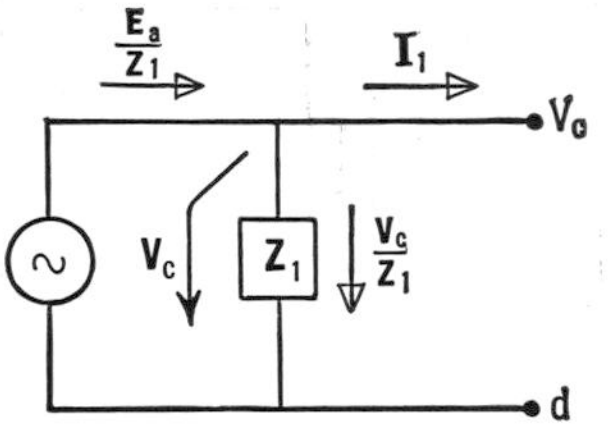

FIG. 49. Equivalent current source of E_a voltage source of Fig. 48.

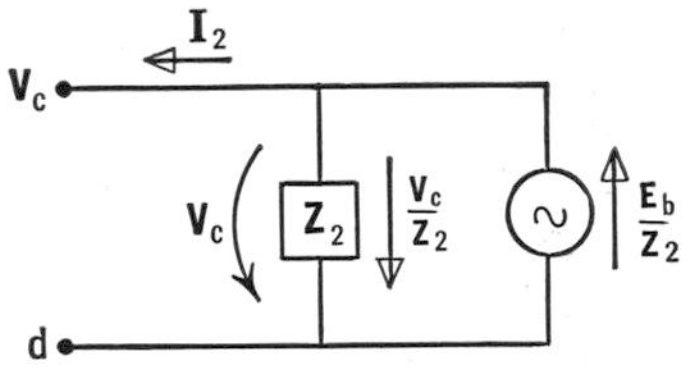

FIG. 50. Equivalent current source of E_b voltage source of Fig. 48.

If now these equivalent current sources are used in Fig. 48 instead of the voltage sources, Fig. 48 takes the form shown in Fig. 51. Employing Fig. 51, the current equation for the node c can be written in terms of voltage drops and admittances as follows:

$$\underset{\text{(current leaving node } c\text{)}}{\mathbf{Y}_1\mathbf{V}_c + \mathbf{Y}_3\mathbf{V}_c + \mathbf{Y}_2\mathbf{V}_c} = \underset{\text{(current entering node } c\text{)}}{\mathbf{Y}_1\mathbf{E}_a + \mathbf{Y}_2\mathbf{E}_b} \tag{85}$$

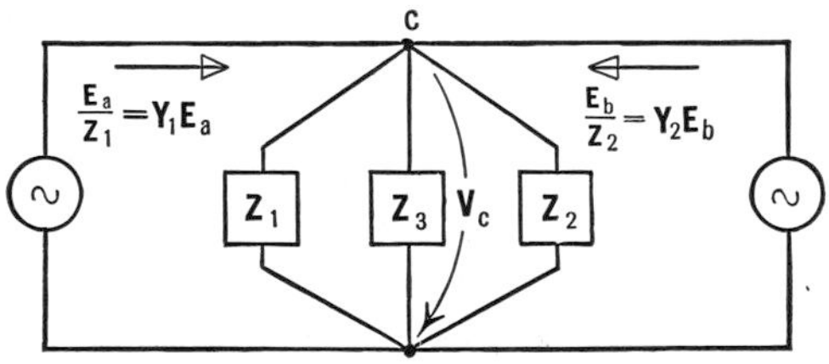

FIG. 51. Transformation of the circuit shown in Fig. 48.

$\mathbf{V}_c$ can be obtained from equation (85) directly in terms of known quantities and all currents thereby calculated.

Example 13. Assume the data for Fig. 48 to be as follows: $\mathbf{E}_a = 100\underline{/0°}$ volts, $\mathbf{E}_b = 50\underline{/90°}$ volts, $\mathbf{Z}_1 = 5\underline{/0°}$ ohms, $\mathbf{Z}_2 = 10\underline{/36.9}$ ohms, and $\mathbf{Z}_3 = 20\underline{/53.1°}$ ohms.

Find the voltage $\mathbf{V}_c$ and currents $\mathbf{I}_1$, $\mathbf{I}_2$, and $\mathbf{I}_3$.

From equation (85),

$$\mathbf{V}_c(\mathbf{Y}_1 + \mathbf{Y}_2 + \mathbf{Y}_3) = \mathbf{Y}_1\mathbf{E}_a + \mathbf{Y}_2\mathbf{E}_b$$

$$\mathbf{V}_c\left(\frac{1}{5\underline{/0°}} + \frac{1}{10\underline{/36.9°}} + \frac{1}{20\underline{/53.1°}}\right) = \frac{100\underline{/0°}}{5\underline{/0°}} + \frac{50\underline{/90°}}{10\underline{/36.9°}}$$

$$\mathbf{V}_c(0.2 + 0.08 - j0.06 + 0.03 - j0.04) = 20 + 5\underline{/53.1^\circ}$$

$$\mathbf{V}_c = 71.6\underline{/27.76^\circ} \text{ volts}$$

$$\mathbf{I}_3 = \mathbf{V}_c\mathbf{Y}_3 = (71.6\underline{/27.76^\circ})\ (0.05\underline{/-53.1^\circ}) = 3.58\underline{/-25.34^\circ} \text{ amperes}$$

As seen from Fig. 49,

$$\mathbf{I}_1 = \mathbf{E}_a\mathbf{Y}_1 - \mathbf{V}_c\mathbf{Y}_1 = (0.2\underline{/0^\circ})\ (100\underline{/0^\circ} - 71.6\underline{/27.76^\circ}) = 7.35 - j6.66 \text{ amperes}$$

and, from Fig. 50,

$$\mathbf{I}_2 = \mathbf{E}_b\mathbf{Y}_2 - \mathbf{V}_c\mathbf{Y}_2 = (0.1\underline{/-36.9^\circ})\ (50\underline{/90^\circ} - 71.6\underline{/27.76^\circ})$$
$$= -4.05 + j5.134 \text{ amperes}$$

The nodal method of analysis is usually superior to the mesh-current method if the number of nodes (after transformation to current sources) does not exceed the number of meshes or loops. If N represents the number of nodes in a network, only $N - 1$ independent node equations are required, and these are obtained by applying Kirchhoff's current law to $N - 1$ nodes.

To arrive at the method of formulating a general system of nodal equations, assume that Fig. 52*a* is the network to be solved. First, replace the voltage sources by constant-current sources as shown in Fig. 52*b*. Assume one node as the reference node, node 4 in this case. The output of the constant-current generator *a* is $\mathbf{E}_a/\mathbf{Z}_a = \mathbf{I}_1$. Similarly the output of constant-current generator *b* is $\mathbf{E}_b/\mathbf{Z}_b = \mathbf{I}_3$. To obtain the current in any impedance, the voltage drop across the impedance is multiplied by the admittance. The voltage drop can always be obtained in terms of the nodal voltages. Remembering that the voltage drop from node 1 to node 2 is the sum of the drops encountered in going from node 1 to 2 by any path, we may write $\mathbf{V}_{12} = \mathbf{V}_{14} + \mathbf{V}_{42} = \mathbf{V}_1 - \mathbf{V}_2$. Hence $\mathbf{I}_{12} = (\mathbf{V}_1 - \mathbf{V}_2)\mathbf{Y}_{12}$. Application of Kirchhoff's current law to node 1 yields

$$\mathbf{Y}_a\mathbf{V}_1 + \mathbf{Y}_1\mathbf{V}_1 + \mathbf{Y}_{12}(\mathbf{V}_1 - \mathbf{V}_2) + \mathbf{Y}_{13}(\mathbf{V}_1 - \mathbf{V}_3) = \mathbf{I}_1 \quad (86)$$

or

$$(\mathbf{Y}_a + \mathbf{Y}_1 + \mathbf{Y}_{12} + \mathbf{Y}_{13})\mathbf{V}_1 - \mathbf{Y}_{12}\mathbf{V}_2 - \mathbf{Y}_{13}\mathbf{V}_3 = \mathbf{I}_1 \quad (87)$$

The sum of all the admittances from node 1 to all other nodes is called the self-admittance and is designated by $\mathbf{Y}_{11}$. The admittance of the impedance connecting node 1 to any other node, say *n*, is called the mutual admittance, $\mathbf{Y}_{1n}$. Thus $\mathbf{Y}_{12}$, $\mathbf{Y}_{13}$, etc., are mutual admittances. When these notations are used, equation (87) becomes

$$\mathbf{Y}_{11}\mathbf{V}_1 - \mathbf{Y}_{12}\mathbf{V}_2 - \mathbf{Y}_{13}\mathbf{V}_3 = \mathbf{I}_1 \quad (88)$$

Similarly, for node 3,

$$\mathbf{Y}_{33}\mathbf{V}_3 - \mathbf{Y}_{32}\mathbf{V}_2 - \mathbf{Y}_{31}\mathbf{V}_1 = \mathbf{I}_3 \tag{89}$$

where $\mathbf{Y}_{33} = \mathbf{Y}_{13} + \mathbf{Y}_3 + \mathbf{Y}_{23} + \mathbf{Y}_b$. And, for node 2,

$$\mathbf{Y}_{22}\mathbf{V}_2 - \mathbf{Y}_{21}\mathbf{V}_1 - \mathbf{Y}_{23}\mathbf{V}_3 = 0 \tag{90}$$

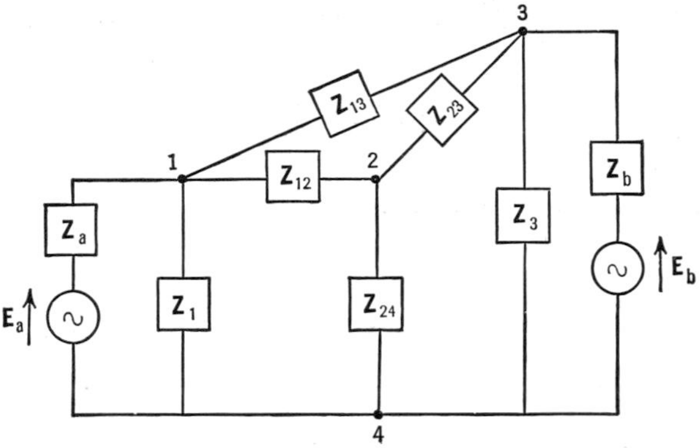

FIG. 52*a*. A network having two voltage sources.

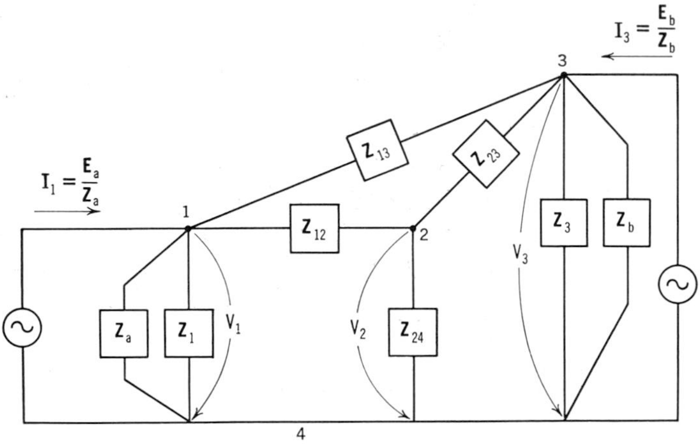

FIG. 52*b*. Transformation of circuit shown in Fig. 52*a*.

An extension of equations (88), (89), and (90) will yield the general system of nodal equations for an n-node system as follows.

$$\left.\begin{aligned} \mathbf{Y}_{11}\mathbf{V}_1 - \mathbf{Y}_{12}\mathbf{V}_2 - \mathbf{Y}_{13}\mathbf{V}_3 - \cdots - \mathbf{Y}_{1n}\mathbf{V}_n &= \mathbf{I}_1 \\ -\mathbf{Y}_{21}\mathbf{V}_1 + \mathbf{Y}_{22}\mathbf{V}_2 - \mathbf{Y}_{23}\mathbf{V}_3 - \cdots - \mathbf{Y}_{2n}\mathbf{V}_n &= \mathbf{I}_2 \\ \cdots\cdots\cdots\cdots\cdots\cdots\cdots\cdots\cdots \\ -\mathbf{Y}_{n1}\mathbf{V}_1 - \mathbf{Y}_{n2}\mathbf{V}_2 - \mathbf{Y}_{n3}\mathbf{V}_3 - \cdots + \mathbf{Y}_{nn}\mathbf{V}_n &= \mathbf{I}_n \end{aligned}\right\}$$ General system of nodal equations where a common node is employed

As previously defined, $\mathbf{I}_1$, $\mathbf{I}_2$, $\cdots$, and $\mathbf{I}_n$ are the output currents of the constant-current generators directed toward the various nodes. The nodal voltages in the general system of equations above may be solved for by determinants. After some practice with these systematic forms of solution, the determinant forms can be established from an inspection of the network after all specified voltage generators have been transformed to equivalent current generators. The writing of the current equations as shown above can therefore be dispensed with and the analysis reduced to a simple routine procedure.

In order to appreciate fully the usefulness of the nodal method, one should apply it to vacuum tube circuits where the plate-to-cathode path of the tube functions as a current sink (or negative current source). This application, however, presupposes an elementary knowledge of the functioning of a vacuum tube, and for this reason the following example may be omitted without loss of continuity by those readers who have no knowledge of the performance of a vacuum tube.

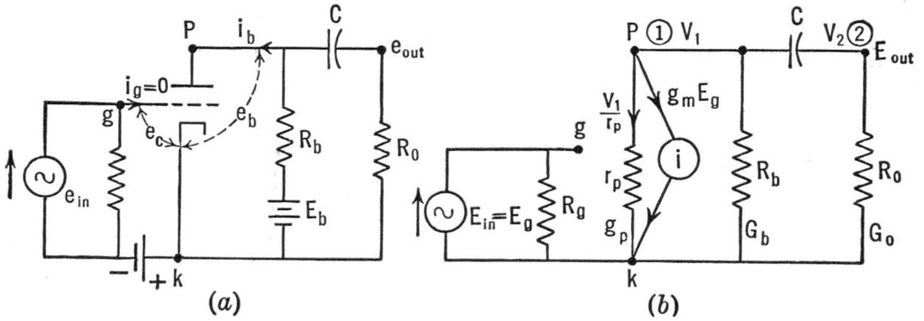

FIG. 53. The a-c equivalent of (*a*) is shown in (*b*).

Example 14. *The Equivalent Plate Circuit of a Vacuum Tube.* For the present, we may accept the fact that the plate current, i_b, of a vacuum tube as shown in Fig. 53*a* is a function of both the plate voltage, e_b, and the control grid voltage, e_c. Both of these potentials are relative to the cathode labeled *k*, as indicated in Fig. 53*a*.

If only small *changes* from the d-c operating values of current and voltage are involved, we may write

$$\Delta i_b = \frac{\partial i_b}{\partial e_b}\Delta e_b + \frac{\partial i_b}{\partial e_c}\Delta e_c \tag{91}$$

and, if the change in plate current Δi_b is called i_p, if the change in plate voltage Δe_b is called e_p, and if the change in grid voltage Δe_c is called e_g, we have

$$i_p = \frac{e_p}{r_p} + g_m e_g \tag{92}$$

where $r_p = \partial e_b/\partial i_b$ is called the variational or plate resistance of the vacuum tube, and $g_m = \partial i_b/\partial e_c$ is called the mutual conductance or transconductance. For a particular condition of d-c operation both r_p and g_m are usually known. The plate current of the vacuum tube so biased that the control grid current is zero is given by equation (92), and it is this equation which permits the use of the equivalent circuit shown in Fig. 53*b* for the plate-to-cathode portion of the vacuum tube shown in Fig. 53*a*.

In Fig. 53 we may replace the instantaneous values of the *e*'s and the *i*'s with effective values if a sinusoidal time variation of e_{in} is assumed and if e_{in} is at no time so large as to permit the contro grid to draw current. It will be observed that the vacuum tube functions as a current sink ($g_m e_g$) in parallel with a resistance path, namely, the r_p path in Fig. 53.

In order to illustrate further the application of the nodal method in a numerical case let it be required to find E_{out} in Fig. 53 if:

$$e_{\text{in}} = 0.707 \sin 3770t \text{ volt} \quad \text{or} \quad E_{\text{in}} = E_g = 0.5\underline{/0^\circ} \text{ volt}$$

$$g_m = 2000 \text{ micromhos} \qquad g_m = 200 \times 10^{-5} \text{ mho}$$

$$r_p = 20{,}000 \text{ ohms} \qquad g_p = 5 \times 10^{-5} \text{ mho}$$

$$R_b = 50{,}000 \text{ ohms} \qquad G_b = 2 \times 10^{-5} \text{ mho}$$

$$R_0 = 200{,}000 \text{ ohms} \qquad G_0 = 0.5 \times 10^{-5} \text{ mho}$$

$$C = 0.00265\ \mu\text{f} \qquad \mathbf{Y}_{12} = \mathbf{Y}_{21} = j\omega C = j10^{-5} \text{ mho}$$

Applying Kirchhoff's current law to node 1 in Fig. 53*b*, we obtain

$$g_p\mathbf{V}_1 + G_b\mathbf{V}_1 + j\omega C(\mathbf{V}_1 - \mathbf{V}_2) = -g_m\mathbf{E}_g = \mathbf{I}_1$$

or

$$\mathbf{Y}_{11}\mathbf{V}_1 - \mathbf{Y}_{12}\mathbf{V}_2 = -g_m\mathbf{E}_g = -100 \times 10^{-5} \text{ ampere}$$

where, in this particular case,

$$\mathbf{Y}_{11} \text{ (the self-admittance of node 1)} = g_p + G_b + j\omega C = (7 + j1)10^{-5} \text{ mho}$$

$$\mathbf{Y}_{12} = \mathbf{Y}_{21} \text{ (the mutual admittance between nodes 1 and 2)} = j\omega C = j10^{-5} \text{ mho}$$

Applying the current law to node 2,

$$G_0\mathbf{V}_2 + j\omega C(\mathbf{V}_2 - \mathbf{V}_1) = 0$$

or

$$-\mathbf{Y}_{21}\mathbf{V}_1 + \mathbf{Y}_{22}\mathbf{V}_2 = 0$$

where

$$\mathbf{Y}_{22} \text{ (the self-admittance of node 2)} = G_0 + j\omega C = (0.5 + j1) \times 10^{-5} \text{ mho}$$

The detailed applications of the current law can be dispensed with as soon as the systematized procedure implied by the subscripts attached to the **Y**'s is understood. The determinant form of the solution for $\mathbf{V}_2$ is

$$\mathbf{V}_2 = \frac{\begin{vmatrix} \mathbf{Y}_{11} & \mathbf{I}_1 \\ -\mathbf{Y}_{21} & 0 \end{vmatrix}}{\begin{vmatrix} \mathbf{Y}_{11} & -\mathbf{Y}_{12} \\ -\mathbf{Y}_{21} & \mathbf{Y}_{22} \end{vmatrix}} = \frac{\begin{vmatrix} (7 + j1) & -100 \\ -j1 & 0 \end{vmatrix} \times 10^{-10}}{\begin{vmatrix} (7 + j1) & -j1 \\ -j1 & (0.5 + j1) \end{vmatrix} \times 10^{-10}}$$

$$\mathbf{V}_2 = \frac{-j100}{3.5 + j7.5} = \frac{100\underline{/-90^\circ}}{8.27\underline{/65^\circ}} = 12.08\underline{/-155^\circ} \text{ volts}$$

The amplification of the circuit arrangement shown in Fig. 53 is

$$\frac{\mathbf{E}_{\text{out}}}{\mathbf{E}_{\text{in}}} = \frac{12.08\underline{/-155^\circ}}{0.5\underline{/0^\circ}} = 24.16\underline{/-155^\circ}$$

which indicates that the magnitude of the output voltage is 24.16 times that of the input voltage and that the output voltage lags the input voltage by 155° or 155/360 part of a cycle.

Norton's Theorem. This theorem states that with respect to any pair of terminals of any active network, the active network may be replaced with a single current source in parallel with an impedance equal to the impedance which is seen looking back into the network

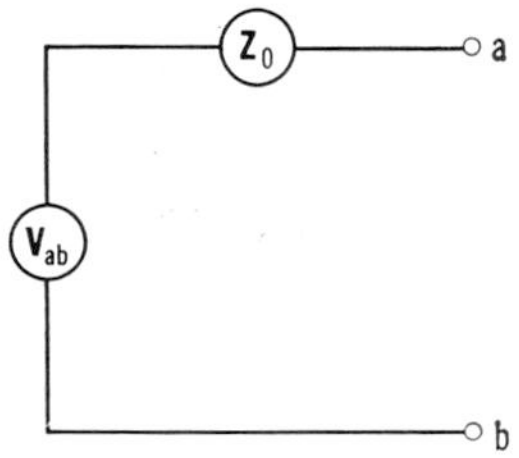

FIG. 54. Equivalent circuit of Fig. 46 as used in the application of Thévenin's theorem.

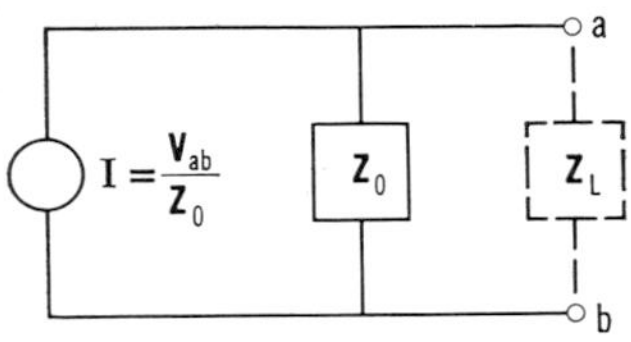

FIG. 55. Equivalent circuit of Fig. 54 employing a constant current generator.

from the specified pair of terminals. As such Norton's theorem is merely a mild variation of Thévenin's theorem since the Thévenin equivalent of an active network (Fig. 54) is readily transformed to the configuration shown in Fig. 55. In this latter figure

$$\mathbf{I} = \mathbf{I}_{\text{source}} = \mathbf{V}_{ab}/\mathbf{Z}_0$$

where $\mathbf{V}_{ab}$ is the open-circuit voltage which appears across the selected terminals and $\mathbf{Z}_0$ is equal to the series impedance of the Thévenin equivalent circuit, Fig. 54. The transformation from Fig. 54 to Fig. 55 is contained essentially in equation (84), page 199.

Example 15. Norton's theorem will be applied to example 12. From example 12 the voltage $\mathbf{V}_{ab} = 200\underline{/0^\circ}$ and the impedance looking back at ab was $\mathbf{Z}_0 = j30$ ohms. This yields a circuit shown by Fig. 54 which was employed in Thévenin's theorem. Converted to a constant-current generator in accordance with the principles shown in the previous article, the circuit of Fig. 55 is obtained. If an impedance load

$\mathbf{Z}_L = 30\underline{/0°}$ is connected across terminals ab the following solution results:

$$\mathbf{I} = \frac{\mathbf{V}_{ab}}{\mathbf{Z}_0} = \frac{200\underline{/0°}}{j30} = -j6.66 \text{ amperes (current source)}$$

$$\mathbf{I}_{ab} = \frac{\dfrac{\mathbf{Z}_L\mathbf{Z}_0}{\mathbf{Z}_L + \mathbf{Z}_0}(-j6.66)}{\mathbf{Z}_L} = \frac{\mathbf{Z}_0}{\mathbf{Z}_L + \mathbf{Z}_0}(-j6.66)$$

$$= \frac{j30}{30 + j30}(-j6.66) = \frac{200}{30 + j30} = 4.72\underline{/-45°} \text{ amperes}$$

which is the same result as obtained in example 12. Thus in accordance with Norton's theorem the circuit of Fig. 55 may be used between terminals ab to replace Fig. 46.

Either Thévenin's or Norton's theorem is often applied where complicated networks relative to a pair of terminals are being analyzed.

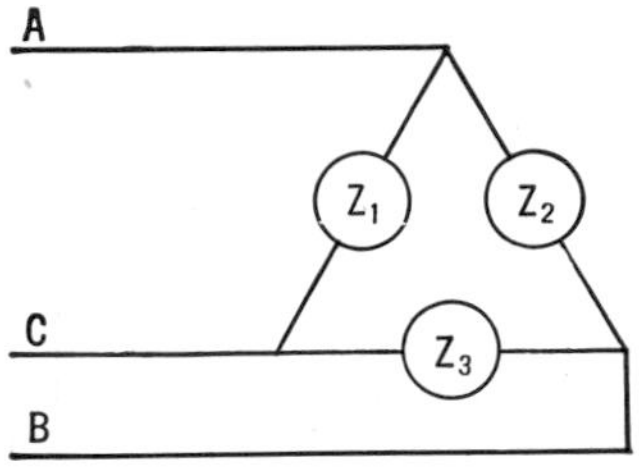

FIG. 56. Delta.

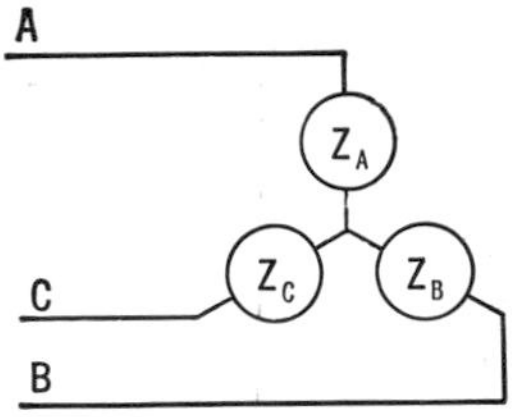

FIG. 57. Wye.

Equivalence of Special Circuits (Wyes and Deltas). Figures 56 and 57 show two types of circuits which are very commonly encountered in the reduction of electrical networks. The first is called a delta system; Fig. 57 is called a wye. It is possible to substitute a wye-connected system of impedances for a delta system, and vice versa, if proper values are given to the substituted impedances. Suppose that it is desired to substitute a wye for a given delta. The two systems will be exactly equivalent if the impedance between any pair of lines A, B, and C, Fig. 58, for the delta is the same as that between the corresponding pair for the wye when the third line is broken. If this condition is imposed, the following equations are obtained:

Line A open: $$\mathbf{Z}_C + \mathbf{Z}_B = \frac{\mathbf{Z}_3(\mathbf{Z}_1 + \mathbf{Z}_2)}{\mathbf{Z}_1 + \mathbf{Z}_2 + \mathbf{Z}_3} \quad (93)$$

Line B open: $$\mathbf{Z}_A + \mathbf{Z}_C = \frac{\mathbf{Z}_1(\mathbf{Z}_2 + \mathbf{Z}_3)}{\mathbf{Z}_1 + \mathbf{Z}_2 + \mathbf{Z}_3} \quad (94)$$

Line C open: $$\mathbf{Z}_A + \mathbf{Z}_B = \frac{\mathbf{Z}_2(\mathbf{Z}_1 + \mathbf{Z}_3)}{\mathbf{Z}_1 + \mathbf{Z}_2 + \mathbf{Z}_3} \quad (95)$$

Solution of these three equations simultaneously for $\mathbf{Z}_A$, $\mathbf{Z}_B$, and $\mathbf{Z}_C$ in terms of the impedances $\mathbf{Z}_1$, $\mathbf{Z}_2$, and $\mathbf{Z}_3$ gives the following:

$$\mathbf{Z}_A = \frac{\mathbf{Z}_1\mathbf{Z}_2}{\mathbf{Z}_1 + \mathbf{Z}_2 + \mathbf{Z}_3} \tag{96}$$

$$\mathbf{Z}_B = \frac{\mathbf{Z}_2\mathbf{Z}_3}{\mathbf{Z}_1 + \mathbf{Z}_2 + \mathbf{Z}_3} \tag{97}$$

$$\mathbf{Z}_C = \frac{\mathbf{Z}_1\mathbf{Z}_3}{\mathbf{Z}_1 + \mathbf{Z}_2 + \mathbf{Z}_3} \tag{98}$$

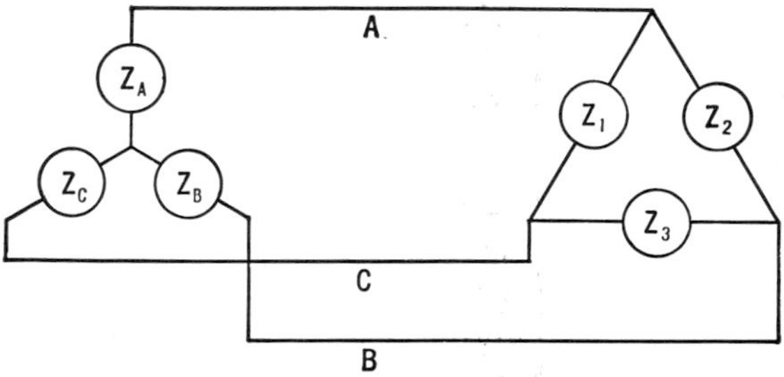

FIG. 58. Circuit for establishment of equivalence between wye and delta systems of impedances.

From equations (96), (97), and (98), the values of the wye impedances $\mathbf{Z}_A$, $\mathbf{Z}_B$, and $\mathbf{Z}_C$ that will replace a system of delta impedances $\mathbf{Z}_1$, $\mathbf{Z}_2$, and $\mathbf{Z}_3$ may be found. These results are easily remembered when it is observed that the denominators are all the same and equal to the sum of the three delta impedances. The numerator for $\mathbf{Z}_A$ is the product of the two delta impedances which connect to $\mathbf{Z}_A$. Similarly the numerator for $\mathbf{Z}_B$ is the product of $\mathbf{Z}_2$ and $\mathbf{Z}_3$.

It should be noticed that the special case of balanced delta impedances yields wye impedances, which are also balanced and equal to

$$\mathbf{Z}_Y = \frac{\mathbf{Z}_\Delta^2}{3\mathbf{Z}_\Delta} = \frac{\mathbf{Z}_\Delta}{3}$$

and

$$\mathbf{Z}_\Delta = 3\mathbf{Z}_Y$$

Example 16. Find I for the circuit and constants shown in Fig. 59. First a wye is substituted for the delta *abc*. The wye and its corresponding impedances are shown dotted.

$$\mathbf{Z}_A = \frac{(1 + j12)\,(4 - j6)}{(4 - j6) + (3 + j0) + (1 + j12)} = 8.6 - j1.2 \text{ ohms}$$

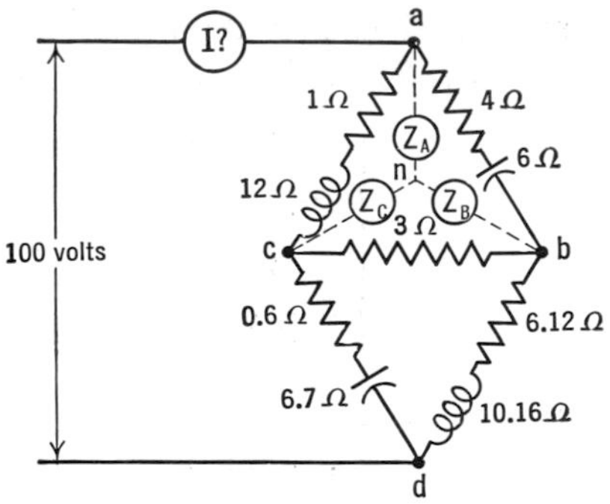

FIG. 59. See example 16.

$$Z_B = \frac{(4 - j6)\,(3)}{8 + j6} = -0.12 - j2.16 \text{ ohms}$$

$$Z_C = \frac{(1 + j12)\,(3)}{8 + j6} = 2.4 + j2.7 \text{ ohms}$$

After the above impedances are substituted, the circuit appears as shown in Fig. 60. It is apparent that a series-parallel circuit results, the method of solution of

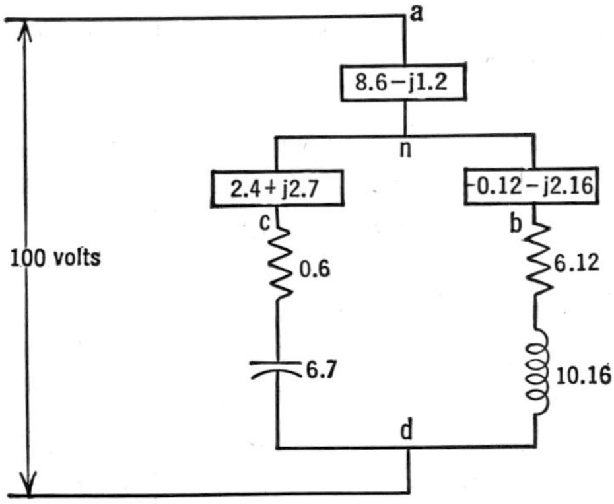

FIG. 60. Reduction from Fig. 59.

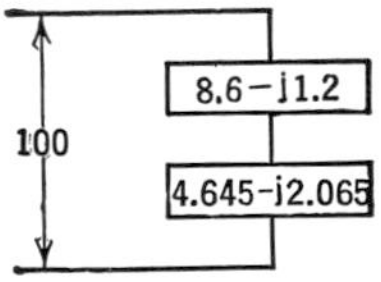

FIG. 61. Reduction from Fig. 60.

which has been given in a previous article. Combining the parallel branches results in the circuit shown in Fig. 61. Thus

$$Z_{ncd} = 3 - j4 \text{ ohms}$$

$$Z_{nbd} = 6 + j8 \text{ ohms}$$

$$Z_{nd} = \frac{(6 + j8)\,(3 - j4)}{(3 - j4) + (6 + j8)} = \frac{50\,(9 - j4)}{(9 + j4)\,(9 - j4)}$$

$$= \frac{450 - j200}{81 + 16} = 4.645 - j2.065 \text{ ohms}$$

$$\mathbf{I} = \frac{100 + j0}{13.245 - j3.265} = 7.14 + j1.76 = 7.355\underline{/14°} \text{ amperes}$$

To find the currents in the various branches, the steps are retraced as follows:

$$\mathbf{V}_{nd} = \mathbf{IZ}_{nd} = (7.14 + j1.76)\,(4.645 - j2.065)$$
$$= 36.73 - j6.57 \text{ volts}$$

$$\mathbf{I}_{ncd} = \frac{(36.73 - j6.57)\,(3 + j4)}{(3 - j4)\,(3 + j4)} = 5.45 + j5.09 \text{ amperes}$$

$$\mathbf{I}_{nbd} = \frac{(36.73 - j6.57)\,(6 - j8)}{(6 + j8)\,(6 - j8)} = 1.69 - j3.33 \text{ amperes}$$

$$\mathbf{V}_{an} = \mathbf{IZ}_{an} = (7.14 + j1.76)\,(8.6 - j1.2) = 63.51 + j6.57 \text{ volts}$$

$$\mathbf{V}_{nc} = \mathbf{I}_{ncd}\mathbf{Z}_{nc} = (5.45 + j5.09)\,(2.4 + j2.7)$$
$$= -0.64 + j26.9 \text{ volts}$$

$$\mathbf{V}_{nb} = \mathbf{I}_{nbd}\mathbf{Z}_{nb} = (1.69 - j3.33)\,(-0.12 - j2.16)$$
$$= -7.403 - j3.25 \text{ volts}$$

$$\mathbf{V}_{ac} = \mathbf{V}_{an} + \mathbf{V}_{nc} = 63.51 + j6.57 - 0.64 + j26.9$$
$$= 62.87 + j33.47 \text{ volts}$$

$$\mathbf{V}_{ab} = \mathbf{V}_{an} + \mathbf{V}_{nb} = 63.51 + j6.57 - 7.403 - j3.25$$
$$= 56.11 + j3.32 \text{ volts}$$

$$\mathbf{I}_{ac} = \frac{(62.87 + j33.47)\,(1 - j12)}{(1 + j12)\,(1 - j12)} = 3.19 - j4.96 \text{ amperes}$$

$$\mathbf{I}_{ab} = \frac{(56.11 + j3.32)\,(4 + j6)}{(4 - j6)\,(4 + j6)} = 3.93 + j6.73 \text{ amperes}$$

Check: $3.19 - j4.96 + 3.93 + j6.73 = 7.12 + j1.77$, which is within slide-rule accuracy of $7.14 + j1.76$ amperes.

$$\mathbf{V}_{cb} = \mathbf{V}_{cn} + \mathbf{V}_{nb} = 0.64 - j26.9 - 7.403 - j3.25$$
$$= -6.763 - j30.15 \text{ volts}$$

$$\mathbf{I}_{cb} = \frac{-6.763 - j30.15}{3} = -2.254 - j10.05 \text{ amperes}$$

$$\mathbf{I}_{cd} = \mathbf{I}_{ac} - \mathbf{I}_{cb} = 3.19 - j4.96 + 2.254 + j10.05$$
$$= 5.444 + j5.09 \text{ amperes}$$

which checks $\mathbf{I}_{ncd}$.

$$\mathbf{I}_{bd} = \mathbf{I}_{cb} + \mathbf{I}_{ab} = -2.254 - j10.05 + 3.93 + j6.73$$
$$= 1.68 - j3.32 \text{ amperes}$$

There are a few occasions when it is convenient and desirable to substitute an equivalent delta for a wye. This is simply the problem of finding the values of $\mathbf{Z}_1$, and $\mathbf{Z}_2$, and $\mathbf{Z}_3$ that will replace the values of $\mathbf{Z}_A$, and $\mathbf{Z}_B$, and $\mathbf{Z}_C$ in Fig. 58. The solution is obtained when equations (93), (94), and (95) are solved algebraically for the impedances $\mathbf{Z}_1$, $\mathbf{Z}_2$, and $\mathbf{Z}_3$ in terms of the impedances $\mathbf{Z}_A$, $\mathbf{Z}_B$, and $\mathbf{Z}_C$. It will usually be found simpler to solve for these quantities from equations (96), (97), and (98), which were derived from equations (93), (94), and (95). The solution gives

$$\mathbf{Z}_1 = \frac{\mathbf{Z}_A\mathbf{Z}_B + \mathbf{Z}_B\mathbf{Z}_C + \mathbf{Z}_C\mathbf{Z}_A}{\mathbf{Z}_B} \tag{99}$$

$$\mathbf{Z}_2 = \frac{\mathbf{Z}_A\mathbf{Z}_B + \mathbf{Z}_B\mathbf{Z}_C + \mathbf{Z}_C\mathbf{Z}_A}{\mathbf{Z}_C} \tag{100}$$

$$\mathbf{Z}_3 = \frac{\mathbf{Z}_A\mathbf{Z}_B + \mathbf{Z}_B\mathbf{Z}_C + \mathbf{Z}_C\mathbf{Z}_A}{\mathbf{Z}_A} \tag{101}$$

Equations (99), (100), and (101) are easy to write when it is observed that the numerator of each is the same and equal to the sum of all

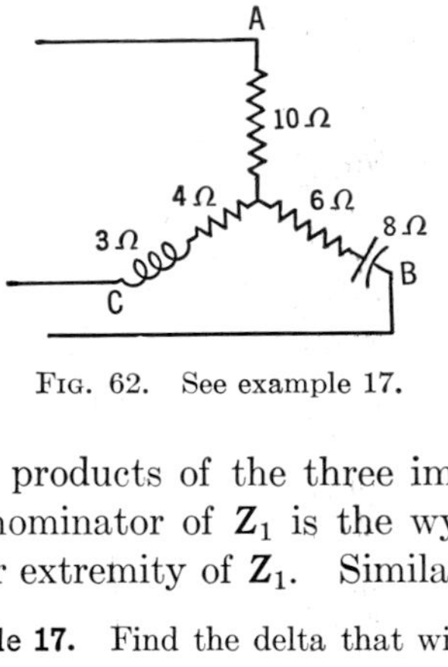

FIG. 62. See example 17.

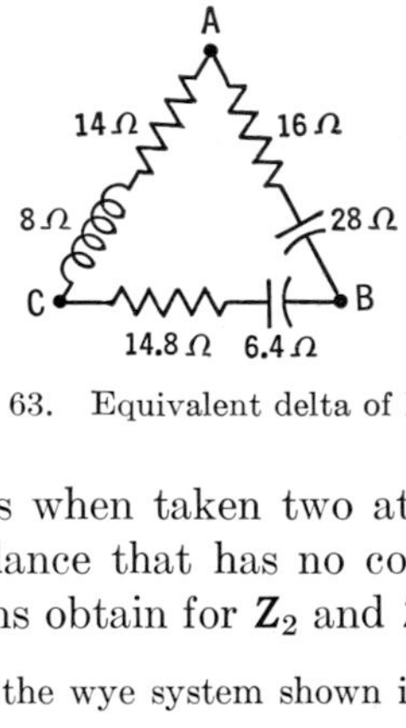

FIG. 63. Equivalent delta of Fig. 62.

possible products of the three impedances when taken two at a time. The denominator of $\mathbf{Z}_1$ is the wye impedance that has no connection to either extremity of $\mathbf{Z}_1$. Similar relations obtain for $\mathbf{Z}_2$ and $\mathbf{Z}_3$.

Example 17. Find the delta that will replace the wye system shown in Fig. 62.

$$\mathbf{Z}_{AB\Delta} = \frac{(10)\,(6 - j8) + (6 - j8)\,(4 + j3) + (10)\,(4 + j3)}{4 + j3}$$

$$= \frac{148 - j64}{4 + j3} = 16 - j28 \text{ ohms}$$

$$\mathbf{Z}_{BC\Delta} = \frac{148 - j64}{10} = 14.8 - j6.4 \text{ ohms}$$

$$\mathbf{Z}_{CA\Delta} = \frac{148 - j64}{6 - j8} = 14 + j8 \text{ ohms}$$

From these three impedances the equivalent delta is found as shown in Fig. 63.

Two commonly used types of networks are the T and π configurations shown, respectively, in Fig. 64*a* and Fig. 64*b*. Viewed as three-terminal networks, these configurations will be recognized as the wye and delta, respectively. The same formulas derived for changing a wye to an equivalent delta are therefore applicable for changing a T to an equivalent π. Likewise formulas for changing a delta to an equivalent wye may be used to change a π to an equivalent T.

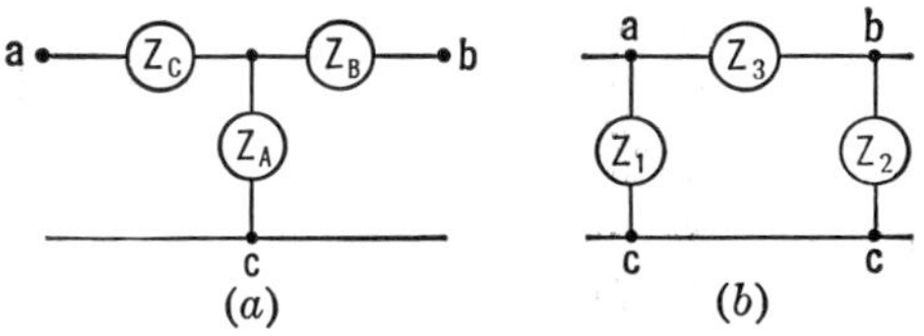

FIG. 64. (*a*) T network, (*b*) π network.

T- and π-sections are used extensively in transmission line and filter-section calculations. In cases of this kind, the T- and π-sections shown in Fig. 64 are usually considered as four-terminal networks because these sections are inserted into a two-wire circuit and are considered to have a pair of " input " terminals and a pair of " output " terminals. The manipulation of T- and π-sections as four-terminal networks will be considered in detail in Chapters X and XI.

PROBLEMS

17. Calculate the current through the impedances of Fig. 65. Find voltage drops across *ab*, *bc*, and *cd*. Draw the vector diagram showing the current and the voltage drop across each resistance or reactance. Calculate the power factor of the complete circuit.

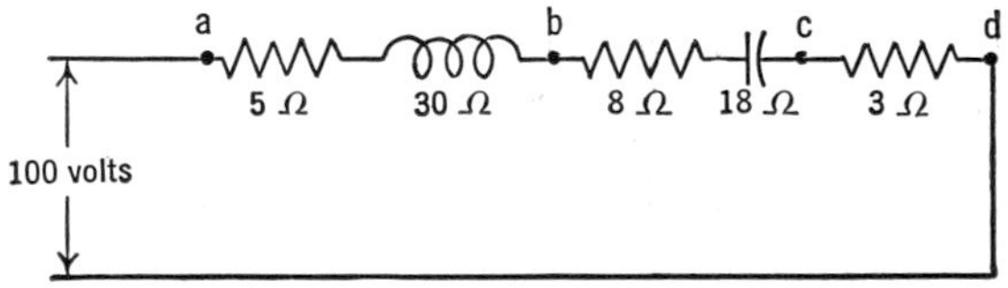

FIG. 65. See Problems 17, 18, and 24.

18. Find all possible values of pure reactance which, when placed in series with the circuit of Fig. 65, will make the overall power factor 0.6. Find the power dissipated in the circuit for this condition.

19. A particular 110-volt, 60-cycle, $\frac{1}{4}$-hp, single-phase induction motor has an efficiency of 60 per cent and a power factor of 0.6 lagging at full load. This motor is to be used temporarily on a 220-volt, 60-cycle line. A resistor (non-inductive) of suitable current capacity and of proper resistance is to be placed in series with the motor.

(*a*) What value of resistance is required if the motor is to have 110 volts across its terminals at rated full load?

(*b*) Draw the complete phasor diagram ($\mathbf{V}_{\text{motor}}$, $\mathbf{IR}_{\text{external}}$, $\mathbf{I}$, and $\mathbf{V}_{\text{line}}$) with $\mathbf{V}_{\text{motor}}$ as reference.

20. A single-phase lagging-power-factor load takes 300 watts and 5 amperes at 120 volts. Find the reactance of a pure capacitor that may be placed in series with this load so that it will operate normally from a 240-volt source.

21. Two single-phase motors are connected in parallel across a 110-volt, 60-cycle source of supply. Motor 1 is a split-phase induction type which takes a lagging current, and motor 2 is a capacitor type which takes a leading current. Find the total power, the combined line current, and the resultant power factor of the two motors operating in parallel from the following data:

Motor	Horsepower Output	Per Unit Efficiency	Per Unit Power Factor
1	$\frac{1}{3}$	0.60	0.70 (lagging)
2	$\frac{1}{2}$	0.75	0.95 (leading)

22. A series circuit on which 100 volts is impressed consists of a 10-ohm resistance, a 5-ohm condenser, a resistance R in which is lost 50 watts, and a reactance X taking 100 inductive vars. Calculate all values of R and X to satisfy the conditions stated and the corresponding currents for each of the combinations.

23. A toaster operates at 115 volts, 60 cycles, and 10 amperes and absorbs 1150 watts at its terminals. A choke coil is to be wound with a ratio of X_L to R of 5, so that, if placed in series with the toaster on a 230-volt, 60-cycle line, the toaster will have 115 volts across its terminals.

(*a*) What is the impedance of the choke coil required? State $\mathbf{Z}$ in polar and in rectangular complex form.

(*b*) Draw the complete vector diagram with V_{toaster} as reference.

(*c*) What is the power factor of the combined toaster and choke coil in series?

24. Find the inductance or capacitance which may be inserted in the circuit of Fig. 65 to put the entire circuit in resonance. Frequency 60 cycles.

25. (*a*) If the impressed voltage on a series circuit containing 5 ohms resistance, 100 ohms inductive reactance at 60 cycles, and a variable capacitance is 100 volts, find the maximum drop across the capacitance and the value of the capacitance for this condition.

(*b*) Repeat the calculation if, instead of the 5-ohm resistance, a 100-ohm resistance is used. Compare the results in the two cases.

26. A series circuit dissipates 800 watts and also requires 1000 volt-amperes when the impressed voltage is 100 volts. Find the equivalent series resistance and possible reactances of this circuit.

27. The frequency range of the pass band as previously defined in this chapter for an RLC circuit is 100 cycles when a coil having a Q of 50 is used. All resistance of the circuit is assumed in the coil.

(*a*) Find the upper and lower frequency limits of the pass band.

(*b*) If a coil with a Q of 200 is used at the same resonant frequency as in (*a*), what will be the frequency range of the pass band?

28. Given the RLC series circuit shown in Fig. 66.

(*a*) Find the resonant frequency of the series circuit.

(*b*) Find the Q of the series circuit at the resonant frequency.

(*c*) At what angular velocities do the half-power points occur?

(*d*) Assuming that L is varied to obtain resonance, at what value of L would V_L be maximum? Assume the frequency in this case to be constant at 159 kc.

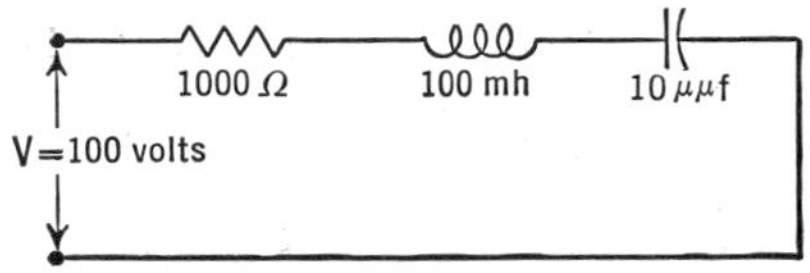

FIG. 66. See Problem 28.

29. Given the circuit shown in Fig. 67.

(*a*) What are the values of X_L that will produce resonance?

(*b*) Find the magnitude of the maximum impedance obtainable with this circuit. Assume that the frequency is held fixed.

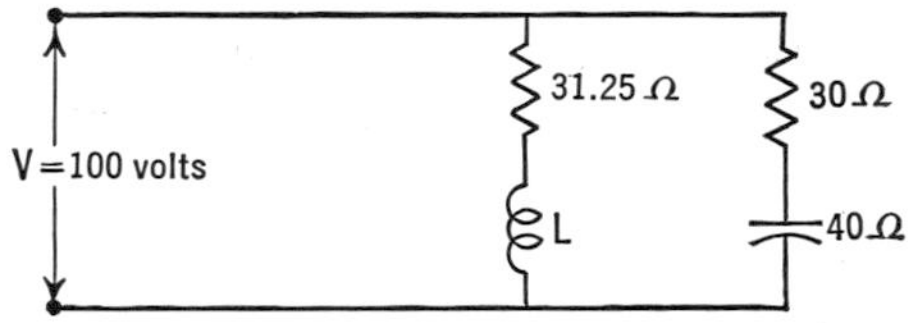

FIG. 67. See Problem 29.

(*c*) If R_L is changed to 30 ohms (R_C remaining the same) and L and C are made 9 millihenrys and 10 μf, respectively, what is the impedance looking into the circuit at 100 cycles per second and 10,000 cycles per second?

(*d*) At what frequency will the circuit as designated in part (*c*) be in resonance?

30. In the following exercises, it is assumed that a coil having L henrys of inductance and R_s ohms of series resistance is placed in resonance with a series capacitor C, so that $\omega_m = 1/\sqrt{LC}$.

(*a*) Show that $Q_s = \omega_m L/R_s$ is

$$Q_s = \frac{\text{reactive factor (of the coil)}}{\text{power factor (of the coil)}}$$

(*b*) Show that

$$\text{Power factor (of the coil)} = \frac{1}{\sqrt{Q_s^2 + 1}}$$

(*c*) Show that

$$Q_s = \frac{\omega_m w}{R_s I^2}$$

where w is the reactive energy stored in L and C at any time and $R_s I^2$ is the average dissipated power of the circuit. *Note:* $w = (Li^2/2) + (Cv_c^2/2) = \text{constant}$.

31. An impedance $Z_1 = 8 - j5$ is in parallel with an impedance $Z_2 = 3 + j7$ ohms. Find the resultant impedance of the combination. What is the overall power factor?

32. If 100 volts are impressed on the parallel impedances of Problem 31, find I_1, I_2, and the resultant current. Draw the vector diagram of the circuit, showing each current, and the voltage drop across each parameter.

33. An impedance load consisting of 12 ohms resistance and 16 ohms inductive reactance is connected across a 60-cycle, 100-volt source. Find the capacitance of a capacitor which may be paralleled with this load to bring the power factor to 1. Assume negligible resistance for the capacitor.

34. Work Problem 33 if a final power factor of 0.8 instead of 1 is desired. Obtain solutions for leading and lagging power factors.

35. Find the value of pure resistance which would be required in parallel with the impedance load of Problem 33 to bring the resultant power factor to 0.8.

36. A capacitor branch having a ratio of X to R of 5 is paralleled with an impedance consisting of 4 ohms resistance and 3 ohms inductive reactance. The power factor of the resulting circuit is 0.8 lead. Find the size of the capacitor in microfarads if the frequency is 60 cycles.

37. A single-phase load on 200 volts takes 5 kw at 0.6 lagging power factor. Find the kva size of capacitor which may be connected in parallel with this motor to bring the resultant power factor to 1.

38. Work Problem 37 if it is desired to bring the power factor to 0.9 lag instead of to 1.

39. The load of Problem 37 is operated in parallel with a synchronous motor that takes 8 kw at 0.5 leading power factor. What are the resultant current supplied by the line and the power factor of the combination?

40. Over the period of a year, an industrial establishment takes an average load of 2000 kw continuously at a (current) lagging power factor of 0.80.

(*a*) What is the annual fixed charge on the kva capacity required to serve this establishment if 1 kva of installed capacity (boiler, generator, transmission line, and transformers) costs $200? The fixed charge (consisting of interest, taxes, and depreciation) may be taken as 8 per cent of the investment.

(*b*) Repeat part (*a*) assuming that the power factor of the establishment is unity.

41. What value of resistance should be placed in parallel with a 50-μf capacitor to give a combined power factor of 0.6 on a 60-cycle system? (Neglect the resistance of the capacitor.)

42. Find the series-circuit resonant frequency of a 100-microhenry inductance and a 400-$\mu\mu$f capacitance.

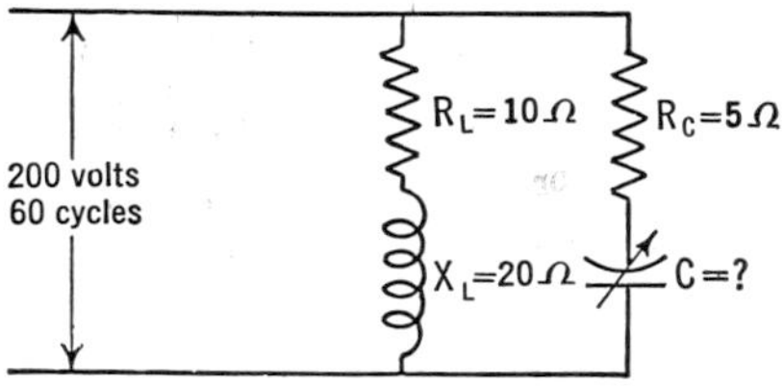

FIG. 68. See Problems 43, 44, and 45.

43. Find C to produce resonance in Fig. 68. How much power is dissipated in R_C at resonance?

44. Find the value of C in Fig. 68 which will yield maximum impedance for the whole circuit.

45. What minimum value of R_C in Fig. 68 would prevent the possibility of attaining resonance by varying C?

46. A fixed condenser is placed in parallel with a fixed resistance and variable inductance of negligible resistance as shown in Fig. 69. Show that the general expression for X_L which will produce unity-power-factor resonance is:

$$X_L = \frac{X_C}{2} \pm \sqrt{\frac{X_C^2}{4} - R^2}$$

Hint: For unity p.f., $b_L = b_C$.

47. Refer to Fig. 69.

(*a*) Draw a to-scale vector diagram of **V**, $\mathbf{I}_C$ and $\mathbf{I}_{RL}$ for $X_L = 0$.

(*b*) On the above diagram draw the loci of $\mathbf{I}_{RL}$ and **I** for X_L variable from 0 to ∞.

(*c*) Determine the values of X_L which will produce unity-power-factor resonance either graphically or analytically.

(*d*) Determine the minimum value of **I** either graphically or analytically, and find the value of X_L which produces this minimum value of **I**.

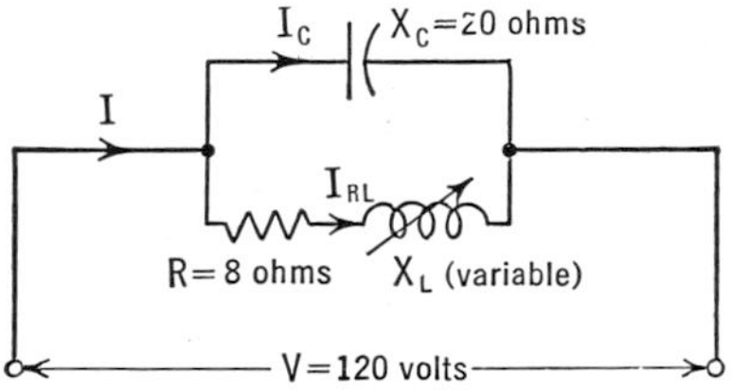

FIG. 69. See Problems 46 and 47.

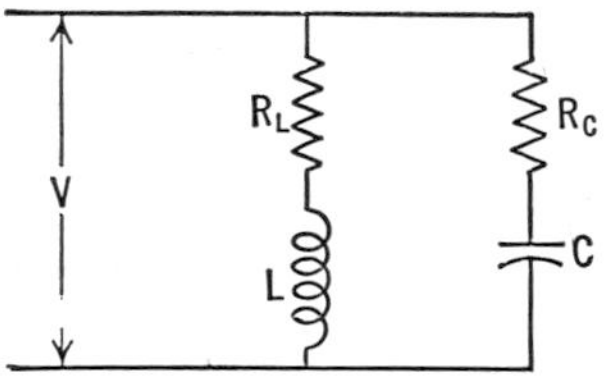

FIG. 70. See Problem 49.

48. A 2-μf capacitance is connected in parallel with a 20-ohm resistance. Plot the magnitudes of the admittance and impedance of the parallel combination against frequency for frequencies of 0, 10,000, 100,000, and 1,000,000 cycles.

49. (*a*) If $L = 0.050$ henry, $C = 200\ \mu$f, and $R_L = R_C = 1.0$ ohm, find the resonant frequency of the parallel branches shown in Fig. 70.

(*b*) If $R_L = 20$ ohms, $L = 0.050$ henry, $C = 100\ \mu$f, find the value of R_C which will yield parallel resonance of the two branches at a frequency of 45 cycles.

(*c*) If $C = 100\ \mu$f, $R_L = 20$ ohms, and $R_C = 20$ ohms, find the value of L that will place the branches in parallel resonance irrespective of frequency.

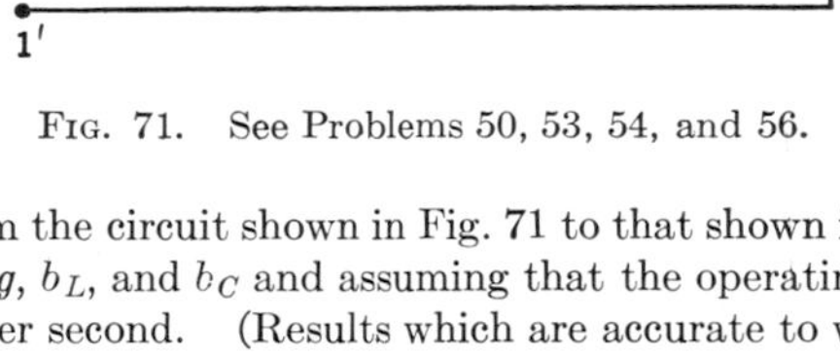

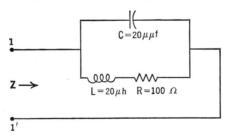

FIG. 71. See Problems 50, 53, 54, and 56.

50. (*a*) Transform the circuit shown in Fig. 71 to that shown in Fig. 72, employing numerical values of g, b_L, and b_C and assuming that the operating angular frequency is 5×10^7 radians per second. (Results which are accurate to within 1 per cent will be considered satisfactory.)

(*b*) If terminals 11′ of Fig. 71 are energized with a current of 2 milliamperes

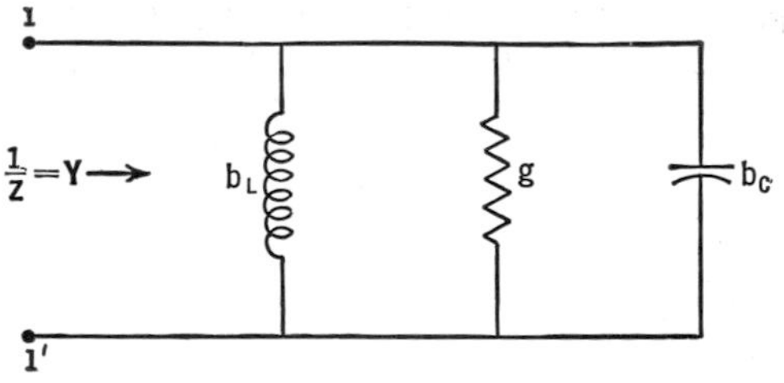

FIG. 72. See Problem 50.

(at $\omega = 5 \times 10^7$ radians per second), what voltage will be developed across these terminals?

(*c*) What is the Q_p of the circuit?

(*d*) Assuming that R is constant, find the resistance component of **Z** in Fig. 71 in terms of L, R, C, and ω.

$$Ans.: \quad R_Z = \frac{R}{(LC\omega^2 - 1)^2 + R^2\omega^2C^2}.$$

51. Given: $R = 2$ ohms, $L = 1$ henry, and $C = 0.1$ farad.

(*a*) If R, L, and C are connected in series, find the pole and zeros of the series impedance, $\mathbf{Z}(\mathbf{s})$, numerically. Evaluate $\mathbf{Z}(\omega)$ at $\omega = 2$ radians per second (or at $\mathbf{s} = j2$ radians per second) graphically from a plot of $\bar{\mathbf{s}}_1$, $\bar{\mathbf{s}}_2$, and $\hat{\mathbf{s}}_1$ and compare the result thus obtained with $\mathbf{Z}(2) = 2 + j(2 - 5) = 3.61\underline{/-56.3°}$ ohms.

(*b*) If R, L, and C are connected in parallel as in Fig. 72, find the pole and zeros of $\mathbf{Y}(\mathbf{s})$ numerically. Evaluate $\mathbf{Y}(\omega)$ at $\omega = 1$ radian per second (or at $\mathbf{s} = j1$ radian per second) graphically from a plot of $\bar{\mathbf{s}}_1$, $\bar{\mathbf{s}}_2$, and $\hat{\mathbf{s}}_1$ and compare the result with

$$\mathbf{Y}(1) = 0.5 + j(0.1 - 1) = 1.03\underline{/-60.9°} \text{ mhos.}$$

(*c*) Repeat part (*b*) for $\omega = 4$ radians per second, and compare with

$$\mathbf{Y}(4) = 0.5 + j(0.4 - 0.25) = 0.522\underline{/16.7°} \text{ mho.}$$

52. (*a*) Find the angular frequency at which R_Z of Problem 50 has its maximum value, employing literal values of L, C, and R.

(*b*) What is the numerical value of the angular frequency for (*a*)?

Ans.: 4.987×10^7 radians per second.

(*c*) Compare the above result with the approximate value of $1/\sqrt{LC}$.

53. What is the maximum numerical value of the resistance component of Z in Fig. 71 as ω is varied from zero to infinity? (A result which is accurate to within 1 per cent will be considered satisfactory.)

54. The series resistance of the 20-microhenry coil shown in Fig. 71 is $R = 100$ ohms. What is the Q of the coil at $\omega = 0.1/\sqrt{LC}$ and at $\omega = 1/\sqrt{LC}$?

55. A coil having L henrys of inductance and R_s ohms of series resistance is placed in resonance with a parallel capacitor, C, having no appreciable series resistance at an angular frequency of ω_m which is essentially equal to $1/\sqrt{LC}$. $R_s^2 \ll \omega_m^2L^2$.

Show that $Q_p = \omega_m C/g$ is essentially equal to

$$Q_p = \frac{\omega_m w}{V^2 g}$$

where V is the effective voltage across the parallel branches, w is the reactive energy stored in L and C at any time, and V^2g is the average dissipated power of the circuit. *Note:* In terms of instantaneous values and letting $v_c = v$, the instantaneous applied voltage,

$$w = \frac{Li_L^2}{2} + \frac{Cv^2}{2} = \text{constant}$$

56. It will be assumed here that the capacitor shown in Fig. 71 has a series resistance of 10 ohms.

(*a*) What is the equivalent parallel resistance of the capacitor at $\omega_m \approx 1/\sqrt{LC}$?

(*b*) What is the equivalent parallel resistance of the two branches at $\omega_m \approx 1/\sqrt{LC}$?

57. Given the circuit arrangement shown in Fig. 73*a*, where the voltage generator has an internal resistance of 20,000 ohms as indicated:

(*a*) Transform the circuit to that shown in Fig. 73*b*.

(*b*) What is the Q_p of the parallel branches facing the current generator in Fig. 73*b* at $\omega = 5 \times 10^7$ radians per second?

(*c*) Compare the result obtained in (*b*) with the Q of the coil itself at $\omega = 5 \times 10^7$ radians per second. The coil has a resistance of 50 ohms as indicated.

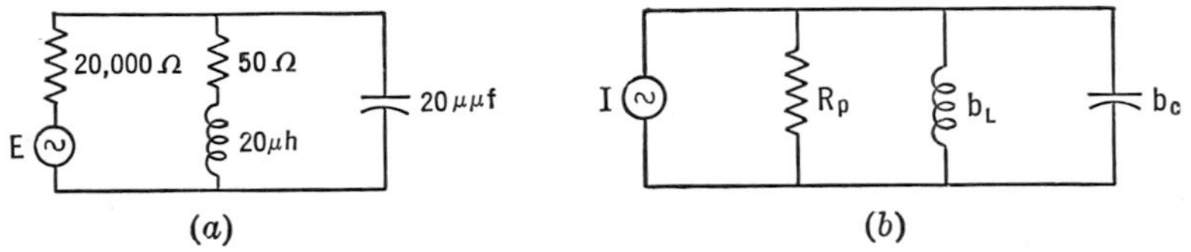

FIG. 73. See Problems 57 and 58.

58. (*a*) If the generator voltage in Fig. 73*a* is 200 volts at $\omega = 5 \times 10^7$ radians per second, what is the magnitude of the current of the equivalent current generator employed in Fig. 73*b*?

(*b*) What voltage is developed across the parallel branches by the current generator at $\omega = 5 \times 10^7$ radians per second?

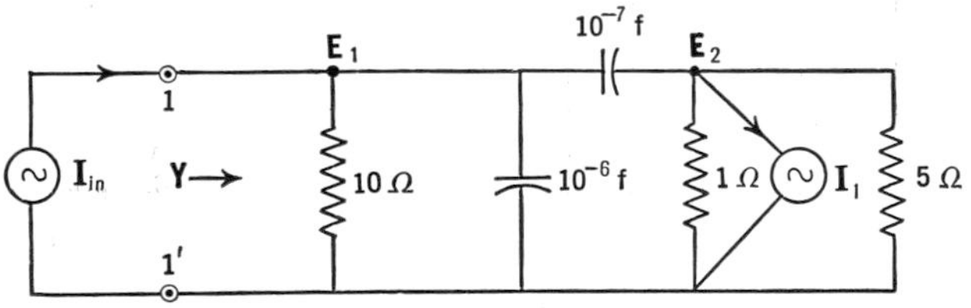

FIG. 74. See Problem 59.

59. Find the admittance Y (looking to the right of terminals 11′) in Fig. 74, and express the result in terms of a resistance R_p in parallel with a condenser C, where R_p and C are expressed numerically in ohms and microfarads, respectively. $\mathbf{I}_1 = 0.1\mathbf{E}_1$.

The I_{in} and I_1 current generators have the polarities indicated, and the operating angular frequency is 10^6 radians per second. *Note:* Current generators are always considered to have infinite internal impedance or zero internal admittance.

60. The parameters in Fig. 75 are:

$$Z_1 = R_1 + jX_{L1} = 10 + j30 \text{ ohms}$$

$$Z_2 = R_2 + jX_{L2} = 5 + j10 \text{ ohms}$$

$$Z_3 = R_3 - jX_{C2} = 4 - j16 \text{ ohms}$$

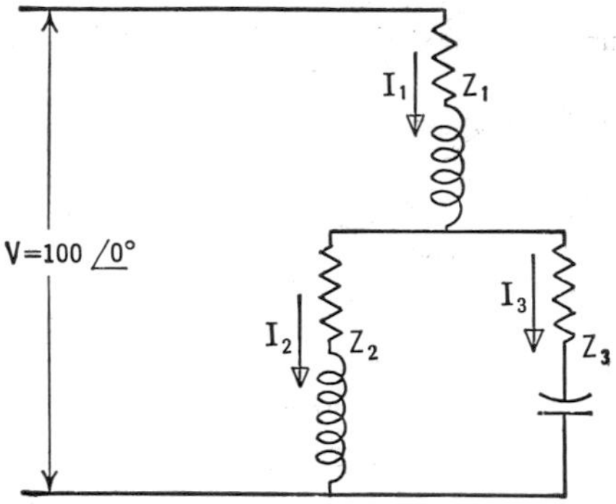

FIG. 75. See Problems 60, 61, and 70.

(*a*) Find $\mathbf{I}_1$, $\mathbf{I}_2$, $\mathbf{I}_3$, $\mathbf{V}_1$, and $\mathbf{V}_{23}$ in complex polar form with respect to applied voltage ($100° \underline{/0°}$ volts) as a reference.

(*b*) Draw a complete phasor diagram of the above voltages and currents.

(*c*) Find the watts and vars input to the entire circuit.

61. Find the power dissipated in each branch of Fig. 75 for the parameters given in Problem 60.

62. Find the pure reactance or reactances X in Fig. 76 which will make the overall power factor 0.707.

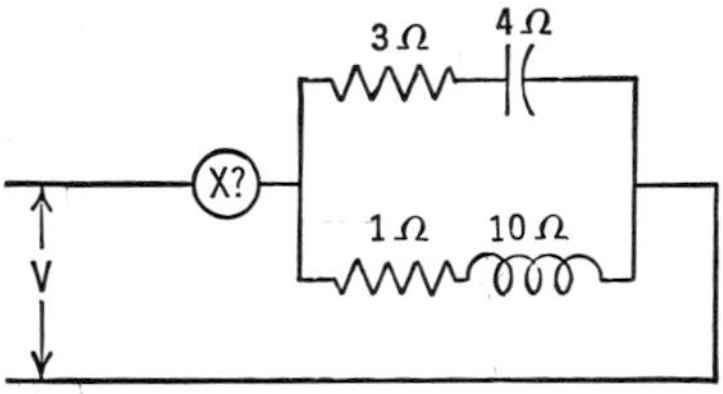

FIG. 76. See Problem 62.

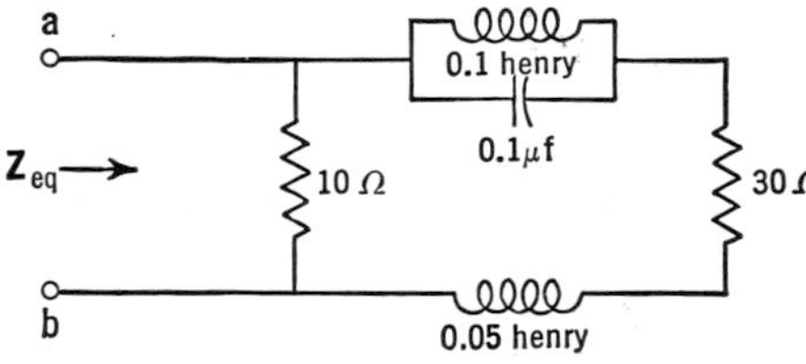

FIG. 77. See Problem 64.

63. A circuit similar to that shown in Fig. 34, page 178, except that L_1 is constant while C_2 is variable, is to pass a 45,000-cycle current with minimum impedance and to block a 15,000-cycle current as effectively as possible. $R_0 = 20$ ohms, $R_1 = 40$ ohms, and $L_1 = 0.002$ henry are fixed. The resistance, R_2, of the C_2 branch is assumed to be negligibly small. Either a fixed C_0 or a fixed L_0 (of negligibly small resistance) is to be placed in series with R_0 to accomplish the desired tuning effect.

(*a*) Solve for C_2 which will put the parallel circuit *bc* into parallel resonance at 15,000 cycles.

(*b*) Calculate the equivalent impedance from *b* to *c* at 45,000 cycles with C_2 set at its 15,000-cycle resonant value. Is *bc* predominantly capacitive or inductive at 45,000 cycles?

(*c*) Must an inductance L_0 or a capacitance C_0 be used to put the branch *ab* into series resonance for 45,000 cycles? Calculate its value.

(*d*) Assuming that branch *ab* has been put into series resonance at 45,000 cycles, what is the actual impedance from *a* to *b* at 45,000 cycles? at 15,000 cycles?

64. Given the circuit shown in Fig. 77, determine the impedance looking into terminals *ab* at 1592 cycles per second.

65. A generating device has an impedance of $0.5 + j1$ ohms and is connected to a load by a line of $0.25 + j2$ ohms. At what load will maximum power transfer be realized? If the generated voltage is 20 volts, what is the power received by the load when adjusted for maximum power transfer? Find the line loss and the loss in the generating device.

66. (*a*) If the resistance of the load in Problem 65 is fixed at 0.75 ohm and only inductive reactance is permitted in the load, for what value of load reactance will maximum load power to the load be realized?

(*b*) What is the maximum load power under these conditions?

67. Work Problem 65 if the receiver impedance is restricted to pure resistance.

68. If a load impedance having a ratio of $X/R = 5$ is used at the end of the line in Problem 65, find the load impedance for maximum power transfer. What is the maximum power the load can receive?

69. Calculate $\mathbf{I}_2$ in Fig. 78 by the superposition theorem if $E_1 = 100\underline{/0°}$ and $E_2 = 50\underline{/60°}$ volts.

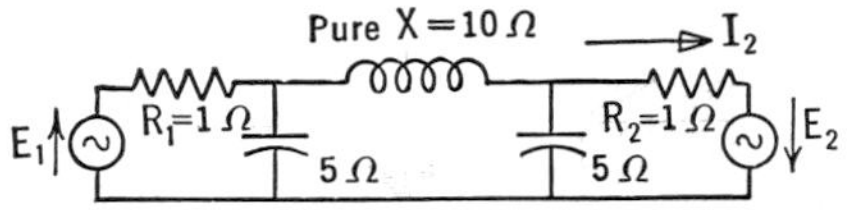

FIG. 78. See Problem 69.

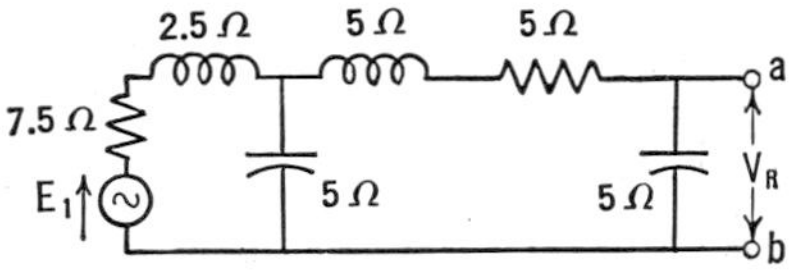

FIG. 79. See Problem 71.

70. The voltage $\mathbf{V} = 100\underline{/0°}$ volts is removed from branch 1 in Fig. 75 and inserted in branch 3. If the upper terminal of $\mathbf{Z}_1$ is connected to the lower common terminal of $\mathbf{Z}_2$ and $\mathbf{Z}_3$, calculate the current $\mathbf{I}_1$. How does this compare with $\mathbf{I}_3$ as calculated in Problem 60? By what theorem could this conclusion be reached?

71. Calculate $\mathbf{V}_R$ in Fig. 79 if $\mathbf{E}_1 = 200\underline{/0°}$ volts. Then use Thévenin's theorem to calculate the current in an impedance $\mathbf{Z}_{ab} = 1.46 + j6.78$ ohms if it is connected to the terminals *ab*.

72. Given the circuit shown in Fig. 80.

(*a*) Using the superposition theorem, determine the current through the resistor marked *A*.

(*b*) Using Thévenin's theorem, determine the current through an impedance $Z_{ab}(= 3 + j3 \text{ ohms})$ that is presumed to be placed across terminals *ab*.

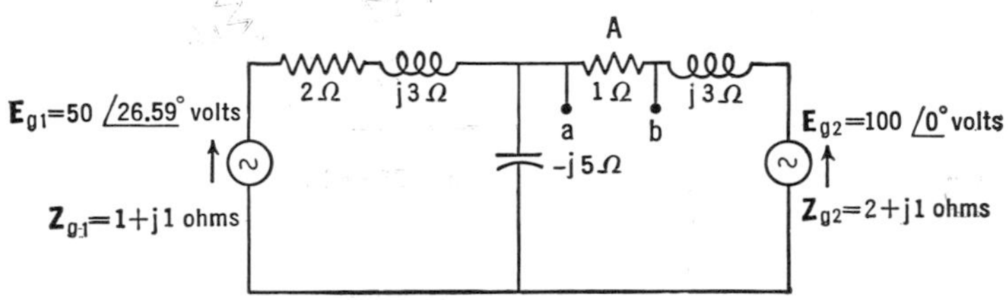

FIG. 80. See Problem 72.

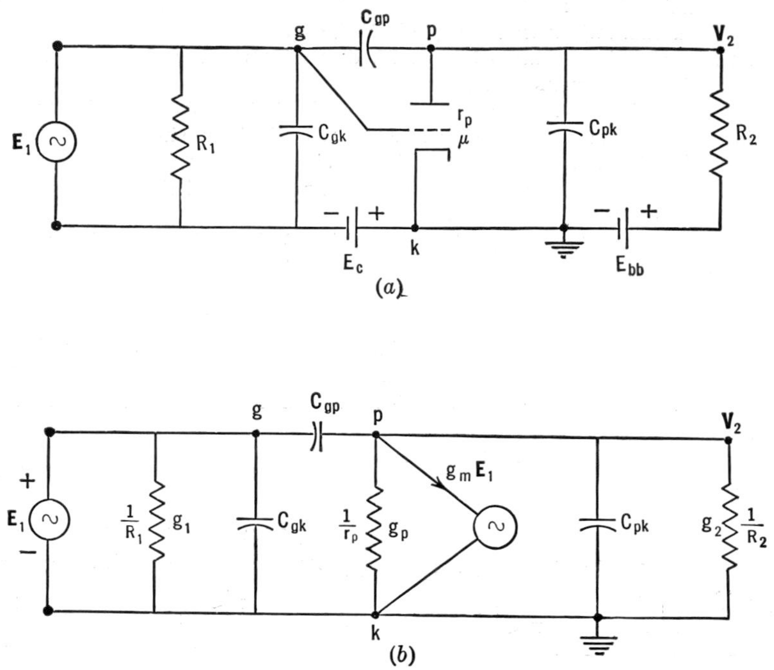

FIG. 81. See Problems 73 and 74.

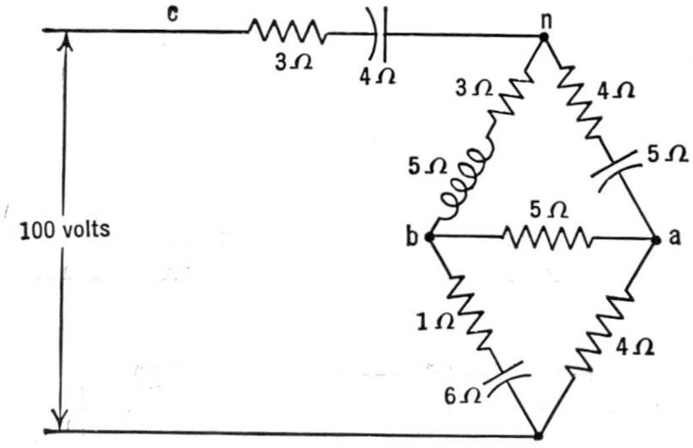

FIG. 82. See Problems 75 and 77.

73. In Fig. 81b: $R_1 = 10^5$ ohms, $R_2 = 5 \times 10^4$ ohms, r_p(of the tube) $= 10^4$ ohms; $C_{gk} = C_{pk} = 40$ $\mu\mu$f, $C_{gp} = 5$ $\mu\mu$f; μ(of the tube) $= 20$; g_m(of the tube) $= \mu/r_p = 2 \times 10^{-3}$ mho.

Find the voltage, V_2, relative to ground if $E_1 = 1\underline{/0°}$ volt. The operating angular frequency is 10^6 radians per second.

Note: In Fig. 81b: $g_1 = 1/R_1$, $g_p = 1/r_p$, $g_2 = 1/R_2$; $j\omega C_{gk} = j\omega C_{pk} = j4 \times 10^{-5}$ mho, and $j\omega C_{gp} = j0.5 \times 10^{-5}$ mho, which is a hint that the problem should probably be solved on the nodal basis, employing E_1 as a known voltage.

74. Find the admittance **Y** (looking to the right of the $\mathbf{E}_1$ generator terminals in Fig. 81b), and express the result in terms of a resistance R_p in parallel with a capacitor C where R_p and C are expressed numerically in ohms and microfarads, respectively.

The parameters and the operating angular frequency are given in Problem 73, and if this problem has been worked $\mathbf{V}_2$ will be a known voltage of $15.6\underline{/159.32°}$ volts.

75. Reduce the impedances shown in Fig. 82 to a single equivalent series impedance. Find the current in branch *ab*.

76. Derive the expressions shown in equations (99), (100), and (101), page 210.

77. Find the equivalent delta system of impedances which will replace the wye *an*, *bn*, *cn*, in Fig. 82.

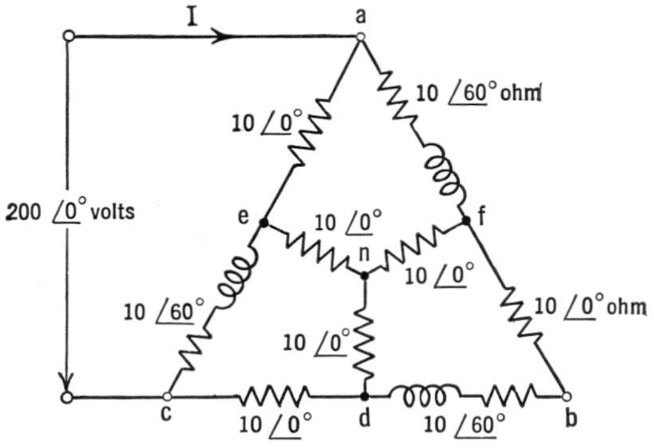

FIG. 83. See Problem 78.

78. Find the voltages $\mathbf{V}_{de}$, $\mathbf{V}_{ef}$, and $\mathbf{V}_{fd}$ in Fig. 83. What is the phase displacement between these voltages?

79. What relationship between the Z's of Fig. 84 will make $I_3 = 0$ regardless of the magnitude of E_{in}? *Hint:* A simple method of solution is to transform the

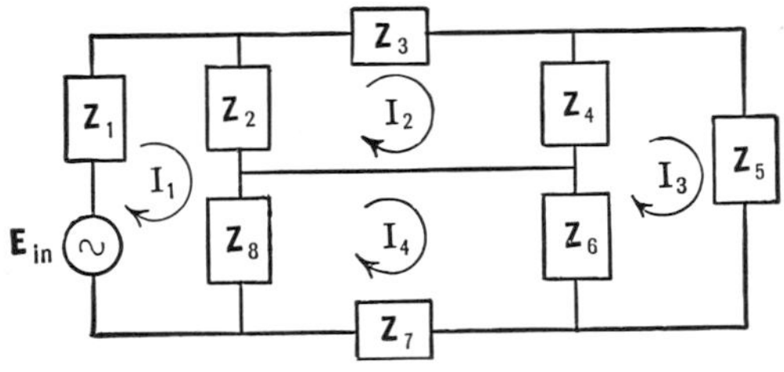

FIG. 84. See Problem 79.

Z_2-Z_3-Z_4 and Z_6-Z_7-Z_8 deltas to equivalent wyes and make the Z_{24} and Z_{68} legs of the latter the negatives of each other to produce a short circuit across the load.

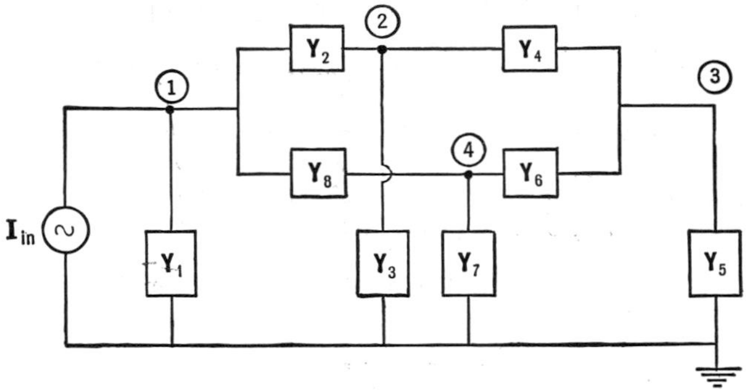

FIG. 85. See Problem 80.

80. What relationship between the Y's of Fig. 85 will make the voltage V_3 (relative to ground) equal to zero regardless of the magnitude of I_{in}?

chapter VI Non-Sinusoidal Waves

Complex Waves. The circuit theory that has been presented in the foregoing chapters has been based upon sine-wave variations of voltage and current, and only sine waves have been considered in the calculations. In many branches of electrical engineering non-sinusoidal waves are as common as sinusoidal waves, and in all branches non-sinusoidal

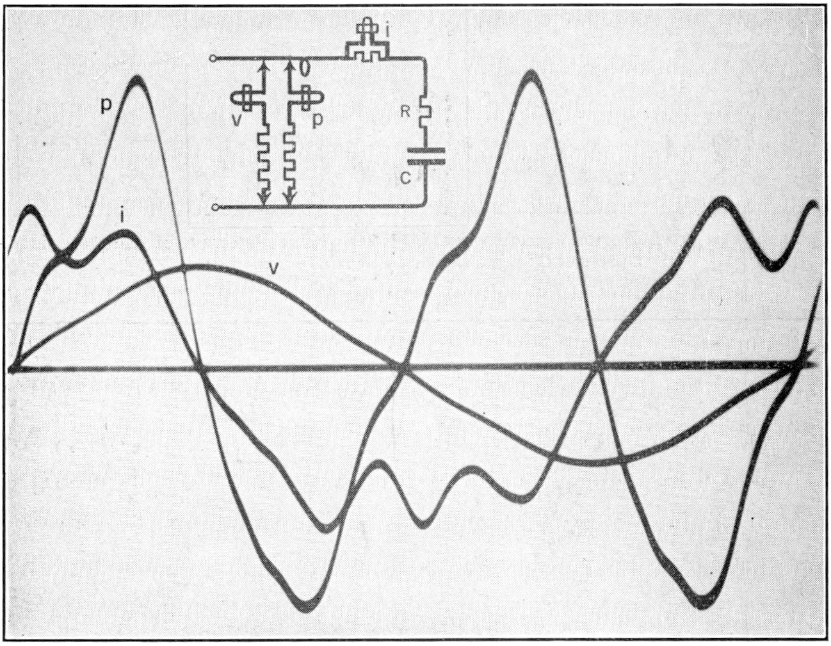

OSCILLOGRAM 1. v-wave form of voltage generated by a particular alternator. i-wave form of current which flows through a capacitive circuit element. Note the relatively larger harmonics in the current wave. p-wave form of instantaneous power. $E = 120$ volts (eff.), $I = 3.9$ amperes (eff.), $P_{av} = 20$ watts, $f = 60$ cycles.

waves must occasionally be given attention. Examples of non-sinusoidal waves are shown in Oscillograms 1, 2, and 3. Even though the voltage wave in Oscillogram 1 is nearly sinusoidal, the current through the capacitive circuit is greatly distorted. Also in Oscillogram 2 the current is non-sinusoidal even though the impressed voltage is practically

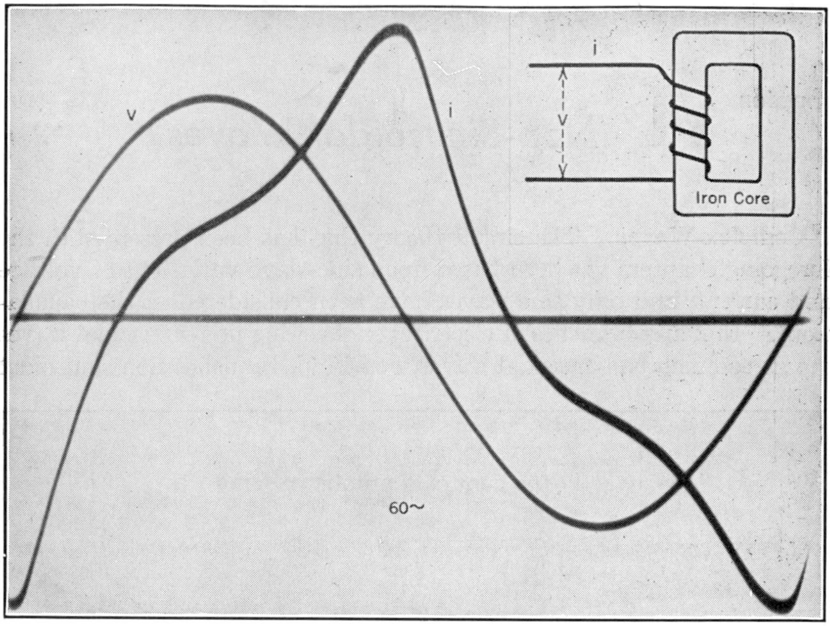

OSCILLOGRAM 2. Distorted current wave, *i*, results when a sine wave of voltage, *v*, is impressed on a particular coil with an iron core.

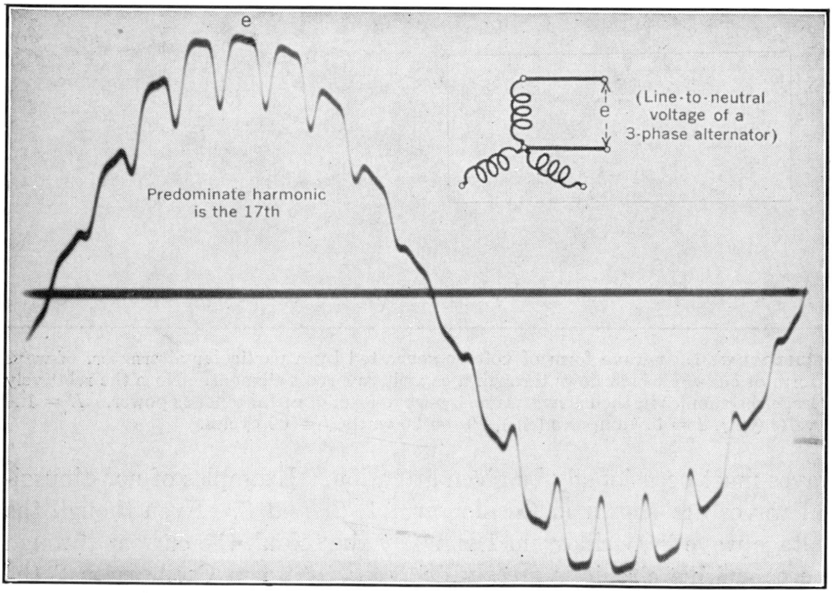

OSCILLOGRAM 3. Wave form produced by an open-slot type of generator.

a sinusoid. Oscillogram 3 shows the effect on the voltage wave form of an alternator due to open slots. The predominant harmonic in this case can easily be determined by the methods discussed in this chapter. The method of making circuit calculations when non-sinusoidal wave forms are encountered will also be given.

Most non-sinusoidal waves found in electrical engineering can be expressed in terms of sine-wave components of different frequencies. Under these conditions each sine component may be handled according to the laws governing the calculations of sine waves. The results of all component analyses are combined according to certain laws to form the composite or final analysis. There are, however, certain limitations to representing non-sinusoidal waves in terms of sine components.

Any periodic wave which is single-valued and continuous except for a finite number of finite discontinuities, and which does not have an infinite number of maxima or minima in the neighborhood of any point, may be represented by the sum of a number of sine waves of different frequencies. As an equation, the above theorem takes the following form and is known as a Fourier series:

$$\begin{aligned} y = f(x) &= A_0 + A_1 \sin x + B_1 \cos x + A_2 \sin 2x + B_2 \cos 2x \\ &+ A_3 \sin 3x + B_3 \cos 3x + \cdots + A_n \sin nx + B_n \cos nx \end{aligned} \quad (1)$$

Except in special cases an infinite number of components are theoretically required. Practically, however, only a few terms are necessary in most instances because of the relatively small effect of the terms of higher frequency. Since the wave which is represented by equation (1) is made up of a number of sine waves of different frequencies, it is called a complex wave. It is apparent that each component of this wave is sinusoidal and that each component in itself may be handled by the methods previously outlined for calculating sine waves. The facility with which sinusoidal components of a complex wave may be manipulated is sufficient justification for expressing a non-sinusoidal wave in such terms as equation (1) even though the equation of the wave may be known in terms of some other function of x.

Wave Analysis. Usually, a photographic record of the wave will be obtained through oscillographic analysis or other means. The determination of the Fourier equation which specifies a particular wave is called wave analysis. Wave analysis consists simply of determining the coefficients A_0, A_1, B_1, etc., of equation (1). These coefficients are determined by some operation on equation (1) that will eliminate all terms except the desired quantity. Then the desired coefficient may be evaluated. Thus, to determine A_0, it is necessary simply to multiply the equation by dx and to integrate between 0 and 2π, as shown below.

$$\int_0^{2\pi} y\,dx = \int_0^{2\pi} A_0\,dx + \int_0^{2\pi} A_1 \sin x\,dx + \int_0^{2\pi} B_1 \cos x\,dx + \int_0^{2\pi} A_2 \sin 2x\,dx + \int_0^{2\pi} B_2 \cos 2x\,dx + \int_0^{2\pi} A_3 \sin 3x\,dx + \int_0^{2\pi} B_3 \cos 3x\,dx + \cdots + \int_0^{2\pi} A_n \sin nx\,dx + \int_0^{2\pi} B_n \cos nx\,dx \quad (2)$$

or

$$\int_0^{2\pi} y\,dx = A_0 \int_0^{2\pi} dx = 2\pi A_0$$

and

$$A_0 = \frac{1}{2\pi} \int_0^{2\pi} y\,dx \quad (3)$$

To find A_1, equation (1) may be multiplied by $\sin x\,dx$ and integrated from 0 to 2π. Thus

$$\int_0^{2\pi} y \sin x\,dx = \int_0^{2\pi} A_0 \sin x\,dx + \int_0^{2\pi} A_1 \sin^2 x\,dx + \int_0^{2\pi} B_1 \cos x \sin x\,dx + \int_0^{2\pi} A_2 \sin 2x \sin x\,dx + \int_0^{2\pi} B_2 \cos 2x \sin x\,dx + \int_0^{2\pi} A_3 \sin 3x \sin x\,dx + \int_0^{2\pi} B_3 \cos 3x \sin x\,dx + \cdots + \int_0^{2\pi} A_n \sin nx \sin x\,dx + \int_0^{2\pi} B_n \cos nx \sin x\,dx \quad (4)$$

It is obvious that $\int_0^{2\pi} A_0 \sin x\,dx$ is zero since it represents the area under a sine wave for a complete cycle. There are four other types of terms. They are

(*a*) $\int_0^{2\pi} \sin^2 x\,dx = \int_0^{2\pi} (\frac{1}{2} - \frac{1}{2}\cos 2x)\,dx = \frac{2\pi}{2} = \pi,$

(*b*) $\int_0^{2\pi} \sin 2x \sin x\,dx$, which is of the general type:

$\int_0^{2\pi} \sin mx \sin nx\,dx = 0$, when m and n are different integers,[1]

(*c*) $\int_0^{2\pi} \cos mx \sin nx\,dx = 0$, when m and n are different integers,[2] and

(*d*) $\int_0^{2\pi} \cos x \sin x\,dx = 0.$

[1] This may be readily proved by substituting for $\sin mx \sin nx$ its equivalent $\frac{1}{2}[\cos(mx - nx) - \cos(mx + nx)]$.

[2] This may be readily proved by substituting for $\cos mx \sin nx$ its equivalent $\frac{1}{2}[\sin(mx + nx) - \sin(mx - nx)]$.

The student should prove statements a, b, c, and d by carrying out the operations indicated. If the above facts are used, equation (4) reduces to

$$\int_0^{2\pi} y \sin x \, dx = A_1\pi$$

or

$$A_1 = \frac{1}{\pi}\int_0^{2\pi} y \sin x \, dx \tag{5}$$

To evaluate the coefficient of the cosine term B_1, equation (1) is multiplied by $\cos x \, dx$ and integrated from 0 to 2π. Thus

$$\int_0^{2\pi} y \cos x \, dx = \int_0^{2\pi} A_0 \cos x \, dx + \int_0^{2\pi} A_1 \sin x \cos x \, dx$$
$$+ \int_0^{2\pi} B_1 \cos^2 x \, dx + \int_0^{2\pi} A_2 \sin 2x \cos x \, dx + \int_0^{2\pi} B_2 \cos 2x \cos x \, dx$$
$$+ \int_0^{2\pi} A_3 \sin 3x \cos x \, dx + \int_0^{2\pi} B_3 \cos 3x \cos x \, dx + \cdots$$
$$+ \int_0^{2\pi} A_n \sin nx \cos x \, dx + \int_0^{2\pi} B_n \cos nx \cos x \, dx \tag{6}$$

If the relations stated above in a, b, c, and d are used, equation (6) becomes

$$\int_0^{2\pi} y \cos x \, dx = B_1 \int_0^{2\pi} \cos^2 x \, dx = B_1\pi$$

or

$$B_1 = \frac{1}{\pi}\int_0^{2\pi} y \cos x \, dx \tag{7}$$

Similarly,

$$A_2 = \frac{1}{\pi}\int_0^{2\pi} y \sin 2x \, dx \tag{8}$$

$$B_2 = \frac{1}{\pi}\int_0^{2\pi} y \cos 2x \, dx \tag{9}$$

$$A_3 = \frac{1}{\pi}\int_0^{2\pi} y \sin 3x \, dx \tag{10}$$

$$B_3 = \frac{1}{\pi}\int_0^{2\pi} y \cos 3x \, dx \tag{11}$$

$$A_n = \frac{1}{\pi}\int_0^{2\pi} y \sin nx \, dx \tag{12}$$

$$B_n = \frac{1}{\pi}\int_0^{2\pi} y \cos nx \, dx \tag{13}$$

Various analytical and graphical methods may be employed to evaluate the coefficients of equations (3), (12), and (13). Two general methods are outlined below.

Analytical Method. If the equation of y in terms of x is known in some mathematical form, the wave may be analyzed analytically. This method is the least laborious but it cannot be employed if the function of x is not known analytically. The function of x employed need not throughout its entire range represent the particular wave to be analyzed. It is necessary to have the function of x only over the interval of periodicity, namely, 2π. Not even a single function of x is necessary. Several different ones may be used and the complete integral from 0 to 2π may be obtained from a sum of the integrals of the several functions, each taken over the interval in which it follows the curve to be analyzed.

The details connected with writing a Fourier series to represent a specified wave form are illustrated by the following examples.

Example 1. Let it be required to write the Fourier series which will represent the sawtooth wave form shown in Fig. 1. It will be observed that this wave form is

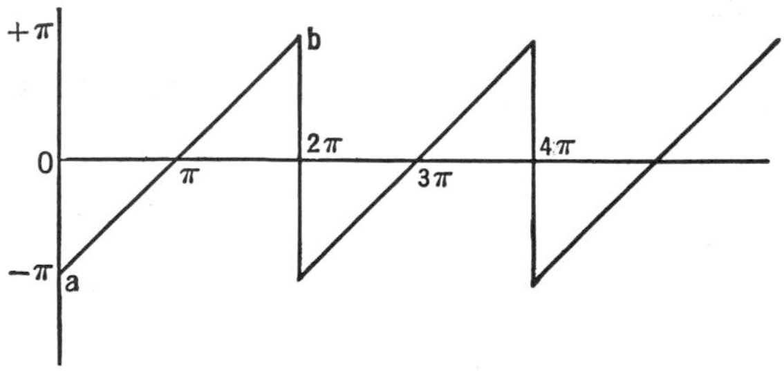

Fig. 1. A type of wave which is easily analyzed by analytical methods.

simply a straight-line variation, ranging from $y = -\pi$ to $y = +\pi$ over one complete cycle. This straight-line variation may be expressed analytically (between $x = 0$ and $x = 2\pi$) as:

$$y = f(x) = x - \pi$$

It should be noted that the above analytical expression for y in terms of x gives no indication of the various harmonics which are present in the wave, whereas a Fourier-series representation of the wave will yield this information.

From equation (3):

$$A_0 = \frac{1}{2\pi}\int_0^{2\pi} (x - \pi)\, dx = \frac{1}{2\pi}\left[\frac{x^2}{2} - \pi x\right]_0^{2\pi} = \frac{1}{2\pi}\left[\frac{4\pi^2}{2} - 2\pi^2\right] = 0$$

The fact that A_0 is zero could have been determined by inspection of Fig. 1 since it is obvious from the figure that the negative half of the wave is equal in area to the positive half.

From equation (12):

$$A_n = \frac{1}{\pi}\int_0^{2\pi}(x-\pi)\sin nx\,dx = \frac{1}{\pi}\left[\int_0^{2\pi} x\sin nx\,dx - \int_0^{2\pi}\pi\sin nx\,dx\right]$$

$$\int_0^{2\pi} x\sin nx\,dx = \left[-\frac{x\cos nx}{n} + \frac{1}{n^2}\sin nx\right]_0^{2\pi}$$

as may be proved by differentiation of the right member and $\int_0^{2\pi}\pi\sin nx\,dx = 0$ for all integral values of n. Therefore:

$$A_n = \frac{1}{\pi}\left[-\frac{x\cos nx}{n} + \frac{1}{n^2}\sin nx\right]_0^{2\pi} = -\frac{2}{n}$$

whence

$$A_1 = -\tfrac{2}{1};\quad A_2 = -\tfrac{2}{2};\quad A_3 = -\tfrac{2}{3};\quad A_4 = -\tfrac{2}{4};\quad \text{etc.}$$

From equation (13):

$$B_n = \frac{1}{\pi}\int_0^{2\pi}(x-\pi)\cos nx\,dx = \frac{1}{\pi}\left[\int_0^{2\pi} x\cos nx\,dx - \int_0^{2\pi}\pi\cos nx\,dx\right]$$

$$\int_0^{2\pi} x\cos nx\,dx = \left[\frac{x\sin nx}{n} + \frac{\cos nx}{n^2}\right]_0^{2\pi}$$

as may be proved by differentiation of the right member and $\int_0^{2\pi}\pi\cos nx\,dx = 0$ for all integral values of n. Therefore:

$$B_n = \frac{1}{\pi}\left[\frac{x\sin nx}{n} + \frac{\cos nx}{n^2}\right]_0^{2\pi} = 0 \quad \text{(for all integral values of } n\text{)}$$

Hence all the coefficients B_1, B_2, B_3, etc., in equation (1) are 0 and the Fourier equation of the wave shown in Fig. 1 becomes:

$$y = -2\left(\sin x + \frac{1}{2}\sin 2x + \frac{1}{3}\sin 3x + \frac{1}{4}\sin 4x + \cdots + \frac{1}{n}\sin nx\right)$$

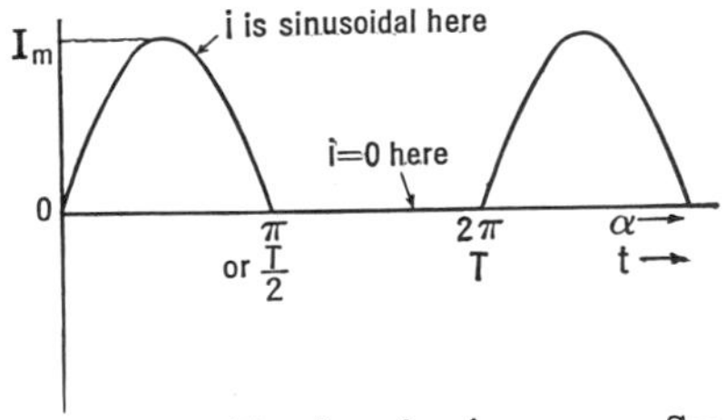

Fig. 2. Half-wave rectification of a sine wave. See example 2.

Example 2. Let it be required to write the first four terms of the Fourier series which will represent the wave form shown in Fig. 2. From Fig. 2, it is plain that i may be expressed analytically between the limits of 0 and 2π as two separate functions. That is:

$$i = I_m \sin\alpha \qquad [\text{between } \alpha \text{ (or } \omega t) = 0 \text{ and } \alpha \text{ (or } \omega t) = \pi]$$

and

$$i = 0 \qquad [\text{between } \alpha \text{ (or } \omega t) = \pi \text{ and } \alpha \text{ (or } \omega t) = 2\pi]$$

From equation (3):

$$A_0 = \frac{1}{2\pi}\left[\int_0^{\pi} I_m \sin\alpha\, d\alpha + \int_{\pi}^{2\pi} 0\, d\alpha\right] = \frac{I_m}{2\pi}\Big[-\cos\alpha\Big]_0^{\pi}$$

$$= \frac{I_m}{\pi} = 0.318 I_m$$

From equation (5):

$$A_1 = \frac{1}{\pi}\left[\int_0^{\pi} (I_m \sin\alpha)\sin\alpha\, d\alpha + \int_{\pi}^{2\pi} (0)\sin\alpha\, d\alpha\right]$$

$$= \frac{I_m}{\pi}\left[\int_0^{\pi} (\tfrac{1}{2} - \tfrac{1}{2}\cos 2\,\alpha)\, d\alpha\right]$$

$$= \frac{I_m}{\pi}\left[\frac{\alpha}{2} - \frac{1}{4}\sin 2\alpha\right]_0^{\pi} = \frac{I_m}{\pi}\left[\frac{\pi}{2}\right] = 0.500 I_m$$

From equation (12) it follows that A_2, A_3, A_4, etc., are all zero because:

$$A_n = \frac{1}{\pi}\left[\int_0^{\pi} (I_m \sin\alpha)\sin n\alpha\, d\alpha\right] = 0 \text{ (for } n \neq 0 \text{ and } n \neq 1)$$

The above evaluation of A_n is evident if $(\sin\alpha \sin n\alpha)$ is replaced by its equivalent $\frac{1}{2}[\cos(n-1)\alpha - \cos(n+1)\alpha]$. Thus A_2, A_3, A_4, etc., are zero because:

$$A_n = \frac{1}{\pi}\int_0^{\pi} \tfrac{1}{2}[\cos(n-1)\alpha - \cos(n+1)\alpha]\, d\alpha$$

$$= \frac{1}{2\pi}\left[\frac{\sin(n-1)\alpha}{(n-1)} - \frac{\sin(n+1)\alpha}{(n+1)}\right]_0^{\pi} = 0 \qquad \begin{cases}\text{for } n \neq 0\\ \text{and } n \neq 1\end{cases}$$

From equation (7):

$$B_1 = \frac{1}{\pi}\left[\int_0^{\pi} (I_m \sin\alpha)\cos\alpha\, d\alpha + \int_{\pi}^{2\pi} (0)\cos\alpha\, d\alpha\right]$$

$$= \frac{I_m}{\pi}\left[\int_0^{\pi} \frac{\sin 2\alpha}{2}\, d\alpha\right] = \frac{I_m}{\pi}\left[-\frac{\cos 2\alpha}{4}\right]_0^{\pi} = 0$$

From equation (13):

$$B_n = \frac{1}{\pi}\left[\int_0^{\pi} (I_m \sin\alpha)\cos n\alpha\, d\alpha\right]$$

$$= \frac{I_m}{\pi}\left[\int_0^{\pi}\left(\frac{\sin(\alpha + n\alpha)}{2} + \frac{\sin(\alpha - n\alpha)}{2}\right) d\alpha\right]$$

$$= \frac{I_m}{\pi}\left[-\frac{\cos(1+n)\alpha}{2(1+n)} - \frac{\cos(1-n)\alpha}{2(1-n)}\right]_0^{\pi} \qquad \begin{cases}\text{for } n \neq 0\\ \text{and } n \neq 1\end{cases}$$

For $n = 2$:

$$B_2 = \frac{I_m}{\pi}\left[-\frac{\cos 3\alpha}{6} - \frac{\cos(-\alpha)}{-2}\right]_0^{\pi} = \frac{I_m}{\pi}\left[+\frac{1}{6} + \frac{1}{6} - \frac{1}{2} - \frac{1}{2}\right]$$

$$= -\frac{2I_m}{3\pi} = -0.212 I_m$$

Similarly for $n = 3$,

$$B_3 = 0$$

and for $n = 4$,

$$B_4 = -0.0424I_m$$

The Fourier series which represents the wave form shown in Fig. 2 is therefore:

$$i = 0.318I_m + 0.500I_m \sin \alpha - 0.212I_m \cos 2\alpha - 0.0424I_m \cos 4\alpha - \cdots$$

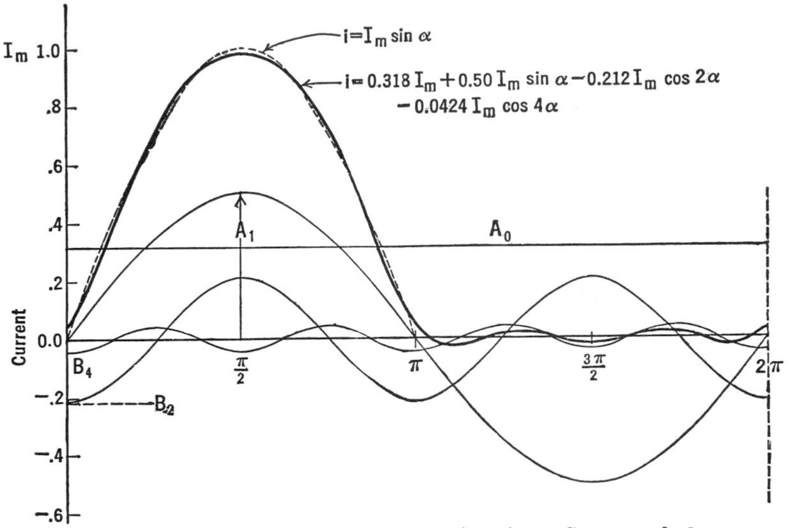

Fig. 3. Components of half-wave rectification. See example 2.

If the above four terms are combined graphically as shown in Fig. 3, the resultant wave approaches the original wave form shown in Fig. 2 to a fair degree of accuracy. The inclusion of more terms in the Fourier series will, of course, improve the correspondence between the resultant wave of Fig. 3 and the original wave form.

Problem 1. (*a*) Write the Fourier series which represents the wave form shown in Fig. 4 out to and including the A_3 term of the series. *Note:* $e = 100$ between $\alpha = 0$ and $\alpha = \pi$, and $e = 0$ between $\alpha = \pi$ and $\alpha = 2\pi$.

Ans.: $e = 50 + 63.7 \sin \alpha + 21.2 \sin 3\alpha$ volts.

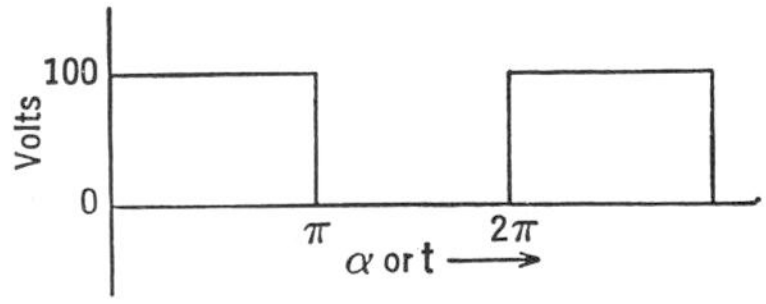

Fig. 4. See Problem 1.

(*b*) Show by means of a sketch the manner in which the above three components combine to approximate the flat-topped wave shown in Fig. 4.

Fourier Analysis of Symmetrical Triangular and Rectangular Waves. Symmetrical waves of triangular and rectangular shape are shown in Figs. 5 (solid lines) and 6 respectively. Since these wave forms are often used in the analyses of certain basic problems, it is convenient to have the Fourier equations of these waves readily available.

Triangular Wave. To facilitate analyzing, the triangular wave may be considered to be composed of several pieces, namely, the straight lines *oa*, *ac*, and *cd*. If the point slope form of equation for a straight line is applied, the equations of these lines will be found to be:

$$y_{oa} = \frac{2x}{\pi}; \quad y_{ac} = -\frac{2x}{\pi} + 2; \quad y_{cd} = \frac{2x}{\pi} - 4$$

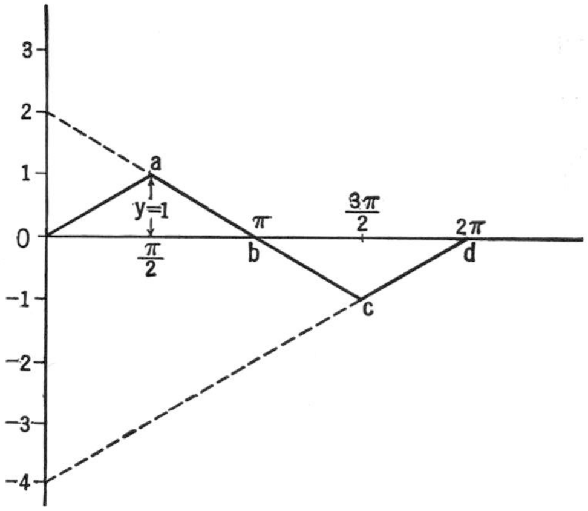

FIG. 5. Symmetrical triangular wave with a maximum value of 1.

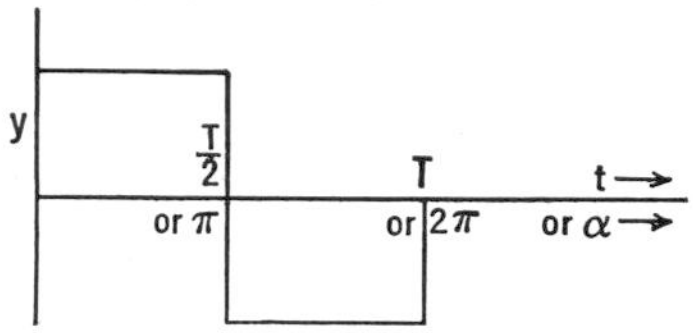

FIG. 6. Symmetrical rectangular wave.

Applying equations (3), (12), and (13) gives:

$$A_0 = \frac{1}{2\pi}\int_0^{2\pi} y\,dx = \frac{1}{2\pi}\left\{\int_0^{\pi/2} \frac{2x}{\pi}\,dx + \int_{\pi/2}^{3\pi/2}\left(\frac{-2x}{\pi}+2\right)dx + \int_{3\pi/2}^{2\pi}\left(\frac{2x}{\pi}-4\right)dx\right\}$$

$$A_n = \frac{1}{\pi}\int_0^{2\pi} y \sin nx\,dx$$

$$= \frac{1}{\pi}\left\{\int_0^{\pi/2} \frac{2x}{\pi}\sin nx\,dx + \int_{\pi/2}^{3\pi/2}\left(\frac{-2x}{\pi}+2\right)\sin nx\,dx + \int_{3\pi/2}^{2\pi}\left(\frac{2x}{\pi}-4\right)\sin nx\,dx\right\}$$

$$B_n = \frac{1}{\pi}\int_0^{2\pi} y \cos nx\,dx$$

$$= \frac{1}{\pi}\left\{\int_0^{\pi/2} \frac{2x}{\pi}\cos nx\,dx + \int_{\pi/2}^{3\pi/2}\left(\frac{-2x}{\pi}+2\right)\cos nx\,dx + \int_{3\pi/2}^{2\pi}\left(\frac{2x}{\pi}-4\right)\cos nx\,dx\right.$$

Evaluation of the above for various values of n by ordinary calculus methods gives the equation of the wave in terms of a Fourier series as follows:

$$y = \frac{8}{\pi^2}\left(\sin x - \frac{1}{3^2}\sin 3x + \frac{1}{5^2}\sin 5x - \frac{1}{7^2}\sin 7x + \cdots \text{etc.}\right) \quad (14)$$

It will be shown later how it is possible to determine from inspection, that, in certain classes of waves as typified by the above example, the terms represented by B_n must be zero.

The results of the above analysis may be generalized and the equation of a symmetrical triangular wave written as

$$y = A_1 \sin \omega t - \frac{A_1}{3^2} \sin 3\omega t + \frac{A_1}{5^2} \sin 5\omega t - \frac{A_1}{7^2} \sin 7\omega t + \cdots \text{etc.} \quad (14a)$$

where x of equation (14) has been replaced by ωt and A_1 equals $8/\pi^2$ times the maximum ordinate of the triangular wave. Theoretically, there is an infinite number of terms and the progression continues as the first four terms indicate.

Rectangular Wave. The rectangular wave is much used in the analysis of a-c machinery and has for its Fourier equation:

$$y = A_1 \sin \omega t + \frac{A_1}{3} \sin 3\omega t + \frac{A_1}{5} \sin 5\omega t + \frac{A_1}{7} \sin 7\omega t + \cdots \text{etc.} \quad (15)$$

where $A_1 = \dfrac{4}{\pi}$ times the height of the rectangle. Again there is an infinite number of terms which may be written as indicated by the first four terms shown. Figure 7 shows a graphical representation of the first three terms and illustrates that a fair approximation to the resultant wave is obtained by the addition of very few terms.

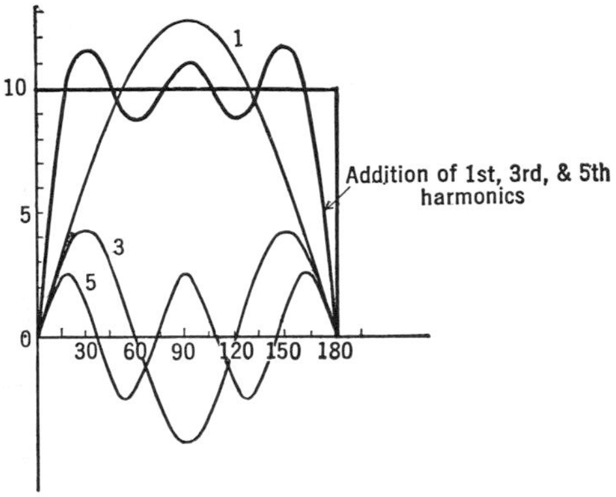

FIG. 7. The addition of only three harmonics gives a fair approximation of the rectangular wave.

Problem 2. Analyze the rectangular wave shown in Fig. 6 by the analytical method to prove the validity of equation (15).

Graphical Method. A second method of evaluating equations (3), (12), and (13) involves the evaluation of the integrals by a step-by-step method. The equation of y in terms of x is usually unknown, and for the majority of waves encountered it would be very cumbersome and laborious to establish equations which would yield pieces of the wave. It is under these conditions that the step-by-step method (sometimes called the graphical method) or its equivalent is employed. The details of this method follow.

Suppose the wave of Fig. 8 is to be analyzed. Equation (3) is simply the average height of the curve over 2π radians. It is found by dividing the area under the curve by the base. Any method of determining the area, such as counting squares or by use of a planimeter, may be employed. If the areas of the positive and negative loops are the same, A_0 is zero. Hence for waves having adjacent loops of the same shape and area with respect to some horizontal axis, the constant A_0 when present simply indicates how much the whole wave has been raised or lowered from symmetry about the axis of abscissas. For graphical analysis, equation (5) may be written

$$A_1 = \frac{1}{\pi} \sum_0^{2\pi} y \sin x \, \Delta x \tag{16}$$

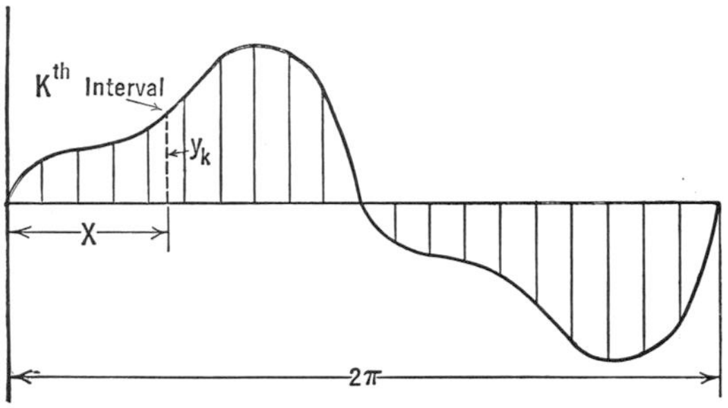

FIG. 8. Preparation of a wave for analysis by the graphical method.

Let 2π radians in Fig. 8 be divided into m equal parts. Then $\Delta x = \frac{2\pi}{m}$ and x, the distance to the midpoint of the kth interval, is $k \frac{2\pi}{m} - \frac{1}{2}\left(\frac{2\pi}{m}\right)$ or $(k - \frac{1}{2}) \frac{2\pi}{m}$. Equation (16) now becomes

$$\begin{aligned} A_1 &= \frac{1}{\pi} \sum_0^m \left[y_k \sin (k - \tfrac{1}{2}) \frac{2\pi}{m} \right] \frac{2\pi}{m} \\ &= \frac{2\pi}{m} \frac{1}{\pi} \sum_0^m y_k \sin \left[(k - \tfrac{1}{2}) \frac{2\pi}{m} \right] \\ &= \frac{2}{m} \sum_0^m y_k \sin \left[(k - \tfrac{1}{2}) \frac{2\pi}{m} \right] \end{aligned} \tag{17}$$

Similarly,

$$B_1 = \frac{2}{m} \sum_0^m y_k \cos (k - \tfrac{1}{2}) \frac{2\pi}{m} \tag{18}$$

and

$$A_2 = \frac{2}{m} \sum_0^m y_k \sin 2 \, (k - \tfrac{1}{2}) \frac{2\pi}{m} \tag{19}$$

The first form of equation (17) shows that A_1 is $1/\pi$ times the area under a *new curve*, which would be obtained by plotting corresponding ordinates of the original curve multiplied by the sine of the angle to the ordinate in question. For A_n the ordinates of the new curve would be obtained by multiplying selected ordinates of the original curve by the sine of n times the fundamental angular distance to the respective ordinates. An analogous procedure is employed for cosine terms. Looked at in another way, equation (17) indicates that A_1 is twice the average ordinate of the *new* curve, which would be obtained by plotting corresponding ordinates of the original curve multiplied by the sine of the angle to the ordinate in question. Multiplying and dividing equation (16) or (17) by 2 makes this statement evident. Thus

$$A_1 = 2\left[\frac{1}{2\pi}\sum_{0}^{2\pi} y \sin x \, \Delta x\right]$$

Similar interpretations may be drawn regarding the other coefficients of the Fourier series. The summations are best carried out in tabular form, and for this purpose a more or less standardized system is used. The tables which are used are called analyzing tables. One form of analyzing tables for odd harmonics up to and including the seventh are shown in heavy type on the following pages. (The light type refers to specific values for an illustrative example.)

It will be shown in a subsequent article that waves having symmetrical positive and negative loops cannot contain even harmonics. Under these conditions it is unnecessary to evaluate A_2, B_2, A_4, B_4, etc. Also, when the wave being analyzed consists of odd harmonics only, it is necessary only to take the summation over the first 180°. Since the summation over the second 180° would be the same as that over the first 180°, the total summation over 360° can be obtained by multiplying the summation over 180° by 2. If m is taken as the number of intervals in 360°, the summation over 180° may be multiplied by $4/m$ instead of multiplying the summation over 360° by $2/m$ as shown in equation (17). Whereas equations (17), (18), and (19) indicate that the midordinate of the interval selected should be used, it is customary to use the ordinate and the angle corresponding to those given in the tables. When the intervals are as small as 5°, the difference between the two schemes is negligible.

Example 3. Given the experimentally determined wave form shown in Oscillogram 4. Find the Fourier equation, employing analyzing tables similar to those given on pages 237–240.

Solution. Ordinates at every 5° are constructed as shown in Oscillogram 4. The magnitude of each is scaled and set in the column for ordinates opposite the corresponding angle in the column for angles. The product of the ordinates and the corresponding sines and cosines of n times the angles are obtained and tabulated as shown in the analyzing tables on pages 237–240.

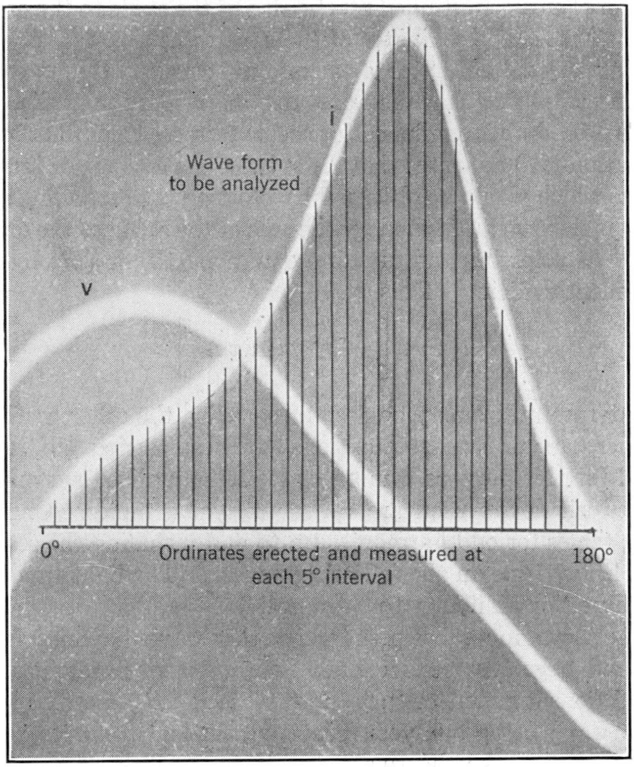

OSCILLOGRAM 4. See example 3.

For the particular wave which is being analyzed:

$$A_1 = 82.45 \text{ units} \qquad A_5 = -5.38 \text{ units}$$
$$B_1 = -22.11 \text{ units} \qquad B_5 = -3.65 \text{ units}$$
$$A_3 = -0.92 \text{ unit} \qquad A_7 = 2.01 \text{ units}$$
$$B_3 = 26.2 \text{ units} \qquad B_7 = -1.29 \text{ units}$$

The Fourier equation of the wave is, therefore,

$$i = 82.45 \sin \omega t - 22.11 \cos \omega t - 0.92 \sin 3\omega t$$
$$+ 26.2 \cos 3\omega t - 5.38 \sin 5\omega t - 3.65 \cos 5\omega t$$
$$+ 2.01 \sin 7\omega t - 1.29 \cos 7\omega t$$

The fundamental frequency in this particular case is 60 cycles per second. Therefore ω is equal to 377 radians per second.

The actual number of terms in the Fourier equation in any particular case can usually be reduced because it is always possible to combine sine and cosine waves of the same frequencies. For example, consider the general wave

$$y = A_1 \sin \omega t + B_1 \cos \omega t + A_2 \sin 2\omega t + B_2 \cos 2\omega t$$
$$+ A_3 \sin 3\omega t + B_3 \cos 3\omega t$$

FUNDAMENTAL

1	2	3	4	5	6	7	8	9
sin x	Products (y sin x)		Ordinate No.	Angle x to ordinate	Meas. ordinate (y)	cos x	Products (y cos x)	
	+	−					+	−
.0872	0.5		1	5°	5.9	.9962	5.9	
.1736	1.7		2	10°	10.0	.9848	9.8	
.2588	3.5		3	15°	13.4	.9659	13.0	
.3420	5.6		4	20°	16.4	.9397	15.4	
.4226	8.2		5	25°	19.4	.9063	17.6	
.5000	10.9		6	30°	21.8	.8660	18.9	
.5736	13.5		7	35°	23.6	.8192	19.3	
.6428	16.6		8	40°	25.9	.7660	19.9	
.7071	19.9		9	45°	28.1	.7071	19.9	
.7660	23.5		10	50°	30.7	.6428	19.7	
.8192	27.8		11	55°	33.9	.5736	19.4	
.8660	32.4		12	60°	37.4	.5000	18.7	
.9063	38.1		13	65°	42.0	.4226	17.7	
.9397	43.9		14	70°	46.7	.3420	16.0	
.9659	51.0		15	75°	52.8	.2588	13.7	
.9848	59.1		16	80°	60.0	.1736	10.4	
.9962	67.5		17	85°	67.7	.0872	5.9	
1.0000	76.4		18	90°	76.4	.0000	0.0	
.9962	86.2		19	95°	86.5	−.0872		7.5
.9848	94.1		20	100°	95.5	−.1736		16.6
.9659	101.5		21	105°	105.1	−.2588		27.2
.9397	106.0		22	110°	112.8	−.3420		38.6
.9063	106.4		23	115°	117.4	−.4226		49.6
.8660	102.7		24	120°	118.5	−.5000		59.3
.8192	93.5		25	125°	114.2	−.5736		65.5
.7660	80.4		26	130°	104.9	−.6428		67.4
.7071	64.6		27	135°	91.4	−.7071		64.6
.6428	50.4		28	140°	78.3	−.7660		60.0
.5736	37.2		29	145°	65.0	−.8192		53.2
.5000	25.6		30	150°	51.1	−.8660		44.3
.4226	16.9		31	155°	40.0	−.9063		36.3
.3420	10.1		32	160°	29.4	−.9397		27.6
.2588	5.5		33	165°	21.3	−.9659		20.6
.1736	2.4		34	170°	14.0	−.9848		13.8
.0872	0.6		35	175°	7.1	−.9962		7.1
.0000	0.0		36	180°	0.0	−1.0000		0.0
Sum of products	1484.2	0					261.2	659.2
	1484.2						−398.0	

$$A_1 = \frac{1484}{36} \times 2 = 82.45$$

$$B_1 = \frac{-398.0}{36} \times 2 = -22.11$$

THIRD HARMONIC

1	2	3	4	5	6	7	8	9
sin 3x	Products (y sin 3x)		Ordinate No.	Angle x to ordinate	Meas. ordinate (y)	cos 3x	Products (y cos 3x)	
	+	−					+	−
.2588	1.5		1	5°	5.9	.9659	5.7	
.5000	5.0		2	10°	10.0	.8660	8.7	
.7071	9.5		3	15°	13.4	.7071	9.5	
.8660	14.2		4	20°	16.4	.5000	8.2	
.9659	18.8		5	25°	19.4	.2588	5.0	
1.0000	21.8		6	30°	21.8	.0000	0.0	
.9659	22.8		7	35°	23.6	−.2588		6.1
.8660	22.4		8	40°	25.9	−.5000		12.9
.7071	19.9		9	45°	28.1	−.7071		19.9
.5000	15.4		10	50°	30.7	−.8660		26.6
.2588	8.8		11	55°	33.9	−.9659		32.8
.0000	0.0		12	60°	37.4	−1.0000		37.4
−.2588		10.9	13	65°	42.0	−.9659		40.6
−.5000		23.4	14	70°	46.7	−.8660		40.5
−.7071		37.4	15	75°	52.8	−.7071		37.4
−.8660		52.0	16	80°	60.0	−.5000		30.0
−.9659		65.5	17	85°	67.7	−.2588		17.5
−1.0000		76.4	18	90°	76.4	−.0000		0.0
−.9659		83.7	19	95°	86.5	.2588	22.4	
−.8660		82.8	20	100°	95.5	.5000	47.8	
−.7071		74.4	21	105°	105.1	.7071	74.4	
−.5000		56.4	22	110°	112.8	.8660	97.7	
−.2588		30.4	23	115°	117.4	.9659	113.6	
.0000		0.0	24	120°	118.5	1.0000	118.5	
.2588	29.6		25	125°	114.2	.9659	110.4	
.5000	52.5		26	130°	104.9	.8660	90.9	
.7071	64.6		27	135°	91.4	.7071	64.6	
.8660	67.9		28	140°	78.3	.5000	39.2	
.9659	62.8		29	145°	65.0	.2588	16.8	
1.0000	51.1		30	150°	51.1	.0000	0.0	
.9659	38.7		31	155°	40.0	−.2588		10.4
.8660	25.5		32	160°	29.4	−.5000		14.7
.7071	15.1		33	165°	21.3	−.7071		15.1
.5000	7.0		34	170°	14.0	−.8660		12.1
.2588	1.8		35	175°	7.1	−.9659		6.9
.0000	0.0		36	180°	0.0	−1.0000		0.0
Sum of products	576.7	593.3					833.4	360.9
	−16.6						+472.5	

$$A_3 = \frac{2(-16.6)}{36} = -0.92$$

$$B_3 = \frac{2(472.5)}{36} = 26.2$$

Fifth Harmonic

1	2	3	4	5	6	7	8	9
sin 5*x*	Products (*y* sin 5*x*)		Ordinate No.	Angle *x* to ordinate	Meas. ordinate (*y*)	cos 5*x*	Products (*y* cos 5*x*)	
	+	−					+	−
.4226	2.5		1	5°	5.9	.9063	5.4	
.7660	7.7		2	10°	10.0	.6428	6.4	
.9659	13.0		3	15°	13.4	.2588	3.5	
.9848	16.2		4	20°	16.4	−.1736		2.8
.8192	15.9		5	25°	19.4	−.5736		11.1
.5000	10.9		6	30°	21.8	−.8660		18.9
.0872	2.1		7	35°	23.6	−.9962		23.5
−.3420		8.9	8	40°	25.9	−.9397		24.4
−.7071		19.9	9	45°	28.1	−.7071		19.9
−.9397		28.8	10	50°	30.7	−.3420		10.5
−.9962		33.8	11	55°	33.9	.0872	3.0	
−.8660		32.4	12	60°	37.4	.5000	18.7	
−.5736		24.1	13	65°	42.0	.8192	34.4	
−.1736		8.1	14	70°	46.7	.9848	46.0	
.2588	13.7		15	75°	52.8	.9659	51.0	
.6428	38.6		16	80°	60.0	.7660	46.0	
.9063	61.4		17	85°	67.7	.4226	28.6	
1.0000	76.4		18	90°	76.4	.0000	0.0	
.9063	78.5		19	95°	86.5	−.4226		36.6
.6428	61.4		20	100°	95.5	−.7660		73.2
.2588	27.2		21	105°	105.1	−.9659		101.6
−.1736		19.6	22	110°	112.8	−.9848		111.1
−.5736		67.4	23	115°	117.4	−.8192		96.2
−.8660		102.7	24	120°	118.5	−.5000		59.2
−.9962		114.0	25	125°	114.2	−.0872		10.0
−.9397		98.5	26	130°	104.9	.3420	35.8	
−.7071		64.6	27	135°	91.4	.7071	64.6	
−.3420		26.8	28	140°	78.3	.9397	73.6	
.0872	5.7		29	145°	65.0	.9962	64.8	
.5000	25.6		30	150°	51.1	.8660	44.3	
.8192	32.7		31	155°	40.0	.5736	23.0	
.9848	29.0		32	160°	29.4	.1736	5.1	
.9659	20.6		33	165°	21.3	−.2588		5.5
.7660	10.7		34	170°	14.0	−.6428		9.0
.4226	3.0		35	175°	7.1	−.9063		6.4
.0000	0.0		36	180°	0.0	−1.0000		0.0
Sum of products	552.8	649.6					554.2	619.9
	−96.8						−65.7	

$$A_5 = \frac{-96.8}{36} \times 2 = -5.38$$

$$B_5 = \frac{-65.7}{36} \times 2 = -3.65$$

SEVENTH HARMONIC

1	2	3	4	5	6	7	8	9
sin 7x	Products (y sin 7x)		Ordinate No.	Angle x to ordinate	Meas. ordinate (y)	cos 7x	Products (y cos 7x)	
	+	−					+	−
.5736	3.4		1	5°	5.9	.8192	4.8	
.9397	9.4		2	10°	10.0	.3420	3.4	
.9659	13.0		3	15°	13.4	−.2588		3.5
.6428	10.5		4	20°	16.4	−.7660		12.6
.0872	1.7		5	25°	19.4	−.9962		19.3
−.5000		10.9	6	30°	21.8	−.8660		18.9
−.9063		21.4	7	35°	23.6	−.4226		10.0
−.9848		24.4	8	40°	25.9	.1736	4.5	
−.7071		19.9	9	45°	28.1	.7071	19.9	
−.1736		5.3	10	50°	30.7	.9848	30.2	
.4226	14.3		11	55°	33.9	.9063	30.8	
.8660	32.4		12	60°	37.4	.5000	18.7	
.9962	41.9		13	65°	42.0	−.0872		3.7
.7660	35.8		14	70°	46.7	−.6428		30.0
.2588	13.7		15	75°	52.8	−.9659		51.0
−.3420		20.5	16	80°	60.0	−.9397		56.5
−.8192		55.5	17	85°	67.7	−.5736		38.8
−1.0000		76.4	18	90°	76.4	.0000		0.0
−.8192		70.9	19	95°	86.5	.5736	49.6	
−.3420		32.6	20	100°	95.5	.9397	89.8	
.2588	27.2		21	105°	105.1	.9659	101.6	
.7660	86.5		22	110°	112.8	.6428	72.5	
.9962	117.0		23	115°	117.4	.0872	10.2	
.8660	102.7		24	120°	118.5	−.5000		59.2
.4226	48.3		25	125°	114.2	−.9063		103.5
−.1736		18.2	26	130°	104.9	−.9848		103.2
−.7071		64.6	27	135°	91.4	−.7071		64.6
−.9848		77.1	28	140°	78.3	−.1736		13.6
−.9063		59.0	29	145°	65.0	.4226	27.5	
−.5000		25.6	30	150°	51.1	.8660	44.3	
.0872	3.5		31	155°	40.0	.9962	39.9	
.6428	18.9		32	160°	29.4	.7660	22.6	
.9659	20.6		33	165°	21.3	.2588	5.5	
.9397	13.6		34	170°	14.0	−.3420		4.8
.5736	4.1		35	175°	7.1	−.8192		5.8
.0000	0.0		36	180°	0.0	−1.0000		0.0
Sum of products	618.5	582.3					575.8	599.0
	36.2						−23.2	

$$A_7 = \frac{36.2}{36} \times 2 = 2.01$$

$$B_7 = \frac{-23.2}{36} \times 2 = -1.29$$

In Fig. 9 the vector OA of magnitude A_1 may be taken to represent the sin ωt. Remembering that the cosine wave leads the sine wave by 90°, the vector OB may be used to represent the cosine term. The vector sum OC of the two vectors OA and OB, therefore, represents the sum of $A_1 \sin \omega t$ and $B_1 \cos \omega t$ in both magnitude and phase. It leads the sin ωt position by $\tan^{-1} \dfrac{B_1}{A_1}$ and it also lags the cos ωt by $\tan^{-1} \dfrac{A_1}{B_1}$. The magnitude OC is $\sqrt{A_1^2 + B_1^2}$. The equation of the combination is $\sqrt{A_1^2 + B_1^2} \sin \left(\omega t + \tan^{-1} \dfrac{B_1}{A_1}\right)$, or $\sqrt{A_1^2 + B_1^2} \cos \left(\omega t - \tan^{-1} \dfrac{A_1}{B_1}\right)$.

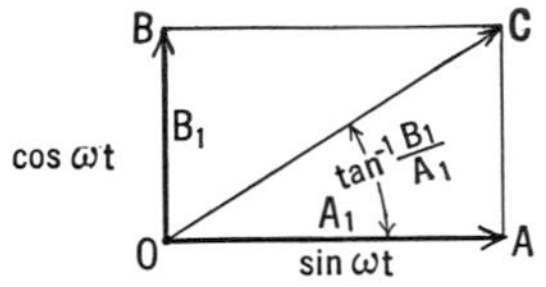

Fig. 9. Vector representation of sin ωt and cos ωt and their sum OC for particular magnitudes A_1 and B_1.

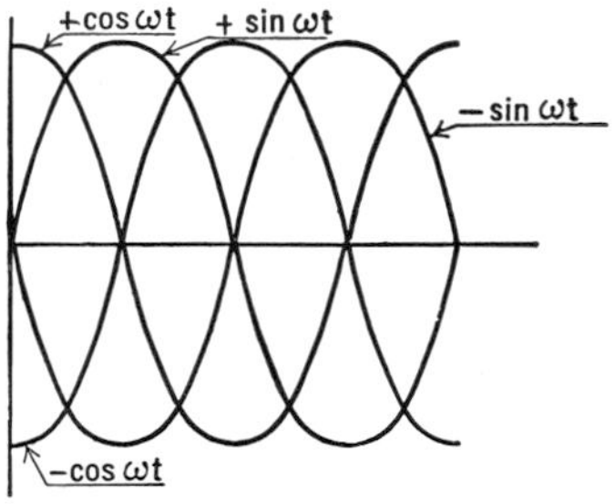

Fig. 10.

The vector representation of the positive and negative sines and cosines forms a convenient way to find trigonometric relations and to make combinations of these waves. For instance, the waves are shown in Fig. 10. The corresponding vector representation of the same waves is shown in Fig. 11. In Fig. 11 it can be seen that the

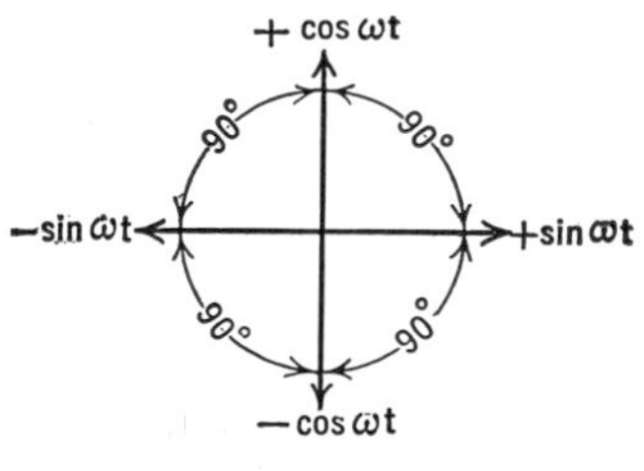

Fig. 11. Vector representation of waves shown in Fig. 10.

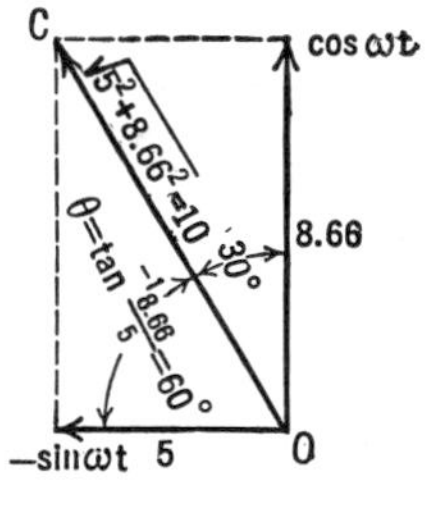

Fig. 12. Combination of $-5 \sin \omega t + 8.66 \cos \omega t$.

sin $(\omega t + 90°)$ gives the +cos ωt, that −cos $(\omega t - 90°)$ gives the −sin ωt, etc. By visualizing Fig. 11, all similar relations become apparent. In like manner, if $[-5 \sin \omega t + 8.66 \cos \omega t]$ is to be reduced to a single trigonometric term, the values would be laid off on Fig. 11 as shown in Fig. 12. The vector addition would then be performed to obtain the resultant OC. OC may be seen to lead the cos ωt by 30° or to lag the −sin ωt by 60°. It also leads the +sin ωt by 120°. Thus the equation of OC is any one of the following: $10 \cos (\omega t + 30°)$, $-10 \sin (\omega t - 60°)$, or $10 \sin (\omega t + 120°)$. There are also other equivalent expressions for the resultant wave.

Example 4. Express the equation obtained from the analysis of the wave of Oscillogram 4 in terms of positive sine components only. The results of the analysis show that:

$$
\begin{array}{lll}
A_1 = 82.45 & B_1 = -22.11 & C_1 = \sqrt{82.45^2 + (-22.11)^2} = 85.50 \text{ units} \\
A_3 = -0.92 & B_3 = 26.2 & C_3 = \sqrt{(-0.92)^2 + 26.2^2} = 26.2 \text{ units} \\
A_5 = -5.38 & B_5 = -3.65 & C_5 = \sqrt{(-5.38)^2 + (-3.65)^2} = 6.50 \text{ units} \\
A_7 = 2.01 & B_7 = -1.29 & C_7 = \sqrt{2.01^2 + (-1.29)^2} = 2.39 \text{ units}
\end{array}
$$

With respect to the $+\sin \omega t$ position of Fig. 11 as a reference:

$$\alpha_1 = \tan^{-1} \frac{-22.11}{82.45} = \tan^{-1} -0.268 = -15^\circ$$

$$\alpha_3 = \tan^{-1} \frac{26.2}{-0.92} = \tan^{-1} -28.5 = 92^\circ$$

$$\alpha_5 = \tan^{-1} \frac{-3.65}{-5.38} = \tan^{-1} 0.678 = 214.2^\circ$$

$$\alpha_7 = \tan^{-1} \frac{-1.29}{2.01} = \tan^{-1} -0.642 = -32.7^\circ$$

It will be noted that the individual signs of the coefficients B and A must be considered in the evaluation of the phase angles.

The equation for the wave form shown in Oscillogram 4 is:

$$
\begin{aligned}
i = {} & 85.50 \sin (\omega t - 15^\circ) + 26.2 \sin (3\omega t + 92^\circ) \\
& + 6.50 \sin (5\omega t + 214.2^\circ) + 2.39 \sin (7\omega t - 32.7^\circ)
\end{aligned}
$$

It is desirable to draw figures, similar to that shown in Fig. 12, for each of the harmonics. This exercise is left to the student. The final test of the correctness of any wave analysis is whether the component parts found by the analysis can be combined to yield the original wave.

Problem 3. Evaluate i in the above equation at 30° intervals of ωt throughout one-half cycle, and plot the resultant curve. Compare the general wave shape thus found with that of the original wave form shown in Oscillogram 4.

Problem 4. Express the equation for the wave shape shown in Oscillogram 4 in terms of positive cosine components.

Wave Analysis (Second Graphical Method). Although the fundamental basis of the previous method of analysis is simple, there are a number of methods which require less time for numerical computation. One of these shorter methods follows.

Equation (1) may be written in the following form:

$$
\begin{aligned}
y = f(x) = {} & A_0 + A_1 \sin x + A_2 \sin 2x + A_3 \sin 3x + \cdots \\
& + A_n \sin nx + B_1 \cos x + B_2 \cos 2x + B_3 \cos 3x \\
& + \cdots + B_n \cos nx
\end{aligned} \tag{20}
$$

If q is a number equal to the order of the harmonic which is under investigation and $f(\pi/2q)$, $f(3\pi/2q)$, etc., are the values of $y = f(x)$ at $x = \pi/2q$, $x = 3\pi/2q$, etc., it can be shown that the following relations are true.[3]

$$2q(A_q - A_{3q} + A_{5q} - A_{7q} + \cdots) = f\left(\frac{\pi}{2q}\right) - f\left(\frac{3\pi}{2q}\right) + f\left(\frac{5\pi}{2q}\right) - \cdots - f\left[\frac{(4q-1)\pi}{2q}\right] \quad (21)$$

$$2q(B_q + B_{3q} + B_{5q} + \cdots) = f(0) - f\left(\frac{\pi}{q}\right) + f\left(\frac{2\pi}{q}\right) - f\left(\frac{3\pi}{q}\right) + \cdots - f\left[\frac{(2q-1)\pi}{q}\right] \quad (22)$$

When equations (21) and (22) are used, it must be remembered that the subscripts $3q$, $5q$, etc., represent the order of the harmonic obtained by multiplication of 3 times q, 5 times q, etc. Thus, if q is 3, B_{3q} would be B_9, B_{5q} would be B_{15}, etc.

Before proceeding to employ equations (21) and (22), it is necessary to estimate the maximum number of harmonics required in the analysis. The procedure is then to start with the highest harmonic and substitute the ordinates at the various angles indicated by the right members of equations (21) and (22). Since it is unlikely that all ordinates required will be given, it is usually necessary to plot the resultant wave in order that the required ordinates may be read from the curve. The necessity of having a graph of the curve will usually entail no extra work in practice because the method will usually be applied only when the resultant wave is obtained from an oscillogram similar to that illustrated in Oscillogram 4, page 236. After the harmonic coefficients are determined, A_0 is evaluated by substituting $x = 0$ in equation (20). Thus

$$f(0) = A_0 + B_1 + B_2 + B_3 + \cdots + B_n \quad (23)$$

$f(0)$ is read from the curve and, since everything except A_0 has been determined, A_0 can be calculated. As an example of the procedure, the wave employed in example 3 will be analyzed.

Example 5. Find the harmonic coefficients through the seventh harmonic for the wave given in Oscillogram 4, page 236, by employing equations (21), (22), and (23).

[3] See "Advanced Mathematics for Engineers," by Reddick and Miller, John Wiley & Sons, Inc., 2nd edition, 1947, p. 202.

For the seventh harmonic, $q = 7$ and equation (21) is used as follows:

$$(2 \times 7)A_7 = f\left(\frac{\pi}{14}\right) - f\left(\frac{3\pi}{14}\right) + f\left(\frac{5\pi}{14}\right) - f\left(\frac{7\pi}{14}\right) + f\left(\frac{9\pi}{14}\right) - f\left(\frac{11\pi}{14}\right)$$
$$+ f\left(\frac{13\pi}{14}\right) - f\left(\frac{15\pi}{14}\right) + f\left(\frac{17\pi}{14}\right) - f\left(\frac{19\pi}{14}\right) + f\left(\frac{21\pi}{14}\right)$$
$$- f\left(\frac{23\pi}{14}\right) + f\left(\frac{25\pi}{14}\right) - f\left(\frac{27\pi}{14}\right)$$

Note that, since the seventh harmonic is the highest required, $A_{3q} = A_{21}$, A_{5q}, etc., are all zero.

$$14A_7 = f(12.86°) - f(38.57°) + f(64.29°) - f(90°) + f(115.7°)$$
$$- f(141.4°) + f(167.2°) - f(193°) + f(218.7°) - f(244.3°)$$
$$+ f(270°) - f(296°) + f(321.5°) - f(347°)$$
$$= 12.4 - 24.5 + 40.5 - 76.4 + 117.6 - 74.6 + 17.5 - (-12.4)$$
$$+ (-24.5) - (-40.5) + (-76.4) - (-117.6) + (-74.6)$$
$$- (-17.5)$$
$$= 25$$

$$A_7 = \frac{25}{14} = 1.79$$

$$14B_7 = f(0) - f(25.7°) + f(51.4°) - f(77.1°) + f(103°) - f(128.7°)$$
$$+ f(154.3°) - f(180°) + f(205.5°) - f(231.3°) + f(257°)$$
$$- f(283°) + f(308.7°) - f(334.5°)$$
$$= 0 - 20 + 32 - 56 + 101 - 107 + 41 - 0 + -20 + 32 - 56$$
$$+ 101 - 107 + 41$$
$$= -18$$

$$B_7 = -\frac{18}{14} = -1.286$$

Because the wave is symmetrical about the 180° point, even harmonics cannot exist. If, however, equations (21) and (22) are used to find the sixth harmonic, zero will be obtained.

Equations (21) and (22) are now used to calculate A_5 and B_5 as follows.

$$(2 \times 5)A_5 = f\left(\frac{\pi}{10}\right) - f\left(\frac{3\pi}{10}\right) + f\left(\frac{5\pi}{10}\right) - f\left(\frac{7\pi}{10}\right) + f\left(\frac{9\pi}{10}\right) - f\left(\frac{11\pi}{10}\right)$$
$$+ f\left(\frac{13\pi}{10}\right) - f\left(\frac{15\pi}{10}\right) + f\left(\frac{17\pi}{10}\right) - f\left(\frac{19\pi}{10}\right)$$

$$10A_5 = f(18°) - f(54°) + f(90°) - f(126°) + f(162°) - f(198°)$$
$$+ f(234°) - f(270°) + f(306°) - f(342°)$$
$$= 15 - 33 + 76.4 - 113 + 26 - (-15) + (-33) - (-76.4)$$
$$+ (-113) - (-26)$$
$$= 2(15 - 33 + 76.4 - 113 + 26) = 2(-28.6) = -57.2$$

$$A_5 = -5.72$$

$$
\begin{aligned}
(2 \times 5)B_5 &= f(0) - f\left(\frac{\pi}{5}\right) + f\left(\frac{2\pi}{5}\right) - f\left(\frac{3\pi}{5}\right) + f\left(\frac{4\pi}{5}\right) - f\left(\frac{5\pi}{5}\right) + f\left(\frac{6\pi}{5}\right) \\
&\quad - f\left(\frac{7\pi}{5}\right) + f\left(\frac{8\pi}{5}\right) - f\left(\frac{9\pi}{5}\right) \\
10B_5 &= f(0) - f(36°) + f(72°) - f(108°) + f(144°) - f(180°) \\
&\quad + f(216°) - f(252°) + f(288°) - f(324°) \\
&= 0 - 24 + 49 - 110 + 68 - 0 + (-24) - (-49) + (-110) \\
&\quad - (-68) \\
&= -34 \\
B_5 &= -3.4
\end{aligned}
$$

Determination of A_3 and B_3:

$$
\begin{aligned}
(2 \times 3)A_3 &= f\left(\frac{\pi}{6}\right) - f\left(\frac{3\pi}{6}\right) + f\left(\frac{5\pi}{6}\right) - f\left(\frac{7\pi}{6}\right) + f\left(\frac{9\pi}{6}\right) - f\left(\frac{11\pi}{6}\right) \\
6A_3 &= f(30°) - f(90°) + f(150°) - f(210°) + f(270°) - f(330°) \\
&= 21.8 - 76.4 + 51.1 - (-21.8) + (-76.4) - (-51.1) \\
&= -7 \\
A_3 &= -1.167
\end{aligned}
$$

$$
\begin{aligned}
6B_3 &= f(0) - f\left(\frac{\pi}{3}\right) + f\left(\frac{2\pi}{3}\right) - f\left(\frac{3\pi}{3}\right) + f\left(\frac{4\pi}{3}\right) - f\left(\frac{5\pi}{3}\right) \\
&= f(0) - f(60°) + f(120°) - f(180°) + f(240°) - f(300°) \\
&= 0 - 37.4 + 118.5 - 0 + (-37.4) - (-118.5) = 162.2 \\
B_3 &= +27.03
\end{aligned}
$$

For the fundamental, equations (21) and (22) become

$$(2 \times 1)(A_1 - A_3 + A_5 - A_7) = f\left(\frac{\pi}{2}\right) - f\left(\frac{3\pi}{2}\right)$$

$$2(A_1 - A_3 + A_5 - A_7) = f(90) - f(270) = 76.4 - (-76.4) = 152.8$$

Substituting the values of A_3, A_5, and A_7 found previously and solving for A_1 gives $A_1 = 82.74$.

In a similar way B_1 may be found as follows.

$$
\begin{aligned}
(2 \times 1)(B_1 + B_3 + B_5 + B_7) &= f(0) - f(\pi) = 0 \\
2(B_1 + 27.03 - 3.4 - 1.286) &= 0 \\
B_1 &= -22.34
\end{aligned}
$$

The foregoing method is easy to apply and entails less labor than the method employing analyzing tables. The accuracy, however, will vary with different wave shapes and will also be dependent upon the estimate of the number of harmonics required. It will be noted that the determination of the fundamental depends upon the values of the harmonics previously determined. It is therefore desirable to start with a high enough order of harmonic so that any higher-order components will be negligible so far as engineering accuracy is concerned. If only a single harmonic of some desired order is required, the method employing the analyzing tables may save time and be more accurate. The error in the method employing analyzing tables depends only upon the size of the intervals chosen and, obviously, approaches zero as the size of the interval is decreased and the number of them is increased. The determination of any one harmonic is independent of the determination of any other harmonics when analyzing tables are employed.

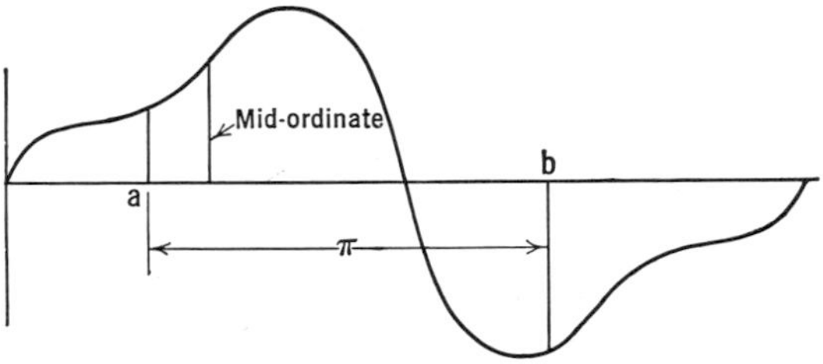

FIG. 13. Wave with unsymmetrical positive and negative loops.

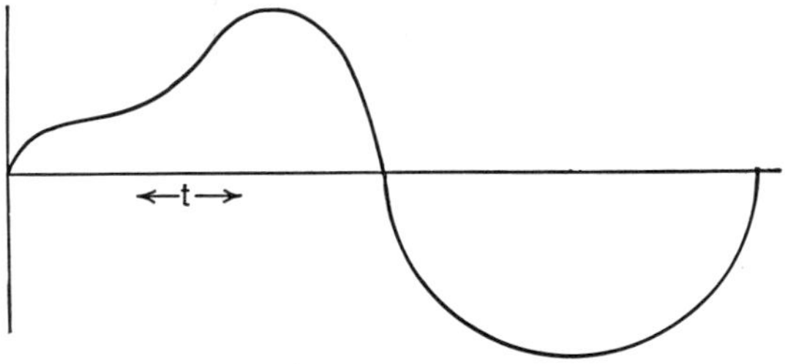

FIG. 14. Wave with unsymmetrical positive and negative loops.

Degrees of Symmetry of Non-Sinusoidal Waves. Non-sinusoidal waves may have symmetrical positive and negative loops, as shown in Fig. 8, or the loops may be unlike, as shown in Figs. 13 and 14. As indicated in the article on wave analysis (page 235), certain types of symmetry in a wave form will automatically eliminate the need for evaluating certain coefficients in the Fourier series which represents the wave.

When the variation from zero to 180° is repeated (except for sign) between 180° and 360°, the wave is said to possess half-wave symmetry. Mathematically a wave of this kind is described as having $[f(x + \pi) = -f(x)]$ symmetry. Expressed in another way, a wave has half-wave symmetry when any ordinate, such as b, Fig. 13, π radians distant from another ordinate, such as a, is equal in magnitude to that at point a but opposite in sign. Thus, the ordinate at any point a for a general wave is:

$$\begin{aligned} y_a &= A_0 + C_1 \sin(\omega t + \alpha_1) + C_2 \sin(2\omega t + \alpha_2) \\ &\quad + C_3 \sin(3\omega t + \alpha_3) + C_4 \sin(4\omega t + \alpha_4) \\ &\quad + C_5 \sin(5\omega t + \alpha_5) + \cdots \end{aligned} \tag{24}$$

The ordinate π radians distant from a is found by adding π radians to ωt. If this angle $(\omega t + \pi)$ is substituted and if it is remembered that $(\omega t + \pi)$ for the fundamental corresponds to $n(\omega t + \pi)$ for the nth harmonic, the following results:

$$\begin{aligned} y_b &= A_0 + C_1 \sin(\omega t + \alpha_1 + \pi) + C_2 \sin(2\omega t + \alpha_2 + 2\pi) \\ &\quad + C_3 \sin(3\omega t + \alpha_3 + 3\pi) + C_4 \sin(4\omega t + \alpha_4 + 4\pi) \\ &\quad + C_5 \sin(5\omega t + \alpha_5 + 5\pi) + \cdots \end{aligned} \tag{25}$$

Since the sine of any angle plus an even multiple of π radians is the same as the sine of the angle, and the sine of an angle plus any odd multiple of π radians is the same as the negative sine of the angle, equation (25) simplifies to:

$$\begin{aligned} y_b &= A_0 - C_1 \sin(\omega t + \alpha_1) + C_2 \sin(2\omega t + \alpha_2) \\ &\quad - C_3 \sin(3\omega t + \alpha_3) + C_4 \sin(4\omega t + \alpha_4) \\ &\quad - C_5 \sin(5\omega t + \alpha_5) + \cdots \end{aligned} \tag{26}$$

The ordinate y_b [equation (26)] would be exactly opposite to that of equation (24) if A_0 and all even harmonics in the wave were absent. Hence a wave is symmetrical with respect to the positive and negative loops if it contains no even harmonics and if A_0 is equal to zero. The converse of the foregoing statement is also true, that is, a wave which has $[f(\omega t) = -f(\omega t + \pi)]$ symmetry can contain neither even harmonics nor A_0. The effect of a second harmonic in destroying half-wave symmetry is shown graphically in Fig. 15. In analyzing waves possessing half-wave symmetry, the analysis need be carried through only ½ cycle or 180°.

A wave possessing half-wave symmetry as defined above may also be symmetrical about the midordinates of its positive and negative loops, namely, its 90° and 270° points. A wave of this kind is said to possess midordinate or quarter-wave symmetry, and the analysis need be carried through only ¼ cycle or 90°. The case where only the positive *or* negative loop is symmetrical about its midordinate is of relatively little importance. Thus the positive loop of the wave shown in Fig. 13 is not symmetrical about its midordinate, whereas that of Fig. 16 is symmetrical with respect to its midordinate. The wave will have the halves of its positive and negative loops symmetrical if its fundamental and all harmonics pass through zero values at the same time, and, further, if all even harmonics are absent. This fact is illustrated graphically in Fig. 17. The second harmonic, shown dotted, adds to the fundamental to the left of the midordinate of the positive loop and subtracts from it on the right-

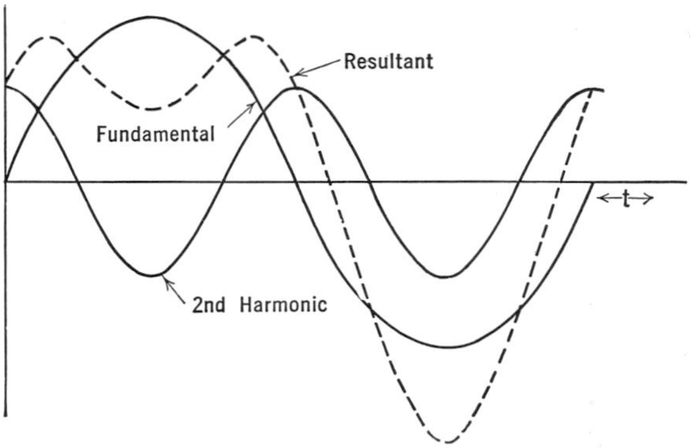

FIG. 15. Effect of second harmonic in destroying half-wave symmetry.

hand side. All the odd harmonics are symmetrical about the midordinate *a* when they pass through zero at the same time as the fundamental. If the zero-ordinate point of the complex wave is chosen as a

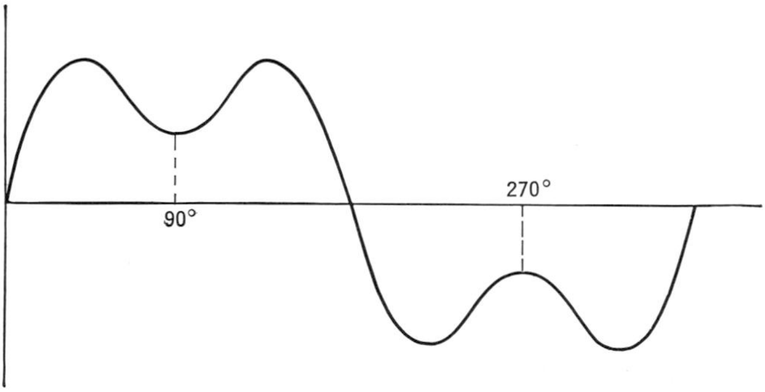

FIG. 16. Wave with positive and negative loops symmetrical about the midordinate (quarter-wave symmetry).

reference, it is plain that only odd sine terms can be present in the equation of a complex wave having quarter-wave symmetry.

Waves of Same Wave Shape. Waves are of the same wave shape if they contain the same harmonics, if the ratio of corresponding harmonics to their respective fundamentals is the same, and if the harmonics are spaced the same with respect to their fundamentals. Expressed in another way, for two waves of the same form the ratio of the magnitudes of corresponding harmonics must be constant, and, when the fundamentals are in phase, all the corresponding harmonics of the two waves must be in phase. The test is to note whether the ratio of corresponding harmonics is constant and then to shift one wave so that the fundamentals coincide. If the phase angles of corresponding harmonics in the two waves are then the same and if the first condition is also fulfilled, the waves are of the same wave shape or wave form.

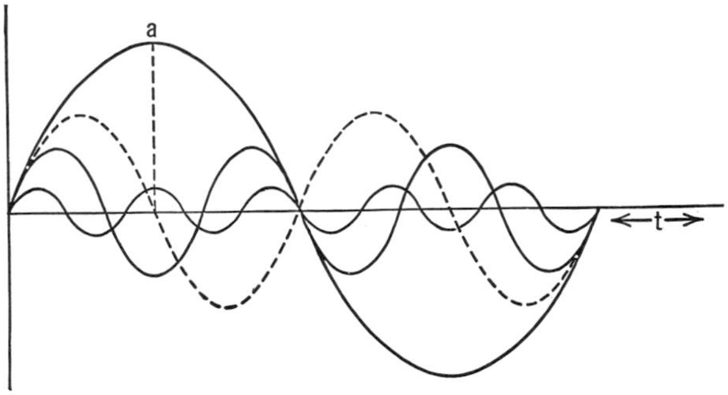

FIG. 17. Symmetry about the midordinate, a, is maintained if all odd harmonics are zero when the fundamental is zero. The second harmonic shown dotted will destroy this symmetry as will other even harmonics.

Example 6. Determine whether the following two waves are of the same shape:

$$e = 100 \sin (\omega t + 30°) - 50 \sin (3\omega t - 60°) + 25 \sin (5\omega t + 40°)$$

$$i = 10 \sin (\omega t - 60°) + 5 \sin (3\omega t - 150°) + 2.5 \cos (5\omega t - 140°)$$

Since all harmonics of the current wave are one-tenth of the corresponding harmonics in the voltage wave, the first requisite is fulfilled. Next, the fundamentals should be brought into phase by shifting the current wave forward 90° or the voltage wave backward 90°. The current wave will be shifted by adding 90° to the phase angle of its fundamental. Shifting the fundamental of a wave by $\alpha°$ corresponds to shifting the nth harmonic by $n\alpha°$. This may be verified by referring to Fig. 17. Suppose the reference axis is changed to the position marked a, thus shifting the wave ahead. This is a shift of 90°, or one quarter cycle for the fundamental. It is a shift of three quarter cycles for the third harmonic, or 270° and five quarter cycles for the fifth harmonic, or 450°. Hence, to maintain the same relation between the fundamental and all harmonics in the current waves, $3 \times 90°$ or 270° will be added to the third, and $5 \times 90°$ or 450° will be added to the fifth harmonic. Then:

$$\begin{aligned} i' &= 10 \sin (\omega t - 60° + 90°) + 5 \sin (3\omega t - 150° + 270°) \\ &\quad + 2.5 \cos (5\omega t - 140° + 450°) \\ &= 10 \sin (\omega t + 30°) + 5 \sin (3\omega t + 120°) + 2.5 \cos (5\omega t + 310°) \\ &= 10 \sin (\omega t + 30°) - 5 \sin (3\omega t - 60°) + 2.5 \sin (5\omega t + 40°) \end{aligned}$$

The corresponding harmonics of the current and voltage waves are hence in phase, and the two waves are of the same shape. Had either the third or fifth harmonic been out of phase with the corresponding harmonic in the voltage wave, the wave shapes would have been different.

The effect on wave shape of shifting a harmonic with respect to the fundamental can be understood through a study of Figs. 18, 19, and 20. In each figure the magnitudes of the fundamental and third harmonic are the same. As the third harmonic is shifted along the axis with respect to the fundamental, the wave form of the resultant is seen to change. This shifting of a harmonic with respect to the fundamental is sometimes spoken of as changing the phase of the harmonic with respect to the fundamental. This should not be construed to mean that there is a definite phase difference between a *vector* representing the fundamental and one representing the third harmonic. Vectors representing a fundamental and a higher harmonic cannot correctly be related on the same vector diagram without special interpretation.

Problem 5. Given the following equations for two wave forms of current:

$$i' = 10 \sin (\omega t + 30°) + 2 \sin 7\omega t$$

$$i'' = 35 \sin (\omega t - 10°) + 7 \sin (7\omega t + 80°)$$

Show that the wave form of the i' variation is like (or unlike) the wave form of the i'' variation. *Ans.:* Same form.

Effective Value of a Non-Sinusoidal Wave. In Chapter III the effective value of any wave was shown to be $\sqrt{\frac{1}{T}\int_0^T [f(t)]^2\, dt}$. Applying this expression to the general complex wave

$$i = I_0 + I_{m1} \sin \omega t + I_{m2} \sin (2\omega t + \alpha_2) + I_{m3} \sin (3\omega t + \alpha_3) + \cdots + I_{mn} \sin (n\omega t + \alpha_n)$$

gives

$$I = \left\{\frac{1}{T}\int_0^T [I_0 + I_{m1} \sin \omega t + I_{m2} \sin (2\omega t + \alpha_2) + I_{m3} \sin (3\omega t + \alpha_3) + \cdots + I_{mn} \sin (n\omega t + \alpha_n)]^2\, dt\right\}^{1/2}$$

$$= \sqrt{I_0^2 + \frac{I_{m1}^2 + I_{m2}^2 + I_{m3}^2 + I_{m4}^2 + \cdots + I_{mn}^2}{2}} \qquad (27)$$

Problem 6. Show by integration, including all steps, that the effective value of

$v = V_{m1} \sin (\omega t + \alpha_1) + V_{m3} \sin (3\omega t + 30°)$ is $\sqrt{\frac{V_{m1}^2 + V_{m3}^2}{2}}$.

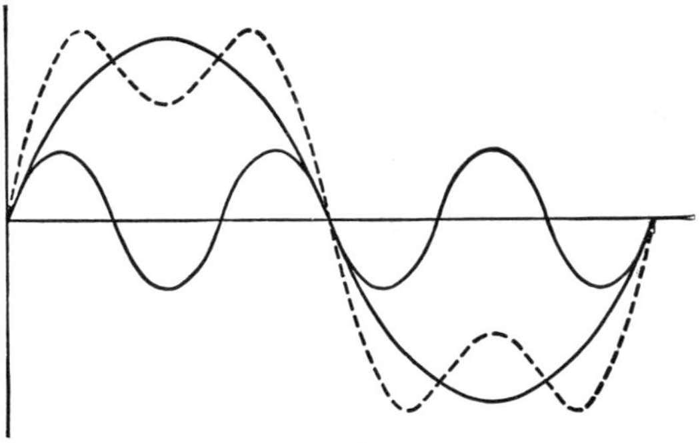

FIG. 18.

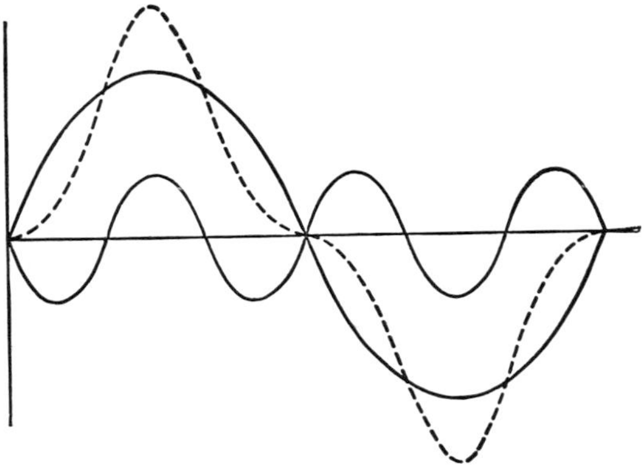

FIG. 19.

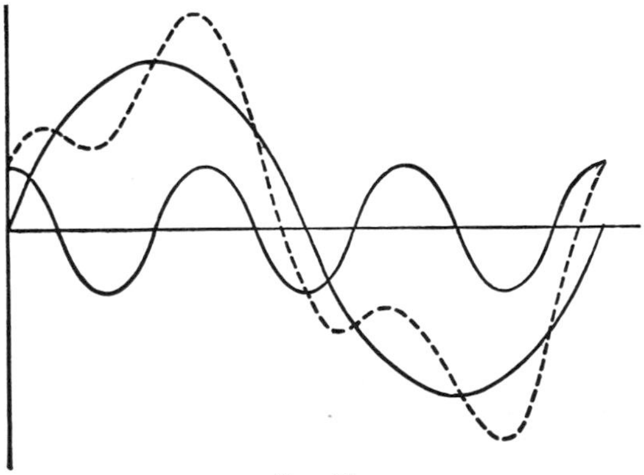

FIG. 20.

Figs. 18, 19, and 20 show the effect on wave shape of shifting a harmonic.

Since

$$\frac{I_{m1}}{\sqrt{2}} = I_1, \qquad \frac{I_{m2}}{\sqrt{2}} = I_2, \qquad \text{etc.}$$

$$I = \sqrt{I_0^2 + I_1^2 + I_2^2 + I_3^2 + I_4^2 + \cdots + I_n^2} \tag{28}$$

Equation (27) is used when the maximum values of the harmonics are given, whereas equation (28) gives the equivalent expression if effective values of the harmonics are available. It is obvious that similar expressions hold for voltages.

Example 7. Find the effective value of the voltage wave used in example 6.

$$E = \sqrt{\frac{100^2 + 50^2 + 25^2}{2}} = 81 \text{ volts}$$

It should be noted that the effective value is the square root of the *sum* of the squares of the maximum values divided by 2, irrespective of the phase angles or signs of the harmonics. A similar statement is true when effective values of the harmonics are used in equation (28).

For one method of analysis in a-c machinery, known as the Blondell two-reaction method, it is necessary to have the effective value of the rectangular wave given by equation (15), page **233**. For this wave, effective value equals $A_1\pi/4$.

Power Due to Non-Sinusoidal Voltages and Currents. The expression for average power in general was given as

$$P = \frac{1}{T}\int_0^T ei\, dt$$

When

$$e = E_{m1} \sin (\omega t + \alpha_1) + E_{m2} \sin (2\omega t + \alpha_2) + E_{m3} \sin (3\omega t + \alpha_3) + \cdots$$

and

$$i = I_{m1} \sin (\omega t + \alpha_1') + I_{m2} \sin (2\omega t + \alpha_2') + I_{m3} \sin (3\omega t + \alpha_3') + \cdots$$

$$P = \frac{1}{T}\int_0^T [E_{m1} \sin (\omega t + \alpha_1) + E_{m2} \sin (2\omega t + \alpha_2) + E_{m3} \sin (3\omega t + \alpha_3) + \cdots] \; [I_{m1} \sin (\omega t + \alpha_1') + I_{m2} \sin (2\omega t + \alpha_2') + I_{m3} \sin (3\omega t + \alpha_3') + \cdots]\, dt \tag{29}$$

Upon expansion, this yields products of terms of unlike frequencies and products of terms of like frequencies. As shown on page 226 the integral of the products of terms of unlike frequencies taken over a complete cycle of the lower frequency is zero. This leaves only the product of terms of like frequency, such as:

$$\frac{1}{T}\int_0^T A \sin (m\omega t + \alpha)\, B \sin (m\omega t + \alpha')\, dt$$

which gives

$$\frac{AB}{2}\cos(\alpha - \alpha') \tag{30}$$

Thus equation (29) becomes

$$P = \frac{E_{m1}I_{m1}}{2}\cos(\alpha_1 - \alpha_1') + \frac{E_{m2}I_{m2}}{2}\cos(\alpha_2 - \alpha_2') + \frac{E_{m3}I_{m3}}{2}\cos(\alpha_3 - \alpha_3') + \cdots \tag{31}$$

Or, since

$$\frac{E_{m1}I_{m1}}{2} = \frac{E_{m1}}{\sqrt{2}}\frac{I_{m1}}{\sqrt{2}} = E_1I_1$$

$$P = E_1I_1\cos(\alpha_1 - \alpha_1') + E_2I_2\cos(\alpha_2 - \alpha_2') + E_3I_3\cos(\alpha_3 - \alpha_3') + \cdots \tag{32}$$

Average power when waves are non-sinusoidal is the algebraic sum of the powers represented by corresponding harmonics of voltage and current. No average power results from components of voltage and current of unlike frequency, provided that the time interval chosen is equal to an integral number of cycles of the lower-frequency variation. The foregoing statement can be proved either mathematically or graphically.

Example 8. Find the power represented by the following:

$$e = 100\sin(\omega t + 30°) - 50\sin(3\omega t + 60°) + 25\sin 5\omega t \text{ volts}$$

$$i = 20\sin(\omega t - 30°) + 15\sin(3\omega t + 30°) + 10\cos(5\omega t - 60°) \text{ amperes}$$

$$P = \frac{100 \times 20}{2}\cos[30° - (-30°)] + \frac{(-50)(15)}{2}\cos[60° - 30°] + \frac{25 \times 10}{2}\cos[-90° - (-60°)]$$

$$= 500 - 324.75 + 108.25$$

$$= 283.5 \text{ watts}$$

An alternative method of obtaining the power for the third-harmonic components follows.

$$e_3 = -50\sin(3\omega t + 60°) = +50\sin(3\omega t - 120°) \text{ volts}$$

$$i_3 = 15\sin(3\omega t + 30°) \text{ amperes}$$

$$P_3 = \frac{50 \times 15}{2}\cos(-120° - 30°) = 375\cos 150° = -324.75 \text{ watts}$$

Problem 7. Find the power delivered by the following:

$$e = 100 \sin \omega t + 50 \sin (5\omega t - 80°) - 40 \cos (7\omega t + 30°) \text{ volts}$$

$$i = 30 \sin (\omega t + 60°) + 20 \sin (5\omega t - 50°) + 10 \sin (7\omega t + 60°) \text{ amperes}$$

Ans.: 1083 watts.

Volt-Amperes. Volt-amperes are determined by the product of the effective voltage and effective current.

Example 9. Find the volt-amperes for the waves in example 8.

$$Va = EI = \sqrt{\frac{100^2 + 50^2 + 25^2}{2}} \sqrt{\frac{20^2 + 15^2 + 10^2}{2}} = 81 \times 19.03$$

$$= 1541 \text{ volt-amperes}$$

In general,

Volt-amperes =

$$\sqrt{\frac{E_{m1}{}^2 + E_{m2}{}^2 + E_{m3}{}^2 + \text{etc.}}{2}} \sqrt{\frac{I_{m1}{}^2 + I_{m2}{}^2 + I_{m3}{}^2 + \text{etc.}}{2}} \quad (33)$$

Power Factor. Power factor for non-sinusoidal waves is defined as the ratio of the power to the volt-amperes. Hence

Power factor =

$$\frac{E_1 I_1 \cos (\alpha_1 - \alpha_1{}') + E_2 I_2 \cos (\alpha_2 - \alpha_2{}') + E_3 I_3 \cos (\alpha_3 - \alpha_3{}') + \text{etc.}}{\sqrt{E_1{}^2 + E_2{}^2 + E_3{}^2 + \text{etc.}} \ \sqrt{I_1{}^2 + I_2{}^2 + I_3{}^2 + \text{etc.}}} \quad (34)$$

Example 10. Find the power factor for the waves given in example 8.

Power from example 8 = 283.5 watts

Volt-amperes from example 9 = 1541

$$\text{Power factor} = \frac{283.5}{1541} = 0.1837$$

The conditions under which the power factor is unity when waves are non-sinusoidal are found from equation (34). To make the power factor 1, the numerator (power) should be as large as possible. Hence

$$\cos (\alpha_1 - \alpha_1{}') = \cos (\alpha_2 - \alpha_2{}') = \cos (\alpha_3 - \alpha_3{}') + \text{etc.} = 1$$

Then

$$\text{p.f.} = \frac{E_1 I_1 + E_2 I_2 + E_3 I_3 + \cdots}{\sqrt{(E_1{}^2 + E_2{}^2 + E_3{}^2 + \text{etc.})(I_1{}^2 + I_2{}^2 + I_3{}^2 + \text{etc.})}}$$

This expression can equal unity only if $E_1/I_1 = E_2/I_2 = E_3/I_3$.

To simplify the algebra, consider only the fundamental and one harmonic.

$$\frac{E_1 I_1 + E_2 I_2}{\sqrt{(E_1{}^2 + E_2{}^2)(I_1{}^2 + I_2{}^2)}} = 1$$

$$E_1I_1 + E_2I_2 = \sqrt{E_1^2I_1^2 + E_1^2I_2^2 + E_2^2I_1^2 + E_2^2I_2^2}$$

$$E_1^2I_1^2 + 2E_1I_1E_2I_2 + E_2^2I_2^2 = E_1^2I_1^2 + E_1^2I_2^2 + E_2^2I_1^2 + E_2^2I_2^2$$

$$2E_1I_1E_2I_2 = E_1^2I_2^2 + E_2^2I_1^2$$

If $E_1/I_1 = E_2/I_2$, $E_1I_2 = E_2I_1$ and the above expression becomes $2E_2^2I_1^2 = 2E_2^2I_1^2$, under which conditions the premise is true. Hence, to have unity power factor, the voltage and current waves must be of the same wave shape and in phase. Even though the voltage and current waves pass through zero at the same instant, the power factor cannot be unity if any harmonic in one wave is absent in the other, or when its magnitude makes the wave shapes different.

Equivalent Sine Waves. Occasionally equivalent sine waves are used for certain calculations and comparisons. They must be used with discretion because calculations based upon them are usually in error by varying amounts. An equivalent sine wave of current or voltage is a sine wave the effective value of which is the same as the effective value of the non-sinusoidal wave which is being represented. When equivalent sine waves of corresponding non-sinusoidal voltages and currents are found, the phase angle between the equivalent sine waves is made such that the power and power factor are the same as those for the actual waves. Whether the equivalent angle of phase difference is one of lead or lag is determined by the angle between the fundamentals of the two waves. If the fundamental of current lags the fundamental of voltage, the equivalent sine wave of current must lag the equivalent sine wave of voltage. If the fundamentals are in phase and the power factor is not unity, the sign of the angle of equivalent phase difference is indeterminate.

Example 11. Find the equivalent sine waves for the current and voltage given in example 8.

$$\text{Effective voltage} = \sqrt{\frac{100^2 + 50^2 + 25^2}{2}} = 81 \text{ volts}$$

$$\text{Effective current} = \sqrt{\frac{20^2 + 15^2 + 10^2}{2}} = 19.03 \text{ amperes}$$

Power factor from example 10 = 0.1837

The angle of equivalent phase difference is $\cos^{-1} 0.1837 = 79.4°$. Since the fundamental of current lags the fundamental of voltage, the angle 79.4° is an angle of lag of current with respect to voltage for the equivalent sine waves. The equivalent sine waves of voltage and current, respectively, are:

$$e = \sqrt{2}\, 81 \sin \omega t \text{ volts}$$

$$i = \sqrt{2}\, 19.03 \sin (\omega t - 79.4°) \text{ amperes}$$

As indicated before, the use of equivalent sine waves in non-sinusoidal circuit analysis will generally lead to large errors, particularly in operations involving the addition or subtraction of the waves. Equivalent sine waves are sometimes used in specifying the deviation from a sine wave.

Problem 8. Find the equivalent sine waves for the waves given in Problem 7.
Ans.: 118.8 sin ωt volts; 37.4 sin $(\omega t + 60.8°)$ amperes.

Deviation Factor. Deviation factor is the ratio of the maximum difference between corresponding ordinates of an actual wave and an

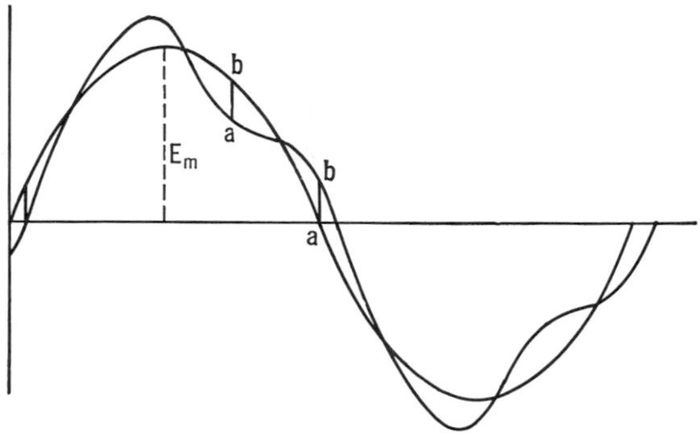

FIG. 21. Deviation of a distorted wave from an equivalent sine wave.

equivalent sine wave of the same length to the maximum ordinate of the equivalent sine wave when the two waves are superposed and shifted along the axis so as to make the maximum difference a minimum. For example, Fig. 21 shows a non-sinusoidal wave and an equivalent sine wave of the same period and length. These waves are shifted in such a way that the maximum difference between corresponding ordinates is as small as possible. In this particular case the maximum difference is *ab*. The ratio of *ab* to the maximum value E_m of the equivalent sine wave is the deviation factor. Deviation factor is sometimes used for specification purposes. A deviation factor of about 0.1 for commercial machines is usually allowable.

Series Circuit Analysis when Waves Are Non-Sinusoidal. The procedure is most readily understood from an example.

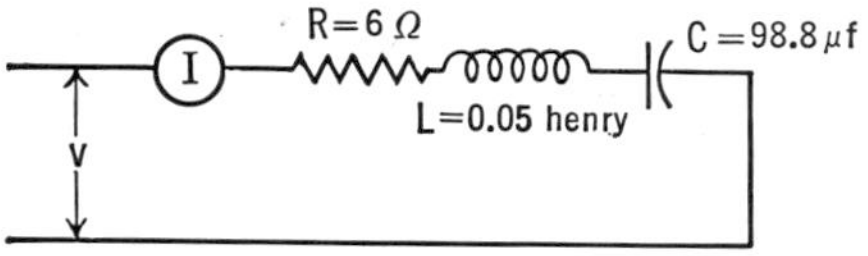

FIG. 22. See example 12.

Example 12. Given the circuit with the parameters shown in Fig. 22. When ω is 377 radians per second and the voltage $v = 141.4 \sin \omega t + 70.7 \sin (3\omega t + 30°) - 28.28 \sin (5\omega t - 20°)$ volts is impressed, find the current, I, that an ammeter would read. Also find the total power dissipated and the effective value of the voltage drop across the inductance. Also find the equation of the current wave.

Since the inductive and condensive reactances are different for different frequencies, each harmonic must be handled *separately*. Subscripts 1, 3, and 5 will designate the fundamental, third, and fifth harmonics, respectively. Either maximum or effective values may be used. If maximum values are used, maximum currents will result; when effective voltages are used, effective currents result. Whichever are used, the result can always be easily changed to give the other if desired. Since the effective values of the harmonic components of voltage in this particular case are more convenient numbers to handle, the solution will be negotiated through the use of effective values immediately.

Fundamental

$$V_1 = \frac{141.4}{\sqrt{2}} = 100 \text{ volts}$$

$$R_1 = 6 \text{ ohms}$$

$$X_{L1} = 377 \times 0.05 = 18.85 \text{ ohms}$$

$$X_{C1} = \frac{10^6}{377 \times 98.8} = 26.85 \text{ ohms}$$

$$\mathbf{Z}_1 = 6 + j18.85 - j26.85 = 6 - j8 \quad \text{or} \quad 10 \text{ ohms}$$

$$I_1 = \frac{V_1}{Z_1} = \frac{100}{10} = 10 \text{ amperes}$$

$$\mathbf{I}_1 \text{ leads } \mathbf{V}_1 \text{ by } \tan^{-1}\frac{8}{6} = 53.12°$$

$$P_1 = 10^2 \times 6 = 600 \text{ watts}$$

$$V_{L1} = I_1 X_{L1} = 10 \times 18.85 = 188.5 \text{ volts}$$

Third Harmonic

$$V_3 = \frac{70.7}{\sqrt{2}} = 50 \text{ volts}$$

$$R_3 = 6 \text{ ohms}$$

$$X_{L3} = 3X_{L1} = 3 \times 18.85 = 56.55 \text{ ohms}$$

$$X_{C3} = \frac{X_{C1}}{3} = \frac{26.85}{3} = 8.95 \text{ ohms}$$

$$\mathbf{Z}_3 = 6 + j56.55 - j8.95 = 6 + j47.6 \quad \text{or} \quad \sqrt{6^2 + 47.6^2} = 48.1 \text{ ohms}$$

$$I_3 = \frac{50}{48.1} = 1.04 \text{ amperes}$$

$$\mathbf{I}_3 \text{ lags } \mathbf{V}_3 \text{ by } \tan^{-1}\frac{47.6}{6} = 82.8°$$

$$P_3 = 1.04^2 \times 6 = 6.48 \text{ watts}$$

$$V_{L3} = 1.04 \times 56.55 = 58.9 \text{ volts}$$

Fifth Harmonic

$$V_5 = \frac{28.28}{\sqrt{2}} = 20 \text{ volts}$$

$$R_5 = 6 \text{ ohms}$$

$$X_{L5} = 5X_{L1} = 5 \times 18.85 = 94.25 \text{ ohms}$$

$$X_{C5} = \frac{X_{C1}}{5} = \frac{26.85}{5} = 5.37 \text{ ohms}$$

$$\mathbf{Z}_5 = 6 + j94.25 - j5.37 = 6 + j88.88 \quad \text{or} \quad \sqrt{6^2 + 88.88^2} = 89 \text{ ohms}$$

$$I_5 = \frac{20}{89} = 0.225 \text{ ampere}$$

$$\mathbf{I}_5 \text{ lags } \mathbf{V}_5 \text{ by } \tan^{-1} \frac{88.88}{6} = 86.1°$$

$$P_5 = I_5^2 R_5 = 0.225^2 \times 6 = 0.304 \text{ watt}$$

$$V_{L5} = 0.225 \times 94.25 = 21.2 \text{ volts}$$

$$I_{\text{total}} = \sqrt{I_1^2 + I_3^2 + I_5^2} = \sqrt{10^2 + 1.04^2 + 0.225^2} = 10.05 \text{ amperes}$$

$$P_{\text{total}} = P_1 + P_3 + P_5 = 600 + 6.48 + 0.304 = 606.8 \text{ watts}$$

$$V_L = \sqrt{188.5^2 + 58.9^2 + 21.2^2} = \sqrt{39510} = 198.8 \text{ volts}$$

Since the fundamental of current leads the fundamental of voltage by 53.12°, the equation of the fundamental of current must be $\sqrt{2}\,10 \sin(\omega t + 53.12°)$. Similarly, for the third harmonic,

$$i_3 = \sqrt{2}\,1.04 \sin(3\omega t + 30° - 82.8°)$$

or

$$i_3 = \sqrt{2}\,1.04 \sin(3\omega t - 52.8°) \text{ amperes}$$

Also

$$i_5 = -\sqrt{2}\,0.225 \sin(5\omega t - 20° - 86.1°)$$
$$= -\sqrt{2}\,0.225 \sin(5\omega t - 106.1°) \text{ amperes}$$

The complete equation is:

$$i = 14.14 \sin(\omega t + 53.12°) + 1.47 \sin(3\omega t - 52.8°) - 0.318 \sin(5\omega t - 106.1°)$$
$$= 14.14 \sin(\omega t + 53.12°) + 1.47 \sin(3\omega t - 52.8°) + 0.318 \sin(5\omega t + 73.9°) \text{ amperes}$$

Parallel Circuit Analysis when Waves Are Non-Sinusoidal. This is not appreciably different from the preceding series-circuit problem.

Example 13. Given the circuit shown in Fig. 23, with the 60-cycle constants as shown. When a voltage $v = 141.4 \sin \omega t + 70.7 \sin(3\omega t + 30°) - 28.28 \sin(5\omega t - 20°)$ volts is impressed, find the ammeter value of the total current, I, the current in each branch, power dissipated by each branch, total power dissipated, and the equation of the resultant current. $\omega = 377$ radians per second.

Fundamental

$$V_1 = \frac{141.4}{\sqrt{2}} = 100 \text{ volts magnitude}$$

$$\mathbf{V}_1 = 100 + j0 \text{ volts}$$

$$\mathbf{I}_{ab1} = \frac{100(5 + j15)}{(5 - j15)(5 + j15)} = 2 + j6 \quad \text{or} \quad 6.33 \text{ amperes}$$

$$\mathbf{I}_{cd1} = \frac{100}{10 + j2} = 9.62 - j1.925 \quad \text{or} \quad 9.82 \text{ amperes}$$

$$\mathbf{I}_{fe1} = \mathbf{I}_{ab1} + \mathbf{I}_{cd1} = 11.62 + j4.075 \quad \text{or} \quad 12.33 \text{ amperes}$$

$\mathbf{I}_{fe1}$ leads the fundamental of voltage by $\tan^{-1}\dfrac{4.075}{11.62} = 19.4°$

$$P_{ab1} = ei + e'i' = 100 \times 2 = 200 \text{ watts}$$

$$P_{cd1} = 100 \times 9.62 = 962 \text{ watts}$$

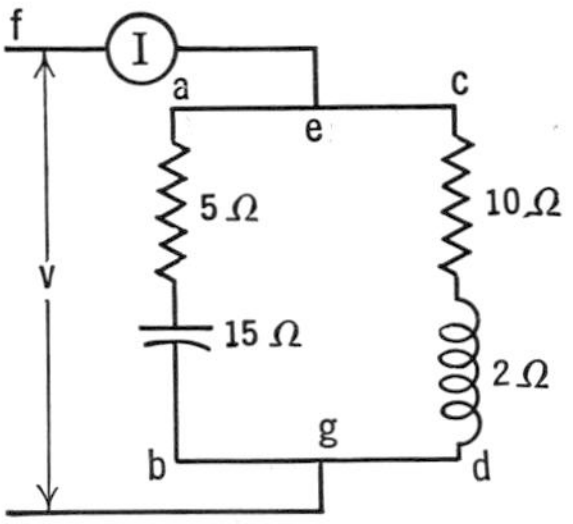

Fig. 23. Circuit with 60-cycle parameters.

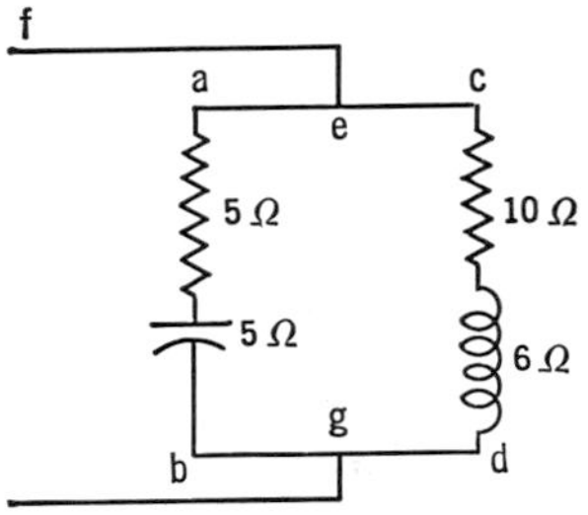

Fig. 24. Circuit of Fig. 23 showing parameters at 180 cycles.

Third Harmonic

The circuit with the parameters for the third harmonic is shown in Fig. 24. Only the reactances need be changed before proceeding as before.

$$V_3 = \frac{70.7}{\sqrt{2}} = 50 \text{ volts magnitude}$$

Take $\mathbf{V}_3$ along the reference axis for the third harmonic. (The most convenient reference axis should be chosen in any particular case in this type of analysis.)

$$\mathbf{V}_3 = 50 + j0 \text{ volts}$$

$$\mathbf{I}_{ab3} = \frac{50}{5 - j5} = 5 + j5 \quad \text{or} \quad 7.07 \text{ amperes}$$

$$\mathbf{I}_{cd3} = \frac{50}{10 + j6} = 3.68 - j2.21 \quad \text{or} \quad 4.3 \text{ amperes}$$

$$\mathbf{I}_{fe3} = 8.68 + j2.79 \quad \text{or} \quad 9.11 \text{ amperes}$$

$$\mathbf{I}_{fe3} \text{ leads } \mathbf{V}_3 \text{ by } \tan^{-1}\frac{2.79}{8.68} = 17.85°$$

$$P_{ab3} = 50 \times 5 = 250 \text{ watts}$$

$$P_{cd3} = 50 \times 3.68 = 184 \text{ watts}$$

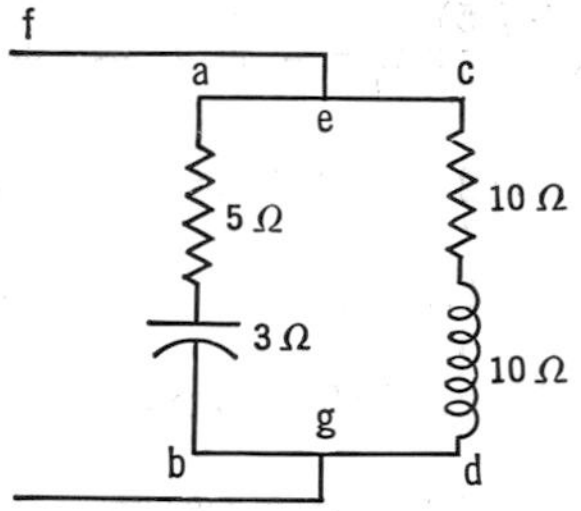

FIG. 25. Circuit of Fig. 23 showing parameters at 300 cycles.

Fifth Harmonic

The circuit with parameters for the fifth harmonic is shown in Fig. 25.

$$V_5 = \frac{28.28}{\sqrt{2}} = 20 \text{ volts}$$

Let $$\mathbf{V}_5 = 20 + j0 \text{ volts}$$

$$\mathbf{I}_{ab5} = \frac{20}{5 - j3} = 2.94 + j1.763 \quad \text{or} \quad 3.43 \text{ amperes}$$

$$\mathbf{I}_{cd5} = \frac{20}{10 + j10} = 1 - j1 \quad \text{or} \quad 1.414 \text{ amperes}$$

$$\mathbf{I}_{fe5} = 3.94 + j0.763 \quad \text{or} \quad 4.01 \text{ amperes}$$

$$\mathbf{I}_{fe5} \text{ leads } \mathbf{V}_5 \text{ by } \tan^{-1}\frac{0.763}{3.94} = 10.95°$$

$$P_{ab5} = 20 \times 2.94 = 58.8 \text{ watts}$$

$$P_{cd5} = 20 \times 1 = 20.0 \text{ watts}$$

$$\text{Ammeter value of total current} = \sqrt{12.33^2 + 9.11^2 + 4.01^2} = 15.9 \text{ amperes}$$

$$\text{Ammeter value of current in } ab = \sqrt{6.33^2 + 7.07^2 + 3.43^2} = 10.1 \text{ amperes}$$

$$\text{Ammeter value of current in } cd = \sqrt{9.82^2 + 4.3^2 + 1.414^2} = 10.81 \text{ amperes}$$

$$P_{ab} = 200 + 250 + 58.8 = 508.8 \text{ watts}$$

$$P_{cd} = 962 + 184 + 20 = 1166 \text{ watts}$$

$$\text{Total power dissipated} = 1674.8 \text{ watts}$$

Since $\mathbf{I}_{fe1}$ leads $\mathbf{V}_1$ by 19.4°, the equation for the fundamental of the current wave must lead the voltage wave 141.4 sin ωt by 19.4°. Hence

$$i_1 = \sqrt{2}\,12.33 \sin(\omega t + 19.4°) \text{ amperes}$$

Similarly

$$i_3 = \sqrt{2}\,9.11 \sin(3\omega t + 30° + 17.85°)$$
$$= \sqrt{2}\,9.11 \sin(3\omega t + 47.85°) \text{ amperes}$$

and

$$i_5 = -\sqrt{2}\,4.01 \sin(5\omega t - 20° + 10.95°)$$
$$= \sqrt{2}\,4.01 \sin(5\omega t + 170.95°) \text{ amperes}$$

Therefore

$$i = i_1 + i_3 + i_5$$
$$= 17.45 \sin(\omega t + 19.4°) + 12.9 \sin(3\omega t + 47.85°)$$
$$+ 5.67 \sin(5\omega t + 171°) \text{ amperes}$$

Addition and Subtraction of Complex Waves. These operations are similar. Subtraction is performed by reversing the sign of the term to be subtracted and then adding. To illustrate, consider the bifurcated circuit shown in Fig. 26. Given

$$i_1 = 10 \sin(\omega t + 30°) - 5 \sin(3\omega t - 40°) \text{ amperes}$$

$$i_3 = 15 \sin(\omega t - 10°) + 10 \sin(3\omega t + 60°) \text{ amperes}$$

Find i_2.

From Kirchhoff's laws, $i_1 + i_2 = i_3$, or $i_2 = i_3 - i_1$.

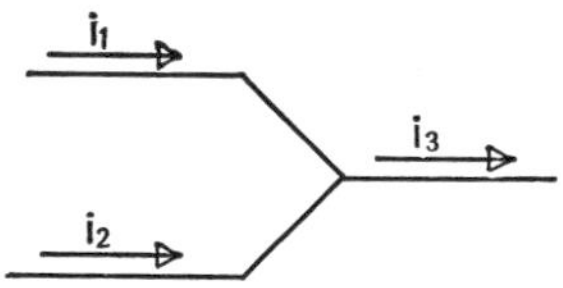

FIG. 26. Bifurcated line.

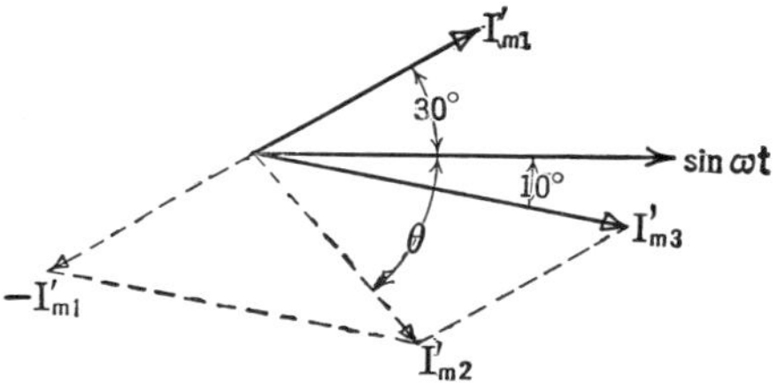

FIG. 27. Vector diagram for currents of fundamental frequency in Fig. 26.

Fundamental

Consider a wave whose equation is of the phase sin ωt as the reference. The solution will follow the vector diagram of Fig. 27. The number of primes on a symbol will indicate the order of the harmonic represented.

$$\mathbf{I}_{m1}' = 10(\cos 30° + j \sin 30°) = 8.66 + j5$$

$$\mathbf{I}_{m3}' = 15(\cos 10° - j \sin 10°) = 14.75 - j2.6$$

$$-\mathbf{I}_{m1}' = -8.66 - j5$$

$$\mathbf{I}_{m2}' = -\mathbf{I}_{m1}' + \mathbf{I}_{m3}' = 6.09 - j7.6 \quad \text{or} \quad 9.74 \text{ amperes}$$

$$\theta = \tan^{-1}\frac{-7.6}{6.09} = -51.3°$$

$$i_2' = 9.74 \sin(\omega t - 51.3°) \text{ amperes}$$

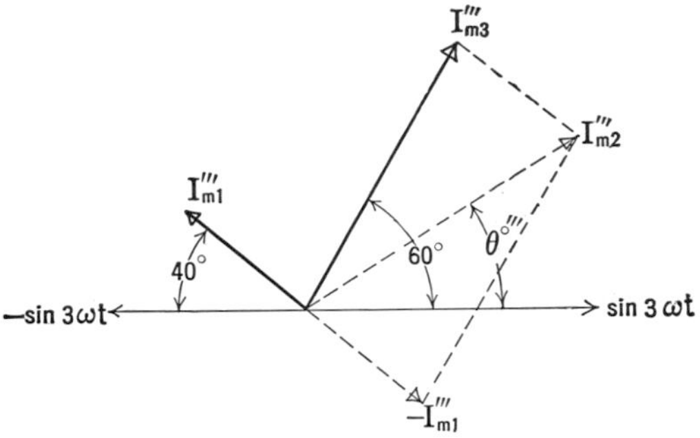

FIG. 28. Vector diagram for third harmonic currents in Fig. 26.

Third Harmonic

A wave of the phase of sin $3\omega t$ will be taken as the reference. Then the vector diagram representing the third-harmonic currents appears as shown in Fig. 28.

$$\mathbf{I}_{m1}''' = 5(\cos 140° + j \sin 140°) = -3.83 + j3.214$$

$$\mathbf{I}_{m3}''' = 10(\cos 60° + j \sin 60°) = 5 + j8.66$$

$$\mathbf{I}_{m2}''' = \mathbf{I}_{m3}''' - \mathbf{I}_{m1}''' = 5 + j8.66 + 3.83 - j3.214 = 8.83 + j5.446$$

or 10.37 amperes

$$\theta''' = \tan^{-1}\frac{5.446}{8.83} = 31.6°$$

$$i_2''' = 10.37 \sin(3\omega t + 31.6°) \text{ amperes}$$

The complete solution is

$$i_2 = i_2' + i_2'''$$
$$= 9.74 \sin(\omega t - 51.3°) + 10.37 \sin(3\omega t + 31.6°) \text{ amperes}$$

Introduction of Harmonics Due to Variation in Circuit Parameters. Harmonics in a current wave may exist even though the voltage causing it is a pure sinusoid. For example, consider a very thin filament of wire which has a high temperature coefficient of resistivity. If the wire is sufficiently thin so that it will heat and cool during a cycle as the current varies from zero to a maximum, the resistance will vary during the cycle. At the maximum point a on the voltage wave, Fig. 29, the resistance will be higher than at point b. The current at a will, therefore, fall below the value that would permit it to be proportional to the voltage. The wave i_1 shows the current wave for a constant resistance, whereas the dotted wave i_2 shows how it will vary when the resistance increases for the higher values of current during a cycle.

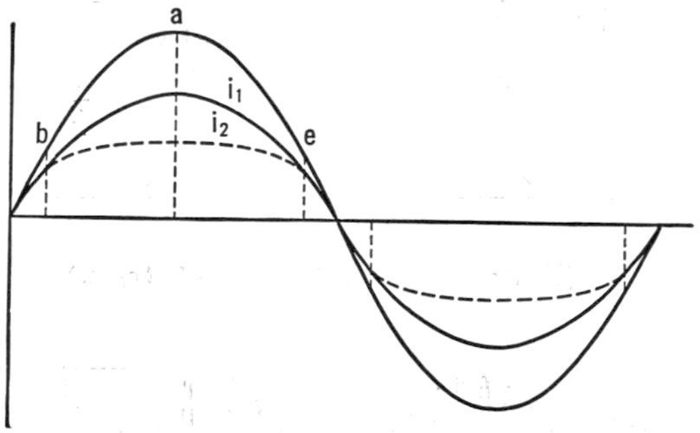

FIG. 29. Shape of i_2 wave is flatter than a sine wave owing to resistance increasing with current.

A very common example of harmonics in a current wave occurs when a sinusoidal voltage wave is impressed on an inductance coil with an iron core. As the current increases, the resulting operation on a higher part of the magnetization or saturation curve causes the inductance to become smaller. When the inductance becomes less, the inductive reactance is reduced and the current, therefore, rises more rapidly than it otherwise would. Thus the current wave becomes more peaked than a sinusoid. This is shown by Oscillogram 2, page 224 which was taken for an iron-core coil.

When the voltage on some device is to be reduced and it is desired to maintain the same wave form, a series resistance cannot be used if the current wave is not sinusoidal. The drop across the resistance will be non-sinusoidal, and this drop subtracted from an original sine wave of voltage will result in a non-sinusoidal wave across the device. In general, but not invariably, the subtraction of a non-sinusoidal voltage drop from a non-sinusoidal voltage will result in a non-sinusoidal wave of different shape from the original.

Modulated Waves. Modulated waves consist of a combination of waves of different frequencies and are, therefore, classified as complex or non-sinusoidal waves. The transmission of radio intelligence is usually accomplished by means of some combination of carrier and audio frequencies. Graphical representations of a carrier wave of relatively high frequency and of a modulating wave of relatively low frequency are shown in Fig. 30*a* and Fig. 30*b*, respectively. The carrier frequencies employed in the program broadcast band range from 540 to 1600 kc, and the modulating audio frequencies usefully employed at the transmitter range from about 30 to 10,000 cycles.

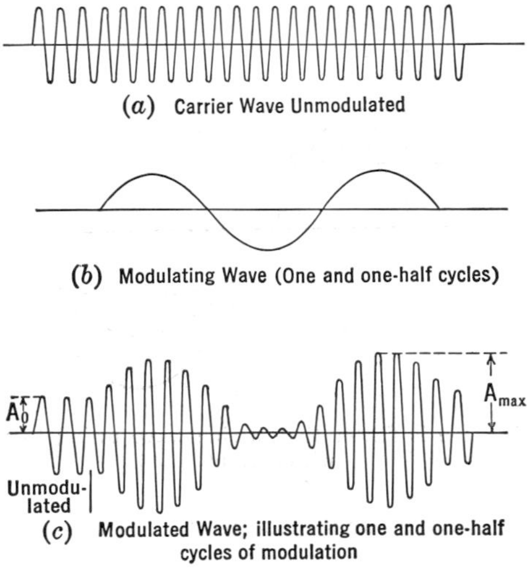

FIG. 30.

The carrier and modulating waves may be combined in a network at the transmitter in such a manner that useful variations in the resultant amplitude or frequency are obtained. Some of the basic principles involved may be understood by considering the case where the carrier frequency is generated by an ordinary type of alternator rather than by a vacuum tube oscillator. The carrier voltage will be represented by

$$e_c = A_0' \sin \omega t \tag{35}$$

where A_0' is the maximum magnitude of the carrier voltage and ω is the carrier angular velocity. Either A_0' or ω may be varied in accordance with the intelligence to be transmitted, thus producing amplitude or frequency modulation. In the case of the ordinary alternator, A_0' could be made to vary by changing the field current sinusoidally and the resultant wave would correspond generally to that shown in Fig. 30*c* or in Oscillogram 5.

Amplitude modulation may be investigated conveniently by letting A_0' of equation (35) take the form $(A_0 + E_m' \sin \omega_1 t)$, where E_m' is the maximum amplitude of the modulating wave that is effectively superimposed on the carrier and ω_1 is the modulating angular velocity. E_m' is a measure of the degree of modulation (for a fixed value of A_0) and usually has values ranging from 50 to 100 per cent of A_0. Percentage modulation is defined as

$$\frac{E_m'}{A_0} \times 100 = \frac{A_{\text{max}} - A_0}{A_0} \times 100$$

where the A's refer to the amplitudes shown in Fig. 30*c*.

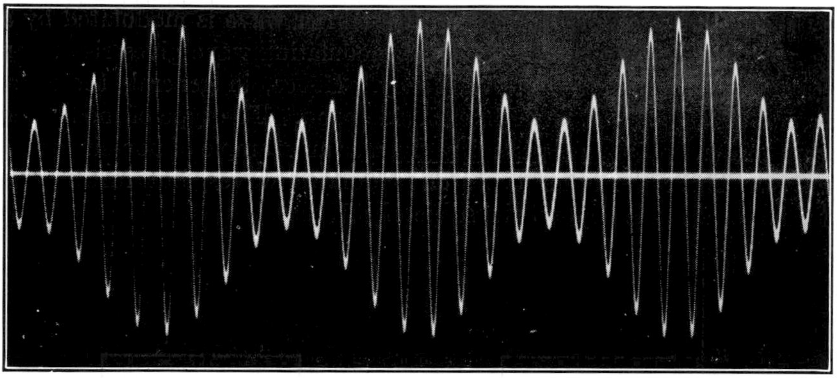

OSCILLOGRAM 5. Photograph of a sinusoidally modulated wave.

In general, the equation of a sinusoidally modulated wave is:

$$\begin{aligned} e &= (A_0 + E_m' \sin \omega_1 t) \sin \omega t \\ &= A_0 \sin \omega t + E_m' \sin \omega_1 t \sin \omega t \end{aligned} \tag{36}$$

The product of two sine waves of different frequencies may be expressed in terms of the following two well-known trigonometric relations.

$$\cos (\omega t - \omega_1 t) = \cos \omega t \cos \omega_1 t + \sin \omega t \sin \omega_1 t \tag{37}$$

$$\cos (\omega t + \omega_1 t) = \cos \omega t \cos \omega_1 t - \sin \omega t \sin \omega_1 t \tag{38}$$

Subtracting equation (38) from (37) gives

$$\cos (\omega t - \omega_1 t) - \cos (\omega t + \omega_1 t) = 2 \sin \omega t \sin \omega_1 t \tag{39}$$

Substituting the value of $\sin \omega t \sin \omega_1 t$ from equation (39) in equation (36) gives

$$\begin{aligned} e &= A_0 \sin \omega t + \frac{E_m'}{2} \cos (\omega t - \omega_1 t) - \frac{E_m'}{2} \cos (\omega t + \omega_1 t) \\ &= A_0 \sin \omega t + \frac{E_m'}{2} \cos 2\pi (f - f_1)t - \frac{E_m'}{2} \cos 2\pi (f + f_1)t \end{aligned} \tag{40}$$

Equation (40) consists of three terms. The first term, $A_0 \sin \omega t$, is of the same frequency as the original wave before modulation. This wave is called the carrier wave, and its frequency the carrier frequency. The second term, $(E_m'/2) \cos 2\pi (f - f_1)t$, has a frequency equal to $(f - f_1)$, the difference between the carrier frequency and the modulating frequency. This frequency $(f - f_1)$ is called the lower side-band frequency. The third term, $(E_m'/2) \cos 2\pi (f + f_1)t$, represents a frequency equal to $f + f_1$, the sum of the carrier and modulating frequencies. It is called the upper side-band frequency. Each of these three frequencies can be separated from the others in the resultant wave by the use of appropriate filters. If a carrier wave is modulated by a complex wave, each harmonic of the modulating wave gives rise to an upper and lower side-band frequency. Hence, in general, there are several different frequencies in each side band. The type of modulated wave presented above is primarily given as an example of non-sinusoidal waves. There are other types of modulated waves, but further discussion of them is beyond the scope of this text.

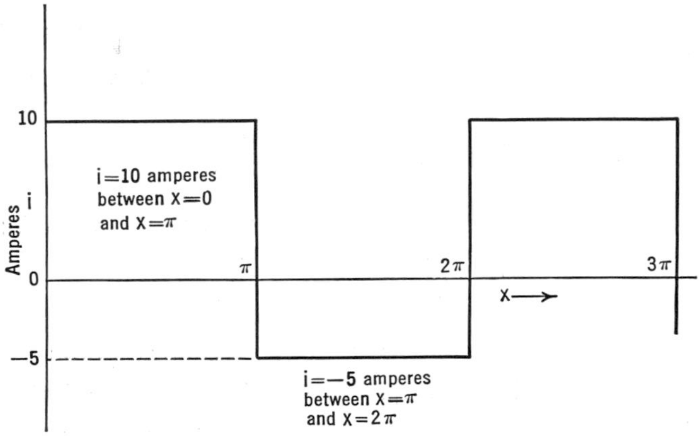

FIG. 31. See Problems 9 and 25.

PROBLEMS

9. (*a*) Employ the analytical method to determine the coefficients of the harmonics through the third harmonic for the wave shown in Fig. 31.

(*b*) Write the Fourier series in terms of sine components for the wave.

(*c*) Sketch the components, indicating the manner in which the components combine to approximate the original wave shape shown in Fig. 31.

10. (*a*) Employ the analytical method to determine the coefficients of the harmonics through the fifth harmonic for the wave shown in Fig. 32.

(*b*) Write the equation of the wave through the fifth harmonic.

(*c*) Sketch the components, indicating the manner in which the components combine to approximate the original wave shown in Fig. 32.

11. A certain current wave has a height of 1 from 0° to 30°, then increases linearly in a positive direction to a value of 3 at 60°, after which it remains at a height of 3 until 120° is reached. It then decreases linearly to a value of zero at 150° and then remains at zero value until 360°. The cycle is then repeated. Find A_0, A_1, and B_1 of the Fourier series terms which represent this wave.

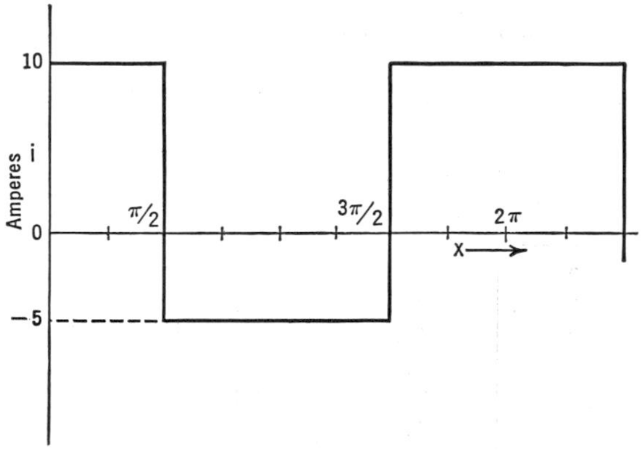

FIG. 32. See Problem 10.

12. A current wave is defined over one complete cycle by the following data:

x (in degrees)	i (in amperes)	x (in degrees)	i (in amperes)
0	−2.000	195	−3.613
15	+0.149	210	−5.000
30	+3.000	225	−6.364
45	+6.364	240	−7.660
60	+9.660	255	−8.634
75	+12.098	270	−9.000
90	+13.000	285	−8.634
105	+12.098	300	−7.660
120	+9.660	315	−6.364
135	+6.364	330	−5.000
150	+3.000	345	−3.613
165	+0.149	360	−2.000
180	−2.000	375	+0.149

(*a*) Employ the analyzing tables on pages 237 to 240, evaluate the Fourier series coefficients A_0, A_1, B_1, A_2, B_2, and A_3 of the above wave form, and write the Fourier series in equational form. (*Note*: Evaluations based on 15° intervals will be sufficiently accurate in this case since the actual Fourier series contains no terms beyond the A_3 term. Call any coefficient zero which is no greater in magnitude than the probable arithmetical error involved.)

(*b*) Graph each of the components and combine these components to form the resultant wave. Check various values on the resultant graph against the original data.

13. Employ the method of equations (21) and (22) and evaluate the Fourier series coefficients through the third harmonic for the wave given in Problem 12.

14. Write the following equation in terms of three sine components only:

$$v = 4.0 \sin \omega t - 3.0 \cos \omega t - 7.66 \sin 2\omega t + 6.43 \cos 2\omega t$$
$$- 2 \sin 3\omega t - 1.5 \cos 3\omega t$$

15. Given an a-c wave form as defined by the following table of measured ordinates:

Ordinate No.	Degrees	Measured Ordinate	Ordinate No.	Degrees	Measured Ordinate
0	0	0.0	19	95	7.1
1	5	0.8	20	100	7.4
2	10	1.7	21	105	8.0
3	15	2.7	22	110	9.0
4	20	3.6	23	115	10.5
5	25	4.5	24	120	12.0
6	30	5.6	25	125	13.2
7	35	6.9	26	130	14.0
8	40	8.2	27	135	14.0
9	45	9.7	28	140	13.0
10	50	10.7	29	145	11.6
11	55	11.0	30	150	10.0
12	60	11.0	31	155	8.0
13	65	10.4	32	160	5.8
14	70	9.8	33	165	4.0
15	75	9.2	34	170	2.5
16	80	8.5	35	175	1.0
17	85	7.8	36	180	0.0
18	90	7.0			

Negative loop similar to positive loop.

(*a*) Graph the wave and analyze it by the Fourier series method for fundamental the third, the fifth, and the seventh harmonics by the use of analyzing tables.

(*b*) Write the equation of the wave in terms of its sine and cosine components.

(*c*) Write the equation of the wave in terms of sine components only.

(*d*) Synthesize the components graphically, and compare the resultant with the original wave.

16. Employ equations (21) and (22) instead of analyzing tables, and find the sine and cosine coefficients of the Fourier series to include the seventh harmonic for the wave in Problem 15. Express the resultant wave in terms of four sine components only.

17. Given an a-c wave form as defined by the measured ordinates shown on page 269.

Analyze the wave by using equations (21) and (22) for the first seven harmonics, and write the Fourier series equation for the wave.

Degrees	Measured Ordinate	Degrees	Measured Ordinate
0	−0.6064	100	0.7848
10	0.1736	110	0.6767
20	0.9484	120	0.4966
30	1.4139	130	0.4200
40	1.4428	140	0.5669
50	1.149	150	0.8832
60	0.79	160	1.1420
70	0.5937	170	1.0880
80	0.6154	180	0.6064
90	0.737		

Negative loop similar to positive loop.

18. Show whether the following waves have symmetry with respect to the positive and negative loops:

$$e = 100 \sin(\omega t + 30°) - 50 \cos 2\omega t + 25 \sin(5\omega t + 150°) \text{ volts}$$

$$i = 20 \sin(\omega t + 40°) + 10 \sin(2\omega t + 30°) - 5 \sin(5\omega t - 50°) \text{ amperes}$$

19. Does either of the waves in Problem 18 possess symmetry about the mid-ordinate of the positive and negative loops? Why?

20. Are the following waves of the same wave form or shape? Give reason.

$$v = 100 \sin(\omega t + 70°) - 60 \sin(2\omega t - 30°) + 30 \sin(3\omega t - 60°)$$

$$i = 50 \cos(\omega t - 60°) + 30 \sin(2\omega t + 70°) - 15 \cos(3\omega t - 90°)$$

21. Are the following two waves of the same wave form? Give reason.

$$e = 100 \sin(\omega t - 20°) + 50 \sin(3\omega t + 60°) - 25 \cos(5\omega t - 30°) \text{ volts}$$

$$i = 20 \cos(\omega t - 60°) - 10 \sin(3\omega t + 15°) + 5 \sin(5\omega t - 70°) \text{ amperes}$$

22. Find the effective values of the voltage and current waves of Problem 18.

23. Find the effective value of:

$$v = 100 \sin(\omega t + 30°) - 40 \sin(2\omega t - 30°) + 40 \sin(2\omega t + 30°) + 20 \cos(5\omega t - 30°)$$

24. A complex wave has harmonics of the following effective values: fundamental 100 volts, third harmonic 70 volts, and fifth harmonic 50 volts. Find the voltmeter value of the complex wave.

25. The Fourier representation of the current variation shown in Fig. 31 is:

$$i = 2.5 + \frac{30}{\pi} \sin x + \frac{30}{3\pi} \sin 3x + \frac{30}{5\pi} \sin 5x + \frac{30}{7\pi} \sin 7x + \frac{30}{9\pi} \sin 9x + \cdots$$

Compare the effective value of the current as calculated by equation (27), page 250 (employing only the first six terms of the series given above), with the true effective value.

26. The current flowing through a particular filter choke is: $i = 5 + 2 \sin x$ amperes, where x $(= 754t)$ represents angular measure. Sketch the wave shape of this current variation.

(*a*) What are the maximum, minimum, and average values of current?

(*b*) Does the maximum value of the a-c component satisfy the relation: $I_{m(ac)} = 0.5\,(I_{\text{max}} - I_{\text{min}})$?

(*c*) What is the effective value of the current: $i = 5 + 2 \sin x$ amperes?

27. Assuming that a pulsating direct current is composed of a d-c component (I_{dc}) and a single-frequency a-c component, the general expression for the current variation is: $i = I_{dc} + I_{m(ac)} \sin x$.

(*a*) If only the average and effective values of the pulsating current were known, would it be possible to find the maximum value of the a-c component, $I_{m(ac)}$?

(*b*) The average value of $i = I_{dc} + I_{m(ac)} \sin x$ is 4 amperes, and the effective value is 5 amperes. Find $I_{m(ac)}$.

28. Considering only second harmonic distortion, the plate current of one class of amplifiers (with sinusoidally varying grid-cathode excitation) is given by the equation:

$$i = I_0 + I_{m1} \sin x - I_{m2} \cos 2x$$

where $I_0 = I_b + I_{m2}$, I_b being the steady plate current with no a-c grid excitation.

(*a*) Sketch the wave form of the current variation for $I_0 = 0.2$, $I_{m1} = 0.1$, and $I_{m2} = 0.01$ ampere. Indicate the value of I_b on the sketch.

(*b*) What are the maximum (I_{max}), minimum (I_{min}), and average values of the wave form sketched in (*a*)? Does the average value of current (I_0) satisfy the relation: $0.5(I_{\text{max}} + I_{\text{min}})$?

29. Refer to the plate current variation given in Problem 28, namely,

$$i = I_0 + I_{m1} \sin x - I_{m2} \cos 2x$$

(*a*) If it is known that the average value of plate current changes from the steady value $I_b = I_0 - I_{m2}$ (with no a-c grid excitation) to the average value I_0 with a-c grid excitation, show either graphically or analytically that:

$$I_{\text{max}} \text{ (with a-c grid excitation)} = I_b + I_{m1} + 2I_{m2}$$

$$I_{\text{min}} \text{ (with a-c grid excitation)} = I_b - I_{m1} + 2I_{m2}$$

$$I_{m1} = 0.5\,(I_{\text{max}} - I_{\text{min}})$$

$$I_{m2} = \frac{(I_{\text{max}} + I_{\text{min}}) - 2I_b}{4}$$

(*b*) Show that the ratio of I_{m2} to I_{m1} expressed in per cent is:

$$\frac{I_{m2}}{I_{m1}} \times 100 = \frac{0.5(I_{\text{max}} + I_{\text{min}}) - I_b}{(I_{\text{max}} - I_{\text{min}})} \times 100$$

Note: The above ratio is called the per cent second harmonic distortion, and, since the values of I_{max}, I_{min}, and I_b may be readily measured under the conditions of steady grid bias, the above relation is sometimes used to determine the per cent second harmonic distortion where unsymmetrical positive and negative peaks of plate current are encountered.

(*c*) Determine the per cent harmonic distortion from $(I_{m2}/I_{m1}) \times 100$ and from the equation given in (*b*) if $I_0 = 0.2$, $I_{m1} = 0.1$, and $I_{m2} = 0.01$ ampere. $(I_b = 0.2 - 0.01$ ampere.)

30. Because of irregularities in the "straight" portion of the plate current-grid voltage characteristic of a vacuum tube, the equation for the plate current sometimes takes the general form

$$i = I_b + I_{m1} \sin x + I_{m3} \sin 3x$$

where I_b is the plate current corresponding to fixed values of grid-cathode and plate-cathode voltages. Find the maximum, the minimum, and the average values of i if $I_b = 0.2$, $I_{m1} = 0.07$, and $I_{m3} = 0.005$ ampere.

31. Calculate the power represented by the voltage and current in Problem 18.

32. Calculate the power represented by the current and voltage of Problem 21.

33. Calculate the power factor for the waves in Problem 18.

34. Determine the power factor for the waves in Problem 21.

35. Given: $v = 100 \sin(\omega t + 60°) - 50 \sin(3\omega t - 30°)$ volts
$i = 10 \sin(\omega t + 60°) + 5 \cos(3\omega t + 60°)$ amperes

(*a*) Calculate the power and power factor for the above waves.

(*b*) If only the magnitude of the third harmonic in the current wave is varied, what would be its value to bring the power factor for the composite waves to 0.8?

36. Determine the equivalent sine waves for the voltage and current in Problem 18.

37. Find the deviation factor for the voltage

$$e = 100 \sin(\omega t - 25.36°) + 50 \sin(3\omega t + 58.92°)$$

38. A voltage $v = 100 \sin(\omega t + 30°) - 50 \sin(3\omega t + 60°) + 30 \cos 5\omega t$ volts is impressed on a resistance of 6 ohms in series with a capacitance of 88.4 μf and an inductance of 0.01061 henry. Find the ammeter value of the current, the power dissipated by the circuit, the power factor of the whole circuit, and the voltage drop across the capacitance if $\omega = 377$ radians per second.

39. A current of $i = 10 \sin(\omega t - 60°) + 5 \sin(2\omega t + 20°)$ amperes flows in a series circuit consisting of 8 ohms resistance, 10 ohms 60-cycle capacitive reactance, and 4 ohms 60-cycle inductive reactance. Find the equation of the impressed voltage wave. $\omega = 377$ radians per second.

40. A branch containing 5 ohms resistance in series with an inductance of 0.00796 henry is in parallel with another branch consisting of a resistance of 6 ohms in series with a 60-cycle capacitive reactance of 15 ohms. For a voltage of $e = 100 \sin(\omega t + 30°) - 50 \cos(3\omega t - 30°)$ volts impressed on the combination, find the equation of the current wave required by the combination. $\omega = 377$ radians per second.

41. Find the ammeter readings in each branch and the supply line to the circuit of Problem 40.

42. Determine the power dissipated in each branch of the circuit of Problem 40 and the total power taken by the whole circuit.

43. Calculate the power factor of the whole circuit in Problem 40 and the power factor of each branch.

44. The following two currents flow toward a certain junction:

$$i_1 = 20 \sin(\omega t + 30°) - 10 \sin(2\omega t - 30°) + 5 \sin(3\omega t - 40°) \text{ amperes}$$

$$i_2 = 15 \cos \omega t + 10 \cos(2\omega t - 60°) + 10 \cos(3\omega t + 50°) \text{ amperes}$$

Find the equation of the current leaving the junction. What is the ammeter or effective value of each of the three currents?

45. Subtract i_2 from i_1 in Problem 44, and find the equation of the resultant.

46. At 60 cycles a certain impedance, Z_1, consists of 4 ohms resistance, 6 ohms capacitive reactance, and 3 ohms inductive reactance in series. Another identical impedance, Z_2, is connected in parallel with Z_1. A third 60-cycle impedance (consisting of 1.5 ohms resistance and 2 ohms inductive reactance in series) is connected in series with the parallel combination of Z_1 and Z_2. If a voltage $v = 100 \sin 377t - 50 \sin 3(377t + 30°)$ volts is impressed on the entire series-parallel circuit, calculate: (*a*) the total rms current taken, (*b*) the rms current in each branch, (*c*) the equation of the current in branch Z_1, (*d*) the total power consumed, (*e*) the power factor of whole circuit.

47. The wave form given in Fig. 33 consists of a fundamental term $A_1 \sin x$ and one and only one other Fourier series term.

(*a*) What are the numerical values of the coefficients of the two terms?

(*b*) Write the equation of the wave. *Note:* It is suggested that the problem be solved by inspection and checked by the second graphical method of analysis, given on pages 242–246.

48. A capacitor having 20 $\mu\mu$f capacitance is connected in parallel with a coil having 20 microhenrys inductance and a series resistance as specified in (*a*) and (*b*) below. This parallel combination is energized with a pulse of current which is zero for $140° \lessgtr \omega t \lessgtr 40°$ during each cycle. The pulse reaches a maximum value of 100 milliamperes at $\omega t = 90°$ and

$$i(45°) = i(135°) = 18 \text{ milliamperes}$$

$$i(55°) = i(125°) = 49 \text{ milliamperes}$$

$$i(65°) = i(115°) = 73.5 \text{ milliamperes}$$

$$i(75°) = i(105°) = 90.5 \text{ milliamperes}$$

$$i(85°) = i(95°) = 99 \text{ milliamperes}$$

where $i(45°)$ means the value of i at $\omega t = 45°$.

Find the effective magnitude of the fundamental component of voltage developed across the parallel branches if $\omega = \frac{5}{3} \times 10^7$ radians per second. Compare this value of voltage with the third harmonic voltage developed across the parallel branches, recognizing the fact that the branches are tuned to the third harmonic. (*a*) Assume that $R = 10\,\Omega$ is the same for the fundamental and third harmonic. (*b*) Assume that $Q = \omega L/R$ is constant, R being $10\,\Omega$ for the fundamental.

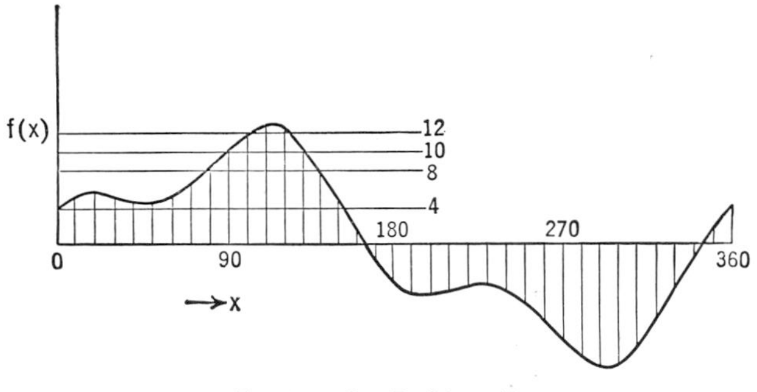

FIG. 33. See Problem 47.

chapter VII Coupled Circuits

Terminology. In electrical-engineering literature, the term " circuit " is used in a variety of ways. At times it is employed to designate a single branch of an electrical network; at other times it is used synonymously with the term " network " to mean a combination of two or more branches which are interrelated either electrically or magnetically, or both. In the present chapter the term " circuit " is employed to mean " any complete electrical loop around which Kirchhoff's emf law can be written."

Two circuits are said to be " coupled " when they are so related that energy interchanges can take place between them. More specifically, this means that a potential difference appears in either of the two circuits which are coupled, if and when the other is energized. The circuits involved may be coupled conductively, electromagnetically, or electrostatically. Various combinations of these principal modes of coupling may exist between circuits. However, the great majority of the circuits in actual practice are coupled either conductively or electromagnetically.

Coupled circuits interact upon one another, and in general the movement of electricity in any particular circuit is governed, not only by the circuit parameters of that circuit, but to some extent by the parameters of all circuits to which the circuit in question is coupled.

Conductively Coupled Circuits. Two circuits which are conductively coupled are shown in Fig. 1. In a circuit arrangement of this kind, circuit 1 may be viewed as the driving or primary circuit and circuit 2 as the receiving or secondary circuit. $\mathbf{Z}_{12}$, the impedance of the branch which is common to both circuits, is called the mutual impedance between circuit 1 and circuit 2. The mutual impedance may consist, theoretically, of a pure resistance, a pure inductance, a pure capacitance, or some combination of these circuit elements.

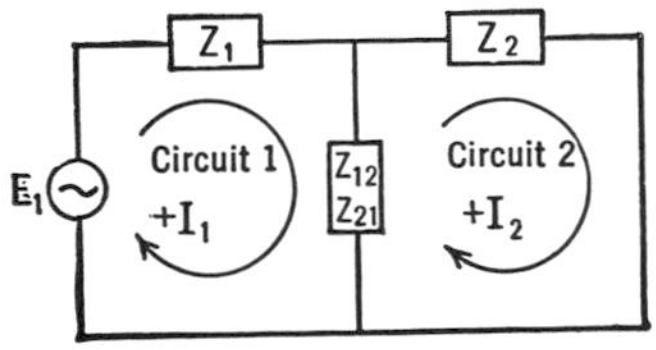

FIG. 1. Conductively coupled circuits.

If the exciting voltage and circuit parameters of Fig. 1 are given, the currents, component voltages, and component powers can be evaluated by simple circuit analysis.

In general the " loop current " method of solution[1] is particularly well suited to coupled circuit solutions. If this method of attack is employed, I_1 and I_2 are considered as the currents which flow around the complete loops of circuit 1 and circuit 2, respectively. The positive circuit directions assigned to I_1 and I_2 are, of course, arbitrary. If positive circuit directions are assigned to I_1 and I_2, as shown in Fig. 1, the actual current in the Z_{12} branch in the $+I_1$ direction is $I_1 - I_2$. The details of the " mesh current " method of solution as applied to Fig. 1 are given below. By definition:

$$\mathbf{Z}_{11} = \mathbf{Z}_1 + \mathbf{Z}_{12} \quad \text{(Impedance of circuit 1 to } I_1\text{)}$$

$$\mathbf{Z}_{22} = \mathbf{Z}_2 + \mathbf{Z}_{21} \quad \text{(Impedance of circuit 2 to } I_2\text{)}$$

If the circuit parameters are constant,

$$\mathbf{Z}_{12} = \mathbf{Z}_{21} \quad \text{(Mutual impedance between circuits 1 and 2)}$$

The application of Kirchhoff's emf law to circuits 1 and 2 of Fig. 1 results in:

$$\mathbf{Z}_{11}\mathbf{I}_1 - \mathbf{Z}_{12}\mathbf{I}_2 = \mathbf{E}_1 \tag{1}$$

$$-\mathbf{Z}_{21}\mathbf{I}_1 + \mathbf{Z}_{22}\mathbf{I}_2 = 0 \tag{2}$$

Employing elementary determinants, the expressions for $\mathbf{I}_1$ and $\mathbf{I}_2$ become:

$$\mathbf{I}_1 = \frac{\begin{vmatrix} \mathbf{E}_1 & -\mathbf{Z}_{12} \\ 0 & \mathbf{Z}_{22} \end{vmatrix}}{\begin{vmatrix} \mathbf{Z}_{11} & -\mathbf{Z}_{12} \\ -\mathbf{Z}_{21} & \mathbf{Z}_{22} \end{vmatrix}} = \frac{\mathbf{E}_1\mathbf{Z}_{22}}{\mathbf{Z}_{11}\mathbf{Z}_{22} - \mathbf{Z}_{12}^2} \tag{3}$$

$$\mathbf{I}_2 = \frac{\begin{vmatrix} \mathbf{Z}_{11} & \mathbf{E}_1 \\ -\mathbf{Z}_{21} & 0 \end{vmatrix}}{\begin{vmatrix} \mathbf{Z}_{11} & -\mathbf{Z}_{12} \\ -\mathbf{Z}_{21} & \mathbf{Z}_{22} \end{vmatrix}} = \frac{\mathbf{E}_1\mathbf{Z}_{21}}{\mathbf{Z}_{11}\mathbf{Z}_{22} - \mathbf{Z}_{12}^2} \tag{4}$$

The above method is generally applicable and may be extended to include any number of coupled circuits.

[1] In general circuit analysis many of the disagreeable details can be avoided by making use of this method. It is sometimes referred to as Maxwell's " cyclic current " method. See " A Treatise on Electricity and Magnetism, " by Maxwell, Vol. 1, 3rd edition. See also Chapter I of this text.

Example 1. Let it be assumed that, in Fig. 1: $\mathbf{E}_1 = 100 \underline{/0°}$ volts, $\mathbf{Z}_1 = 3 + j4$ ohms, $\mathbf{Z}_{12} = 10 + j0$ ohms, and $\mathbf{Z}_2 = 4 - j8$ ohms. The impedance of the generator is considered to be negligibly small, or else its impedance is included in $\mathbf{Z}_1$.

$$\mathbf{Z}_{11} = (3 + j4) + (10 + j0) = 13 + j4 = 13.6\underline{/17.1°} \text{ ohms}$$

$$\mathbf{Z}_{22} = (4 - j8) + (10 + j0) = 14 - j8 = 16.1\underline{/-29.7°} \text{ ohms}$$

$$\mathbf{Z}_{11}\mathbf{Z}_{22} = 219\underline{/-12.6°} = 214 - j47.8$$

$$\mathbf{Z}_{11}\mathbf{Z}_{22} - \mathbf{Z}_{12}{}^2 = 114 - j47.8 = 123.7\underline{/-22.7°}$$

$$\mathbf{I}_1 = \frac{(100\underline{/0°})(16.1\underline{/-29.7°})}{123.7\underline{/-22.7°}} = 13.0\underline{/-7°} \text{ amperes}$$

$$\mathbf{I}_2 = \frac{(100\underline{/0°})(10\underline{/0°})}{123.7\underline{/-22.7°}} = 8.08\underline{/22.7°} \text{ amperes}$$

The current in the $\mathbf{Z}_{12}$ branch in the direction of $\mathbf{I}_1$ is $\mathbf{I}_{12} = (\mathbf{I}_1 - \mathbf{I}_2)$.

$$\begin{aligned}\mathbf{I}_{12} &= 13.0\,(0.992 - j0.122) - 8.08\,(0.922 + j0.386)\\ &= (12.9 - j1.59) - (7.45 + j3.12)\\ &= 5.45 - j4.71 = 7.21\underline{/-40.8°} \text{ amperes}\end{aligned}$$

The total power generated by the generator E_1 is:

$$\begin{aligned}P_{\text{gen}} &= E_1 I_1 \cos\theta\Big]_{\mathbf{I}_1}^{\mathbf{E}_1} = 100 \times 13.0 \cos(-7°)\\ &= 1290 \text{ watts (approximately)}\end{aligned}$$

The total power absorbed by the network is:

$$\begin{aligned}I_1{}^2R_1 + I_2{}^2R_2 + I_{12}{}^2R_{12} &= 13.0^2 \times 3 + 8.08^2 \times 4 + 7.21^2 \times 10\\ &= 1288 \text{ watts (approximately)}\end{aligned}$$

Problem 1. Solve for $\mathbf{I}_1$, $\mathbf{I}_2$, and $\mathbf{I}_{12}$ in the above illustrative example by first reducing the coupled circuits to an equivalent series impedance. Draw the vector diagram of $\mathbf{E}_1$, $\mathbf{I}_1$, $\mathbf{I}_2$, $\mathbf{I}_{12}$, $\mathbf{V}_{12}$, illustrating vectorially that $\mathbf{V}_{12} = \mathbf{E}_1 - \mathbf{I}_1\mathbf{Z}_1$.

Ans.: Given in the above illustrative example.

Mutual Impedance. Before proceeding with particular types of coupled circuits, we shall state some general definitions which will be useful later in this chapter and also in radio courses where the coefficient of coupling plays a far more prominent role than it does in a first course.

The mutual impedance between, say, circuits 1 and 2 of a general network is defined as the ratio of the voltage developed in circuit 2 per unit current in circuit 1 when all circuits except circuit 1 are open-circuited. This mutual impedance has already been employed in the foregoing section as $\mathbf{Z}_{21}$. If linear bilateral circuit elements are employed in the coupling of the two circuits, it should be plain that $\mathbf{Z}_{12}$, the ratio of the voltage developed in circuit 1 per unit current in circuit 2 with all circuits except circuit 2 open-circuited, is equal to $\mathbf{Z}_{21}$.

The definition given above for mutual impedance between two circuits can be generalized to apply to two pairs of terminals, 11′ and 22′, as shown in Fig. 2 where the network in the box may be any con-

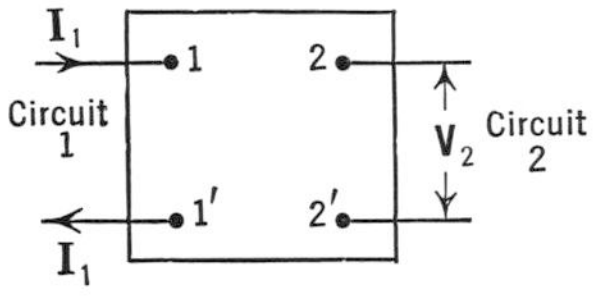

FIG. 2. Circuit 1 coupled to circuit 2 through an arbitrary network not shown.

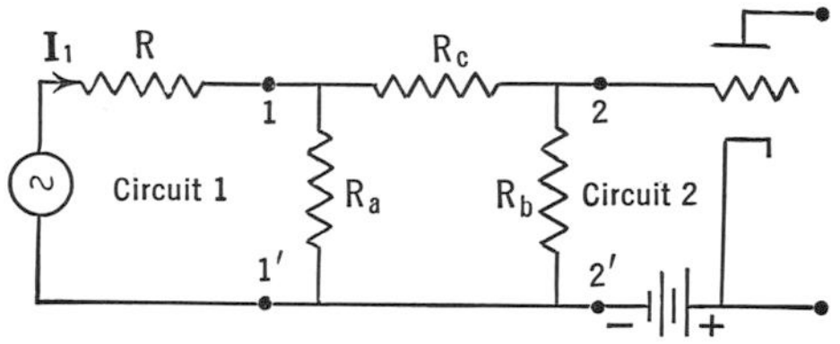

FIG. 3. Circuit 1 coupled to circuit 2 through a π set of resistances.

figuration of impedances. If, for example, the terminals 11′ and 22′ of Fig. 3 are selected, we would find upon measurement that

$$\mathbf{Z}_{21} = \frac{\mathbf{V}_2}{\mathbf{I}_1} = \frac{\mathbf{V}_b}{\mathbf{I}_1} = \frac{\dfrac{\mathbf{V}_a}{R_b + R_c} R_b}{\dfrac{\mathbf{V}_a(R_a + R_b + R_c)}{R_a(R_b + R_c)}} = \frac{R_a R_b}{R_a + R_b + R_c}$$

where $\mathbf{V}_b$ is the voltage developed across R_b (terminals 22′) and $\mathbf{V}_a$ is the voltage drop across R_a. The same result would have been obtained had the π set of resistors ($R_a - R_b - R_c$) been transformed to an equivalent $\mathbf{Y}$ set of resistors.

In many networks, particularly in the field of radio, the direct currents must be confined to specified paths and a-c energy is transferred from

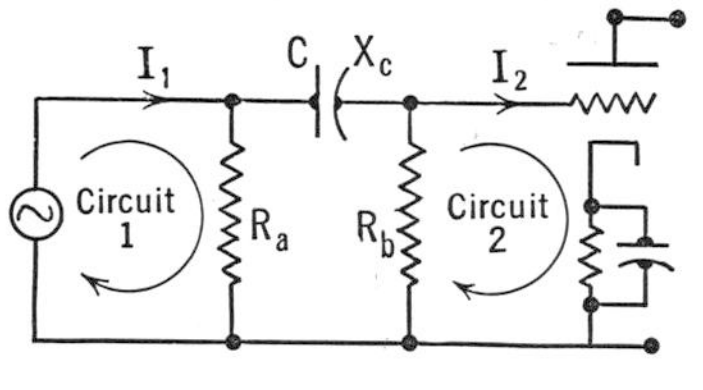

FIG. 4. Circuits coupled through R_a-C-R_b network.

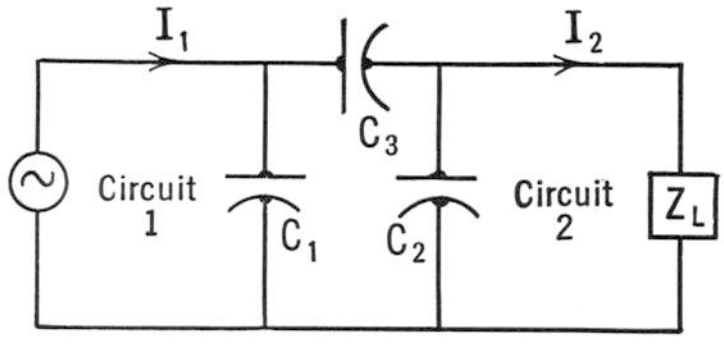

FIG. 5. Circuits coupled through C_1-C_3-C_2 network.

one circuit to another through the agency of an electric or magnetic field. In Fig. 4, for example, a-c energy may be transferred from circuit 1 to circuit 2 by way of the electric field existing between the plates of the coupling condenser, C.

A particular form of capacitive coupling is shown in Fig. 5. If the coupling reactance between circuit 1 and circuit 2 is defined as the voltage developed in circuit 2, namely, the voltage across C_2, per unit current in circuit 1, this coupling reactance is:

$$X_{\text{coupling}} = \frac{\dfrac{V_1}{X_2 + X_3} X_2}{\dfrac{V_1(X_1 + X_2 + X_3)}{X_1(X_2 + X_3)}} = \frac{X_1 X_2}{X_1 + X_2 + X_3}$$

where V_1 is the voltage across C_1 and the X's are the capacitive reactances of the respective condensers. The coupling capacitance between circuit 1 and circuit 2 (or vice versa) is:

$$C_{\text{coupling}} = \frac{1}{\omega X_{\text{coupling}}} = \frac{1}{\omega \dfrac{(1/\omega C_1)(1/\omega C_2)}{(1/\omega C_1) + (1/\omega C_2) + (1/\omega C_3)}}$$

$$= C_1 + C_2 + \frac{C_1 C_2}{C_3}$$

Problem 2. Show that the voltage developed across condenser C_1 per unit current flowing in circuit 2 of Fig. 5 is:

$$\frac{X_1 X_2}{X_1 + X_2 + X_3} = X_{\text{coupling}}$$

where $X_1 = 1/\omega C_1$, $X_2 = 1/\omega C_2$, and $X_3 = 1/\omega C_3$.

Problem 3. Consider R_a, R_b, and X_c of Fig. 4 to be a coupling device between circuit 1 and circuit 2. Show that the coupling impedance between the two circuits is:

$$\mathbf{Z}_{\text{coupling}} = \frac{(R_a^2 R_b + R_a R_b^2) + jR_a R_b X_c}{(R_a + R_b)^2 + X_c^2}$$

Note:

$$\mathbf{Z}_{\text{coupling}} = \frac{\mathbf{V}_b}{\mathbf{I}_1}$$

where $\mathbf{V}_b$ is the voltage developed across R_b by $\mathbf{I}_1$, or

$$\mathbf{Z}_{\text{coupling}} = \frac{\mathbf{V}_a}{\mathbf{I}_2}$$

where V_a is the voltage developed across R_a by $\mathbf{I}_2$.

Coefficient of Coupling. Given two pairs of terminals, 11′ and 22′, as shown in Fig. 2. The coefficient of coupling between circuit 11′ and circuit 22′ will be defined as:

$$\mathbf{k} = \frac{\mathbf{Z}_{12}}{\sqrt{\mathbf{Z}_{11'}\mathbf{Z}_{22'}}} = \frac{\mathbf{Z}_{21}}{\sqrt{\mathbf{Z}_{11'}\mathbf{Z}_{22'}}}$$

where $\mathbf{Z}_{12}$ is the mutual impedance between circuits 2 and 1. $\mathbf{Z}_{21} = \mathbf{Z}_{12}$.

$\mathbf{Z}_{11'}$ is the impedance seen looking into terminals 11′ with terminals 22′ open-circuited.

$\mathbf{Z}_{22'}$ is the impedance seen looking into terminals 22′ with terminals 11′ open-circuited.

Example 2. Consider terminals 11′ and 22′ of Fig. 3. Let it be required to find the coefficient of coupling between circuits 1 and 2.

It has been shown that

$$\mathbf{Z}_{21} = \mathbf{Z}_{12} = \frac{R_a R_b}{R_a + R_b + R_c}$$

$$\mathbf{Z}_{11'} = \frac{R_a(R_b + R_c)}{R_a + R_b + R_c}$$

$$\mathbf{Z}_{22'} = \frac{R_b(R_a + R_c)}{R_a + R_b + R_c}$$

$$\mathbf{k} = \frac{R_a R_b}{\sqrt{R_a(R_b + R_c) R_b(R_a + R_c)}}$$

If, for example, $R_c = 0$, the coefficient of coupling is unity. It should be noted that, with the general definition of coupling coefficient which has been given, $\mathbf{k}$ may be complex and greater than unity. In most cases, however, the coefficient of coupling is real and less than unity as in this example.

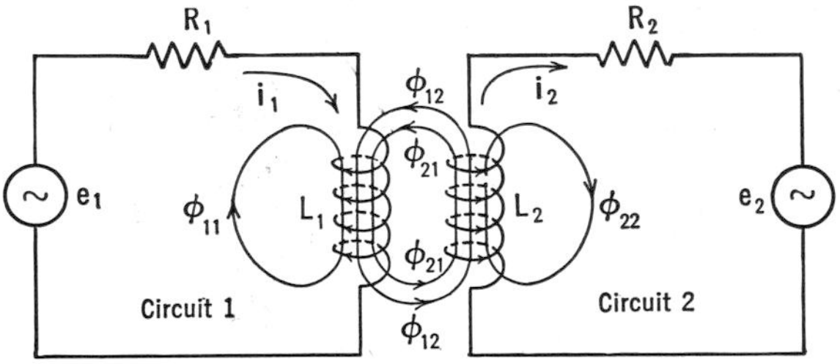

FIG. 6. Illustrating the four component fluxes ϕ_{11}, ϕ_{12}, ϕ_{22}, and ϕ_{21} into which the resultant magnetic field is separated for the purpose of analysis.

Magnetic Coupling. If a portion of the magnetic flux established by one circuit interlinks with a second circuit, the two circuits are coupled magnetically and energy may be transferred from one circuit to the other by way of the magnetic field which is common to the two circuits. The practical operation of many devices depends upon this type of coupling.

Separation of Magnetic Flux into Hypothetical Components. Magnetic coupling between two individual circuits is shown in Fig. 6. For the purpose of analysis, the total flux which is established by i_1, namely,

ϕ_1, is divided into two components. One component of ϕ_1 is that part which links with circuit 1 but not with circuit 2, namely, ϕ_{11}. The second component of ϕ_1 is ϕ_{12}, that part which links with both circuit 2 and circuit 1. In a similar manner, the flux established by i_2 is separated into two components for the sake of detailed analysis.

By definition:

$$\phi_1 = \phi_{11} + \phi_{12} \tag{5}$$

and

$$\phi_2 = \phi_{22} + \phi_{21} \tag{6}$$

The four component fluxes are shown in Fig. 6, and a recapitulation of their definitions is given below:

ϕ_{11} the fractional part of ϕ_1 which links *only* with the turns of circuit 1. This is the leakage flux of circuit 1 with respect to circuit 2.

ϕ_{12} the fractional part of ϕ_1 which links with the turns of circuit 2. This is the mutual flux produced by circuit 1.

ϕ_{22} the fractional part of ϕ_2 which links *only* with the turns of circuit 2. This is the leakage flux of circuit 2 with respect to circuit 1.

ϕ_{21} the fractional part of ϕ_2 which links with the turns of circuit 1. This is the mutual flux produced by circuit 2.

It should be recognized that the actual flux established by i_1 or i_2 does not conform to the simple configurations shown in Fig. 6. For example, part of ϕ_{11} links with only a fraction of the total turns of circuit 1, and likewise a part of ϕ_{12} links with only a fractional part of the turns of circuit 2. ϕ_{11} is a hypothetical flux which, when linking with all the turns, N_1, produces the same total flux linkages as the true flux linkages in question. Similar concepts are held for the other component fluxes, and, when used quantitatively in this manner, they represent accurately the true condition of affairs as regards induced voltages.

Mutual Inductance. In order to describe the magnetic interaction between circuits or between portions of the same circuit, the circuit parameter M is introduced. It is called the coefficient of mutual inductance, or simply mutual inductance, and is dimensionally equivalent to the coefficient of self-inductance, L. The similarity between the concept of mutual inductance of (or between) two circuits and the concept of self-inductance may be shown in the following manner. Refer to Fig. 6. For the purpose at hand we shall define the self-inductance of circuit 1 as:

$$L_1 = \frac{N_1\phi_1}{i_1} \left[\text{flux linkages of circuit 1 per unit current in circuit 1}\right] \tag{7}$$

On the same basis of reckoning, the mutual inductance of circuit 1 with respect to circuit 2 is:

$$M_{21} = \frac{N_1\phi_{21}}{i_2} \left[\text{flux linkages of circuit 1 per unit current in circuit 2}\right] \tag{8}$$

Also the mutual inductance of circuit 2 with respect to circuit 1 is:

$$M_{12} = \frac{N_2\phi_{12}}{i_1} \left[\text{flux linkages of circuit 2 per unit current in circuit 1}\right] \tag{9}$$

If the ϕ/i characteristics in equations (7), (8), and (9) are not straight lines, then L_1, M_{21}, and M_{12} are variable circuit parameters and for certain types of analyses can best be written in the forms:

$$L_1 = N_1 \frac{d\phi_1}{di_1} \tag{7a}$$

$$M_{21} = N_1 \frac{d\phi_{21}}{di_2} \tag{8a}$$

$$M_{12} = N_2 \frac{d\phi_{12}}{di_1} \tag{9a}$$

If, however, the flux is proportional to the current (i.e., permeability constant), both self-inductance and mutual inductance in equations (7), (8), and (9) are constant and as such are very useful circuit parameters in classical circuit theory.

Under the condition of constant permeability, the reluctance of the *mutual flux path* ($\mathcal{R}_{21}$ or $\mathcal{R}_{12}$) is a fixed quantity and $\mathcal{R}_{21} = \mathcal{R}_{12}$.

$$M_{21} = \frac{N_1\phi_{21}}{i_2} = \frac{KN_1N_2}{\mathcal{R}_{21}} \tag{10}$$

$$M_{12} = \frac{N_2\phi_{12}}{i_1} = \frac{KN_2N_1}{\mathcal{R}_{12}} \tag{11}$$

where K is a constant which depends for its value upon the units employed in evaluating $\phi = KNi/\mathcal{R}$. Therefore, if the permeability of the mutual flux path is constant, M_{21} and M_{12} are constant and $M_{21} = M_{12} = M$. This fact may also be proved in terms of the energies stored in the magnetic field when both circuits are energized.

If the permeability of the mutual flux path is not constant, neither M_{21} nor M_{12} will be constant and the following method of representing mutually induced voltages in terms of M loses much of its effectiveness. Unless otherwise stated, absence of ferromagnetic material will be assumed, in which case $M_{21} = M_{12} = M$.

The units in which mutual inductance is expressed are identical with the units in which self-inductance is expressed, usually the henry or millihenry. If the flux linkages in equations (8) or (9) are expressed in weber-turns (10^8 maxwell-turns) and the current is expressed in amperes, M is given in henrys.

Problem 4. Refer to Fig. 6, page 278, and assume that the L_1 coil consists of 50 turns and that the L_2 coil consists of 500 turns.

(*a*) What is the mutual inductance between the two circuits (in millihenrys) if 5 amperes in circuit 1 establishes a total equivalent flux (ϕ_1) of 30,000 maxwells 27,500 maxwells of which link with the turns of the L_2 coil?

(*b*) What is the self-inductance of the L_1 coil?

Ans.: (*a*) $M_{12} = 27.5$ millihenrys; (*b*) $L_1 = 3$ millihenrys.

Mutual Reactance, X_M. It is evident that any change in i_2 of Fig. 6 will cause a corresponding change in ϕ_{21}. In accordance with Lenz's law, any time rate of change of ϕ_{21} will manifest itself in circuit 1 in the form of a generated or induced voltage the value of which is:

$$e_{12} = -N_1 \frac{d\phi_{21}}{dt} \quad \text{or} \quad v_{12} = N_1 \frac{d\phi_{21}}{dt} \tag{12}$$

where e_{12} is considered as a voltage rise or generated voltage and v_{12} is considered as a voltage drop.

Similarly any change in i_1 will manifest itself in circuit 2 as:

$$e_{21} = -N_2 \frac{d\phi_{12}}{dt} \quad \text{or} \quad v_{21} = N_2 \frac{d\phi_{12}}{dt} \tag{13}$$

It is through the agency of these mutually induced voltages that the phenomenon known as mutual inductance can be taken into account in circuit analysis.

The basic equations of voltage for the two circuits shown in Fig. 6 are:

$$R_1 i_1 + N_1 \frac{d\phi_1}{dt} + N_1 \frac{d\phi_{21}}{dt} = e_1 \tag{14}$$

and

$$R_2 i_2 + N_2 \frac{d\phi_2}{dt} + N_2 \frac{d\phi_{12}}{dt} = e_2 \tag{15}$$

If the permeability of the flux paths is assumed constant, the above equations can be written in more convenient forms, since:

$$N_1\phi_1 = L_1 i_1 \quad \therefore N_1 \frac{d\phi_1}{dt} = L_1 \frac{di_1}{dt} \tag{16}$$

$$N_1\phi_{21} = M_{21} i_2 \therefore N_1 \frac{d\phi_{21}}{dt} = M_{21} \frac{di_2}{dt} \tag{17}$$

$$N_2\phi_2 = L_2 i_2 \quad \therefore N_2 \frac{d\phi_2}{dt} = L_2 \frac{di_2}{dt} \tag{18}$$

$$N_2\phi_{12} = M_{12} i_1 \therefore N_2 \frac{d\phi_{12}}{dt} = M_{12} \frac{di_1}{dt} \tag{19}$$

Equations (14) and (15) may, therefore, be written in the following manner:

$$R_1 i_1 + L_1 \frac{di_1}{dt} + M_{21} \frac{di_2}{dt} = e_1 \tag{14a}$$

$$R_2 i_2 + L_2 \frac{di_2}{dt} + M_{12} \frac{di_1}{dt} = e_2 \tag{15a}$$

It will be observed that the effects of mutual inductance are entered into the basic voltage equations as voltage drops ($+M\,di/dt$). If, for example, $i_1 = I_{m1} \sin \omega t$, the voltage drop in circuit 2 due to mutual inductance is:

$$M_{12} \frac{di_1}{dt} = \omega M_{12} I_{m_1} \cos \omega t = X_{M_{12}} I_{m_1} \cos \omega t \tag{20}$$

In general, $\omega M = X_M$. It is called the mutual reactance and is an impedance function which expresses the ratio of the voltage of mutual inductance to the exciting current. It will be noted that the voltage of mutual inductance leads the exciting current by 90°. Hence the vector expression for the mutual reactance is:

$$\mathbf{X}_M = j\omega M = \omega M \underline{/90°} \tag{21}$$

Circuit configurations in which M may possess either a positive or negative sign will be considered presently.

Problem 5. An inductance coil has a resistance of 10 ohms, a self-inductance of 1/37.7 henry, and a mutual inductance of 0.02 henry with respect to a neighboring coil. ($M_{12} = M_{21}$.) A voltage of 50 sin 377t volts is impressed across the terminals of the primary coil. Find the ohmic value of the mutual reactance and the effective value of the voltage across the open-circuited terminals of the neighboring coil.

Ans.: $X_M = 7.54$ ohms, $V_2 = 18.85$ volts.

Problem 6. Let the effective values of the primary voltage and current of Problem 5 be known as V_1 and I_1, and draw a vector diagram illustrating $\mathbf{V}_1$, $\mathbf{I}_1$, $R_1\mathbf{I}_1$, $jX_{L1}\mathbf{I}_1$, $jX_M\mathbf{I}_1$, and $\mathbf{E}_{21}$. (*Note:* Considered as a generated voltage, $\mathbf{E}_{21}$ is 180° out of phase with $jX_M\mathbf{I}_1$, since the latter is a component voltage drop in circuit 2 in the same sense that $R\mathbf{I}_1$ and $jX_{L1}\mathbf{I}_1$ are component voltage drops in circuit 1.)

Ans.: $\mathbf{V}_1 = \dfrac{50}{\sqrt{2}}\underline{/0^\circ}$ volts, $\mathbf{I}_1 = 2.5\underline{/-45^\circ}$ amperes, $\mathbf{E}_{21} = 18.85\underline{/-135^\circ}$ volts.

Coefficient of Magnetic Coupling. The fractional part of ϕ_1 which links with N_2, ϕ_{12}/ϕ_1, and the fractional part of ϕ_2 which links with N_1, (ϕ_{21}/ϕ_2), are indices of the degree of coupling that exists between two windings. Where the windings are widely separated or are so situated in space that these fractions are small, the coupling is said to be loose. With closer proximity and proper orientation of the windings, ϕ_{12}/ϕ_1 and ϕ_{21}/ϕ_2 approach unity as a theoretical upper limit.

The coefficient of coupling between two windings which individually possess L_1 and L_2 units of self-inductance is defined as:

$$k_M = \sqrt{\left(\frac{\phi_{12}}{\phi_1}\right)\left(\frac{\phi_{21}}{\phi_2}\right)} = \sqrt{\frac{(M_{12}i_1/N_2)}{(L_1i_1/N_1)}\frac{(M_{21}i_2/N_1)}{(L_2i_2/N_2)}} = \sqrt{\left(\frac{M_{12}}{L_1}\right)\left(\frac{M_{21}}{L_2}\right)} \tag{22}$$

Under the condition of constant permeability, $M_{12} = M_{21} = M$. Therefore, if the permeability is constant,

$$k_M = \sqrt{\left(\frac{M}{L_1}\right)\left(\frac{M}{L_2}\right)} = \frac{M}{\sqrt{L_1L_2}} \tag{23}$$

Thus k_M is the geometric mean of the fractions (ϕ_{12}/ϕ_1) and (ϕ_{21}/ϕ_2) or between the fractions (M/L_1) and (M/L_2). Numerically the coefficient of coupling in practical installations may range from approximately 0.01 between certain types of radio circuits to as high as 0.98 or 0.99 between iron-core transformer windings.

Example 3. Let the number of turns of the two windings shown in Fig. 6 be $N_1 = 50$ and $N_2 = 500$. It will be assumed that 6000 maxwells link with the turns N_1, of circuit 1, per ampere of exciting current i_1, of which 5500 also link with N_2. Under the assumption of similar concentrated windings and of constant permeability of the flux paths, 60,000 maxwells will link with the turns N_2, of circuit 2, per ampere of exciting current i_2, and 55,000 of these flux lines will also link with N_1. The purpose of this numerical example is to specify the coefficient of coupling in terms of the fractions (ϕ_{12}/ϕ_1) and (ϕ_{21}/ϕ_2) and also in terms of the fractions (M_{12}/L_1) and (M_{21}/L_2). For 1 ampere of primary exciting current and for 1 ampere of secondary current:

$$\phi_1 = 6000 \text{ maxwells}$$
$$\phi_{12} = 5500 \text{ maxwells}$$
$$\phi_2 = 60{,}000 \text{ maxwells}$$
$$\phi_{21} = 55{,}000 \text{ maxwells}$$

$$k_M = \sqrt{\left(\frac{\phi_{12}}{\phi_1}\right)\left(\frac{\phi_{21}}{\phi_2}\right)} = \sqrt{\left(\frac{55}{60}\right)\left(\frac{55}{60}\right)} = 0.917$$

$$L_1 = \frac{N_1\phi_1}{i_1} = \frac{50 \times 6000}{1} \times 10^{-8} = 0.003 \text{ henry}$$

$$M_{12} = \frac{N_2\phi_{12}}{i_1} = \frac{500 \times 5500}{1} \times 10^{-8} = 0.0275 \text{ henry}$$

$$L_2 = \frac{N_2\phi_2}{i_2} = \frac{500 \times 60{,}000}{1} \times 10^{-8} = 0.30 \text{ henry}$$

$$M_{21} = \frac{N_1\phi_{21}}{i_2} = \frac{50 \times 55{,}000}{1} \times 10^{-8} = 0.0275 \text{ henry}$$

$$k_M = \sqrt{\left(\frac{M_{12}}{L_1}\right)\left(\frac{M_{21}}{L_2}\right)} = \frac{M}{\sqrt{L_1L_2}} = \frac{0.0275}{\sqrt{0.003 \times 0.30}} = 0.917$$

Problem 7. The individual self-inductances of two windings are 0.094 henry and 0.0108 henry. The coefficient of coupling between the windings is 0.805. Find the mutual inductance of the two windings. *Ans.:* 0.0256 henry.

Problem 8. A winding of 1000 turns has a (ϕ_1/i_1) characteristic of 9400 maxwells per ampere and is coupled magnetically to a second winding of 338 turns. Assuming constant permeability of the flux paths and similar concentrated windings, find L_1, L_2, and M in henrys if the coefficient of coupling is 0.805.
Ans.: $L_1 = 0.094$ henry, $L_2 = 0.0108$ henry, $M = 0.0256$ henry.

Circuit Directions and the Sign of *M*. If only one circuit of an a-c network includes a generating device, the positive directions of the currents may be arbitrarily assigned if it is understood that the positive circuit direction given to the current through the generator arbitrarily defines the positive circuit direction of the generated voltage. When more than one generating device is present in an electrical network, the relative polarities and time phases of the generating devices with respect to the common branches must be taken into account in assigning the positive circuit directions of the currents in the coupled circuits.

In a given circuit or portion thereof the voltage of mutual inductance, $M\,di/dt$, may aid or oppose the voltage of self-inductance, $L\,di/dt$. If more than one circuit is involved, the currents are first given their positive circuit directions. When the positive circuit directions of the currents have been determined from the relative polarities of the several generating devices (if more than one generator exists), or when the positive circuit directions of the currents for a single generator have been arbitrarily assigned, the sign of M is considered positive if in a given winding the induced voltage of mutual inductance acts in the same direction as the induced voltage of self-inductance. If the induced voltage of mutual inductance opposes the induced voltage of self-inductance in a given winding, M is considered as a negative quantity.

In determining the sign of M, each particular case must be analyzed as to the relative positive circuit directions of the currents, the relative modes of winding of the coils involved, and the actual physical placement of one winding with respect to the other. It will be shown later that the sign of M between circuits which are not electrically connected and which are energized with a single generator in one circuit is wholly dependent upon the arbitrary positive circuit directions which are assigned to the currents in the separate circuits.

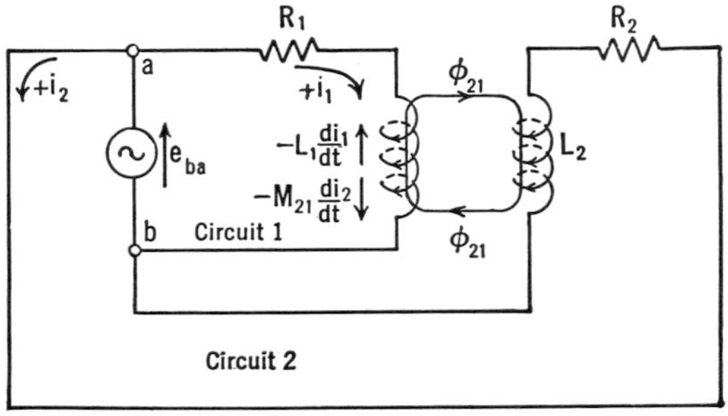

FIG. 7. Illustrating a particular case wherein the voltage of mutual inductance acts in circuit opposition to the voltage of self-inductance in a given coil.

Example 4. Consider the hypothetical arrangement of the two circuits shown in Fig. 7. If the clockwise direction around circuit 1 is taken as the positive circuit direction of i_1, the generator emf possesses a positive circuit direction from b to a through the generator. The latter direction fixes the positive circuit direction of i_2 as counter-clockwise around circuit 2.

By Lenz's law, the voltage of self-inductance in the L_1 coil *considered as an induced voltage* acts in a counter-clockwise direction around circuit 1 when di_1/dt is positive. If the positive circuit direction of i_2 and the modes of winding of the coils are considered, it is plain that voltage which is induced in the L_1 coil by the variation of ϕ_{21} is a clockwise direction around circuit 1 when di_2/dt or $d\phi_{21}/dt$ is positive.

Since $M\ di_2/dt$ acts oppositely to $L_1\ di_1/dt$ in circuit 1, M must be considered negative if L_1 is considered positive. The general equation for voltage equilibrium in circuit 1 is:

$$R_1 i_1 + L_1 \frac{di_1}{dt} + (-M)\frac{di_2}{dt} = e_{ba}$$

A simple way to determine the sign of M is to call M positive if the mmf's caused by the two currents combine to increase the total flux. If the mmf's oppose, the sign of M is negative.

Problem 9. Show, by means of detailed and independent analysis, that the general equation for voltage equilibrium in circuit 2 of Fig. 7 is:

$$R_2 i_2 + L_2 \frac{di_2}{dt} - M \frac{di_1}{dt} = e_{ba}$$

Instead of showing the actual modes of winding, a conventional method employing a dot-marked terminal, as shown in Fig. 8, is often used to yield the same information. This practice has been used for many years in the marking of iron-core instrument transformers, where the dots are known as polarity marks. The dots are placed so that a current entering the dot-marked terminal of any coil will produce a magnetomotive force and corresponding flux in the *same* direction around the magnetic circuit. Thus in Fig. 8 a current *entering* the dot-marked terminal of coil 1 causes a counter-clockwise flux in the magnetic circuit and a current *entering* the dot-marked terminal of coil 2 also causes a counter-clockwise flux in the same magnetic circuit. Hence the dots alone are sufficient to determine the relative modes

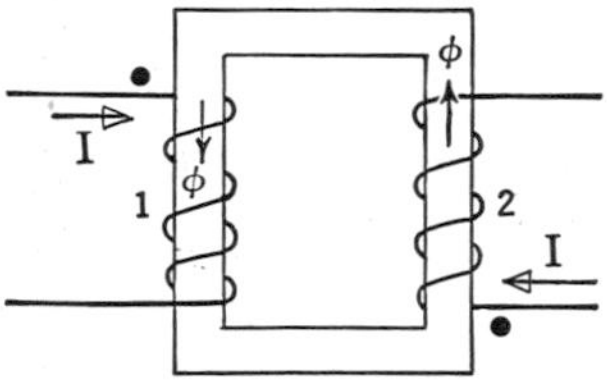

FIG. 8. Dot marks used to define relative polarities of two coils.

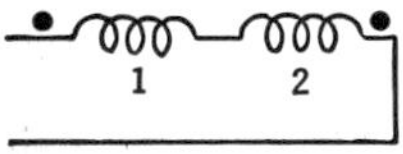

FIG. 9. Dot marks indicate $-M$.

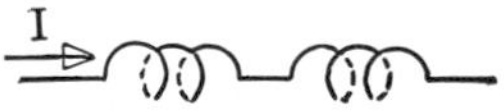

FIG. 10. Mode of winding and physical placement indicate $-M$.

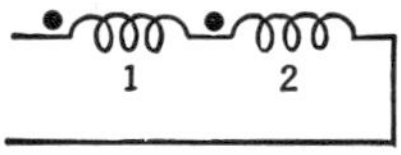

FIG. 11. Dot marks indicate $+M$.

of winding. The use of this convention is illustrated in Fig. 9. If a current entering the dot-marked terminal of coil 1 is assumed to produce a flux through the coils from left to right, this same current, since it is leaving the dot-marked terminal of coil 2, would cause a flux from right to left through the coils. Therefore, for the purpose of setting up an equation of voltage drops, M must be considered negative. Hence the relative modes of winding must be as shown in Fig. 10. If the coils of Fig. 9 were marked as shown in Fig. 11, a current entering the dot-marked terminal of coil 1 would also enter the dot-marked terminal of coil 2, the mmf's of the two coils would be additive, and the sign of M would be positive.

Mutual Inductance between Portions of the Same Circuit. Mutual inductance may be a significant factor in governing the flow of electricity in a single-series circuit where two or more portions of the circuit are coupled magnetically. A particular example is shown in Fig. 12. The arrangement consists of two magnetically coupled inductance coils connected in electrical series. Individually the coils possess L_a and L_b units of self-inductance together with R_a and R_b units of resistance, respectively.

If the coils are wound in the manner shown in Fig. 12, it is apparent that, in coil a, the voltage

$$-M_{ba}\frac{di}{dt} = -N_a\frac{d\phi_{ba}}{dt}$$

acts in the same circuit direction as the voltage $-L_a\,di/dt$. Likewise the voltage

$$-M_{ab}\frac{di}{dt} = -N_b\frac{d\phi_{ab}}{dt}$$

acts in the same circuit direction as $-L_b\,di/dt$. Hence M is positive.

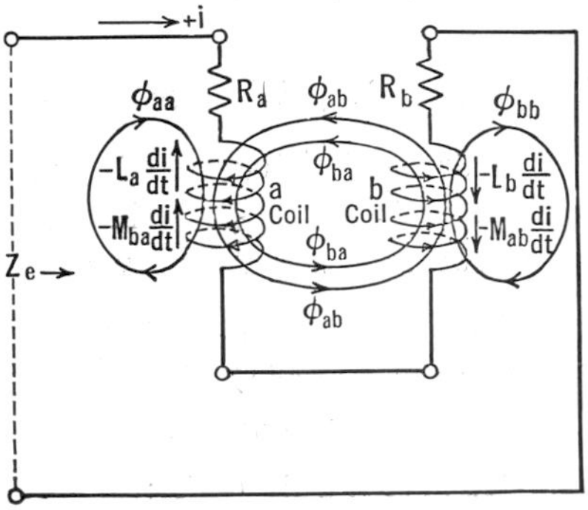

FIG. 12. Two inductance coils connected series-aiding.

Considered as voltage drops, the component voltages referred to above have circuit directions which agree with that of the applied voltage, v. Considered as voltage rises, the induced voltages are, of course, in circuit opposition to the applied voltage, v.

The facts involved can be stated in equation form as follows:

$$R_ai + L_a\frac{di}{dt} + M_{ba}\frac{di}{dt} + R_bi + L_b\frac{di}{dt} + M_{ab}\frac{di}{dt} = v \tag{24}$$

If the mutual flux path is of constant permeability, the above equation reduces to:

$$(R_a + R_b)\,i + (L_a + L_b + 2M)\frac{di}{dt} = v \tag{25}$$

If v varies sinusoidally with time and if all circuit parameters are constant, equation (25) may be written in terms of effective values as follows:

$$(R_a + R_b)\mathbf{I} + j\omega(L_a + L_b + 2M)\mathbf{I} = \mathbf{V} \tag{26}$$

It will be noted that M enters into the voltage equation in exactly the same manner as L. Hence ωM is a mutual reactance. The equivalent impedance of the series circuit shown in Fig. 12 follows directly from equation (26).

$$\mathbf{Z}_e = \frac{\mathbf{V}}{\mathbf{I}} = \sqrt{[R_a + R_b]^2 + [\omega(L_a + L_b + 2M)]^2} \bigg/ \tan^{-1}\frac{\omega(L_a + L_b + 2M)}{(R_a + R_b)} \tag{27}$$

Equation (27) may also be written:

$$\mathbf{Z}_e = (R_a + R_b) + j\omega(L_a + L_b + 2M) = \mathbf{Z}_a + \mathbf{Z}_b + 2\mathbf{Z}_M \tag{27a}$$

where

$$\mathbf{Z}_a = R_a + j\omega L_a,\ \mathbf{Z}_b = R_b + j\omega L_b \quad \text{and} \quad \mathbf{Z}_M = 0 + j\omega M$$

If the two coils were connected together in the opposite sense, that is, with a polarity opposite to that shown in Fig. 12, the signs of the M terms in the above equations would be reversed.

Example 5. An inspection of equations (25), (26), and (27) will show that the equivalent inductance of the two coils connected in additive series is:

$$L_{e(\text{add})} = L_a + L_b + 2M$$

If the two coils are connected in subtractive series:

$$L_{e(\text{sub})} = L_a + L_b - 2M$$

The value of M may, therefore, be found experimentally by measuring $L_{e(\text{add})}$ and $L_{e(\text{sub})}$ since, from the above relations:

$$M = \frac{L_{e(\text{add})} - L_{e(\text{sub})}}{4}$$

Example 6. Let it be required to find the coefficient of coupling, the equivalent series-circuit impedance, and the magnitude of the current in a circuit arrangement similar to that shown in Fig. 12 if:

R_a = 1.0 ohm	M = +3 millihenrys
L_a = 4.0 millihenrys	ω = 1000 radians per second
R_b = 6.0 ohms	V = 40.5 volts, the applied voltage
L_b = 9.0 millihenrys	

(*a*) The coefficient of coupling is:

$$k = \frac{M}{\sqrt{L_a L_b}} = \frac{+3}{\sqrt{4 \times 9}} = +0.5$$

(b) The equivalent series-circuit impedance is:

$$\mathbf{Z}_e = (R_a + R_b) + j\omega(L_a + L_b + 2M)$$
$$= (1 + 6) + j(1000)(0.004 + 0.009 + 0.006)$$
$$= 7 + j19 = 20.25 \underline{/69.8^\circ} \text{ ohms}$$

(c) The series current is:

$$I = \frac{40.5}{20.25} = 2.0 \text{ amperes}$$

A vector diagram of **V**, **I**, $\mathbf{V}_a$, and $\mathbf{V}_b$ is shown in Fig. 13 together with the component voltages of $\mathbf{V}_a$ and $\mathbf{V}_b$.

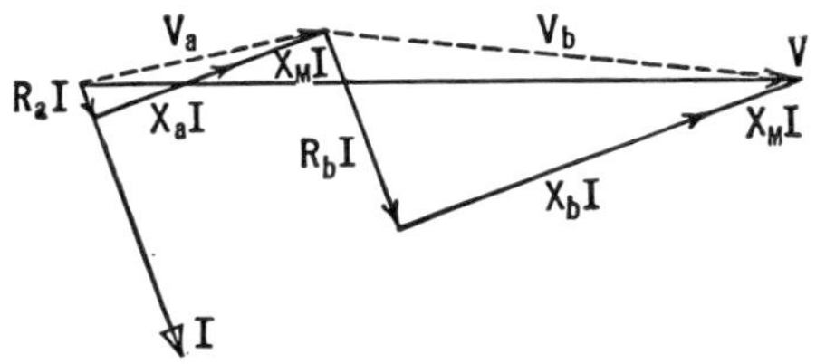

FIG. 13. Vector diagram of example 6.

Problem 10. Find the magnitude of the current in the above example if the two coils are connected in subtractive series, that is, $M = -3$ millihenrys. Draw a vector diagram illustrating the vector positions of **V**, **I**, $\mathbf{V}_a$, $\mathbf{V}_b$, and the various R**I** and X**I** component voltages. *Ans.*: $I = 4.09$ amperes.

Mutual Inductance between Parallel Branches. Reference to Fig. 14 will show that, in coil 1, $M_{21}\, di_2/dt$ acts in circuit opposition to $L_1\, di_1/dt$.

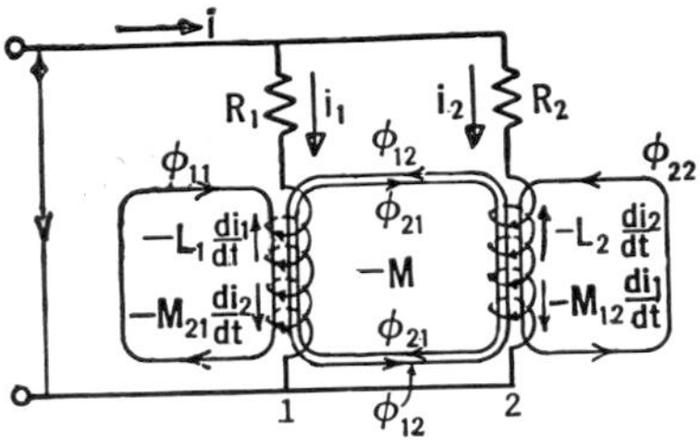

FIG. 14. Parallel arrangement of two inductance coils which are coupled magnetically. For the mode of winding shown and the assumed positive directions of currents as indicated, M is negative.

Similarly, in coil 2, $M_{12}\, di_1/dt$ acts in circuit opposition to $L_2\, di_2/dt$. In equation form:

$$R_1 i_1 + L_1 \frac{di_1}{dt} - M_{21} \frac{di_2}{dt} = v \tag{28}$$

$$R_2 i_2 + L_2 \frac{di_2}{dt} - M_{12} \frac{di_1}{dt} = v \tag{29}$$

It will be noted that the individual branch currents have been employed in the above equations.

If the circuit parameters are constant and a sinusoidal variation of v is assumed, the above equations may be written in terms of effective values as follows:

$$(R_1 + j\omega L_1)\mathbf{I}_1 - j\omega M\mathbf{I}_2 = \mathbf{V} \tag{30}$$

$$(R_2 + j\omega L_2)\mathbf{I}_2 - j\omega M\mathbf{I}_1 = \mathbf{V} \tag{31}$$

Let

$$(R_1 + j\omega L_1) = \mathbf{Z}_1 \tag{32}$$

$$(R_2 + j\omega L_2) = \mathbf{Z}_2 \tag{33}$$

$$0 + j\omega M = \mathbf{Z}_M \tag{34}$$

With the above abbreviations, equations (30) and (31) reduce to:

$$\mathbf{Z}_1\mathbf{I}_1 - \mathbf{Z}_M\mathbf{I}_2 = \mathbf{V} \tag{35}$$

$$-\mathbf{Z}_M\mathbf{I}_1 + \mathbf{Z}_2\mathbf{I}_2 = \mathbf{V} \tag{36}$$

The individual branch currents, $\mathbf{I}_1$ and $\mathbf{I}_2$, may be found from the simultaneous solutions of equations (35) and (36).

$$\mathbf{I}_1 = \frac{\begin{vmatrix} \mathbf{V} & -\mathbf{Z}_M \\ \mathbf{V} & \mathbf{Z}_2 \end{vmatrix}}{\begin{vmatrix} \mathbf{Z}_1 & -\mathbf{Z}_M \\ -\mathbf{Z}_M & \mathbf{Z}_2 \end{vmatrix}} = \frac{\mathbf{V}(\mathbf{Z}_2 + \mathbf{Z}_M)}{\mathbf{Z}_1\mathbf{Z}_2 - \mathbf{Z}_M^{\ 2}} \tag{37}$$

$$\mathbf{I}_2 = \frac{\begin{vmatrix} \mathbf{Z}_1 & \mathbf{V} \\ -\mathbf{Z}_M & \mathbf{V} \end{vmatrix}}{\begin{vmatrix} \mathbf{Z}_1 & -\mathbf{Z}_M \\ -\mathbf{Z}_M & \mathbf{Z}_2 \end{vmatrix}} = \frac{\mathbf{V}(\mathbf{Z}_1 + \mathbf{Z}_M)}{\mathbf{Z}_1\mathbf{Z}_2 - \mathbf{Z}_M^{\ 2}} \tag{38}$$

$$\mathbf{I} = \mathbf{I}_1 + \mathbf{I}_2 = \frac{\mathbf{V}(\mathbf{Z}_1 + \mathbf{Z}_2 + 2\mathbf{Z}_M)}{\mathbf{Z}_1\mathbf{Z}_2 - \mathbf{Z}_M^{\ 2}} \tag{39}$$

The equivalent impedance of the two parallel branches shown in Fig. 14 for the case of negative M is:

$$\mathbf{Z}_e = \frac{\mathbf{V}}{\mathbf{I}} = \frac{\mathbf{Z}_1\mathbf{Z}_2 - \mathbf{Z}_M^{\ 2}}{\mathbf{Z}_1 + \mathbf{Z}_2 + 2\mathbf{Z}_M} \tag{40}$$

Example 7. In the circuit arrangement shown in Fig. 14 it will be assumed that:

$R_1 = 3.3$ ohms $L_2 = 0.0108$ henry

$L_1 = 0.094$ henry $M = -0.0256$ henry

$R_2 = 0.775$ ohm $\omega = 377$ radians per second

$\mathbf{V} = 50 \underline{/0^\circ}$ volts

Let it be required to find $\mathbf{I}$, $\mathbf{I}_1$, $\mathbf{I}_2$, and the total power spent in the two parallel branches.

$\mathbf{Z}_1$ (individually) $= 3.3 + j35.4 = 35.5 \underline{/84.7^\circ}$ ohms

$\mathbf{Z}_2$ (individually) $= 0.775 + j4.07 = 4.17 \underline{/79.25^\circ}$ ohms

$\mathbf{Z}_M = 0 + j\omega M = 0 + j9.65 = 9.65 \underline{/90^\circ}$ ohms

Note: $\mathbf{Z}_M$ is herein considered as inherently positive since the appropriate negative signs have been introduced into equations (30) and (31).

$$\mathbf{Z}_e = \frac{\mathbf{Z}_1\mathbf{Z}_2 - \mathbf{Z}_M^2}{\mathbf{Z}_1 + \mathbf{Z}_2 + 2\mathbf{Z}_M} = \frac{63.6\underline{/140°}}{59.0\underline{/86°}} = 1.078\underline{/54°} \text{ ohms}$$

$$\mathbf{I} = \frac{\mathbf{V}}{\mathbf{Z}_e} = \frac{50\underline{/0°}}{1.078\underline{/54°}} = 46.4\underline{/-54°} \text{ amperes}$$

$$\mathbf{I}_1 = \frac{\mathbf{V}(\mathbf{Z}_2 + \mathbf{Z}_M)}{\mathbf{Z}_1\mathbf{Z}_2 - \mathbf{Z}_M^2} = \frac{(50\underline{/0°})(13.73\underline{/86.8°})}{63.6\underline{/140°}}$$

$$\mathbf{I}_1 = 10.8\underline{/-53.2°} \text{ amperes}$$

$$\mathbf{I}_2 = \frac{\mathbf{V}(\mathbf{Z}_1 + \mathbf{Z}_M)}{\mathbf{Z}_1\mathbf{Z}_2 - \mathbf{Z}_M^2} = \frac{(50\underline{/0°})(45.1\underline{/85.8°})}{63.6\underline{/140°}}$$

$$\mathbf{I}_2 = 35.4\underline{/-54.2°} \text{ amperes}$$

$$P = VI\cos\theta\Big]_{\mathbf{I}}^{\mathbf{V}} = 50 \times 46.4 \times \cos 54° = 1365 \text{ watts}$$

Check:

$$\mathbf{I} = \mathbf{I}_1 + \mathbf{I}_2 = 10.8\underline{/-53.2°} + 35.4\underline{/-54.2°}$$

$$\mathbf{I} = (6.46 - j8.65) + (20.8 - j28.8) = 27.26 - j37.45$$

$$\mathbf{I} = 46.4\underline{/-54°} \text{ amperes}$$

$$P = I_1^2R_1 + I_2^2R_2 = 385 + 973 = 1358 \text{ watts}$$

Problem 11. Assume that the inductance coils in the above illustrative example are connected in parallel as shown in Fig. 14, except that the terminals of one coil are reversed from that shown in the figure. Show that, under these conditions:

$$\mathbf{Z}_e = 3.095\underline{/61.40°} \text{ ohms}$$

$$\mathbf{I} = 16.16\underline{/-61.40°} \text{ amperes } (\mathbf{V} \text{ as reference})$$

$$\mathbf{I}_1 = 4.43\underline{/-222.1°} \text{ amperes}$$

$$\mathbf{I}_2 = 20.4\underline{/-57.30°} \text{ amperes}$$

$$P = VI\cos\theta\Big]_{\mathbf{I}}^{\mathbf{V}} = 386 \text{ watts}$$

Draw the vector diagram of **V**, **I**, $\mathbf{I}_1$, and $\mathbf{I}_2$, and illustrate the manner in which the three component voltages in each branch combine vectorially to equal the applied voltage, **V**.

The Air-Core Transformer. In the conventional transformer arrangement shown schematically in Fig. 15, the individual circuits are not connected electrically. Circuit 1, energized by means of an alternating potential difference, is called the primary. Circuit 2 is called the secondary. As a result of the magnetic coupling between the circuits, circuit 2 has induced in it a voltage which is equal to:

$$-N_2 \frac{d\phi_{12}}{dt} = -M_{12} \frac{di_1}{dt} \tag{41}$$

The magnitude of the voltage induced in circuit 2 is proportional to the number of secondary turns, N_2, and is dependent upon the degree of coupling between the two windings.

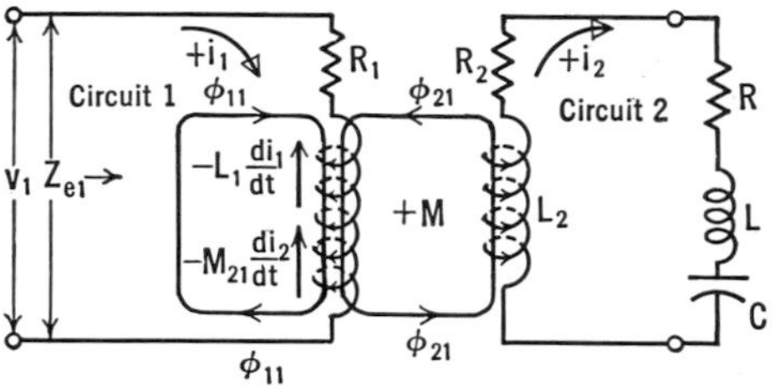

FIG. 15. Conventional air-core transformer arrangement.

The sign of M in the conventional transformer arrangement is dependent upon the arbitrary choice of the positive circuit direction of i_2. The majority of writers prefer to use the positive circuit direction of i_2 which allows them to employ the positive sign of M. For the relative modes of winding shown in Fig. 15, the positive clockwise direction of i_2 requires the use of $+M$, since under these conditions $M_{21}\, di_2/dt$ acts in the same circuit direction as $L_1\, di_1/dt$ in the primary winding. If the counter-clockwise direction around circuit 2 is taken as the positive circuit direction of i_2, then, of course, M must be considered negative. The resulting solutions will be identical in either case, except that all secondary currents and voltages will be reversed in sign. Experience with detailed solutions will convince the reader that the two different methods of attack yield identical physical results.

If the positive circuit directions are employed as indicated in Fig. 15, the mathematical analysis of the ordinary air-core transformer may be carried out as follows:

$$R_1 i_1 + L_1 \frac{di_1}{dt} + M_{21} \frac{di_2}{dt} = v_1 \tag{42}$$

$$(R_2 + R)i_2 + (L_2 + L) \frac{di_2}{dt} + \frac{\int i_2\, dt}{C_2} + M_{12} \frac{di_1}{dt} = 0 \tag{43}$$

If v_1 is assumed to have sinusoidal wave form and all circuit parameters are constant, the above equations may be written in terms of effective values as follows:

$$(R_1 + j\omega L_1)\mathbf{I}_1 + j\omega M\mathbf{I}_2 = \mathbf{V}_1 \tag{44}$$

$$(R_2 + j\omega L_2)\mathbf{I}_2 + \left[R + j\left(\omega L - \frac{1}{\omega C}\right)\right]\mathbf{I}_2 + j\omega M\mathbf{I}_1 = 0 \tag{45}$$

For the sake of simplicity in writing, the following abbreviations are adopted:

$\mathbf{Z}_1 = (R_1 + j\omega L_1)$ (Individual primary winding impedance) (46)

$\mathbf{Z}_2 = (R_2 + j\omega L_2)$ (Individual secondary winding impedance) (47)

$\mathbf{Z}_M = (0 + j\omega M)$ (Mutual impedance assuming no core loss) (48)

$\mathbf{Z} = \left[R + j\left(\omega L - \frac{1}{\omega C}\right)\right]$ (General expression for load impedance) (49)

Equations (44) and (45) become:

$$\mathbf{Z}_1\mathbf{I}_1 + \mathbf{Z}_M\mathbf{I}_2 = \mathbf{V}_1 \qquad (44)\text{–}(50)$$

$$\mathbf{Z}_M\mathbf{I}_1 + (\mathbf{Z}_2 + \mathbf{Z})\mathbf{I}_2 = 0 \qquad (45)\text{–}(51)$$

The simultaneous solutions of the above equations for $\mathbf{I}_1$ and $\mathbf{I}_2$ yield:

$$\mathbf{I}_1 = \frac{\begin{vmatrix} \mathbf{V}_1 & \mathbf{Z}_M \\ 0 & (\mathbf{Z}_2 + \mathbf{Z}) \end{vmatrix}}{\begin{vmatrix} \mathbf{Z}_1 & \mathbf{Z}_M \\ \mathbf{Z}_M & (\mathbf{Z}_2 + \mathbf{Z}) \end{vmatrix}} = \frac{\mathbf{V}_1(\mathbf{Z}_2 + \mathbf{Z})}{\mathbf{Z}_1(\mathbf{Z}_2 + \mathbf{Z}) - \mathbf{Z}_M{}^2} \tag{52}$$

$$\mathbf{I}_2 = \frac{\begin{vmatrix} \mathbf{Z}_1 & \mathbf{V}_1 \\ \mathbf{Z}_M & 0 \end{vmatrix}}{\begin{vmatrix} \mathbf{Z}_1 & \mathbf{Z}_M \\ \mathbf{Z}_M & (\mathbf{Z}_2 + \mathbf{Z}) \end{vmatrix}} = \frac{-\mathbf{V}_1\mathbf{Z}_M}{\mathbf{Z}_1(\mathbf{Z}_2 + \mathbf{Z}) - \mathbf{Z}_M{}^2} \tag{53}$$

If $\mathbf{I}_1$ has been evaluated, it may, in certain cases, be more convenient to solve for $\mathbf{I}_2$ directly from equation (51).

$$\mathbf{I}_2 = \frac{-\mathbf{Z}_M\mathbf{I}_1}{(\mathbf{Z}_2 + \mathbf{Z})} \tag{54}$$

The secondary terminal voltage, or the voltage which appears across the load impedance, is:

$$\mathbf{V}_2 = \mathbf{Z}\mathbf{I}_2 = -\mathbf{Z}_M\mathbf{I}_1 - \mathbf{Z}_2\mathbf{I}_2 \tag{55}$$

Also:

$$\mathbf{V}_2 = \frac{-\mathbf{V}_1\mathbf{Z}_M\mathbf{Z}}{\mathbf{Z}_1(\mathbf{Z}_2 + \mathbf{Z}) - \mathbf{Z}_M{}^2} \tag{56}$$

The above relations follow directly from equations (51) and (53). Equation (55) shows that the secondary circuit may be thought of as experiencing an induced voltage equal to $-\mathbf{Z}_M\mathbf{I}_1$, from which the internal secondary impedance drop, $\mathbf{Z}_2\mathbf{I}_2$, must be subtracted in order to obtain the secondary terminal voltage, $\mathbf{V}_2$.

Equivalent Impedance. The equivalent impedance of the transformer arrangement shown in Fig. 15 referred to the primary side is defined as the ratio of the applied voltage to the primary current. Thus:

$$\mathbf{Z}_{e1} = \frac{\mathbf{V}_1}{\mathbf{I}_1} = \frac{\mathbf{Z}_1(\mathbf{Z}_2 + \mathbf{Z}) - \mathbf{Z}_M{}^2}{(\mathbf{Z}_2 + \mathbf{Z})} \tag{57}$$

A more convenient form of the above equation is:

$$\mathbf{Z}_{e1} = \mathbf{Z}_1 - \frac{\mathbf{Z}_M{}^2}{(\mathbf{Z}_2 + \mathbf{Z})} = \mathbf{Z}_1 + \frac{\omega^2 M^2}{\mathbf{Z}_2 + \mathbf{Z}} \tag{58}$$

Equations (57) and (58) show that the air-core transformer, with respect to its primary terminals, is reducible to an equivalent series circuit.

Example 8 (for Z = 0). It will be assumed that, in Fig. 16*a*:

$R_1 = 3.3$ ohms $\qquad M = 0.0256$ henry

$L_1 = 0.094$ henry $\qquad \mathbf{Z} = 0$

$R_2 = 0.775$ ohm $\qquad \omega = 377$ radians per second

$L_2 = 0.0108$ henry $\qquad \mathbf{V}_1 = 50\,/0^\circ$ volts

$$\mathbf{Z}_1 = 3.3 + j35.4 = 35.5\,/84.7^\circ \text{ ohms}$$

$$\mathbf{Z}_2 = 0.775 + j4.07 = 4.14\,/79.25^\circ \text{ ohms}$$

$$\mathbf{Z}_M = 0 + j9.65 = 9.65\,/90^\circ \text{ ohms}$$

$$\mathbf{Z}_{e1} = \mathbf{Z}_1 - \frac{\mathbf{Z}_M{}^2}{\mathbf{Z}_2} = (3.3 + j35.4) + \frac{93.1\,/0^\circ}{4.14\,/79.25^\circ}$$

$$\mathbf{Z}_{e1} = (3.3 + j35.4) + (4.20 - j22.1) = 7.50 + j13.3 = 15.27\,/60.55^\circ \text{ ohms}$$

$$\mathbf{I}_1 = \frac{\mathbf{V}_1}{\mathbf{Z}_{e1}} = \frac{50\,/0^\circ}{15.27\,/60.55^\circ} = 3.28\,/-60.55^\circ \text{ amperes}$$

$$\mathbf{I}_2 = \frac{-\mathbf{I}_1\mathbf{Z}_M}{\mathbf{Z}_2} = \frac{(3.28\,/119.45^\circ)(9.65\,/90^\circ)}{4.14\,/79.25^\circ}$$

$$\mathbf{I}_2 = 7.66\,/130.2^\circ \text{ amperes}$$

The total power dissipated in the two circuits is:

$$P = V_1 I_1 \cos\theta \Big]_{\mathbf{I}_1}^{\mathbf{V}_1} = 50 \times 3.28 \times \cos(-60.55^\circ) = 80.8 \text{ watts}$$

or

$$P = I_1{}^2 R_1 + I_2{}^2 R_2 = 3.28^2 \times 3.3 + 7.66^2 \times 0.775 = 81.0 \text{ watts}$$

The vector diagram of $\mathbf{V}_1$, $\mathbf{I}_1$, $\mathbf{I}_2$, and $-\mathbf{Z}_M\mathbf{I}_1$ is shown in Fig. 16*b*. In the particular case shown in Fig. 16*b*, the voltage induced in circuit 2, $-\mathbf{Z}_M\mathbf{I}_1$, is balanced entirely by the internal secondary impedance drop, namely, $\mathbf{Z}_2\mathbf{I}_2$. If the counter-clockwise direction around circuit 2 had been taken as the positive circuit direction, $\mathbf{I}_2$ and $\mathbf{Z}_M\mathbf{I}_1$ would appear on the vector diagram 180° from the positions shown in Fig. 16*b*.

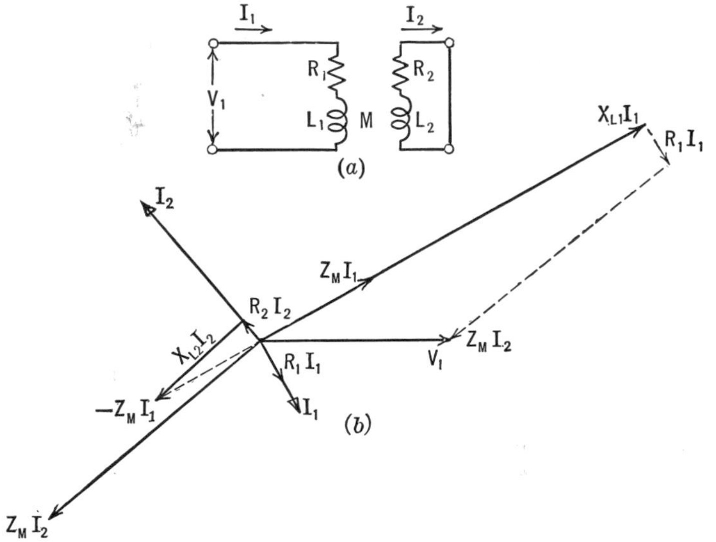

FIG. 16. Voltage and current relations in an air-core transformer the secondary of which is short-circuited. Note the manner in which $X_{L1}I_1$, R_1I_1, and Z_MI_2 combine vectorially to balance the applied voltage V_1.

Oscillogram 1 illustrates the instantaneous variations of v_1, i_1, and i_2 for the above numerical case. The salient features of the numerical solution are clearly shown. The primary current lags the applied voltage by approximately 60°, and the secondary current lags the primary current by approximately 170°. Within the limits of oscillographic accuracy, the maximum magnitudes of i_1 and i_2 agree with the results of the above numerical example.

Example 9 (for $\mathbf{Z} = 14.5 + j21.2$ ohms). It will be assumed that in Fig. 17*a*:

$R_1 = 3.3$ ohms $\qquad M = 0.0256$ henry

$L_1 = 0.094$ henry $\qquad \mathbf{Z} = 14.5 + j21.2$ ohms

$R_2 = 0.775$ ohm $\qquad \omega = 377$ radians per second

$L_2 = 0.0108$ henry $\qquad \mathbf{V}_1 = 50\underline{/0°}$ volts

$$\mathbf{Z}_1 = 3.3 + j35.4 = 35.5\underline{/84.7°} \text{ ohms}$$

$$\mathbf{Z}_2 = 0.775 + j4.07 = 4.14\underline{/79.25°} \text{ ohms}$$

$$\mathbf{Z}_M = 0 + j9.65 = 9.65\underline{/90°} \text{ ohms}$$

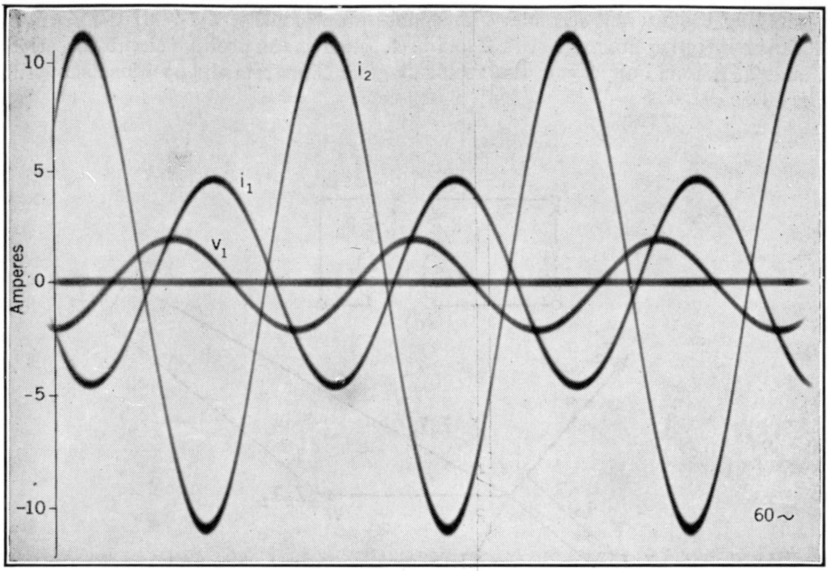

OSCILLOGRAM 1. Illustrating the time phase relations of primary and secondary currents of an air-core transformer with respect to the applied voltage wave. (For a short-circuited secondary. See Fig. 16*a*.) $v_1 = 70.7 \sin 377t$ volts.

$$\mathbf{Z}_{e1} = \mathbf{Z}_1 - \frac{\mathbf{Z}_M{}^2}{\mathbf{Z}_2 + \mathbf{Z}} = 35.5\,\underline{/84.7^\circ} + \frac{93.1\,\underline{/0^\circ}}{15.28 + j25.3}$$

$$\mathbf{Z}_{e1} = (3.3 + j35.4) + (1.63 - j2.7) = 4.93 + j32.7$$

$$\mathbf{Z}_{e1} = 33.0\,\underline{/81.4^\circ}\text{ ohms}$$

$$\mathbf{I}_1 = \frac{\mathbf{V}_1}{\mathbf{Z}_{e1}} = \frac{50\,\underline{/0^\circ}}{33\,\underline{/81.4^\circ}} = 1.515\,\underline{/-81.4^\circ}\text{ amperes}$$

$$\mathbf{I}_2 = \frac{-\mathbf{I}_1\mathbf{Z}_M}{(\mathbf{Z}_2 + \mathbf{Z})} = \frac{(1.515\,\underline{/98.6^\circ})(9.65\,\underline{/90^\circ})}{29.6\,\underline{/58.9^\circ}}$$

$$\mathbf{I}_2 = 0.494\,\underline{/129.7^\circ}\text{ amperes}$$

$$\mathbf{V}_2\text{ (terminal voltage)} = \mathbf{I}_2\mathbf{Z}$$

$$\mathbf{V}_2 = (0.494\,\underline{/129.7^\circ})(25.7\,\underline{/55.6^\circ}) = 12.7\,\underline{/185.3^\circ}\text{ volts}$$

The input power to the primary terminals is:

$$P_{\text{input}} = V_1 I_1 \cos\theta \Big]_{\mathbf{I}_1}^{\mathbf{V}_1} = 50 \times 1.515 \times \cos 81.4^\circ$$

$$= 50 \times 1.515 \times 0.1495 = 11.3\text{ watts}$$

The power delivered to the load is:

$$P_{\text{load}} = V_2 I_2 \cos\theta \Big]_{I_2}^{V_2} = 12.7 \times 0.494 \cos 55.6°$$

$$= 12.7 \times 0.494 \times 0.565 = 3.55 \text{ watts}$$

The efficiency of this particular air-core transformer working under the conditions stated above is 3.55/11.3 or 31.4 per cent.

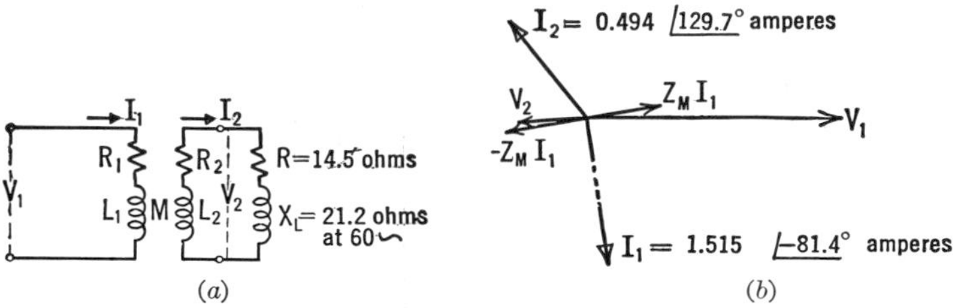

FIG. 17. Voltage and current relations in an air-core transformer the secondary of which is loaded as shown in (*a*).

Figure 17*b* is a vector diagram of $\mathbf{V}_1$, $\mathbf{I}_1$, $-\mathbf{Z}_M\mathbf{I}_1$, $\mathbf{I}_2$, and $\mathbf{V}_2$. Oscillogram 2 illustrates the variations of v_1, i_1, and i_2 for the particular case under discussion. The phase positions of the primary and secondary currents with respect to the applied voltage are shown in rectangular-coordinate form and agree with the calculated

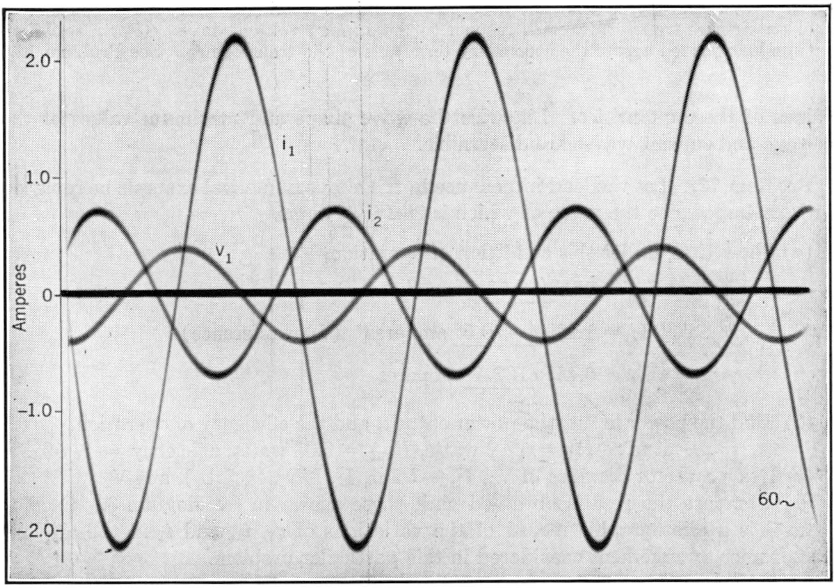

OSCILLOGRAM 2. Illustrating the time-phase relations of primary and secondary currents of an air-core transformer with respect to the applied voltage wave. (For an inductive-type load placed across the secondary terminals of the transformer. See Fig. 17*a*.)

v_1 represents the applied voltage wave (effective value = 50 volts)

i_1 represents the primary current wave (effective value = 1.5 amperes)

i_2 represents the secondary current wave (effective value = 0.5 ampere)

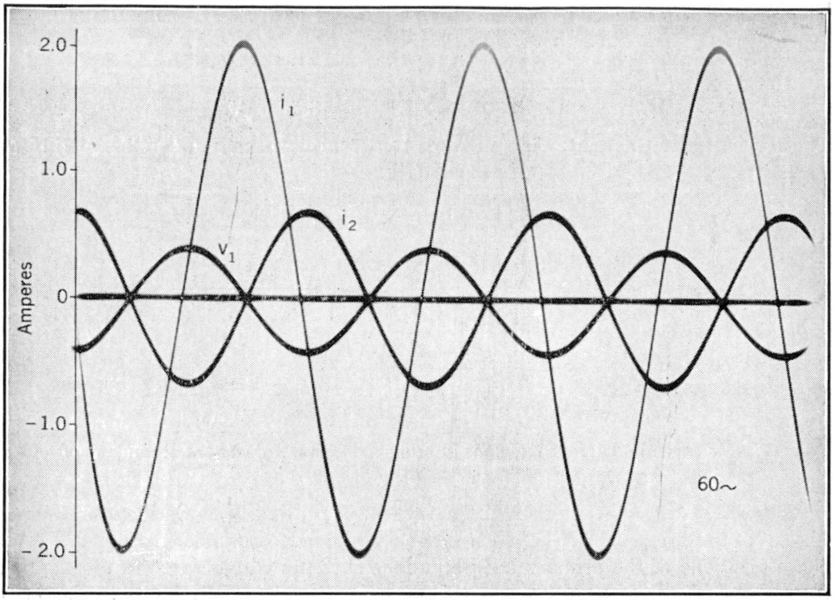

OSCILLOGRAM 3. Illustrating the time-phase relations of primary and secondary currents of an air-core transformer with respect to the applied voltage wave. (For a resistive-type load placed across the secondary terminals of the transformer. See Problem 12.)

values of these quantities. Likewise the wave shape and maximum values of the voltage and current waves are discernible.

Problem 12. Let the load impedance in the above numerical example be replaced with an impedance the value of which is $28.15\,\underline{/0^\circ}$ ohms.

(*a*) Show that, under this condition of operation,

$$\mathbf{Z}_{e1} = 35.5\,\underline{/79.5^\circ} \text{ ohms}$$

$$\mathbf{I}_1 = 1.409\,\underline{/-79.5^\circ} \text{ amperes} \quad (\mathbf{V}_1 \text{ as reference})$$

$$\mathbf{I}_2 = 0.465\,\underline{/182.4^\circ} \text{ amperes}$$

(*b*) Find the power input, the power output, and the efficiency of operation.

Ans.: $P_{\text{in}} = 12.8$ watts, $P_{\text{out}} = 6.08$ watts, efficiency $= 47.5\%$.

(*c*) Draw a vector diagram of $\mathbf{V}_1$, $\mathbf{I}_1$, $-\mathbf{I}_1\mathbf{Z}_M$, $\mathbf{I}_2$, $\mathbf{I}_2R_2$, $\mathbf{I}_2(j\omega L_2)$, and $\mathbf{V}_2$.

(*d*) Compare the results obtained with those shown in Oscillogram 3. Oscillogram 3 is a photographic record of the variations of v_1, i_1, and i_2 in the air-core transformer arrangement considered in this particular problem.

Transferred Impedance. One of the primary considerations in communication circuits is that of transferring maximum power from a low-power generating device to a receiver. It has been shown in Chapter V that maximum power is transferred (for a fixed generator voltage) when the impedance of the receiver (in complex form) is the conjugate of the impedance of the generator and associated transmission lines. That is, if $\mathbf{Z}_{gen} = R + jX$, then $\mathbf{Z}_{rec}$ should equal $R - jX$ for maximum power transfer. For impedance matches which will prevent reflection losses, $\mathbf{Z}_{gen} = \mathbf{Z}_{rec}$. (See Chapters X and XI.)

At audio frequencies, iron-core transformers may be used successfully for transforming voltage magnitudes and for matching impedances, but at radio frequencies air-core transformers are generally used. In iron-core transformers where the coefficient of coupling is relatively high and where $(\omega L_2)^2 \gg R_2'^2$, a resistance, R, placed across an N_2-turn secondary, *may* appear at the terminals of an N_1-turn primary as $(N_1/N_2)^2R$, approximately. The term "*may* appear" is used because several conditions must be fulfilled simultaneously before the $(N_1/N_2)^2$ factor can be used successfully, as will be shown presently.

Classical methods will be employed to show how an impedance placed across the secondary terminals of an air-core transformer appears at the primary terminals in modified form.[2]

Reference to equation (58) will show that the equivalent impedance of an air-core transformer referred to the primary side is:

$$\mathbf{Z}_{e1} = \mathbf{Z}_1 - \frac{\mathbf{Z}_M^2}{\mathbf{Z}_2'} = (R_1 + jX_1) + \frac{X_M^2}{(R_2' + jX_2')} \tag{59}$$

where $\mathbf{Z}_2' = (\mathbf{Z}_2 + \mathbf{Z})$, the total secondary impedance.

Since $\mathbf{Z}_M^2 = -\omega^2M^2$, and $\mathbf{Z}_2' = R_2' + j\omega L_2'$ (for a predominantly inductive secondary circuit), it follows that:

$$\mathbf{Z}_{e1} = (R_1 + j\omega L_1) + \left(\frac{\omega^2M^2}{R_2' + j\omega L_2'}\right) \tag{60}$$

Rationalizing equation (60) yields:

$$\mathbf{Z}_{e1} = \left[R_1 + \frac{\omega^2M^2R_2'}{R_2'^2 + \omega^2L_2'^2}\right] + j\omega\left[L_1 - \frac{\omega^2M^2L_2'}{R_2'^2 + \omega^2L_2'^2}\right] \tag{61}$$

It will be observed that R_2' appears at the primary terminals in modified form, namely, as:

$$\left[\frac{\omega^2M^2}{R_2'^2 + \omega^2L_2'^2}\right]R_2' = \frac{X_M^2}{Z_2'^2}R_2'$$

[2] It should be recognized that classical methods are applicable only where $M_{21} = M_{12}$ = a constant. Where iron-core transformers are involved, the $(N_1/N_2)^2$ factor is often used as an approximation, but since detailed analyses of iron-core transformers are usually considered in a-c machinery courses they will not be given here.

If R_2' is very small compared with $\omega_2 L_2'$, if $L_2' = N_2\phi_2/i_2$, that is, if all of L_2' is concentrated in the secondary winding, and if $M = \sqrt{L_1 L_2'}$, then R_2' appears at the primary terminals as:

$$\left(\frac{N_1}{N_2}\right)^2 R_2' \quad \text{approximately}$$

Thus, if a high value of R_2' is to appear at the primary terminals at an apparently reduced value, N_1/N_2 must be made less than unity by the appropriate amount. The above transfer factor, $(N_1/N_2)^2$, can be theoretically approached only in the case of an ideal transformer the coefficient of coupling of which is unity. Even with unity coupling, R_2' is not actually transferred by the exact square of the turn ratio, N_1/N_2, as is sometimes supposed. In the iron-core transformer the conditions required to make $(N_1/N_2)^2$ the correct transfer factor are fulfilled to a degree which makes calculations fall well within engineering accuracy when this factor is applied. As a result, it is customary to use this factor in iron-core transformer practice.

Equation (61) reveals another interesting fact, namely, that the effective inductance at the primary terminals of a loaded transformer approaches zero only when $R_2'^2$ is negligibly small compared with $\omega^2 L_2'^2$ and when L_2' is entirely concentrated in the secondary winding. Under these conditions and if the coefficient of coupling is equal to unity,

$$\left[L_1 - \frac{\omega^2 M^2 L_2'}{\omega^2 L_2'^2}\right] = \left[L_1 - \frac{\omega^2 L_1 L_2'^2}{\omega^2 L_2'^2}\right] = 0$$

Example 10. Given an air-core (or constant-permeability) transformer, in which $N_1 = 500$ and $N_2 = 5000$. For the particular arrangement considered:

$$R_1 = 1.0 \text{ ohm} \qquad R_2 = 10 \text{ ohms}$$

$$L_1 = 0.03 \text{ henry} \qquad L_2 = 3.0 \text{ henrys}$$

$$M = 0.275 \text{ henry}$$

$$\mathbf{Z} = 90\underline{/0^\circ} \text{ ohms}$$

At 265.5 cycles per second, $\omega = 1667$ radians per second and

$$X_M = \omega M = 1667 \times 0.275 = 458.4 \text{ ohms}$$

$$X_M^2 = 458.4^2 = 210{,}000$$

$$\mathbf{Z}_2' = (10 + j5000) + (90 + j0) = 100 + j5000 \text{ ohms}$$

$$\mathbf{Z}_{e1} = (1 + j50) + \frac{210{,}000}{100 + j5000}$$

$$\mathbf{Z}_{e1} = (1 + j50) + (0.84 - j42) = 1.84 + j8.0 = 8.2\underline{/77^\circ} \text{ ohms}$$

It will be noted that $\mathbf{Z}_2' = (100 + j5000)$ ohms appears at the primary terminals as $(0.84 - j42)$ ohms. This result emphasizes the wide discrepancy that may exist between ideal transformer operation and that actually obtained in an air-core transformer the coefficient of coupling of which is 0.917.

Under ideal conditions, the load impedance, $\mathbf{Z} = 90\underline{/0^\circ}$ ohms, would appear at the primary terminals as

$$\left[\frac{N_1}{N_2}\right]^2 \times 90 = \frac{500^2}{5000^2} \times 90 = 0.90 \text{ ohm}$$

The ideal conditions referred to are: (1) perfect coupling, and (2) zero resistance in the transformer windings.

The reactive term in $\mathbf{Z}_{e1}$ may, of course, be neutralized with a series condenser in the primary circuit if a low resistive impedance at the primary circuit terminals is desired.

Problem 13. A generator which develops 10 volts (effective) at 265.5 cycles and which has an internal impedance of $2\underline{/0^\circ}$ ohms is to be used to energize the 90-ohm load resistance of the above example in the two following ways:

(*a*) Directly. That is, with the generator terminals directly across the terminals of the 90-ohm load.

(*b*) Through the transformer of the above example and a primary series condenser the capacitive reactance of which is 8 ohms.

Find the power delivered to the 90-ohm load in (*a*) and in (*b*).

Ans.: (*a*) 1.063 watts; (*b*) 5.13 watts.

Primary Unity-Power-Factor Resonance. The inductive reactance of $\mathbf{Z}_{e1}$ caused by the introduction of a transformer may be neutralized in any one of several different ways. If, upon evaluation in a particular case, $\mathbf{Z}_{e1}$ possesses an inductive reactive component, suitable neutralizing capacitors may be placed in either the primary or the secondary circuits, and these capacitors may be arranged either in series or in parallel with the transformer windings. For the sake of analysis, let $\mathbf{Z}_{e1}$ be written in the form given in equation (61).

$$\mathbf{Z}_{e1} = \left[R_1 + \frac{\omega^2 M^2 R_2'}{R_2'^2 + \omega^2 L_2'^2}\right] + j\omega\left[L_1 - \frac{\omega^2 M^2 L_2'}{R_2'^2 + \omega^2 L_2'^2}\right] \tag{61}$$

R_2' is the total secondary circuit resistance. L_2' is the total secondary circuit self-inductance.

$$\mathbf{Z}_{e1} = R_{e1} + jX_{e1} \tag{62}$$

where

$$X_{e1} = \left[\omega L_1 - \frac{\omega^3 M^2 L_2'}{R_2'^2 + \omega^2 L_2'^2}\right] = \left[X_1 - \frac{X_M{}^2 X_2'}{R_2'^2 + X_2'^2}\right] \tag{63}$$

Series Primary Capacitor. Primary unity power factor can be obtained by introducing a capacitor in series with the primary, which has a capacitive reactance equal in magnitude to the inductive reactance represented in equation (63).

$$X_{C1(\text{series})} = \left[X_1 - \frac{X_M{}^2X_2{}'}{R_2{}'^2 + X_2{}'^2}\right] \tag{64}$$

Parallel Primary Capacitor. A capacitor, placed in parallel with the primary terminals, can be used to produce primary unity power factor. It is simply necessary to make the susceptance (b_C) of the parallel capacitor equal in magnitude to the susceptance (b_L) of $\mathbf{Y}_{e1}$, where:

$$\mathbf{Y}_{e1} = \frac{1}{R_{e1} + jX_{e1}} = \frac{R_{e1}}{R_{e1}{}^2 + X_{e1}{}^2} - j\frac{X_{e1}}{R_{e1}{}^2 + X_{e1}{}^2} \tag{65}$$

The inductive susceptance of the uncompensated transformer looking into the primary terminals is given by the j component of the above equation. The capacitive susceptance of the parallel primary capacitor must, therefore, be equal to:

$$b_{C1(\text{parallel})} = \frac{X_{e1}}{R_{e1}{}^2 + X_{e1}{}^2} \tag{66}$$

Secondary Capacitors. Under the assumptions that have been made concerning equations (61), (62), and (63), $X_2{}'$ is an inductive reactance. The introduction of a capacitor in series with the secondary circuit or the introduction of a capacitor in parallel with the secondary load terminals will tend to neutralize the original inductive reactance and cause the net inductive $X_2{}'$ to be smaller in magnitude. If $R_2{}'^2$ is not too great, the lower value of $X_2{}'$ increases the magnitude of the subtractive term of equation (63), namely,

$$\left[\frac{X_M{}^2X_2{}'}{R_2{}'^2 + X_2{}'^2}\right]$$

Provided $R_2{}'^2$ is sufficiently small in comparison with $X_2{}'^2$ to permit the required increase in the above expression, X_{e1} may be made equal to zero with the proper adjustment of the secondary capacitance. The correct value of secondary capacitance to employ in a particular case is not difficult to determine. However, the general algebraic expressions for the proper sizes of capacitors are of rather awkward algebraic form. In the circuits where this type of tuning is employed the desired effect is very often accomplished by means of a variable condenser which can be adjusted experimentally to the proper capacitance.

Adjustment of M. Assume that X_1 or $X_2{}'$ of equation (63) possesses a capacitive reactive component which is at least large enough to make

$$X_{e1} = \left[X_1 - \frac{X_M{}^2 X_2{}'}{R_2{}'^2 + X_2{}'^2}\right] = 0 \tag{67}$$

when the two windings are in their position of closest coupling. If now X_M is made smaller by decreasing the coefficient of coupling, X_{e1} will take on positive values, thus indicating a resulting inductive reactance. In general, the capacitive element employed would be adjusted to make X_{e1} slightly capacitive for the condition of maximum X_M. The primary current could thus be made to lead or lag the primary voltage by adjusting the degree of coupling between the two transformer windings.

Example 11. Let it be required to find the condenser of proper size to place in parallel with the primary terminals of Fig. 17*a* to produce primary unity power factor. The circuit parameters, and so forth, are given on page 295. For the case considered: $\mathbf{Z}_1 = 3.3 + j35.4$, $\mathbf{Z}_M = 0 + j9.65$, and $\mathbf{Z}_2{}' = (\mathbf{Z}_2 + \mathbf{Z}) = 15.28 + j25.27$ ohms at 60 cycles. Without the condenser:

$$\mathbf{Z}_{e1} = 4.93 + j32.7 \text{ ohms}$$

$$\mathbf{Y}_{e1} = \frac{4.93}{1094} - \frac{j32.7}{1094} = (0.0045 - j0.0299) \text{ mho}$$

Neglecting the resistance of the capacitor which is to be used:

$$b_{c1\,(\text{parallel})} = \frac{1}{X_{C1}} = 2\pi f C$$

$$C = \frac{0.0299}{377} = 79.3 \times 10^{-6} \text{ farad} = 79.3\ \mu\text{f}$$

Problem 14. Find the primary series capacitance to employ in the above example to produce primary unity power factor. *Ans.:* 81.1 μf.

Problem 15. Solve equation (63) for the value of $X_2{}'$ which will make $X_{e1} = 0$.

Ans.: $X_2{}' = \dfrac{X_M{}^2}{2X_1} \pm \sqrt{\dfrac{X_M{}^4}{4X_1{}^2} - R_2{}'^2}$.

Problem 16. Can a secondary series capacitance be employed in example 11 to produce primary unity power factor?

Ans.: No; $R_2{}'$ is too large for the specified values of X_1 and X_M.

Partial Resonance. In the coupled circuits of the type shown in Fig. 18, the two chief concerns are usually: (*a*) maximum value of I_2 (and of V_{C2}) for a given value of V_1; (*b*) sharply defined peak of I_2 for variable X_2, X_M, or ω.

In considering the salient features of these tuned coupled circuits, a slight modification in notation is desirable. Thus far we have distinguished between the impedance of the primary winding ($\mathbf{Z}_1$), the impedance of the secondary winding ($\mathbf{Z}_2$), and the impedance of the load ($\mathbf{Z}$). It is plain from the development preceding equations (52) and (53), page 293, that no restrictions have been imposed on the nature of $\mathbf{Z}_1$. $\mathbf{Z}_1$ is simply the equivalent series-circuit impedance of the primary circuit. Similarly $\mathbf{Z}_2 + \mathbf{Z}$ is the equivalent series-circuit impedance of the secondary circuit. The equations in the remainder of this chapter will be simpler to write and easier to grasp if $\mathbf{Z}_1$ is under-

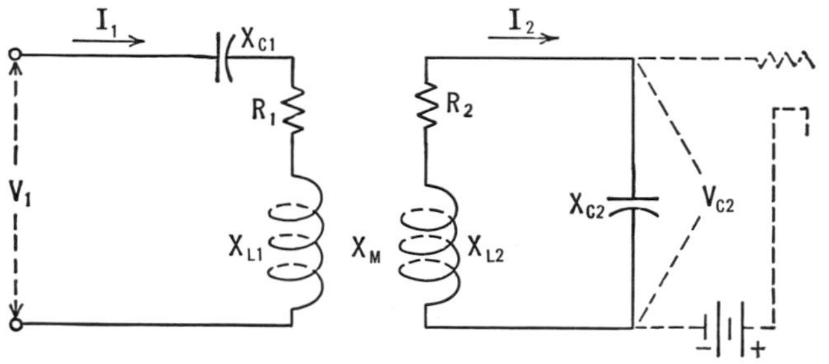

FIG. 18. A double-tuned circuit arrangement.

stood to be the total series impedance of the primary circuit and if $\mathbf{Z}_2$ is understood to be the total series impedance of the secondary circuit. Thus:

$$\mathbf{Z}_1 = R_1 + j(X_{L1} - X_{C1}) = R_1 + jX_1 \tag{68}$$

$$\mathbf{Z}_2 = R_2 + j(X_{L2} - X_{C2}) = R_2 + jX_2 \tag{69}$$

$$\mathbf{Z}_M = jX_M = j\omega M \quad \text{(as before)} \tag{70}$$

The equation for the secondary current $\mathbf{I}_2$ [as given in equation (53), page 293] becomes:

$$\mathbf{I}_2 = \frac{-\mathbf{V}_1\mathbf{Z}_M}{\mathbf{Z}_1\mathbf{Z}_2 - \mathbf{Z}_M{}^2} = \frac{-\mathbf{V}_1(jX_M)}{(R_1 + jX_1)(R_2 + jX_2) + X_M{}^2} \tag{71}$$

or

$$\mathbf{I}_2 = \frac{-\mathbf{V}_1X_M[(X_1R_2 + X_2R_1) + j(R_1R_2 - X_1X_2 + X_M{}^2)]}{(X_1R_2 + X_2R_1)^2 + (R_1R_2 - X_1X_2 + X_M{}^2)^2} \tag{72}$$

For simplicity in writing, let

$$a = X_1R_2 + X_2R_1 \quad \text{and} \quad b = R_1R_2 - X_1X_2 + X_M{}^2$$

Then:

$$\mathbf{I}_2 = \frac{-\mathbf{V}_1X_M(a + jb)}{a^2 + b^2} \tag{73}$$

The magnitude of $\mathbf{I}_2$ is:

$$I_2 = V_1 X_M \sqrt{\frac{a^2 + b^2}{(a^2 + b^2)^2}} = \frac{V_1 X_M}{\sqrt{a^2 + b^2}} \tag{74}$$

or

$$I_2 = \frac{V_1 X_M}{\sqrt{X_1^2 R_2^2 + X_2^2 R_1^2 + R_1^2 R_2^2 + 2R_1 R_2 X_M^2 + X_1^2 X_2^2 - 2X_1 X_2 X_M^2 + X_M^4}} \tag{75}$$

In solving for I_2, where numerical values are involved, it is often more convenient to use equation (71) than equation (75). This is particularly true where X_1 or X_2 is equal to zero. Equation (75), however, is useful in determining maximum values of I_2 that can be obtained by varying any one of the parameters.

Partial resonance in coupled circuits is obtained when any one parameter is so varied as to cause maximum effective secondary current, I_2, under the condition of constant applied voltage, V_1.

From equation (75) it is evident that partial resonance can be obtained by adjusting any one of the five parameters: R_1, R_2, X_1, X_2, or X_M. (For fixed values of R_1, L_1, C_1, M, R_2, L_2, and C_2, partial resonance may be obtained by adjustment of the frequency.) Partial resonance will obviously be produced by adjusting any parameter which appears only in the positive terms of the denominator of equation (75) to zero. Hence partial resonance obtains, theoretically, when either R_1 or R_2 is equal to zero. Practically, neither R_1 nor R_2 can be zero and, as will be shown presently, the value of $R_1 R_2$ determines the optimum value of I_2 that can be obtained.

The values of X_1, X_2, or X_M which will produce partial resonance may, in general, be found by differentiating the expression for I_2 [as given in equation (75)] with respect to the proper X and equating dI_2/dX equal to zero. For example, the value of X_1 which will produce partial resonance may be determined by equating dI_2/dX_1 equal to zero and solving for X_1 in terms of the other parameters. Thus:

$$\frac{dI_2}{dX_1} = 0 = -V_1 X_M \tfrac{1}{2}[2X_1(R_2^2 + X_2^2) - 2X_2 X_M^2] \tag{76}$$

The only useful relationship which can be derived from the above is:

$$X_1(R_2^2 + X_2^2) = X_2 X_M^2 \tag{77}$$

The value of X_1 which will produce partial resonance is, therefore:

$$X_{1\,(\text{res})} = \frac{X_2 X_M^2}{R_2^2 + X_2^2} = \frac{X_2 X_M^2}{Z_2^2} \tag{78}$$

Reference to equation (63), page 301, will show that the above value of X_1 is also the unity-power-factor-resonance value of X_1. In making this comparison it should be recognized that R_2 and X_2 of equation (78) mean the same as R_2' and X_2' of equation (63) because of the shift in notation which was made at the beginning of this section. In a similar manner, it may be shown that the value of X_2 for partial resonance is:

$$X_{2(\text{res})} = \frac{X_1 X_M^2}{R_1^2 + X_1^2} = \frac{X_1 X_M^2}{Z_1^2} \tag{79}$$

The interpretation of the above equation is that X_2 must have the value stated to produce maximum I_2. If $X_1 = 0$, then X_2 should be tuned to zero to produce maximum I_2 for a fixed value of X_M. If the primary circuit is not tuned to $X_{L1} - X_{C1} = 0$, then the secondary must be detuned to the value $X_1 X_M^2/Z_1^2$. Where sharpness of secondary tuning is of more importance than an optimum value of I_2, the primary is often purposely detuned to effect a pronounced peak in the I_2 versus X_{C2} graph. (See Problem 17, page 309.)

If X_1 and X_2 are both equal to zero (by virtue of $X_{L1} - X_{C1} = 0$ and $X_{L2} - X_{C2} = 0$), equation (75) reduces to

$$I_{2(\max)} = \frac{V_1 X_M}{R_1 R_2 + X_M^2} \tag{80}$$

If, now, X_M is varied by changing the coefficient of coupling between the coils, the optimum value of I_2 is obtained when

$$\frac{dI_{2(\max)}}{dX_M} = \frac{V_1(R_1 R_2 + X_M^2) - 2V_1 X_M^2}{(R_1 R_2 + X_M^2)^2} = 0 \tag{81}$$

or when

$$X_M = \omega M = \pm \sqrt{R_1 R_2} \quad \text{(called critical coupling)} \tag{82}$$

Under these conditions:

$$I_{2(\text{opt})} = \frac{V_1 \sqrt{R_1 R_2}}{R_1 R_2 + R_1 R_2} = \frac{V_1}{2\sqrt{R_1 R_2}} \tag{83}$$

The relationships stated in equations (78), (79), (82), and (83) are of considerable importance in voltage amplification in radio circuits. Some of the essential features involved are illustrated numerically in the following examples and in graphical form in Figs. 19 and 20. For fixed values of the other parameters, there is a value of X_M or a coefficient of coupling which will produce maximum I_2 as shown in the graphs of Fig. 19. Frequency responses of coupled circuits for fixed values of R_1, L_1, C_1, M, R_2, L_2, and C_2 are shown in Fig. 20. Graphs of I_2 and V_{C2} versus X_{C2} are reserved for student exercises.

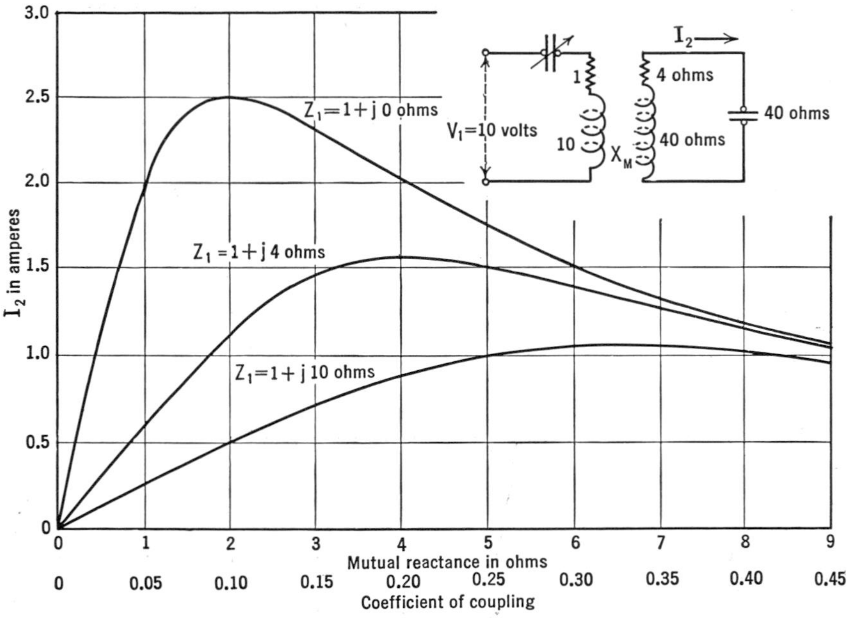

FIG. 19. Variation of secondary current with coefficient of coupling for different values of primary impedance. See example 12.

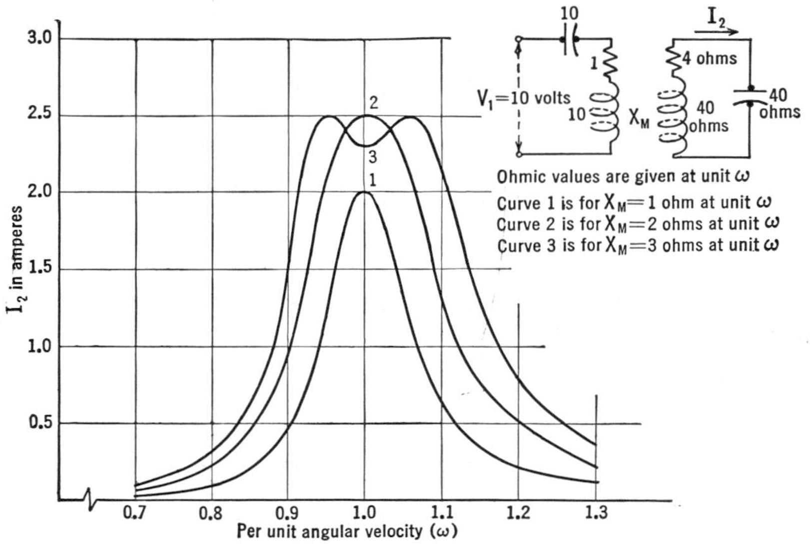

FIG. 20. Frequency responses of double-tuned circuits.

Example 12. (*a*) Consider the coupled circuits shown in Fig. 19 under the following conditions:

$$\mathbf{Z}_1 = 1 + j10 \text{ ohms} \quad \mathbf{Z}_2 = 4 + j(40 - 40) \text{ ohms} \quad X_M \text{ variable}$$

In this case the primary is not tuned and the secondary is tuned, that is, $X_{C2} = X_{L2} = 40$ ohms at the frequency of the impressed voltage, V_1.

Solutions of equation (71) for $V_1 = 10$ volts and for various values of X_M will show the manner in which I_2 varies with the degree of coupling between the coils. The results of a series of such calculations are shown in the lower curve of Fig. 19. It will be observed that, for $\mathbf{Z}_1 = 1 + j10$ ohms, I_2 attains a maximum value at X_M equal to 6.5 ohms or at a coefficient of coupling of 0.325. Closer or looser coupling than 0.325 results in lesser values of I_2 and hence of $V_{C2} = I_2X_{C2}$.

Calculations will show that in this case

$$V_{C2(\text{max})} = 1.063 \times 40 = 42.52 \text{ volts}$$

(*b*) The response of I_2 to variable X_M when the primary is partially tuned is shown in the middle graph of Fig. 19. In this case, 6 ohms of capacitive reactance is employed in the primary circuit and

$$\mathbf{Z}_1 = 1 + j4 \text{ ohms} \quad \mathbf{Z}_2 = 4 + j0 \text{ ohms} \quad X_M \text{ variable}$$

I_2 attains a maximum value at $X_M = 4.3$ ohms of 1.565 amperes. The maximum value of the secondary condenser voltage is:

$$V_{C2(\text{max})} = 1.565 \times 40 = 62.6 \text{ volts}$$

(*c*) The upper graph of Fig. 19 shows the response of I_2 to a variable X_M when both primary and secondary are tuned.

$$\mathbf{Z}_1 = 1 + j0 \text{ ohms} \quad \mathbf{Z}_2 = 4 + j0 \text{ ohms}, \quad X_M \text{ variable}$$

In accordance with equations (82) and (83), I_2 attains its optimum value of $V_1/2\sqrt{R_1R_2}$ at $X_M = \sqrt{R_1R_2}$.

$$I_{2(\text{opt})} = \frac{V_1}{2\sqrt{R_1R_2}} = \frac{10}{2 \times 2} = 2.5 \text{ amperes}$$

$$V_{C2(\text{opt})} = I_{2(\text{opt})}X_{C2} = 2.5 \times 40 = 100 \text{ volts}$$

The Q (or $\omega L/R$) of the coils in this case is equal to 10, and it will be observed that $V_{C2(\text{opt})}$ is equal to the driving voltage (10 volts) times the Q of the coils. That is, $V_{C2(\text{opt})} = V_1Q = 10 \times 10 = 100$ volts. This fact is generally true where $X_{L2} = 4X_{L1}$, provided that both primary and secondary circuits are tuned to resonance and provided that the coupling reactance is adjusted to its critical value, namely, $\sqrt{R_1R_2}$. Under these conditions,

$$Q = \frac{X_{L1}}{R_1} = \frac{X_{L2}}{R_2} \quad \text{and} \quad R_1R_2 = \frac{X_{L1}X_{L2}}{Q^2}$$

$$I_{2(\text{opt})} = \frac{V_1}{2\sqrt{R_1R_2}} = \frac{V_1Q}{\sqrt{4X_{L1}X_{L2}}} = \frac{V_1Q}{X_{L2}}$$

$$V_{C2(\text{opt})} = I_{2(\text{opt})}X_{C2} = I_{2(\text{opt})}X_{L2} = V_1Q$$

Thus it will be seen that the voltage developed across the secondary condenser of the coupled circuits shown in Fig. 18 may be equal to Q times the applied voltage. If, for example, the Q of the coils is 50, a voltage amplification of 50 can be obtained simply with the aid of the tuned coupled circuits. As indicated in Fig. 18, the voltage developed across the secondary condenser may be applied between the control grid and cathode of a vacuum tube in order to obtain further voltage amplification.

Example 13. The response of a coupled circuit to a constant driving voltage of variable frequency is shown in Fig. 20 for three different values of X_M. Since the critical coupling at unit angular velocity is 2 ohms, the graphs shown in Fig. 20 represent couplings which are less than, equal to, and greater than critical coupling.

In these graphs, unit angular velocity is called the angular velocity at which $X_{L1} - X_{C1} = 0$ and at which $X_{L2} - X_{C2} = 0$. At unit angular velocity,

$$\mathbf{Z}_1 = 1 + j(10 - 10), \quad \mathbf{Z}_2 = 4 + j(40 - 40) \quad X_M = 1, 2, \text{ or } 3 \text{ ohms}$$

At other values of ω, the X_L's and X_M vary directly as ω, and the X_C's vary inversely as ω.

For coupling less than critical coupling the maximum value of the secondary current is less than for critical coupling, and for couplings greater than critical coupling the current response is generally similar to the double-peaked curve shown in Fig. 20.

If a single pronounced peak of I_2 versus ω is desired, the coupling should not be greater than critical coupling, and the Q of the coils should be as high as practicable. If the Q of the coils is made higher than that used in Fig. 20, the peaks of the curves will be sharper and more clearly defined. Sharpness of tuning is particularly important in radio receiver circuits.

Problem 17. In the coupled circuits shown in Fig. 18, page 304:

$R_1 = 1.0$ ohm	$R_2 = 4.0$ ohms
$X_{L1} = 10$ ohms	$X_{L2} = 40$ ohms
$X_{C1} = 10$ ohms	X_{C2} is variable
$X_M = 2$ ohms	$V_1 = 10$ volts

Graph I_2 and V_{C2} versus X_{C2} between the limits of $X_{C2} = 20$ ohms and $X_{C2} = 60$ ohms.

Ans.: $I_{2(\text{max})} = 2.5$ amperes at $X_{C2} = 40$ ohms.
$V_{C2(\text{max})} = 102$ volts at $X_{C2} = 41.7$ ohms, approximately.

Note: The fact that circuits of this kind tune more sharply but to lesser peak values when one member is partially detuned may be shown by repeating the above problem using $\mathbf{Z}_1 = 1 + j4$ ohms rather than $\mathbf{Z}_1 = 1 + j0$.

Double-Tuned Circuit Analysis and Design in Terms of $f/f_0 - f_0/f$. The double-tuned circuit shown in Fig. 21a is widely used in radio engineering practice, and it is the purpose of this section to derive design equations which will specify the Q's of the circuits and the coefficient of coupling in terms of the band width and the degree of irregularity which can be tolerated in the response characteristic. The current generator (g_mE_g) in parallel with R_p is the plate circuit representation of a vacuum tube. $\left(di_b = \frac{\partial i_b}{\partial e_g} de_g + \frac{\partial i_b}{\partial e_b} de_b \text{ or } i_p = g_m e_g + \frac{e_p}{R_p}.\right)$ See page 203.

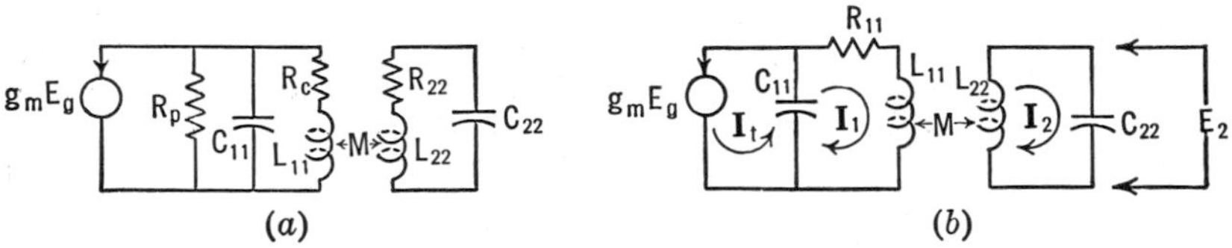

FIG. 21. The actual double-tuned circuit shown in (a) transforms readily to that shown in (b).

Wherever inductive and capacitive reactances are combined as shown in Fig. 22 the analysis is simplified considerably by letting

$$\frac{\omega}{\omega_0} - \frac{\omega_0}{\omega} = \frac{f}{f_0} - \frac{f_0}{f} = F \tag{84}$$

where $\omega_0 = 1/\sqrt{L_{11}C_{11}} = 1/\sqrt{L_{22}C_{22}}$ under the assumption that the primary and secondary circuits will be tuned to the same frequency.

It will be noted that F as defined above is the difference between two dimensionless quantities (f/f_0 and f_0/f) which individually characterize the variations of inductive and capacitive reactances relative to variations in frequency.

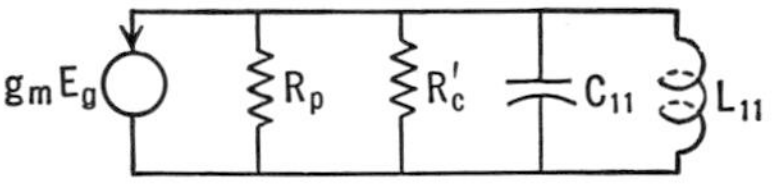

FIG. 22.

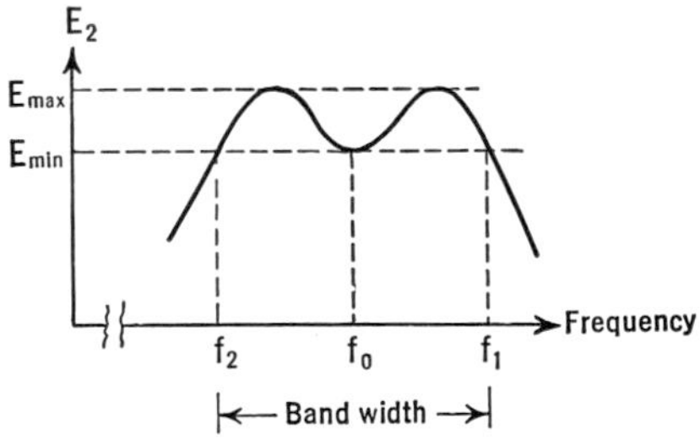

FIG. 23. Response curve of double-tuned circuit. $f_0 = \sqrt{f_1f_2}$ is the center frequency.

As shown in Fig. 23, $f_1 - f_2$ will be called the band width and it will be assumed that $f_1 - f_2$ is small compared with f_0. For narrow-band responses of this kind, E_2 has a value of E_{min} within the pass band at

$$f_0 = \sqrt{f_1f_2}$$

where f_1 and f_2 are the frequencies (other than f_0) at which the response, E_2, has values of E_{min}. See Fig. 23. In this connection it will be noted that, if F_{min} symbolizes the value of F where $E_2 = E_{\text{min}}$, say at $f = f_1$, then

$$F_{\text{min}} = \frac{f_1}{f_0} - \frac{f_0}{f_1} = \frac{f_1}{f_0} - \frac{f_2}{f_0} \tag{85}$$

since $f_0 = \sqrt{f_1 f_2}$. If the band width is specified, F_{min} is known.

If we let $a = 1/Q_1$, $b = 1/Q_2$, and $k = M/\sqrt{L_{11}L_{22}}$:

$$\mathbf{Z}_{11}\,(\text{in Fig. 21}b) = R_{11} + j\left(\omega L_{11} - \frac{1}{\omega C_{11}}\right) = \omega_{01}L_{11}(a + jF_{11}) \tag{86}$$

$$\mathbf{Z}_{22} = \omega_{02}L_{22}(b + jF_{22}) \tag{87}$$

$$\mathbf{Z}_{12} = \mathbf{Z}_{21} = j\omega M = j\omega k\sqrt{L_{11}L_{22}} \tag{88}$$

We assume that C_{11} and C_{22} will be so adjusted that

$$\omega_{01} = \frac{1}{\sqrt{L_{11}C_{11}}} = \omega_{02} = \frac{1}{\sqrt{L_{22}C_{22}}} = \omega_0$$

where

$$\omega_0^2 = \frac{1}{\sqrt{L_{11}L_{22}C_{11}C_{22}}}$$

The problem is essentially that of expressing a, b, and k in terms of F_{min} and $(E_{\text{max}} - E_{\text{min}})$.

Employing the loop current method of analysis in Fig. 21b and treating g_mE_g as a known value of current, say I_t, circulating in the left-hand loop, we have

$$\left.\begin{aligned} \mathbf{Z}_{11}\mathbf{I}_1 + \mathbf{Z}_{12}\mathbf{I}_2 &= j\frac{g_mE_g}{\omega C_{11}} = j\frac{I_t}{\omega C_{11}} \\ \mathbf{Z}_{21}\mathbf{I}_1 + \mathbf{Z}_{22}\mathbf{I}_2 &= 0 \end{aligned}\right\} \tag{89}$$

The output voltage is

$$\mathbf{E}_2 = -j\frac{1}{\omega C_{22}}\mathbf{I}_2 = \frac{\left(-j\frac{1}{\omega C_{22}}\right)\left(-j\frac{I_t}{\omega C_{11}}\right)(j\omega k\sqrt{L_{11}L_{22}})}{\omega_0^2L_{11}L_{22}[(ab - F^2) + j(a + b)F] + \omega^2k^2L_{11}L_{22}} \tag{90}$$

$$\mathbf{E}_2 = \frac{\dfrac{-jI_tk\sqrt{L_{11}L_{22}}}{\omega C_{11}C_{22}}}{\omega_0^2L_{11}L_{22}\left[\left(ab + \dfrac{\omega^2}{\omega_0^2}k^2 - F^2\right) + j(a + b)F\right]} \tag{91}$$

Since we are interested particularly in the region shown in Fig. 23 where any ω is close to ω_0 if the per unit band width is small, we may set $\omega^2/\omega_0{}^2 \approx 1$ in equation (91) and obtain

$$\mathbf{E}_2 = \frac{-jI_tk}{\omega\sqrt{C_{11}C_{22}}[(k^2 + ab - F^2) + j(a + b)F]} \tag{92}$$

At $\omega = \omega_0$, the center angular frequency $F = 0$ and

$$\mathbf{E}_{20} = \mathbf{E}_0 = \frac{-jI_tk}{\omega_0\sqrt{C_{11}C_{22}}\,(k^2 + ab)} \tag{93}$$

Consider now the ratio of the magnitudes of E_2 and E_0 and let the ratio ω/ω_0 again be reckoned as unity. Under these conditions

$$\left(\frac{E_2}{E_0}\right)^2 = \frac{1}{1 + \dfrac{F^4 + (a^2 + b^2 - 2k^2)F^2}{(k^2 + ab)^2}} \tag{94}$$

or

$$\frac{E_2}{E_0} = \frac{1}{\sqrt{1 + \dfrac{F^4 + (a^2 + b^2 - 2k^2)F^2}{(k^2 + ab)^2}}} \tag{95}$$

From equation (95) it is plain that the shape of the E_2 curve (reckoned in per unit values relative to E_0) will be determined by the relative magnitudes of $a^2 + b^2$ and $2k^2$. If $a^2 + b^2 \geqq 2k^2$, then a single-peaked curve is obtained since, as F takes on values greater than 0 (f different from f_0), the E_2/E_0 curve will decrease continuously from its maximum value of unity, the value of E_2/E_0 when $F = 0$ or when $f = f_0$.

If, however, $a^2 + b^2 < 2k^2$, the denominator of equation (95) takes on a minimum value or E_2/E_0 takes on a maximum value where $f(F^2) = F^4 + (a^2 + b^2 - 2k^2)F^2$ is a minimum. This minimum may be found from

$$\frac{df(F^2)}{d(F^2)} = 2(F^2) - (2k^2 - a^2 - b^2) = 0$$

or where

$$F^2 = F_{\max}{}^2 = \frac{2k^2 - a^2 - b^2}{2} \tag{96}$$

When plotted versus actual frequency, the response takes the form shown in Fig. 23 or, when plotted versus F, the form shown in Fig. 24.

We may write an expression for $(E_2/E_0)_{\max} = E_{\max}$ from equations (95) and (96), and, since $E_{\min}$ is taken as unity, we may write

$$\frac{E_{\max}{}^2}{E_{\min}{}^2} = \frac{1}{1 - \dfrac{(2k^2 - a^2 - b^2)^2}{4(k^2 + ab)^2}} \tag{97}$$

Let

$$\alpha^2 = 1 - \frac{E_{\min}{}^2}{E_{\max}{}^2} = \frac{(2k^2 - a^2 - b^2)^2}{4(k^2 + ab)^2} = \frac{F_{\min}{}^4}{4(k^2 + ab)^2} \tag{98}$$

where $F_{\min}{}^2 = (2k^2 - a^2 - b^2)$. [See Fig. 24 and equation (95.)] It follows that

$$\alpha = \frac{F_{\min}{}^2}{2(k^2 + ab)} \tag{99}$$

and

$$\frac{E_2}{E_0} = \frac{1}{\sqrt{1 + \dfrac{4\alpha^2 F^2 (F^2 - F_{\min}{}^2)}{F_{\min}{}^4}}} \tag{100}$$[3]

$F_{\min} = \sqrt{2k^2 - a^2 - b^2} \approx (f_1 - f_2)/f_0$ is the value of F at the edge of the pass band where $E_2/E_0 = 1 = E_{\min}$.

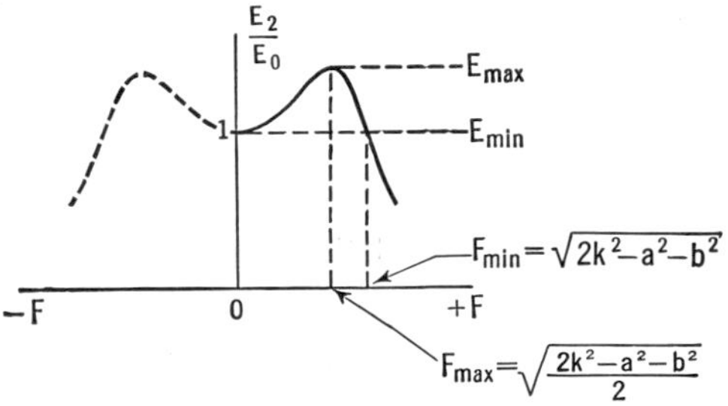

FIG. 24. A response curve, E_2/E_0 versus the variable F for $a^2 + b^2 < 2k^2$. $(F = f/f_0 - f_0/f.)$

Equation (100) is a convenient working equation since it includes α, a measure of the response irregularity which can be tolerated within the pass band $(f_1 - f_2)$, and $F_{\min}$, a measure of the pass band width $(f_1 - f_2)$. From a design point of view, α and $F_{\min}$ would normally be specified (at least indirectly), and k, a, and b would then be so chosen

[3] These results are due to Dr. T. C. G. Wagner of the University of Maryland who has developed design formulas for double-, triple-, and quadruple-tuned circuits.

that the specified values of α and $f_1 - f_2$ would be obtained in the final design. See Problem 45, page 324, and example 14 for applications.

Example 14. Let it be required to design a double-tuned circuit which will have a per unit band width $[(f_1 - f_2)/f_0]$ of 0.05 and a ratio of E_{max} to E_{min} equal to 1.25. If we make $a = b$ $(Q_1 = Q_2)$, we may readily show that:

$$a^2 = b^2 = \frac{F_{min}^2(1 - \alpha)}{4\alpha} \quad \text{and} \quad k^2 = \frac{F_{min}^2(1 + \alpha)}{4\alpha}$$

since $\alpha = F_{min}^2/2(k^2 + ab)$ and $F_{min}^2 = 2k^2 - a^2 - b^2$. In the particular case under discussion

$$F_{min}^2 = \left(\frac{f_1 - f_2}{f_0}\right)^2 = 0.05^2 = 0.0025 \text{ [see equation (85)]}$$

and

$$\alpha^2 = 1 - \frac{E_{min}^2}{E_{max}^2} = 1 - \frac{16}{25} \quad \text{or} \quad \alpha = 0.6$$

Thus

$$a^2 = b^2 = \frac{0.0025(0.4)}{2.4} = 0.000417 \quad \text{and} \quad Q_1 = Q_2 = 49$$

$$k^2 = \frac{0.0025(1.6)}{2.4} = 0.00167 \quad \text{and} \quad k = 0.041$$

Component Fluxes and Voltages in the Air-Core Transformer. Figure 25*a* shows diagrammatically the flux components in an air-core transformer. The current I_2 in the secondary produces an mmf which may be considered to cause two component fluxes: one the leakage flux ϕ_{22}, which links the turns of winding 2 only, and ϕ_{21}, which links both windings 2 and 1. The same conditions regarding the flux linkages as explained on page 279 for Fig. 6 apply to the present discussion, namely, that ϕ_{22} is a hypothetical component which, when linking all the turns of winding 2, produces the same total flux linkages as obtained from the true flux linkages in question. The current I_1 causes two component fluxes, ϕ_{12}, which links both windings, and ϕ_{11}, which links winding 1 only. Reference to example 9 on page 295 and application of Lenz's law will reveal in a general way the reason for the phase angle shown between $\mathbf{I}_1$ and $\mathbf{I}_2$ in the vector diagram (Fig. 25*b*). The component fluxes produced by $\mathbf{I}_1$ and $\mathbf{I}_2$ are also shown. It is plain from Fig. 25*a* that the resultant mutual flux is $\phi_M = \phi_{12} + \phi_{21}$. The total flux through winding 2 is $\phi_{2R} = \phi_M + \phi_{22} = \phi_2 + \phi_{12}$. Also the total flux through winding 1 is $\phi_{1R} = \phi_M + \phi_{11} = \phi_1 + \phi_{21}$. All these combinations are shown on the vector diagram. Equal numbers of turns on windings 1 and 2 are assumed.

Since $e = -N(d\phi/dt)$, the induced voltage due to a flux lags the flux by 90 degrees. Thus, on the vector diagram, $\mathbf{E}_{2R}$ is caused by ϕ_{2R}, $\mathbf{E}_{M2}$

by ϕ_M, and $\mathbf{E}_{22}$ by ϕ_{22}. The resultant induced emf in winding 2 is therefore $\mathbf{E}_{2R}$. Because of the resistance R_2 of winding 2 the terminal voltage must be less than $\mathbf{E}_{2R}$ by the $\mathbf{I}_2R_2$ drop as shown. Hence $\mathbf{V}_2$ is the secondary terminal voltage. It is seen to be ahead of $\mathbf{I}_2$ by the secondary load power-factor angle.

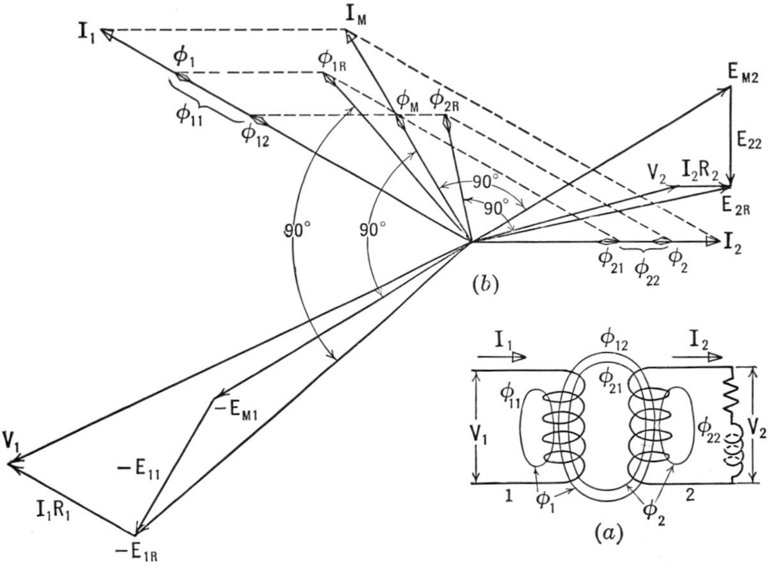

FIG. 25. Vector diagram of the air-core transformer.

The voltage drop impressed on winding 1 must be equal to the sum of all the drops through winding 1. Thus one component of the total drop must be the drop $-\mathbf{E}_{1R}$, which is equal and opposite to the induced voltage $\mathbf{E}_{1R}$ (not shown) in winding 1 caused by all the flux linking that winding. The remaining component drop is the $\mathbf{I}_1R_1$. Hence $\mathbf{V}_1 = \mathbf{I}_1R_1 + (-\mathbf{E}_{1R})$. The components of $-\mathbf{E}_{1R}$ are the voltage drops $-\mathbf{E}_{11}$ and $-\mathbf{E}_{M1}$, which overcome the induced voltages due to the primary leakage and mutual fluxes, respectively.

The leakage flux ϕ_{22} is (even for all practical purposes in iron-core transformers) proportional to the current $\mathbf{I}_2$. $\mathbf{E}_{22}$ is an induced voltage rise and is directly proportional to $\mathbf{I}_2$. The voltage $-\mathbf{E}_{22}$ is opposite to $\mathbf{E}_{22}$ and therefore leads the current by 90 degrees. It is thus in the direction of a reactance drop, and, since it is proportional to the current, a constant reactance may be multiplied by the current $\mathbf{I}_2$ to represent correctly the drop $-\mathbf{E}_{22}$. Such a reactance which may be used to replace the effect of the leakage flux is called a leakage reactance, and the corresponding drop a leakage reactance drop. The vector diagram which is commonly used is shown in Fig. 26. Only the flux ϕ_M in Fig. 25 is shown, and the drops $-\mathbf{E}_{22}$ and $-\mathbf{E}_{11}$ are replaced by their corresponding leakage reactance drops $\mathbf{I}_2\mathbf{X}_2$ and $\mathbf{I}_1\mathbf{X}_1$, respectively.

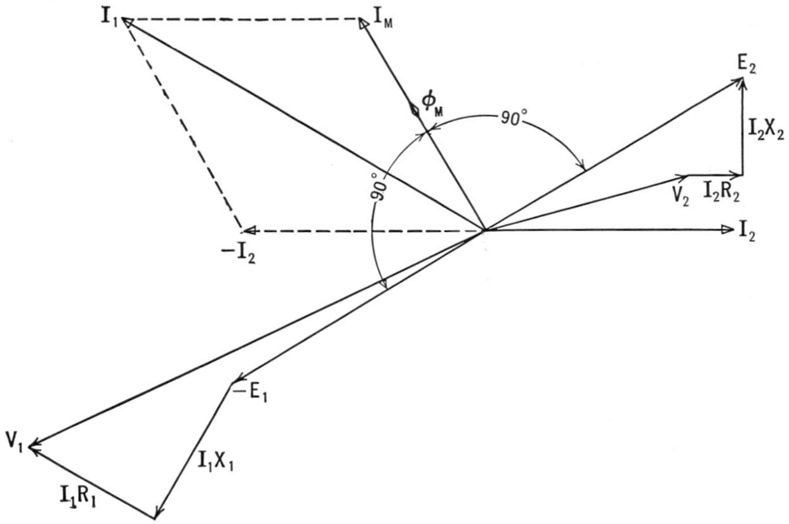

FIG. 26. Commonly used vector diagram for the air-core transformer shown in Fig. 25.

Leakage Reactance. Leakage reactance may be defined as $2\pi f$ times the leakage inductance. This may be shown as follows. By referring to Fig. 25a, leakage inductance

$$L_{S2} = \frac{N_2\phi_{22}}{I_2} \quad \text{or} \quad N_2\frac{d\phi_{22}}{di_2} \tag{101}$$

$$e_{22} = -N_2\frac{d\phi_{22}}{dt} \tag{102}$$

Dividing equation (102) by equation (101) gives

$$e_{22} = -L_{S2}\frac{di_2}{dt}$$

For sine waves

$$i_2 = I_{m2}\sin\omega t \tag{103}$$

and

$$e_{22} = -L_{S2}I_{m2}\omega\cos\omega t \tag{104}$$

Hence

$$E_{m22} = I_{m2}\omega L_{S2}$$

Also

$$E_{22} = \frac{I_{m2}}{\sqrt{2}} \omega L_{S2} = I_2 \omega L_{S2}$$

The magnitude of the leakage reactance drop has been defined equal to $E_{22} = I_2\omega L_{S2} = I_2X_2$. Therefore

$$X_2 = \omega L_{S2} \tag{105}$$

Since e_{22} in equation (104) is a voltage rise, the drop is $-e_{22} = L_{S2}\omega I_{m2} \cos \omega t$. Because this voltage drop is 90 degrees ahead of the current (equation 103), the complex expression for leakage reactance must be

$$X_2 = +j\omega L_{S2} \tag{106}$$

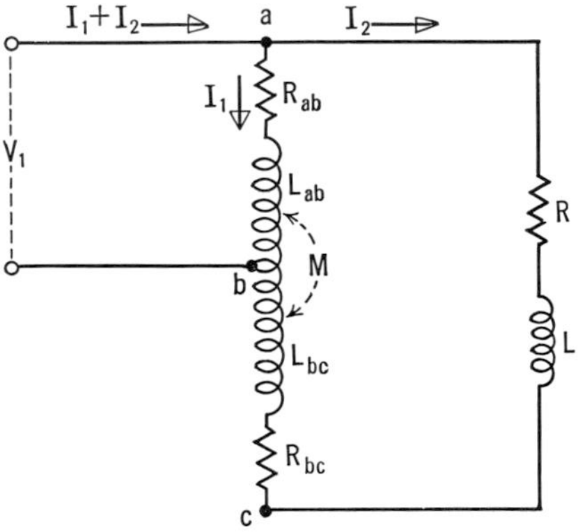

FIG. 27. Air-core autotransformer connected as a step-up voltage device.

The Air-Core Autotransformer. Two inductance coils arranged as shown in Fig. 27 are called an autotransformer. If the driving voltage is applied to the terminals *ab* and the load connected across the terminals *ac*, the autotransformer functions as a step-up voltage device; whereas, if the driving voltage is applied to the terminals *ac* and the load connected to terminals *ab* or *bc*, it functions as a step-down voltage device. The mathematical analysis of the air-core autotransformer is reserved for student exercises. (See Problems 37, 38, and 39 at the end of this chapter.)

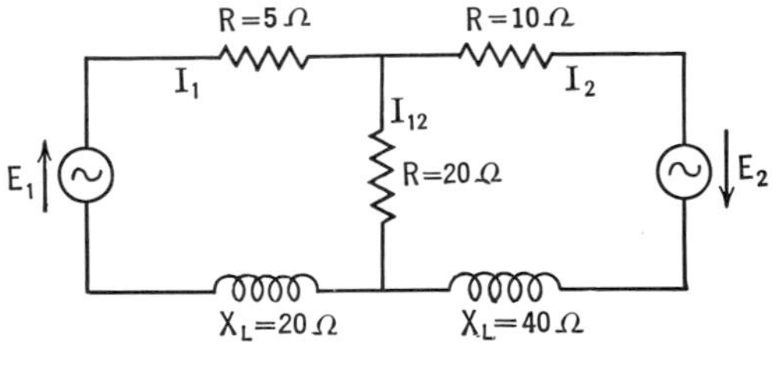

FIG. 28. See Problem 18.

PROBLEMS

18. In Fig. 28, $\mathbf{E}_1 = 100\underline{/0°}$ volts and $\mathbf{E}_2 = 100\underline{/+120°}$ volts. The physical meaning of the foregoing statement is that the E_2 generator develops a maximum generated emf ($\sqrt{2} \times 100$ volts) in its arrow direction $\frac{1}{3}$ of a cycle or 120° before the E_1 generator develops its maximum generated emf in its arrow direction. Assuming that the resistances and reactances given in Fig. 28 include the generator impedances, find $\mathbf{I}_1$, $\mathbf{I}_2$, and $\mathbf{I}_{12}$.

19. In Fig. 2, page 276, it is found experimentally that $\mathbf{I}_1 = 1\underline{/90°}$ ampere and $\mathbf{V}_{22'} = 4\underline{/0°}$ volts (with terminals 22′ open-circuited) when $\mathbf{E}_1$ (the voltage applied to terminals 11′) is $6\underline{/0°}$ volts. When a voltage of $6\underline{/0°}$ volts is applied to terminals 22′ (with terminals 11′ open-circuited), $\mathbf{I}_2 = 1.5\underline{/90°}$ amperes and $\mathbf{V}_{11'} = 6\underline{/0°}$ volts.

(*a*) Find $\mathbf{Z}_{21}$ and $\mathbf{Z}_{12}$ from the above data.

(*b*) Find the coefficient of coupling between the two circuits.

(*c*) Draw a circuit configuration that might actually exist within the 11′2′2 box and that is consistent with the specified data.

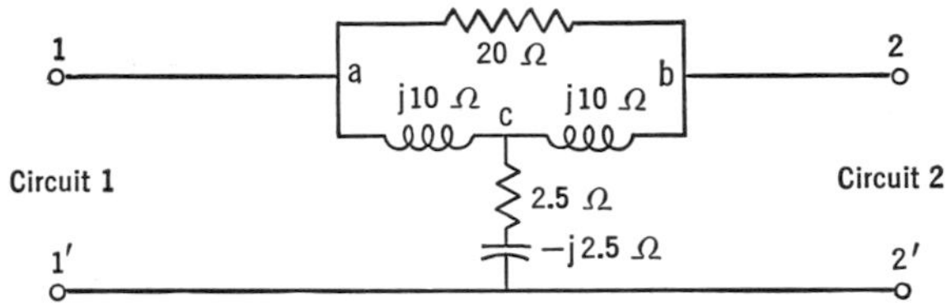

FIG. 29. See Problem 20.

20. Find the coefficient of coupling between circuits 1 and 2 in Fig. 29. *Hint:* Transform the *abc* delta to an equivalent wye, and then determine $\mathbf{Z}_{12}$ or $\mathbf{Z}_{21}$ of the equivalent circuit.

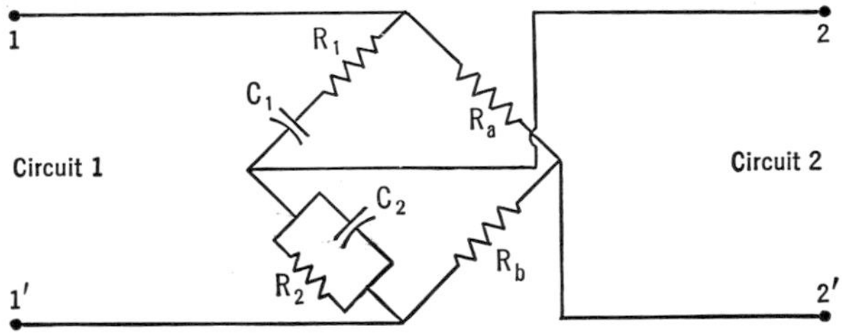

FIG. 30. See Problem 21.

21. Show that the coupling coefficient between circuits 1 and 2 in Fig. 30 is equal to zero if $\omega = 1/\sqrt{R_1R_2C_1C_2}$, $R_a = R_b$, $R_2 = 2R_1$, and $C_1 = 2C_2$.

22. Figures 31*a*, 31*b*, and 31*c* are the approximate equivalent circuits that are sometimes used in making voltage amplification calculations in resistance-coupled audio amplifiers. Show that the expressions given for E_2 in terms of μE_g are correct for each of the three configurations.

23. Two air-core inductance coils possess, individually, 60 and 30 millihenrys self-inductance, respectively. Measurements show that, if the two coils are connected in additive series as shown in Fig. 12, page 287, the equivalent self-inductance of the combination is 120 millihenrys.

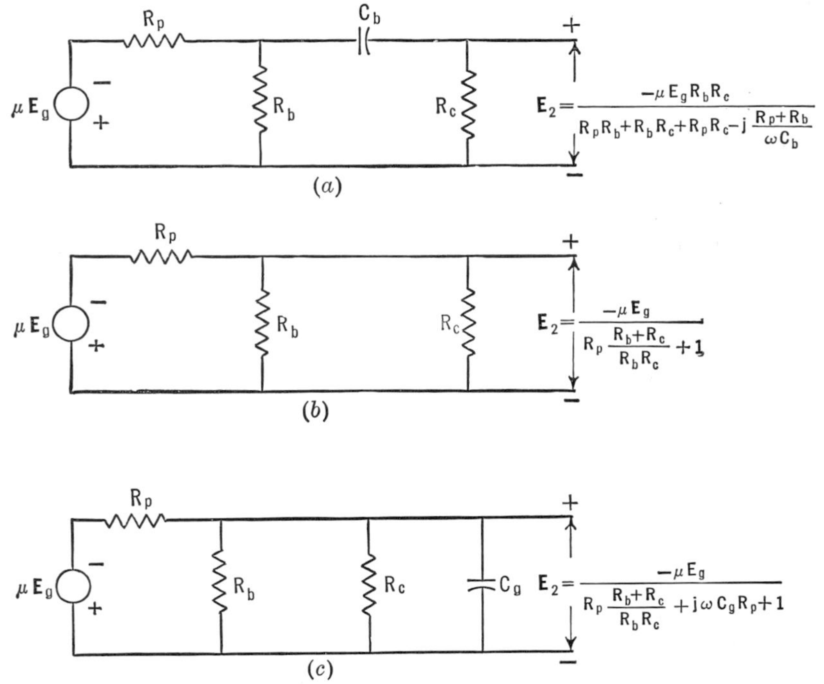

FIG. 31. Approximate equivalent circuits of resistance-capacitance coupled amplifiers. See Problem 22. (*a*) is for low-frequency range, (*b*) is for intermediate-frequency range, and (*c*) is for high-frequency range where the impedance of the blocking condenser C_b may be neglected.

(*a*) If the coils are connected in subtractive series, find the equivalent self-inductance of the combination.

(*b*) Find the coefficient of coupling between the coils.

24. Two inductance coils are connected in additive series. For 100 volts impressed on the combination, the current is 5 amperes and the power consumed is 200 watts. When the coils are reconnected in subtractive series and 100 volts are impressed, 8 amperes flow. Calculate the mutual inductance if the frequency for the above measurements is 69.5 cycles.

25. If the two coils in Problem 24 have equal resistances and the voltage drop across coil 1 is 36.05 volts for the additive series connection in Problem 24, (*a*) calculate L_1 and L_2 and the drop across coil 2 for this condition; (*b*) also calculate the coefficient of coupling.

26. The individual self-inductances of the two windings shown in Fig. 6, page 216, are 0.100 and 0.050 henry, respectively. The coefficient of coupling between the windings is 0.56. If the current in the 0.100-henry winding is a 60-cycle sinusoidal variation, the maximum magnitude of which is 10 amperes, find the effective value of voltage induced in the 0.050-henry winding as a result of the current variation in the 0.100-henry winding. Also find the magnitude of the rms induced voltage in the 0.1-henry winding.

27. In Fig. 32, $e_{ba} = 141.4 \sin 1131t$ volts and $e_{cd} = 70.7 \sin (1131t - 90°)$ volts.

(*a*) Find I_{ba} and I_{cd}, assuming that Fig. 32 correctly represents the modes of winding as well as the physical placement of the two inductance coils. The internal impedances of the generators may be assumed to be negligibly small.

(*b*) Find the power generated by each generator.

(*c*) Draw a vector diagram of $\mathbf{E}_{ba}$, $\mathbf{I}_{ba}$, $\mathbf{I}_{ba}\mathbf{R}_1$, $\mathbf{I}_{ba}\mathbf{X}_{L1}$, $\mathbf{E}_{cd}$, $\mathbf{I}_{cd}$, $\mathbf{I}_{cd}\mathbf{R}_2$, $\mathbf{I}_{cd}\mathbf{X}_{L2}$, $\mathbf{I}_{cd}\mathbf{X}_M$, and $\mathbf{I}_{ba}\mathbf{X}_M$.

28. Branch 1 of two parallel branches consists of a resistance of 2 ohms in series with an inductive reactance of 3 ohms. Branch 2 consists of a resistance of 5 ohms in series with an inductive reactance of 12 ohms. The coefficient of coupling between the two inductances is 0.8, and the inductances are wound so that the mmf's

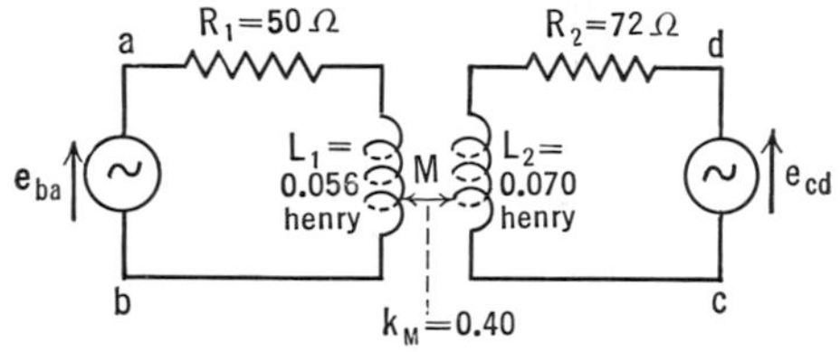

FIG. 32. See Problem 27.

due to I_1 and I_2 taken in the same direction from the junction are additive. If 100 volts are impressed on the two parallel branches, find I_1, I_2, the power supplied conductively to branch 2, the power supplied branch 2 electromagnetically, and the voltage drop across only the inductance of branch 2. What is the phase angle between the latter drop and the current in branch 2?

29. The coefficient of coupling for the coils in Fig. 33 is 0.5. Find the current in the resistance.

30. Calculate the phase and magnitude of the voltage drop V_{be} with respect to the total drop from *a* to *c* in Fig. 34. $X_{L1} = 5\,\Omega$; $X_{L2} = 5\,\Omega$; $X_M = 4\,\Omega$.

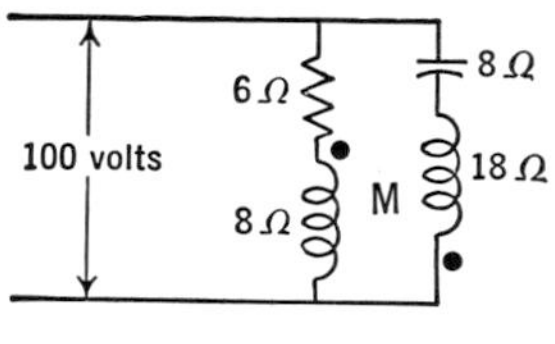

FIG. 33. See Problem 29.

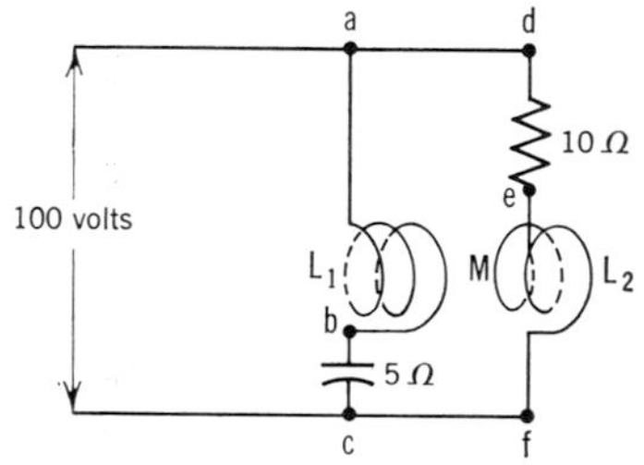

FIG. 34. See Problem 30.

31. In the coupled circuits shown in Fig. 18, page 304,

$$R_1 = 4.0 \text{ ohms} \qquad R_2 = 10 \text{ ohms}$$

$$X_{L1} = 40 \text{ ohms} \qquad X_{L2} = 100 \text{ ohms}$$

$$X_{C1} = 40 \text{ ohms} \qquad X_{C2} = 120 \text{ ohms}$$

$$X_M = 50 \text{ ohms} \qquad V_1 = 100 \text{ volts}$$

Find I_2 and V_{C2}.

32. In the coupled circuits shown in Fig. 18, page 304,

$$R_1 = 4 \text{ ohms} \qquad R_2 = 10 \text{ ohms}$$

$$X_{L1} = 40 \text{ ohms} \qquad X_{L2} = 100 \text{ ohms}$$

$$X_{C1} = 40 \text{ ohms} \qquad X_{C2} = 120 \text{ ohms}$$

$$X_M = 50 \text{ ohms} \qquad V_1 = 100 \text{ volts}$$

Find the equivalent primary impedance, Z_{e1}, of the coupled circuits and the ohmic value of the secondary-circuit impedance referred to the primary terminals. How many ohms reactance does the secondary reflect into the primary, and is it inductive or capacitive?

33. Assume that an 83-μf capacitance is placed in series with the primary of Fig. 17*a*. Except for the insertion of the 83-μf capacitance into the primary circuit, the parameters are as given on page 295. Find the value of M which will produce unity-power-factor resonance.

34. Show that the partial resonance which can be obtained by adjustment of the secondary reactance, X_2 (in coupled circuits of the kind shown in Fig. 18, page 304), occurs when $X_2 = X_1 X_M^2 / Z_1^2$. (See equation 79, page 306.)

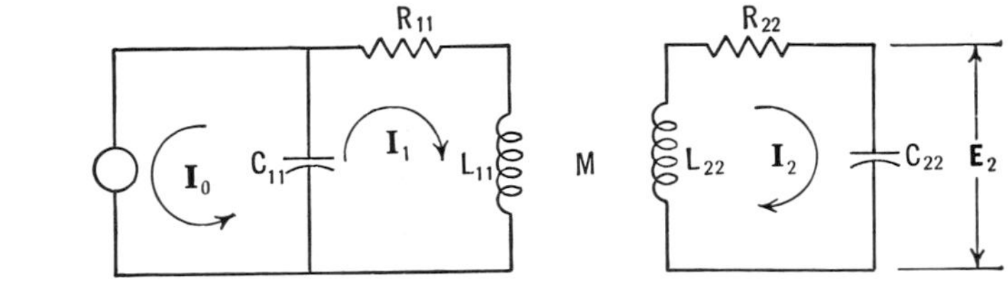

FIG. 35. See Problems 35, 41, 42, 43, 44, and 45.

35. In Fig. 35 $R_{11} = 10$, $L_{11} = 0.01$ henry, $L_{22} = 0.05$ henry, $M = 0.02$ henry, $R_{22} = 40\,\Omega$, $C_{22} = 20.0\ \mu$f, and $\omega = 1000$ radians per second. (*a*) Find the value of C_{11} that will make the whole circuit, looking into the lines connecting to the source, a pure resistance. (*b*) Find the value of the pure resistance.

36. Circuits 1 and 2 are inductively coupled. Circuit 1 consists of 2 ohms resistance in series with a coil of 16 ohms reactance and negligible resistance. Circuit 2 consists of 10 ohms resistance in series with an inductance coil of 100 ohms reactance and a capacitor of 100 ohms.

(*a*) If the coefficient of coupling is 0.05, what is the drop across the capacitor when 10 volts are applied to circuit 1?

(*b*) If a capacitor is placed in series with circuit 1 so as to tune circuit 1 to resonance ($\omega L_1 = 1/\omega C_1$), what will be the drop across the capacitor in circuit 2 for the same coefficient of coupling as before?

(*c*) If the coupling can be adjusted in part (*b*), what will be the greatest voltage drop across the secondary capacitor?

37. Write the general differential equations for voltage equilibrium in the two circuits shown in Fig. 27, page 317, in terms of R_{ab}, L_{ab}, R_{bc}, L_{bc}, M, R, and L, and the branch currents i_1 and i_2. Note that this is essentially two parallel branches which are coupled.

38. Assuming that v_1 varies sinusoidally, write the general voltage equations for Fig. 27, page 317, in terms of the effective values of the branch currents, I_1 and I_2. Solve the equations thus found for $\mathbf{I}_1$ and $\mathbf{I}_2$. What circuit considered earlier in this chapter has similar equations for $\mathbf{I}_1$ and $\mathbf{I}_2$?

39. Assume that, in Fig. 27, page 317,

$$R_{ab} = 4.0 \text{ ohms} \qquad M = 0.02 \text{ henry}$$

$$L_{ab} = 0.07 \text{ henry} \qquad R = 10 \text{ ohms}$$

$$R_{bc} = 0.5 \text{ ohm} \qquad L = 0.00 \text{ henry}$$

$$L_{bc} = 0.01 \text{ henry} \qquad \omega = 377 \text{ radians per second}$$

If $\mathbf{V}_1 = 100\underline{/0°}$ volts, find $\mathbf{I}_1$, $\mathbf{I}_2$, and $\mathbf{I}_1 + \mathbf{I}_2$. Also calculate the total power supplied and that dissipated in each of circuits 1 and 2. Draw the complete vector diagram of the voltages and currents.

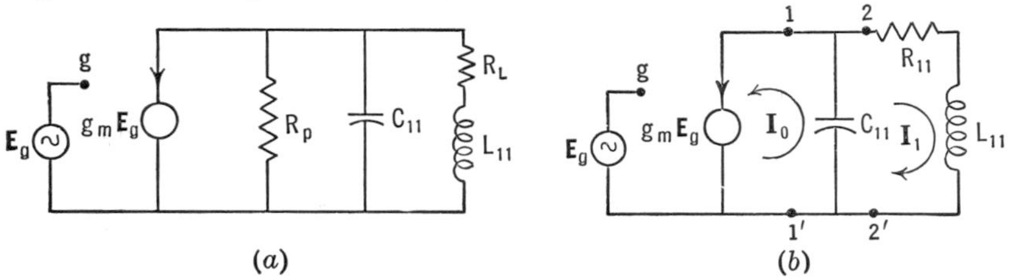

FIG. 36. See Problem 40.

40. Given the circuit arrangement shown in Fig. 36*a*, where the g_mE_g current generator in parallel with R_p is the equivalent a-c circuit of a pentode which has a voltage of E_g volts applied to its control grid.

(*a*) If $R_p = 750{,}000$ ohms, $R_L = 12$ ohms, $L_{11} = 382$ microhenrys, and C_{11} is adjusted to resonate the $L_{11}C_{11}$ parallel branches at 500 kc, find R_{11} of the equivalent circuit shown in Fig. 36*b*.

(*b*) What is the Q of the coil itself, namely, $\omega_m L_{11}/R_L$, at 500 kc?

(*c*) What is the Q of the $C_{11} - R_{11}L_{11}$ parallel combination of Fig. 36*b* at 500 kc?

(*d*) Can I_1 in Fig. 36*b* be evaluated from the relation $\mathbf{Z}_{11}\mathbf{I}_1 = -(\mathbf{I}_0)\left(-j\dfrac{1}{\omega C_{11}}\right)$, where $\mathbf{Z}_{11} = R_{11} + j\left(\omega L_{11} - \dfrac{1}{\omega C_{11}}\right)$?

41. In Problem 40, it has been shown that the current generators of Fig. 36*b* and Fig. 35 can be replaced by equivalent voltage generators which have voltages of $-(\mathbf{I}_0)\left(-j\dfrac{1}{\omega C_{11}}\right)$.

Show that the equivalent primary impedance (including the reflected impedance from the secondary) which the equivalent voltage generator in Fig. 35 sees is:

$$\mathbf{Z}_{11\text{eq}} = \frac{j\dfrac{\mathbf{I}_0}{\omega C_{11}}}{\mathbf{I}_1} = \mathbf{Z}_{11} + \frac{\omega^2 M^2}{\mathbf{Z}_{22}} = \omega_{m1}L_{11}\left[(a + jF_{11}) + \frac{\omega^2 k^2}{\omega_{m1}\omega_{m2}(b + jF_{22})}\right]$$

where

$$\omega_{m1} = \frac{1}{\sqrt{L_{11}C_{11}}} \qquad \omega_{m2} = \frac{1}{\sqrt{L_{22}C_{22}}}$$

$$\mathbf{Z}_{11} = R_{11} + j\left(\omega L_{11} - \frac{1}{\omega C_{11}}\right) \qquad \mathbf{Z}_{22} = R_{22} + j\left(\omega L_{22} - \frac{1}{\omega C_{22}}\right)$$

$$a = \frac{1}{Q_1} = \frac{R_{11}}{\omega_{m1} L_{11}} \qquad b = \frac{1}{Q_2} = \frac{R_{22}}{\omega_{m2} L_{22}}$$

$$F_{11} = \left(\frac{\omega}{\omega_{m1}} - \frac{\omega_{m1}}{\omega}\right) \qquad F_{22} = \left(\frac{\omega}{\omega_{m2}} - \frac{\omega_{m2}}{\omega}\right)$$

$$k = \frac{M}{\sqrt{L_{11} L_{22}}}$$

42. The results of Problem 41 are to be employed in the following exercises.

(*a*) Show that a voltmeter across L_{11} of Fig. 35 will read a maximum value when C_{11} is adjusted to $1/L_{11}\omega^2$ if loop 2 is open-circuited and that this voltage will be

$$\mathbf{V}_{L_{11}\max} = \frac{\mathbf{K}}{\omega_{m1} L_{11} a}$$

where $\mathbf{K} = [-(\mathbf{I}_0/\omega C_{11})](\omega L_{11})$.

(*b*) With C_{11} left at the value found above $(1/L_{11}\omega_{m1}^2)$, show that the voltmeter (which is across the L_{11} coil) will read a minimum value of

$$\mathbf{V}_{L_{11}\min} = \frac{\mathbf{K}}{\omega_{m1} L_{11}\left(a + \frac{k^2}{b}\right)}$$

when C_{22} is adjusted to $1/L_{22}\omega_{m1}^2$.

(*c*) Show that, if the experimental procedure outlined in (*a*) and (*b*) is followed, the coupling coefficient between the two coils is

$$k = \sqrt{ab\left(\frac{V_{L_{11}\max}}{V_{L_{11}\min}} - 1\right)}$$

43. In Fig. 35: $L_{11} = L_{22} = 500$ microhenrys; $C_{11} = C_{22} = 2000\ \mu\mu f$; $M = 8.66$ microhenrys; $a = R_{11}/\omega_{m1}L_{11} = b = R_{22}/\omega_{m2}L_{22} = 0.01$.

(*a*) Find the magnitude of the voltage across the C_{22} capacitor per milliampere of I_0 at $\omega = \omega_m = 1/\sqrt{L_{11}C_{11}}$ radians per second.

(*b*) Will the voltage found in part (*a*) be the maximum value of E_2 if the frequency is varied slightly about the value ω_m specified above?

44. (*a*) Make a sketch of $\dfrac{E_{C22}}{E_{C22(\omega=\omega_m)}}$ versus F for the circuit shown in Fig. 35 employing the circuit parameters specified in Problem 43. Calculate points for this sketch at

$$\omega = 1.010\omega_m \quad \text{or} \quad F = 2 \times 10^{-2}$$
$$\omega = 1.00707\omega_m \quad \text{or} \quad F = \sqrt{2} \times 10^{-2}$$
$$\omega = 1.005\omega_m \quad \text{or} \quad F = 10^{-2}$$
$$\omega = \omega_m \quad \text{or} \quad F = 0$$

using equation (95), namely:

$$\frac{E_{C22}}{E_{C22(\omega=\omega_m)}} = \frac{1}{\sqrt{1 + \dfrac{F^4 + (a^2 + b^2 - 2k^2)F^2}{(k^2 + ab)^2}}}$$

(*b*) Make a sketch of E_{C22} per milliampere of I_0 versus ω/ω_m employing the results of part (*a*). It may be assumed that the response curve is symmetrical about the center frequency ω_m.

45. Design a current-fed double-tuned circuit like that shown in Fig. 35 which has a per unit band width of 0.02 centered at $\omega_m = 10^6$ radians per second. Use $L_{11} = L_{22} = 500$ microhenrys. The permissible variation in the response curve over the pass band is 1.2516 decibels reckoned from E_{min} as reference. ($\alpha = 0.5$)

Note: Where $Q_1 = Q_2$, a design of this kind amounts simply to specifying some appropriate value for the Q's of the coils and then calculating the coefficient of coupling to employ between these coils to meet the conditions imposed. In this case, ${F_{min}}^2/\alpha = 0.0004/0.5 = 2(k^2 + ab) = 2(k^2 + a^2)$. In a more general case, one of the Q's may be chosen almost arbitrarily. Then ${F_{min}}^2/\alpha = 2(k^2 + ab)$ and ${F_{min}}^2 = (2k^2 - a^2 - b^2)$ may be solved simultaneously for k and the other Q to meet the specified values of F_{min} and α.

chapter VIII Balanced Polyphase Circuits

Generation of Polyphase Voltages. Polyphase voltages are generated in the same way as single-phase voltages. A polyphase system is simply several single-phase systems which are displaced in time phase from one another. The single-phase systems which form the polyphase systems are generally interconnected in some way.

In Fig. 1 is shown a single coil aa' on the armature of a two-pole machine. When the poles are in the position shown, the emf of conductor a of coil aa' is a maximum, and its direction is away from the reader. If a conductor is placed 120° from a at position b, it would

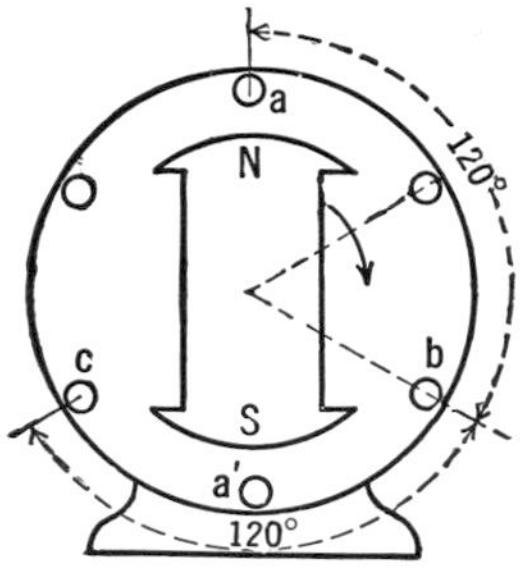

FIG. 1. Elementary three-phase generator.

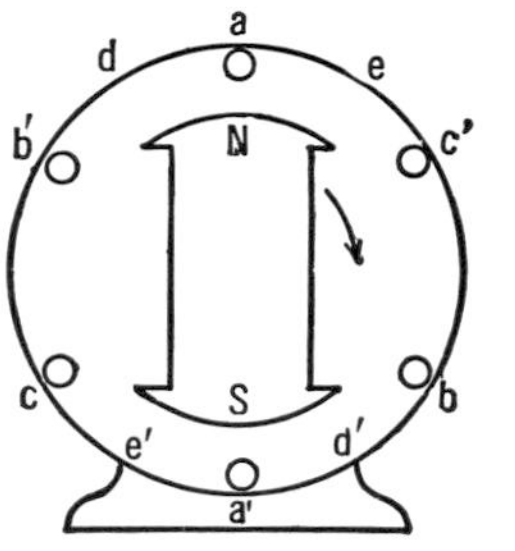

FIG. 2.

experience maximum emf in a direction away from the reader when the north pole axis was at b, or 120° later than when the pole axis was at a. In like manner, the maximum emf in the direction away from the reader for a conductor at c would occur 120° later than that at b, and 240° later than that at a. The placement of such conductors and the coils of which they are a part are shown in Fig. 2. Thus the coils aa', bb', and cc' would have emf's that are 120° out of time phase, as pictured in Fig. 3. This system is called three-phase because there are three waves of different time phase. In practice the space on the armature is completely covered with coils (except in single phase). For instance, the conductor of another coil could be placed in the slot to the right of conductor a in Fig. 2, and another to the left. The one to the right would have an emf which would lag that in a by the same angle that the one to the left would lead. The sum of the three emf's would give a resultant emf of the same phase as that in a. Conductors for phase a

would cover the periphery from d to e and from d' to e'. The distance from d to e is called a phase belt. The emf of all the coils in series for the whole phase would have the same phase relation as the emf of the center conductor of the phase belt. For this reason only the center conductors of the phase belts will be considered. It is apparent that any number of phases could be developed through properly spacing the coils on the stator.

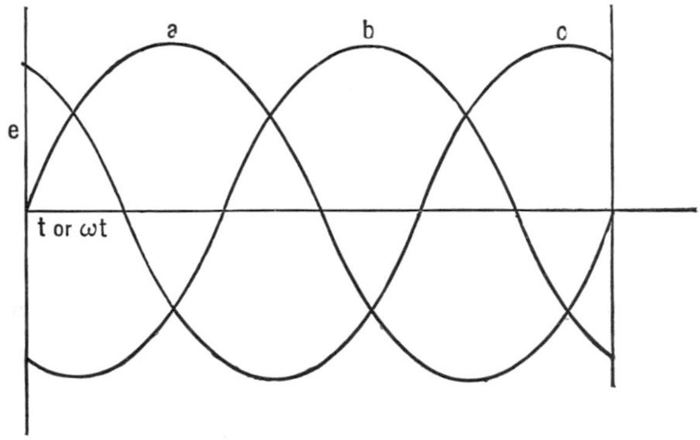

FIG. 3. Waves of emf generated by a three-phase generator.

In general, the electrical displacement between phases for a balanced n-phase system is $360/n$ electrical degrees. Three-phase systems are the most common, although for certain special applications a greater number of phases is used. For instance, practically all mercury-arc rectifiers for power purposes are either six- or twelve-phase. Most rotary converters are six-phase. Practically all modern generators are three-phase. Three-phase is also invariably used for transmitting large amounts of power. In general, three-phase apparatus is more efficient, uses less material for a given capacity, and costs less than single-phase apparatus. It will be shown later that, for a fixed amount of power to be transmitted a fixed distance at a fixed line loss with a fixed voltage between conductors, three-phase is more economical in the use of copper than any other number of phases.

In the development of the three-phase voltages in Fig. 3, clockwise rotation of the field structure of the alternator in Fig. 2 was assumed. This assumption made the emf of phase b lag that of a by 120°. Also, the emf of phase c lagged that of phase b by 120°. In other words, the order in which the emf's of phases a, b, and c came to their corresponding maximum values was *abc*. This is called the phase order or sequence *abc*. If the rotation of the field structure in Fig. 2 is reversed, the order in which the phases would attain their corresponding maximum voltages would be reversed. The phase sequence would be *acb*. This means that the emf of phase *c* would then lag that of phase *a* by 120° instead of by 240° as in the first case. In general, the phase sequence of the voltages applied to a load is fixed by the order in which the three-phase lines are connected. Interchanging any pair of lines reverses the phase sequence. For three-phase induction motors the effect of reversing the sequence is to reverse the direction of rotation. For three-phase unbalanced loads the effect is, in general, to cause a completely different set of values for line currents; hence when calculating such systems it is essential that phase sequence be specified or confusion may arise.

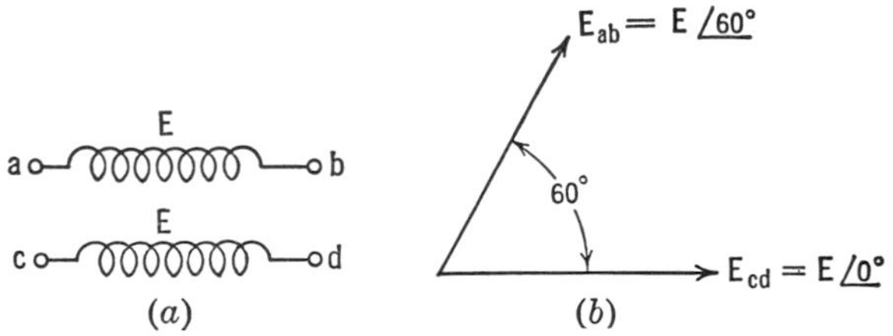

FIG. 4. Coils having induced emf's shown in part (*b*).

Vector Diagrams and Double-Subscript Notation. When drawing vector diagrams of polyphase circuits it is imperative that directions in which the circuit is being traced be noted and recorded. For example, let us assume that the two coils shown in Fig. 4*a* possess induced voltages or emf's that are 60° out of phase and that the coils are to be connected in additive series, that is, in such a manner that the emf's add at a 60°

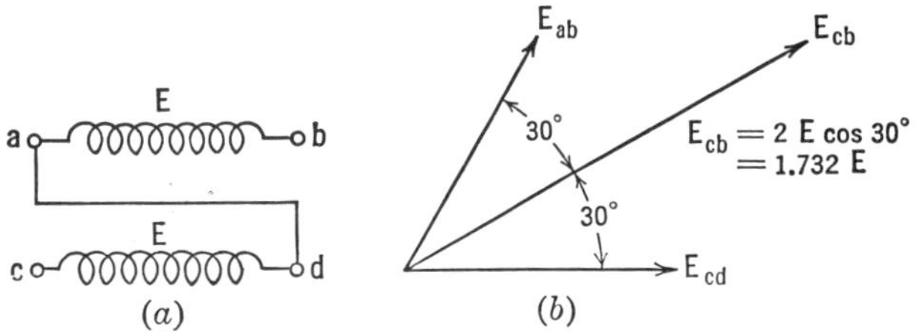

FIG. 5. Resultant emf shown in (*b*) for connection of coils shown in (*a*).

angle. From the information given it would be impossible to know whether terminal *a* should be connected to terminal *c* or terminal *d*. But if it were stated that the emf from *a* to *b* is 60° out of phase with that from *c* to *d* as shown in Fig. 4*b*, the way to connect the coils would be definitely fixed. Under such conditions, double-subscript notation is very convenient.

The order in which the subscripts are written denotes the direction in which the circuit is being traced. Thus the emf from *a* to *b* in Fig. 4*a* may be designated as $\mathbf{E}_{ab}$ and that from c to d as $\mathbf{E}_{cd}$. (See Fig. 4*b*.) If d is connected to a as shown in Fig. 5*a*, the emf from c to b is determined by adding all the emf's *in the directions encountered* as the circuit is traced from c to b. Hence $\mathbf{E}_{cb} = \mathbf{E}_{cd} + \mathbf{E}_{ab}$ as shown in Fig. 5*b*. This procedure will be further illustrated in succeeding articles.

Problem 1. In Fig. 4*a*, connect terminal b to terminal c and compare the resultant voltage $\mathbf{E}_{ad}$ with voltage $\mathbf{E}_{cb}$ of Fig. 5*b*.

Ans.: $\mathbf{E}_{ad} = \mathbf{E}_{cb}$.

Problem 2. (*a*) Connect terminal d to terminal b in Fig. 4*a* and find the voltage $\mathbf{E}_{ca}$ if $E = 120$ volts. $\mathbf{E}_{ab}$ and $\mathbf{E}_{cd}$ have the same vector relation as shown in Fig. 4*b*.

Ans.: $\mathbf{E}_{ca} = 120 \underline{/-60°}$ volts.

(*b*) With terminal d connected to terminal b as above, find $\mathbf{E}_{ac}$.

Ans.: $\mathbf{E}_{ac} = 120 \underline{/120°}$ volts.

A vector diagram is simply a means of representing certain electrical quantities that are related by a circuit. A vector diagram therefore must always be drawn in conjunction with a circuit. Sometimes circuits may be visualized instead of actually drawn, but without a definite picture of the circuit represented a vector diagram means nothing and cannot be intelligently drawn. It should be clearly recognized, however, that a circuit vector diagram of voltages and currents represents time-phase relations and not space relations of the circuit. This means that the space configuration of a circuit diagram is in no way indicative of the time-phase relations of the voltages or currents.

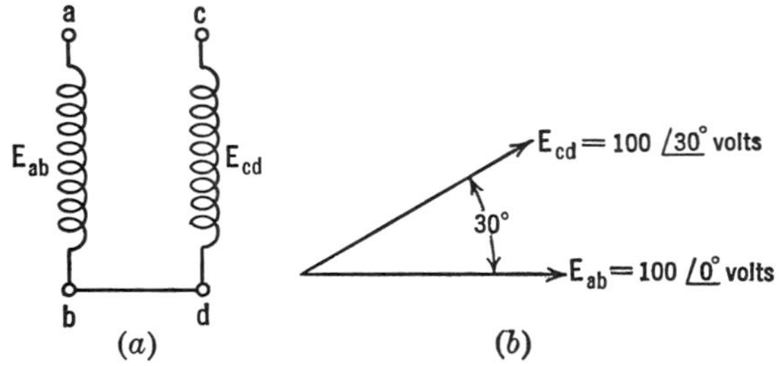

FIG. 6. See Problem 3.

Problem 3. Find the magnitude and vector position of voltage $\mathbf{E}_{ca}$ in Fig. 6*a* if $\mathbf{E}_{ab}$ and $\mathbf{E}_{cd}$ are displaced from each other by 30° in time phase as shown in Fig. 6*b*.

Ans.: $\mathbf{E}_{ca} = 51.76 \underline{/105°}$ volts.

Two- and Four-Phase Systems. A two-phase system is an electrical system in which the voltages of the phases are 90° out of time phase. A two-phase system is pictured by the drum and Gramme ring windings in Figs. 7 and 8. From the position of the coils on the armature in Fig. 8 it can be seen that the emf's of the four coils are related in time phase as shown in Fig. 9. If the zero terminals of coils $a0$ and $c0$ are connected, the emf from a to c is $\mathbf{E}_{a0} + \mathbf{E}_{0c}$. This operation is shown in Fig. 10. Likewise, when the zeros of coils $b0$ and $d0$ are connected

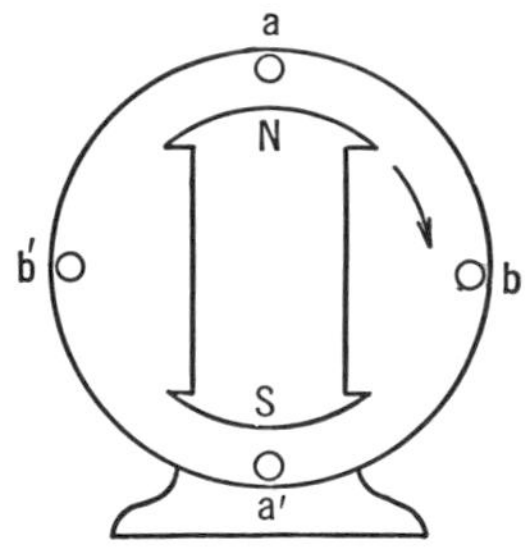

FIG. 7. Elementary drum-type two-phase generator.

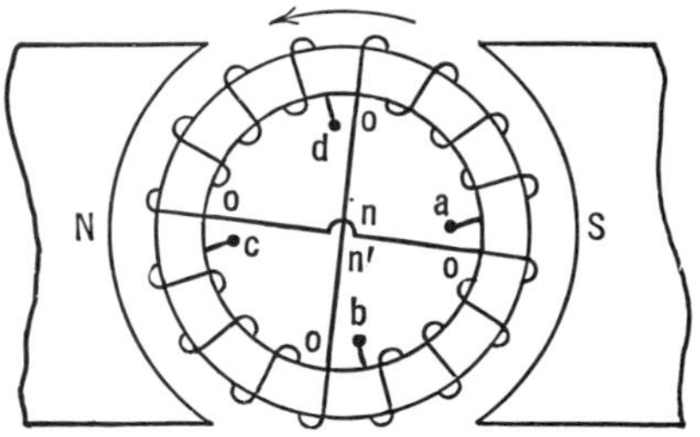

FIG. 8. Elementary Gramme ring-type two-phase generator.

$\mathbf{E}_{bd} = \mathbf{E}_{b0} + \mathbf{E}_{0d}$. This is also shown in Fig. 10. The emf's $\mathbf{E}_{ac}$ and $\mathbf{E}_{bd}$ are 90° apart in time phase, and the system shown in Fig. 8 constitutes a two-phase system. A two-phase system is the equivalent of two separate single-phase systems that are separated 90° in time phase.

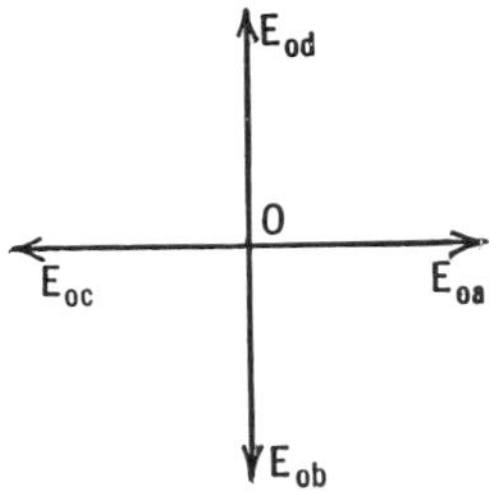

FIG. 9. Emf's of coils on generator in Fig. 8.

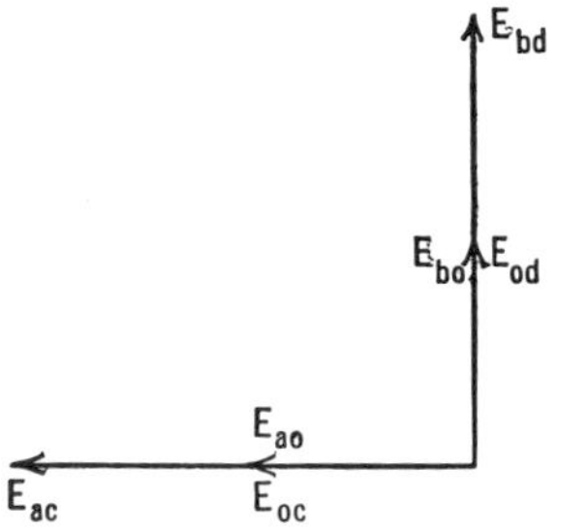

FIG. 10. Resultant emf's of two coils in series connected as shown in Fig. 8.

A four-phase and a two-phase system differ only in internal connections. Thus if connection is made between the two windings at n and n', the system would be called a four-phase system. The vector diagram of phase or coil voltages is shown in Fig. 9. Since there now is an electrical connection between the two groups of coils that constituted the two-phase system, there will be emf's between terminals d and a and also between b and c, as may be seen by studying the diagrammatic representation of the coils shown in Fig. 11. This connection is called a four-phase star. The voltages E_{da}, E_{ab}, E_{bc}, and E_{cd} are called the line voltages, while voltages E_{0a}, E_{0b}, E_{0c}, and E_{0d} are called the phase voltages, or voltages to neutral. From the circuit it is evident that

$\mathbf{E}_{da} = \mathbf{E}_{d0} + \mathbf{E}_{0a}$. This combination and similar ones for all the line voltages are shown in Fig. 12. Another method of showing the same thing is illustrated in Fig. 13. Thus, in the four-phase star, line voltage is the $\sqrt{2}$ times phase voltage and it is either 45° or 135° out of phase with the phase voltage, depending upon which voltages are considered.

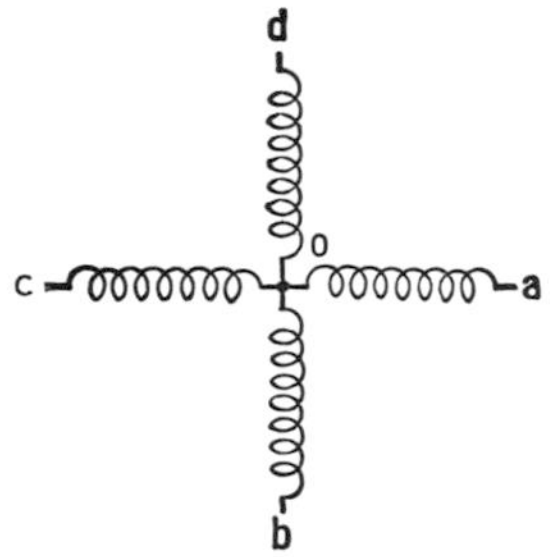

FIG. 11. Diagrammatic representation of Fig. 8 when n and n' are connected to form point o.

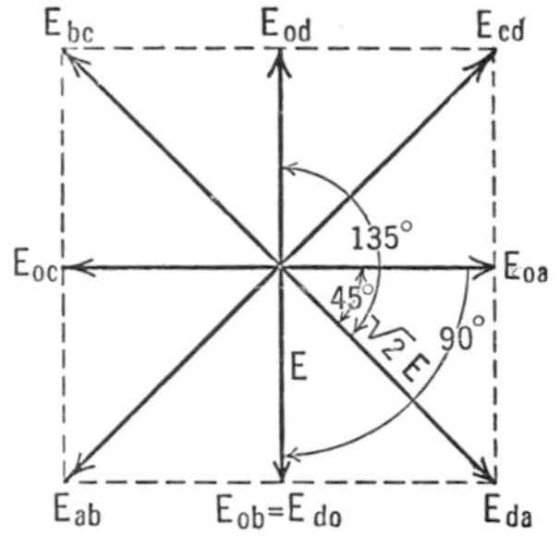

FIG. 12. Voltages of the four-phase star shown in Fig. 11.

Since $\mathbf{E}_{0a} + \mathbf{E}_{0b} + \mathbf{E}_{0c} + \mathbf{E}_{0d} = 0$, it would be possible to connect the four coils shown in Figs. 8 and 11 so that their voltages add in this way and no current would flow in the series circuit of the coils. This connection, shown in Fig. 14, is called a mesh connection, and in this case it would be known as a four-phase mesh. The line connections

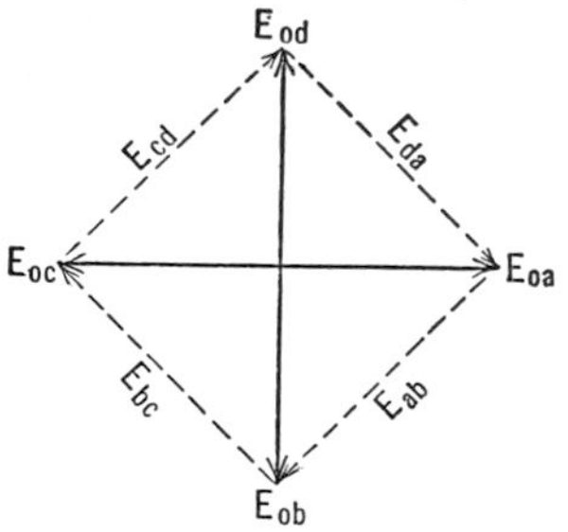

FIG. 13. Alternative representation of Fig. 12.

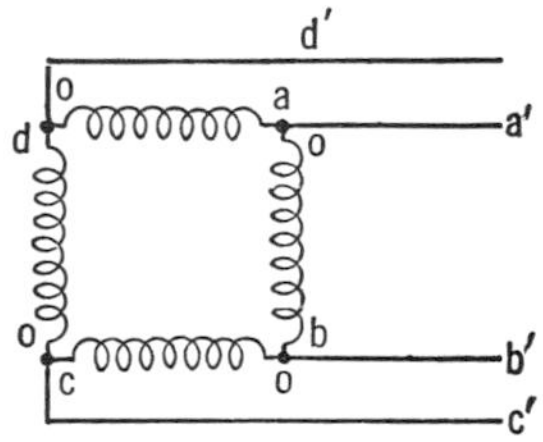

FIG. 14. Four-phase mesh.

are made at points a, b, c, and d. The vector diagram of the emf's for this system is shown in Fig. 15. For balanced loads the currents in adjacent phases are 90° out of phase as shown in Fig. 16. The aa' line current is $\mathbf{I}_{aa'} = \mathbf{I}_{da} + \mathbf{I}_{ba}$, as shown in Fig. 16. Thus line current of a balanced four-phase mesh is the $\sqrt{2}$ times phase current and is either 45° or 135° out of phase with the phase currents, according to which are being considered. Note that what was true about line and phase voltages in the star is true about line and phase currents in the mesh.

Inspection of the star system shows that line and phase currents must be identical, and the same thing is true regarding line and phase voltages in the mesh.

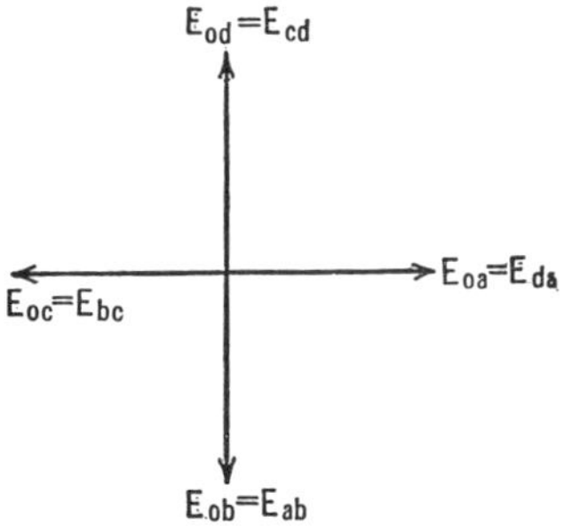

FIG. 15. Vector diagram of emf's of the four-phase mesh shown in Fig. 14.

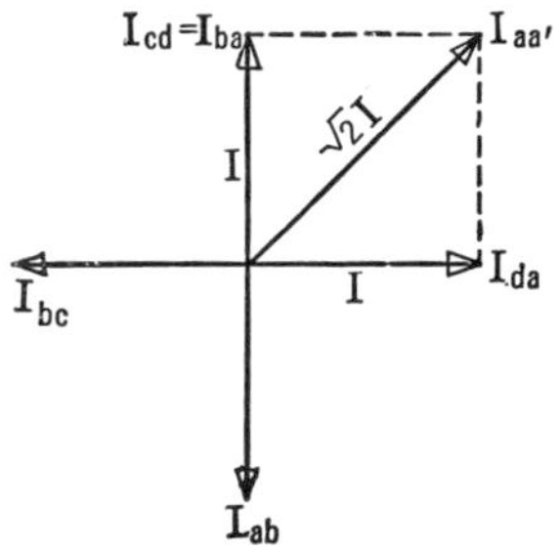

FIG. 16. Vector diagram of currents of the four-phase mesh shown in Fig. 14 under conditions of balanced load.

Sometimes a two-phase system is used with only three wires. When this is done, one wire is common to both phases. The circuit diagram of Fig. 8 when connected for such use is shown in Fig. 17, and the vector diagram is shown in Fig. 18. It will be noted that this is essentially half of the four-phase system shown in Fig. 11 when line wires are connected to points 0, *d*, and *c*.

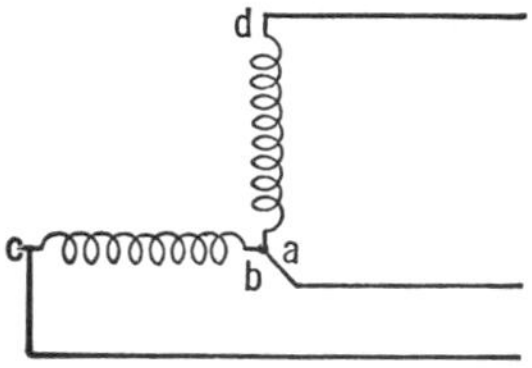

FIG. 17. Two-phase three-wire system.

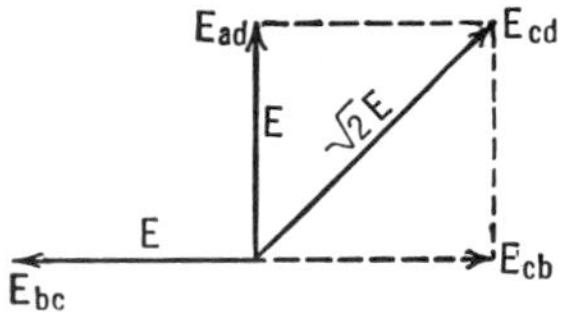

FIG. 18. Vector diagram of voltages for Fig. 17.

Three-Phase, Four-Wire Systems of Generated Emf's. The generation of three-phase was explained at the beginning of this chapter. If six wires were connected to terminals a, a', b, b', c, and c' of Fig. 2, the system might be called a six-wire, three-phase system. Such a generator could be loaded with three independent single-phase loads. Though such a system is not used, one that is widely used may be derived from it by making a common connection between terminals a', b', and c'. Four wires are all that would then be necessary, three for terminals a, b, and c, and one for the common connection $a'b'c'$. Such a system, called a four-wire, three-phase system, is shown diagrammatically in Fig. 19. This system is now extensively used for a-c networks and is rapidly displacing the formerly much used d-c networks in the downtown areas of large cities. The common wire connecting to n is called the neutral. Lighting loads are placed from line to neutral; motor and other three-phase power loads are connected between the three lines a, b, and c. The generated voltage waves of this system are shown in Fig. 3, and the vector diagram that portrays the same thing is shown in Fig. 20. The three voltages shown are called phase voltages or line-

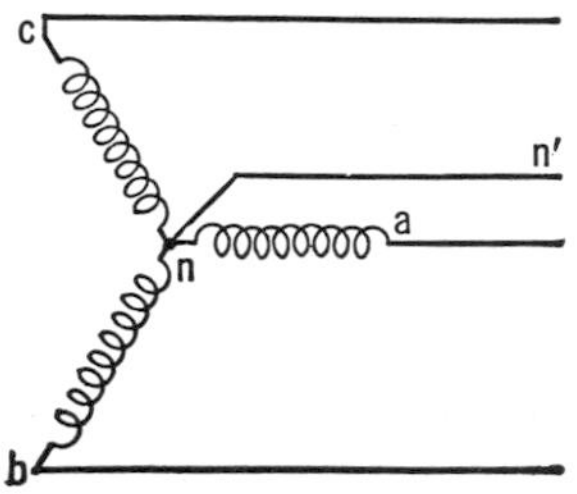

FIG. 19. Three-phase four-wire system.

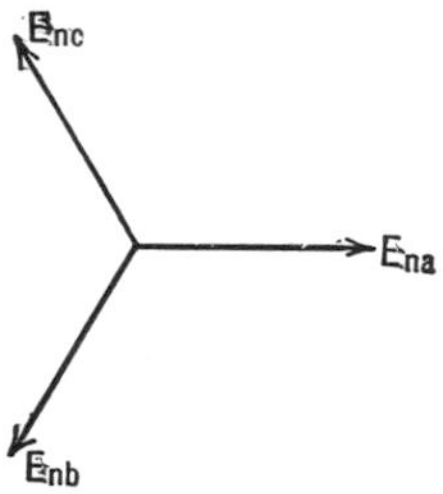

FIG. 20. Line-to-neutral voltages of Fig. 19.

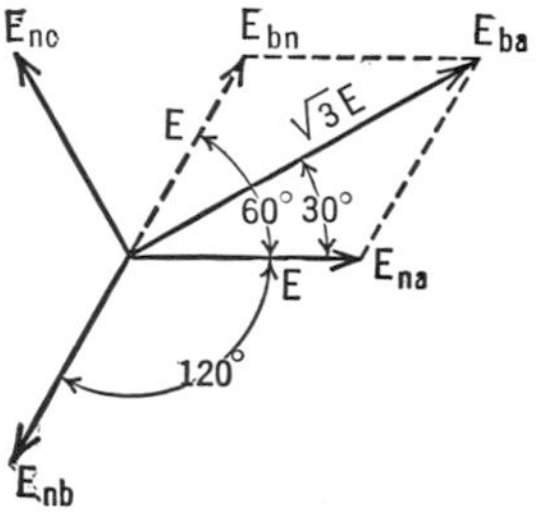

FIG. 21. Line voltage equals phase voltage times $\sqrt{3}$ in the wye connection.

to-neutral voltages. They are sometimes called the wye voltages of the system, and the connection of Fig. 19 is called a wye connection. The voltages between terminals a, b, and c are called the line or terminal voltages. Under balanced conditions they are definitely related to the phase voltages, as the following shows:

$$\mathbf{E}_{ba} = \mathbf{E}_{bn} + \mathbf{E}_{na}$$

This combination is shown in Fig. 21 where the magnitude of the phase

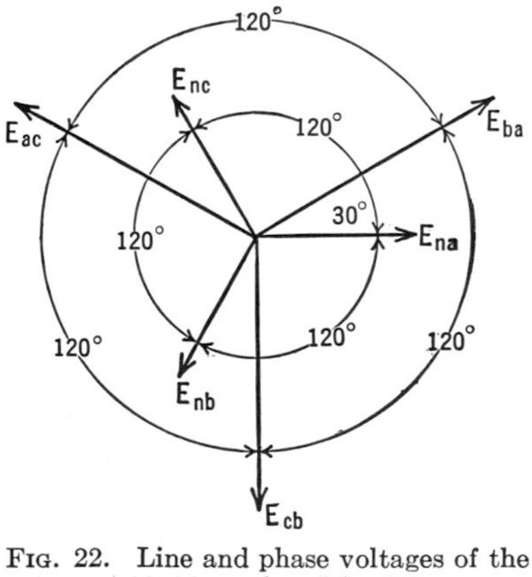

FIG. 22. Line and phase voltages of the wye connection (Fig. 19).

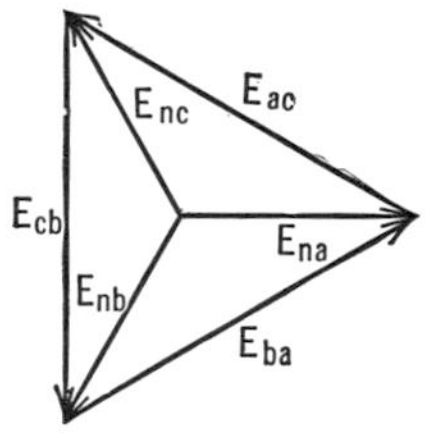

FIG. 23. Alternative representation of Fig. 22.

voltage is considered as E. Hence line voltage in the balanced three-phase star or wye connection is the $\sqrt{3}$ times the phase voltage and makes an angle with the component phase voltages of either 30° or 150°, depending upon which are considered. The complete vector diagram showing all line voltages is given in Fig. 22. Figure 23 shows the same system in terms of a polar vector diagram of phase voltages and a funicular diagram of line voltages. Oscillogram 1 shows these relationships as obtained from an actual load.

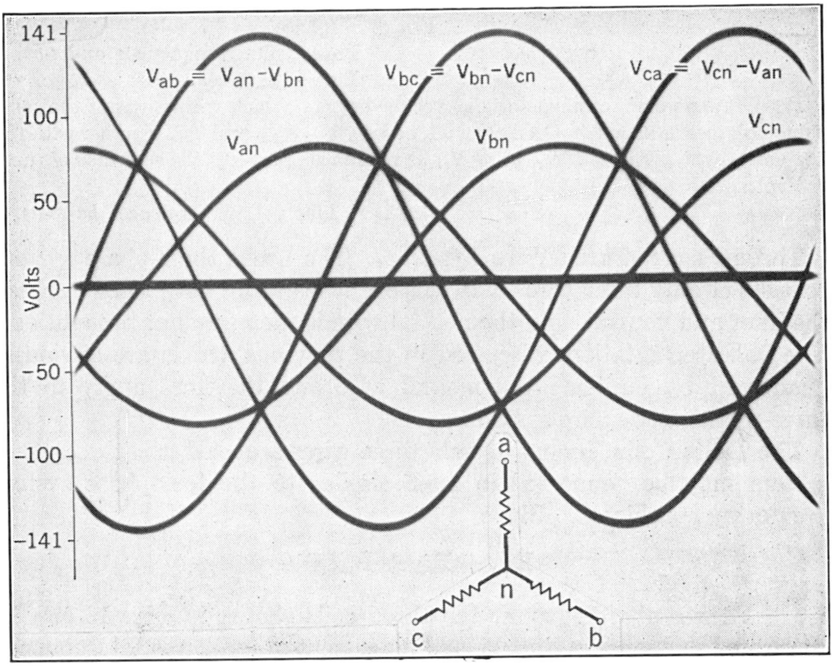

OSCILLOGRAM 1. Illustrating the 30° angular displacement between the phase voltages and the systematically labeled line-to-line voltages in a balanced, three-phase, wye-connected load. Effective value of each line-to-line voltage is 100 volts.

When the system is balanced, the currents in the three phases are all equal in magnitude and differ by 120° in time phase, as shown in Fig. 24. The phase of currents with respect to the wye voltages is defined by the circuit parameters in any particular case. An inspection of Fig. 19 shows that line and phase currents are identical. The current in the neutral wire is obtained through the application of Kirchhoff's current law. Thus

$$\mathbf{I}_{n'n} = \mathbf{I}_{na} + \mathbf{I}_{nb} + \mathbf{I}_{nc}$$

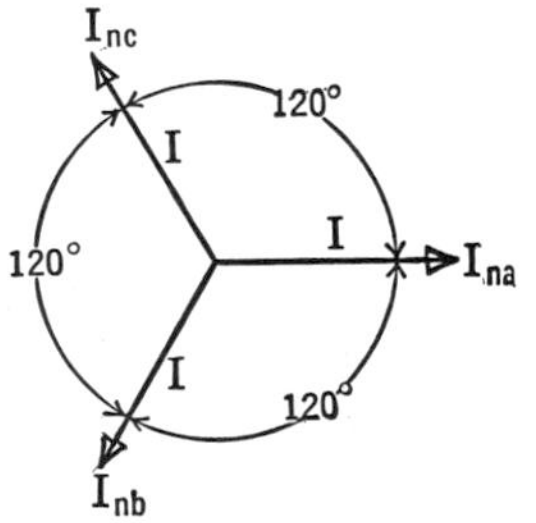

FIG. 24. Currents in a balanced-wye system.

If the system is balanced, $\mathbf{I}_{na}$, $\mathbf{I}_{nb}$, and $\mathbf{I}_{nc}$ are equal in magnitude and displaced from one another in time phase by 120° as shown in Fig. 24. Under these conditions it is apparent that the current in the neutral is zero since $\mathbf{I}_{na} + \mathbf{I}_{nb} + \mathbf{I}_{nc} = 0$.

Problem 4. (*a*) Draw a polar (or single-origin) vector diagram which will represent the same phase voltages and the same line voltages as shown in Oscillogram 1 using $\mathbf{V}_{bn}$ as reference. Specify the effective magnitude of the phase voltages, the sequence of the phase voltages, and the sequence of the line voltages.

Ans.: V/phase = 57.7 volts.
Phase voltage sequence: *an-bn-cn.*
Line voltage sequence: *ab-bc-ca.*

(*b*) Draw a polar (or single-origin) vector diagram which will represent the same phase voltages as shown in Oscillogram 1, namely $\mathbf{V}_{an}$, $\mathbf{V}_{bn}$, and $\mathbf{V}_{cn}$, together with the line voltages $\mathbf{V}_{ba}$, $\mathbf{V}_{cb}$, and $\mathbf{V}_{ac}$, using $\mathbf{V}_{cn}$ as reference. Specify the sequence of these line voltages.

Ans.: Line voltage sequence: *ba-cb-ac.*

Three-Phase, Three-Wire Systems. The usual three-phase system consists of only three wires. In this event loads are not placed between the lines and neutral, and the neutral wire is therefore not brought out. The balanced relations discussed in the previous article are obviously unaffected by omitting the neutral wire and therefore apply to the three-phase, three-wire system.

The Delta Connection. If only three wires are used, the three-phase system may be connected in mesh similar to the four-phase system previously considered. Since

$$\mathbf{E}_{na} + \mathbf{E}_{nb} + \mathbf{E}_{nc} = 0$$

for the three-phase system, the three coils shown in Fig. 19 can be connected as shown in Fig. 25, and no current of fundamental frequency

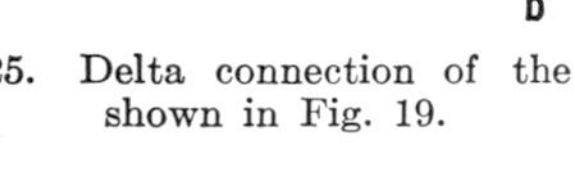

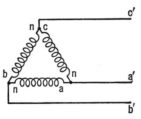

FIG. 25. Delta connection of the coils shown in Fig. 19.

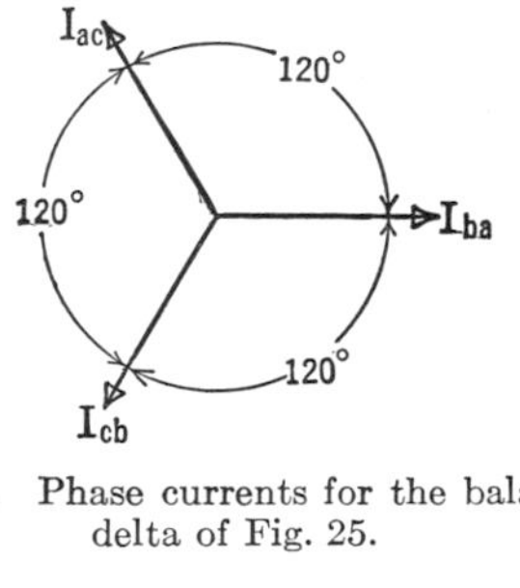

FIG. 26. Phase currents for the balanced delta of Fig. 25.

will flow around the series circuit of the three coils. This three-phase mesh connection is called a delta connection. It will be noted that star and mesh are general terms applicable to any number of phases, but wye and delta are special cases of the star and mesh when three-phase is considered. Inspection of Fig. 25 shows that phase voltages and line voltages are identical but that line and phase currents are different. The vector diagram of phase currents for a balanced load is shown in Fig. 26. Line currents are found through the application of Kirchhoff's current law. Thus

$$\mathbf{I}_{aa'} = \mathbf{I}_{ba} + \mathbf{I}_{ca}$$

This operation is carried out in Fig. 27. For a balanced system, line current is the $\sqrt{3}$ times phase current in magnitude and is out of phase with the component-phase currents by either 30° or 150°, depending

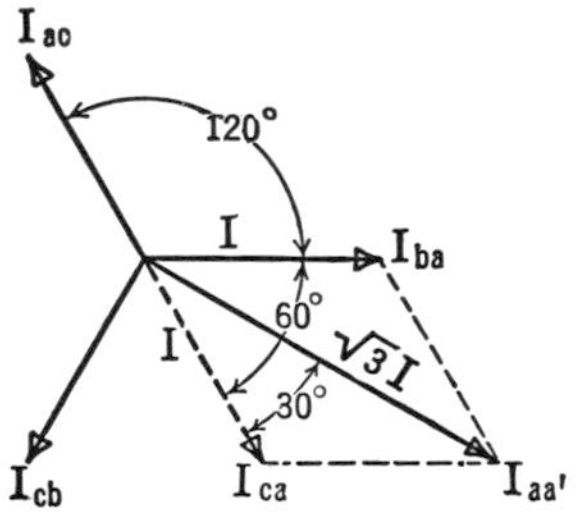

FIG. 27. Combination of phase currents gives line current for Fig. 25.

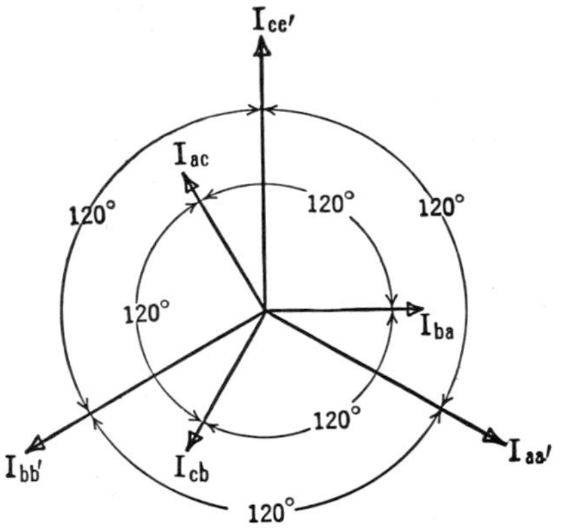

FIG. 28. Vector diagram of currents for a balanced delta is shown in Fig. 25.

upon which are considered. The complete vector diagram of currents for the three-phase balanced delta connection is shown in Fig. 28. Oscillogram 2 shows the relations discussed above as obtained from an actual load labeled as in the accompanying circuit diagram.

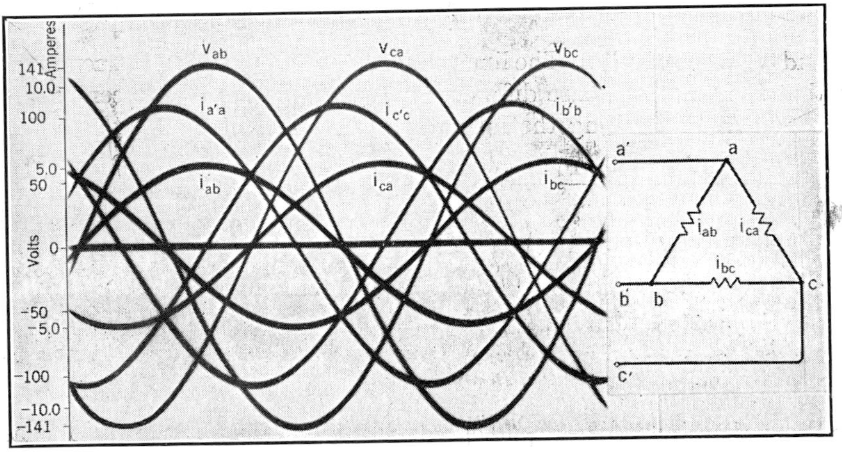

OSCILLOGRAM 2. Oscillographic study of a balanced, delta-connected, unity-power-factor load. The line-to-line voltages (or phase voltages) together with the phase currents and line currents are illustrated.

It should be understood that all the vectors on a vector diagram like that shown in Fig. 28 may be reversed, that is, changed individually through 180°, and, if a reversal in the order of subscripts accompanies this change, the resulting vector diagram will represent the same thing as does Fig. 28. As applied to the circuit shown on Oscillogram 2, for example, it is immaterial whether $\mathbf{I}_{ab}$ is considered to flow in the direction of $\mathbf{V}_{ab}$ or whether $\mathbf{I}_{ba}$ is considered to flow in the direction of $\mathbf{V}_{ba}$. Those who prefer to consider line voltages *ab*, *ca*, and *bc* rather than line voltages *ba*, *ac*, and *cb* will label a circuit diagram like that shown on Oscillogram 2, whereas those who prefer to consider line voltages *ba*, *ac*, and *cb* will employ $\mathbf{I}_{ba}$, $\mathbf{I}_{ac}$, and $\mathbf{I}_{cb}$ as the delta-phase currents.

Problem 5. Refer to Oscillogram 2. Draw a complete vector diagram of $\mathbf{V}_{ab}$, $\mathbf{V}_{bc}$, $\mathbf{V}_{ca}$, $\mathbf{I}_{ab}$, $\mathbf{I}_{bc}$, $\mathbf{I}_{ca}$, $\mathbf{I}_{a'a}$, $\mathbf{I}_{b'b}$, and $\mathbf{I}_{c'c}$ employing $\mathbf{V}_{bc}$ as reference. From the scaled ordinates given on Oscillogram 2, determine the effective values of line (or phase) voltage, phase current, and line current.

Ans.: $V = 100$ volts; $I_p = 3.5$ amperes; $I_l = 6$ amperes.

The *n*-Phase Star and Mesh. The circuit and vector diagrams of two adjacent phases of an *n*-phase star system are shown in Figs. 29

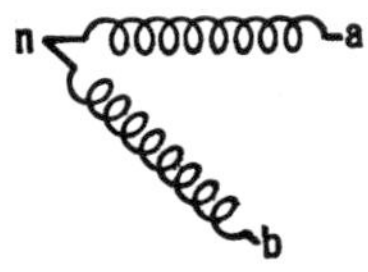

FIG. 29. Two adjacent phases of an *n*-phase star.

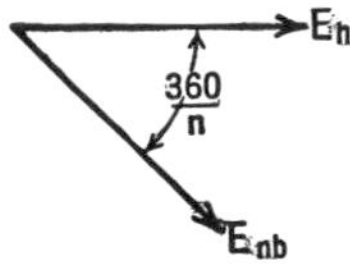

FIG. 30. Line-to-neutral voltages of adjacent phases of an *n*-phase star (Fig. 29).

and 30, respectively. The line voltage $\mathbf{E}_{ab}$ is $\mathbf{E}_{an} + \mathbf{E}_{nb}$. Remembering that the angle of phase difference between voltages of adjacent phases is $360°/n$, and calling the magnitude of phase voltage E_p, the general calculation of the line voltage can be understood from the vector relations shown in Fig. 31. Hence the line voltage is

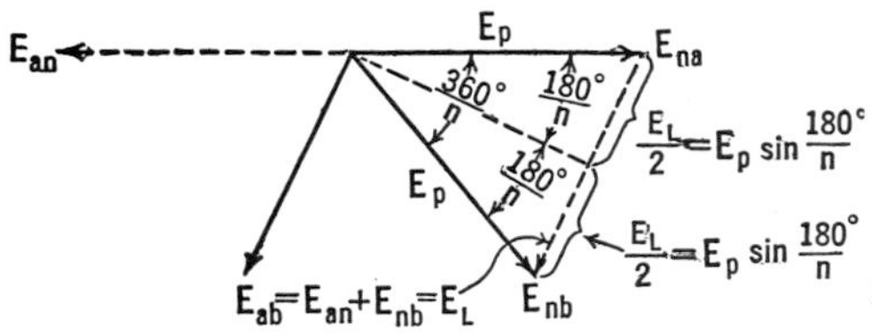

FIG. 31. Combination of line-to-neutral voltages to give line-to-line voltages in an *n*-phase star.

$$E_L = 2E_p \sin \frac{180°}{n} \qquad (1)$$

From the circuit of Fig. 29 it is evident that line current and phase current are identical. Hence

$$I_L = I_p$$

From the circuit and vector diagrams shown for part of an n-phase mesh system in Fig. 32, the use of previously outlined principles will show that

$$E_L = E_p$$

and

$$I_L = 2I_p \sin \frac{180°}{n} \tag{2}$$

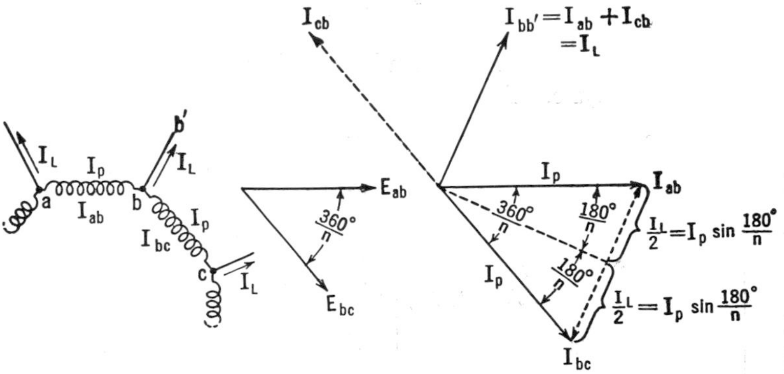

FIG. 32. Circuit diagram of adjacent phases and corresponding vector diagrams for an n-phase mesh.

Example 1. The line currents issuing from a balanced four-phase, mesh-connected generator (like that shown in Fig. 14, page 267) are known to be 70.7 amperes in magnitude. Let it be required to find the magnitude of the phase currents employing the general relationship stated in equation (2).

$$I_p = \frac{70.7}{2 \sin \frac{180°}{4}} = \frac{70.7}{2 \sin 45°} = \frac{70.7}{1.414} = 50 \text{ amperes}$$

Problem 6. Find the magnitude of the line currents issuing from a balanced six-phase, mesh-connected generator if the phase currents are known to be 100 amperes in magnitude. Illustrate solution by means of a vector diagram.

Ans.: $I_L = I_p = 100$ amperes.

Problem 7. Find the voltage between *adjacent* lines of a balanced twelve-phase, star-connected system if the phase voltages are 50 volts in magnitude. Illustrate solution by means of a vector diagram.

Ans.: 25.88 volts.

Problem 8. Find the voltage between *alternate* lines of a balanced six-phase, star-connected system if the phase voltages are 132.8 volts in magnitude.

Ans.: 230 volts.

Balanced Wye Loads. When three identical impedances are connected to a common point, n, Fig. 33, they constitute a balanced wye load. If balanced three-phase voltages are impressed on such a load, it would seem that all impedances should have equal voltage drops across them and that the ratio and phase of line and phase voltages should be the same as those discussed for the wye-connected generators. Application of Kirchhoff's laws as discussed in the next chapter shows that this is true. Hence the voltage drop V_p across each impedance in terms of the line voltage is

$$V_p = \frac{V_L}{\sqrt{3}}$$

The current, power, etc., may then be found in accordance with single-phase circuit analysis. As a general rule, all balanced three-phase circuits are calculated on a *per phase* basis in exactly the same manner as the corresponding calculations are made for any single-phase circuit. If this procedure is followed it is important that *per phase* values of V and I are not confused with line voltages and line currents even though line currents in a wye connection are the same as the phase currents, and the line voltages in a delta connection are the same as the phase voltages. As a general rule, all balanced three-phase circuits are calculated per phase just as the calculations were made for single-phase circuits.

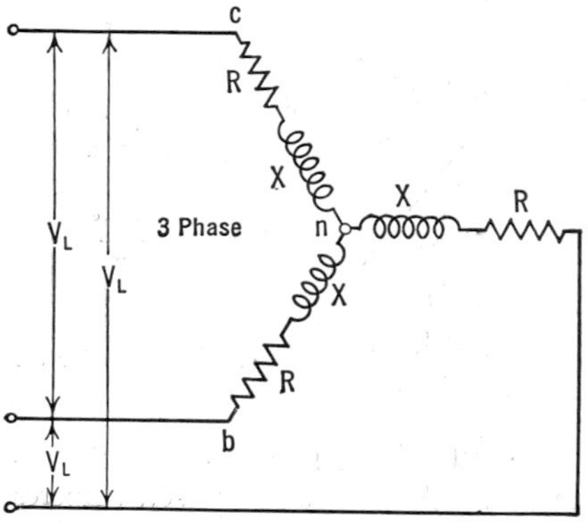

FIG. 33. Balanced wye load.

Example 2. Given the line voltages V_L in Fig. 33 as 220 volts balanced three-phase, and R and X of each phase 6 ohms resistance and 8 ohms inductive reactance. Find the line current, power per phase, and total power.

$$V_p = \frac{V_L}{\sqrt{3}} = \frac{220}{\sqrt{3}} = 127 \text{ volts}$$

$$I_L = I_p = \frac{127}{\sqrt{6^2 + 8^2}} = \frac{127}{10} = 12.7 \text{ amperes}$$

$$\text{Power per phase} = I_p{}^2R_p = 12.7^2 \times 6 = 968 \text{ watts}$$
$$\text{Total power} = 3 \times 968 = 2904 \text{ watts}$$

The example given could have been worked by means of complex numbers. Since there was no need for the vector expressions of voltages and currents, it was simpler to use magnitudes only. When it is necessary to combine the line current due to some particular load with that from another load, the vector expressions or their equivalents are required. To illustrate the vector method of handling the above example, assume the phase sequence V_{ba}, V_{cb}, V_{ac}. This means that $\mathbf{V}_{cb}$ lags $\mathbf{V}_{ba}$ by 120°. It would be possible to use any line voltage or any phase voltage as a reference. The vector diagram of a similar set of voltages to those required here is shown in Fig. 22 where E is used instead of V. The phase voltage of phase na will be taken as the reference (sometimes called the standard phase). Thus:

$$\mathbf{V}_{na} = 127 + j0 \text{ volts}$$

$$\mathbf{V}_{nb} = 127 \angle{-120°} = 127 (\cos 120° - j \sin 120°) = -63.5 - j110 \textbf{ volts}$$

$$\mathbf{V}_{nc} = 127 \angle{120°} = -63.5 + j110 \text{ volts}$$

If the vector expressions for line voltages are desired, they may be obtained by the following procedure.

$$\mathbf{V}_{ba} = \mathbf{V}_{bn} + \mathbf{V}_{na} = 63.5 + j110 + 127 + j0 = 190.5 + j110 \text{ volts, etc.}$$

$$\mathbf{I}_{na} = \frac{\mathbf{V}_{na}}{\mathbf{Z}_{na}} = \frac{127 + j0}{6 + j8} = 7.62 - j10.16 = 12.7 \angle{-53.13°} \text{ amperes}$$

$$\mathbf{I}_{nb} = \frac{\mathbf{V}_{nb}}{\mathbf{Z}_{nb}} = \frac{-63.5 - j110}{6 + j8} = \frac{127 \angle{-120°}}{10 \angle{53.13°}} = 12.7 \angle{-173.13°} \text{ amperes}$$

$$\mathbf{I}_{nc} = \frac{\mathbf{V}_{nc}}{\mathbf{Z}_{nc}} = \frac{127 \angle{120°}}{10 \angle{53.13°}} = 12.7 \angle{66.87°} \text{ amperes}$$

$$P_{na} = vi + v'i' = 127 \times 7.62 = 968 \text{ watts}$$

or

$$P_{nb} = 127 \times 12.7 \cos (120° - 173.13°) = 968 \text{ watts}$$

The vector diagram of the voltages and currents for this load as drawn from the vector solution is shown in Fig. 34.

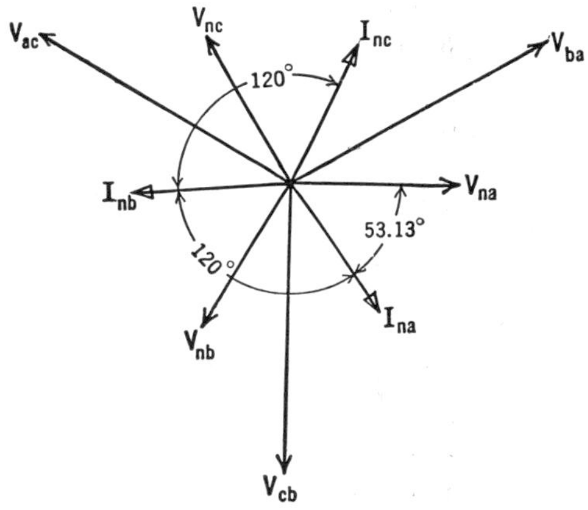

FIG. 34. Vector diagram of load in example 2.

Balanced Delta Loads. Three identical impedances connected as shown in Fig. 35 constitute a balanced delta load. The voltage drop across each impedance is known when the line voltage is given. Hence the phase currents may be determined directly as V_p/Z_p. The magnitudes of the line currents are simply phase currents multiplied by $\sqrt{3}$.

Example 3. Reconnect the impedances given in example 2 in delta, and calculate phase current, line current, phase power, and total power. (R = 6 ohms and X = 8 ohms per phase.)

$$V_L = V_p = 220 \text{ volts}$$

$$I_p = \frac{220}{\sqrt{6^2+8^2}} = 22 \text{ amperes}$$

$$I_L = \sqrt{3} \times 22 = 38.1 \text{ amperes}$$

Power per phase $= 22^2 \times 6 = 2904$ watts.

Total power $= 2904 \times 3 = 8712$ watts.

Alternative vector solution using sequence $\mathbf{V}_{ba}$, $\mathbf{V}_{cb}$, $\mathbf{V}_{ac}$. Use $\mathbf{V}_{ba}$ as the reference voltage.

$$\mathbf{V}_{ba} = 220 \,\underline{/\,0°} \text{ volts}$$

$$\mathbf{V}_{cb} = 220 \,\underline{/-120°} \text{ volts}$$

$$\mathbf{V}_{ac} = 220 \,\underline{/120°} \text{ volts}$$

$$\mathbf{I}_{ba} = \frac{220 \,\underline{/0°}}{10 \,\underline{/53.13°}} = 22 \,\underline{/-53.13°} = 13.2 - j17.6 \text{ amperes}$$

$$\mathbf{I}_{cb} = \frac{220 \,\underline{/-120°}}{10 \,\underline{/53.13°}} = 22 \,\underline{/-173.13°} = -21.85 - j2.63 \text{ amperes}$$

$$\mathbf{I}_{ac} = \frac{220 \,\underline{/120°}}{10 \,\underline{/53.13°}} = 22 \,\underline{/66.87°} = 8.65 + j20.2 \text{ amperes}$$

$$P_{ba} = 220 \times 22 \cos 53.13° = 2904 \text{ watts}$$

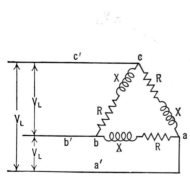

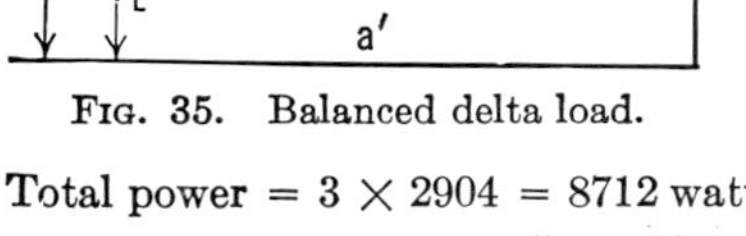

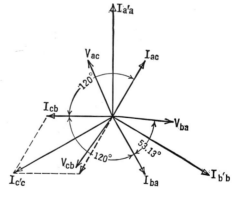

FIG. 35. Balanced delta load.

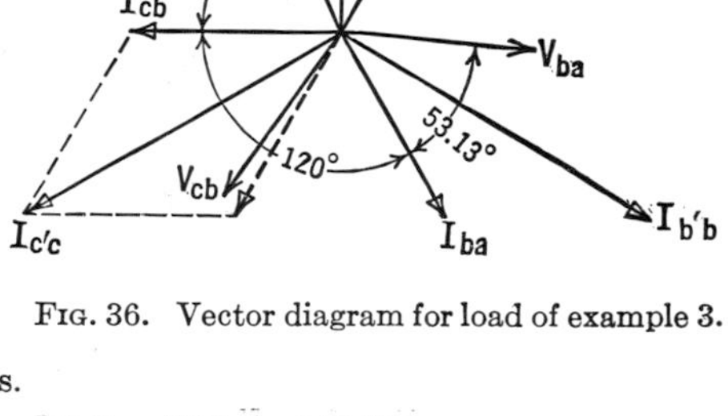

FIG. 36. Vector diagram for load of example 3.

Total power $= 3 \times 2904 = 8712$ watts.

$$\mathbf{I}_{c'c} = \mathbf{I}_{cb} + \mathbf{I}_{ca} = -30.5 - j22.8 = 38.1 \,\underline{/-143.13°} \text{ amperes}$$

$$\mathbf{I}_{b'b} = \mathbf{I}_{bc} + \mathbf{I}_{ba} = +35.05 - j15 = 38.1 \,\underline{/-23.13°} \text{ amperes}$$

$$\mathbf{I}_{a'a} = \mathbf{I}_{ab} + \mathbf{I}_{ac} = -4.55 + j37.8 = 38.1 \,\underline{/96.87°} \text{ amperes}$$

The vector diagram of this delta load as drawn from the vector solution is shown in Fig. 36.

Three-Origin Vector Diagram of a Balanced Three-Phase System. Figure 37 shows a polar vector diagram of a three-phase balanced unity-power-factor wye load. Figure 38 shows a vector diagram of a

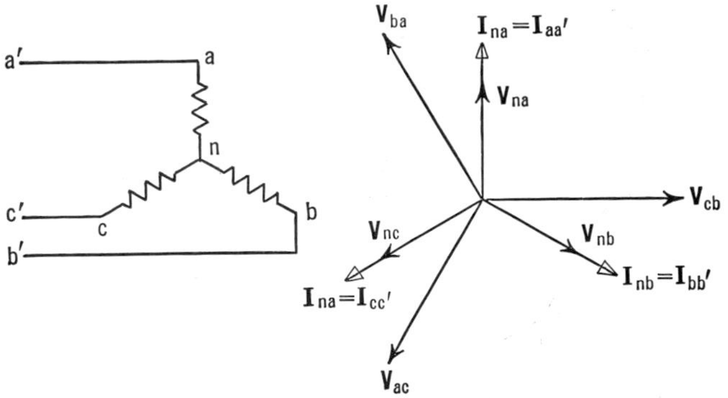

FIG. 37. Polar vector diagram of unity-power-factor, balanced wye-connected load.

balanced unity-power-factor delta load. A comparison of these two diagrams will show that the phase relation between *line* currents and *line* voltages is identical for both loads. Therefore a single vector diagram can be used to represent the relations between line currents and line

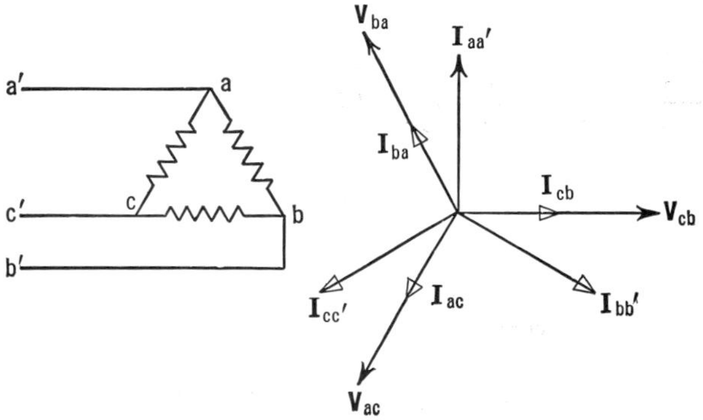

FIG. 38. Polar vector diagram of unity-power-factor, balanced delta-connected load.

voltages for a balanced three-phase load whether the load is wye- or delta-connected. In other words, it is not necessary to know which connection is used in order to represent properly the phase relations of line voltages and currents. This fact makes it convenient in many cases to use a three-origin vector diagram which is explained as follows.

If it is remembered that a vector can be translated without changing its value, the line voltages for the above loads may be arranged to form a closed triangle, as shown in Fig. 39. Also the line currents may be drawn from the corners of the triangle so formed as indicated. The three corners comprise the three origins; hence the name of the diagram.

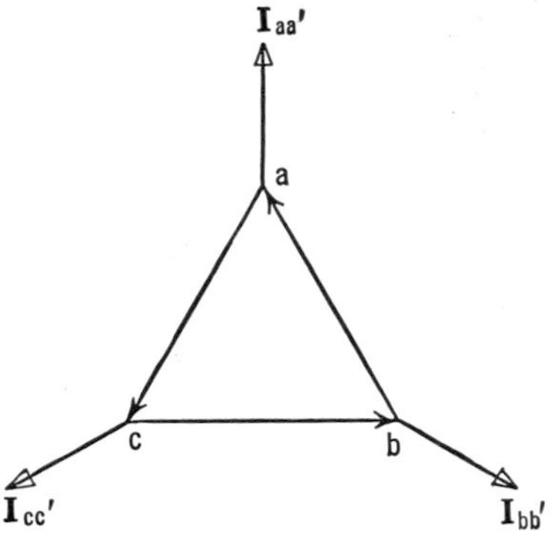

FIG. 39. Three-origin vector diagram of line voltages (*cb-ac-ba*) and line currents ($I_{bb'}$, $I_{cc'}$, $I_{aa'}$).

It will be observed that, at unity power factor, line current $I_{aa'}$ bisects the angle at origin a made by the line voltages at that point. A similar situation obtains for the other line currents. The bisectors of these angles may therefore be called the unity-power-factor positions of the line currents for a balanced three-phase load regardless of delta or wye connection. If a load having a power-factor angle of θ is to be represented, it is necessary only to let the three line currents swing from their unity-power-factor positions by the angle θ. That this is true is evident from a study of the changes in Figs. 37 and 38 when a load having a power-factor angle θ is represented.

It should be recognized that the three-origin diagram is essentially the equivalent wye diagram where the line voltages are drawn between extremities of the wye voltages to neutral, and these latter voltages, if shown, would be drawn from the corners of the triangle to the geometrical neutral. Inspection of the diagrams, Fig. 40*b* and *c*, shows the power-factor angle is actually the angle between the line current and the equivalent wye voltage or voltage to neutral. To show how the

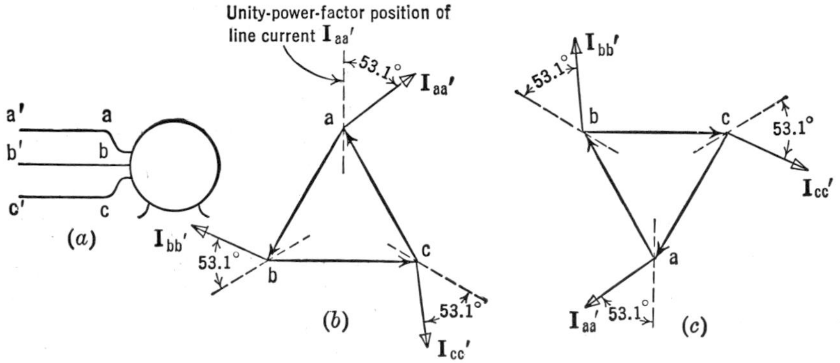

FIG. 40. Three-origin vector diagrams for both sequences of line voltages.

three-origin diagram might be used to represent a three-phase load, study the following example.

Example 4. A balanced three-phase, 0.6 p.f. lagging load takes 10 kva at 200 volts. Show the vector diagram of the line voltages and currents.

The load is represented by the circle, and the lines are labeled a, b, and c, as shown in Fig. 40. Assume $\mathbf{V}_{bc}$ as a reference, and complete the line voltage triangle as shown in (b) or (c) according to the sequence desired. The bisectors of the angles are shown dotted and are the unity-power-factor positions of the respective currents leaving points a, b, and c. The actual power-factor angle for the load is $\cos^{-1} 0.6 = 53.1°$, and the currents are therefore drawn lagging their unity-power-factor positions by this angle, as shown. Had the load operated at a leading power factor, the currents would have swung ahead of their unity-power-factor positions by 53.1°.

The above type of diagram lends itself to a simple visualization of line voltages and currents for a balanced three-phase load and contributes to an easy understanding of operating conditions in individual transformers for certain types of connections when supplying balanced loads. They may also be used to effect the proper combination of line currents from several balanced three-phase loads independent of whether the loads themselves are delta- or wye-connected. It should be recognized from this discussion that, as far as phase relations between line currents and line voltages are concerned, one is at liberty to assume a delta- or wye-connected load even though the actual type of connection is known or unknown. Also, if convenient, the directions of the currents shown in Fig. 40 may be reversed and so labeled.

Power Calculations in Balanced Systems. The determination of power in balanced polyphase systems is based upon calculations per phase. If the voltage per phase is V_p, the phase current I_p, and the angle between them θ_p, the power per phase is

$$P_p = V_p I_p \cos \theta_p \tag{3}$$

The power for all phases of an n-phase system is

$$P_t = nP_p = nV_p I_p \cos \theta_p \tag{4}$$

The universality of three-phase warrants the development of equation (4) to give power in terms of line current I_L and the line voltage V_L. Consider the wye connection. Then

$$P_t = 3V_p I_p \cos \theta_p = 3 \frac{V_L}{\sqrt{3}} I_L \cos \theta_p$$

$$= \sqrt{3} V_L I_L \cos \theta_p \tag{5}$$

For the delta connection

$$P_t = 3V_p I_p \cos \theta_p = 3V_L \frac{I_L}{\sqrt{3}} \cos \theta_p$$

$$= \sqrt{3} V_L I_L \cos \theta_p \tag{6}$$

The equations for power in terms of line voltages and line currents for *balanced three-phase* loads whether delta- or wye-connected are identical and equal to $\sqrt{3}V_LI_L \cos \theta_p$. In this expression, $\sqrt{3}V_LI_L \cos \theta_p$, for balanced three-phase power, it must be remembered that θ_p is the angle between *phase voltage and phase current* and *not* between line voltage and line current.

Problem 9. Three-phase line voltages of 2300 volts magnitude are impressed on a balanced wye-connected load which consists of 100 ohms resistance per phase in series with 173.2 ohms inductive reactance per phase. Find the line current and the total power taken by the three-phase load. Calculate P_t as $3I_p{}^2R_p$, as $3V_pI_p \cos \theta_p$, and as $\sqrt{3}V_LI_L \cos \theta_p$.

Ans.: $I_L = I_p = 6.64$ amperes, $P_t = 13.22$ kw.

Problem 10. Repeat Problem 9, assuming that the three impedances are connected in delta (rather than in wye) across the same line voltages.

Ans.: $I_L = 19.92$ amperes, $P_t = 39.66$ kw.

Volt-Amperes. The volt-amperes of a *balanced* three-phase system are defined as the sum of the volt-amperes of the separate phases or three times the number of volt-amperes per phase. Hence

$$\text{va}_t = 3\text{va}_p = 3V_pI_p$$

In terms of line voltage and line current, volt-amperes are

For delta:
$$3V_L \frac{I_L}{\sqrt{3}} = \sqrt{3}V_LI_L \tag{7}$$

For wye:
$$3 \frac{V_L}{\sqrt{3}} I_L = \sqrt{3}V_LI_L \tag{8}$$

For an n-phase system under balanced conditions the total volt-amperes are n times the volt-amperes per phase.

Reactive Volt-Amperes. The reactive volt-amperes for a balanced three-phase system are defined as the sum of the reactive volt-amperes for each phase, or three times the reactive volt-amperes per phase. In terms of line voltage and line current the reactive volt-amperes or reactive power is

For wye:
$$P_X = 3V_pI_p \sin \theta_p = 3 \frac{V_L}{\sqrt{3}} I_L \sin \theta_p$$
$$= \sqrt{3}V_LI_L \sin \theta_p \tag{9}$$

For delta:
$$P_X = 3V_pI_p \sin \theta_p = 3V_L \frac{I_L}{\sqrt{3}} \sin \theta_p$$
$$= \sqrt{3}V_LI_L \sin \theta_p \tag{10}$$

Summarizing for either *balanced* delta or wye, the totals for the systems are

$$P = \sqrt{3}V_L I_L \cos\theta_p \tag{11}$$

$$\text{va} = \sqrt{3}V_L I_L \tag{12}$$

$$P_X = \sqrt{3}V_L I_L \sin\theta_p \tag{13}$$

The sine of the angle between phase voltage and phase current ($\sin\theta_p$) is called the *reactive factor* of a *balanced* system.

Problem 11. Three-phase line voltages of 440 volts are impressed on a balanced delta-connected load which consists of 8 ohms resistance in series with 6 ohms inductive reactance per phase.

(*a*) Find the volt-amperes per phase, the reactive volt-amperes per phase, and the reactive factor of each phase.

Ans.: $\text{va}_p = 19{,}360$, $\text{rva}_p = 11{,}616$, r.f. $= 0.6$.

(*b*) Find the total volt-amperes of the system, the total reactive volt-amperes of the system, and the reactive factor of the system.

Ans.: $\text{va}_t = 58{,}080$, $\text{rva}_t = 34{,}848$, r.f. $= 0.6$.

Power Factor. The power factor of a balanced three-phase system, when the wave forms of voltage and current are sinusoidal, is defined as the cosine of the angle between *phase voltage* and *phase current* independent of whether the connection is delta or wye. It should be noted that the volt-amperes of equation (12) are equal to $\sqrt{P^2 + P_X{}^2}$. Thus

$$\begin{aligned}\text{va} &= \sqrt{(\sqrt{3}V_L I_L \cos\theta_p)^2 + (\sqrt{3}V_L I_L \sin\theta_p)^2} \\ &= \sqrt{3}V_L I_L \sqrt{\cos^2\theta_p + \sin^2\theta_p} = \sqrt{3}V_L I_L\end{aligned} \tag{14}$$

From equation (11),

$$\text{p.f.} = \cos\theta_p = \frac{P}{\sqrt{3}V_L I_L} \tag{15}$$

From equation (13),

$$\text{r.f.} = \sin\theta_p = \frac{P_X}{\sqrt{3}V_L I_L} \tag{16}$$

From equations (15) and (14),

$$\text{p.f.} = \frac{P}{\sqrt{P^2 + P_X{}^2}} \tag{17}$$

From equations (16) and (14),

$$\text{r.f.} = \frac{P_X}{\sqrt{P^2 + P_X{}^2}} \tag{18}$$

Example 5. A 5-horsepower, 220-volt, three-phase motor has an efficiency of 85 per cent and operates at 86 per cent power factor. Find the line current.

$$\text{Power input} = \sqrt{3}V_L I_L \text{ p.f.} = \frac{5 \times 746}{0.85} = 4390 \text{ watts}$$

$$I_L = \frac{4390}{\sqrt{3}\,220 \times 0.86} = 13.4 \text{ amperes}$$

Balanced Three-Phase Loads in Parallel. The combination of a number of balanced loads which are in parallel may be effected through changing all loads to equivalent delta loads and then combining the impedances of corresponding phases according to the law governing parallel circuits. Also all loads may be changed to equivalent wye loads and the impedances of corresponding phases paralleled. In addition to these methods, the power of the several loads may be added arithmetically and the reactive volt-amperes may be added algebraically. The total volt-amperes will then be obtained as $\sqrt{P^2 + P_X{}^2}$.

Example 6. A 3-phase motor takes 10 kva at 0.6 power factor lagging from a source of 220 volts. It is in parallel with a balanced delta load having 16 ohms resistance and 12 ohms capacitive reactance in series in each phase. Find the total volt-amperes, power, line current, and power factor of the combination.

Solution a. Assume motor to be Y-connected.

$$\text{Motor line current} = \text{phase current} = \frac{10{,}000}{\sqrt{3}\,220} = 26.25 \text{ amperes}$$

$$\text{Equivalent impedance per phase of motor} = \frac{220}{\sqrt{3}\,26.25} = 4.84 \text{ ohms}$$

$$R = 4.84 \cos\theta = 4.84 \times 0.6 = 2.904 \text{ ohms}$$

$$X = 4.84 \sin\theta = 4.84 \times 0.8 = 3.872 \text{ ohms}$$

$$\text{Equivalent wye of delta load } \mathbf{Z}_p = \frac{16 - j12}{3} = 5.33 - j4 \text{ ohms}$$

$$\mathbf{Z}_0 = \frac{(5.33 - j4)\,(2.904 + j3.872)}{5.33 - j4 + 2.904 + j3.872} = 3.91\,\underline{/17.17^\circ} \text{ ohms}$$

$$I_0 = \frac{220}{\sqrt{3}\,3.91} = 32.5 \text{ amperes}$$

$$\text{va} = \sqrt{3}\,220 \times 32.5 = 12{,}370 \text{ volt-amperes}$$

$$\text{p.f.}_0 = \cos 17.17^\circ = 0.955$$

$$P = 12{,}370 \times 0.955 = 11{,}810 \text{ watts}$$

Solution b. The motor may be assumed delta-connected and the delta-phase impedances combined after which delta phase currents and line currents can be found. The remaining procedure is similar to that in solution *a*.

Solution c. Line currents for each load are determined and shown on a diagram of the type shown in Fig. 39 where the equivalent voltage to neutral V_{na} is drawn

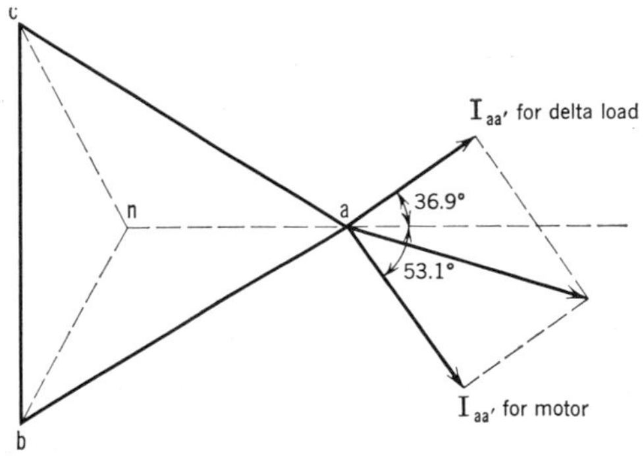

FIG. 41.

along the horizontal as shown in Fig. 41. Currents are then combined as indicated on Fig. 41.

$$\text{Motor line current} = \frac{10{,}000}{\sqrt{3}\,220} = 26.25 \text{ amperes}$$

$$\text{Delta-load line current} = \frac{220}{\sqrt{16^2 + 12^2}}\sqrt{3} = 19.05 \text{ amperes}$$

$$I_{aa'\text{motor}} = 26.25\,/\underline{-53.1^\circ} = 15.75 - j21$$

$$I_{aa'\text{delta load}} = 19.05\,/\underline{36.9^\circ} = 15.24 + j11.43$$

$$I_{aa'} = I_{aa'\text{motor}} + I_{aa'\text{delta load}} = 30.99 - j9.57 = 32.5\,/\underline{-17.17^\circ} \text{ amperes}$$

$$\text{va} = \sqrt{3}\,220 \times 32.5 = 12{,}370 \text{ volt-amperes}$$

$$\text{p.f.}_0 = \cos 17.17^\circ = 0.955$$

$$P = 12{,}370 \times 0.995 = 11{,}810 \text{ watts.}$$

Solution d. For the delta load, phase current is $220/\sqrt{16^2 + 12^2} = 11$ amperes.

$$P = 11^2 \times 16 \times 3 = 5810 \text{ watts for all phases}$$

$$P_X = 11^2 \times 12 \times 3 = 4350 \text{ vars for all phases (capacitive)}$$

For the motor

$$P = 10 \times 0.6 = 6 \text{ kw}$$

$$P_X = 10 \times 0.8 = 8 \text{ kilovars (inductive)}$$

$$\text{Summation of power} = 5.81 + 6 = 11.81 \text{ kw}$$

$$\text{Summation of kilovars} = 8 - 4.35 = 3.65 \text{ kilovars}$$

$$\text{kva}_0 = \sqrt{11.81^2 + 3.65^2} = 12.37$$

$$I_0 = \frac{12{,}370}{\sqrt{3}\,220} = 32.5 \text{ amperes}$$

$$\text{p.f.}_0 = \frac{11.81}{12.37} = 0.955$$

Of the four solutions, that which is most convenient for the quantities given should be employed.

Single-Phase and Balanced Three-Phase Power. A comparison of the variation with respect to time of instantaneous single-phase and three-phase power brings out certain fundamental differences. As shown in Chapter II, single-phase power follows a double-frequency sine law with respect to time plus a constant. The instantaneous power for each of three phases, when currents and voltages are sine waves, of a balanced three-phase system is given by the following general equations.

$$p_a = V_m I_m \sin \omega t \sin (\omega t - \theta)$$

$$p_b = V_m I_m \sin (\omega t - 120°) \sin (\omega t - 120° - \theta)$$

$$p_c = V_m I_m \sin (\omega t - 240°) \sin (\omega t - 240° - \theta)$$

The total three-phase power is

$$p_3 = P_a + P_b + P_c = V_m I_m [\sin \omega t \sin (\omega t - \theta) + \sin (\omega t - 120°) \sin (\omega t - 120° - \theta) + \sin (\omega t - 240°) \sin (\omega t - 240° - \theta)]$$

$$p_3 = 1.5 V_m I_m \cos \theta \tag{19}$$

For single-phase, say phase a,

$$p_1 = V_m I_m \sin \omega t \sin (\omega t - \theta) = \frac{V_m I_m}{2} \cos \theta - \frac{V_m I_m}{2} \cos (2\omega t - \theta) \tag{20}$$

Equation (19) shows the instantaneous value of three-phase power to be independent of time. In other words, balanced three-phase power under steady-state conditions is constant from instant to instant. In contrast, equation (20) for single-phase power shows it to follow a double-frequency variation with respect to time. This comparison is graphically illustrated in Fig. 42.

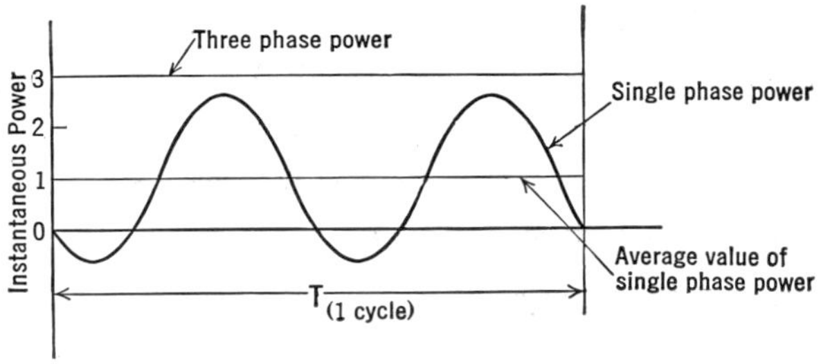

FIG. 42. Comparison of variations of single- and balanced three-phase power.

Power Measurement in Balanced Systems. A wattmeter gives a reading proportional to the product of the current through its current coil, the voltage across its potential coil, and the cosine of the angle between this voltage and current. Since the total power in a three-phase circuit is the sum of the powers of the separate phases, the total power could be measured by placing a wattmeter in each phase, as shown in Fig. 43. It is not generally feasible to break into the phases of a delta-connected load. Therefore the method shown in part (*a*) of Fig. 43

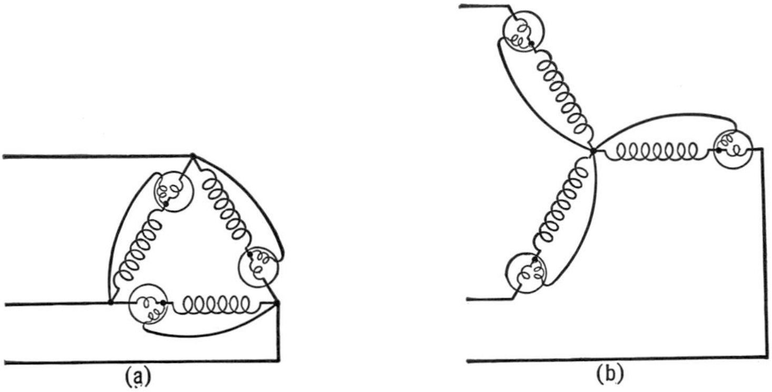

Fig. 43. A wattmeter in each phase may be used to measure three-phase power.

is not applicable. For the wye load shown in part (*b*), it is necessary to connect to the neutral point. This point is not always accessible. Hence another method making use of only two wattmeters is generally employed in making three-phase power measurements. This connection is shown in Fig. 44. To show that two such wattmeters may be used to measure power, the readings of each will be established and their sum compared with equation (11), which has been shown to be

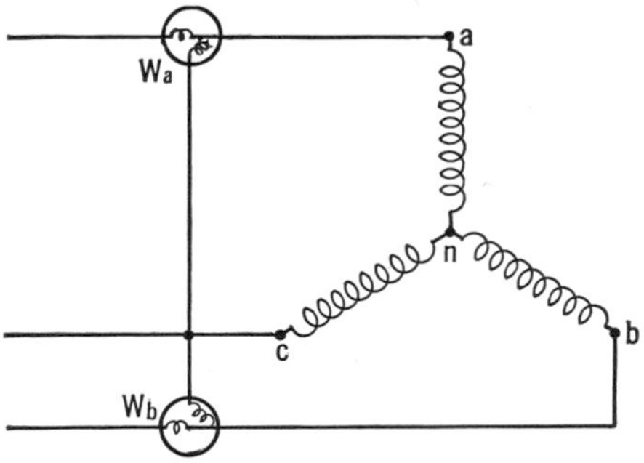

Fig. 44. Connection of two wattmeters to measure three-phase power.

correct for balanced three-phase power. It is important to take the direction of the voltage through the circuit the same as that taken for current when establishing wattmeter readings. Thus if the current coil of W_a, Fig. 44, is considered carrying current I_{an}, the potential across the voltage coil should be taken from a through the circuit, which in this particular case is V_{ac}. Figure 45 shows the vector diagram of the voltages and currents for a balanced system like that of Fig. 44. From this figure the power represented by the currents and voltages of each wattmeter is

$$W_a = V_{ac}I_{an} \cos(\theta - 30°) \tag{21}$$

$$W_b = V_{bc}I_{bn} \cos(\theta + 30°) \tag{22}$$

In equations (21) and (22) the subscripts serve only to assist in seeing which voltages and currents were used. Since the load is balanced, $V_{ac} = V_{bc}$, $I_{an} = I_{bn}$ and only magnitudes are involved. Dropping the subscripts gives

$$W_a = VI \cos(\theta - 30°) \tag{23}$$

$$W_b = VI \cos(\theta + 30°) \tag{24}$$

$$\begin{aligned} W_a + W_b &= VI \cos(\theta - 30°) + VI \cos(\theta + 30°) \\ &= VI [\cos\theta \cos 30° + \sin\theta \sin 30° + \cos\theta \cos 30° - \sin\theta \sin 30°] \\ &= \sqrt{3} VI \cos\theta \end{aligned} \tag{25}$$

Hence $W_a + W_b$ correctly measures the power in a balanced three-phase system of any power factor. As will be shown later, the algebraic sum of the readings of two wattmeters will give the correct value for power under any conditions of unbalance, wave form, or power factor.

For each value of θ (i.e., for each power factor) there is a definite ratio of W_a/W_b. If the ratio of the smaller to the larger reading is always taken and plotted against the corresponding $\cos\theta$ (i.e., power factor), a curve called the watt ratio curve results. This curve is shown in Fig. 46. Reference to the vector diagram of Fig. 45 and the curve of Fig. 46 shows that at 0.5 power factor one wattmeter reads zero. For the case under discussion 0.5 lagging power factor makes W_b read zero, while 0.5 leading power factor makes W_a read zero. When the power factor is zero, each wattmeter has the same deflection but the readings are of opposite signs. The foregoing facts are easily deducible from the vector diagram shown in Fig. 45 and also follow from equations (23) and (24). It is essential in the two-wattmeter method that the proper sign be given the wattmeter readings and that the sum be taken algebraically.

There are several ways to determine whether a wattmeter reading

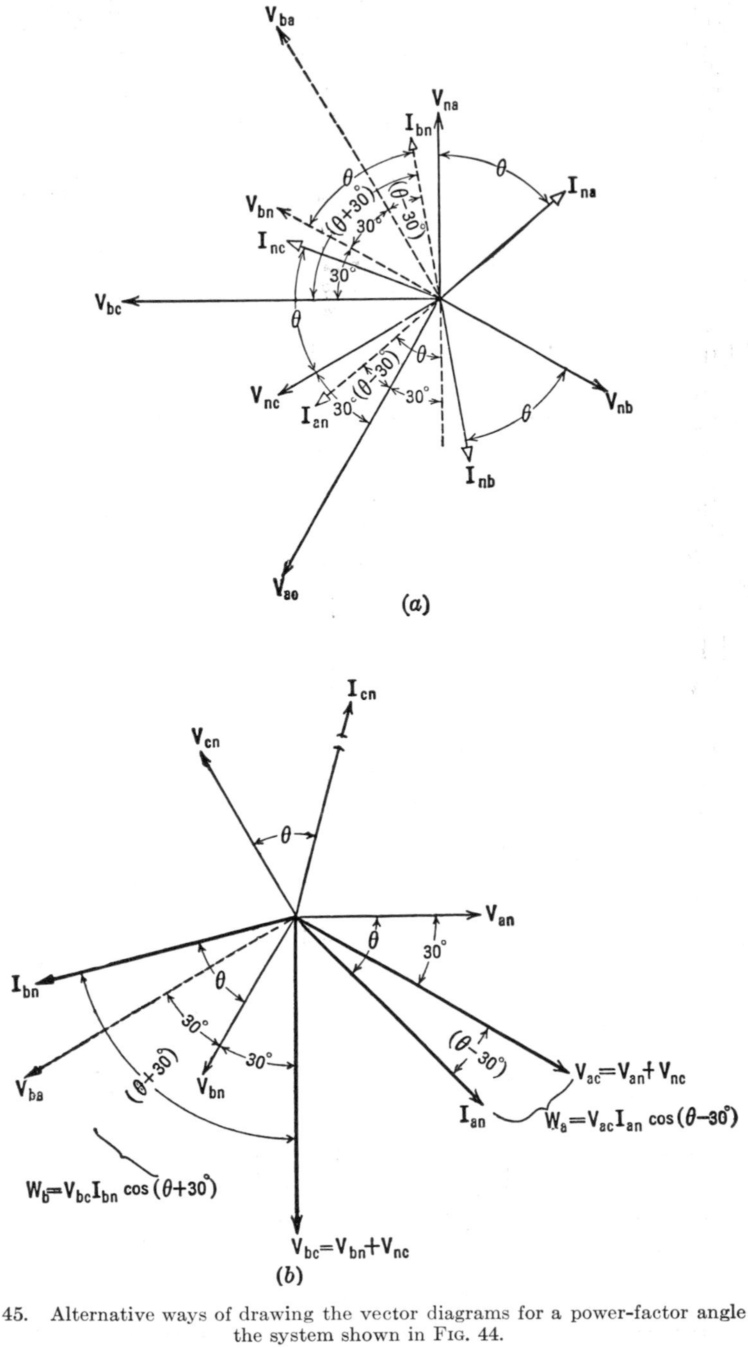

FIG. 45. Alternative ways of drawing the vector diagrams for a power-factor angle θ of the system shown in FIG. 44.

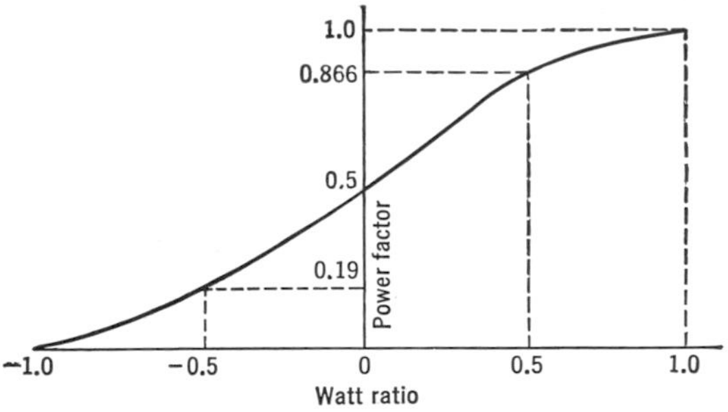

FIG. 46. Watt ratio curve for two-wattmeter method of measuring power (applicable only to balanced loads).

should be taken positive or negative. One of the best methods follows. Refer to Fig. 44. Open line *a*. Then all power must be transferred to the load over lines *b* and *c*. If wattmeter *b* is connected so that it reads "up scale," it will then be known to have this deflection when the power it reads is going to the load. Next reconnect line *a* and open line *b*. Then connect W_a so that it reads up scale. Now close line *b*. If at any time after this either wattmeter needle goes backward against the down-scale stop, power through this wattmeter channel is being transferred to the generator and this power must be of opposite sign to that registered by the other. Either the potential or current coil will have to be reversed to secure an up-scale reading. The foregoing test is applicable under any conditions of loading, although it may not always be feasible because of the necessity for opening the lines.

A second test applicable only when the load is practically *balanced* is to disconnect from the common potential point *c* of Fig. 44 the potential coil of the wattmeter which has the smaller reading and connect it to the line containing the current coil of the other wattmeter. If the needle goes against the down-scale stop, the wattmeter reading was negative. The foregoing is best explained through a consideration of the circuit diagram of Fig. 44 and the corresponding vector diagram of Fig. 45. As previously shown, W_a reads the power represented by V_{ac} and I_{an} while W_b reads that due to V_{bc} and I_{bn}. Since the angle $(\theta + 30°)$ between V_{bc} and I_{bn} is larger than the angle $(\theta - 30°)$ between V_{ac} and I_{an} for the load represented by Fig. 45, wattmeter W_b will have the smaller deflection. If the potential coil of W_b is now removed from line *c* in Fig. 44 and connected to line *a*, the meter will deflect because of the potential V_{ba} and current I_{bn}. The angle between V_{ba} and I_{bn} is seen to be $(\theta - 30°)$ or the same as that between the voltage and current for wattmeter W_a. W_a and W_b will then read alike.

Furthermore, since W_b was connected to read up scale when the angle between its voltage and current was less than 90°, it will continue to read up scale when it receives the potential V_{ba}. If, however, the power factor was below 0.5, the angle $(\theta + 30°)$ on Fig. 45 would be more than 90°. If the wattmeter W_b were made to read up scale under such conditions, it would reverse its deflection when given the potential V_{ba} as outlined above since it would then be subjected to a voltage and current of $(\theta - 30°)$, which is less than 90° out of phase. When the potential coil connection of W_b is moved from line c to a in Fig. 44, this wattmeter receives a potential of V_{ba}, while that for W_a (taken similarly from the line containing the current coil) is V_{ac}. These potentials are in the same order or direction around the diagram. Hence the potential coils are said to be connected in the same cyclic order about the circuit, and under these conditions both wattmeters would be expected to show the same deflection. This was found to be true in the above analysis.

Example 7. In a circuit like that shown in Fig. 44, W_a reads 800 and W_b reads 400 watts. When the potential coil of W_b is disconnected at c and connected at a, the needle goes against the down-scale stop.

Solution. The test indicates that W_b is reading -400 watts. Hence

$$P = W_a + W_b = 800 + (-400) = 400 \text{ watts}$$

$$\text{Watt ratio} = \frac{W_b}{W_a} = \frac{-400}{800} = -0.5$$

From a watt ratio curve like that shown on page 352, the power factor may be determined directly as 0.19.

The power factor, $\cos\theta$, could also have been calculated from a simultaneous solution of equations (23) and (24) since

$$\cos\theta = \cos\left(\tan^{-1}\frac{\sqrt{3}\,(W_a - W_b)}{W_a + W_b}\right)$$

This relation is made apparent in the next article.

Reactive Volt-Amperes. The reactive volt-amperes in a balanced three-phase circuit may be expressed by

$$P_X = \sqrt{3}\,(W_a - W_b) \tag{26}$$

This may be shown as follows:

$$\begin{aligned}\sqrt{3}\,(W_a - W_b) &= \sqrt{3}\,[VI\cos(\theta - 30°) - VI\cos(\theta + 30°)]\\ &= \sqrt{3}VI\,[\cos\theta\cos 30° + \sin\theta\sin 30° - \cos\theta\cos 30°\\ &\quad + \sin\theta\sin 30°]\\ &= \sqrt{3}VI\sin\theta\end{aligned}$$

This is the same as equation (13) for reactive power given on page 345. Since the ratio of the reactive volt-amperes, $\sqrt{3}V_LI_L \sin\theta$, to the power, $\sqrt{3}V_LI_L \cos\theta$, is the $\tan\theta$, it follows from equations (25) and (26) that

$$\tan\theta = \frac{\sqrt{3}\,(W_a - W_b)}{W_a + W_b} \tag{27}$$

where θ is the power-factor angle.

Example 8. The power factor in the preceding example could have been easily calculated by means of the relation stated in equation (26). Thus

$$P_X = \sqrt{3}\;(W_a - W_b) = \sqrt{3}\;[800 - (-400)] = 2078 \text{ vars}$$

$$(P = W_a + W_b = 800 - 400 = 400 \text{ watts})$$

$$\text{va} = \sqrt{P^2 + P_X{}^2} = \sqrt{400^2 + 2078^2} = 2114 \text{ volt-amperes}$$

$$\text{p.f.} = \frac{P}{\text{va}} = \frac{400}{2114} = 0.19$$

Three-Phase, Four-Wire Systems. If a three-phase, four-wire system is balanced, the fourth wire or neutral will carry no current. The system is the same as when the neutral is omitted, in which case it is the same as a balanced three-phase, three-wire system. It can therefore be metered as previously shown for the three-wire system. Another method is given later. Under any other conditions three meters or their equivalent are necessary. Unbalanced systems are considered in the next chapter.

Delta Systems. The measurement of power in a three-phase system was discussed with reference to a wye-circuit diagram and the corresponding vector diagram. When it is remembered that a delta system can always be replaced by an equivalent wye system, the preceding discussion will be seen to apply to the delta system. Furthermore only line voltages and line currents were involved in the discussion of the two-wattmeter method of measuring power, and there is no difference between these quantities for the delta and wye systems.

Oscillograms 3 and 4, which were obtained from a delta system as shown and labeled in Fig. 47, may be profitably studied.

Problem 12. Refer to Oscillogram 3. (*a*) If the line-to-line voltages have instantaneous maximum values of 155.5 volts and the delta-line currents have instantaneous maximum values of 14.14 amperes, find the average power readings of the wattmeters $W_{ab\text{-}a'a}$ and $W_{cb\text{-}c'c}$.

(*b*) Draw a vector diagram indicating all currents and voltages shown on Oscillogram 3. Use $\mathbf{V}_{ab}$ as reference, and include the delta-phase currents $\mathbf{I}_{ab}$, $\mathbf{I}_{bc}$, and

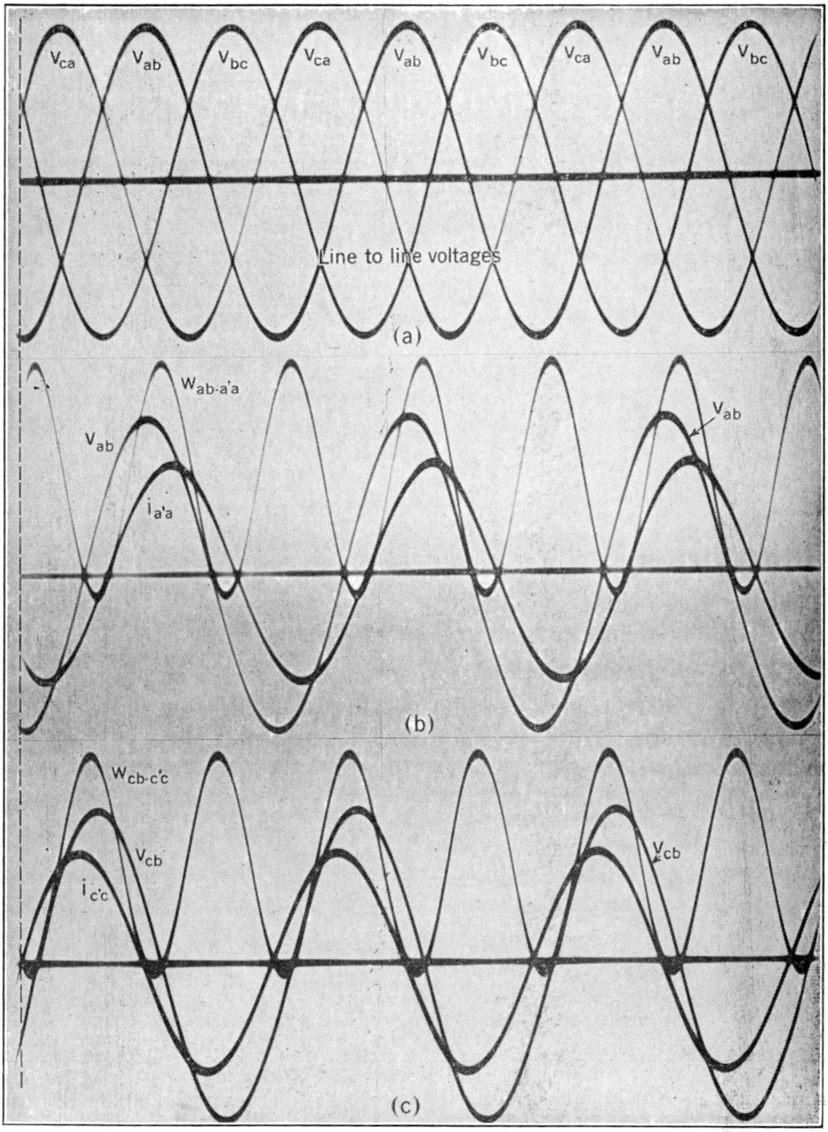

OSCILLOGRAM 3. Oscillographic representation of all voltages and currents involved in the two-wattmeter method of measuring balanced three-phase power at unity power factor. In (*a*) the sequence of line-to-line voltages is shown. v_{ca} is the voltage not used. In (*b*) $w_{ab-a'a}$ is a graph of the instantaneous driving torque of the wattmeter element which is operated by v_{ab} and $i_{a'a}$. In (*c*) $w_{cb-c'c}$ is a graph of the instantaneous driving torque of the wattmeter element which is operated by v_{cb} and $i_{c'c}$.

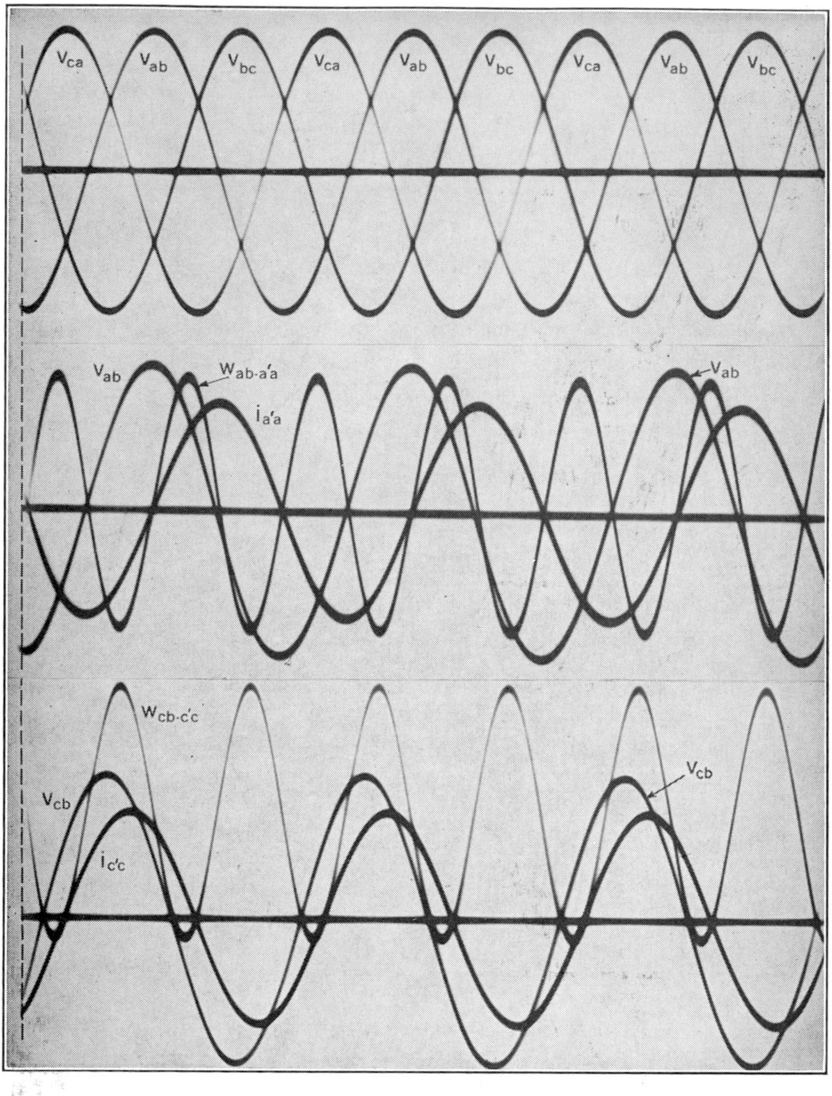

Oscillogram 4. Oscillographic representation of all voltages and currents involved in the two-wattmeter method of measuring balanced three-phase power at 0.5 p.f. lag, the condition under which one wattmeter reads zero. In the upper oscillogram, the sequence of line-to-line voltages is shown. The voltage v_{ca} is the voltage not used in the two-wattmeter method in this case. (In the center oscillogram, $w_{ab-a'a}$ is a graph of the instantaneous driving torque of the wattmeter element which is operated by v_{ab} and $i_{a'a}$. In the lower oscillogram, $w_{cb-c'c}$ is a graph of the instantaneous driving torque of the wattmeter element which is operated by v_{cb} and $i_{c'c}$.

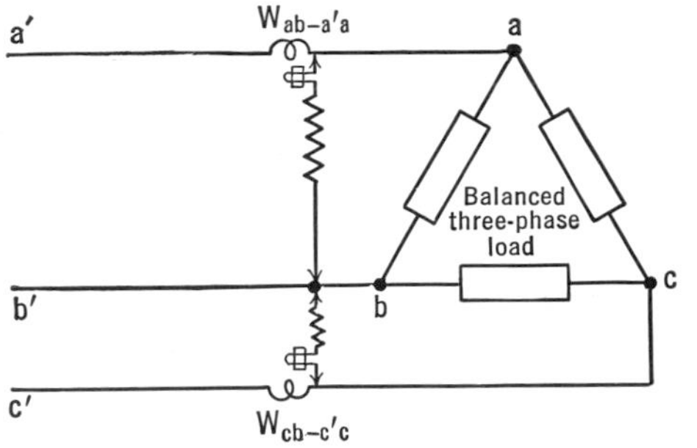

FIG. 47. Circuit arrangement for which Oscillograms 3 and 4 were taken.

$\mathbf{I}_{ca}$ which are not shown on the oscillogram but which combine to form the delta-line currents $\mathbf{I}_{a'a}$ and $\mathbf{I}_{c'c}$.

Ans.: (*a*) $W_{ab\text{-}a'a} = W_{cb\text{-}c'c} = 952.6$ watts.
(*b*) *ab-bc-ca* sequence of line-to-line voltages; $\mathbf{I}_{ab}$ in time phase with $\mathbf{V}_{ab}$; $\mathbf{I}_{a'a}$ lags $\mathbf{V}_{ab}$ by 30°; $\mathbf{I}_{c'c}$ leads $\mathbf{V}_{cb}$ by 30°.

General *n*-Wire Balanced System. The total power taken by a balanced *n*-phase system is *n* times the power per phase. A single wattmeter connected to measure the product of the current, potential, and the cosine of the angle between the current and potential may be used to obtain the power of a balanced *n*-phase system. The wattmeter reading obtained is multiplied by *n*. If it is not possible to break into a phase of a mesh-connected load or to obtain the neutral of a star-connected one, power may still be measured with a single wattmeter. For the *n*-phase system, *n* equal resistances may be connected in star and then to the lines. A neutral is thus established, and power is measured as though the neutral wire of a star system were available. The method is shown in Fig. 48. If the number of phases is even, as, for example, in Fig. 48, only a single resistance is necessary provided that the potential coil of the wattmeter can be connected at the midpoint of this resistance. The resistance must be connected between two lines having the largest potential difference. The wattmeter reading must

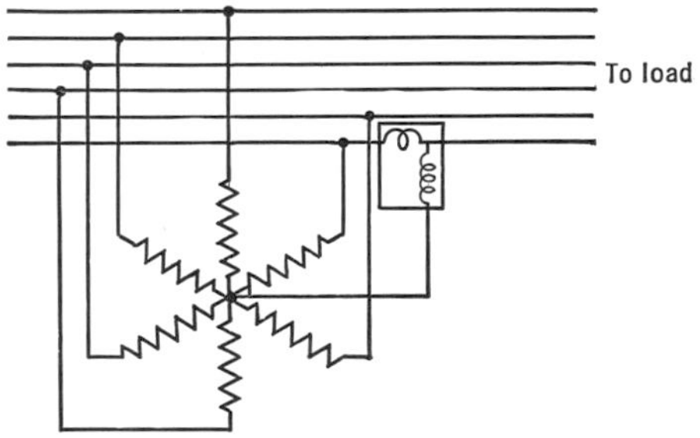

FIG. 48. A method for measuring power to an *n*-phase balanced load (load not shown).

be multiplied by n, the number of phases, to obtain the total power. If the number of phases is even, the potential coil may be connected from the line containing the current coil to the line which yields the highest potential difference. The total power is then the wattmeter indication multiplied by $n/2$. These connections may be used only for balanced systems.

Copper Required to Transmit Power under Fixed Conditions. All systems will be compared on the basis of a fixed amount of power transmitted a fixed distance with the same amount of loss and at the same maximum voltage between conductors. In all cases the total weight of copper will be directly proportional to the number of wires, since the distance is fixed, and inversely proportional to the resistance of each wire. First, three-phase will be compared with single-phase. Since the same voltage and power factor are to be assumed, the same respective symbols for these quantities for single- and three-phase will suffice.

$$P_1 = VI_1 \cos\theta$$

$$P_3 = \sqrt{3}VI_3 \cos\theta$$

Since

$$P_1 = P_3$$

$$VI_1 \cos\theta = \sqrt{3}VI_3 \cos\theta$$

$$I_1 = \sqrt{3}I_3$$

Also

$$I_1^2R_1 \times 2 = I_3^2R_3 \times 3$$

or

$$\frac{R_1}{R_3} = \frac{3I_3^2}{2I_1^2} = \frac{3I_3^2}{3I_3^2 \times 2} = \frac{1}{2}$$

$$\frac{\text{Copper three-phase}}{\text{Copper single-phase}} = \frac{\text{No. of wires three-phase}}{\text{No. of wires single-phase}} \times \frac{R_1}{R_3} = \frac{3}{2} \times \frac{1}{2} = \frac{3}{4}$$

The above shows that the same amount of power may be transmitted a fixed distance with a fixed line loss with only three-fourths of the amount of copper that would be required for single-phase, or one-third more copper is required for single-phase than would be necessary for three-phase.

Comparison of Three-Phase with Four-Phase.

$$P_3 = \sqrt{3}VI_3 \cos\theta$$

$$P_4 = 4\frac{V}{2}I_4 \cos\theta$$

(*Note:* V is highest voltage between any pair of wires.) Therefore

$$\sqrt{3}VI_3 \cos\theta = 4\frac{V}{2}I_4 \cos\theta$$

$$\sqrt{3}I_3 = \frac{4}{2}I_4$$

$$\frac{I_3}{I_4} = \frac{2}{\sqrt{3}}$$

$$3I_3^2R_3 = 4I_4^2R_4$$

$$\frac{R_4}{R_3} = \frac{3I_3^2}{4I_4^2} = \frac{3}{4} \times \frac{4}{3} = 1$$

$$\frac{\text{Copper three-phase}}{\text{Copper four-phase}} = \frac{3}{4} \times \frac{1}{1} = \frac{3}{4}$$

This is the same relation as shown for single-phase. If other systems are compared with three-phase in this manner, it will be found that three-phase is more economical in the use of copper than any other number of phases.

When a fixed amount of power is transmitted a fixed distance with a fixed loss for the same voltage to neutral, there is no difference between any of the systems. Consider three-phase and single-phase. The voltage to neutral single-phase is half the voltage between lines. This point is called the neutral, since the potential from either line to it is the same.

$$P_3 = P_1$$

$$3V_nI_3 \cos\theta = 2V_nI_1 \cos\theta$$

$$\frac{I_3}{I_1} = \frac{2}{3}$$

$$3I_3^2R_3 = 2I_1^2R_1$$

$$\frac{R_1}{R_3} = \frac{3I_3^2}{2I_1^2} = \frac{3}{2} \times \frac{4}{9} = \frac{2}{3}$$

$$\frac{\text{Copper three-phase}}{\text{Copper single-phase}} = \frac{3}{2} \times \frac{2}{3} = 1 \quad \text{(for same voltage to neutral)}$$

Comparison of Three-Phase with n-Phase for the Same Voltage to Neutral.

$$P_3 = P_n$$

$$3V_nI_3 \cos\theta = nV_nI_n \cos\theta$$

$$\frac{I_3}{I_n} = \frac{n}{3}$$

$$3I_3{}^2R_3 = nI_n{}^2R_n$$

$$\frac{R_n}{R_3} = \frac{3}{n}\frac{I_3{}^2}{I_n{}^2} = \frac{3}{n}\frac{n^2}{3^2} = \frac{n}{3}$$

$$\frac{\text{Copper three-phase}}{\text{Copper } n\text{-phase}} = \frac{3}{n}\frac{n}{3} = 1 \quad \text{(for same voltage to neutral)}$$

There is no difference in the amount of copper required between any of the systems if the voltage to neutral is fixed and if the same amount of power is transmitted a fixed distance at a fixed line loss.

Two-phase transmission was not considered in the above comparisons. When it is recognized that two-phase is the same as two independent single-phase systems, it is evident that two-phase, four-wire transmission requires the same amount of copper as single-phase. There are twice as many wires, but each is only one-half of the cross section of those necessary for single-phase.

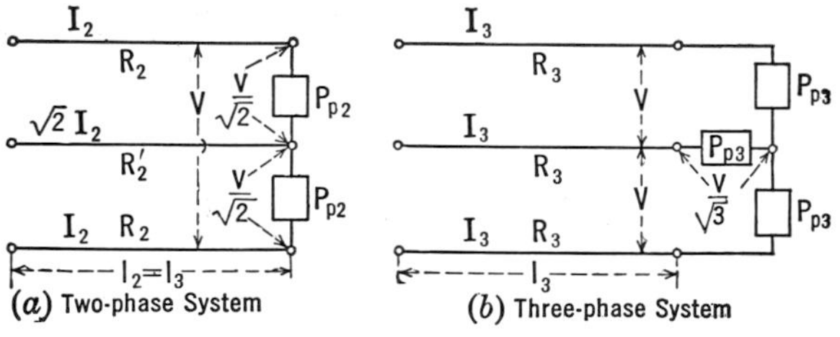

FIG. 49. See Problem 13.

Problem 13. Refer to Fig. 49. Find the ratio of the copper required for two-phase, three-wire transmission to that required for three-phase, three-wire transmission under the following conditions, all imposed simultaneously.

(*a*) A fixed amount of power transmitted.
(*b*) The same distance.
(*c*) With the same total line loss.
(*d*) With the same highest line voltage between any pair of lines in the two systems.
(*e*) With the same current density in the three two-phase conductors.

Hint:

From condition (*a*): $P_{2t} = 2V_{p2}I_2 \cos\theta = P_{3t} = 3V_{p3}I_3 \cos\theta$

From condition (*d*): $I_2 = \dfrac{\sqrt{3}}{\sqrt{2}} I_3$

From condition (*c*): $2I_2{}^2R_2 + (\sqrt{2}I_2)^2R_{2'} = 3I_3{}^2R_3$

From condition (*e*): Area of $R_{2'}$ wire $= \sqrt{2} \times$ area of R_2 wire

From condition (*b*): $R_{2'} = \dfrac{R_2}{\sqrt{2}}$ *Ans.:* 1.94.

Harmonics in the Wye System. An emf generated in a conductor will be sinusoidal only when the flux cutting the conductor varies according to a sine law. In a-c generators it is rather difficult, if not entirely impossible, to obtain an exact sine wave of distribution of the field flux. The slots and teeth change the reluctance of the path for the flux and cause ripples in the flux wave. Even if the distribution of the field flux were sinusoidal at no load, the distribution would be altered as the load came on, owing to the effect of the armature reaction of the current in the armature. The result is to induce in each phase an emf wave that is somewhat distorted from a true sine wave. In modern machines this distortion is relatively small. Through certain arrangements of the inductors on the armature and through certain ways of connecting them, some of the harmonics in the wave are reduced or are made to cancel entirely. When iron-core transformers are connected in wye, or any other way for that matter, the exciting current cannot be sinusoidal even though the impressed voltage is a perfect sine wave. This is due to the varying reluctance of the magnetic circuit with the consequent requirement of more ampere-turns to produce a given change in flux when the core operates at the higher flux densities. It therefore becomes of some importance to consider the effects of certain harmonics of currents and voltages in the phases of a three-phase system in affecting the line voltage of the system.

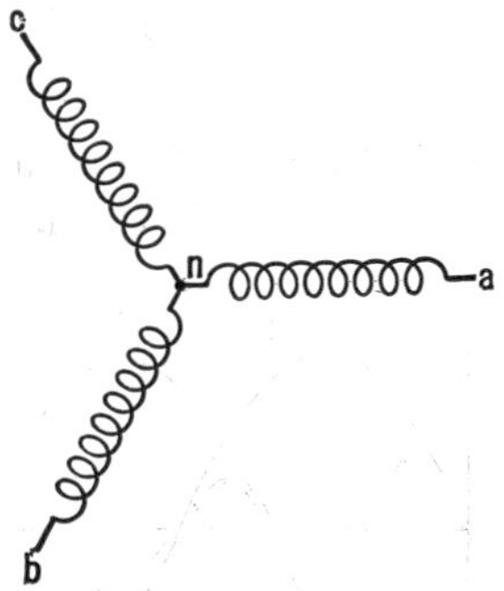

FIG. 50. Diagrammatic sketch of a wye-connected generator.

Assume that the emf induced in phase *a* of the wye-connected generator diagrammatically shown in Fig. 50 is

$$e_{na} = E_{m1} \sin \omega t + E_{m3} \sin (3\omega t + \alpha_3) + E_{m5} \sin (5\omega t + \alpha_5) + E_{m7} \sin (7\omega t + \alpha_7) \quad (28)$$

The sequence e_{na}, e_{nb}, e_{nc} will be used. Hence the fundamental of emf in phase nb will lag that in na by 120°, while that in phase nc will lag phase na by 240°. As usual, a shift of one degree for the fundamental will be a shift of n degrees for the nth harmonic. Then

$$\begin{aligned} e_{nb} &= E_{m1} \sin (\omega t - 120°) + E_{m3} \sin (3\omega t + \alpha_3 - 360°) \\ &\quad + E_{m5} \sin (5\omega t + \alpha_5 - 600°) + E_{m7} \sin (7\omega t + \alpha_7 - 840°) \\ &= E_{m1} \sin (\omega t - 120°) + E_{m3} \sin (3\omega t + \alpha_3) \\ &\quad + E_{m5} \sin (5\omega t + \alpha_5 - 240°) + E_{m7} \sin (7\omega t + \alpha_7 - 120°) \end{aligned} \tag{29}$$

$$\begin{aligned} e_{nc} &= E_{m1} \sin (\omega t - 240°) + E_{m3} \sin (3\omega t + \alpha_3) \\ &\quad + E_{m5} \sin (5\omega t + \alpha_5 - 120°) + E_{m7} \sin (7\omega t + \alpha_7 - 240°) \end{aligned} \tag{30}$$

The equations of the phase voltages show that all third harmonics are in phase. Also the phase sequence for the fifth harmonic is reversed from that of the fundamental. The sequence of the seventh is the same

TABLE 1

DISPLACEMENT BETWEEN VARIOUS HARMONICS IN THE PHASES OF FIG. 50

Displacement in electrical degrees

Harmonic	1	3	5	7	9	11	13
Phase A	0	0	0	0	0	0	0
Phase B	120	0	240	120	0	240	120
Phase C	240	0	120	240	0	120	240

as that for the fundamental. In general it will be found that the fundamental and all harmonics obtained by adding a multiple of 6 to the fundamental will have the same sequence. These are first, seventh, thirteenth, nineteenth, twenty-fifth, and so on. In like manner, the fifths, elevenths, seventeenths, twenty-thirds, etc., have like sequences but opposite to that of the fundamentals. Also the third, ninth, and all multiples of the third will be found to be in phase. These results are tabulated in Table 1. The relation between the fundamentals and third harmonics in each phase for $\alpha_3 = 0$ in equations (28), (29), and (30) is shown in Fig. 51.

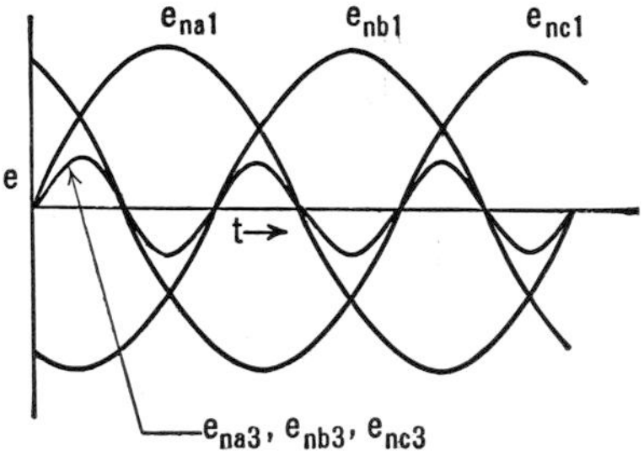

FIG. 51. Fundamental and third harmonic voltages.

The line voltage of the wye may be found by summing up the potentials encountered in passing through the circuit between the line terminals in question. With reference to Fig. 50,

$$e_{ba} = e_{bn} + e_{na}$$

Each harmonic must be handled separately. The combination of e_{bn} and e_{na} is shown by vector diagrams in Fig. 52. For the funda-

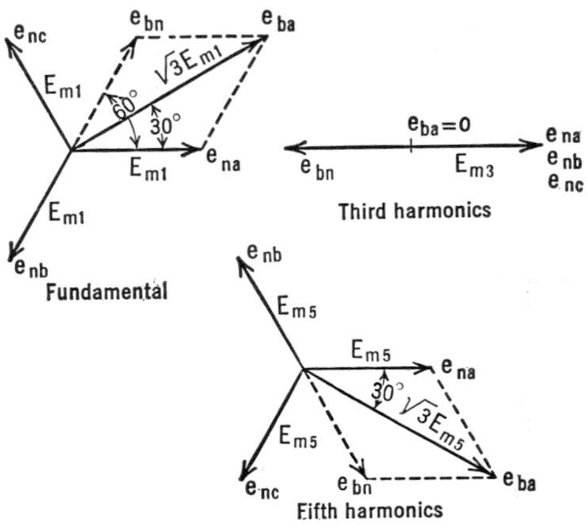

FIG. 52. Line voltages in Fig. 50 are found for each harmonic separately.

mental, e_{ba} is 30° ahead of e_{na}. Since $e_{na_1} = E_{m1} \sin \omega t$, $e_{ba_1} = \sqrt{3}E_{m1} \sin (\omega t + 30°)$. For the third harmonic, $e_{ba_3} = 0$. For the fifth, e_{ba_5} lags e_{na_5} by 30°. Hence $e_{ba_5} = \sqrt{3}E_{m5} \sin (5\omega t + \alpha_5 - 30°)$. The seventh-harmonic vector diagram is similar to that for the fundamental. The complete equation for the line voltage e_{ba} is

$$e_{ba} = \sqrt{3}E_{m1} \sin (\omega t + 30°) + \sqrt{3}E_{m5} \sin (5\omega t + \alpha_5 - 30°) + \sqrt{3}E_{m7} \sin (7\omega t + \alpha_7 + 30°) \quad (31)$$

Similarly,

$$e_{ac} = \sqrt{3}E_{m1} \sin (\omega t + 150°) + \sqrt{3}E_{m5} \sin (5\omega t + \alpha_5 - 150°) + \sqrt{3}E_{m7} \sin (7\omega t + \alpha_7 + 150°) \quad (32)$$

$$e_{cb} = \sqrt{3}E_{m1} \sin (\omega t - 90°) + \sqrt{3}E_{m5} \sin (5\omega t + \alpha_5 + 90°) + \sqrt{3}E_{m7} \sin (7\omega t + \alpha_7 - 90°) \quad (33)$$

The vector diagram of the third-harmonic voltages shows that the third harmonics in the two phases between any pair of terminals are in opposition and cancel. The third harmonics cannot contribute anything to line voltage, although they do contribute toward the total voltage between one terminal and neutral. The rms magnitude of the voltage to neutral in the example just considered is

$$E_{na} = \sqrt{\frac{E_{m1}{}^2 + E_{m3}{}^2 + E_{m5}{}^2 + E_{m7}{}^2}{2}}$$

The rms magnitude of the voltage between terminals is

$$E_{ba} = \sqrt{3}\sqrt{\frac{E_{m1}{}^2 + E_{m5}{}^2 + E_{m7}{}^2}{2}}$$

The ratio of line and phase voltage of a wye connection can be the $\sqrt{3}$ only when there is no third harmonic or its multiples in the wave of phase voltage.

Consider next the harmonics in the current waves for the wye. Kirchhoff's current law applied to the wye connection without a neutral wire connected states that

$$i_{na} + i_{nb} + i_{nc} = 0$$

Under balanced conditions this equation can be fulfilled only when the three currents are equal in magnitude and 120° apart in time phase, or when the magnitudes of each current are equal to zero. Since the third harmonics and their multiples are the only ones that are not 120° apart, each of them must be zero to fulfil the conditions imposed by Kirchhoff's current law. The vector diagrams for the harmonics of current appear exactly as those for phase voltages in Fig. 52. If, in each phase, e is replaced by i, the diagrams will represent currents. If the third harmonics of current do exist, there must be a neutral connection. This neutral or fourth wire furnishes the return path for the third harmonics of each phase. Since all third harmonics, in accordance with the diagram in Fig. 52, would have to be in phase, their arithmetic sum would flow in the neutral. A third-harmonic pressure or voltage may exist in each phase, but, unless a path through the neutral is provided, the three voltages do not have a closed circuit upon which they can act and, therefore, no third-harmonic current can flow. In a balanced wye-connected circuit without neutral connection, therefore, all harmonics except the third and its multiples can exist. In a four-wire, three-phase circuit (neutral wire connected) all harmonics in the current wave can exist.

Harmonics in the Delta System. If three coils having induced voltages as given by e_{na}, e_{nb}, and e_{nc} in the previous article are connected in delta, those voltages that do not add to zero around the loop will cause a circulating current to flow. Under any circumstances, in the delta of Fig. 53, the sum of the three terminal voltages taken in the same direction around the delta must be zero. Expressed algebraically,

$$v_{ca} + v_{ab} + v_{bc} = 0 \qquad (34)$$

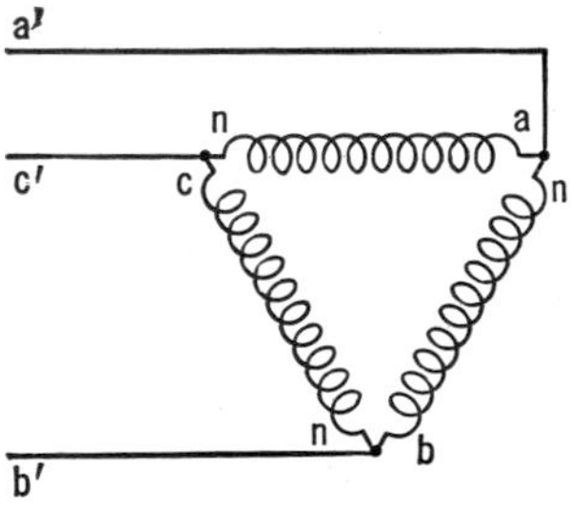

FIG. 53. Coils of Fig. 50 reconnected in delta.

Because the sum of the generated emf's, $e_{na} + e_{nb} + e_{nc}$, is equal to zero for all except triple-frequency voltages and its multiples, no circulatory current of other than triple frequency and its multiples can exist. Hence there will be no impedance drops at no load, and the generated voltages for all except the third harmonic and its multiples will appear across the terminals. For the third harmonic and its multiples the situation is different. Since the third-harmonic generated voltages of all phases of a three-phase system were shown to be equal and in phase,

$$e_{na_3} + e_{nb_3} + e_{nc_3} = 3E_{m3} \sin (3\omega t + \alpha_3)$$

will cause a current to circulate in the delta. This current multiplied by the impedance of the loop will be equal to the resultant third-harmonic voltage $3E_{m3} \sin (3\omega t + \alpha_3)$. Since the terminal voltage is equal to the generated voltage minus the internal drop, there will be no third-harmonic voltage between terminals in the delta if the phase emf's and impedances are balanced. In this way equation (34) is fulfilled for the third-harmonic voltages.

There is no third harmonic in the terminal voltage of the wye; neither is the wye connection subject to a third-harmonic circulating current. In the wye the third-harmonic voltages between terminals do not appear, as the result of their being in opposition between two terminals and neutralizing. In the delta, the third-harmonic voltage does not appear in the terminal voltage because it is short-circuited by the mesh connection and is consumed in the form of internal impedance drop. The equations of the terminal voltages of the delta generator or transformer at no load are the same as the generated voltages of each phase with the third-harmonic voltage and its multiples omitted. Thus

$$v_{ca} = E_{m1} \sin \omega t + E_{m5} \sin (5\omega t + \alpha_5) + E_{m7} \sin (7\omega t + \alpha_7) \quad (35)$$

$$v_{ab} = E_{m1} \sin (\omega t - 120°) + E_{m5} \sin (5\omega t + \alpha_5 - 240°) + E_{m7} \sin (7\omega t + \alpha_7 - 120°) \quad (36)$$

$$v_{bc} = E_{m1} \sin (\omega t - 240°) + E_{m5} \sin (5\omega t + \alpha_5 - 120°) + E_{m7} \sin (7\omega t + \alpha_7 - 240°) \quad (37)$$

Compare equations (35), (36), and (37) with equations (28), (29), and (30).

All harmonics of current are possible in the phases of the delta, since it is simply a closed series loop. Thus for phase *ca*, Fig. 53, we may have

$$i_{ca} = I_{m1} \sin \omega t + I_{m3} \sin (3\omega t + \alpha_3) + I_{m5} \sin (5\omega t + \alpha_5) + I_{m7} \sin (7\omega t + \alpha_7) \quad (38)$$

If the sequence is such that phase *ab* lags *ca* by 120°, the currents in the other phases are found by displacing the fundamentals by the usual 120° and the *n*th harmonic by *n* times this angle. Thus

$$\begin{aligned} i_{ab} &= I_{m1} \sin (\omega t - 120°) + I_{m3} \sin (3\omega t + \alpha_3 - 360°) \\ &\quad + I_{m5} \sin (5\omega t + \alpha_5 - 600°) + I_{m7} \sin (7\omega t + \alpha_7 - 840°) \\ &= I_{m1} \sin (\omega t - 120°) + I_{m3} \sin (3\omega t + \alpha_3) \\ &\quad + I_{m5} \sin (5\omega t + \alpha_5 - 240°) + I_{m7} \sin (7\omega t + \alpha_7 - 120°) \end{aligned} \quad (39)$$

$$i_{bc} = I_{m1} \sin (\omega t - 240°) + I_{m3} \sin (3\omega t + \alpha_3) + I_{m5} \sin (5\omega t + \alpha_5 - 120°) + I_{m7} \sin (7\omega t + \alpha_7 - 240°) \quad (40)$$

The line currents are obtained in terms of phase current as indicated below.

$$i_{a'a} = i_{ac} + i_{ab}$$

$$i_{b'b} = i_{ba} + i_{bc}$$

$$i_{c'c} = i_{ca} + i_{cb}$$

These operations are performed similarly to those illustrated in the vector diagrams of Fig. 52 for voltages. The results are

$$i_{a'a} = \sqrt{3}I_{m1} \sin (\omega t - 150°) + \sqrt{3}I_{m5} \sin (5\omega t + \alpha_5 + 150°) + \sqrt{3}I_{m7} \sin (7\omega t + \alpha_7 - 150°) \quad (41)$$

$$i_{b'b} = \sqrt{3}I_{m1} \sin (\omega t + 90°) + \sqrt{3}I_{m5} \sin (5\omega t + \alpha_5 - 90°) + \sqrt{3}I_{m7} \sin (7\omega t + \alpha_7 + 90°) \quad (42)$$

$$i_{c'c} = \sqrt{3}I_{m1} \sin (\omega t - 30°) + \sqrt{3}I_{m5} \sin (5\omega t + \alpha_5 + 30°) + \sqrt{3}I_{m7} \sin (7\omega t + \alpha_7 - 30°) \quad (43)$$

Equations (41), (42), and (43) show that no third-harmonic currents can exist in the lines of a delta. The third-harmonic current in one phase coming to a line connection exactly equals the third-harmonic current in the other phase leaving the junction. This leaves no third-harmonic current to flow in the line connection.

The magnitude of the phase current is

$$I_p = \sqrt{\frac{I_{m1}{}^2 + I_{m3}{}^2 + I_{m5}{}^2 + I_{m7}{}^2}{2}}$$

The magnitude of the line current is

$$I_L = \sqrt{\frac{(\sqrt{3}I_{m1})^2 + (\sqrt{3}I_{m5})^2 + (\sqrt{3}I_{m7})^2}{2}}$$

$$= \sqrt{3}\sqrt{\frac{I_{m1}{}^2 + I_{m5}{}^2 + I_{m7}{}^2}{2}}$$

The ratio of line to phase current can be $\sqrt{3}$ only when no third-harmonic currents exist.

Example 9. Only fundamentals and third harmonics are assumed to exist in the voltages of a wye connection like that shown in Fig. 50. Voltmeter readings as follows are obtained: $V_{na} = 150$, $V_{ba} = 220$. Calculate the magnitude of the third-harmonic voltage.

Solution. Since V_{ba} contains only fundamental voltage, the fundamental to neutral is $220/\sqrt{3} = 127$.

$$V_{na} = \sqrt{V_1{}^2 + V_3{}^2} \quad \text{or} \quad V_3 = \sqrt{150^2 - 127^2} = 79.9$$

The possibility of a third-harmonic circulating current in a delta makes this connection for a-c generators somewhat less desirable than the wye, although there are several other more important factors that make wye connection for generators predominate. Although the third-harmonic current is undesirable in the delta generator it *is* desirable in transformers, since there it acts as a component of the magnetizing current for the core which is essential if a sine wave of flux and induced voltage is to be obtained. Some high-voltage transformers which are connected wye on both primary and secondary have a third winding which is delta-connected to allow a third-harmonic circulating current to flow, thus supplying the transformers with the necessary triple-frequency component of magnetizing current. A delta-connected winding of this kind is called a tertiary winding.

PROBLEMS

14. What is the phase voltage and also the voltage between adjacent lines of a six-phase star connection if the greatest voltage between any pair of lines is 156 volts?

15. The voltage between adjacent lines of a twelve-phase star is 100 volts. Find the voltage to neutral, the voltage between alternate lines, and the greatest voltage between any pair of lines.

16. Find the phase current in a six-phase mesh if the line current is 10 amperes; also for a twelve-phase mesh for the same line current.

17. Given six coils each having an induced voltage of 63.5 volts. Adjacent coil voltages are 60° apart. In how many ways may you connect these coils to form a balanced three-phase wye system of voltages if all coils must be used for each system and if the magnitude of the line voltages of each system must be different? What are the line voltages for each wye system?

18. A generator has six coils, adjacent coils being displaced 30 electrical degrees. If each coil voltage is 114 volts, show how to connect them and calculate the line or terminal voltage for three-phase star. Repeat for three-phase mesh. Repeat for two-phase, where line voltage is taken as the phase voltage.

19. A generator has six coils, adjacent coils being displaced 30 electrical degrees. If all coils are used to form a three-phase mesh, what must be the emf of each coil to yield balanced three-phase voltages of 230 volts each? If all coils are connected for three-phase star, what must be the emf of each coil to give an emf between lines of 230 volts?

20. Draw vector diagrams which represent the currents and voltages shown in Oscillograms 3 and 4, pages 355 and 356, and label them in accordance with the labeling on the oscillogram.

21. Three-phase line voltages of 230 volts are impressed on a balanced wye load having 16 ohms resistance and 12 ohms reactance in series in each phase. Find the line current and total power. If the three impedances are reconnected in delta and placed across the same line voltages, what are the line and phase currents and the total power?

22. A current of 10 amperes flows in the lines to a twelve-phase mesh-connected load having 5 ohms resistance and 8 ohms capacitive reactance in series in each phase. What is the voltage between alternate lines on the load? Draw the vector diagram of the voltages and phase currents of two adjacent phases, and also show the line current from the junction of these two phases.

23. A balanced wye load consists of 3 ohms resistance and 4 ohms capacitive reactance in series per phase. Balanced three-phase voltages of 100 volts each are impressed across the lines at the load. If the load is connected to a generator through three lines of equal impedance, each line containing a resistance of 1 ohm and an inductive reactance of 4 ohms, find the voltage at the generator terminals.

24. A balanced wye load having 8 ohms resistance and 6 ohms inductive reactance in series in each phase is supplied through lines each having 1 ohm resistance and 2 ohms inductive reactance. If the sending-end voltage between lines is 250 volts, what will be the voltage between lines at the load?

25. A balanced delta load contains a resistance of 12 ohms and a capacitive reactance of 16 ohms in series in each phase. If the balanced impressed line voltages on the load are 115 volts each, calculate the line and phase currents.

26. A balanced delta load having 18 ohms resistance and 24 ohms capacitive reactance in series in each phase is supplied through lines each having 1 ohm resistance and 2 ohms inductive reactance. If the line-to-line voltage at the sending end is 250 volts, find the line-to-line voltage at the load terminals. Also find the total power consumed by the load.

27. A balanced wye inductive load takes 5.4 kw at 0.6 power factor at a line voltage of 200 volts. It is in parallel with a pure resistive balanced wye load taking 5 kw. Find the resultant line current supplied the combination.

28. The total power supplied two balanced three-phase loads in parallel is 12 kw at 0.8 power factor lagging. One of the loads takes 10 kva at 0.8 power-factor lead. The second load is a delta-connected balanced load. Find the resistance and reactance per phase of the delta load if the line voltage is 230 volts. If the unknown load were wye-connected, what would be the resistance and reactance per phase?

29. Each phase of a delta load has 6 ohms resistance and 9 ohms capacitive reactance in series. Each phase of a wye load has 8 ohms resistance and 6 ohms inductive reactance in series. The two loads are connected in parallel across three-phase line voltages of 100 volts. Calculate the resultant line current, the total power consumed, and the power factor of the combination.

30. A three-phase, 5-hp, 220-volt induction motor (balanced load) has an efficiency of 86 per cent and operates at 86.6 per cent lagging power factor. It is paralleled with a three-phase resistance furnace consisting of three 36-ohm resistances connected in delta. Find the kilovolt-amperes demanded by the combination, the power factor, and the line current.

31. A three-phase generator supplies balanced voltages of 230 volts each at its terminals when it carries a load which requires 10 amperes. If the power factor at the generator terminals is 0.8 leading, calculate the voltage at the load if the load is connected through lines each having 1 ohm resistance and 5 ohms inductive reactance.

32. A balanced three-phase load requires 10 kva at 0.5 lagging power factor. Find the kva size of a condenser bank which may be paralleled with the load to bring the power factor of the combination to 0.866 lag, and also to 0.866 lead.

33. If the line voltage for Problem 32 is 230 volts and the frequency 60 cycles, find the capacitance in microfarads of capacitors required in each phase of the capacitor bank if they are delta-connected. What capacitance is required if they are wye-connected?

34. Three $15\underline{/60^\circ}$-ohm load impedances are connected in delta and supplied by lines, each line containing 1 ohm resistance and 1 ohm inductive reactance. If the line voltages on the supply side of the line impedances are balanced three-phase of 115 volts each, find the voltage across the load impedances. Also calculate the power loss in the supply lines and the power dissipated by the load itself.

35. If the current through each of the load impedances in Problem 34 is 20 amperes, find the required voltage on the supply side of the line impedances.

36. A three-phase line has three capacitors, each having a reactance of 300 ohms connected in delta across the lines at the source. Three similar capacitors are so connected between the lines at the load. Between these two sets of capacitors each line has a series inductive reactance of 10 ohms. If a balanced three-phase load of 100 kva at 0.6 power-factor lag requires 2300 volts between lines, what voltage between lines will be required at the source? What will be the power input to the lines and the power factor at the source?

37. The motor M in Fig. 54 has 2300 volts balanced three-phase voltages impressed at its terminals and takes 120 kva at 0.6 leading power factor. Calculate the line volts, power input, and the power factor at a, b, c.

38. If the motor in Fig. 54 is removed from the circuit and balanced three-phase

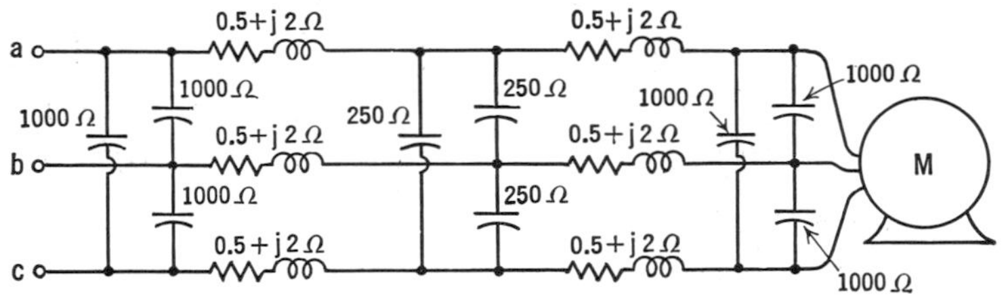

FIG. 54. See Problems 37 and 38.

line voltages of 2300 volts each are impressed at a, b, and c, how many volts will appear between lines at the motor end of the line?

39. A three-phase resonant shunt is connected to three-phase, 2300-volt lines to furnish a low impedance for a certain frequency so as to reduce the inductive interference with a telephone line. The shunt consists of three 10-kva, 60-cycle, 2300-volt capacitors connected in delta. In series with each line terminal from the delta is an inductance of 2.5 millihenrys. At what frequency does this three-phase combination resonate, that is, offer minimum impedance? Assume that resistances of capacitors and inductances are negligible.

40. (a) Three coils each having 36 ohms resistance and 100 millihenrys inductance are connected in delta. Find the microfarad capacitance of each capacitor which may be placed in each of the three lines from the delta to produce resonance (unity p.f.) of the system as a whole for a frequency of 800 cycles. This is a type of resonant shunt sometimes connected to power lines to reduce inductive interference with telephone circuits.

(b) Assume that the capacitors calculated for each line in (a) are removed and connected in delta. Find how many henrys of inductance would be required in each line from this delta to bring the power factor of the combination to unity at 800 cycles.

41. Find the readings of W_a and W_b in Fig. 55 for the sequence V_{na}, V_{nc}, V_{nb}. Find the power dissipated in each phase.

42. A balanced three-phase load takes 5 kw and 20 reactive kva. Find the readings of two wattmeters properly connected to measure the total power.

43. In Fig. 55 find the reading of W_R. Also calculate the total reactive volt-amperes taken by the load. What is the ratio of the total reactive volt-amperes taken to the reading of W_R?

44. Prove that the ratio of the reading of W_R of Fig. 55 to the total reactive volt-amperes obtained in Problem 43 will obtain for all balanced loads when the impressed voltages are sinusoidal balanced three-phase.

45. (a) Calculate analytically the power-factor angle for a balanced three-phase circuit in which two wattmeters properly connected to measure three-phase power read +1000 and +800 watts, respectively.

(b) Also calculate the angle if the meters read +1000 and −800 watts, respectively.

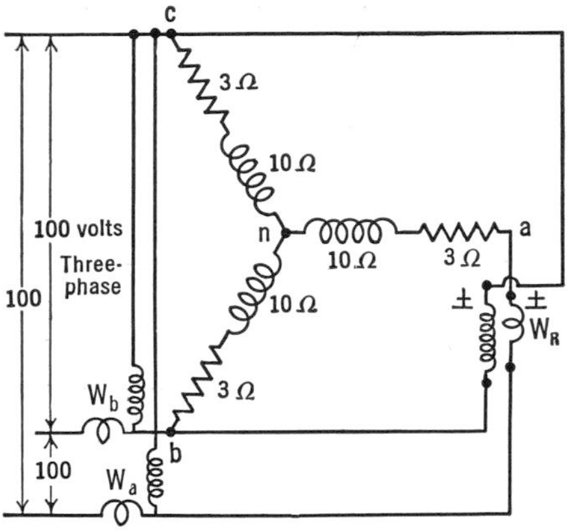

FIG. 55. See Problems 41, 43, and 44.

46. Two wattmeters measuring power to a balanced three-phase load read 1200 and −400 watts, respectively. How many volt-amperes does the load take? At what power factor?

47. The power to a balanced three-phase leading-power-factor load is measured by two wattmeters. The wattmeter having its current coil in line A and its potential coil from line A to line C indicates +1000 watts. The other wattmeter with its current coil in line B and its potential coil from line B to line C indicates +400 watts. What is the voltage sequence? What is the power factor of the load?

48. Each phase of a balanced twelve-phase star-connected load consists of 3 ohms resistance and 4 ohms inductive reactance in series. Balanced twelve-phase line voltages of 51.76 volts between adjacent lines are applied to the load. Calculate the line current, power factor, and total power consumed by the load.

49. The voltage induced in phase na of a three-phase wye-connected generator is

$$e_{na} = 127 \sin \omega t + 50 \sin (3\omega t - 30°) + 30 \sin (5\omega t + 40°)$$

If the sequence is e_{na}, e_{nb}, e_{nc}, find the equation with respect to time of the line voltage e_{ab}. *Note:* Phase voltages of polyphase generators differ only in phase angle.

50. If the phases of the generator in Problem 49 are reconnected in delta, what will be the equation with respect to time of the line voltage across phase na?

51. A wye-connected generator has a generated voltage per phase which contains only the fundamental, third, fifth, and seventh harmonics. The line voltage as measured by a voltmeter is 230 volts; the voltage to neutral is 160 volts. Calculate the magnitude of the third harmonic in the generated voltage.

52. The induced emf of a delta generator with one corner of the delta open as shown in Fig. 56 contains only odd harmonics up to the seventh. A voltmeter across ac reads 2500 volts, and, across bb' when negligible current flows, 1800 volts. Find the reading of a voltmeter connected from a to b'.

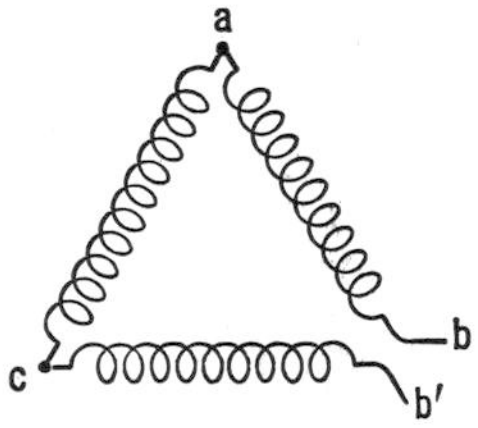

FIG. 56. See Problems 52 and 53.

53. The induced phase voltage of a delta generator with one corner open as shown in Fig. 56 contains odd harmonics up to the seventh. A voltmeter connected from a to b' reads 2500 volts, and from a to c it reads 2200 volts when negligible current flows. What should it read from b to b'?

54. Figure 57 shows a generator connected to a balanced pure resistance load. An ammeter in the neutral reads 15 amperes, and the wattmeter shown reads 600 watts. A voltmeter shows a balanced line voltage of 230 volts. Find the line currents to the load and the voltage from line to neutral at the load, assuming that the generated voltage contains only fundamental and third-harmonic components.

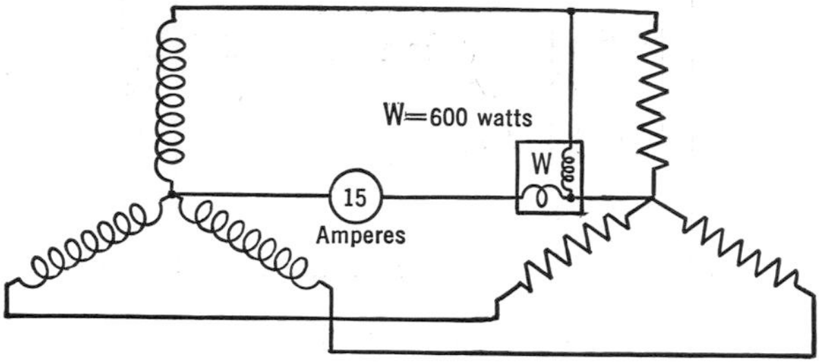

Fig. 57. See Problem 54.

chapter IX Unbalanced Polyphase Circuits

Unbalanced Loads. The previous chapter developed the method of calculating the currents in the various branches of balanced polyphase loads when the impedances and impressed voltages are known. In the present chapter, methods of calculating the various branch currents will be developed when known voltages are impressed upon unbalanced loads. Any polyphase load in which the impedance in one or more phases differs from those of other phases is said to be unbalanced. Even though the load impedances of the various phases are identical, one of the methods of calculating unbalanced loads must be employed if the voltages impressed on the load are unequal and differ in phase by angles which are not equal. Some of the simpler types of unbalanced loads which are solvable by rather simple direct methods will be considered first.

Unbalanced Delta Loads. If the three-phase line voltages across the terminals of an unbalanced delta load are fixed, the voltage drop across each phase impedance is known. The currents in each phase can therefore be determined directly. The line currents can be found by adding vectorially the two component currents coming toward or flowing away from the line terminal in question as was done in series-parallel circuit analysis. The following example will illustrate the procedure.

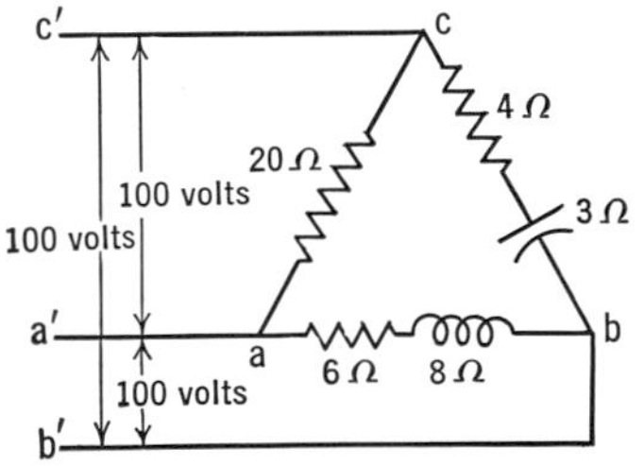

FIG. 1. Unbalanced delta load. See example 1.

Example 1. Given the unbalanced delta load shown in Fig. 1. Calculate all currents for the three-phase balanced voltages shown on the figure, if the voltage sequence is *ab–ca–bc*.

Since the voltages shown are assumed to be maintained at the terminals *a*, *b*, and *c*, the complex expressions for the phase voltages may be established. Take some phase voltage as a reference, say $\mathbf{V}_{ab}$ for this example. Therefore,

$$\mathbf{V}_{ab} = 100 + j0$$

$$\mathbf{V}_{bc} = 100 \underline{/120^\circ} = -50 + j86.6$$

$$\mathbf{V}_{ca} = 100 \underline{/-120^\circ} = -50 - j86.6 \text{ volts}$$

Then

$$\mathbf{I}_{ab} = \frac{\mathbf{V}_{ab}}{\mathbf{Z}_{ab}} = \frac{100 + j0}{6 + j8} = 6 - j8 = 10 \underline{/-53.1^\circ} \text{ amperes}$$

$$\mathbf{I}_{bc} = \frac{\mathbf{V}_{bc}}{\mathbf{Z}_{bc}} = \frac{-50 + j86.6}{4 - j3} = -18.39 + j7.856 = 20 \underline{/156.9^\circ} \text{ amperes}$$

$$\mathbf{I}_{ca} = \frac{\mathbf{V}_{ca}}{\mathbf{Z}_{ca}} = \frac{-50 - j86.6}{20 + j0} = -2.5 - j4.33 = 5 \underline{/-120^\circ} \text{ amperes}$$

The line currents are:

$$\mathbf{I}_{a'a} = \mathbf{I}_{ab} + \mathbf{I}_{ac} = 6 - j8 + 2.5 + j4.33 = 8.5 - j3.67$$
$$= 9.26 \underline{/-23.4^\circ} \text{ amperes}$$

$$\mathbf{I}_{b'b} = \mathbf{I}_{ba} + \mathbf{I}_{bc} = -6 + j8 - 18.39 + j7.856$$
$$= -24.39 + j15.856 = 29 \underline{/146.9^\circ} \text{ amperes}$$

$$\mathbf{I}_{c'c} = \mathbf{I}_{ca} + \mathbf{I}_{cb} = -2.5 - j4.33 + 18.39 - j7.856$$
$$= 15.89 - j12.186 = 20 \underline{/-37.3^\circ} \text{ amperes}$$

Unbalanced Wye Loads. If the load voltages at the terminals a, b, and c of an unbalanced wye load like that shown in Fig. 2 can be assumed to remain constant at their specified values, then the phase currents of an equivalent delta which replaces the wye can be found directly as shown in example 1. The line currents to this equivalent delta are obviously the currents in the phases of the wye load.

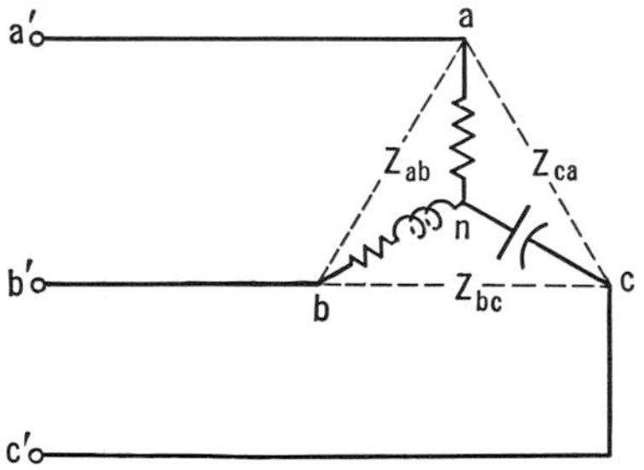

FIG. 2. Conversion from a wye-connected load to an equivalent delta-connected load.

Example 2. A balanced set of three-phase voltages is connected to an unbalanced set of wye-connected impedances as shown in Fig. 2. The following values are assumed to be known:

$$\mathbf{V}_{ab} = 212 \underline{/90^\circ} \text{ volts} \qquad \mathbf{Z}_{an} = 10 + j0 \text{ ohms}$$
$$\mathbf{V}_{bc} = 212 \underline{/-150^\circ} \text{ volts} \qquad \mathbf{Z}_{bn} = 10 + j10 \text{ ohms}$$
$$\mathbf{V}_{ca} = 212 \underline{/-30^\circ} \text{ volts} \qquad \mathbf{Z}_{cn} = 0 - j20 \text{ ohms}$$

The line currents $\mathbf{I}_{a'a}$, $\mathbf{I}_{b'b}$, and $\mathbf{I}_{c'c}$ are to be determined by the wye to delta conversion method. (See Chapter V, page 210, for the general theory involved in making wye to delta conversions.)

In Fig. 2 the equivalent delta impedances may be expressed in terms of the wye impedances as follows:

$$\mathbf{Z}_{ab} = \frac{(\mathbf{Z}_{an}\mathbf{Z}_{bn} + \mathbf{Z}_{bn}\mathbf{Z}_{cn} + \mathbf{Z}_{cn}\mathbf{Z}_{an})}{\mathbf{Z}_{nc}} = \frac{\mathbf{S}}{\mathbf{Z}_{nc}}$$

$$\mathbf{Z}_{bc} = \frac{\mathbf{S}}{\mathbf{Z}_{an}} \quad \text{and} \quad \mathbf{Z}_{ca} = \frac{\mathbf{S}}{\mathbf{Z}_{bn}}$$

Numerically, the equivalent delta impedances are:

$$\mathbf{Z}_{ab} = \frac{300 - j300}{0 - j20} = (15 + j15) = 21.2 \underline{/45^\circ} \text{ ohms}$$

$$\mathbf{Z}_{bc} = \frac{300 - j300}{10 - j0} = (30 - j30) = 42.4 \underline{/-45^\circ} \text{ ohms}$$

$$\mathbf{Z}_{ca} = \frac{300 - j300}{10 + j10} = (0 - j30) = 30.0 \underline{/-90^\circ} \text{ ohms}$$

The load currents in the equivalent delta are:

$$\mathbf{I}_{ab} = \frac{\mathbf{V}_{ab}}{\mathbf{Z}_{ab}} = \frac{212 \underline{/90^\circ}}{21.2 \underline{/45^\circ}} = 10 \underline{/45^\circ} \text{ amperes}$$

$$\mathbf{I}_{bc} = \frac{\mathbf{V}_{bc}}{\mathbf{Z}_{bc}} = \frac{212 \underline{/-150^\circ}}{42.4 \underline{/-45^\circ}} = 5.0 \underline{/-105^\circ} \text{ amperes}$$

$$\mathbf{I}_{ca} = \frac{\mathbf{V}_{ca}}{\mathbf{Z}_{ca}} = \frac{212 \underline{/-30^\circ}}{30 \underline{/-90^\circ}} = 7.07 \underline{/60^\circ} \text{ amperes}$$

The actual line and load currents are:

$$\begin{aligned}\mathbf{I}_{a'a} &= \mathbf{I}_{ab} - \mathbf{I}_{ca} \\ &= 10 \underline{/45^\circ} - 7.07 \underline{/60^\circ} = 3.66 \underline{/15^\circ} \text{ amperes} \\ \mathbf{I}_{b'b} &= \mathbf{I}_{bc} - \mathbf{I}_{ab} \\ &= 5 \underline{/-105^\circ} - 10 \underline{/45^\circ} = 14.56 \underline{/-125.1^\circ} \text{ amperes} \\ \mathbf{I}_{c'c} &= \mathbf{I}_{ca} - \mathbf{I}_{bc} \\ &= 7.07 \underline{/60^\circ} - 5 \underline{/-105^\circ} = 11.98 \underline{/66.2^\circ} \text{ amperes}\end{aligned}$$

As a single check on the above arithmetic let the calculated value of $[\mathbf{I}_{a'a}\mathbf{Z}_{an} - \mathbf{I}_{b'b}\mathbf{Z}_{bn}]$ be compared with the originally specified value of $\mathbf{V}_{ab}$, which was $212 \underline{/90^\circ}$ volts.

$$\begin{aligned}[\mathbf{I}_{a'a}\mathbf{Z}_{an} - \mathbf{I}_{b'b}\mathbf{Z}_{bn}] &= (35.4 + j9.48) - (35.35 - j202.6) \\ &= (0.05 + j212.1) \text{ volts} \qquad \textit{(Check)}\end{aligned}$$

The conversion of a wye to its equivalent delta along with the solution of the delta as illustrated in the above example will usually require an equal or greater amount of work than the direct solution of the wye employing two simultaneous equations obtained by the application of Kirchhoff's laws.

Vector diagrams of the voltages and currents involved in the foregoing example are given in Fig. 3.

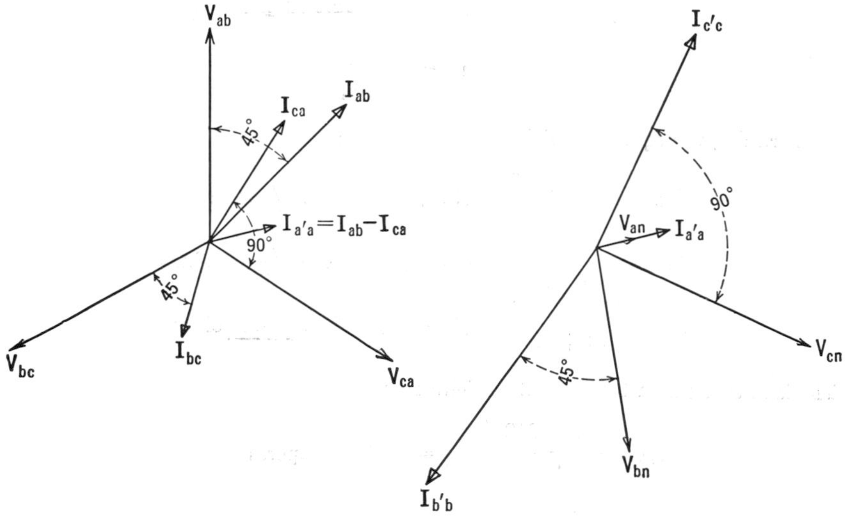

FIG. 3. Vector diagrams for example 2.

Problem 1. Determine the values of $\mathbf{V}_{an}$, $\mathbf{V}_{bn}$, and $\mathbf{V}_{cn}$ in example 2.

Ans.: $\mathbf{V}_{an} = 36.6 \underline{/15°}$; $\mathbf{V}_{bn} = 205.6 \underline{/-80.1°}$; $\mathbf{V}_{cn} = 239.6 \underline{/-23.8°}$ volts.

Problem 2. Determine the power dissipated in each of the three phases (*an*, *bn*, and *cn*) of example 2.

Ans.: $P_{an} = 134$; $P_{bn} = 2120$; $P_{cn} = 0$ watts.

Problem 3. Find the magnitudes of $\mathbf{I}_{a'a}$, $\mathbf{I}_{b'b}$, and $\mathbf{I}_{c'c}$ in Fig. 2 if $\mathbf{V}_{ab} = 212 \underline{/90°}$, $\mathbf{V}_{bc} = 212 \underline{/-30°}$, and $\mathbf{V}_{ca} = 212 \underline{/-150°}$ volts. As in example 2, $\mathbf{Z}_{an} = (10 + j0)$, $\mathbf{Z}_{bn} = (10 + j10)$, and $\mathbf{Z}_{cn} = (0 - j20)$ ohms.

Ans.: $I_{a'a} = 13.65$; $I_{b'b} = 6.20$; $I_{c'c} = 7.54$ amperes.

Combined Delta and Wye Loads. Delta-connected loads are sometimes operated in conjunction with wye-connected loads as shown in Fig. 4. If the three-phase, line-to-line voltages $\mathbf{V}_{ab}$, $\mathbf{V}_{bc}$, and $\mathbf{V}_{ca}$ remain sensibly constant irrespective of load conditions, a relatively simple solution may be effected by first converting the wye load to an equivalent delta load. The two parallel deltas may then be combined to form a single equivalent delta-connected load and the equivalent delta currents calculated directly as

$$\mathbf{I}_{ab(\text{eq})} = \frac{\mathbf{V}_{ab}}{\mathbf{Z}_{ab(\text{eq})}} \quad \mathbf{I}_{bc(\text{eq})} = \frac{\mathbf{V}_{bc}}{\mathbf{Z}_{bc(\text{eq})}} \quad \mathbf{I}_{ca(\text{eq})} = \frac{\mathbf{V}_{ca}}{\mathbf{Z}_{ca(\text{eq})}}$$

The above currents may be combined in the usual manner to find the line currents $\mathbf{I}_{a'a}$, $\mathbf{I}_{b'b}$, and $\mathbf{I}_{c'c}$. The details are reserved for student analysis. (See Problem 15, page 404.)

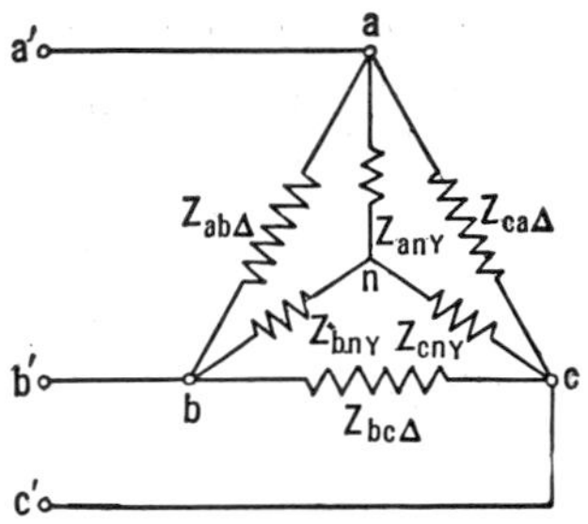

FIG. 4. Delta and wye loads on the same system of voltages.

Network Solutions. The solutions of unbalanced polyphase circuits are simply applications of Kirchhoff's laws. Some of the details are illustrated in the following example which refers to Fig. 5.

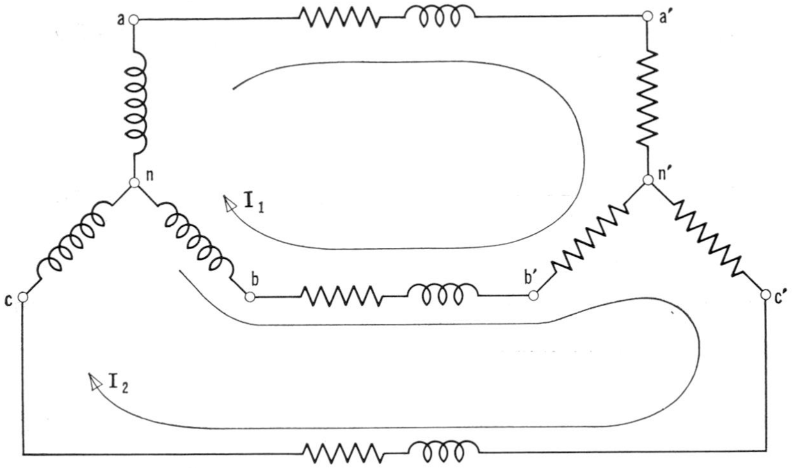

FIG. 5.

Example 3. The generated voltages and impedances for Fig. 5 are given as follows:

$$\mathbf{E}_{na} = 1000 + j0 = 1000\underline{/0°}$$

$$\mathbf{E}_{nb} = -500 - j866 = 1000\underline{/-120°}$$

$$\mathbf{E}_{nc} = -500 + j866 = 1000\underline{/-240°}$$

$\mathbf{Z}_{na} = 2 + j8$, $\mathbf{Z}_{aa'} = 1 + j2$, $\mathbf{Z}_{a'n'} = 19 + j18 = 26.2\underline{/43.45°}$, $\mathbf{Z}_{nb} = 2 + j8$, $\mathbf{Z}_{bb'} = 1 + j2$, $\mathbf{Z}_{b'n'} = 49 - j2 = 49.04\underline{/-2.34°}$, $\mathbf{Z}_{nc} = 2 + j8$, $\mathbf{Z}_{cc'} = 1 + j2$, and $\mathbf{Z}_{c'n'} = 29 + j50 = 57.8\underline{/59.9°}$.

In unbalanced polyphase circuits specification of the sequence employed is important because different solutions result from the two possible voltage sequences. For this example the sequence *abc* is assumed. This means that voltage of phase *b* lags that of phase *a* by 120°. All impedances in series are additive. Therefore the impedance of *naa'n'* is $\mathbf{Z}_a = 2 + j8 + 1 + j2 + 19 + j18 = 22 + j28 = 35.6\underline{/51.8°}$ ohms.

Likewise $\mathbf{Z}_b = 52 + j8 = 52.6\angle 8.8^\circ$ and $\mathbf{Z}_c = 32 + j60 = 68.0\angle 61.9^\circ$. The mesh-current solution will be illustrated first and for this solution the labeling of mesh currents is shown in Fig. 5. The equations are

$$(\mathbf{Z}_a + \mathbf{Z}_b)\mathbf{I}_1 - \mathbf{Z}_b\mathbf{I}_2 = \mathbf{E}_{na} + \mathbf{E}_{bn} = \mathbf{E}_{na} - \mathbf{E}_{nb} \tag{1}$$

$$(\mathbf{Z}_b + \mathbf{Z}_c)\mathbf{I}_2 - \mathbf{Z}_b\mathbf{I}_1 = \mathbf{E}_{nb} + \mathbf{E}_{cn} = \mathbf{E}_{nb} - \mathbf{E}_{nc} \tag{2}$$

Inserting the numerical values in the above two equations gives

$$(74 + j36)\mathbf{I}_1 - (52 + j8)\mathbf{I}_2 = 1500 + j866 \tag{3}$$

$$-(52 + j8)\mathbf{I}_1 + (84 + j68)\mathbf{I}_2 = -j1732 \tag{4}$$

$$\mathbf{I}_1 = \frac{\begin{vmatrix} (1500 + j866) & -(52 + j8) \\ -j1732 & (84 + j68) \end{vmatrix}}{\begin{vmatrix} (74 + j36) & -(52 + j8) \\ -(52 + j8) & (84 + j68) \end{vmatrix}} = 16.0\angle -34.9^\circ \text{ amperes} = \mathbf{I}_{aa'}$$

$$\mathbf{I}_2 = \frac{\begin{vmatrix} (74 + j36) & (1500 + j866) \\ (52 + j8) & -j1732 \end{vmatrix}}{\begin{vmatrix} (74 + j36) & -(52 + j8) \\ (52 + j8) & (84 + j68) \end{vmatrix}} = 20.7\angle -109.2^\circ \text{ amperes} = \mathbf{I}_{c'c}$$

$$\mathbf{I}_{bb'} = -\mathbf{I}_1 + \mathbf{I}_2 = -16\angle -34.9^\circ + 20.7\angle -109.2^\circ = 22.5\angle -152.5^\circ \text{ amperes}$$

The voltage drops at the load may now be determined as

$$\mathbf{V}_{a'n'} = \mathbf{I}_{aa'}\mathbf{Z}_{a'n'} = 16\angle -34.9^\circ \;\; 26.2\angle 43.45^\circ = 419\angle 8.55^\circ \text{ volts}$$

$$\mathbf{V}_{b'n'} = \mathbf{I}_{bb'}\mathbf{Z}_{b'n'} = 22.5\angle -152.5^\circ \;\; 49.04\angle -2.34^\circ = 1105\angle -154.84^\circ \text{ volts}$$

$$\mathbf{V}_{c'n'} = \mathbf{I}_{cc'}\mathbf{Z}_{c'n'} = 20.7\angle -109.2^\circ \;\; 57.8\angle 59.9^\circ = 1197\angle -49.3^\circ \text{ volts}$$

The line-to-line voltages at the load are obtained by adding the voltages encountered in tracing through the load circuit from one line to the other as follows:

$$\begin{aligned} \mathbf{V}_{a'b'} &= \mathbf{V}_{a'n'} + \mathbf{V}_{n'b'} = \mathbf{V}_{a'n'} - \mathbf{V}_{b'n'} = 419\angle 8.55^\circ - 1105\angle -154.84^\circ \\ &= 1512\angle 20.6^\circ \text{ volts} \end{aligned}$$

$$\mathbf{V}_{b'c'} = \mathbf{V}_{b'n'} + \mathbf{V}_{n'c'} = 1835\angle 166.2^\circ \text{ volts}$$

$$\mathbf{V}_{c'a'} = \mathbf{V}_{c'n'} + \mathbf{V}_{n'a'} = 1039\angle -69.3^\circ \text{ volts}$$

The above line voltages could be calculated from the generated voltage and line drops. Thus the application of Kirchhoff's voltage law gives

$$\mathbf{E}_{bn} + \mathbf{E}_{na} = \mathbf{I}_{aa'}(\mathbf{Z}_{na} + \mathbf{Z}_{aa'}) + \mathbf{V}_{a'b'} + \mathbf{I}_{b'b}\,(\mathbf{Z}_{bb'} + \mathbf{Z}_{nb})$$

or

$$\begin{aligned} \mathbf{V}_{a'b'} &= (\mathbf{E}_{bn} + \mathbf{E}_{na}) - \mathbf{I}_{aa'}(\mathbf{Z}_{na} + \mathbf{Z}_{aa'}) - \mathbf{I}_{b'b}(\mathbf{Z}_{bb'} + \mathbf{Z}_{nb}) \\ &= 1500 + j866 - 16.0\angle -34.9^\circ\,(3 + j10) + 22.5\angle -152.5^\circ\,(3 + j10) \\ &= 1413.2 + j531.6 = 1512\angle 20.6^\circ \text{ volts} \qquad \textit{(Check)} \end{aligned}$$

This calculation indicates that line and generator drops can be subtracted from the generated voltages to obtain the load voltages but the computation must be made with due regard to the proper phase of all quantities. Power in any branch is obtained in the usual way from the voltage and current in the particular branch.

The phasor diagrams of all voltages and currents may be obtained by plotting the complex quantities calculated for this example.

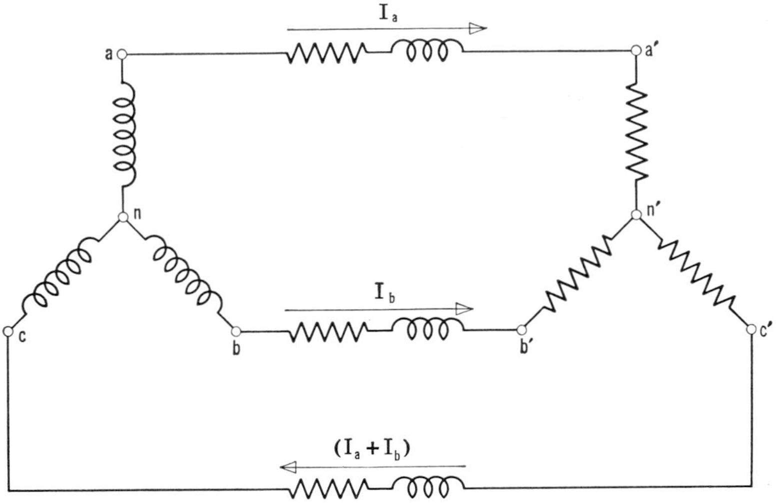

FIG. 6.

An alternative method of solving this problem is to label the circuit as shown in Fig. 6 and set up equations as follows:

$$\mathbf{Z}_a\mathbf{I}_a - \mathbf{Z}_b\mathbf{I}_b = \mathbf{E}_{bn} + \mathbf{E}_{na} = \mathbf{E}_{na} - \mathbf{E}_{nb} \quad (5)$$

$$\mathbf{Z}_b\mathbf{I}_b + \mathbf{Z}_c(\mathbf{I}_a + \mathbf{I}_b) = \mathbf{E}_{cn} + \mathbf{E}_{nb} = \mathbf{E}_{nb} - \mathbf{E}_{nc} \quad (6)$$

or

$$\mathbf{Z}_c\mathbf{I}_a + (\mathbf{Z}_b + \mathbf{Z}_c)\mathbf{I}_b = \mathbf{E}_{nb} - \mathbf{E}_{nc} \quad (6a)$$

Equations (5) and (6*a*) may be solved for the currents. This method is equivalent to the loop-current method, previously demonstrated. As a matter of fact if the current $\mathbf{I}_{aa'}$ in Fig. 6 were labeled $\mathbf{I}_1$ the current $\mathbf{I}_{c'c}$ labeled $\mathbf{I}_2$, and $\mathbf{I}_{b'b}$ labeled $(\mathbf{I}_1 - \mathbf{I}_2)$, equations identical with (1) and (2) would result if the same loops are employed.

Positive Circuit Directions. A great deal of needless confusion exists in the minds of many students relative to the correct positive circuit directions of the quantities involved in polyphase circuit analysis. The basic principles concerning circuit direction have been presented in the earlier chapters. (See pages 95–96, 284–285, and 327.) These principles are, of course, entirely applicable to polyphase circuits as well as to single-phase circuits.

In general, all generated emf's in polyphase systems have specified *relative* polarities and angular positions with respect to one another. This information must be known either directly or indirectly if the circuit investigation is to proceed. For example, if a three-phase alternator is connected in wye it may be assumed that the individual phases are connected subtractively at a common junction as shown in Fig. 7.

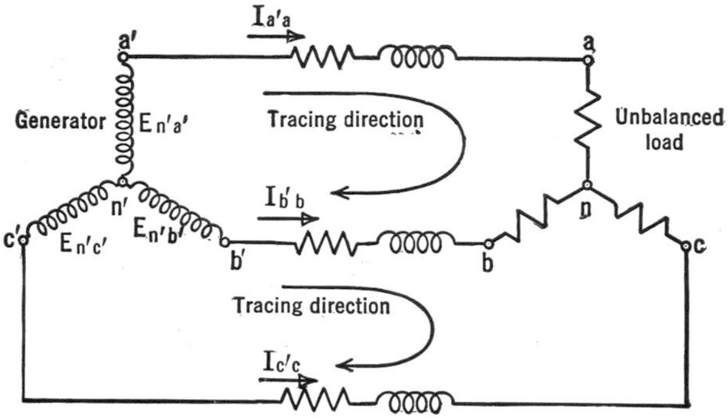

FIG. 7. A three-wire three-phase network. (See pages 380–382.)

It is only by means of subtractive polarities that a three-phase, wye-connected machine can give balanced line-to-line voltages. Unless otherwise specified, the individual phase generated emf's of a three-phase machine may be assumed to be 120° apart in time phase. The foregoing facts are sufficient for a specification of the positive circuit directions in the network shown in Fig. 7.

A positive circuit direction may be arbitrarily assigned to any one generated emf. For example, if the *a* phase generated emf in Fig. 7 is considered, either $\mathbf{E}_{n'a'}$ or $\mathbf{E}_{a'n'}$ may be taken as positive. One of these having been selected as positive, the positive circuit directions of the other systematically labeled emf's are fixed because of the relatively fixed polarities that the generated emf's bear toward one another. If $\mathbf{E}_{n'a'}$ is taken as positive, then $\mathbf{E}_{n'b'}$ and $\mathbf{E}_{n'c'}$ are also taken as the positive circuit directions because only when all phase voltages are considered away from the neutral or when all are considered toward the neutral does the usual 120° phase angle between adjacent phase voltages in a three-phase system exist. Thus either of the two following systems of generated voltages may be employed in analyzing the network shown in Fig. 7.

(1) $\mathbf{E}_{n'a'}, \mathbf{E}_{n'b'}, \mathbf{E}_{n'c'}$

or

(2) $\mathbf{E}_{a'n'}, \mathbf{E}_{b'n'}, \mathbf{E}_{c'n'}$

With the generated voltage relations established the solution is effected by employing the same methods used to solve any network, two of which were illustrated in example 3.

The Wye-Wye System with Neutral Connection. Four-wire, three-phase systems similar to the one shown in Fig. 8 are sometimes employed in the transmission and distribution of electrical energy. The connection of the point n' of the wye-connected generator (or transformer bank) to the point n of the wye-connected load distinguishes Fig. 8 from the three-wire, three-phase system shown in Fig. 7.

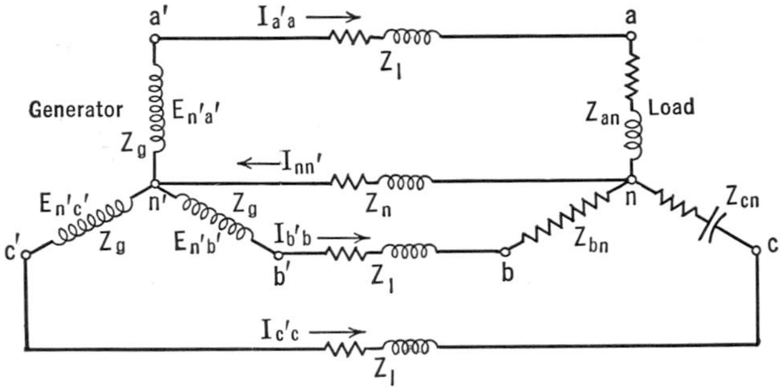

FIG. 8. A four-wire three-phase system.

In general, the details involved in solving for $\mathbf{I}_{a'a}$, $\mathbf{I}_{b'b}$, $\mathbf{I}_{c'c}$, and $\mathbf{I}_{nn'}$ of Fig. 8 are similar to those which have been presented for the wye-wye system without neutral connection. If the wye-wye system of Fig. 8 is solved straightforwardly by the determinant method, three-row, three-column matrices are encountered, and a considerable amount of labor is involved in effecting a complete solution in a perfectly general case. Because of the inherent symmetry of the basic voltage equations, however, several simplifications may be made. If, for example, Kirchhoff's emf law is applied to loops $n'a'ann'$, $n'b'bnn'$, and $n'c'cnn'$, it is plain that

$$\mathbf{I}_{a'a} = \frac{\mathbf{E}_{n'a'} - \mathbf{I}_{nn'}\mathbf{Z}_n}{(\mathbf{Z}_g + \mathbf{Z}_l + \mathbf{Z}_{an})}; \quad \mathbf{I}_{b'b} = \frac{\mathbf{E}_{n'b'} - \mathbf{I}_{nn'}\mathbf{Z}_n}{(\mathbf{Z}_g + \mathbf{Z}_l + \mathbf{Z}_{bn})};$$

$$\mathbf{I}_{c'c} = \frac{\mathbf{E}_{n'c'} - \mathbf{I}_{nn'}\mathbf{Z}_n}{(\mathbf{Z}_g + \mathbf{Z}_l + \mathbf{Z}_{cn})}$$

Since

$$\mathbf{I}_{a'a} + \mathbf{I}_{b'b} + \mathbf{I}_{c'c} = \mathbf{I}_{nn'} \tag{7}$$

it follows that

$$\frac{\mathbf{E}_{n'a'} - \mathbf{I}_{nn'}\mathbf{Z}_n}{\mathbf{Z}_a} + \frac{\mathbf{E}_{n'b'} - \mathbf{I}_{nn'}\mathbf{Z}_n}{\mathbf{Z}_b} + \frac{\mathbf{E}_{n'c'} - \mathbf{I}_{nn'}\mathbf{Z}_n}{\mathbf{Z}_c} = \mathbf{I}_{nn'} \tag{8}$$

where, for simplicity in writing,

$$\mathbf{Z}_g + \mathbf{Z}_l + \mathbf{Z}_{an} = \mathbf{Z}_a \tag{9}$$

$$\mathbf{Z}_g + \mathbf{Z}_l + \mathbf{Z}_{bn} = \mathbf{Z}_b \tag{10}$$

$$\mathbf{Z}_g + \mathbf{Z}_l + \mathbf{Z}_{cn} = \mathbf{Z}_c \tag{11}$$

The remaining details are reserved for student analysis. (See Problem 4 below and Problem 16 at the close of the chapter.)

Problem 4. Solve equation (8) explicitly for $\mathbf{I}_{nn'}$ and state in words how to find $\mathbf{I}_{a'a}$, $\mathbf{I}_{b'b}$, and $\mathbf{I}_{c'c}$ after $\mathbf{I}_{nn'}$ has been evaluated.

$$\textit{Ans.:}\quad \mathbf{I}_{nn'} = \frac{\mathbf{E}_{n'a'}\mathbf{Z}_b\mathbf{Z}_c + \mathbf{E}_{n'b'}\mathbf{Z}_c\mathbf{Z}_a + \mathbf{E}_{n'c'}\mathbf{Z}_a\mathbf{Z}_b}{\mathbf{Z}_a\mathbf{Z}_b\mathbf{Z}_c + \mathbf{Z}_n(\mathbf{Z}_b\mathbf{Z}_c + \mathbf{Z}_c\mathbf{Z}_a + \mathbf{Z}_a\mathbf{Z}_b)}\,.$$

Note: If the numerator and denominator of the above answer are divided by $\mathbf{Z}_a\mathbf{Z}_b\mathbf{Z}_c$, both sides of the equation multiplied by $\mathbf{Z}_n$, and all of the impedances of the right member written in terms of admittances, there results a simple formula for the voltage between neutral points. If this voltage is solved for initially, substitution of the result in the three unnumbered equations on page 381 will yield the line currents directly.

The Wye-Delta System. A three-phase, wye-connected generator is shown connected to a delta load in Fig. 9. The solution of this system

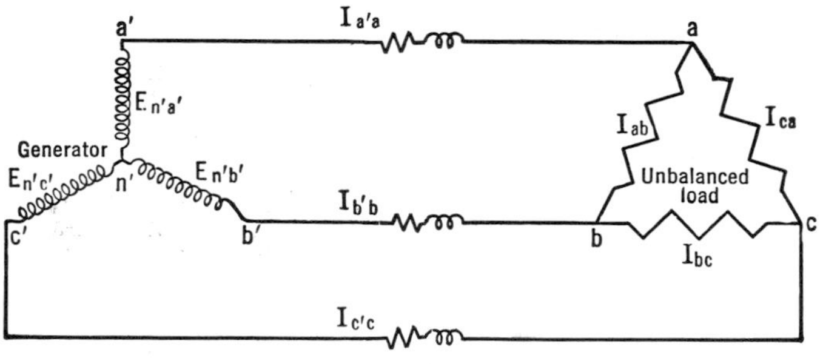

FIG. 9. A wye-delta circuit arrangement.

for currents in all branches may be effected by application of conventional Kirchhoff's laws which would require establishment of three emf equations and three current equations. Another method would consist of first converting the delta to an equivalent wye-connected load and then solving by employing two equations. However the least amount of work will usually be encountered if the loop-current method or the Kirchhoff's law equivalent employing three unknown currents is applied directly to the original circuit. This solution requires only three equations which are readily solved by determinants.

Phase-Sequence Effects. The direction of rotation of polyphase induction motors is dependent upon the phase sequence of the applied voltages. Also, the two wattmeters in the two-wattmeter method of measuring three-phase power interchange their readings when subjected to a reversal of phase sequence even though the system is balanced. But the magnitudes of the various currents and component voltages in balanced systems are not affected by a reversal of phase sequence.

In an unbalanced polyphase system, a reversal of voltage phase sequence will, in general, cause certain branch currents to change in magnitude as well as in time-phase position, although the total watts and vars generated remain the same. (See example following.)

Unless otherwise stated, the term " phase sequence " refers to voltage phase sequence. It should be recognized that, in unbalanced systems, the line currents and phase currents have their own phase sequence which may or may not be the same as the voltage sequence.

Example 4. The effects of reversal of voltage sequence upon the magnitudes of the currents in the wye-connected load of Fig. 2 are illustrated by the results of example 2 and of Problem 3.

For the *ab–ca–bc* voltage sequence of example 2, page 374,

$$I_{a'a} = 3.66,\ I_{b'b} = 14.56, \text{ and } I_{c'c} = 11.98 \text{ amperes}$$

For the *ab–bc–ca* voltage sequence of Problem 3, page 376,

$$I_{a'a} = 13.65,\ I_{b'b} = 6.20, \text{ and } I_{c'c} = 7.54 \text{ amperes}$$

Methods of Checking Voltage Phase Sequence. Sometimes in practice it becomes desirable and even necessary to know the phase sequence of a particular polyphase system. There are two general methods for checking voltage phase sequence: one based on direction of rotation of induction motors; the other, on unbalanced polyphase circuit phenomena.

Method One. Small polyphase induction motors which have previously been checked against a known phase sequence can be employed to test the phase sequence of a given system. In two- and three-phase systems, only two different phase sequences are possible, and consequently the direction in which the motor rotates can be used as an indicator of phase sequence. The principle of operation involves rotating magnetic field theory which rightfully belongs in the domain of a-c machinery.

Method Two. In general, any unbalanced set of load impedances can be employed as a voltage phase sequence checker. The different effects produced by changes in phase sequence can be determined theoretically, and when an effect peculiar to one sequence is noted in the actual installation, that effect can be used to designate the phase sequence of the system.

One of the most common devices for checking phase sequence in three-phase systems is the unbalanced circuit arrangement shown in Fig. 10. The three line wires, the voltage phase sequence of which is to be tested, are arbitrarily labeled. The free end of one lamp is connected to the line marked *a*. The other lamp is connected to line *c*, and the inductance coil is connected to line *b* as shown in Fig. 10. *If lamp 'a' is brighter than lamp 'c,' the phase sequence of the line-to-line voltages is ab–bc–ca. If lamp 'c' is brighter than lamp 'a,' the phase sequence is ab–ca–bc.*

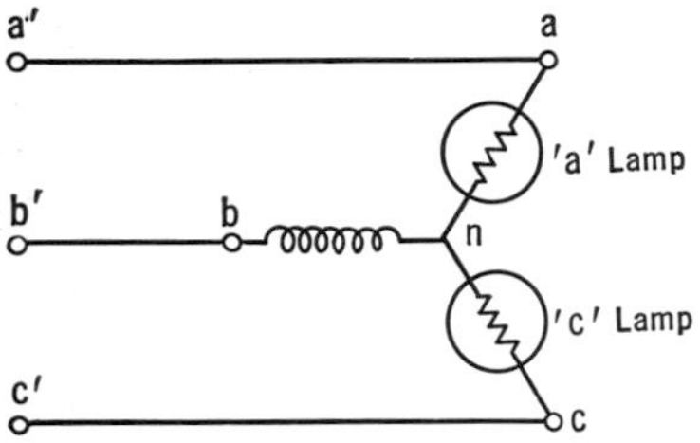

FIG. 10. A two-lamp method for checking phase sequence in three-phase systems. Lamp '*a*' is brighter for *ab–bc–ca* sequence, lamp '*c*' is brighter for *ab–ca–bc* sequence.

The foregoing statements are based upon the results of theoretical analyses, the details of which are outlined below. Assuming that the lamps are similar, their brightnesses will depend upon the voltages $Z_{an}I_{an}$ and $Z_{cn}I_{cn}$. These voltages may be determined by the Kirchhoff equation method as shown below:

$$\mathbf{I}_{an} + \mathbf{I}_{bn} + \mathbf{I}_{cn} = 0 \tag{12}$$

$$\mathbf{Z}_{an}\mathbf{I}_{an} - \mathbf{Z}_{bn}\mathbf{I}_{bn} = \mathbf{V}_{ab} \tag{13}$$

$$\mathbf{Z}_{bn}\mathbf{I}_{bn} - \mathbf{Z}_{cn}\mathbf{I}_{cn} = \mathbf{V}_{bc} \tag{14}$$

Upon the elimination of $\mathbf{I}_{cn}$ from equation (14), there results

$$\mathbf{Z}_{cn}\mathbf{I}_{an} + (\mathbf{Z}_{bn} + \mathbf{Z}_{cn})\mathbf{I}_{bn} = \mathbf{V}_{bc} \tag{15}$$

Equations (13) and (15) can now be solved by inspection for $\mathbf{I}_{an}$ and the result multiplied by $\mathbf{Z}_{an}$. The voltage across the *a* lamp is

$$\mathbf{Z}_{an}\mathbf{I}_{an} = \mathbf{Z}_{an}\left[\frac{\mathbf{V}_{ab}(\mathbf{Z}_{bn} + \mathbf{Z}_{cn}) + \mathbf{V}_{bc}\mathbf{Z}_{bn}}{\mathbf{Z}_{an}(\mathbf{Z}_{bn} + \mathbf{Z}_{cn}) + \mathbf{Z}_{cn}\mathbf{Z}_{bn}}\right] \tag{16}$$

The voltage across the *c* lamp is

$$\mathbf{Z}_{cn}\mathbf{I}_{cn} = \mathbf{V}_{ca} + \mathbf{Z}_{an}\mathbf{I}_{an} \tag{17}$$

Example 5. For the sake of illustrating the effect of reversal of phase sequence upon the magnitudes of $\mathbf{Z}_{an}\mathbf{I}_{an}$ and $\mathbf{Z}_{cn}\mathbf{I}_{cn}$, a numerical case will be considered. The lamps $\mathbf{Z}_{an}$ and $\mathbf{Z}_{cn}$ of Fig. 10 will be assumed to be pure resistances each of 100 ohms magnitude. $\mathbf{Z}_{bn}$ will be assumed equal to $100\underline{/90^\circ}$ ohms, that is, a hypothetically pure inductance. The magnitude of the line-to-line voltages will be taken as 100 volts each and will first be assigned the following vector positions:

$$\mathbf{V}_{ab} = 100\underline{/0^\circ} \text{ volts}$$

$$\mathbf{V}_{bc} = 100\underline{/-120^\circ} \text{ volts}$$

$$\mathbf{V}_{ca} = 100\underline{/-240^\circ} \text{ volts}$$

Under these conditions

$$\mathbf{Z}_{an}\mathbf{I}_{an} = 100\underline{/0^\circ}\left[\frac{(100\underline{/0^\circ})\ (141.4\underline{/45^\circ}) + (100\underline{/-120^\circ})\ (100\underline{/90^\circ})}{22{,}380\underline{/63.45^\circ}}\right]$$

$$= 86.4\underline{/-48.45^\circ} \text{ volts} \tag{18}$$

$$\mathbf{Z}_{cn}\mathbf{I}_{cn} = (100\underline{/-240^\circ}) + (86.3\underline{/-48.45^\circ})$$
$$= 23.2\underline{/71.55^\circ} \text{ volts} \tag{19}$$

The *a* lamp is therefore brighter than the *c* lamp for phase sequence *ab–bc–ca*.

Now let the line-to-line voltages be assigned vector positions which represent a reversal of phase sequence, namely,

$$\mathbf{V}_{ab} = 100\underline{/0^\circ} \text{ volts}$$

$$\mathbf{V}_{bc} = 100\underline{/-240^\circ} \text{ volts}$$

$$\mathbf{V}_{ca} = 100\underline{/-120^\circ} \text{ volts}$$

For *ab–ca–bc* phase sequence

$$\mathbf{Z}_{an}\mathbf{I}_{an} = 100\underline{/0^\circ}\left[\frac{(100\underline{/0^\circ})\ (141.1\underline{/45^\circ}) + (100\underline{/-240^\circ})\ (100\underline{/90^\circ})}{22{,}380\underline{/63.45^\circ}}\right]$$

$$= 23.2\underline{/11.55^\circ} \text{ volts} \tag{20}$$

$$\mathbf{Z}_{cn}\mathbf{I}_{cn} = 100\underline{/-120^\circ} + 23.2\underline{/11.55^\circ}$$
$$= 86.4\underline{/-108.45^\circ} \text{ volts} \tag{21}$$

The *c* lamp is therefore brighter than the *a* lamp for phase sequence *ab–ca–bc*. The above numerical results would be somewhat different if the resistance of the inductance coil had been considered. However, if the ratio (X_L/R) of the coil is relatively high, the difference between the lamp voltages is easily discernible.

Example 6. Another convenient form of voltage sequence checker is shown in Fig. 11*a*. It consists of a condenser (X_C), a resistor (R), and a voltmeter (Vm).

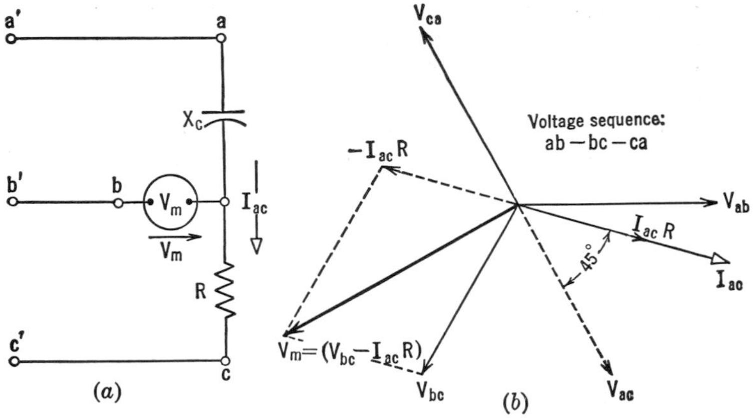

FIG. 11. A voltmeter method of checking phase sequence in three-phase systems. See example 6 and Problems 5 and 6.

The voltmeter (whose current consumption is negligibly small compared with the current through X_C and R) is connected between the line labeled b and the junction between X_C and R. X_C and R are connected in series across the voltage $\mathbf{V}_{ac}$ (or $\mathbf{V}_{ca}$) with the condenser connected to the a line and the resistor to the c line. If $X_C = 100$ ohms, $R = 100$ ohms, and $V_{ab} = V_{bc} = V_{ca} = 141.4$ volts,

$$\mathbf{I}_{ac} = \frac{141.4\underline{/-60^\circ}}{141.4\underline{/-45^\circ}} = 1\underline{/-15^\circ} \text{ amperes} \left\{ \begin{array}{l} \text{for sequence } ab\text{–}bc\text{–}ca \text{ as shown} \\ \text{in Fig. 11}b. \end{array} \right.$$

$$\mathbf{V}_{bc} = \mathbf{Vm} + \mathbf{I}_{ac}R \quad \text{or} \quad \mathbf{Vm} = \mathbf{V}_{bc} - \mathbf{I}_{ac}R$$

$$\begin{aligned} \mathbf{Vm} &= (141.4\underline{/-120^\circ}) - (1\underline{/-15^\circ})\,(100\underline{/0^\circ}) \\ &= -167.3 - j96.6 = 193\underline{/-150^\circ} \text{ volts} \end{aligned}$$

The above result shows that the voltmeter (Vm) reads above the line voltage (in the ratio of 193 to 141 in this case) for voltage sequence *ab–bc–ca*. The same general result is obtained with any combination of X_C and R provided X_C is roughly equal in ohmic value to R or greater in ohmic value than R.

Problem 5. Show by means of a qualitative vector diagram that the voltmeter (Vm) of Fig. 11*a* reads below line voltage for voltage sequence *ab–ca–bc*.

Problem 6. What is the magnitude of the voltmeter reading in Fig. 11*a* if $X_C = 100$ ohms, $R = 100$ ohms, and $V_{ab} = V_{bc} = V_{ca} = 141.4$ volts if the voltage sequence is *ab–ca–bc*?

Ans.: 51.8 volts.

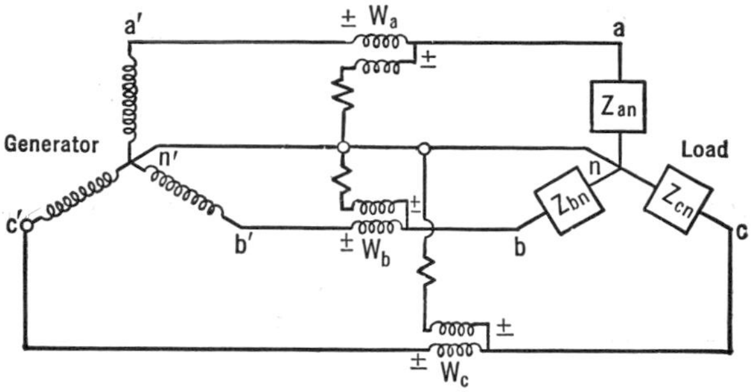

FIG. 12. The three-wattmeter method of measuring four-wire, three-phase power.

The Three-Wattmeter Method of Measuring Three-Phase Power. The total power delivered to a three-phase, wye-connected load with neutral connection can obviously be measured with three wattmeters connected as shown in Fig. 12. W_a measures the *an* phase power, W_b measures the *bn* phase power, and W_c measures the *cn* phase power. The sum of the three wattmeter readings therefore equals the total power consumed by the load. It is plain that if each individual phase of the wye-connected load is dissipative in character all the wattmeters shown in Fig. 12 will indicate positive power.

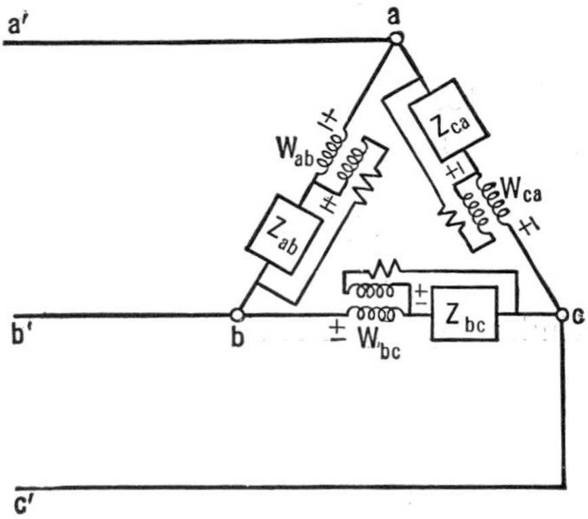

FIG. 13. The three-wattmeter method of measuring individual phase powers in a delta-connected load.

The total power absorbed by an unbalanced delta-connected load can be measured with the aid of three wattmeters as shown in Fig. 13. Individual phase powers are measured by the wattmeters. This method of measuring power would not, in general, be used unless the individual phase powers were desired.

The Two-Wattmeter Method of Measuring Three-Wire, Three-Phase Power. Except for inherent meter losses and errors, the three wattmeters connected as shown in Fig. 14 will measure accurately the power consumed by the three-phase load *abc*. A general proof of the foregoing statement will be given, and then certain important deductions will be made therefrom.

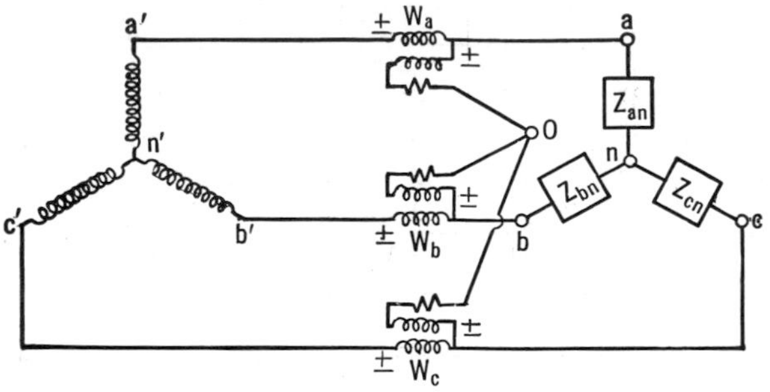

FIG. 14. A three-wattmeter method of measuring three-phase power which is independent of the potential and hence of the physical position of the point O.

The total average power delivered to the three-phase load shown in Fig. 14 over a time interval T is

$$P_{abc} = \frac{1}{T}\int_0^T (v_{an}i_{a'a} + v_{bn}i_{b'b} + v_{cn}i_{c'c})\,dt \tag{22}$$

The total average power measured by the three wattmeters shown in Fig. 14 is

$$P_{\text{meters}} = \frac{1}{T}\int_0^T (v_{a0}i_{a'a} + v_{b0}i_{b'b} + v_{c0}i_{c'c})\,dt \tag{23}$$

Under any condition it is plain that

$$v_{a0} = v_{an} - v_{0n} \tag{24}$$

$$v_{b0} = v_{bn} - v_{0n} \tag{25}$$

$$v_{c0} = v_{cn} - v_{0n} \tag{26}$$

Equation (23) may therefore be written as

$$P_{\text{meters}} = \frac{1}{T}\int_0^T (v_{an}i_{a'a} + v_{bn}i_{b'b} + v_{cn}i_{c'c})\,dt - \frac{1}{T}\int_0^T v_{0n}(i_{a'a} + i_{b'b} + i_{c'c})\,dt \tag{27}$$

Since $(i_{a'a} + i_{b'b} + i_{c'c}) = 0$, it follows that

$$P_{\text{meters}} = \frac{1}{T}\int_0^T (v_{an}i_{a'a} + v_{bn}i_{b'b} + v_{cn}i_{c'c})\,dt \tag{28}$$

It is thus shown that the three wattmeters in Fig. 14 measure the load power irrespective of voltage or current balance, of wave form, and of the potential of the point O. The last fact is highly significant. It indicates that the wattmeter potential coils need not have equal resistances when employed as shown in Fig. 14. It also indicates that the point O can be placed on any one of the three lines, thereby reducing one wattmeter reading to zero. Although the proof was based on a wye-connected load, the entire proof holds equally well for delta-connected loads. A simple way of extending the proof to cover delta loads is to recognize the fact that any delta load can be reduced to an equivalent wye-connected load. (See Chapter V, pages 206–209.)

The practical significance of placing point O on one of the three lines is that only two wattmeters are required to measure the total three-phase power. This expedient is widely utilized in measuring three-wire, three-phase power because it possesses no inherent limitations as regards balance or wave form.

The two wattmeters used to measure three-phase power may be placed in the circuit as shown in Fig. 15a, b, or c. The three combina-

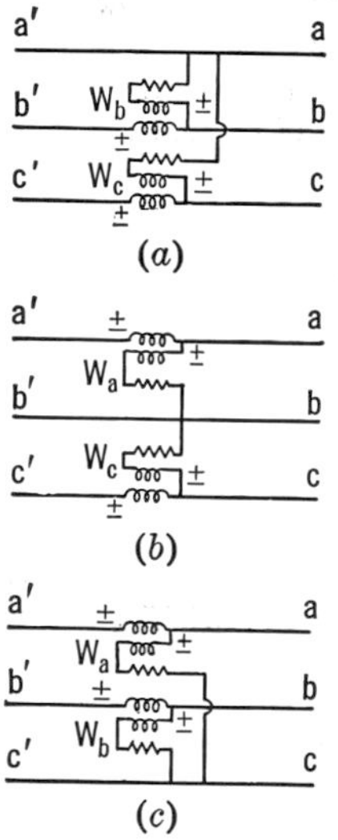

W_b reads $V_{ba}I_{b'b}\cos\theta\,\Big]_{I_{b'b}}^{V_{ba}}$

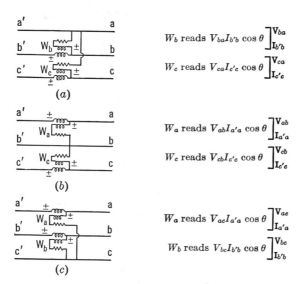

W_c reads $V_{ca}I_{c'c}\cos\theta\,\Big]_{I_{c'c}}^{V_{ca}}$

W_a reads $V_{ab}I_{a'a}\cos\theta\,\Big]_{I_{a'a}}^{V_{ab}}$

W_c reads $V_{cb}I_{c'c}\cos\theta\,\Big]_{I_{c'c}}^{V_{cb}}$

W_a reads $V_{ac}I_{a'a}\cos\theta\,\Big]_{I_{a'a}}^{V_{ac}}$

W_b reads $V_{bc}I_{b'b}\cos\theta\,\Big]_{I_{b'b}}^{V_{bc}}$

Fig. 15. Different circuit positions that the two wattmeters employed to measure three-phase power can take.

tions are obtained by placing the point O of Fig. 14 on lines a, b, and c, respectively.

For the relative polarities of the wattmeter coils shown in Figs. 14

and 15 the instruments will read up-scale if positive power is being metered. Under the condition of sinusoidal wave form of current and voltage, positive power is indicated if the current through the current coil in the ± direction is less than 90° out of phase with the voltage which is across the potential circuit in the ± direction. If one of the meters reads down-scale when connected as shown in Fig. 15, the relative polarity of the coils is changed to obtain up-scale reading and this reading is reckoned as negative power in finding the algebraic sum of the wattmeter readings.

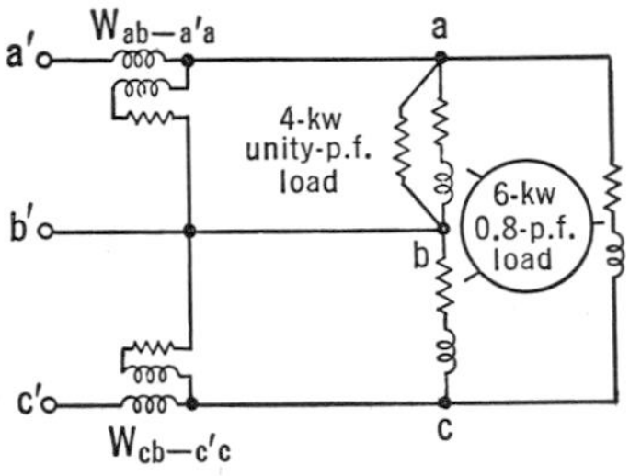

FIG. 16. A particular unbalanced three-phase load.

Example 7. In Fig. 16, *abc* represents a balanced three-phase system of voltages. The magnitude of each voltage is 200 volts, and the phase sequence is *ab–ca–bc*.

A balanced, 0.8-power-factor, induction motor load of 6 kw is connected across *abc* and a 4-kw, unity-power-factor load is connected across *ab* as shown in the diagram.

Let it be required to find the individual readings of the wattmeters, $W_{ab-a'a}$ and $W_{cb-c'c}$, which are connected to measure the total load power. The subscripts designate the voltage and current which are operative in a given meter in producing positive up-scale deflection. Obviously, the meter will read down-scale, thus indicating negative power if the operative voltage and current are separated by more than 90° in time phase.

Let $\mathbf{V}_{ab}$ be selected as reference. Then

$$\mathbf{V}_{ab} = 200\underline{/0^\circ},\ \mathbf{V}_{bc} = 200\underline{/-240^\circ}, \quad \text{and} \quad \mathbf{V}_{ca} = 200\underline{/-120^\circ} \text{ volts}$$

The current in each phase of the induction motor is

$$I_\phi = \frac{2000}{200 \times 0.8} = 12.5 \text{ amperes}$$

and these phase currents lag the applied phase voltages by $\cos^{-1} 0.8$ or 36.9°. The unity-power-factor load current is, of course, in phase with $\mathbf{V}_{ab}$. Therefore

$$\begin{aligned} \mathbf{I}_{ab} &= \frac{4000}{200}\underline{/0^\circ} + 12.5\underline{/-36.9^\circ} \\ &= (20 + j0) + (10 - j7.5) \\ &= (30 - j7.5) \text{ amperes} \end{aligned}$$

$$\begin{aligned} \mathbf{I}_{bc} &= 12.5\underline{/-240^\circ - 36.9^\circ} = 12.5\underline{/83.1^\circ} \\ &= (1.5 + j12.4) \text{ amperes} \end{aligned}$$

$$\begin{aligned} \mathbf{I}_{ca} &= 12.5\underline{/-120^\circ - 36.9^\circ} = 12.5\underline{/-156.9^\circ} \\ &= (-11.5 - j4.90) \text{ amperes} \end{aligned}$$

The line currents are

$$\mathbf{I}_{a'a} = (30 - j7.5) - (-11.5 - j4.90)$$
$$= 41.5 - j2.60 = 41.6\underline{/-3.58} \text{ amperes}$$
$$\mathbf{I}_{b'b} = (1.5 + j12.4) - (30 - j7.5)$$
$$= -28.5 + j19.9 = 34.7\underline{/145^\circ} \text{ amperes}$$
$$\mathbf{I}_{c'c} = (-11.5 - j4.90) - (1.5 + j12.4)$$
$$= -13.0 - j17.3 = 21.7\underline{/-127^\circ} \text{ amperes}$$

A vector diagram of the voltages and currents is shown in Fig. 17. Since the magnitudes and relative time-phase positions of the line-to-line voltages and the line currents are known, the wattmeter readings can be determined.

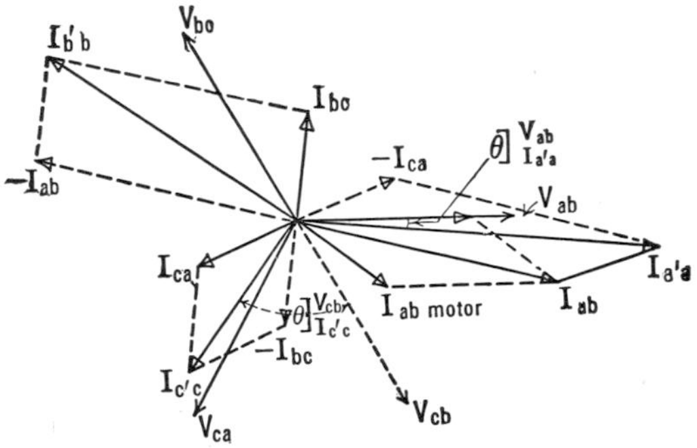

Fig. 17. Vector or phasor diagram of voltages and currents in a particular unbalanced three-phase circuit. (See Fig. 16.)

$$W_{ab-a'a} = V_{ab}I_{a'a}\cos\theta\Big]_{\mathbf{I}_{a'a}}^{\mathbf{V}_{ab}}$$
$$= 200 \times 41.6 \cos 3.58^\circ = 8300 \text{ watts}$$
$$W_{cb-c'c} = V_{cb}I_{c'c}\cos\theta\Big]_{\mathbf{I}_{c'c}}^{\mathbf{V}_{cb}}$$
$$= 200 \times 21.7 \cos 67^\circ = 1700 \text{ watts}$$

The other wattmeter combinations which will correctly measure the three-phase power are

(1) $W_{ac-a'a}$ together with $W_{bc-b'b}$,

(2) $W_{ba-b'b}$ together with $W_{ca-c'c}$.

In the present example

$$W_{ac-a'a} = V_{ac}I_{a'a}\cos\theta\Big]_{\mathbf{I}_{a'a}}^{\mathbf{V}_{ac}}$$
$$= 200 \times 41.6 \times \cos 63.58^\circ = 3705 \text{ watts}$$
$$W_{bc-b'b} = V_{bc}I_{b'b}\cos\theta\Big]_{\mathbf{I}_{b'b}}^{\mathbf{V}_{bc}}$$
$$= 200 \times 34.7 \times \cos 25^\circ = 6295 \text{ watts}$$

Problem 7. Calculate the readings of $W_{ba-b'b}$ and $W_{ca-c'c}$ in the above example and compare the sum of the wattmeter readings thus found with the total connected load.

Ans.: $W_{ba-b'b} = 5685$, $W_{ca-c'c} = 4315$ watts.

The Use of $n - 1$ Wattmeters to Measure n-Wire Power. In general, $n - 1$ wattmeter elements can be employed to measure n-wire power. The wattmeter elements may take the form of individual wattmeters, in which case the total power is equal to the algebraic sum of the wattmeter readings; or all movable members may be connected to a common shaft in which case the total power is indicated directly on one scale. The latter type of instrument is called a polyphase wattmeter.

Reactive Volt-Amperes in Unbalanced Four-Wire, Three-Phase Systems. The reactive volt-amperes of each individual phase of the load shown in Fig. 18 can be measured with three reactive volt-ampere

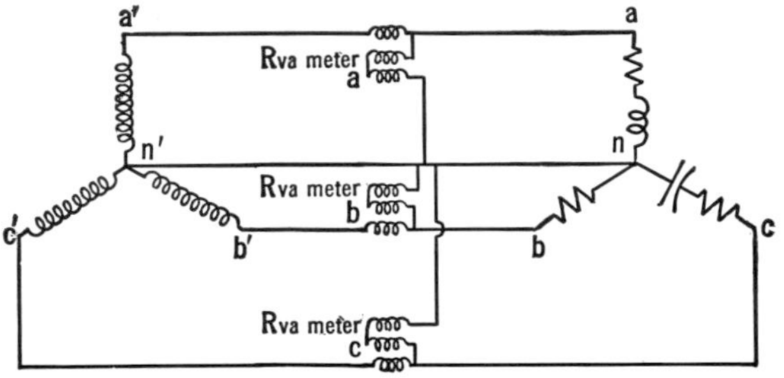

FIG. 18. Measurement of total reactive volt-amperes in a four-wire, three-phase system with three reactive volt-ampere meters.

meters. Sinusoidal wave forms of currents and voltages are assumed since the term " reactive volt-amperes " as well as any measurements of that quantity are ambiguous when other than sinusoidal wave forms are encountered.

In Fig. 18

$$\text{Meter } a \text{ reads } V_{an}I_{an} \sin \theta \Big]_{I_{an}}^{V_{an}} \text{ vars}$$

$$\text{Meter } b \text{ reads } V_{bn}I_{bn} \sin \theta \Big]_{I_{bn}}^{V_{bn}} \text{ vars}$$

$$\text{Meter } c \text{ reads } V_{cn}I_{cn} \sin \theta \Big]_{I_{cn}}^{V_{cn}} \text{ vars}$$

The algebraic sum of the above readings is of practical importance.

Assume the phase angle to be positive if the current lags the voltage and negative if the current leads the voltage. These conventions are merely matters of definition. (See page 97.) A meter properly connected to give up-scale readings for lagging-current reactive volt-amperes will read down-scale when subjected to leading-current reactive volt-amperes. If then in a particular case a meter reads down-scale, the relative polarities of the current and potential circuits of the meter are reversed. The resulting up-scale reading is considered as negative reactive volt-amperes in finding the total reactive volt-amperes of the system. With negative reactive volt-amperes defined as it is, the total vars of a system may, of course, be negative.

Example 8. In Fig. 18 let

$$\mathbf{V}_{an} = 100\underline{/0^\circ} \text{ volts} \qquad \mathbf{Z}_{an} = 25\underline{/45^\circ} \text{ ohms}$$

$$\mathbf{V}_{bn} = 100\underline{/-120^\circ} \text{ volts} \qquad \mathbf{Z}_{bn} = 50\underline{/0^\circ} \text{ ohms}$$

$$\mathbf{V}_{cn} = 100\underline{/-240^\circ} \text{ volts} \qquad \mathbf{Z}_{cn} = 20\underline{/-60^\circ} \text{ ohms}$$

The individual readings of the three reactive volt-ampere meters and the algebraic sum of the readings are to be determined.

$$\mathbf{I}_{an} = \frac{100\underline{/0^\circ}}{25\underline{/45^\circ}} = 4.0\underline{/-45^\circ} \text{ amperes}$$

$$\mathbf{I}_{bn} = \frac{100\underline{/-120^\circ}}{50\underline{/0^\circ}} = 2.0\underline{/-120^\circ} \text{ amperes}$$

$$\mathbf{I}_{cn} = \frac{100\underline{/-240^\circ}}{20\underline{/-60^\circ}} = 5.0\underline{/180^\circ} \text{ amperes}$$

The relative vector positions of the phase voltages and phase currents which actuate the meters are shown in Fig. 19.

Reactive volt-ampere meter a reads

$$(100 \times 4 \times 0.707) = 283 \text{ vars}$$

Reactive volt-ampere meter b reads

$$(100 \times 2 \times 0.0) = 0 \text{ var}$$

Reactive volt-ampere meter c reads

$$(100 \times 5 \times -0.866) = -433 \text{ vars}$$

The algebraic sum of the meter readings or the " total " number of vars is -150.

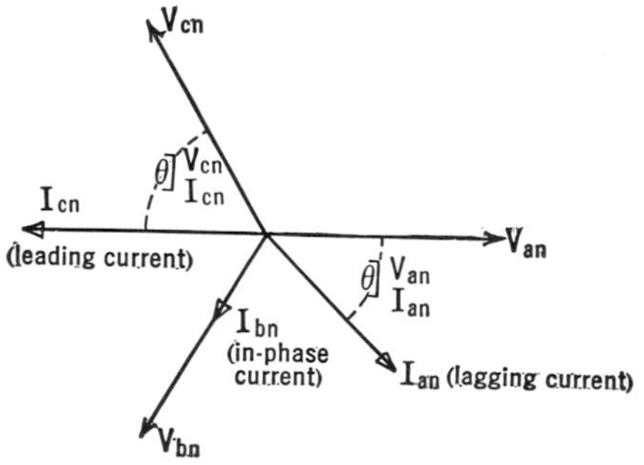

FIG. 19. Phasor diagram of the phase voltages and phase currents of the four-wire, three-phase load shown in Fig. 18 for a particular set of load impedances.

If wattmeters were to replace the reactive volt-ampere meters shown in Fig. 18, their readings would be as shown below:

$$W_a = 100 \times 4 \times 0.707 = 283 \text{ watts}$$

$$W_b = 100 \times 2 \times 1.000 = 200 \text{ watts}$$

$$W_c = 100 \times 5 \times 0.500 = 250 \text{ watts}$$

The total number of watts is 733.

Power Factor in Unbalanced Three-Phase Systems. Power factor in a single-phase system or in a balanced polyphase system has a definite physical significance. It is the ratio of the phase watts to the phase volt-amperes. Under conditions of sinusoidal wave form, power factor is equivalent to the cosine of the time-phase angular displacement between phase voltage and phase current.

In an unbalanced polyphase system each phase has its own particular power factor. The result is that the term " power factor " as applied to the combined unbalanced polyphase system can have only such meaning as is given to it by definition. The average of the individual phase power factors is a good general indication of the ratio of total watts to total volt-amperes in certain cases where the phase loads are all inductive or all capacitive. Where both capacitive and inductive phase loads are encountered, the compensating effect of capacitive reactive volt-amperes and inductive reactive volt-amperes is not taken into account. Another serious limitation to " average " power factor concept is that the individual phase power factors are not easily determined in many practical installations. " Average " power factor is generally not considered when specifying the power factor of an unbalanced polyphase system.

One recognized definition called vector power factor of an unbalanced polyphase system is

$$\text{Vector p.f.} = \frac{\sum VI \cos\theta}{\sqrt{(\sum VI \sin\theta)^2 + (\sum VI \cos\theta)^2}} \tag{29}$$

$$\sum VI \cos\theta = V_a I_a \cos\theta_a + V_b I_b \cos\theta_b + V_c I_c \cos\theta_c + \cdots \tag{30}$$

$$\sum VI \sin\theta = V_a I_a \sin\theta_a + V_b I_b \sin\theta_b + V_c I_c \sin\theta_c + \cdots \tag{31}$$

The subscripts employed in the above equations refer to individual phase values. For example, θ_a is the angular displacement between phase voltage and phase current in the a phase of the system. $\sum VI \cos\theta$ is the total power consumed by the polyphase load, the power factor of which is under investigation. $\sum VI \sin\theta$ is the algebraic sum of the individual phase reactive volt-amperes. In evaluating $\sum VI \sin\theta$ in any particular case due regard must be given to the sign of each component.

It is evident that the denominator of equation (29) can be evaluated as if it were the magnitude of a resultant vector, the right-angle components of which are $(\sum VI \cos\theta)$ and $(\sum VI \sin\theta)$. This fact is illustrated graphically in Fig. 20 for the particular three-phase system

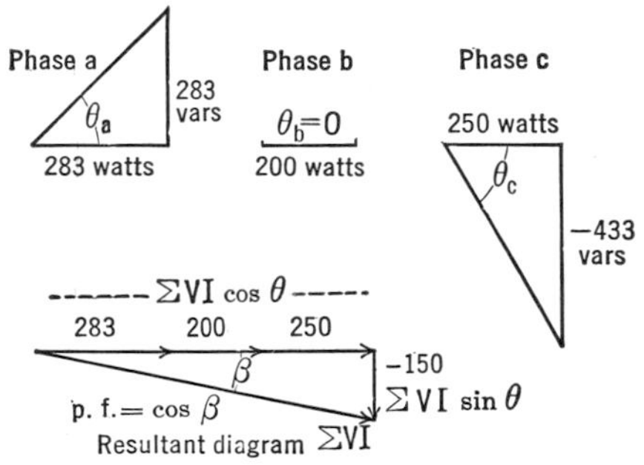

FIG. 20. Illustrating the concept of vector volt-amperes in a particular case.

discussed on pages 392–394. Considering watts and vars as the right-angle components which go to form " vector volt-amperes " it is plain that

$$\sum \mathbf{VI} = \sqrt{(\sum VI \sin\theta)^2 + (\sum VI \cos\theta)^2} \underline{/\beta} \tag{32}$$

or

$$\sum \mathbf{VI} = V_a I_a \underline{/\theta_a} + V_b I_b \underline{/\theta_b} + V_c I_c \underline{/\theta_c} \tag{33}$$

Power factor, as defined by equation (29), can now be written in any one of several different ways.

$$\text{Vector p.f.} = \cos\tan^{-1}\frac{(\sum VI \sin\theta)}{(\sum VI \cos\theta)} = \cos\beta \tag{34}$$

or

$$\text{Vector p.f.} = \frac{\sum VI \cos\theta}{\text{magnitude of } \sum \mathbf{VI}} \tag{35}$$

Example 9. The " average " power factor of the unbalanced load described on pages 392–394 is to be compared with the power factor as defined by equations (29),

(34), or (35). The circuit arrangement is shown in Fig. 18, and the previously determined values are indicated below.

$$\mathbf{V}_{an} = 100\underline{/0^\circ} \text{ volts} \qquad \mathbf{I}_{an} = 4.0\underline{/-45^\circ} \text{ amperes}$$

$$\mathbf{V}_{bn} = 100\underline{/-120^\circ} \text{ volts} \qquad \mathbf{I}_{bn} = 2.0\underline{/-120^\circ} \text{ amperes}$$

$$\mathbf{V}_{cn} = 100\underline{/-240^\circ} \text{ volts} \qquad \mathbf{I}_{cn} = 5.0\underline{/180^\circ} \text{ amperes}$$

a-phase vars = 283 $\qquad$ a-phase watts = 283

b-phase vars = 000 $\qquad$ b-phase watts = 200

c-phase vars = -433 $\qquad$ c-phase watts = 250

$\sum VI \sin\theta = -150$ vars $\qquad$ $\sum VI \cos\theta = 733$ watts

The individual phase power factors are

$$\text{P.f.}_a = 0.707 \text{ (result of lagging current)}$$

$$\text{P.f.}_b = 1.000 \text{ (result of in-phase current)}$$

$$\text{P.f.}_c = 0.500 \text{ (result of leading current)}$$

The arithmetical average of the above phase power factors is

$$\text{P.f.}_{\text{av}} = \frac{2.207}{3} = 0.736$$

The power factor of the unbalanced load as defined by equation (29) is

$$\text{Vector p.f.} = \frac{733}{\sqrt{(-150)^2 + (733)^2}} = \frac{733}{748} = 0.98$$

Inasmuch as the latter determination of power factor recognizes the compensating effect of "leading" and "lagging" reactive volt-amperes it is somewhat more significant than the "average" power factor.

Measurement of $\sum VI \sin\theta$ in a Three-Wire, Three-Phase Circuit. Power factors in three-wire, three-phase systems are very often measured in terms of $\sum VI \cos\theta$ and $\sum VI \sin\theta$. $\sum VI \cos\theta$ can be measured with the aid of either two or three wattmeters as shown in previous articles. It may be shown that $\sum VI \sin\theta$ can also be measured in a three-wire, three-phase system with either two or three reactive volt-ampere meters. Only the two-meter method of measuring $\sum VI \sin\theta$ will be considered.

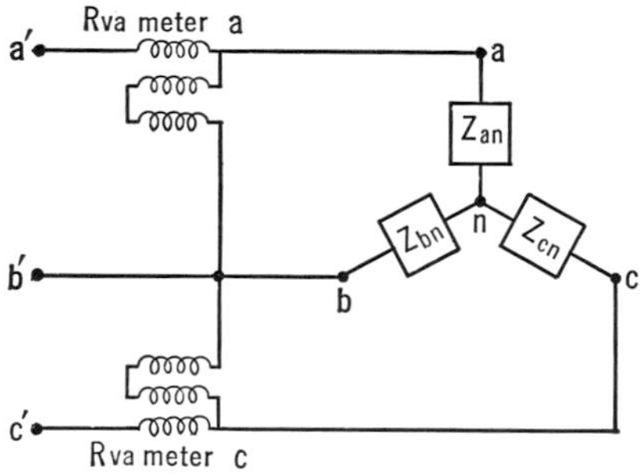

FIG. 21. The two reactive volt-ampere meter method of measuring $\Sigma VI \sin\theta$ in a three-wire, three-phase system.

The two meters shown in Fig. 21 are assumed to be reactive volt-ampere meters which are capable of reading $VI \sin \theta \Big]_{\mathbf{I}}^{\mathbf{V}}$. These meters are connected into the circuit in a manner which is exactly like two wattmeters in the two-wattmeter method of measuring three-phase power. It will be shown presently that, when they are connected in this fashion, the algebraic sum of the two reactive volt-ampere meter readings is equal to $\sum VI \sin \theta$ of the three-phase circuit. $\sum VI \sin \theta$ for a polyphase system has been defined in equation (31) of the present chapter.

Connected as shown in Fig. 21

$$\text{Reactive volt-ampere meter } a \text{ reads } \left\{ V_{ab} I_{a'a} \sin \theta \Big]_{\mathbf{I}_{a'a}}^{\mathbf{V}_{ab}} \right\}$$

$$\text{Reactive volt-ampere meter } c \text{ reads } \left\{ V_{cb} I_{c'c} \sin \theta \Big]_{\mathbf{I}_{c'c}}^{\mathbf{V}_{cb}} \right\}$$

For the sake of analysis, the above readings will be expressed temporarily in terms of the complex components of the voltages and currents. In Chapter IV it was shown that under the conditions of sinusoidal wave form

$$VI \sin \theta \Big]_{\mathbf{I}}^{\mathbf{V}} = v'i - vi' \tag{36}$$

where

$$\mathbf{V} = v + jv' \quad \text{and} \quad \mathbf{I} = i + ji'$$

Reference to Fig. 21 will show that $\mathbf{I}_{a'a} = \mathbf{I}_{an}$ and that $\mathbf{I}_{c'c} = \mathbf{I}_{cn}$. Also $\mathbf{V}_{ab} = \mathbf{V}_{an} - \mathbf{V}_{bn}$ and $\mathbf{V}_{cb} = \mathbf{V}_{cn} - \mathbf{V}_{bn}$.

$$\begin{aligned} V_{ab} I_{a'a} \sin \theta \Big]_{\mathbf{I}_{a'a}}^{\mathbf{V}_{ab}} &= V_{ab} I_{an} \sin \theta \Big]_{\mathbf{I}_{an}}^{\mathbf{V}_{ab}} \\ &= (v'_{ab} i_{an} - v_{ab} i'_{an}) \\ &= (v'_{an} i_{an} - v'_{bn} i_{an} - v_{an} i'_{an} + v_{bn} i'_{an}) \\ &= (v'_{an} i_{an} - v_{an} i'_{an}) + (v_{bn} i'_{an} - v'_{bn} i_{an}) \end{aligned} \tag{37}$$

$$\begin{aligned} V_{cb} I_{c'c} \sin \theta \Big]_{\mathbf{I}_{c'c}}^{\mathbf{V}_{cb}} &= V_{cb} I_{cn} \sin \theta \Big]_{\mathbf{I}_{cn}}^{\mathbf{V}_{cb}} \\ &= (v'_{cb} i_{cn} - v_{cb} i'_{cn}) \\ &= (v'_{cn} i_{cn} - v'_{bn} i_{cn} - v_{cn} i'_{cn} + v_{bn} i'_{cn}) \\ &= (v'_{cn} i_{cn} - v_{cn} i'_{cn}) + (v_{bn} i'_{cn} - v'_{bn} i_{cn}) \end{aligned} \tag{38}$$

It will be noticed that $(v_{bn}i'_{an} - v'_{bn}i_{an})$ of equation (37) and $(v_{bn}i'_{cn} - v'_{bn}i_{cn})$ of equation (38) can be added so as to yield

$$v_{bn}(i'_{an} + i'_{cn}) - v'_{bn}(i_{an} + i_{cn}) = (v'_{bn}i_{bn} - v_{bn}i'_{bn}) \tag{39}$$

Therefore the sum of equations (37) and (38) reduces to

$$(v'_{an}i_{an} - v_{an}i'_{an}) + (v'_{bn}i_{bn} - v_{bn}i'_{bn}) + (v'_{cn}i_{cn} - v_{cn}i'_{cn})$$

which in turn is easily recognized as the total reactive volt-amperes of the three-phase load or $\sum VI \sin\theta$.

No restrictions as to the balance of either voltage or current have been imposed upon the foregoing derivation. Two reactive volt-ampere meters connected into a three-wire, three-phase circuit as shown in Fig. 21 will, therefore, measure $\sum VI \sin\theta$ regardless of the condition of balance. Although the generality is rather difficult to incorporate into the derivation, the algebraic sum of the readings will be equal to $\sum VI \sin\theta$ whenever the reactive volt-amperes are restricted to those cases where both voltages and current wave forms are sinusoidal, provided the reactive volt-ampere meters are connected into the three-wire, three-phase line in a manner similar to the wattmeters shown in Fig. 15*a*, *b*, or *c*.

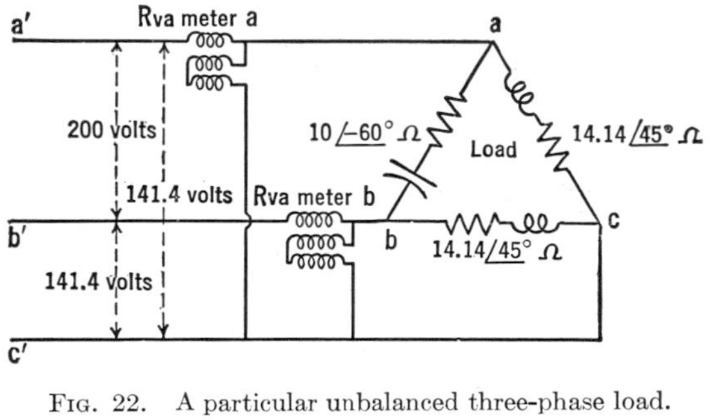

FIG. 22. A particular unbalanced three-phase load.

Example 10. In Fig. 22, *abc* represents an unbalanced three-phase system of voltages, the phase sequence of which is *ab–bc–ca*. In magnitude

$$V_{ab} = 200, \ V_{bc} = 141.4 \quad \text{and} \quad V_{ca} = 141.4 \text{ volts}$$

If $\mathbf{V}_{ab}$ is assumed to occupy the reference axis position, then

$$\mathbf{V}_{ab} = 200\underline{/0^\circ}, \ \mathbf{V}_{bc} = 141.4\underline{/-135^\circ}, \ \mathbf{V}_{ca} = 141.4\underline{/-225^\circ} \text{ volts}$$

It will be assumed that the load impedances have the values shown on the circuit diagram, namely,

$$\mathbf{Z}_{ab} = 10\underline{/-60^\circ} \text{ ohms}$$

$$\mathbf{Z}_{bc} = 14.14\underline{/45^\circ} \text{ ohms}$$

$$\mathbf{Z}_{ca} = 14.14\underline{/45^\circ} \text{ ohms}$$

Assuming that the line-to-line voltages remain fixed at the values given above, the delta-phase currents are

$$\mathbf{I}_{ab} = \frac{200\underline{/0^\circ}}{10\underline{/-60^\circ}} = 20\underline{/60^\circ} \text{ amperes}$$

$$\mathbf{I}_{bc} = \frac{141.4\underline{/-135^\circ}}{14.14\underline{/45^\circ}} = 10\underline{/180^\circ} \text{ amperes}$$

$$\mathbf{I}_{ca} = \frac{141.4\underline{/-225^\circ}}{14.14\underline{/45^\circ}} = 10\underline{/90^\circ} \text{ amperes}$$

From which

$$\mathbf{I}_{a'a} = \mathbf{I}_{ab} - \mathbf{I}_{ca} = 10 + j7.32 = 12.4\underline{/36.2^\circ} \text{ amperes}$$

$$\mathbf{I}_{b'b} = \mathbf{I}_{bc} - \mathbf{I}_{ab} = -20 - j17.32 = 26.45\underline{/-139.1^\circ} \text{ amperes}$$

$$\mathbf{I}_{c'c} = \mathbf{I}_{ca} - \mathbf{I}_{bc} = 10 + j10 = 14.14\underline{/45^\circ} \text{ amperes}$$

The voltages and currents are represented graphically in Fig. 23.

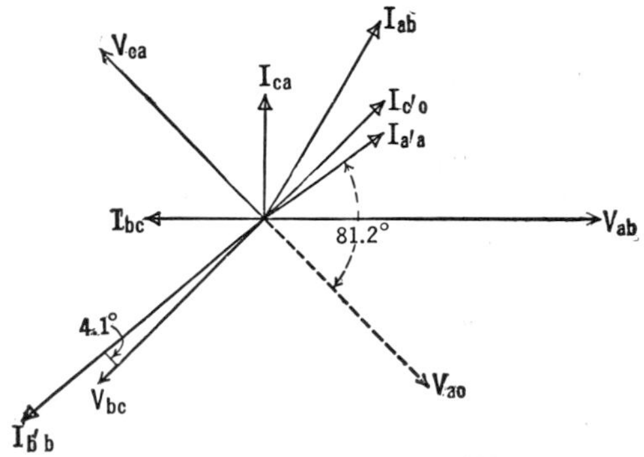

FIG. 23. Phasor voltages and currents in the three-phase circuit shown in Fig. 22.

The meters shown in Fig. 22 are assumed to be reactive volt-ampere meters, and the present example concerns itself with the predetermination of their readings.

Reactive volt-ampere meter a reads

$$V_{ac}I_{a'a}\sin\theta\Big]_{\mathbf{I}_{a'a}}^{\mathbf{V}_{ac}} = 141.4 \times 12.4 \times \sin -81.2^\circ = -1732 \text{ vars}$$

Reactive volt-ampere meter b reads

$$V_{bc}I_{b'b}\sin\theta\Big]_{\mathbf{I}_{b'b}}^{\mathbf{V}_{bc}} = 141.4 \times 26.45 \sin 4.1^\circ = 268 \text{ vars}$$

The algebraic sum of the meter readings is

$$-1732 + 268 = -1464 \text{ vars}$$

The actual value of $\sum VI \sin\theta$ as determined from the individual phase voltages and currents is

$$\sum VI \sin\theta = -(200 \times 20 \times 0.866) + (141.4 \times 10 \times 0.707) + (141.4 \times 10 \times 0.707) = -1464 \text{ vars}$$

Problem 8. If the reactive volt-ampere meters shown in Fig. 22 are placed so that the current coils carry $I_{a'a}$ and $I_{c'c}$, what will be the individual meter readings in vars? It is assumed that the potential circuits of the meters are connected in such a manner that the algebraic sum of the readings will be equal to $\sum VI \sin\theta$.

Ans.: Meter *a* reads −1464 vars; meter *c* reads zero.

Problem 9. What is the power factor of the unbalanced load shown in Fig. 22 as determined from $\sum VI \sin\theta$ and $\sum VI \cos\theta$?

Ans.: 0.939.

Phasor Relations as Found from Experimentally Determined Magnitudes of Current and Voltage. Phasor diagrams of the voltages of polyphase loads may be formed from measurements of the voltages by forming in a closed polygon those line voltages which according to Kirchhoff's laws add to zero when tracing from one line in a continuous direction to each adjacent line in sequence until the starting point is reached. Line-to-neutral voltages in a star connection may then be inscribed in the polygon so that they combine according to Kirchhoff's laws to form the line voltages. The principle of duality indicates a similar procedure may be followed to establish phasor diagrams of line and phase currents in a mesh connection. The phase relations may then be found by solving the diagrams either graphically or analytically and the solutions adapted to any desired sequence. See Problems 31 and 32.

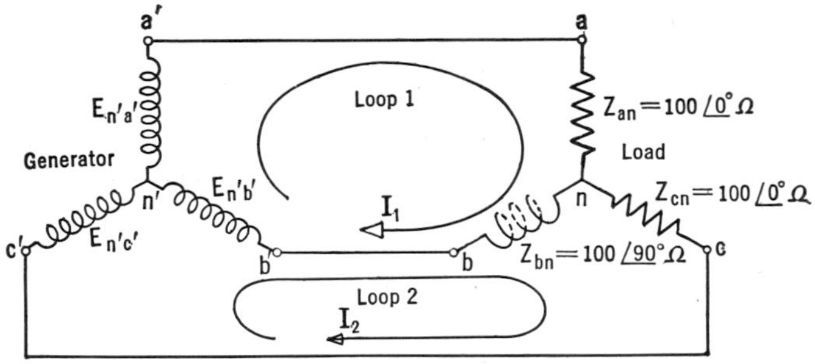

FIG. 24. Loop-current method of labeling. See example 11.

Example 11. Let it be required to find the branch currents $\mathbf{I}_{an}$, $\mathbf{I}_{bn}$, and $\mathbf{I}_{cn}$ of Fig. 24 by the loop-current method if

$$\mathbf{E}_{n'a'} = 57.7\underline{/-30°}, \quad \mathbf{E}_{n'b'} = 57.7\underline{/-150°}, \quad \text{and} \quad \mathbf{E}_{n'c'} = 57.7\underline{/90°} \text{ volts}$$

Since only two loop currents are required to traverse all the branches,

$$\mathbf{Z}_{11}\mathbf{I}_1 - \mathbf{Z}_{12}\mathbf{I}_2 = \mathbf{E}_1 = \mathbf{E}_{b'n'} + \mathbf{E}_{n'a'} = 100\underline{/0^\circ} \text{ volts}$$

$$-\mathbf{Z}_{21}\mathbf{I}_1 + \mathbf{Z}_{22}\mathbf{I}_2 = \mathbf{E}_2 = \mathbf{E}_{c'n'} + \mathbf{E}_{n'b'} = 100\underline{/-120^\circ} \text{ volts}$$

where the minus signs account for the opposite directions of $\mathbf{I}_1$ and $\mathbf{I}_2$ through $\mathbf{Z}_{n'b'bn}$. If the generator impedances of Fig. 24 are neglected,

$$\mathbf{Z}_{11} = 100\underline{/0^\circ} + 100\underline{/90^\circ} = 141.4\underline{/45^\circ} \text{ ohms}$$

$$\mathbf{Z}_{22} = 100\underline{/90^\circ} + 100\underline{/0^\circ} = 141.4\underline{/45^\circ} \text{ ohms}$$

Without regard for sign, which has been taken care of in the above voltage equations

$$\mathbf{Z}_{12} = \mathbf{Z}_{21} = 100\underline{/90^\circ} \text{ ohms}$$

The voltage equations may be solved directly for $\mathbf{I}_1$ and $\mathbf{I}_2$ as shown below:

$$\mathbf{I}_1 = \mathbf{I}_{an} = \frac{\begin{vmatrix} 100\underline{/0^\circ} & -100\underline{/90^\circ} \\ 100\underline{/-120^\circ} & 141.4\underline{/45^\circ} \end{vmatrix}}{\begin{vmatrix} 141.4\underline{/45^\circ} & -100\underline{/90^\circ} \\ -100\underline{/90^\circ} & 141.4\underline{/45^\circ} \end{vmatrix}} = \frac{19{,}320\underline{/15^\circ}}{22{,}380\underline{/63.45^\circ}} = 0.864\underline{/-48.45^\circ} \text{ ampere}$$

$$\mathbf{I}_2 = \mathbf{I}_{nc} = \frac{\begin{vmatrix} 141.4\underline{/45^\circ} & 100\underline{/0^\circ} \\ -100\underline{/90^\circ} & 100\underline{/-120^\circ} \end{vmatrix}}{22{,}380\underline{/63.45^\circ}} = \frac{5185\underline{/-45^\circ}}{22{,}380\underline{/63.45^\circ}} = 0.232\underline{/-108.45^\circ} \text{ ampere}$$

$\mathbf{I}_{cn} = -\mathbf{I}_{nc} = 0.232\underline{/71.55^\circ}$, and $\mathbf{I}_{bn} = \mathbf{I}_2 - \mathbf{I}_1$

Example 12. In Fig. 25 are shown three load mpedances $\mathbf{Z}_{an}$, $\mathbf{Z}_{bn}$, and $\mathbf{Z}_{cn}$ which are energized by $\mathbf{V}_{ab}$, $\mathbf{V}_{bc}$ (and, of course, $\mathbf{V}_{ca}$). The *an* coil is assumed to be coupled magnetically to the *cn* coil and, as shown in Fig. 25, the coefficient of coupling between

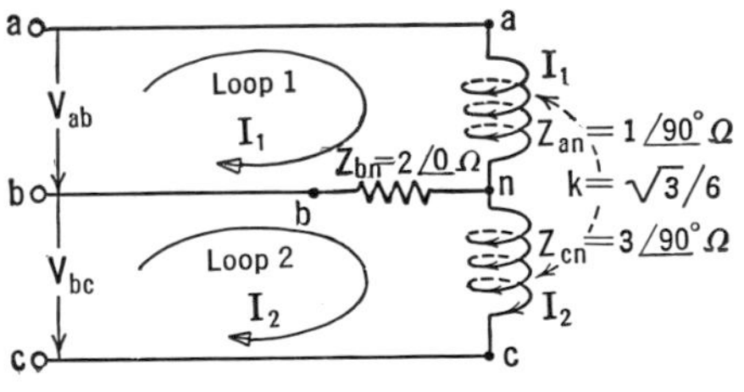

FIG. 25. See example 12.

the coils is assumed to be $\sqrt{3}/6$. If the network is to be analyzed by the loop-current method employing $\mathbf{I}_1$ and $\mathbf{I}_2$ in the directions shown,

$$\omega M_{ac} = \omega M_{ca} = \frac{\sqrt{3}}{6}\sqrt{\omega L_{an} \times \omega L_{cn}} = \frac{\sqrt{3}}{6}\sqrt{1 \times 3} = 0.5 \text{ ohm}$$

The positive sign of M is used here because the coils magnetize along a common axis in the same direction if wound as shown and if positive values of $\mathbf{I}_1$ and $\mathbf{I}_2$ are present. (See page 284.) Assume $\mathbf{V}_{ab} = 100\underline{/0^\circ}$ volts and $\mathbf{V}_{bc} = 100\underline{/-120^\circ}$ volts.

For the network shown in Fig. 25, the basic voltage equations become

$$\mathbf{Z}_{11}\mathbf{I}_1 + \mathbf{Z}_{12}\mathbf{I}_2 = \mathbf{V}_{ab} = 100\underline{/0^\circ} \text{ volts}$$

$$\mathbf{Z}_{21}\mathbf{I}_1 + \mathbf{Z}_{22}\mathbf{I}_2 = \mathbf{V}_{bc} = 100\underline{/-120^\circ} \text{ volts}$$

$$\mathbf{Z}_{11} = (2 + j1),\ \mathbf{Z}_{22} = (2 + j3), \quad \text{and} \quad \mathbf{Z}_{12} = \mathbf{Z}_{21} = (-2 + j0.5) \text{ ohms}$$

Note: The minus sign in $\mathbf{Z}_{12}$ accounts for the fact that $\mathbf{I}_2$ flows through $\mathbf{Z}_{bn}$ opposite to $\mathbf{I}_1$ and $+j0.5$ in $\mathbf{Z}_{12}$ accounts for the fact that the $(j\omega M\mathbf{I}_2)$ voltage drop acts in the same direction in loop 1 as the $(j\omega L\mathbf{I}_1)$ voltage drop.

$$\mathbf{I}_1 = \frac{\begin{vmatrix} (100 + j0) & (-2 + j0.5) \\ (-50 - j86.6) & (2 + j3) \end{vmatrix}}{\begin{vmatrix} (2 + j1) & (-2 + j0.5) \\ (-2 + j0.5) & (2 + j3) \end{vmatrix}} = \frac{56.7 + j152}{-2.75 + j10} = 12.68 - j9.15$$

$$= 15.6\underline{/-35.8^\circ} \text{ amperes}$$

$$\mathbf{I}_2 = \frac{\begin{vmatrix} (2 + j1) & (100 + j0) \\ (-2 + j0.5) & (-50 - j86.6) \end{vmatrix}}{(-2.75 + j10)} = \frac{186.6 - j273}{-2.75 + j10} = -30.15 - j10.36$$

$$= 31.8\underline{/-161^\circ} \text{ amperes}$$

The branch currents follow directly from $\mathbf{I}_1$ and $\mathbf{I}_2$ as shown in example 11.

Example 13. The network shown in Fig. 26 represents two generators operating

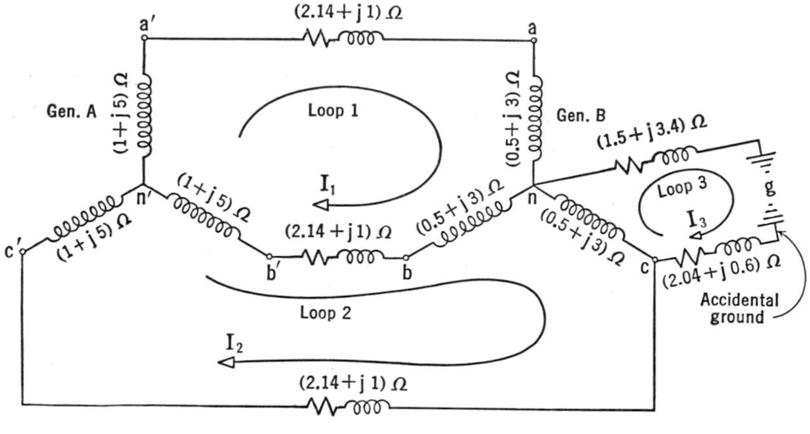

Fig. 26. See example 13.

in parallel. An accidental ground on the line leading out from terminal c is assumed to exist as shown and the problem is that of determining the short-circuit current $\mathbf{I}_{ngc}$ or loop current $\mathbf{I}_3$ in Fig. 26.

A study of Fig. 26 will show that the self-impedances of loops 1, 2, and 3 are, respectively,

$$\mathbf{Z}_{11} = (7.28 + j18) = 19.4\underline{/68^\circ} \text{ ohms}$$

$$\mathbf{Z}_{22} = (7.28 + j18) = 19.4\underline{/68^\circ} \text{ ohms}$$

$$\mathbf{Z}_{33} = (4.04 + j7.0) = 8.08\underline{/60^\circ} \text{ ohms}$$

Next, the mutual impedances will be obtained from an inspection of Fig. 26 and minus signs will be affixed to those mutual impedances that carry loop currents of opposite directions.

$$\mathbf{Z}_{12} = \mathbf{Z}_{21} = -(3.64 + j9.0) = -9.7\underline{/68^\circ} \text{ ohms}$$

$$\mathbf{Z}_{23} = \mathbf{Z}_{32} = -(0.50 + j3.0) = -3.04\underline{/80.5^\circ} \text{ ohms}$$

$$\mathbf{Z}_{13} = \mathbf{Z}_{31} = 0 \text{ (Since loops 1 and 3 have no common path.)}$$

Assume the generated phase voltages are

$$\mathbf{E}_{n'a'} = \mathbf{E}_{na} = 4000\underline{/0^\circ} \text{ volts}$$

$$\mathbf{E}_{n'b'} = \mathbf{E}_{nb} = 4000\underline{/-120^\circ} \text{ volts}$$

$$\mathbf{E}_{n'c'} = \mathbf{E}_{nc} = 4000\underline{/-240^\circ} \text{ volts}$$

The resultant voltages which exist in the three loops of Fig. 26 are

$$\mathbf{E}_1 = \mathbf{E}_{n'a'} - \mathbf{E}_{na} + \mathbf{E}_{nb} - \mathbf{E}_{n'b'} = 0$$

$$\mathbf{E}_2 = \mathbf{E}_{n'b'} - \mathbf{E}_{nb} + \mathbf{E}_{nc} - \mathbf{E}_{n'c'} = 0$$

$$\mathbf{E}_3 = -\mathbf{E}_{nc}$$

$$= -4000\underline{/-240^\circ} = 4000\underline{/-60^\circ} \text{ volts}$$

The equations for voltage equilibrium in the three meshes of Fig. 26 are

$$\begin{aligned}
(19.4\underline{/68^\circ})\mathbf{I}_1 - (9.7\underline{/68^\circ})\mathbf{I}_2 \quad + 0 \qquad\qquad &= 0\\
-(9.7\underline{/68^\circ})\mathbf{I}_1 + (19.4\underline{/68^\circ})\mathbf{I}_2 - (3.04\underline{/80.5^\circ})\mathbf{I}_3 &= 0\\
0 - (3.04\underline{/80.5^\circ})\mathbf{I}_2 + (8.08\underline{/60^\circ})\mathbf{I}_3 &= 4000\underline{/-60^\circ}
\end{aligned}$$

The above equations will be solved simultaneously for $\mathbf{I}_1$, $\mathbf{I}_2$, and $\mathbf{I}_3$ with the aid of elementary determinant theory. The common denominator of each current solution is

$$\mathbf{D} = \begin{vmatrix} (19.4\underline{/68^\circ}) & -(9.7\underline{/68^\circ}) & 0 \\ -(9.7\underline{/68^\circ}) & (19.4\underline{/68^\circ}) & -(3.04\underline{/80.5^\circ}) \\ 0 & -(3.04\underline{/80.5^\circ}) & (8.08\underline{/60^\circ}) \end{vmatrix}$$

$$\mathbf{D} = [-2920 - j837] - [(-117.8 - j135.4) + (-733 - j210)]$$
$$= (-2068 - j492) = 2122\underline{/193.4^\circ} \text{ ohms}^3$$

The desired current in the present instance is $\mathbf{I}_{ngc}$ or $\mathbf{I}_3$.

$$\mathbf{I}_3 = \frac{\begin{vmatrix} (19.4\underline{/68^\circ}) & -(9.7\underline{/68^\circ}) & 0 \\ -(9.7\underline{/68^\circ}) & (19.4\underline{/68^\circ}) & 0 \\ 0 & -(3.04\underline{/80.5^\circ}) & (4000\underline{/-60^\circ}) \end{vmatrix}}{2122\underline{/193.4^\circ}}$$

$$\mathbf{I}_3 = \frac{1{,}131{,}000\underline{/76^\circ}}{2122\underline{/193.4^\circ}} = 533\underline{/-117.4^\circ} \text{ amperes}$$

Problem 10. Find the magnitudes of $\mathbf{I}_{a'a}$, $\mathbf{I}_{b'b}$, and $\mathbf{I}_{c'c}$ in Fig. 26 utilizing the calculations of example 13 in so far as they are helpful.

Ans.: $I_{a'a} = 55.6$, $I_{b'b} = 55.6$; and $I_{c'c} = 111.2$ amperes.

PROBLEMS

11. An unbalanced delta system labeled *abc* at the corners consists of $\mathbf{Z}_{ab} = 10\underline{/-60°}$, $\mathbf{Z}_{bc} = 5\underline{/0°}$, and $\mathbf{Z}_{ca} = 10\underline{/60°}$ ohms. If $\mathbf{V}_{cb} = 100\underline{/0°}$ and the voltage sequence is *cb-ba-ac*, find the vector expressions for the currents entering the terminals *a*, *b*, and *c*. The three-phase supply voltages are balanced. Also solve for the opposite sequence.

12. An unbalanced load labeled *abc* at the corners consists of $\mathbf{Z}_{ab} = 5\underline{/40°}$, $\mathbf{Z}_{bc} = 10\underline{/-30°}$, and $\mathbf{Z}_{ca} = 8\underline{/45°}$ ohms. Three-phase balanced line voltages of 115 volts each are applied. If the sequence is *cb-ac-ba*, calculate the complex expressions for the line currents leaving terminals *a*, *b*, and *c* for $\mathbf{V}_{cb} = 115\underline{/0°}$ volts.

13. Refer to Fig. 27. V_{AB} and V_{CB} represent a balanced two-phase system of voltage drops, the magnitude of each being 115 volts. The voltage phase sequence

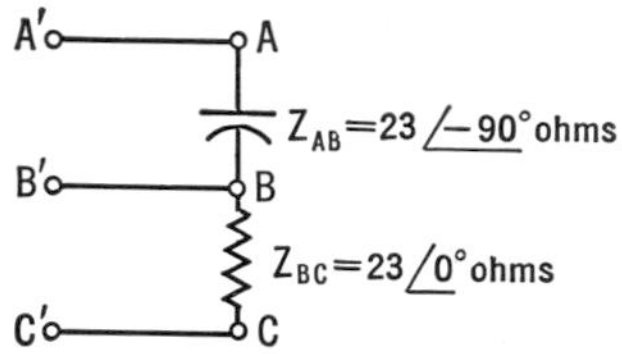

FIG. 27. See Problem 13.

is *AB-CB*. V_{AB} is to be used as reference. Find $\mathbf{I}_{AB}$, $\mathbf{I}_{CB}$, $\mathbf{I}_{BB'}$ and draw a vector diagram of the voltages and currents.

14. A wye-connected set of impedances consists of $\mathbf{Z}_{an} = 5\underline{/0°}$, $\mathbf{Z}_{bn} = 5\underline{/60°}$, and $\mathbf{Z}_{cn} = 5\underline{/-60°}$ ohms. Find the equivalent delta-connected impedances $\mathbf{Z}_{ab}$, $\mathbf{Z}_{bc}$, and $\mathbf{Z}_{ca}$ which can be used to replace the wye-connected set of impedances.

15. Refer to Fig. 28. The terminals $a'b'c'$ represent a balanced three-phase system of voltages the sequence of which is $b'c'$-$a'b'$-$c'a'$. The magnitude of each

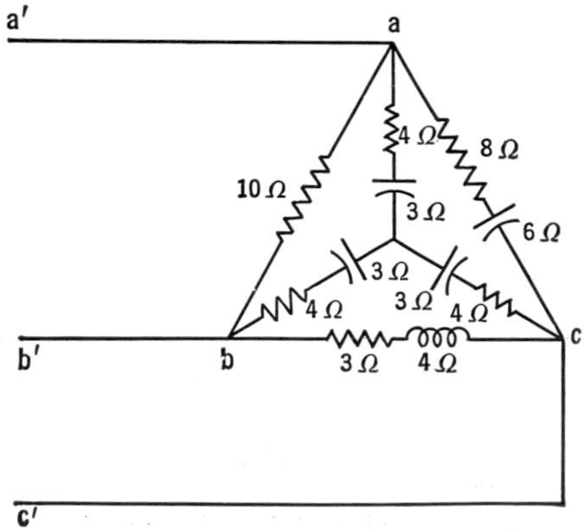

FIG. 28. See Problem 15.

line-to-line voltage is 230 volts. Find the readings of ammeters placed in the $a'a$, $b'b$, and $c'c$ lines.

16. In Fig. 7, page 380, it will be assumed that the generated voltages are

$\mathbf{E}_{n'a'} = 100\underline{/0^\circ}$, $\mathbf{E}_{n'b'} = 100\underline{/-120^\circ}$, $\mathbf{E}_{n'c'} = 100\underline{/-240^\circ}$ volts and that

$$\mathbf{Z}_{n'a'an} = (2 - j1) \text{ ohms}$$

$$\mathbf{Z}_{n'b'bn} = (1 - j3) \text{ ohms}$$

$$\mathbf{Z}_{n'c'cn} = (3 + j4) \text{ ohms}$$

Find the line currents $\mathbf{I}_{a'a}$, $\mathbf{I}_{b'b}$, and $\mathbf{I}_{c'c}$. Draw a vector diagram of the line-to-line voltages and the line currents.

17. Refer to Fig. 8, page 381. Let it be assumed that the following quantities are known:

$$\mathbf{E}_{n'a'} = 1000 + j0 = 1000\underline{/0^\circ} \text{ volts}$$

$$\mathbf{E}_{n'b'} = -500 - j866 = 1000\underline{/-120^\circ} \text{ volts}$$

$$\mathbf{E}_{n'c'} = -500 + j866 = 1000\underline{/120^\circ} \text{ volts}$$

$$\mathbf{Z}_{an} = 20 - j20 = 28.28\underline{/-45^\circ} \text{ ohms}$$

$$\mathbf{Z}_{bn} = 50 + j0 = 50.0\underline{/0^\circ} \text{ ohms}$$

$$\mathbf{Z}_{cn} = 30 + j52 = 60.0\underline{/60^\circ} \text{ ohms}$$

$$\mathbf{Z}_{g} = 2 + j8 = 8.25\underline{/76^\circ} \text{ ohms}$$

$$\mathbf{Z}_{l} = 1 + j1 = 1.41\underline{/45^\circ} \text{ ohms}$$

$$\mathbf{Z}_{n} = 2.5 + j1 = 2.70\underline{/21.8^\circ} \text{ ohms}$$

Write the expressions for $\mathbf{I}_{aa'}$, $\mathbf{I}_{bb'}$, and $\mathbf{I}_{cc'}$, employing determinants and the numerical values of the **E**'s and **Z**'s specified above. Use loop currents $\mathbf{I}_1 = \mathbf{I}_{a'a}$, $\mathbf{I}_2 = \mathbf{I}_{b'b}$, and $\mathbf{I}_3 = \mathbf{I}_{c'c}$ all returning through line nn'. (Results may be left in the form of the ratio of two matrices.)

18. A delta-connected set of impedances consists of $\mathbf{Z}_{ab} = 5\underline{/0^\circ}$, $\mathbf{Z}_{bc} = 5\underline{/60^\circ}$, and $\mathbf{Z}_{ca} = 5\underline{/-60^\circ}$ ohms. Find the equivalent wye-connected impedances $\mathbf{Z}_{an}$, $\mathbf{Z}_{bn}$, and $\mathbf{Z}_{cn}$ which can be employed to replace the above delta-connected impedances.

19. Refer to Fig. 9, page 382. Assume that the generator is capable of maintaining a balanced three-phase system of voltages $\mathbf{E}_{b'a'}$, $\mathbf{E}_{a'c'}$, $\mathbf{E}_{c'b'}$, the sequence of which is $b'a'$-$a'c'$-$c'b'$. The magnitude of each line voltage is 100 volts. $\mathbf{Z}_{a'a} = \mathbf{Z}_{b'b} = \mathbf{Z}_{c'c} = 0.5 + j0.5$ ohm. $\mathbf{Z}_{ab} = 10\underline{/0^\circ}$, $\mathbf{Z}_{bc} = 10\underline{/60^\circ}$, and $\mathbf{Z}_{ca} = 10\underline{/-60^\circ}$ ohms. Find $\mathbf{I}_{a'a}$, $\mathbf{I}_{b'b}$, $\mathbf{I}_{ab}$, $\mathbf{I}_{bc}$, and $\mathbf{I}_{ca}$ with respect to $\mathbf{V}_{a'b'}$ as a reference.

20. Explain, by means of qualitative vector diagrams, the operation of a three-phase-sequence indicator that employs an inductance coil in place of the condenser shown in Fig. 11*a*, page 386. Does the voltmeter read above or below line voltage for sequence *ab-ca-bc*?

21. Devise some scheme for checking the phase sequence of two-phase voltages.

22. Find the reading of a wattmeter which has its current coil in the $A'A$ line and its potential coil across the voltage V_{AC} in Problem 13 and Fig. 27.

23. Refer to Fig. 13, page 387. $\mathbf{V}_{ab} = 200$, $\mathbf{V}_{bc} = 141.4$, and $\mathbf{V}_{ca} = 141.4$ volts. Sequence *ab-bc-ca*. $\mathbf{Z}_{ab} = \mathbf{Z}_{bc} = \mathbf{Z}_{ca} = (8 - j6)$ ohms. Find the reading of each of the wattmeters. Find reading of a wattmeter with its current coil in line a and potential coil from a to b; also one with current coil in line c and potential coil from c to b.

24. (a) If a wattmeter W_a has its current coil in line a and its potential coil from line a to c of Fig. 1, page 373, what will it read for a sequence V_{ab}-V_{ca}-V_{bc}? If another wattmeter W_b has its current coil in line b and its potential coil connected from line b to c, what will it read?

(b) If W_a and W_b were varmeters what would they read?

25. (a) Find readings of wattmeters W_a and W_b with their current coils in lines a and b, respectively, supplying the load of Problem 11 if the potential coils are properly connected so that the sum of the readings will give the total power consumed by the load.

(b) Find readings if W_a and W_b are varmeters.

26. Refer to Fig. 29. $\mathbf{V}_{a'b'}$, $\mathbf{V}_{b'c'}$, and $\mathbf{V}_{c'a'}$ represent a balanced three-phase system of voltage drops, the magnitude of each being 200 volts. The voltage

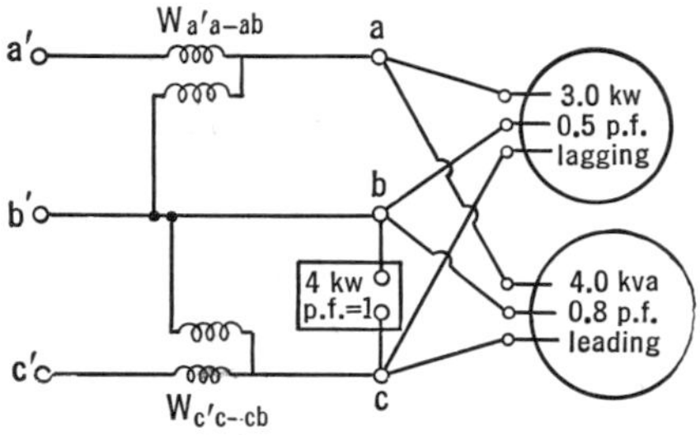

FIG. 29. See Problem 26.

sequence is $a'b'$-$b'c'$-$c'a'$. Two balanced three-phase loads indicated by the circles are connected to the terminals abc as shown in Fig. 29. In addition to the two balanced loads, a single-phase, 4-kw, unity-power-factor load is placed across the bc terminals as indicated.

(a) Find the reading of $W_{a'a\text{-}ab}$ and $W_{c'c\text{-}cb}$.

(b) If reactive volt-ampere meters replaced $W_{a'a\text{-}ab}$ and $W_{c'c\text{-}cb}$, find their respective readings.

(c) Find the combined vector power factor of the composite load.

27. In Fig. 21, page 396, it will be assumed that $\mathbf{V}_{a'b'}$, $\mathbf{V}_{b'c'}$, and $\mathbf{V}_{c'a'}$ represent a balanced three-phase system of voltages the sequence of which is $a'b'$-$c'a'$-$b'c'$. $\mathbf{Z}_{an} = 10\underline{/0°}$, $\mathbf{Z}_{bn} = 10\underline{/-60°}$, and $\mathbf{Z}_{cn} = 10\underline{/90°}$ ohms. Assume line-to-line voltage of 100 volts.

(a) Find the readings of the two reactive volt-ampere meters shown in Fig. 21.

(b) Find the readings of wattmeters placed at similar positions in the circuit, namely, at the $a'a$-ab and the $c'c$-cb positions.

(c) Find the vector power factor of the unbalanced load as recognized by the A.I.E.E.

28. In Fig. 30, $\mathbf{V}_{ab}$, $\mathbf{V}_{bc}$, $\mathbf{V}_{ca}$ are balanced three-phase voltages each having a magnitude of 200 volts and a phase sequence of ab-bc-ca. Determine the readings of the two wattmeters shown in the figure.

29. In Fig. 31, $\mathbf{E}_{n'a'}\mathbf{E}_{n'b'}\mathbf{E}_{n'c'}$ are balanced three-phase voltages with magnitudes

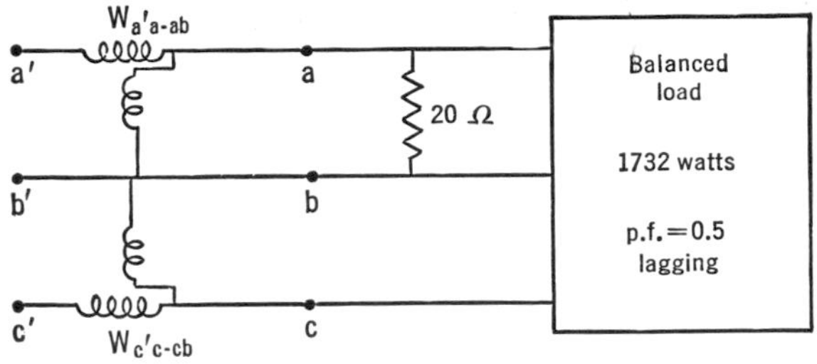

FIG. 30. See Problem 28.

of 115.4 volts and a phase sequence of $n'a'$-$n'b'$-$n'c'$. Find the following quantities and express all complex quantities with reference to $\mathbf{V}_{ab}$.

(*a*) $\mathbf{V}_{ab}$, $\mathbf{V}_{bc}$, $\mathbf{V}_{ca}$.

(*b*) $\mathbf{I}_{ab}$, $\mathbf{I}_{bc}$, $\mathbf{I}_{ca}$.

(*c*) $\mathbf{I}_{a'a}$, $\mathbf{I}_{b'b}$, $\mathbf{I}_{c'c}$.

(*d*) The sum of the readings of the wattmeters W_a, W_b, W_c when they are connected as shown.

(*e*) The individual readings of wattmeters W_a, W_b, W_c if the common point O is connected to line $b'b$.

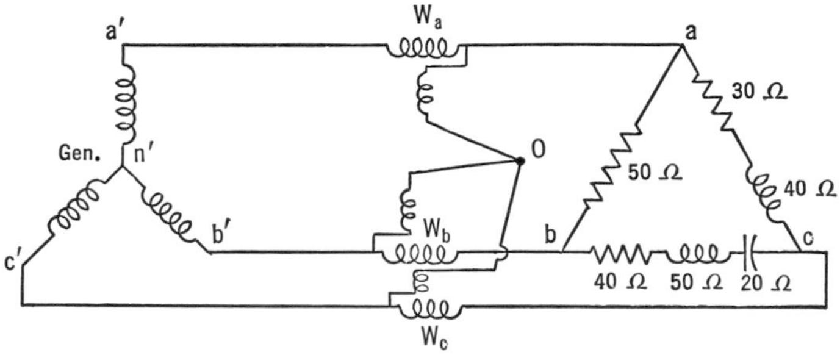

FIG. 31. See Problem 29.

30. The line-to-line voltages of a three-phase system are $V_{ab} = 200$, $V_{bc} = 150$, and $V_{ca} = 120$ volts. Write the polar expressions for $\mathbf{V}_{ab}$, $\mathbf{V}_{bc}$, and $\mathbf{V}_{ca}$ with respect to $\mathbf{V}_{ab}$ as reference for both phase sequences.

31. Refer to Fig. 2. In a particular case measurements yield $V_{ab} = 140$, $V_{bc} = 120$, $V_{ca} = 150$, $V_{an} = 200$, $V_{bn} = 80$, and $V_{cn} = 104.2$ volts. Draw the qualitative phasor diagram of the voltages for sequence *abc*, and determine analytically the complex expressions for each of the voltages with respect to V_{ab} as a reference.

32. Refer to Fig. 1. In a particular case measurements yield $I_{a'a} = 20$, $I_{b'b} = 14$, $I_{c'c} = 15$, $I_{ab} = 12$, $I_{bc} = 2$, and $I_{ca} = 15$ amperes. For the line-current sequence of $a'a$–$c'c$–$b'b$ solve the qualitative phasor diagram analytically, and determine the complex expressions for each of the currents with respect to I_{ab} as a reference.

33. Calculate the line currents in Problem 16 by the loop-current method.

34. Refer to example 13, pages 402–403, including Fig. 26. Solve for $\mathbf{I}_1$, $\mathbf{I}_2$, and $\mathbf{I}_3$ by the loop-current method, neglecting the resistive components of *all* branch impedances for a voltage sequence E_{na}–E_{nc}–E_{nb}. (Results may be left in the form of the ratio of two matrices.)

35. In Fig. 32, $L_{ab} = L_{cb} = 0.01$ henry and the coefficient of coupling is 0.5. Assume no resistances or inductances except as indicated on the figure. The sequence of the balanced driving voltages is $n'a'$–$n'b'$–$n'c'$, and $\mathbf{E}_{n'a'} = 57.7\underline{/90°}$ volts. For $\omega = 1000$ radians per second calculate the line and phase currents for the load. Use Maxwell's cyclic-current method.

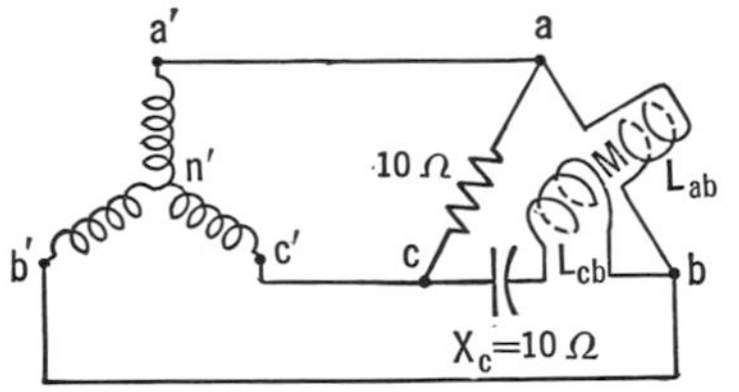

FIG. 32. See Problems 35 and 36.

36. Set up the determinant form of the solution for $I_{aa'}$ in Problem 35 if 3 ohms pure resistance is inserted in each line to the load and the same sequence and reference as specified in Problem 35 are employed. For uniformity in checking results, use loop currents as follows:

$$\text{Loop current } I_1 = I_{a'acc'}$$

$$\text{Loop current } I_2 = \mathbf{I}_{c'cbb'}$$

$$\text{Loop current } I_3 = I_{a'n'b'ba}$$

37. Solve for $I_{a'a}$, $I_{b'b}$, and $I_{c'c}$ in Fig. 33 if $E_{n'a'} = 1350 + j0$ volts, $E_{n'b'} = -675 - j1170$ volts, and $E_{n'c'} = -675 + j1170$ volts.

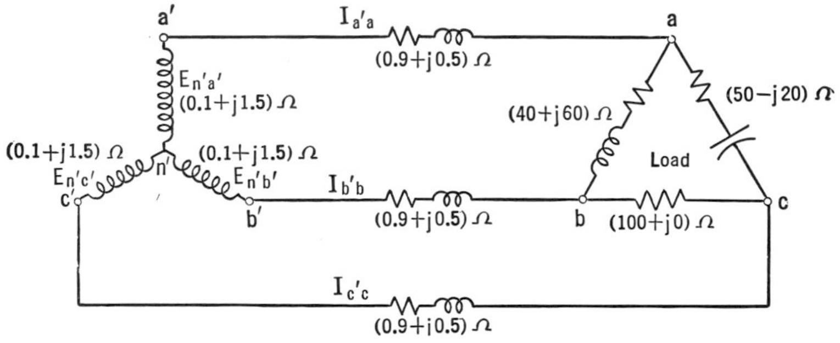

FIG. 33. See Problem 37.

chapter X Transmission Line Calculations

Line Constituents. A transmission line consists of the equivalent of two or more electrical conductors for the purpose of transmitting electric energy. For single-phase transmission the line may consist of a single conductor with a ground return or of two ordinary wires. For three-phase transmission, three wires are generally used although in some installations a neutral wire or its equivalent is employed. The wires of a transmission line are separated by some dielectric as air for overhead transmission, or by other insulating materials as in cables. Since the two conductors are separated by a dielectric, they form a condenser, the capacitance of which is uniformly distributed along the wires. When a difference of potential is applied between the wires, charging current flows. This effect could be simulated by a large number of condensers connected between the two wires as shown in Fig. 1. V_s denotes the sending-end voltage, and V_r represents receiver-end voltage. A representation of this kind is approximate because it shows the shunted capacitance lumped at certain points instead of being uniformly distributed. Within reasonable limits of accuracy it is permissible to make line calculations on the basis of lumped capacitance. Under the conditions of relatively low voltage and relatively short distances the shunted capacitance can even be neglected without seriously affecting the accuracy.

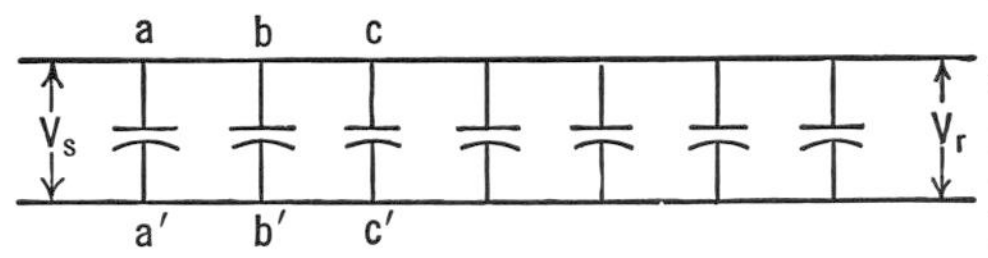

FIG. 1. Distributed shunted capacitance of a transmission line simulated by a large number of shunted condensers.

In addition to shunted capacitance the line has series resistance and inductance or inductive reactance. Thus the sections between con-

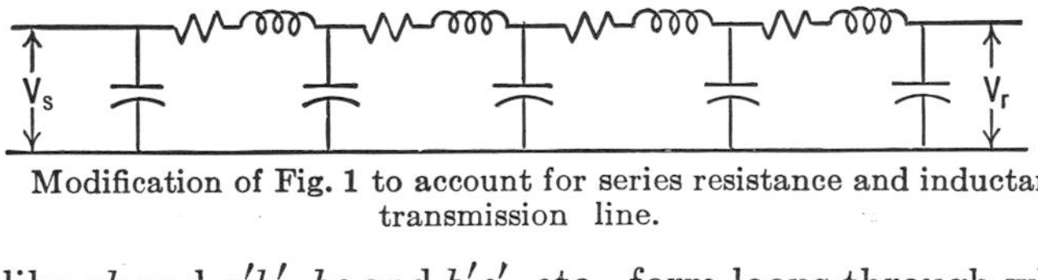

FIG. 2. Modification of Fig. 1 to account for series resistance and inductance of a transmission line.

densers, like ab and $a'b'$, bc and $b'c'$, etc., form loops through which flux will be set up by the mmf of the current flowing in the wires. These sections also have resistance. Hence, to account for these parameters, Fig. 1 should be modified to appear as shown in Fig. 2. Strictly speaking, each condenser should be shunted by a non-inductive resistance to account for any leakage of current from conductor to conductor because of imperfect insulation, moisture content of the air, and other factors. On a clear dry day the leakage is so small that it may usually be neglected. The greater the number of sections, like those shown in Fig. 2, into which the line is divided, the more nearly it will simulate the actual line which has uniformly distributed parameters. If more than two or three shunted condensers are used, it is just about as simple to calculate the line by assuming uniformly distributed parameters instead of concentrated quantities. Three of the usual arrangements of concentrated parameters will be considered.

The T Line. The T representation of a line is shown in Fig. 3. When all the shunted capacitance, C, of the line is concentrated in one condenser and half of the total series impedance, Z, is placed in each arm as indicated in Fig. 3, the circuit is known as the nominal T line. It is called nominal because the representation is only approximately correct. When the circuit parameters indicated in Fig. 3 are multiplied by certain hyperbolic correction factors,[1] the T thus formed represents the line exactly between terminals (V_s and V_r) and it then becomes the exact equivalent T. Calling Y the admittance due to the shunted capacitance C and using the quantities as labeled in Fig. 3, the determination of V_s in terms of the receiver voltage and current is made as follows.

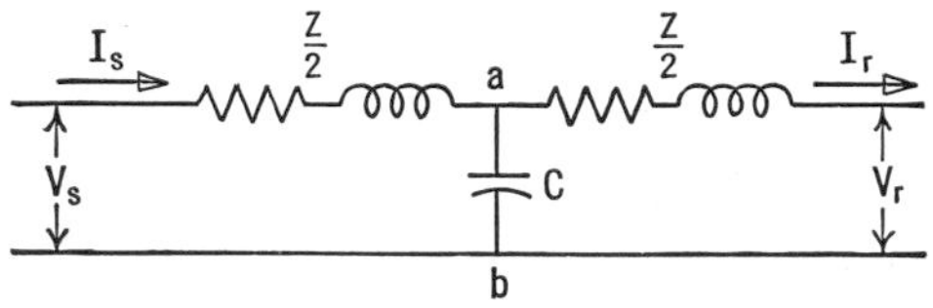

FIG. 3. T representation of a transmission line.

$$\mathbf{V}_{ab} = \mathbf{V}_r + \mathbf{I}_r\frac{\mathbf{Z}}{2}$$

$$\mathbf{I}_{ab} = \mathbf{V}_{ab}\mathbf{Y}$$

$$\mathbf{I}_s = \mathbf{I}_r + \mathbf{I}_{ab} = \mathbf{I}_r + \mathbf{Y}\left(\mathbf{V}_r + \mathbf{I}_r\frac{\mathbf{Z}}{2}\right) \qquad (1)$$

$$\mathbf{V}_s = \mathbf{V}_{ab} + \mathbf{I}_s\frac{\mathbf{Z}}{2}$$

$$= \left(\mathbf{V}_r + \mathbf{I}_r\frac{\mathbf{Z}}{2}\right) + \left[\mathbf{I}_r + \mathbf{Y}\left(\mathbf{V}_r + \mathbf{I}_r\frac{\mathbf{Z}}{2}\right)\right]\frac{\mathbf{Z}}{2}$$

$$= \mathbf{V}_r\left(1 + \frac{\mathbf{YZ}}{2}\right) + \mathbf{I}_r\left(\mathbf{Z} + \frac{\mathbf{YZ}^2}{4}\right) \qquad (2)$$

[1] See "Hyperbolic Functions Applied to Electrical Engineering," by A. E. Kennelly or "Electric Circuits Theory and Applications," by O. G. C. Dahl.

From equation (1),

$$\mathbf{I}_s = \mathbf{I}_r\left(1 + \frac{\mathbf{YZ}}{2}\right) + \mathbf{YV}_r \tag{3}$$

Equations (2) and (3) give the sending-end voltage and current in complex form. As indicated, all quantities in the equations must be expressed in vector form. The receiver current must be properly related in complex form to the receiver voltage. The power factor of the load determines the angle between $\mathbf{V}_r$ and $\mathbf{I}_r$. $\mathbf{V}_s$ and $\mathbf{I}_s$ being in complex form, power input may be determined in the usual way. The vector diagram of the T circuit of Fig. 3 is shown in Fig. 4. This diagram follows the above equations for calculating $\mathbf{V}_s$ and $\mathbf{I}_s$.

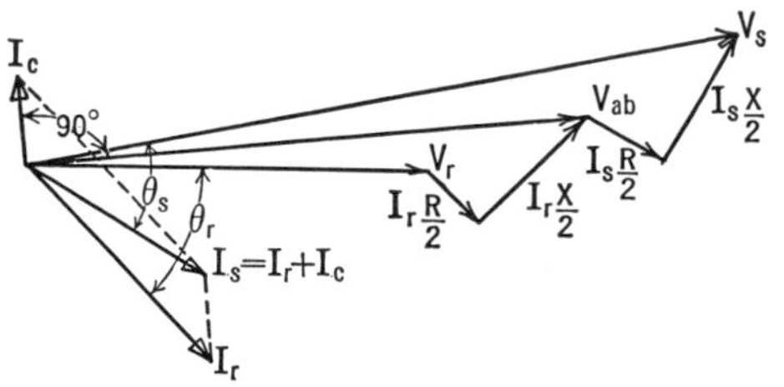

FIG. 4. Vector diagram of T representation in FIG. 3.

Problem 1. A 60-cycle, 3-phase line 200 miles long has a shunted capacitance to neutral per mile of 146×10^{-4} μf, an inductive reactance of 0.78 ohm per wire per mile, and a resistance of 0.42 ohm per wire per mile. The receiver voltage is 100,000 volts between lines. Use the nominal T line, and find the sending voltage and current for an 0.8 power-factor lagging load requiring 75 amperes per line at the receiver. *Ans.* 64,600 $\underline{/7.4°}$ volts, 62.3 $\underline{/24°}$ amperes.

The π Line. If one-half of the total line capacitance is concentrated at each end of the line and all the series resistance and reactance are concentrated at the center as shown in Fig. 5, the resultant configuration portrays the nominal π representation of a transmission line. Like the T line it is possible to alter the parameters by applying hyperbolic correction factors to obtain a π circuit which yields the correct relations between terminals. A π circuit thus corrected is called an exact equivalent π.

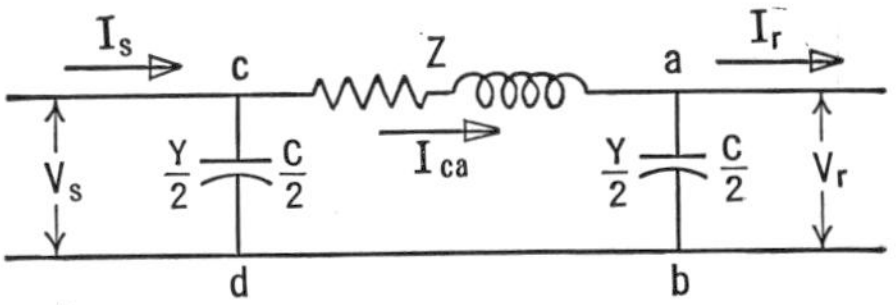

FIG. 5. π representation of a transmission line.

The π circuit is easily solved through a procedure similar to that employed for the T circuit.

$$\mathbf{I}_{ab} = \mathbf{V}_r\frac{\mathbf{Y}}{2}$$

$$\mathbf{I}_{ca} = \mathbf{I}_r + \mathbf{I}_{ab} = \mathbf{I}_r + \mathbf{V}_r\frac{\mathbf{Y}}{2}$$

$$\mathbf{V}_s = \mathbf{V}_r + \mathbf{I}_{ca}\mathbf{Z} = \mathbf{V}_r + \left(\mathbf{I}_r + \mathbf{V}_r\frac{\mathbf{Y}}{2}\right)\mathbf{Z}$$

$$= \mathbf{V}_r\left(1 + \frac{\mathbf{ZY}}{2}\right) + \mathbf{I}_r\mathbf{Z} \tag{4}$$

$$\mathbf{I}_s = \mathbf{I}_{ca} + \mathbf{I}_{cd}$$

$$\mathbf{I}_{cd} = \mathbf{V}_s\frac{\mathbf{Y}}{2} = \left[\mathbf{V}_r\left(1 + \frac{\mathbf{ZY}}{2}\right) + \mathbf{I}_r\mathbf{Z}\right]\frac{\mathbf{Y}}{2}$$

$$\mathbf{I}_s = \mathbf{I}_r + \mathbf{V}_r\frac{\mathbf{Y}}{2} + \left[\mathbf{V}_r\left(1 + \frac{\mathbf{ZY}}{2}\right) + \mathbf{I}_r\mathbf{Z}\right]\frac{\mathbf{Y}}{2}$$

$$= \mathbf{I}_r\left(1 + \frac{\mathbf{ZY}}{2}\right) + \mathbf{V}_r\mathbf{Y}\left(1 + \frac{\mathbf{ZY}}{4}\right) \tag{5}$$

Equations (4) and (5) are the solution of the π representation of a transmission line. The vector diagram of the π circuit is shown in Fig. 6, and the above calculations follow this diagram.

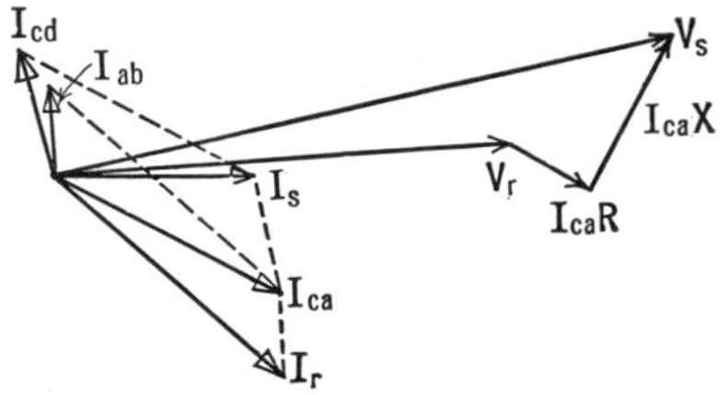

FIG. 6. Vector diagram of π line in Fig. 5.

Problem 2. Use the nominal π-line representation and solve Problem 1.
Ans.: 65,300 $/7.4°$ volts, 59.75 $/22.2°$ amperes.

The Steinmetz Representation of the Transmission Line. Another representation of the transmission line suggested by C. P. Steinmetz which yields approximately correct results is shown in Fig. 7. In the

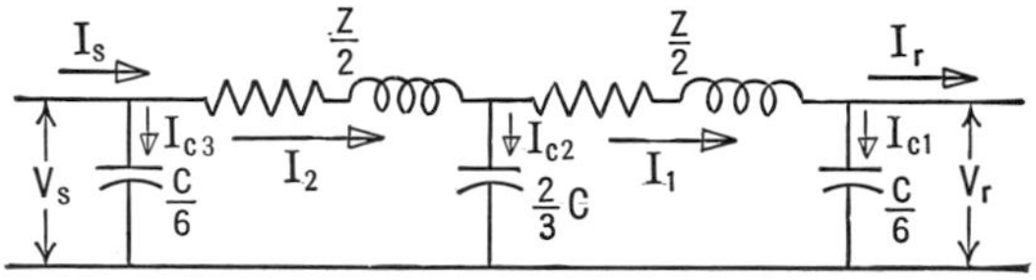

FIG. 7. Steinmetz representation of a transmission line.

figure, Z represents the total series impedance and C the total shunted capacitance. The student can work out the details of the solution by following the methods employed for the T and π lines. This circuit and the solution are slightly more cumbersome, but the results are generally somewhat closer to the theoretically correct values than those obtained from the use of the nominal T or π sections. The calculations must follow the vector diagram shown in Fig. 8.

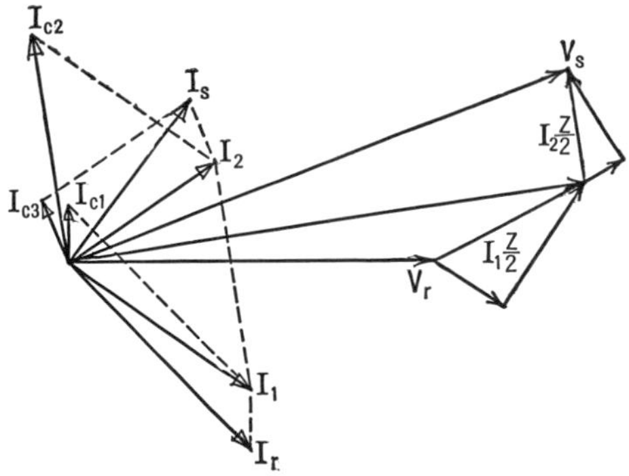

FIG. 8. Vector diagram of Fig. 7.

Problem 3. Derive the equations for the sending-end voltage and current in terms of the receiver quantities for the Steinmetz representation of a transmission line.

$$\textit{Ans.:}\ \mathbf{V}_s = \left(1 + \frac{\mathbf{ZY}}{2} + \frac{\mathbf{Z}^2\mathbf{Y}^2}{36}\right)\mathbf{V}_r + \mathbf{Z}\left(1 + \frac{\mathbf{ZY}}{6}\right)\mathbf{I}_r$$

$$\mathbf{I}_s = \left(1 + \frac{5\mathbf{ZY}}{36} + \frac{\mathbf{Z}^2\mathbf{Y}^2}{216}\right)\mathbf{YV}_r + \left(1 + \frac{\mathbf{ZY}}{2} + \frac{\mathbf{Z}^2\mathbf{Y}^2}{36}\right)\mathbf{I}_r$$

Problem 4. Solve Problem 1 according to the Steinmetz representation of the line.

Ans.: 64,900 $\underline{/7.3°}$ volts, 60.9 $\underline{/22.9°}$ amperes.

Exact Solution of a Long Line with Uniformly Distributed Parameters. In the line shown in Fig. 9 let the series impedance per mile be **Z**, the shunted admittance per mile **Y**, and the length of the line considered l.

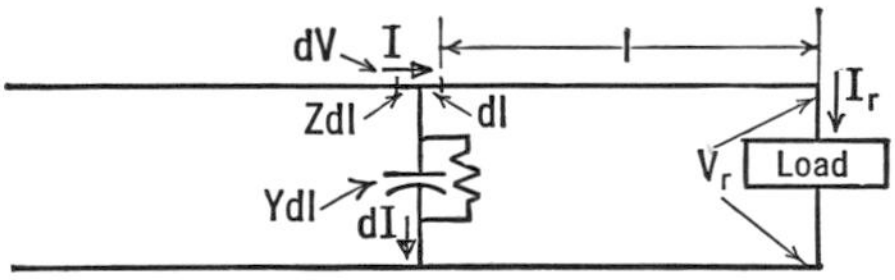

FIG. 9. Circuit used for deriving the exact solution of a transmission line.

The elementary voltage drop in the element dl is the current **I** in the element times the impedance **Z** dl of the element. Considering only the space variation of **V** and **I**,

$$d\mathbf{V} = \mathbf{IZ}\,dl \tag{6}$$

The current leaving the line over the length dl is the voltage **V** times the shunted admittance **Y** dl for the element. Thus

$$d\mathbf{I} = \mathbf{VY}\, dl \tag{7}$$

Equations (6) and (7) are solved for **V** and **I** as follows:

$$\frac{d\mathbf{V}}{dl} = \mathbf{IZ} \tag{8}$$

$$\frac{d\mathbf{I}}{dl} = \mathbf{VY} \tag{9}$$

Differentiating equation (8) with respect to l gives

$$\frac{d^2\mathbf{V}}{dl^2} = \mathbf{Z}\frac{d\mathbf{I}}{dl} \tag{10}$$

Substituting equation (9) in equation (10),

$$\frac{d^2\mathbf{V}}{dl^2} = \mathbf{ZYV} \tag{11}$$

This is a linear differential equation of the second order, the solution of which can be shown[2] to be of the form

$$\mathbf{V} = C_1\epsilon^{\mathbf{m}_1 l} + C_2\epsilon^{\mathbf{m}_2 l}$$

where C_1 and C_2 are constants of integration and m_1 and m_2 are roots of the auxiliary equation, namely,

$$\mathbf{m}^2 = \mathbf{ZY}$$

$$\mathbf{m} = +\sqrt{\mathbf{ZY}} \quad \text{or} \quad -\sqrt{\mathbf{ZY}} \tag{12}$$

The two roots $\mathbf{m}_1$ and $\mathbf{m}_2$ are respectively $+\sqrt{\mathbf{ZY}}$ and $-\sqrt{\mathbf{ZY}}$. Therefore

$$\begin{aligned} \mathbf{V} &= C_1\epsilon^{\mathbf{m}_1 l} + C_2\epsilon^{\mathbf{m}_2 l} \\ &= C_1\epsilon^{\sqrt{\mathbf{ZY}}l} + C_2\epsilon^{-\sqrt{\mathbf{ZY}}l} \end{aligned} \tag{13}$$

From equation (8),

$$\mathbf{I} = \frac{1}{\mathbf{Z}}\frac{d\mathbf{V}}{dl} \tag{14}$$

[2] See any book on differential equations, such as "Differential Equations," by D. A. Murray, p. 63.

Differentiating equation (13) and substituting the result in (14) gives

$$\mathbf{I} = C_1 \frac{\sqrt{\mathbf{ZY}}}{\mathbf{Z}} \epsilon^{\sqrt{\mathbf{ZY}}l} - \frac{C_2\sqrt{\mathbf{ZY}}}{\mathbf{Z}} \epsilon^{-\sqrt{\mathbf{ZY}}l}$$

$$= C_1\sqrt{\mathbf{Y}/\mathbf{Z}}\, \epsilon^{\sqrt{\mathbf{ZY}}l} - C_2\sqrt{\mathbf{Y}/\mathbf{Z}}\, \epsilon^{-\sqrt{\mathbf{ZY}}l} \qquad (15)$$

The constants of integration C_1 and C_2 in equations (13) and (15) can be evaluated from known boundary conditions. In this case the boundary conditions at the receiver are assumed to be known. Thus in Fig. 9 when

$$l = 0 \qquad (16)$$

$$\mathbf{I} = \mathbf{I}_r \qquad (17)$$

and

$$\mathbf{V} = \mathbf{V}_r \qquad (18)$$

Substituting equations (16), (17), and (18) in equations (13) and (15),

$$\mathbf{V}_r = C_1 + C_2 \qquad (19)$$

$$\mathbf{I}_r = C_1 \sqrt{\mathbf{Y}/\mathbf{Z}} - C_2 \sqrt{\mathbf{Y}/\mathbf{Z}} \qquad (20)$$

Equations (19) and (20) are now solved simultaneously for C_1 and C_2. Multiplying equation (19) by $\sqrt{\mathbf{Y}/\mathbf{Z}}$ gives

$$\mathbf{V}_r\sqrt{\mathbf{Y}/\mathbf{Z}} = C_1 \sqrt{\mathbf{Y}/\mathbf{Z}} + C_2 \sqrt{\mathbf{Y}/\mathbf{Z}} \qquad (21)$$

Adding equations (20) and (21),

$$\mathbf{I}_r + \sqrt{\mathbf{Y}/\mathbf{Z}}\, \mathbf{V}_r = 2C_1 \sqrt{\mathbf{Y}/\mathbf{Z}}$$

$$C_1 = \frac{\mathbf{V}_r + \mathbf{I}_r\sqrt{\mathbf{Z}/\mathbf{Y}}}{2} \qquad (22)$$

Subtracting equation (20) from equation (21),

$$\mathbf{V}_r \sqrt{\mathbf{Y}/\mathbf{Z}} - \mathbf{I}_r = 2C_2 \sqrt{\mathbf{Y}/\mathbf{Z}}$$

$$C_2 = \frac{\mathbf{V}_r - \mathbf{I}_r \sqrt{\mathbf{Z}/\mathbf{Y}}}{2} \qquad (23)$$

It is apparent that C_1 and C_2 in the above equations are complex coefficients and might have been written in bold-face type. The expressions for voltage and current at any distance l from the receiver are obtained by substituting equations (22) and (23) in equations (13) and (15). Then

$$\mathbf{V} = \left(\frac{\mathbf{V}_r + \mathbf{I}_r\sqrt{\mathbf{Z}/\mathbf{Y}}}{2}\right)\epsilon^{\sqrt{\mathbf{ZY}}l} + \left(\frac{\mathbf{V}_r - \mathbf{I}_r\sqrt{\mathbf{Z}/\mathbf{Y}}}{2}\right)\epsilon^{-\sqrt{\mathbf{ZY}}l} \tag{24}$$

$$\mathbf{I} = \left(\frac{\mathbf{I}_r + \mathbf{V}_r\sqrt{\mathbf{Y}/\mathbf{Z}}}{2}\right)\epsilon^{\sqrt{\mathbf{ZY}}l} + \left(\frac{\mathbf{I}_r - \mathbf{V}_r\sqrt{\mathbf{Y}/\mathbf{Z}}}{2}\right)\epsilon^{-\sqrt{\mathbf{ZY}}l} \tag{25}$$

Equations (24) and (25) may be used as the working equations for the exact solution of long lines. Under certain conditions it is convenient to have equations (24) and (25) expressed in terms of hyperbolic functions. This is done as follows.

From equation (24),

$$\mathbf{V} = \frac{\mathbf{V}_r}{2}\epsilon^{\sqrt{\mathbf{ZY}}l} + \frac{\mathbf{I}_r\sqrt{\mathbf{Z}/\mathbf{Y}}}{2}\epsilon^{\sqrt{\mathbf{ZY}}l} + \frac{\mathbf{V}_r}{2}\epsilon^{-\sqrt{\mathbf{ZY}}l} - \frac{\mathbf{I}_r\sqrt{\mathbf{Z}/\mathbf{Y}}}{2}\epsilon^{-\sqrt{\mathbf{ZY}}l}$$

$$= \mathbf{V}_r\left(\frac{\epsilon^{\sqrt{\mathbf{ZY}}l} + \epsilon^{-\sqrt{\mathbf{ZY}}l}}{2}\right) + \mathbf{I}_r\sqrt{\mathbf{Z}/\mathbf{Y}}\left(\frac{\epsilon^{\sqrt{\mathbf{ZY}}l} - \epsilon^{-\sqrt{\mathbf{ZY}}l}}{2}\right)$$

Since the analytic definition of

$$\sinh\theta = \frac{\epsilon^{\theta} - \epsilon^{-\theta}}{2}$$

and

$$\cosh\theta = \frac{\epsilon^{\theta} + \epsilon^{-\theta}}{2}$$

$$\mathbf{V} = \mathbf{V}_r\cosh\sqrt{\mathbf{ZY}}l + \mathbf{I}_r\sqrt{\mathbf{Z}/\mathbf{Y}}\sinh\sqrt{\mathbf{ZY}}l \tag{26}$$

Similarly

$$\mathbf{I} = \mathbf{I}_r\cosh\sqrt{\mathbf{ZY}}l + \mathbf{V}_r\sqrt{\mathbf{Y}/\mathbf{Z}}\sinh\sqrt{\mathbf{ZY}}l \tag{27}$$

Equations (26) and (27) are particularly convenient to use if tables of complex hyperbolic functions are available; otherwise, equations (24) and (25) may be more convenient.[3]

Physical Interpretation of Equations for Exact Solution. Equations (24) and (25) may be modified somewhat to make their physical significance more apparent. Since $\sqrt{\mathbf{ZY}}$ is a complex expression, we may substitute an expression such as $(\alpha + j\beta)$ for it. Also, letting

[3] See "Tables" or "Charts of Complex Hyperbolic Functions," by A. E. Kennelly, Harvard University Press.

$Z_0 = \sqrt{Z/Y}$ and $Y_0 = \sqrt{Y/Z}$, equations (24) and (25) may be written:

$$V = \left(\frac{V_r + I_rZ_0}{2}\right)\epsilon^{(\alpha+j\beta)\,l} + \left(\frac{V_r - I_rZ_0}{2}\right)\epsilon^{-(\alpha+j\beta)\,l} \qquad (28)$$

$$I = \left(\frac{I_r + V_rY_0}{2}\right)\epsilon^{(\alpha+j\beta)\,l} + \left(\frac{I_r - V_rY_0}{2}\right)\epsilon^{-(\alpha+j\beta)\,l} \qquad (29)$$

Recognizing that $\epsilon^{(\alpha+j\beta)\,l} = \epsilon^{\alpha l}\epsilon^{j\beta l}$ and that $\epsilon^{-(\alpha+j\beta)\,l} = \epsilon^{-\alpha l}\epsilon^{-j\beta l}$, we may write equations (28) and (29) as follows:

$$V = \left(\frac{V_r + I_rZ_0}{2}\right)\epsilon^{\alpha l}\epsilon^{j\beta l} + \left(\frac{V_r - I_rZ_0}{2}\right)\epsilon^{-\alpha l}\epsilon^{-j\beta l} \qquad (30)$$

$$I = \left(\frac{I_r + V_rY_0}{2}\right)\epsilon^{\alpha l}\epsilon^{j\beta l} + \left(\frac{I_r - V_rY_0}{2}\right)\epsilon^{-\alpha l}\epsilon^{-j\beta l} \qquad (31)$$

The quantity $\sqrt{ZY} = (\alpha + j\beta)$ is called the propagation constant. It determines how the wave is propagated with reference to change in magnitude and phase along the line. Equation (30) consists of two parts. The first, $\left(\frac{V_r + I_rZ_0}{2}\right)\epsilon^{\alpha l}\,\epsilon^{j\beta l}$, represents a quantity that increases in magnitude ($\epsilon^{\alpha l}$ increases) as we go from the receiver to the sending end or it becomes smaller as we proceed from the sending to the receiver end. This term must therefore represent a voltage wave which is being propagated from the sending to the receiver end. Hence it is called the direct wave or direct component. The direct component is analogous to a wave started in a body of water. As the wave leaves the source it becomes smaller and smaller. The second part of equation (30) is $\left(\frac{V_r - I_rZ_0}{2}\right)\epsilon^{-\alpha l}\,\epsilon^{-j\beta l}$. As we proceed from the load to the generator this component becomes smaller, since l increases and $\epsilon^{-\alpha l}$ decreases. Hence this wave must be originating at the receiver, and it is therefore called the reflected wave. It is analogous to the phenomena in a body of water as a wave strikes a bank. A reflection occurs, and a wave is then seen traveling away from the bank with gradually diminishing magnitude. Since, for a given distance of travel, α determines the magnitude of the wave, it is a measure of how much the wave is increased or decreased in magnitude, or, in other words, attenuated. For this reason it is called the attenuation constant or factor. The attenuation factor is the real part of the propagation constant. The factors $\epsilon^{j\beta l}$ and $\epsilon^{-j\beta l}$ will be recognized as operators which produce opposite rotations. The operator $\epsilon^{j\beta l}$ causes the direct component to advance in phase from its position at the load as we proceed from the receiving to the sending end, while $\epsilon^{-j\beta l}$ causes the reflected wave to fall behind its phase position at the receiver. Since β determines the change in phase for a given distance l along the line, it is called the phase constant. It is sometimes called the wave length constant because it determines the distance along the line over which a complete wave is subtended. This will be explained in more detail later. The loci of the variation of the direct and reflected waves can be represented as spirals, as shown in Fig. 10. The sum od of the direct and reflected waves of voltage at any point along the line such as at βl gives the resultant voltage at that point. When βl is 90°, the direct component of voltage oa is opposite to the reflected component ob. The resultant oc, which is the voltage of the line at this 90° or quarter-wave-length point, may be very small because of the cancellation effect of the two waves. A generator producing a low voltage, if connected at this point, could subtend a comparatively high voltage at the receiver. This is essentially a resonance phenomenon and is called quarter-wave resonance. As βl increases from this 90° point the voltage of the line increases until βl becomes 180°.

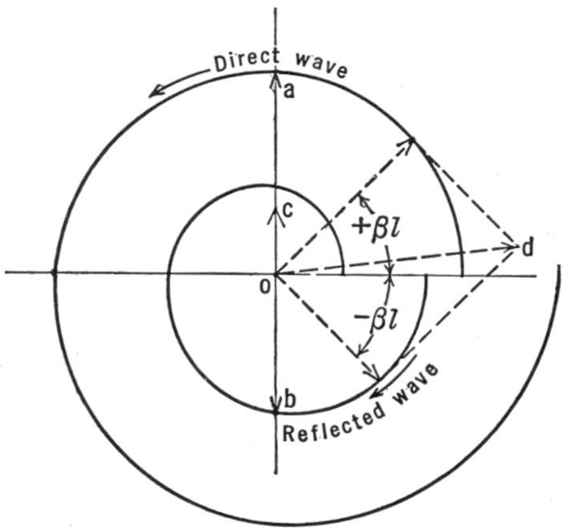

Fig. 10. Variation of direct and reflected waves of voltage with respect to the line angle βl for a particular case.

Here the direct and reflected waves add. This phenomenon is called half-wave resonance. As βl increases to 270° the direct and reflected waves are again opposite (as at quarter-wave) and we then have three-quarter-wave resonance.

Surge Impedance. Inspection of equation (28) makes it apparent that dimensionally $I_r Z_0$ must be a voltage. Hence Z_0 must be an impedance. Further evidence of this fact is obtained when it is remembered that $Z_0 = \sqrt{Z/Y}$. The reciprocal of Y is dimensionally an impedance, and the $\sqrt{Z/Y}$ then becomes $\sqrt{\text{impedance}^2}$ which is an impedance. Hence the quantity $Z_0 = \sqrt{Z/Y}$ is called the surge impedance of the line. The reciprocal, $\sqrt{Y/Z}$, is called surge admittance. The surge impedance is the impedance offered to the propagation of a wave along a line. In effect it is the impedance an advancing wave of voltage or current encounters as it travels along the line.

Terminal Reflections. The receiver voltage $\mathbf{V}_r$ is $\mathbf{I}_r\mathbf{Z}_r$ where $\mathbf{Z}_r$ is the impedance of the load. If $\mathbf{Z}_r$ is made equal to $\mathbf{Z}_0$ the receiver voltage $\mathbf{V}_r$ would equal $\mathbf{I}_r\mathbf{Z}_0$. Then the reflected wave in equation (30) is zero and the equation of the voltage along the line becomes

$$\mathbf{V} = \left(\frac{\mathbf{V}_r + \mathbf{V}_r}{2}\right)\epsilon^{\alpha l}\epsilon^{j\beta l} = \mathbf{V}_r\epsilon^{\alpha l}\epsilon^{j\beta l} \tag{32}$$

This variation is exponential in character, and no terminal reflections exist. The voltage, V, increases exponentially in magnitude as we proceed from the receiving end to the sending end. Simultaneously with the increase in magnitude there is a uniform advance in phase of $\mathbf{V}$ with respect to the load voltage $\mathbf{V}_r$. The wave encounters the same impedance (surge impedance) at the load as it did while advancing along the line. This termination makes the line behave as if it were infinitely long. Hence a line terminated in its surge impedance is sometimes called an infinite line. In communication work, terminating a line in an impedance equal to the surge impedance is sometimes called matching.

If a long line is short-circuited at the receiver $V_r = 0$ and equation (30) becomes

$$\mathbf{V} = \frac{\mathbf{I}_r\mathbf{Z}_0}{2}\epsilon^{\alpha l}\epsilon^{j\beta l} - \frac{\mathbf{I}_r\mathbf{Z}_0}{2}\epsilon^{-\alpha l}\epsilon^{-j\beta l} \tag{33}$$

Where l is 0,

$$\begin{aligned}\mathbf{V}_{l=0} &= \frac{\mathbf{I}_r\mathbf{Z}_0}{2} - \frac{\mathbf{I}_r\mathbf{Z}_0}{2}\\ &= \text{direct wave} - \text{reflected wave}\end{aligned}$$

Thus it may be said that the voltage is reflected with a change in sign. The current wave under the same conditions becomes

$$\begin{aligned}\mathbf{I}_{l=0} &= \frac{\mathbf{I}_r}{2} + \frac{\mathbf{I}_r}{2}\\ &= \text{direct wave} + \text{reflected wave}\end{aligned}$$

It follows, then, that the current wave is reflected with the same sign or the direct and reflected waves of current add arithmetically at the receiver.

If the line is open-circuited at the receiver, $I_r = 0$. Imposing this condition on equations (30) and (31) shows the voltage wave to be reflected with the same sign and the current with a change in sign.

Velocity of Propagation. In the foregoing equations, distance along the line, namely l, has been considered the independent variable. The other independent variable, time, has been tacitly taken into account by the use of vector quantities. In the evaluation of the velocity of propagation the interrelation of time-phase and space-phase effects must be recognized.

It is evident from the use of β in the foregoing equations that this quantity determines the phase shift of **V** or **I** per unit length of line, and as such it represents a number of radians per unit length of line. The length of line required to effect a complete cycle or 2π radians of phase shift is

$$\lambda = \frac{2\pi}{\beta} \text{ units} \tag{34}$$

where λ and β are expressed in any consistent set of units. To simplify visualizing the phenomenon, consider only the voltage wave.

Since λ is the distance for a phase shift of 2π radians, it is the distance along the line (see Fig. 11) from one zero value say at a on the voltage wave to a corresponding zero value at b, 2π radians or 360° from the first zero point. The distance λ thus represents the length of line over which a complete space wave or cycle of voltage is subtended, and in consequence λ is called the wave length of the propagated wave. As time

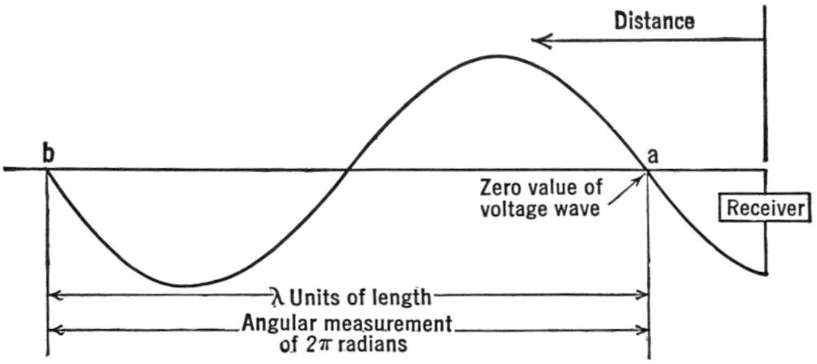

FIG. 11. A space wave or cycle from a to b.

elapses, the alternating voltage at point a will rise to a positive maximum, decrease to zero, then increase to a negative maximum, thence to zero. In this length of time, point b on the wave will have arrived at a in Fig. 11. In other words, during this length of time, the time for one cycle, $1/f$, all points on the wave will have traveled a distance of λ. The velocity of travel or propagation must then be $\frac{\lambda}{1/f}$, or λf units of length per second. Hence the velocity of propagation is

$$v = \lambda f = \frac{2\pi}{\beta} f \tag{35}$$

Equation (34) shows that the wave length for any line is determined by the quantity β. Hence β is often termed the wave-length constant, and it may be evaluated in terms of the circuit parameters from the original substitution, namely, $\sqrt{\mathbf{ZY}} = \alpha + j\beta$. Since $\mathbf{Z} = R + jX$ and $\mathbf{Y} = g - jb$, it follows that

$$\alpha + j\beta = \sqrt{(R + jX)\,(g - jb)} \tag{36}$$

$$\alpha^2 + j2\alpha\beta - \beta^2 = Rg - jRb + jgX + bX$$

$$\alpha^2 - \beta^2 = Rg + bX \tag{37}$$

$$2\alpha\beta = gX - Rb \tag{38}$$

Solving equations (37) and (38) simultaneously for β gives

$$\beta = \sqrt{\frac{\pm ZY - (Rg + bX)}{2}} \tag{39}$$

The preceding derivation shows that all terms in equation (39) are expressed algebraically and not in complex form. All the quantities are per unit values, that is, per centimeter, per mile, etc.

It is interesting to find the velocity of propagation under the conditions of zero series resistance and a negligibly small value of g. Imposing these conditions gives

$$\beta = \sqrt{\frac{\pm bX - bX}{2}} = \sqrt{-bX}$$

The two signs before ZY in equation (39) and before bX above resulted from the solution of a quadratic equation. As often occurs, one of such solutions has no physical reality. If the plus sign were used in the algebraic manipulation above, β would be zero, which would in turn give an infinite velocity of propagation. Obviously, this is impossible. When making arithmetic computations the proper sign to employ is that which will give a physically possible and plausible result. Had the equations been based on $g + jb$, it would have been necessary to use the plus sign before the ZY and bX above. Since b is the shunted susceptance due to the line capacitance, it must carry a negative sign upon substitution of a numerical value for it in accordance with the conventions employed in this book. Substituting the value of β above in equation (35) gives

$$v = \frac{2\pi f}{\sqrt{-bX}} = \frac{2\pi f}{\sqrt{2\pi f C \times 2\pi f L}} = \frac{1}{\sqrt{LC}} \text{ (for } r = 0 \text{ and } g = 0\text{)} \tag{40}$$

In equation (40) v is in miles per second if L is expressed in henrys per mile and C in farads per mile. If one further assumption is made in equation (40), namely, that the inductance due to the flux within the conductor is negligible, the velocity will be the same as that of light. This is illustrated by example 2, pages 429–433.

Example 1. An open-wire telephone line has a resistance of 10.26 ohms, an inductance of 0.00366 henry, and a capacitance of 0.00822 μf per loop mile (one mile of outgoing plus one mile of return conductor). Calculate the velocity of propagation for a 200-cycle and also for a 2000-cycle frequency, assuming that the values of R, L, and C are the same at both frequencies. Assume $g = 0$ in both cases.

At 200 cycles

$$X = 2\pi\, 200 \times 0.00366 = 4.6 \text{ ohms per loop mile}$$
$$Z = \sqrt{10.26^2 + 4.6^2} = 11.22 \text{ ohms per loop mile}$$
$$b = -2\pi f C = -2\pi\, 200 \times 0.00822 \times 10^{-6} = -10.32 \times 10^{-6} \text{ mho per loop mile}$$
$$Y = 10.32 \times 10^{-6} \text{ mho per loop mile}$$
$$\beta = \sqrt{\frac{\pm 11.22 \times 10.32 \times 10^{-6} - (-10.32 \times 10^{-6} \times 4.6)}{2}}$$
$$= \sqrt{\frac{163.5 \times 10^{-6}}{2}} = 9.05 \times 10^{-3}$$
$$v = \frac{2\pi f}{\beta} = \frac{2\pi\, 200}{9.05 \times 10^{-3}} = 139 \times 10^3 = 139{,}000 \text{ miles per second}$$

At 2000 cycles

$$X = 2\pi\, 2000 \times 0.00366 = 46 \text{ ohms per loop mile}$$
$$Z = \sqrt{10.26^2 + 46^2} = 47.1 \text{ ohms per loop mile}$$
$$b = -2\pi f C = -2\pi\, 2000 \times 0.00822 \times 10^{-6}$$
$$= -103.2 \times 10^{-6} \text{ mho per loop mile}$$
$$Y = 103.2 \times 10^{-6} \text{ mho per loop mile}$$
$$\beta = \sqrt{\frac{\pm 47.1 \times 103.2 \times 10^{-6} - (-103.2 \times 10^{-6} \times 46)}{2}}$$
$$= \sqrt{\frac{9610 \times 10^{-6}}{2}} = 69.3 \times 10^{-3}$$
$$v = \frac{2\pi f}{\beta} = \frac{2\pi\, 2000}{69.3 \times 10^{-3}} = 181{,}400 \text{ miles per second}$$

If parameters per mile to ground or neutral were used, Z would be halved, Y and b doubled and β would be the same.

Confusion sometimes arises as to what the velocity of propagation refers to physically. The velocity of propagation of a voltage or current wave is the velocity at which the impulse or pressure travels. It is not the velocity of current flow. The velocity of current flow for normal current densities in copper is very low, although the velocity of the pressure wave is high. The phenomenon is somewhat analogous to the application of pressure at one end of a long pipe filled with water. The pressure appears at the far end of the pipe very soon after it is applied at the near end. However, the actual rate of flow of water in the pipe may be very low, especially if only a comparatively small stream is permitted to emerge at the far end.

Determination of Transmission Line Parameters. 1. *Inductance.* The inductance per wire is used in transmission line calculations. It may be derived as follows. Consider two parallel conductors as shown in

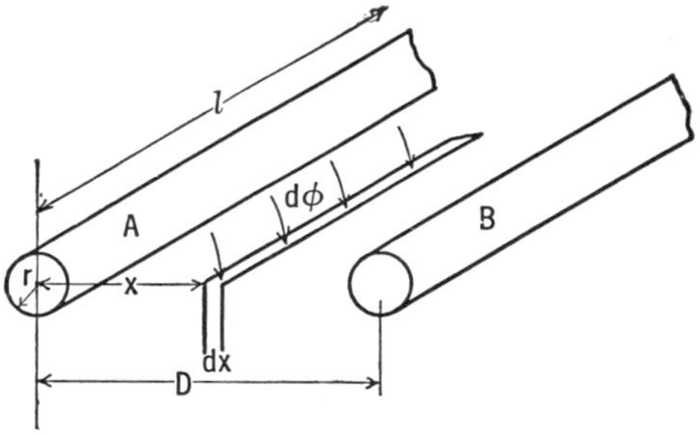

FIG. 12. Part of a two-wire line.

Fig. 12, each having a radius r and separated a distance D between centers. The fundamental equation of inductance when permeability is constant is

$$L = \frac{N\phi}{I} 10^{-9} \text{ henry}$$

where I is in abamperes and ϕ is in maxwells. The field intensity based on the law of Biot-Savart, at a distance of x centimeters from a long straight conductor carrying a current is $2I/x$ gilberts per centimeter, which in air is numerically equal to the flux density. Referring now to the open-wire line shown in Fig. 12,

$$d\phi = \left(\frac{2I}{x}\right)(l\,dx)$$

The total flux that exists outside of conductor A which causes an inductive effect on conductor A is

$$\phi_1 = \int_r^D \frac{2I}{x} l\,dx = 2lI \log_\epsilon \frac{D}{r}$$

$$L_1 = \frac{N\phi_1}{I} 10^{-9} = 2l \log_\epsilon \frac{D}{r} 10^{-9}$$

$$= 2 \times 2.3026 l \log_{10} \frac{D}{r} 10^{-9} \text{ henry} \quad (41)$$

where l is expressed in centimeters.

The flux included from $x = (D - r)$ to $x = (D + r)$ has some effect in inducing a net emf in the two conductors connected in series to form a coil. The effect is due to this flux linking all of conductor A and only part of conductor B. Integrating between the limits $x = r$ and $x = D$ includes the full effectiveness of the flux from $x = (D - r)$ to $x = D$ in causing the inductance. This balances the partial effectiveness of the flux from $x = D$ to $x = (D + r)$ which is neglected in taking the limits from r to D. The flux from $x = (D + r)$ to $x = \infty$ links both conductors and therefore produces equal and opposing emf's around the loop. Hence it has no net inductive effect. Equation (41) gives the inductance of conductor A due to all the flux on the outside of conductor A which is effective. The flux within the conductor causes some inductance which may be calculated as follows.

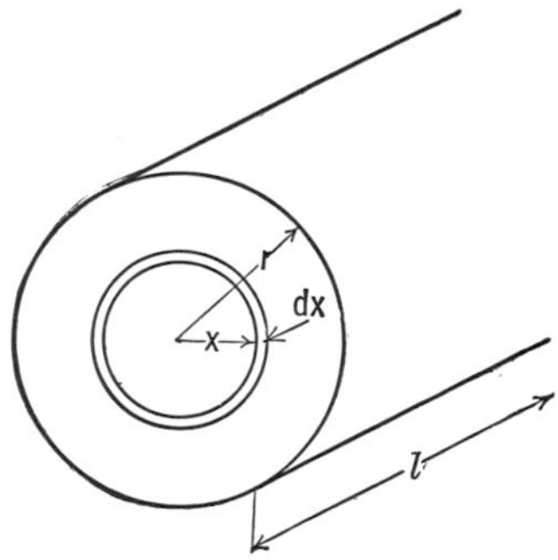

FIG. 13.

Assume that the current in conductor A is uniformly distributed across the cross-section. Let I' be the current per unit area. Refer to the cross-section of conductor A shown in Fig. 13. The total current responsible for the mmf causing flux through the element dx is $\pi x^2 I'$.

$$\text{mmf} = 4\pi NI = 4\pi\ (\pi x^2 I')$$

If the permeability of the conductor material is unity, the reluctance of the flux path formed by the element dx and a length of conductor l is

$$\mathcal{R} = \frac{2\pi x}{l\,dx} \text{ cgs units when } x \text{ is in centimeters}$$

$$d\phi = \frac{4\pi^2 x^2 I'}{\dfrac{2\pi x}{(l\,dx)}} = 2\pi x I' l\,dx \text{ maxwells}$$

The flux $d\phi$ links only the fibers of the conductor from the center to a distance x or $K\pi x^2$ fibers. To obtain the flux which links the whole conductor that produces the same effect as the actual flux which links $K\pi x^2$ fibers, it is only necessary to find the flux linking $K\pi r^2$ fibers (the entire conductor), which is equivalent to the flux $d\phi$ linking $K\pi x^2$ fibers. Calling the flux in question $d\phi_e$, we have for equivalent linkages

$$d\phi_e K\pi r^2 = d\phi K\pi x^2$$

or

$$d\phi_e = \frac{x^2}{r^2} d\phi$$

Hence

$$d\phi_e = \frac{x^2}{r^2}(2\pi x I' l\, dx)$$

$$\phi_e = \int_0^r \frac{2\pi x^3 I' l\, dx}{r^2} = \left(\frac{2\pi I' l}{r^2}\right)\left(\frac{r^4}{4}\right)$$

$$= \frac{\pi r^2 I' l}{2}$$

But $\pi r^2 I'$ is the total current I. Therefore

$$\phi_e = \frac{Il}{2}$$

The inductance due to this flux is

$$L_2 = \frac{N\phi_e}{I} 10^{-9} = \frac{1 \times Il\, 10^{-9}}{2I} = \frac{l\, 10^{-9}}{2} \text{ henry} \tag{42}$$

The total inductance of conductor A is the sum of equations (41) and (42).

$$L = L_1 + L_2 = \left[\frac{l}{2} + 4.6052 l \log_{10}\frac{D}{r}\right] 10^{-9} \text{ henry} \tag{43}$$

The inductance per mile is

$$L_{\text{mile}} = 0.5 \times 5280 \times 30.48\, 10^{-9}$$
$$+ 4.6052 \times 5280 \times 30.48 \times 10^{-9} \log_{10}\frac{D}{r}$$
$$= 0.805\, 10^{-4} + 0.741 \times 10^{-3} \log_{10}\frac{D}{r} \text{ henry} \tag{44}$$

Equation (44) is the working equation. Usually the reactance is desired. It is found by multiplying the values obtained from equation (44) by the angular velocity $2\pi f$.

2. *Capacitance between Wires and to Ground.* The defining equation for capacitance is $C = Q/V$. The defining equation for difference of potential V is

$$V = \frac{W}{Q} = \frac{\text{work}}{\text{charge}}$$

The difference of electrostatic potential between two conductors is the work done in carrying a unit charge from the surface of one conductor to the other. Work is the product of force and the distance through which the force acts. By definition, if all quantities are expressed in the cgs electrostatic system of units, the force on a unit charge is numerically equal to the electrostatic field intensity. The electrostatic field intensity at point p, Fig. 14, at a perpendicular distance of r centimeters from a long straight wire is found as follows.

Let all quantities be expressed in the cgs electrostatic system of units, and let σ be the charge per unit length of wire. From Coulomb's law $f = QQ'/d^2$ dynes. Hence the force on a unit charge at point p due to a length of conductor dl is

$$df' = \frac{1 \times \sigma\, dl}{\rho^2}$$

where ρ is the distance in centimeters from p to dl. As θ varies between minus and plus 90° (on the basis of an infinite length of wire), it is

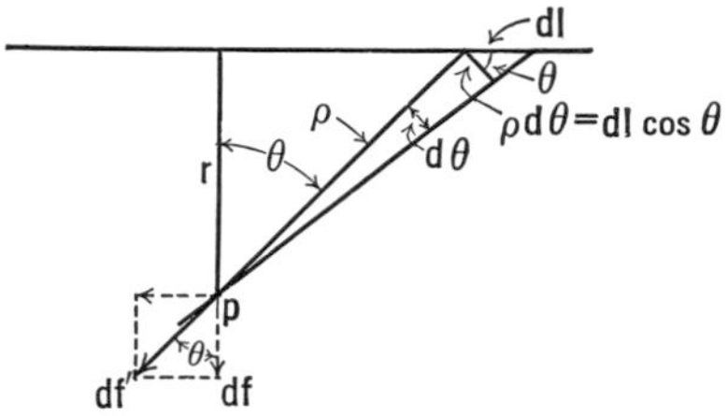

Fig. 14.

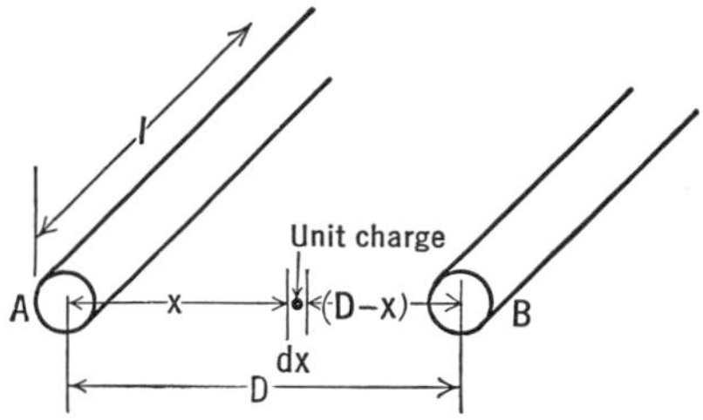

Fig. 15.

apparent that all the components of df' parallel to the wire add to zero. Therefore only the components perpendicular to the conductor need be added to obtain the resultant force on the unit charge.

$$\begin{aligned} df &= df' \cos\theta \\ &= \frac{\sigma\, dl}{\rho^2}\cos\theta = \frac{\sigma\rho\, d\theta}{\rho^2} = \frac{\sigma\, d\theta}{\rho} \\ &= \frac{\sigma\, d\theta}{r/\cos\theta} = \frac{\sigma}{r}\cos\theta\, d\theta \end{aligned}$$

$$f = \int_{-\pi/2}^{\pi/2} \frac{\sigma}{r}\cos\theta\, d\theta = \frac{2\sigma}{r}\text{ dynes} \tag{45}$$

The force on the unit charge in Fig. 15 is due to the effect of conductor A (say + charge) and that of conductor B (negative charge if A is positive).

$$f_A = \frac{2\sigma}{x}$$

$$f_B = \frac{2\sigma}{D - x}$$

$$f = f_A + f_B = \frac{2\sigma}{x} + \frac{2\sigma}{D - x} \tag{46}$$

$$dW = f\,dx = \left(\frac{2\sigma}{x} + \frac{2\sigma}{D - x}\right) dx$$

$$W = V = \int_r^{D-r} \left(\frac{2\sigma}{x} + \frac{2\sigma}{D - x}\right) dx = 4\sigma \log_\epsilon \frac{D - r}{r} \tag{47}$$

The charge on the line for a length l is σl. Therefore

$$C = \frac{Q}{V} = \frac{\sigma l}{4\sigma \log_\epsilon \dfrac{D - r}{r}} = \frac{l}{4 \log_\epsilon \dfrac{D - r}{r}} \text{ cgs esu} \tag{48}$$

where r now represents the radius of the conductor and is not the same as in the derivation of equation (45). All quantities in equation (48) are in the cgs or absolute electrostatic system of units, giving C in esu or statfarads.

Equation (48) gives the capacitance between two parallel wires. The capacitance to ground or neutral is usually desired in the calculation of transmission lines. Since the plane of neutral potential is symmetrically located between positive and negative charges (assuming a uniform dielectric such as air), the potential between one wire and neutral,[4] or what is also ground potential, is one-half of the potential

[4] The preceding and following equations of capacitance are only approximately correct because they are based on several assumptions which are only partially fulfilled. First, the charge on the conductor is assumed uniform. This assumption requires in part that the conductors be removed an infinite distance from all charged bodies and that the conductors are circular in shape. Under such conditions the distribution of the electrostatic field is pictured in Fig. 16. Equipotential surfaces are those in which all electrostatic lines of force enter and leave perpendicularly. One equipotential surface XX' is shown in Fig. 16. This surface is at a distance halfway between the two conductors and is therefore at a potential midway between the positively and negatively charged conductors. Such a surface is said to be at zero potential, and it is sometimes called the neutral plane between conductors, or simply the neutral. If the earth is considered a conductor and to be at zero potential, it may be assumed to be the same as the equipotential plane XX'. Hence the potential and capacitance to earth or ground may be taken the same as that to the equipotential surface XX' in Fig. 16 provided $D/2$ is relatively small compared with the physical height of the conductor above actual ground. Even though all the above assumptions are not completely fulfilled, the equations given yield results which are sufficiently accurate for most work concerning transmission lines. For more accurate derivations of capacitance the reader is referred to works on electrostatics and electrodynamics.

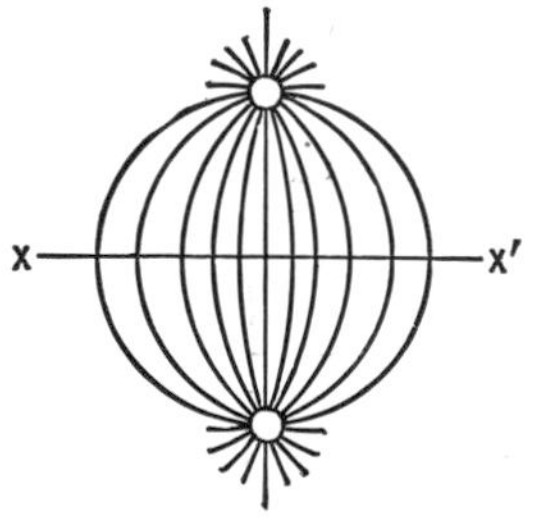

FIG. 16. Equipotential line XX' is at a potential midway between the positively charged top and negatively charged lower conductors.

[given in equation (47)] between wires. Hence

$$V_g = \frac{1}{2}\left(4\sigma \log_\epsilon \frac{D-r}{r}\right) = 2\sigma \log_\epsilon\left(\frac{D-r}{r}\right)$$

and

$$C_g = \frac{\sigma l}{2\sigma \log_\epsilon \dfrac{D-r}{r}} = \frac{l}{2 \log_\epsilon \dfrac{D-r}{r}} \text{esu} \tag{49}$$

Expressed in farads per mile, equations (48) and (49) for the capacitance between conductors and between one conductor and ground become:

$$C_{\text{farads per mile}} = \frac{1940 \times 10^{-11}}{\log_{10} \dfrac{D-r}{r}} \tag{50}$$

$$C_{g\ \text{farads per mile}} = \frac{3880 \times 10^{-11}}{\log_{10} \dfrac{D-r}{r}} \tag{51}$$

Equations (50) and (51) are the working equations. As long as D and r are expressed in the same units, the actual units are immaterial.

Equations (44), (50), and (51) form the basis of tables wherein values of L or C may be immediately determined when the size of wire and spacings are known. Samples of tables where the quantities are expressed in units per thousand feet are shown in Tables I and II.[5]

When equations (44), (50), and (51) are applied to three-phase transmission the distance D is that for equilateral spacing, as shown in Fig. 17. These equations are often applied to plane spacings, as shown

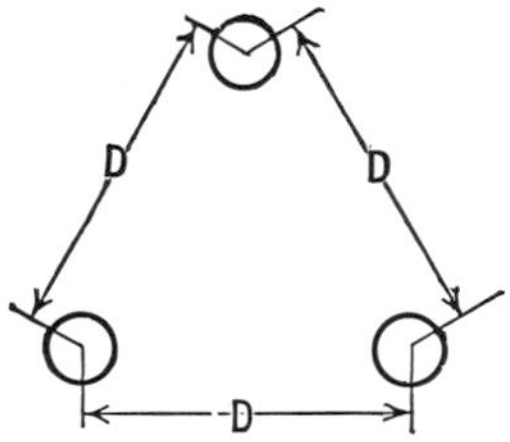

FIG. 17. Equilateral spacing of a transmission line.

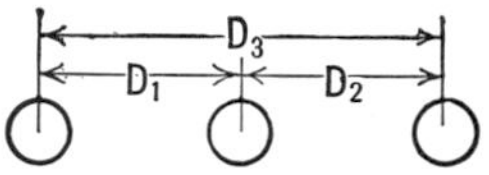

FIG. 18. Plane spacing of a transmission line.

in Fig. 18, in which cases D is taken as the geometric mean distance, that is, $D = \sqrt[3]{D_1D_2D_3}$. The results thus obtained are sufficiently accurate for most computations.

[5] Reprinted by permission from "Electrical Engineers' Handbook: Electric Power," fourth edition, edited by Pender and Del Mar, pp. 14–39 and 14–34, John Wiley & Sons, Inc., 1949.

TABLE I

SELF-INDUCTANCE OF SOLID NON-MAGNETIC WIRES*

Millihenrys per 1000 FEET of each wire of a single-phase or of a symmetrical three-phase line

Size of Wire, cir mils or A.W.G.	Diam. of Wire, inches	Inches between Wires, center to center							
		1	3	6	9	12	18	24	30
1,000,000	1.0000	0.05750	0.1245	0.1667	0.1915	0.2090	0.2337	0.2512	0.2648
750,000	0.8660	0.06627	0.1332	0.1755	0.2002	0.2178	0.2425	0.2600	0.2736
500,000	0.7071	0.07863	0.1456	0.1879	0.2126	0.2301	0.2548	0.2724	0.2860
350,000	0.5916	0.08950	0.1565	0.1987	0.2235	0.2410	0.2657	0.2832	0.2968
250,000	0.5000	0.09976	0.1667	0.2090	0.2337	0.2512	0.2760	0.2935	0.3071
0000	0.4600	0.1048	0.1718	0.2141	0.2388	0.2563	0.2810	0.2986	0.3122
000	0.4096	0.1119	0.1789	0.2211	0.2459	0.2634	0.2881	0.3057	0.3193
00	0.3648	0.1190	0.1860	0.2282	0.2529	0.2705	0.2952	0.3127	0.3263
0	0.3249	0.1260	0.1930	0.2353	0.2600	0.2775	0.3022	0.3198	0.3334
1	0.2893	0.1331	0.2001	0.2423	0.2671	0.2846	0.3093	0.3269	0.3405
2	0.2576	0.1402	0.2072	0.2494	0.2741	0.2917	0.3164	0.3339	0.3475
4	0.2043	0.1543	0.2213	0.2635	0.2883	0.3058	0.3305	0.3481	0.3617
6	0.1620	0.1685	0.2354	0.2777	0.3024	0.3199	0.3447	0.3622	0.3758
8	0.1285	0.1826	0.2496	0.2918	0.3165	0.3341	0.3588	0.3763	0.3899
10	0.1019	0.1967	0.2637	0.3060	0.3307	0.3482	0.3729	0.3905	0.4041
12	0.08081	0.2109	0.2778	0.3201	0.3448	0.3623	0.3871	0.4046	0.4182
14	0.06408	0.2250	0.2920	0.3342	0.3590	0.3765	0.4012	0.4187	0.4323
16	0.05082	0.2391	0.3061	0.3484	0.3731	0.3906	0.4153	0.4329	0.4465

Size of Wire, cir mils or A.W.G.	Feet between Wires, center to center								
	3	4	5	6	8	10	15	20	25
1,000,000	0.2760	0.2935	0.3071	0.3182	0.3358	0.3494	0.3741	0.3916	0.4052
750,000	0.2847	0.3023	0.3159	0.3270	0.3445	0.3581	0.3828	0.4004	0.4140
500,000	0.2971	0.3146	0.3282	0.3393	0.3569	0.3705	0.3952	0.4127	0.4263
350,000	0.3080	0.3255	0.3391	0.3502	0.3678	0.3814	0.4061	0.4236	0.4372
250,000	0.3182	0.3358	0.3494	0.3605	0.3780	0.3916	0.4163	0.4339	0.4475
0000	0.3233	0.3408	0.3544	0.3656	0.3831	0.3967	0.4214	0.4390	0.4526
000	0.3304	0.3479	0.3615	0.3726	0.3902	0.4038	0.4285	0.4460	0.4596
00	0.3374	0.3550	0.3686	0.3797	0.3972	0.4108	0.4356	0.4531	0.4667
0	0.3445	0.3620	0.3756	0.3867	0.4043	0.4179	0.4426	0.4601	0.4737
1	0.3516	0.3691	0.3827	0.3938	0.4114	0.4250	0.4497	0.4672	0.4808
2	0.3586	0.3762	0.3898	0.4009	0.4184	0.4320	0.4568	0.4743	0.4879
4	0.3728	0.3903	0.4039	0.4150	0.4326	0.4462	0.4709	0.4884	0.5020
6	0.3869	0.4045	0.4181	0.4292	0.4467	0.4603	0.4850	0.5026	0.5162
8	0.4011	0.4186	0.4322	0.4433	0.4608	0.4744	0.4992	0.5167	0.5303
10	0.4152	0.4327	0.4463	0.4574	0.4750	0.4886	0.5133	0.5308	0.5444
12	0.4293	0.4469	0.4605	0.4716	0.4891	0.5027	0.5274	0.5450	0.5586
14	0.4435	0.4610	0.4746	0.4857	0.5033	0.5169	0.5416	0.5591	0.5727
16	0.4576	0.4751	0.4887	0.4998	0.5174	0.5310	0.5557	0.5732	0.5868

* The inductances given in this table also apply, with a practically negligible error (about 1 per cent), to ordinary stranded wires of the *same cross-section.*

Example 2. Exact Solution of a Transmission Line. A 60-cycle transmission line 200 miles long consists of three No. 0000 solid conductors with 10-ft equilateral spacing. Calculate the sending voltage when the receiver voltage is 110 kv between lines and when the line is supplying a balanced load of 18,000 kw at 0.8 power-factor lag. Also calculate the sending-end current and the efficiency of the line at 25° C. Assume that the conductance to ground is negligible.

TABLE II

CAPACITANCE TO NEUTRAL* OF SMOOTH ROUND WIRES

Microfarads per 1000 FEET of each wire of a single-phase or of a symmetrical three-phase line

Size of Wire, A.W.G.	Diam. of Wire, inches	Inches between Wires, center to center							
		1	3	6	9	12	18	24	30
0000	0.4600	0.01199	0.006608	0.005192	0.004618	0.004282	0.003884	0.003643	0.003477
000	0.4096	0.01099	0.006317	0.005013	0.004477	0.004161	0.003783	0.003555	0.003396
00	0.3648	0.01016	0.006055	0.004847	0.004344	0.004045	0.003688	0.003470	0.003319
0	0.3249	0.009458	0.005812	0.004692	0.004218	0.003936	0.003597	0.003390	0.003245
1	0.2893	0.008855	0.005587	0.004546	0.004100	0.003833	0.003511	0.003313	0.003174
2	0.2576	0.008332	0.005381	0.004408	0.003988	0.003735	0.003428	0.003239	0.003107
4	0.2043	0.007455	0.005010	0.004157	0.003781	0.003553	0.003274	0.003102	0.002980
6	0.1620	0.006753	0.004688	0.003933	0.003595	0.003388	0.003134	0.002975	0.002863
8	0.1285	0.006177	0.004406	0.003732	0.003426	0.003238	0.003005	0.002859	0.002755
10	0.1019	0.005693	0.004155	0.003551	0.003273	0.003100	0.002886	0.002751	0.002655
12	0.08081	0.005277	0.003931	0.003386	0.003132	0.002974	0.002776	0.002651	0.002562
14	0.06408	0.004921	0.003730	0.003235	0.003003	0.002858	0.002675	0.002558	0.002475

Size of Wire, A.W.G.	Feet between Wires, center to center								
	3	4	5	6	8	10	15	20	25
0000	0.003351	0.003171	0.003043	0.002947	0.002806	0.002706	0.002542	0.002436	0.002361
000	0.003276	0.003103	0.002981	0.002889	0.002753	0.002657	0.002498	0.002396	0.002323
00	0.003204	0.003039	0.002922	0.002833	0.002702	0.002610	0.002456	0.002358	0.002287
0	0.003135	0.002977	0.002864	0.002779	0.002653	0.002564	0.002416	0.002320	0.002251
1	0.003069	0.002917	0.002809	0.002727	0.002606	0.002520	0.002376	0.002284	0.002217
2	0.003006	0.002860	0.002756	0.002677	0.002560	0.002477	0.002338	0.002249	0.002184
4	0.002887	0.002752	0.002656	0.002582	0.002474	0.002396	0.002266	0.002182	0.002121
6	0.002777	0.002652	0.002563	0.002494	0.002392	0.002319	0.002197	0.002118	0.002061
8	0.002676	0.002559	0.002476	0.002412	0.002317	0.002248	0.002133	0.002059	0.002004
10	0.002581	0.002473	0.002395	0.002335	0.002245	0.002181	0.002073	0.002002	0.001951
12	0.002493	0.002392	0.002319	0.002262	0.002178	0.902118	0.002016	0.001949	0.001900
14	0.002411	0.002316	0.002247	0.002194	0.002115	0.002058	0.001961	0.001898	0.001852

* The capacitance *between* wires equals one-half the values given in this table.

All calculations will be made per phase to neutral or ground.

$$V_n = \frac{110{,}000}{\sqrt{3}} = 63{,}500 \text{ volts}$$

$$I_r = \frac{18{,}000{,}000}{\sqrt{3}\ 110{,}000 \times 0.8} = 118 \text{ amperes}$$

From wire tables the 60-cycle resistance per mile of No. 0000 at 25° C is 0.271 ohm. The diameter of No. 0000 wire is 460 mils.

$$L_{\text{mile}} = 0.805 \times 10^{-4} + 0.741 \times 10^{-3} \log_{10} \frac{120}{0.23}$$

$$= 0.805 \times 10^{-4} + 0.741 \times 10^{-3} \times 2.718$$

$$= 0.805 \times 10^{-4} + 2.01 \times 10^{-3}$$

$$= 20.9 \times 10^{-4} \text{ henry per mile}$$

Reactance per mile $= 2\pi\, 60 \times 20.9 \times 10^{-4} = 0.788$ ohm

$$b = \frac{-1}{X_c} = -2\pi fC$$

$$C_{\text{mile}} = \frac{3880 \times 10^{-11}}{\log_{10} \dfrac{120 - 0.23}{0.23}} = 1430 \times 10^{-11} \text{ farad}$$

Susceptance per mile $= -2\pi\, 60 \times 1430 \times 10^{-11} = -0.538 \times 10^{-5}$ mho

$$\mathbf{Y} = g - jb = +j0.538 \times 10^{-5} = 0.538 \times 10^{-5} \underline{/90^\circ} \text{ mho}$$

$$\mathbf{Z} = r + jX = 0.271 + j0.788 = 0.834 \underline{/71.05^\circ} \text{ ohms}$$

$$\sqrt{\mathbf{ZY}} = \sqrt{0.834 \underline{/71.05^\circ}\, 0.538 \times 10^{-5} \underline{/90^\circ}} = 2.12 \times 10^{-3} \underline{/80.5^\circ}$$

$$\sqrt{\mathbf{Z/Y}} = \sqrt{\frac{0.834 \underline{/71.05^\circ}}{0.538 \times 10^{-5} \underline{/90^\circ}}} = 3.94 \times 10^2 \underline{/-9.48^\circ} \text{ ohms}$$

$$\sqrt{\mathbf{Y/Z}} = 0.254 \times 10^{-2} \underline{/9.48^\circ} \text{ mhos}$$

For $l = 200$ miles,

$$\epsilon^{\sqrt{\mathbf{ZY}}l} = \epsilon^{0.424 \underline{/80.5^\circ}} = \epsilon^{0.07+j0.418} = \epsilon^{0.07}\epsilon^{j23.9^\circ}$$

$$\mathbf{V}_r = 63{,}500 + j0 \text{ volts}$$

$$\mathbf{I}_r = 118 \underline{/-36.9^\circ} \text{ amperes}$$

$$\left(\frac{\mathbf{V}_r + \mathbf{I}_r\sqrt{\mathbf{Z/Y}}}{2}\right) = \left(\frac{63{,}500 + 118 \underline{/-36.9^\circ} \times 3.94 \times 10^2 \underline{/-9.48^\circ}}{2}\right)$$

$$= 47{,}800 - j16{,}800 \text{ volts}$$

$$\left(\frac{\mathbf{V}_r + \mathbf{I}_r\sqrt{\mathbf{Z/Y}}}{2}\right)\epsilon^{\sqrt{\mathbf{ZY}}l} = (47{,}800 - j16{,}800)\epsilon^{0.07}\epsilon^{j23.9^\circ}$$

$$= (51{,}300 - j18{,}050)\epsilon^{j23.9^\circ}$$

$$= 54{,}400 \underline{/-19.4^\circ}\, \underline{/23.9^\circ}$$

$$= 54{,}400 \underline{/4.5^\circ} \text{ volts}$$

$$\left(\frac{\mathbf{V}_r - \mathbf{I}_r\sqrt{\mathbf{Z/Y}}}{2}\right)\epsilon^{\sqrt{\mathbf{ZY}}l} = (15{,}700 + j16{,}800)\epsilon^{-0.07}\epsilon^{-j23.9^\circ}$$

$$= (14{,}610 + j15{,}630)\epsilon^{-j23.9^\circ}$$

$$= 21{,}400 \underline{/46.9^\circ}\, \underline{/-23.9^\circ}$$

$$= 21{,}400 \underline{/23^\circ} \text{ volts}$$

$$\mathbf{V}_s = \left(\frac{\mathbf{V}_r + \mathbf{I}_r\sqrt{\mathbf{Z/Y}}}{2}\right)\epsilon^{\sqrt{\mathbf{ZY}}l} + \left(\frac{\mathbf{V}_r - \mathbf{I}_r\sqrt{\mathbf{Z/Y}}}{2}\right)\epsilon^{-\sqrt{\mathbf{ZY}}l}$$

$$= 54{,}400 \underline{/4.5^\circ} + 21{,}400 \underline{/23^\circ}$$

$$= 54{,}200 + j4270 + 19{,}680 + j8355$$

$$= 73{,}880 + j12{,}625 = 74{,}970 \underline{/9.7^\circ} \text{ volts}$$

The current at the sending end could be calculated in a similar way. However, for illustrative purposes it will be calculated from equation (27).

$$\mathbf{I}_s = \mathbf{I}_r \cosh \sqrt{\mathbf{ZY}}l + \mathbf{V}_r \sqrt{\mathbf{Y}/\mathbf{Z}} \sinh \sqrt{\mathbf{ZY}}l$$

The following relations are convenient to use when dealing with hyperbolic functions of complex angles:

$$\sinh (x \pm y) = \sinh x \cosh y \pm \cosh x \sinh y$$
$$\cosh (x \pm y) = \cosh x \cosh y \pm \sinh x \sinh y$$
$$\sinh jx = j \sin x$$
$$\cosh jx = \cos x$$

$$\sqrt{\mathbf{ZY}}l = 2.12 \times 10^{-3} \underline{/80.5^\circ} \times 200 = 0.424 \underline{/80.5^\circ} = 0.07 + j0.418$$

$$\begin{aligned}\cosh (0.07 + j0.418) &= \cosh 0.07 \cosh j0.418 + \sinh 0.07 \sinh j0.418\\ &= \cosh 0.07 \cos 0.418 + j \sinh 0.07 \sin 0.418\\ &= \cosh 0.07 \cos 23.9^\circ + j \sinh 0.07 \sin 23.9^\circ\\ &= 1.00245 \times 0.9143 + j0.07 \times 0.4051\\ &= 0.915 + j0.02835\end{aligned}$$

$$\begin{aligned}\sinh (0.07 + j0.418) &= \sinh 0.07 \cosh j0.418 + \cosh 0.07 \sinh j0.418\\ &= \sinh 0.07 \cos 23.9^\circ + j \cosh 0.07 \sin 23.9^\circ\\ &= 0.07 \times 0.9143 + j1.00245 \times 0.4051\\ &= 0.0639 + j0.406\end{aligned}$$

$$\mathbf{V}_r \sqrt{\mathbf{Y}/\mathbf{Z}} = 63{,}500 \times 0.254 \times 10^{-2} \underline{/9.48^\circ} = 161.30 \underline{/9.48^\circ} \text{ amperes}$$

$$\begin{aligned}\mathbf{V}_r \sqrt{\mathbf{Y}/\mathbf{Z}} \sinh \sqrt{\mathbf{ZY}}l &= 161.3 \underline{/9.48^\circ} (0.0639 + j0.406)\\ &= -0.66 + j66.3 \text{ amperes}\end{aligned}$$

$$\mathbf{I}_r \cosh \sqrt{\mathbf{ZY}}l = (118 \underline{/-36.9^\circ})(0.915 + j0.0284) = 88.4 - j62.1 \text{ amperes}$$

$$\begin{aligned}\mathbf{I}_s &= 88.4 - j62.1 - 0.66 + j66.3\\ &= 87.8 + j4.2 = 87.9 \underline{/2.8^\circ} \text{ amperes}\end{aligned}$$

As a check on the sending voltage, V_s will be calculated by the hyperbolic equation

$$\mathbf{V}_r \cosh \sqrt{\mathbf{ZY}}l + \mathbf{I}_r \sqrt{\mathbf{Z}/\mathbf{Y}} \sinh \sqrt{\mathbf{ZY}}l$$

$$\begin{aligned}\mathbf{V}_s &= 63{,}500 \times 0.915 \underline{/1.75^\circ} + (118 \underline{/-36.9^\circ} \times 3.94 \times 10^2 \underline{/-9.48^\circ})(0.0639 + j0.406)\\ &= 58{,}100 + j1770 + 15{,}700 + j10{,}880\\ &= 73{,}800 + j12{,}652 = 74{,}850 \underline{/9.7^\circ} \text{ volts}\end{aligned}$$

$$\begin{aligned}P_s = vi + v'i' &= 73{,}800 \times 87.8 + 12{,}652 \times 4.2\\ &= 6{,}490{,}000 + 53{,}100\\ &= 6{,}543{,}000 \text{ watts per phase}\end{aligned}$$

$$\text{Efficiency} = \frac{6000}{6543} = 0.917$$

If tables of complex hyperbolic functions are available, the hyperbolic solution is greatly simplified.

Calculation of Velocity of Propagation. From equations (35) and (39),

$$v = \frac{2\pi f}{\beta}$$

$$\beta = \sqrt{\frac{\pm ZY - (Rg + bX)}{2}}$$

$$ZY = [2.12 \times 10^{-3}]^2 = 4.5 \times 10^{-6}$$

$$Rg = 0$$

$$bX = -0.538 \times 10^{-5} \times 0.788 = -0.424 \times 10^{-5}$$

$$\beta = \sqrt{\frac{\pm 4.5 \times 10^{-6} + 4.24 \times 10^{-6}}{2}} = 2.09 \times 10^{-3}$$

$$v = \frac{377}{2.09 \times 10^{-3}} = 180{,}300 \text{ miles per second}$$

If the resistance and the inductance due to the flux within the conductor are neglected, the velocity from equation (40) is

$$\frac{1}{\sqrt{LC}} = \frac{1}{\sqrt{2.01 \times 10^{-3} \times 1430 \times 10^{-11}}}$$

$$= 186{,}400 \text{ miles per second, or the velocity of light}$$

PROBLEMS

5. Solve Problem 1, page 411, by the exact method of calculating transmission lines.

6. Points A and B are 150 miles apart and are connected by a parallel-wire line having parameters as follows:

Effective resistance per loop mile at 1000 cycles, 60 ohms
Effective inductance per loop mile at 1000 cycles, 0.0042 henry
Effective capacitance per loop mile at 1000 cycles, 0.00755 μf
Shunted conductance is negligible.

The line is assumed to be terminated at point B with an impedance equal to its surge impedance. Find the voltage, current, and power received at point B when 50 volts at 1000 cycles are impressed at A. (A loop mile consists of one mile of outgoing plus one mile of return conductor.) Use $\mathbf{V}_A$ as reference.

7. Calculate by means of the formula the inductance in henrys per mile of No. 0000 wire with an equilateral spacing of 6 feet.

8. Calculate the capacitance per mile between wires and between one wire and neutral or ground for the line in Problem 7.

9. A 3-phase 60-cycle transmission line is 150 miles long and consists of three No. 0000 wires spaced at corners of an equilateral triangle which are 15 feet apart. The line is to deliver 138,000 line-to-line volts and 45,000 kw total power at 0.8 p.f. lagging at the receiver. Calculate the required sending-end voltage, current, power factor, and efficiency of transmission if the nominal T line is used. See bottom of page 430 for resistance of No. 0000 wire. Use $\mathbf{V}_{\text{line-to-neutral}}$ as reference.

10. Work Problem 9 if the nominal π line is employed.

11. Work Problem 9 if the Steinmetz three-condenser method of representing the line is used.

12. Work Problem 9 if the exact method of calculating long lines is employed.

13. Calculate the velocity of propagation of the wave in Problem 12.

14. (*a*) If 138,000 line-to-line volts were maintained at the sending end of the line in Problem 9, what would be the receiver-end voltage with the receiver end open? Employ the exact method of solution. (*b*) What is the magnitude of the direct wave at the receiver? (*c*) of the reflected wave?

15. What is the velocity of propagation of the wave in Problem 6?

16. What is the attenuation in decibels per mile of the transmission line described in Problem 6?

chapter XI Electric Wave Filters

The frequency characteristics of certain types of networks can be employed to separate waves of different frequencies. The separation may be effected primarily for the purpose of selecting a desired band of frequencies or for the purpose of rejecting an undesired band. Selected bands are called pass or transmission bands, and rejected bands are called stop or attenuation bands. Any network which possesses definite properties of frequency discrimination and which is capable of separating electric waves of different frequencies is called an *electric wave filter* or, simply, a *filter*.

Selective Properties of Circuit Elements and Elementary Circuits. Single reactive circuit elements are sometimes employed to pass or reject frequency bands when only broad discrimination is to be made. Thus *blocking* condensers in many vacuum tube circuits discriminate very satisfactorily between waves of zero frequency (direct current) and high-frequency waves. Inductance coils can be employed to pass direct current and practically eliminate frequencies which are of the order of 1000 kilocycles.

High-Frequency Line Drain. A high-frequency disturbance can be drained from a low-frequency, two-wire line with a condenser arrangement similar to that shown in Fig. 1*a*. The condensers constitute a

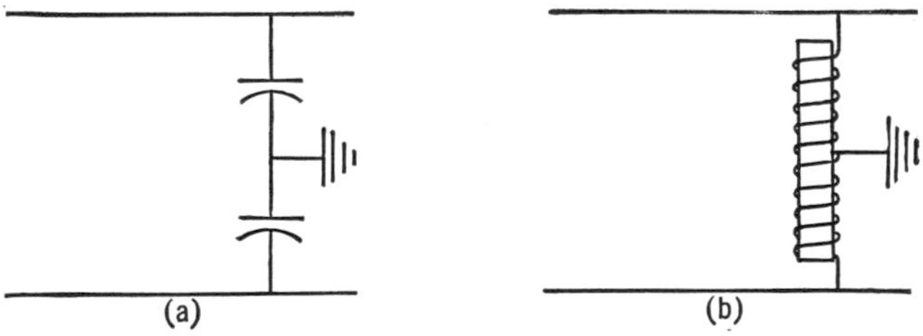

FIG. 1. Devices for draining induced disturbances from two-wire lines.

relatively high impedance to the low-frequency line voltage, both line-to-line and line-to-ground. At the same time a relatively low line-to-ground impedance is presented to the high-frequency variation which in the present case is assumed to be the result of an induced disturbance.

Low-Frequency Line Drain. A method sometimes used to drain a low-frequency induced disturbance from a two-wire line is shown diagrammatically in Fig. 1*b*. The drain coil is ironclad and offers a relatively high impedance to current which tends to flow from line-to-line. If, however, both lines are raised simultaneously above (or below) ground potential by induction, the currents which flow from the lines to ground magnetize the core in opposite directions. With respect to the induced currents, the two halves of the coil are in series opposition with the result that the impedances offered to these currents to ground are relatively very low. The device can be used to drain charges from telephone lines which are electrostatically induced from neighboring power lines.

Typical Smoothing Network. A very common form of filter is the elementary π-section shown in Fig. 2. This particular type of filter section is widely used to give d-c output from rectified a-c wave forms.

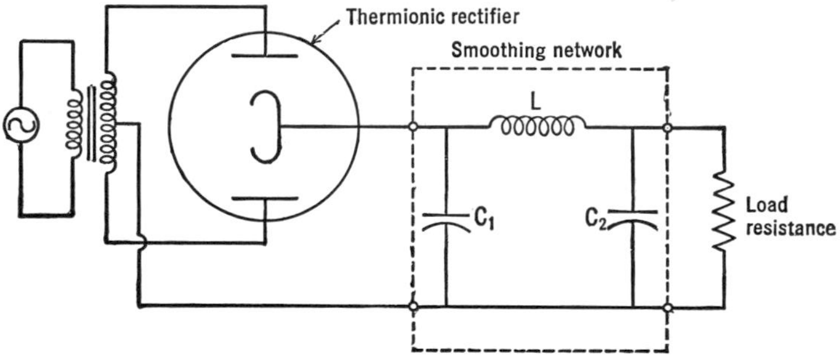

FIG. 2. A commonly used filter section.

The output voltage of the rectifying device, namely, that which appears across the input terminals of the filter section, will take the following general form:

$$v = V_{dc} + V_{m1} \sin (\omega_1 t + \alpha_1) + \text{higher harmonics}$$

where V_{dc} is the average value of the rectified wave and ω_1 is the angular velocity of the lowest-frequency component present in the voltage variation. A typical voltage input variation is shown in Oscillogram 1*a*.

If, for example, both halves of 60-cycle wave are rectified symmetrically, the lowest frequency component in the rectified voltage wave will be that of 120 cycles, in which case $\omega_1 = 754$ radians per second. In unsymmetrical rectification ω_1 is generally equal to the fundamental angular velocity of the alternating variation which is being rectified.

Under ideal conditions the filter section shown in Fig. 2 should pass waves of zero frequency with no attenuation and absolutely stop waves which are of other than zero frequency. Obviously, these ideal conditions of operation can only be approached in practice, but the

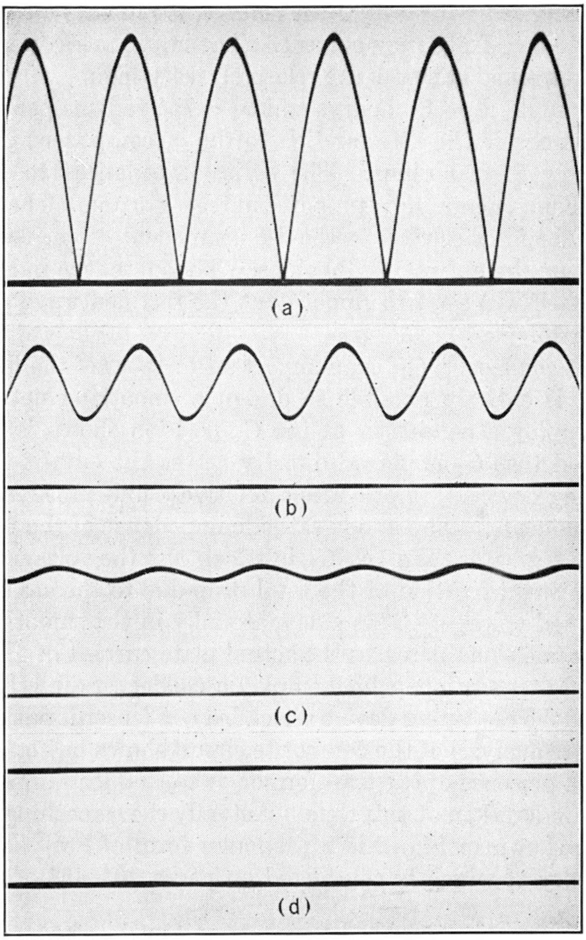

Oscillogram 1.
(*a*) Rectified a-c wave, no filtering.
(*b*) Rectified a-c wave, choke filtering only.
(*c*) Rectified a-c wave, choke and input condenser filtering.
(*d*) Rectified a-c wave, complete π-section filtering. (See Fig. 2.)

difference between ideal operation and actual operation can be made exceedingly small by proper design. See Oscillogram 1*d*.

For full-wave, 60-cycle rectification satisfactory filtering can usually be obtained if C_1 and C_2 of Fig. 2 are about 4 or 5 μf each and L is about 30 or 40 henrys. The permissible voltage regulation will, to a large extent, determine the amount of resistance that can be present in the inductance coil in any particular instance. In any case R is very small as compared with $\omega_1 L$. The result is that, when the π-section is energized with a rectified voltage, it presents a relatively low impedance to zero-frequency current. The impedances offered to other than zero-frequency currents are relatively very high.

If, for example, $L = 30$ henrys and ω_1 is 754 radians per second, the series impedance of the filter section to the ω_1 component of current is approximately 22,600 ohms. The series impedances to the higher-frequency components are proportionately greater. The series impedance of the filter section to the d-c component of current may, in a particular case, be only 20 or 30 ohms. Therefore, the inductance coil acting by itself will tend to smooth out the rectified wave as shown in Oscillogram 1*b*.

The input condenser, C_1, is an important member of the filter section, although it is entirely possible to design a smoothing network which does not employ a condenser at the C_1 position shown in Fig. 2. It will be noted that C_1 is placed directly across the output terminals of the rectifying device. It provides a relatively low-impedance path for all a-c components. The anode-cathode impedance of the tube may be 10 or 20 times greater than $1/\omega_1 C_1$, in which case the voltage drop across C_1 is only a small fraction of the total drop due to the a-c components of the rectified voltage. This aids materially in the smoothing process but at the same time increases the actual plate current of the rectifying elements. Filter sections which employ a condenser directly across the terminals of the rectifying device are called condenser input sections.[1]

A complete analysis of the composite circuit shown in Fig. 2 is complicated by the presence of the transformer, tube, and load impedances and will not be undertaken at this time. Actually the smoothing network or ripple filter shown in Fig. 2 is a particular form of low-pass filter, the general theory of which is considered on pages 464–468 of the present chapter.

Image Impedances of Four-Terminal Networks. Most filter sections take the form of a four-terminal network, and as such they possess one pair of input terminals and one pair of output terminals. With this arrangement of terminals, a filter section can be inserted directly into a two-wire line.

General four-terminal network theory is rather elaborate and is not

[1] For details see "Electrical Engineers' Handbook: Electric Communication and Electronics," fourth edition, edited by Pender and McIlwain, pp. 7–106, 7–108, John Wiley & Sons, Inc., 1950.

considered to be suitable first-course material. There are certain aspects of the subject, however, that are essential to a proper understanding of elementary filter theory. One of these is the concept of image impedances.

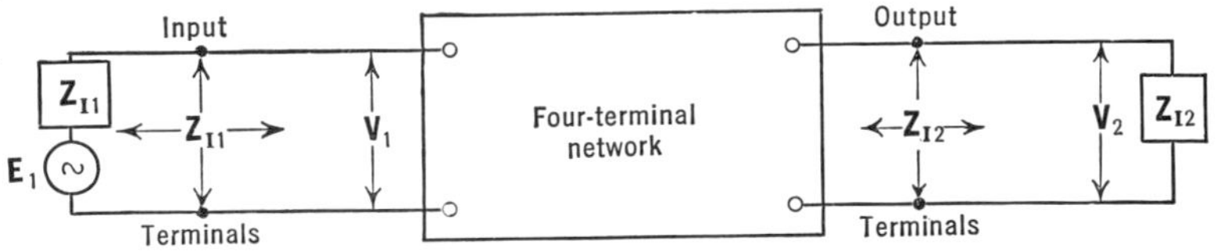

FIG. 3. Four-terminal network terminated on the image impedance basis.

The rectangle shown in Fig. 3 is assumed to be any form of four-terminal network, the internal circuit elements of which may or may not be accessible. It is also assumed that the individual circuit elements are linear. Circuit elements are linear if effects are proportional to causes, for example, if currents are proportional to applied voltages.

The image impedances of a four-terminal network are called $\mathbf{Z}_{I1}$ and $\mathbf{Z}_{I2}$ and are defined in the following manner. (Refer to Fig. 3.) If the impedance across the input terminals (looking into the network) is $\mathbf{Z}_{I1}$ when the output terminals are closed through $\mathbf{Z}_{I2}$, and if the impedance across the output terminals (looking into the network) is $\mathbf{Z}_{I2}$ when the input terminals are closed through $\mathbf{Z}_{I1}$, then $\mathbf{Z}_{I1}$ and $\mathbf{Z}_{I2}$ are called the image impedances of the network. If a four-terminal network is terminated in its image impedances, $\mathbf{Z}_{I1}$ and $\mathbf{Z}_{I2}$, the impedance looking either way from the input terminals is $\mathbf{Z}_{I1}$ and the impedance looking either direction from the output terminals is $\mathbf{Z}_{I2}$. The network is correctly matched when the input impedance is $\mathbf{Z}_{I1}$ and the output impedance is $\mathbf{Z}_{I2}$ and under these conditions the network is said to be terminated on the image basis.

A special case of image impedance termination is employed in elementary filter theory. The assumption is made that $\mathbf{Z}_{I1} = \mathbf{Z}_{I2}$, and this particular value of impedance is called the characteristic impedance of the filter section.

The image impedance at either end of a given network can be determined from the open-circuit and short-circuit impedances. By open-circuit impedance, $\mathbf{Z}_{o\text{-}c}$, is meant the impedance looking into one set of terminals when the other set of terminals is open-circuited. By short-circuit impedance, $\mathbf{Z}_{s\text{-}c}$, is meant the impedance looking into one set of terminals when the other set of terminals is short-circuited. It can be shown that image impedance at either end of a four-terminal network is the geometric mean of the open-circuit and short-circuit impedances.

Thus in Fig. 3:

$$\mathbf{Z}_{I1} = \sqrt{\mathbf{Z}_{o\text{-}c1}\mathbf{Z}_{s\text{-}c1}} \tag{1}$$

and

$$\mathbf{Z}_{I2} = \sqrt{\mathbf{Z}_{o\text{-}c2}\mathbf{Z}_{s\text{-}c2}} \tag{2}$$

Generalized proofs of the above equations will not be given but it will be shown presently that the relations stated are correct when $\mathbf{Z}_{I1} = \mathbf{Z}_{I2}$, the condition which is of special importance in elementary filter theory.

Characteristic Impedances of T- and π-Sections. The basic units of elementary filter theory are the symmetrical T- and π-sections shown in Fig. 4. Although both of these sections are essentially three-terminal networks, they are usually inserted into a two-wire line in the same manner as a four-terminal network. Viewed as three-terminal networks, the T-section is a wye-connected set of impedances and the π-section is a delta-connected set of impedances. It should not be supposed that the $\mathbf{Z}_1$ and $\mathbf{Z}_2$ values given in Fig. 4*a* and Fig. 4*b* are, in

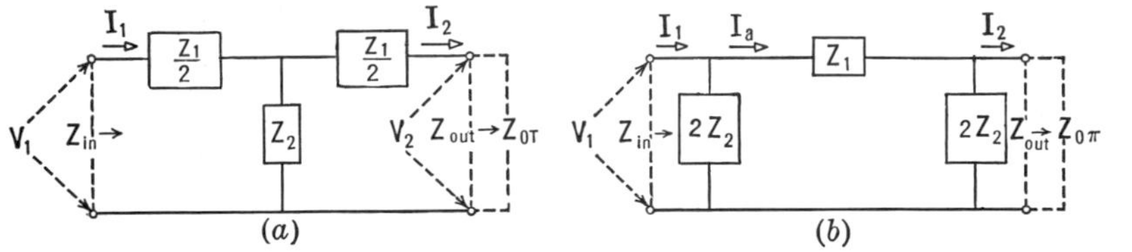

FIG. 4. Symmetrical T- and π-sections.

general, equivalent wye and delta values. The circuit elements are usually labeled as indicated in Fig. 4 in order to make the algebraic expressions for several of the filtering characteristics the same for both the T- and π-sections.

The series impedance of a symmetrical T-section is composed of two similar units, each of which is labeled $\mathbf{Z}_1/2$ in Fig. 4*a*. The impedance labeled $\mathbf{Z}_2$ in Fig. 4*a* is called the shunt impedance of the T-section. The shunt impedance of a symmetrical π-section is composed of two equal branches, each labeled $2\mathbf{Z}_2$ in Fig. 4*b*, and these shunt branches are located on either side of the series impedance $\mathbf{Z}_1$. If the series and shunt impedances are designated in accordance with Fig. 4, ladder structures formed by the cascade arrangement of successive sections are generally similar. (See Fig. 10 and Fig. 11.)

If the output terminals of the T-section shown in Fig. 4*a* are closed through an impedance $\mathbf{Z}_{oT}$, the impedance across the input terminals (looking into the network) is:

$$\mathbf{Z}_{in} = \frac{\mathbf{Z}_1}{2} + \frac{\mathbf{Z}_2\left(\frac{\mathbf{Z}_1}{2} + \mathbf{Z}_{oT}\right)}{\mathbf{Z}_2 + \frac{\mathbf{Z}_1}{2} + \mathbf{Z}_{oT}} \tag{3}$$

In order for $\mathbf{Z}_{in}$ to equal $\mathbf{Z}_{oT}$, it follows that:

$$\mathbf{Z}_{oT} = \frac{\mathbf{Z}_1}{2} + \frac{\frac{\mathbf{Z}_1\mathbf{Z}_2}{2} + \mathbf{Z}_2\mathbf{Z}_{oT}}{\frac{\mathbf{Z}_1}{2} + \mathbf{Z}_2 + \mathbf{Z}_{oT}} \tag{4}$$

The above equation may be solved for $\mathbf{Z}_{oT}$ and the result stated in terms of $\mathbf{Z}_1$ and $\mathbf{Z}_2$. Thus it can be shown that *the characteristic impedance of the* T-*section* is:

$$\mathbf{Z}_{oT} = \sqrt{\mathbf{Z}_1\mathbf{Z}_2 + \frac{\mathbf{Z}_1^2}{4}} = \sqrt{\mathbf{Z}_1\mathbf{Z}_2\left(1 + \frac{\mathbf{Z}_1}{4\mathbf{Z}_2}\right)} \tag{5}$$

If the output terminals of the π-section shown in Fig. 4*b* are closed through an impedance $\mathbf{Z}_{o\pi}$, the impedance across the input terminals (looking into the network) is:

$$\mathbf{Z}_{in} = \frac{2\mathbf{Z}_2\left(\mathbf{Z}_1 + \frac{2\mathbf{Z}_2\mathbf{Z}_{o\pi}}{2\mathbf{Z}_2 + \mathbf{Z}_{o\pi}}\right)}{2\mathbf{Z}_2 + \mathbf{Z}_1 + \frac{2\mathbf{Z}_2\mathbf{Z}_{o\pi}}{2\mathbf{Z}_2 + \mathbf{Z}_{o\pi}}} \tag{6}$$

In order to determine the conditions under which $\mathbf{Z}_{in}$ is equal to $\mathbf{Z}_{o\pi}$ it is simply necessary to set $\mathbf{Z}_{in} = \mathbf{Z}_{o\pi}$ in the above equation and solve the resulting equation for $\mathbf{Z}_{o\pi}$. After $\mathbf{Z}_{in}$ has been set equal to $\mathbf{Z}_{o\pi}$ and all fractions cleared, it will be found that:

$$\mathbf{Z}_{o\pi}^2\,(\mathbf{Z}_1 + 4\mathbf{Z}_2) = 4\mathbf{Z}_1\mathbf{Z}_2^2$$

From which *the characteristic impedance of the* π-*section* is

$$\mathbf{Z}_{o\pi} = \sqrt{\frac{4\mathbf{Z}_1\mathbf{Z}_2^2}{\mathbf{Z}_1 + 4\mathbf{Z}_2}} = \sqrt{\frac{\mathbf{Z}_1\mathbf{Z}_2}{\left(1 + \frac{\mathbf{Z}_1}{4\mathbf{Z}_2}\right)}} \tag{7}$$

Equations (5) and (7) are important relations in filter theory because they define the characteristic impedances $\mathbf{Z}_{oT}$ and $\mathbf{Z}_{o\pi}$ in terms of the series and shunt elements out of which the T- and π-sections are composed. If a filter section is terminated in its characteristic impedance, the impedance across the input terminals (looking into the network) is the same as the receiving-end impedance. (The importance of designing filter sections to have particular characteristic impedances will become more evident after composite filter sections are studied.) It should be noted that a given filter section terminated at both ends in its characteristic impedance is terminated on the image basis and that in this particular case $\mathbf{Z}_{I1}$ and $\mathbf{Z}_{I2}$ are equal. (See Fig. 3.) Reference to equations (5) and (7) will show that:

$$\mathbf{Z}_{oT}\mathbf{Z}_{o\pi} = \mathbf{Z}_1\mathbf{Z}_2 \tag{8}$$

and

$$\mathbf{Z}_{o\pi} = \frac{\mathbf{Z}_1\mathbf{Z}_2}{\mathbf{Z}_{oT}} \tag{9}$$

Equations (8) and (9) define a rather important relationship that exists between the characteristic impedances of T- and π-sections, the $\mathbf{Z}_1$'s and $\mathbf{Z}_2$'s of which are equal.

Filter theory is based upon $\mathbf{Z}_1$, $\mathbf{Z}_2$, $\mathbf{Z}_{oT}$, and $\mathbf{Z}_{o\pi}$ to such an extent that the physical significance of each of these four impedances should be clearly understood. The reader who is unfamiliar with filter theory nomenclature should at this stage review the definitions which have been given for $\mathbf{Z}_1$, $\mathbf{Z}_2$, $\mathbf{Z}_{oT}$, and $\mathbf{Z}_{o\pi}$. [See Fig. 4 and equations (5) and (7).]

Example 1. In Fig. 4*a*, let each $\mathbf{Z}_1/2$ take the form of an inductance coil, the inductance of which is 0.047 henry and the resistance of which is 1 ohm. The shunt arm, namely, $\mathbf{Z}_2$, is to take the form of a 300-μf condenser. (*Note:* This is an unconventional set of parameters for this type of filter section but since some of the experimental results which follow are based upon these particular values they will be used here to illustrate the calculation of $\mathbf{Z}_{oT}$.)

The method of calculating $\mathbf{Z}_{oT}$ at 50 cycles is as follows:

$$\frac{\mathbf{Z}_1}{2} = \frac{R_1}{2} + j\omega\frac{L_1}{2} = 1 + j14.77 = 14.8\,\underline{/86.1^\circ}\text{ ohms}$$

$$\mathbf{Z}_1 = 29.6\,\underline{/86.1^\circ}\text{ ohms} \quad \text{(Full series arm impedance.)}$$

$$\mathbf{Z}_2 = 0 - j\frac{1}{\omega C_2} = 0 - j10.61 = 10.61\,\underline{/-90^\circ}\text{ ohms}$$

$$\mathbf{Z}_{oT} = \sqrt{\mathbf{Z}_1\mathbf{Z}_2 + \frac{\mathbf{Z}_1^2}{4}}$$

$$= \sqrt{(29.6\,\underline{/86.1^\circ})(10.61\,\underline{/-90^\circ}) + \frac{(29.6\,\underline{/86.1^\circ})^2}{4}}$$

$$= 9.83\,\underline{/2.5^\circ} = 9.81 + j0.43\text{ ohms}$$

The physical significance of the above value of $\mathbf{Z}_{oT}$ is that, if an impedance of $9.83\,\underline{/2.5^\circ}$ ohms is placed across the output terminals of this symmetrical T-section, *the impedance looking into the input terminals is also* $9.83\,\underline{/2.5^\circ}$ *ohms.*

Problem 1. Neglect the resistances of the two inductance coils that form the series impedance of the filter section in the illustrative example given above and find $\mathbf{Z}_{oT}$ at 50 cycles and at 100 cycles. (It may be of interest to know that this symmetrical T-section forms a low-pass filter that passes all frequencies up to 60 cycles and attenuates those above 60 cycles.)

Ans.: At 50 cycles, $\mathbf{Z}_{oT} = 9.76 \underline{/0^\circ}$ ohms.
At 100 cycles, $\mathbf{Z}_{oT} = 23.65 \underline{/90^\circ}$ ohms.

Problem 2. The series impedance, $\mathbf{Z}_1$, of a symmetrical π-section (like that shown in Fig. 4*b*) consists of a 0.02-henry inductance coil, the resistance of which is assumed to be negligibly small. Each of the shunt arms, namely, $2\mathbf{Z}_2$, is composed of a 2.0-μf condenser. (This symmetrical π-section forms a low-pass filter which passes all frequencies below 900 cycles without attenuation as will be shown later.)

Find the characteristic impedance of this section at 200 cycles and at 2000 cycles. Use equation (7) and recognize that

$$\mathbf{Z}_1 = 0.02\omega \underline{/90^\circ} \quad \text{and} \quad \mathbf{Z}_2 = \frac{10^6}{4\omega} \underline{/-90^\circ} \text{ ohms}$$

Ans.: At 200 cycles, $\mathbf{Z}_{o\pi} = 71.8 \underline{/0^\circ}$ ohms.
At 2000 cycles, $\mathbf{Z}_{o\pi} = 48 \underline{/-90^\circ}$ ohms.

Characteristic Impedance as a Function of Open-Circuit and Short-Circuit Impedances. Reference to Fig. 5*a* will show that the open-circuit impedance of a T-section (looking into the section) is:

$$\mathbf{Z}_{o\text{-}c} = \frac{\mathbf{Z}_1}{2} + \mathbf{Z}_2 \tag{10}$$

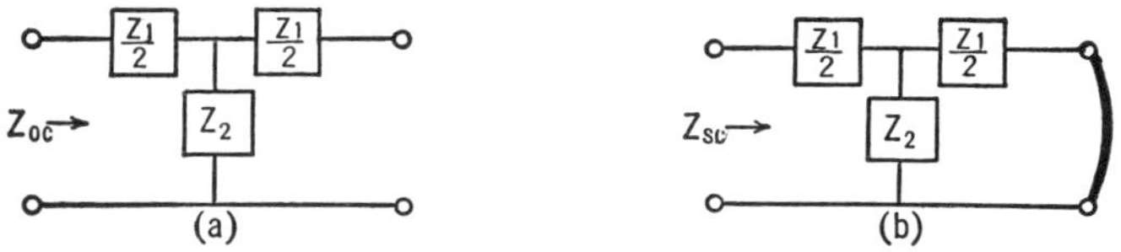

FIG. 5. $\mathbf{Z}_{oc}$ and $\mathbf{Z}_{sc}$ of a symmetrical T-section.

When the output terminals are short-circuited as shown in Fig. 5*b* the impedance of the T-section (looking into the section) is:

$$\mathbf{Z}_{s\text{-}c} = \frac{\mathbf{Z}_1}{2} + \frac{\dfrac{\mathbf{Z}_1}{2}\mathbf{Z}_2}{\dfrac{\mathbf{Z}_1}{2} + \mathbf{Z}_2} = \frac{\dfrac{\mathbf{Z}_1^2}{4} + \mathbf{Z}_1\mathbf{Z}_2}{\dfrac{\mathbf{Z}_1}{2} + \mathbf{Z}_2} \tag{11}$$

The geometric mean of $\mathbf{Z}_{o\text{-}c}$ and $\mathbf{Z}_{s\text{-}c}$ is:

$$\sqrt{\mathbf{Z}_{o\text{-}c}\mathbf{Z}_{s\text{-}c}} = \sqrt{\mathbf{Z}_1\mathbf{Z}_2 + \frac{\mathbf{Z}_1^2}{4}} \tag{12}$$

It has already been shown that

$$\mathbf{Z}_{oT} = \sqrt{\mathbf{Z}_1\mathbf{Z}_2 + \frac{\mathbf{Z}_1^2}{4}} \quad \text{[See equation (5).]}$$

Therefore,

$$\mathbf{Z}_{oT} = \sqrt{\mathbf{Z}_{o\text{-}c}\mathbf{Z}_{s\text{-}c}} \tag{13}$$

The fact that $\mathbf{Z}_{oT}$ is equivalent to the geometric mean of $\mathbf{Z}_{o\text{-}c}$ and $\mathbf{Z}_{s\text{-}c}$ provides the basis for a simple experimental method of determining the characteristic impedance of a given section.

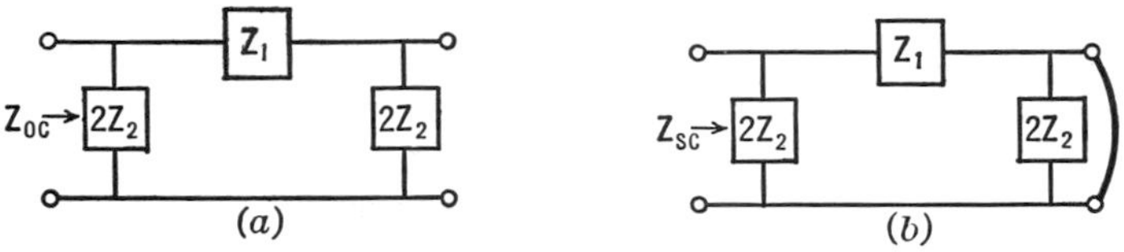

FIG. 6. $\mathbf{Z}_{oc}$ and $\mathbf{Z}_{sc}$ of a symmetrical π-section.

Reference to Fig. 6*a* will show that the open-circuit impedance of a symmetrical π-section (looking into the section) is:

$$\mathbf{Z}_{o\text{-}c} = \frac{2\mathbf{Z}_2(\mathbf{Z}_1 + 2\mathbf{Z}_2)}{\mathbf{Z}_1 + 4\mathbf{Z}_2} \tag{14}$$

If the output terminals of the π-section are short-circuited as shown in Fig. 6*b*, the input impedance is:

$$\mathbf{Z}_{s\text{-}c} = \frac{2\mathbf{Z}_2\mathbf{Z}_1}{\mathbf{Z}_1 + 2\mathbf{Z}_2} \tag{15}$$

$$\sqrt{\mathbf{Z}_{o\text{-}c}\mathbf{Z}_{s\text{-}c}} = \sqrt{\frac{4\mathbf{Z}_1\mathbf{Z}_2^2}{\mathbf{Z}_1 + 4\mathbf{Z}_2}} \tag{16}$$

Comparison of the above relation with equation (7) will show that:

$$\mathbf{Z}_{o\pi} = \sqrt{\mathbf{Z}_{o\text{-}c}\mathbf{Z}_{s\text{-}c}} \tag{17}$$

Equations (13) and (17) indicate that the characteristic impedance of either the T- or π-section is equal to the geometric mean of their respective open- and short-circuit impedances. It should be evident that the symbols $\mathbf{Z}_{o\text{-}c}$ and $\mathbf{Z}_{s\text{-}c}$ in equations (13) and (17) refer to open- and short-circuit impedances of the particular section that is under investigation. In general $\mathbf{Z}_{oT} \neq \mathbf{Z}_{o\pi}$.

Problem 3. Referring to Fig. 7 find (*a*) $\mathbf{Z}_{o\text{-}c}$, (*b*) $\mathbf{Z}_{s\text{-}c}$, and (*c*) $\mathbf{Z}_{oT}$ at 200 cycles.
Ans.: (*a*) $186.2 \underline{/-90^\circ}$, (*b*) $26.0 \underline{/90^\circ}$, and (*c*) $69.5 \underline{/0^\circ}$ ohms.

Problem 4. Referring to Fig. 8, find (*a*) $\mathbf{Z}_{o-c}$, (*b*) $\mathbf{Z}_{s-c}$, and (*c*) $\mathbf{Z}_{o\pi}$ at 200 cycles. *Ans.:* (*a*) $192.5 \underline{/-90°}$, (*b*) $26.8 \underline{/90°}$, and (*c*) $71.8 \underline{/0°}$ ohms.

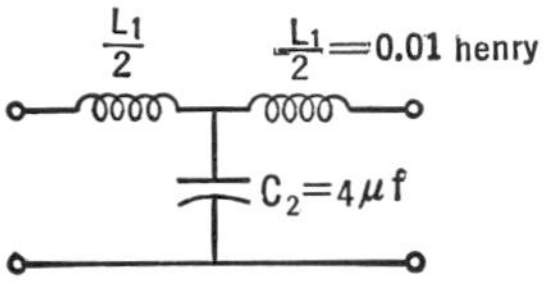

FIG. 7. A particular symmetrical T-section for use with Problem 3

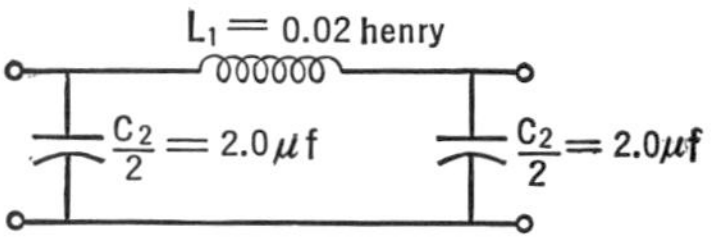

FIG. 8. A particular symmetrical π-section for use in connection with Problem 4.

Physical Operation of Symmetrical T- and π-Sections. The T- and π-sections shown in Fig. 4 possess some remarkable properties when their output terminals are connected to the characteristic impedances $\mathbf{Z}_{oT}$ and $\mathbf{Z}_{o\pi}$ respectively. Before considering the filtering properties of these sections, some of the basic relationships that follow directly from elementary circuit theory will be established.

The conditions imposed on equations (4) and (6), page 441, make $\mathbf{Z}_{\text{in}} = \mathbf{Z}_{\text{out}}$ for either type of section. Hence $\mathbf{I}_1 = \mathbf{V}_1/\mathbf{Z}_o$ and $\mathbf{I}_2 = \mathbf{V}_2/\mathbf{Z}_o$, where $\mathbf{Z}_o$ symbolizes the characteristic impedance of the particular type of section considered. It follows directly that

$$\frac{\mathbf{I}_1}{\mathbf{I}_2} = \frac{\mathbf{V}_1}{\mathbf{V}_2} \quad \text{and} \quad \frac{W_1}{W_2} = \frac{V_1 I_1 \cos\theta}{V_2 I_2 \cos\theta} = \frac{I_1^2}{I_2^2} \tag{18}$$

where the subscripts 1 refer to input quantities and the subscripts 2 refer to output quantities. Since the impedance looking into the input terminals is the same as the terminating impedance, the angle between $\mathbf{V}_1$ and $\mathbf{I}_1$ is equal to the angle between $\mathbf{V}_2$ and $\mathbf{I}_2$. This angle is symbolized as θ in equation (18) and is equal to $\tan^{-1}(X_o/R_o)$, where X_o and R_o are the reactive and resistive components of the characteristic impedance $\mathbf{Z}_o$. The basic relationships contained in equation (18) are illustrated photographically for a particular T-section in Oscillogram 2, page 446. These relationships will be used later in defining the attenuation of filter sections.

The next basic relationship to be established is that the ratio of input current to output current, namely, $\mathbf{I}_1/\mathbf{I}_2$, is completely defined by the series arm impedance ($\mathbf{Z}_1$) and the shunt arm impedance ($\mathbf{Z}_2$) out of which the symmetrical T- or π-section is composed. For the T-section shown in Fig. 4*a* it is plain from Kirchhoff's emf law that

$$\frac{\mathbf{Z}_1}{2}\mathbf{I}_1 + \frac{\mathbf{Z}_1}{2}\mathbf{I}_2 + \mathbf{Z}_{oT}\mathbf{I}_2 = \mathbf{V}_1 = \mathbf{Z}_{oT}\mathbf{I}_1 \tag{19}$$

Whence

$$\frac{\mathbf{I}_1}{\mathbf{I}_2} = \frac{\mathbf{Z}_{oT} + \dfrac{\mathbf{Z}_1}{2}}{\mathbf{Z}_{oT} - \dfrac{\mathbf{Z}_1}{2}} \quad \text{(for T-sections)} \tag{20}$$

Referring to Fig. 4*b* for the π-section and remembering that $\mathbf{V}_1 = \mathbf{I}_1\mathbf{Z}_{o\pi}$ and that $\mathbf{V}_2 = \mathbf{I}_2\mathbf{Z}_{o\pi}$, the current $\mathbf{I}_{\text{series}}$ in the series arm is:

$$\mathbf{I}_{\text{series}} = \mathbf{I}_1 - \frac{\mathbf{I}_1\mathbf{Z}_{o\pi}}{2\mathbf{Z}_2} = \mathbf{I}_2 + \frac{\mathbf{I}_2\mathbf{Z}_{o\pi}}{2\mathbf{Z}_2} \tag{21}$$

from which

$$\mathbf{I}_1 \frac{(2\mathbf{Z}_2 - \mathbf{Z}_{o\pi})}{2\mathbf{Z}_2} = \mathbf{I}_2 \frac{(2\mathbf{Z}_2 + \mathbf{Z}_{o\pi})}{2\mathbf{Z}_2} \tag{22}$$

and

$$\frac{\mathbf{I}_1}{\mathbf{I}_2} = \frac{2\mathbf{Z}_2 + \mathbf{Z}_{o\pi}}{2\mathbf{Z}_2 - \mathbf{Z}_{o\pi}} \tag{23}$$

Reference to equations (20) and (23) above and to equations (5) and (7), page 441, will show that the ratio $\mathbf{I}_1/\mathbf{I}_2$ is defined wholly in terms of $\mathbf{Z}_1$ and $\mathbf{Z}_2$ for either T- or π-sections. It will be shown later that the

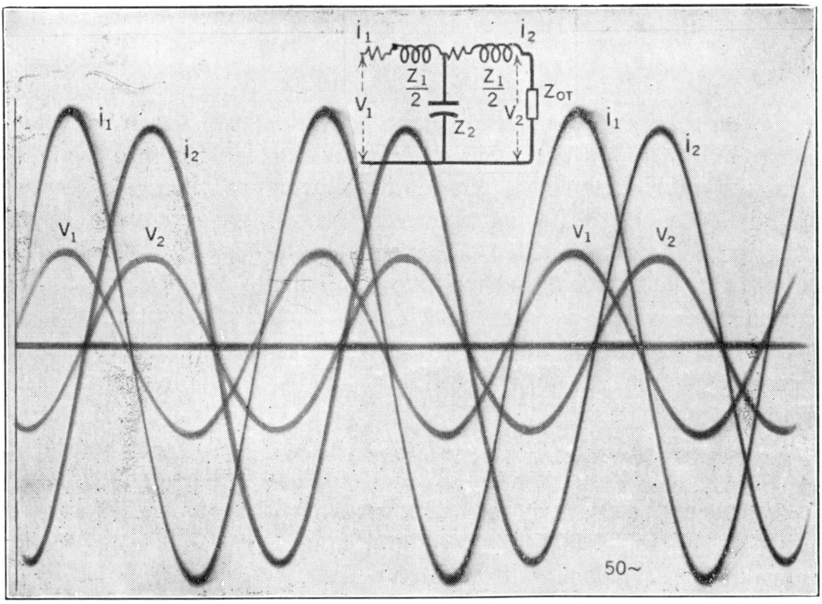

OSCILLOGRAM 2. Illustrating attenuation and phase shift in a symmetrical T-section. v_1 and i_1 are input voltage and current respectively. v_2 and i_2 are output voltage and current respectively.

right members of equations (20) and (23) are identically equal when written wholly in terms of $\mathbf{Z}_1$ and $\mathbf{Z}_2$. For the present, equation (20) will be used to define the ratio $\mathbf{I}_1/\mathbf{I}_2$ in T-sections and equation (23) will be used to define this ratio in π-sections.

Example 2. Refer to the symmetrical T-section shown in Fig. 9*a*. Let it be required to evaluate the ratio $\mathbf{I}_1/\mathbf{I}_2$ at $f = 50$ cycles. Since this is the same T-section as described in example 1, page 442, the results of example 1 may be used here to define $\mathbf{Z}_1$, $\mathbf{Z}_2$, and $\mathbf{Z}_{oT}$.

$$\frac{\mathbf{Z}_1}{2} = (1 + j14.77),\ \mathbf{Z}_2 = (0 - j10.61),\quad \text{and}\quad \mathbf{Z}_{oT} = (9.81 + j0.43)\ \text{ohms}$$

$$\frac{\mathbf{I}_1}{\mathbf{I}_2} = \frac{\mathbf{Z}_{oT} + \dfrac{\mathbf{Z}_1}{2}}{\mathbf{Z}_{oT} - \dfrac{\mathbf{Z}_1}{2}} = \frac{(9.81 + j0.43) + (1 + j14.77)}{(9.81 + j0.43) - (1 + j14.77)}$$

$$= \frac{(10.81 + j15.20)}{(8.81 - j14.34)} = \frac{18.7\ \underline{/54.6^\circ}}{16.8\ \underline{/-58.4^\circ}} = 1.11\ \underline{/113^\circ}$$

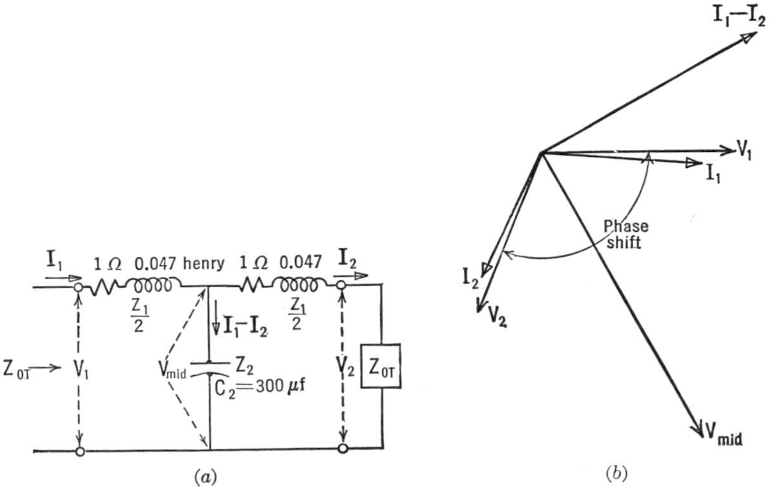

FIG. 9. A symmetrical T-section terminated in its characteristic impedance, together with a vector diagram of the currents and voltages in a particular case.

The physical significance of the above complex number is that the magnitude of $\mathbf{I}_1$ is 1.11 times as great as the magnitude of $\mathbf{I}_2$ and that $\mathbf{I}_1$ *leads* $\mathbf{I}_2$ by 113°. (See Fig. 9*b*.) It will be shown presently that the ratio I_1/I_2 defines the *attenuation* of the filter section and that the associated angle of $\mathbf{I}_1/\mathbf{I}_2$ defines the *phase shift* of the section.

A worthwhile exercise for the student at this stage is that of correlating the results given above with those determined by elementary circuit analysis. Let $\mathbf{V}_1$ of Fig. 9*a* $= 100\ \underline{/0^\circ}$ volts and solve for $\mathbf{I}_1$ and $\mathbf{I}_2$ by ordinary methods. The results are illustrated in Fig. 9*b* and in Oscillogram 2 which is a photographic record of v_1, i_1, v_2, and i_2 for the particular T-section shown in Fig. 9*a*.

Example 3. Let it be required to find the ratio $\mathbf{I}_1/\mathbf{I}_2$ in Fig. 9*a* if the resistances of the inductance coils are neglected, assuming that the frequency of the supply voltage is 50 cycles.

$$\frac{\mathbf{Z}_1}{2} = (0 + j14.77), \quad \mathbf{Z}_2 = (0 - j10.61), \quad \frac{\mathbf{Z}_1^{\,2}}{4} = (j14.77)^2$$

$$\mathbf{Z}_{oT} = \sqrt{\mathbf{Z}_1\mathbf{Z}_2 + (\mathbf{Z}_1/2)^2} = \sqrt{(j29.54)(-j10.61) + (j14.77)^2}$$
$$= \sqrt{313.4 - 218.2} = \sqrt{95.2} = 9.76\underline{/0^\circ} \text{ ohms}$$

Employing equation (20):

$$\frac{\mathbf{I}_1}{\mathbf{I}_2} = \frac{9.76 + j14.77}{9.76 - j14.77} = \frac{17.7\underline{/56.5^\circ}}{17.7\underline{/-56.5^\circ}} = 1\underline{/113^\circ}$$

Thus the output current $\mathbf{I}_2$ is shown to be as great in magnitude as the input current $\mathbf{I}_1$. This condition exists generally in symmetrical T- and π-sections when the resistances are negligibly small provided the characteristic impedance for the frequency considered is a pure ohmic resistance.

Example 4. Let it be required to find the characteristic impedance and the current ratio $\mathbf{I}_1/\mathbf{I}_2$ in Fig. 9*a* if the frequency of the supply is 100 cycles and if the resistances of the inductance coils are neglected. Under these conditions:

$$\frac{\mathbf{Z}_1}{2} = (0 + j29.54), \quad \mathbf{Z}_2 = (0 - j5.305), \quad \frac{\mathbf{Z}_1^{\,2}}{4} = (j29.54)^2$$

$$\mathbf{Z}_{oT} = \sqrt{(j59.08)(-j5.305) + (j29.54)^2}$$
$$= \sqrt{(313\underline{/0^\circ}) + (873\underline{/+180^\circ})}$$
$$= \sqrt{560\underline{/+180^\circ}} = 23.66\underline{/90^\circ} \text{ ohms}$$

The characteristic impedance of the filter section has changed from a pure resistance (of 9.76 ohms) to a pure inductive reactance of 23.66 ohms as a result of changing the frequency from 50 cycles to 100 cycles. *Note:* The values of L_1 and C_2 used in Fig. 9*a* make this section a low-pass filter section which starts to attenuate at 60 cycles, as will be shown later. See equation (55), page 465. At 100 cycles:

$$\frac{\mathbf{I}_1}{\mathbf{I}_2} = \frac{\mathbf{Z}_{oT} + \dfrac{\mathbf{Z}_1}{2}}{\mathbf{Z}_{oT} - \dfrac{\mathbf{Z}_1}{2}} = \frac{(23.66\underline{/90^\circ}) + (29.54\underline{/90^\circ})}{(23.66\underline{/90^\circ}) - (29.54\underline{/90^\circ})}$$

$$= \frac{53.2\underline{/90^\circ}}{5.88\underline{/-90^\circ}} = 9.04\underline{/+180^\circ}$$

It will be observed that, at 100 cycles, I_1 is 9.04 times as great as I_2 which indicates that marked attenuation is taking place. It will also be observed that the phase shift is 180°, a condition that always obtains in a resistanceless filter section which is operating in the attenuation band and which is terminated in its characteristic impedance.

The importance of the ratio $\mathbf{I}_1/\mathbf{I}_2$ has been emphasized in the foregoing examples because the physical operation of a filter section is concisely defined by this ratio.

Problem 5. Find the ratio $\mathbf{I}_1/\mathbf{I}_2$ of the symmetrical π-section shown in Fig. 8 page 445, at 200 cycles and at 2000 cycles. Neglect the resistance of the inductance coil and recognize that $\mathbf{Z}_1 = (0 + j0.02\omega)$ is the full series arm and that $\mathbf{Z}_2 = \left(0 - j\dfrac{10^6}{4\omega}\right)$ is the combined shunt arm since the total series inductance (L_1) is 0.02 henry and the combined shunt capacitance (C_2) is 4 μf. (See Fig. 4*b* and Fig. 8.) Note also that $2\mathbf{Z}_2 = \left(0 - j\dfrac{10^6}{2\omega}\right)$ ohms.

Ans.: At 200 cycles $\mathbf{I}_1/\mathbf{I}_2 = 1\underline{/+20.5°}$.
At 2000 cycles $\mathbf{I}_1/\mathbf{I}_2 = 10.6\underline{/-180°}$.

Problem 6. Find the current ratio $\mathbf{I}_1/\mathbf{I}_2$ of the symmetrical T-section shown in Fig. 7, page 445, at 200 cycles and at 2000 cycles. Neglect the resistances of the inductance coils.

Ans.: At 200 cycles $\mathbf{I}_1/\mathbf{I}_2 = 1\underline{/20.5°}$.
At 2000 cycles $\mathbf{I}_1/\mathbf{I}_2 = 10.6\underline{/+180°}$.

Transmission Constant of a Filter Section. A transmission constant which applies to a generator feeding a resistance load has been defined in equation (80), page 136. It will be remembered that the reference used in that case was selected with a view toward including the effects of a possible mismatch between the resistance of the generator and the resistance of the load. Another transmission constant which applies to long lines was used in Chapter X. In this case it was called the *propagation* constant, the term usually employed for the transmission constant of long lines.

Where a filter section or other four-terminal network is terminated on an image impedance basis as shown in Fig. 3, the impedance match between the generator and load is already effected and the definition of the transmission constant is somewhat different from that given in equation (80), page 136. Assuming that the filter section is terminated on an image impedance basis and that we wish to specify a measure of the attenuation and phase shift of the filter itself, we employ the following definition of the transmission constant:

$$\boldsymbol{\gamma} = \alpha + j\beta = \log_\epsilon \frac{\mathbf{Z}_T'}{\mathbf{Z}_{I1}} = \log_\epsilon \frac{\mathbf{V}_1/\mathbf{I}_2}{\mathbf{V}_1/\mathbf{I}_1} = \log_\epsilon \frac{\mathbf{I}_1}{\mathbf{I}_2} \tag{24}$$

where $\mathbf{Z}_T'$ is the transfer impedance from the input terminals of the filter section to the output terminals, namely, $\mathbf{V}_1/\mathbf{I}_2$

$\mathbf{Z}_{I1}$ is the image impedance seen looking to the right of the input terminals, namely, $\mathbf{V}_1/\mathbf{I}_1$

α is called the attenuation of the filter section

β is called the phase-shift constant of the filter section.

Actually the α and β defined in equation (24) apply to any four-terminal network which is terminated on an image impedance basis as shown in Fig. 3. As such they apply directly to a filter section which is terminated in its characteristic impedance, since characteristic impedance termination is but a special case of image impedance termination where $\mathbf{Z}_{I1} = \mathbf{Z}_{I2}$.

The attenuation, α, is a measure of the ratio of the power input to the power output of a filter section which is terminated in its characteristic impedance, since under these conditions the real part of equation (24) may be written as:

$$\alpha = \log_\epsilon \frac{\sqrt{I_1^2 R_0}}{\sqrt{I_2^2 R_0}} = \frac{1}{2} \log_\epsilon \frac{I_1^2 R_0}{I_2^2 R_0} = \frac{1}{2} \log_\epsilon \frac{W_1}{W_2} \tag{25}$$

where R_0 is the resistive component of $\mathbf{Z}_0$
W_1 is the power entering the input terminals
W_2 is the power leaving the output terminals.

From equation (24) it is plain that

$$\frac{\mathbf{I}_1}{\mathbf{I}_2} = \epsilon^{(\alpha + j\beta)} = \epsilon^{\alpha}\epsilon^{j\beta} = K \underline{/\beta} \tag{26}$$

where $K = \epsilon^{\alpha} = I_1/I_2$
β = angle of lead of $\mathbf{I}_1$ with respect to $\mathbf{I}_2$.

As applied to a series or cascade arrangement of filter sections like those shown in Fig. 10, page 452:

$$\frac{\mathbf{I}_1}{\mathbf{I}_2} = \frac{\mathbf{I}_2}{\mathbf{I}_3} = \frac{\mathbf{I}_3}{\mathbf{I}_4} \tag{27}$$

and the transmission constant (together with the attenuation and phase-shift) may be reckoned on a per section (or $\mathbf{I}_1/\mathbf{I}_2$) basis or on a combined basis of $\mathbf{I}_1/\mathbf{I}_4$, since both arrangements are presumably terminated on a characteristic impedance basis.

Units of Attenuation or Transmission Loss. Filter section attenuation is usually expressed in either nepers or decibels. (See pages 136–137.) These units of transmission loss are both defined on a logarithmic basis, since their greatest field of application is in the transmission of sound, the loudness of which is a logarithmic function of the sound energy.

The Neper. The general definition of attenuation expressed in nepers is:

$$(\text{Attenuation in nepers}) = \tfrac{1}{2} \log_\epsilon \frac{W_{(\text{general})}}{W_{(\text{reference})}} \tag{28}$$

or

$$(\text{Attenuation in nepers}) = 1.151 \log_{10} \frac{W_{(\text{general})}}{W_{(\text{reference})}} \tag{29}$$

where $W_{(\text{general})}$ is any particular power level which might be under discussion

$W_{(\text{reference})}$ is the power level employed as reference from which $W_{(\text{general})}$ is to be measured.

Reference to equation (18) or to equation (25) will show that, for a filter section which is terminated in its characteristic impedance, the output power W_2 is employed as the reference power level and

$$(\text{Attenuation in nepers}) = \tfrac{1}{2} \log_\epsilon \frac{W_1}{W_2} = \tfrac{1}{2} \log_\epsilon \frac{I_1^2 R_0}{I_2^2 R_0} = \log_\epsilon \epsilon^\alpha = \alpha \tag{30}$$

If the filter section is not terminated in its characteristic impedance, equation (28) is employed and W_1 is used for $W_{(\text{general})}$ and W_2 is used for $W_{(\text{reference})}$.

The Decibel. The decibel is an arbitrarily defined unit of transmission loss (or gain) which has come into general use since about 1925.[2] The customary abbreviation is db. The general definition of attenuation expressed in decibels is

$$(\text{Attenuation in decibels}) = 10 \log_{10} \frac{W_{(\text{general})}}{W_{(\text{reference})}} \tag{31}$$

where $W_{(\text{general})}$ and $W_{(\text{reference})}$ have the same meanings as employed in connection with equation (28).

If the filter section is terminated on a characteristic impedance basis, reference to equation (18) or to equation (25) will show that

$$(\text{Attenuation in decibels}) = 10 \log_{10} \left[\frac{I_1}{I_2}\right]^2 = 10 \log_{10} \epsilon^{2\alpha}$$

$$= 20\alpha \log_{10} \epsilon = 8.686\alpha \tag{32}$$

Comparison of equations (30) and (32) will show that the decibel is a transmission unit which is 1/8.686 times as large as the neper (or napier). In practice the decibel is used almost exclusively in the United States. Because of its rationality, the neper is widely used in theoretical derivations.

It should be noted that transmission loss (or attenuation) units define power ratios and under special conditions define current and voltage

[2] Originally the decibel was called the "transmission unit" (abbreviated TU). See "The Transmission Unit and Telephone Transmission Reference Systems," by W. H. Martin, *Bell System Technical Journal*, Vol. 3, p. 400.

ratios. These units do not specify the actual loss (or gain) in either watts, amperes, or volts. If, for example, it is known that the ratio of power input to power output in a particular case is 3, the transmission loss or attenuation is:

$$\tfrac{1}{2} \log_\epsilon 3 = 0.55 \text{ neper} \quad \text{or} \quad 10 \log_{10} 3 = 4.77 \text{ decibels}$$

If the current ratio is 3 and the input and output impedances are equal, the transmission loss is:

$$\tfrac{1}{2} \log_\epsilon 3^2 = 1.1 \text{ nepers} \quad \text{or} \quad 10 \log_{10} 3^2 = 9.54 \text{ decibels}$$

The actual values of power or current are not specified in the statements given above, only logarithmic functions of the ratios.

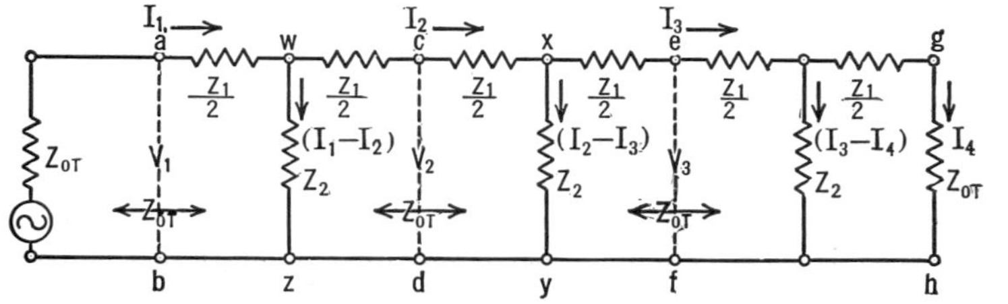

Fig. 10. Three symmetrical T-sections terminated on a characteristic impedance basis.

Example 5. If the vector current ratio per section of each of the three T-sections shown in Fig. 10 is $3\,\underline{/30°}$ or $3\,\underline{/\pi/6}$ radian:

$$\frac{\mathbf{I}_1}{\mathbf{I}_2} = \frac{\mathbf{I}_2}{\mathbf{I}_3} = \frac{\mathbf{I}_3}{\mathbf{I}_4} = \epsilon^{\gamma_1} = \epsilon^{\alpha_1}\epsilon^{j\beta_1} = 3\,\underline{/30°}$$

from which

$$\epsilon^{\alpha_1} = 3 \quad \text{or} \quad \alpha_1 = \log_\epsilon 3 = 1.1 \text{ neper per section}$$

$$\beta_1 = 30° \quad \text{or} \quad \pi/6 \text{ radian, phase shift of } \mathbf{I}_2 \text{ behind } \mathbf{I}_1$$

On a three-section basis:

$$\frac{\mathbf{I}_1}{\mathbf{I}_4} = \epsilon^{\gamma_3} = \epsilon^{\alpha_3}\epsilon^{j\beta_3} = 27\,\underline{/90°}$$

From which the attenuation and phase shift of the three sections may be calculated as

$$\epsilon^{\alpha_3} = 27 \quad \text{or} \quad \alpha_3 = \log_\epsilon 27 = 3.3 \text{ nepers}$$
$$= 28.6 \text{ decibels}$$

$\beta_3 = 90°$ or $\pi/2$ radians, phase shift of $\mathbf{I}_4$ behind $\mathbf{I}_1$.

Problem 7. The current ratio in a particular filter section is known to be $1.11\,\underline{/113°}$ as in example 2, page 448. If the section is terminated in its characteristic impedance, find the attenuation in nepers and in decibels.

Ans.: 0.1043 neper, 0.905 decibel.

Problem 8. Calculate the attenuation in decibels and in nepers for the various power and current ratios indicated below. In the case of the current ratios, it is assumed that the filter sections to which they apply are terminated on a characteristic impedance basis. The few calculated values that appear in the table may be used as guide.

W_1/W_2	db	nepers	I_1/I_2	db	nepers
1	0	0	1	0	0
10	10	1.15	10	20	2.3
100			100		
1,000			1,000		
5,000			10,000		

With respect to a specified reference power level, any particular circuit power may be measured in plus or minus decibels, depending on whether the circuit power is greater or less than the reference power level. Several reference power levels have been used in sound engineering, namely, 6 milliwatts in telephone circuits, 12.5 milliwatts in public address systems, and a relatively new reference level which is designed to be generally applicable and which is specified as " 1 milliwatt in 600 ohms." Thus, 6 milliwatts might be reckoned as $10 \log_{10} (6/1) = +7.78$ db with respect to a 1-milliwatt reference or as $10 \log_{10} (6/12.5) = -3.19$ db with respect to a 12.5-milliwatt reference.

General Considerations. Elementary filter theory concerns itself with uniform ladder structures which are composed of either conventional T- or π-sections. With the definitions which have been given to $\mathbf{Z}_1$ and $\mathbf{Z}_2$ in T- and π-sections, the ladder structures formed by cascade arrangements of these sections are equivalent except for their terminations.

Figure 10 illustrates a ladder structure composed of symmetrical T-sections which is midseries terminated. A ladder structure is said to be midseries terminated when it is terminated at the midpoint of a series arm such as wx. It will be noted that g is the midpoint of such a series arm. Under ideal conditions the structure is terminated at both sending and receiving ends in impedances which are equal to the characteristic impedance of a T-section, namely, $\mathbf{Z}_{oT}$. (Methods will be considered later whereby generating devices of one impedance can be properly matched to a load device of a different impedance.)

Figure 11 illustrates a ladder structure composed of symmetrical π-sections. Comparison of Fig. 10 and Fig. 11 will show the general circuit equivalence of T- and π-sections except for the terminations. The arrangement shown in Fig. 11 may be thought of as symmetrical T-sections which are terminated at planes such that the shunt arm $\mathbf{Z}_2$ is bisected longitudinally, leaving $2\mathbf{Z}_2$ directly across the input and output terminals. This form of termination is called midshunt termination. It has a certain practical significance which will be discussed in a later article.

A *low-pass* filter is a network designed to pass currents of all frequencies below a critical or cut-off frequency and materially to reduce the amplitude of currents of all frequencies above this critical frequency. Under certain ideal conditions which will be considered, a low-pass filter will pass all frequencies from zero up to a predetermined number of cycles with theoretical zero attenuation. The frequency at which the theoretical attenuation takes on a finite value is called the cut-off frequency.

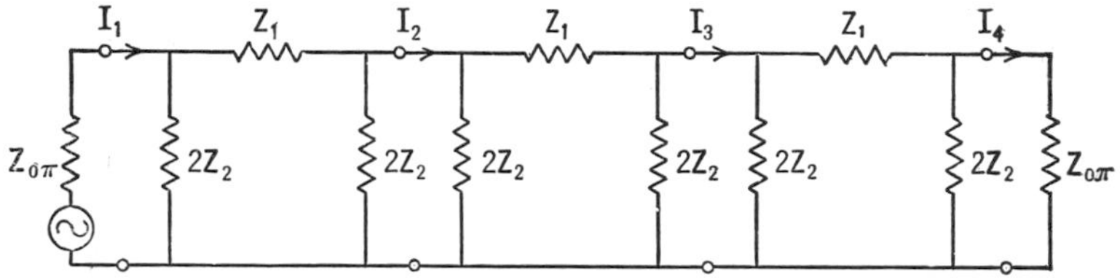

FIG. 11. Three symmetrical π-sections terminated on a characteristic impedance basis.

The general arrangements of circuit elements for elementary low-pass filter sections are illustrated in Fig. 14, page 465.

A *high-pass* filter is a network designed to pass currents of all frequencies above a critical or cut-off frequency and materially to reduce the amplitude of currents of all frequencies below this critical frequency. Under ideal conditions, a high-pass filter attenuates all frequencies from zero up to a predetermined number of cycles and transmits higher frequencies with theoretical zero attenuation. In a high-pass filter the lowest frequency at which theoretical zero attenuation obtains is called cut-off frequency. Elementary high-pass filter sections are shown in Fig. 16, page 468.

A Fundamental Filter Equation. An equation which defines the propagation constant of a filter section wholly in terms of an arbitrarily selected series arm ($\mathbf{Z}_1$) and an arbitrarily selected shunt arm ($\mathbf{Z}_2$) is necessary in the design of filter sections.

Reference to equations (20) and (23), page 446, and to equation (24), page 449, shows that

$$\frac{\mathbf{I}_1}{\mathbf{I}_2} = \epsilon^{\gamma} = \frac{\mathbf{Z}_{oT} + \dfrac{\mathbf{Z}_1}{2}}{\mathbf{Z}_{oT} - \dfrac{\mathbf{Z}_1}{2}} \quad \text{(for T-sections)} \tag{33}$$

$$\frac{\mathbf{I}_1}{\mathbf{I}_2} = \epsilon^{\gamma} = \frac{2\mathbf{Z}_2 + \mathbf{Z}_{o\pi}}{2\mathbf{Z}_2 - \mathbf{Z}_{o\pi}} \quad \text{(for } \pi\text{-sections)} \tag{34}$$

After the value of $\mathbf{Z}_{oT}$ as given in equation (5), page 441, is substituted in equation (33), the following form may be obtained:

$$\frac{\mathbf{I}_1}{\mathbf{I}_2} = \epsilon^{\gamma} = \frac{\sqrt{1 + \frac{\mathbf{Z}_1}{4\mathbf{Z}_2}} + \sqrt{\frac{\mathbf{Z}_1}{4\mathbf{Z}_2}}}{\sqrt{1 + \frac{\mathbf{Z}_1}{4\mathbf{Z}_2}} - \sqrt{\frac{\mathbf{Z}_1}{4\mathbf{Z}_2}}} \quad \text{(for T-sections)} \tag{35}$$

After substituting the value of $\mathbf{Z}_{o\pi}$ as given in equation (7) into equation (34), the following form may be obtained:

$$\frac{\mathbf{I}_1}{\mathbf{I}_2} = \epsilon^{\gamma} = \frac{\sqrt{1 + \frac{\mathbf{Z}_1}{4\mathbf{Z}_2}} + \sqrt{\frac{\mathbf{Z}_1}{4\mathbf{Z}_2}}}{\sqrt{1 + \frac{\mathbf{Z}_1}{4\mathbf{Z}_2}} - \sqrt{\frac{\mathbf{Z}_1}{4\mathbf{Z}_2}}} \quad \text{(for } \pi\text{-sections)} \tag{36}$$

Hence, for like values of $\mathbf{Z}_1$ and $\mathbf{Z}_2$;

$$\frac{\mathbf{I}_1}{\mathbf{I}_2} \text{ (for T-sections)} = \frac{\mathbf{I}_1}{\mathbf{I}_2} \text{ (for } \pi\text{-sections)} \tag{37}$$

Since $\epsilon^{\gamma} = \epsilon^{(\alpha + j\beta)}$, it follows that

$$\epsilon^{(\alpha + j\beta)} = \frac{\left(\sqrt{1 + \frac{\mathbf{Z}_1}{4\mathbf{Z}_2}} + \sqrt{\frac{\mathbf{Z}_1}{4\mathbf{Z}_2}}\right)^2}{1} \tag{38}$$

Although equation (38) defines both α and β in terms of $\mathbf{Z}_1$ and $\mathbf{Z}_2$, a different form is usually employed in the actual evaluation process.[3] An algebraic rearrangement of the quantities involved in equation (38) will show that:

$$\alpha + j\beta = 2 \log_{\epsilon} \left(\sqrt{1 + \frac{\mathbf{Z}_1}{4\mathbf{Z}_2}} + \sqrt{\frac{\mathbf{Z}_1}{4\mathbf{Z}_2}}\right) \tag{39}$$

The above relation is one form of fundamental filter equation, since the

[3] A fundamental filter equation which is sometimes called Campbell's equation (after G. A. Campbell who discovered the filtering properties of various lumped impedance networks) is:

$$\cosh \gamma = 1 + \frac{\mathbf{Z}_1}{2\mathbf{Z}_2} = (\cosh \alpha \cos \beta + j \sinh \alpha \sin \beta)$$

The above form need not be used here but, for the reader who is familiar with the manipulation of complex hyperbolic functions, Campbell's equation is much more elegant than is equation (39). See "Physical Theory of the Wave-Filter," by G. A. Campbell, *Bell System Technical Journal*, Vol. I, November, 1922.

attenuation constant and the phase-shift constant are defined wholly in terms of the *full series arm impedance* ($\mathbf{Z}_1$) and the *full shunt arm impedance* ($\mathbf{Z}_2$). The analysis of any symmetrical T- or π-section composed of series and shunt arms of $\mathbf{Z}_1$ and $\mathbf{Z}_2$, respectively, may be carried through with the aid of equation (39).

Since the right-hand member of equation (39) is, in general, a complex number, it is capable of defining both α and β of either T- or π-sections which are terminated on a characteristic impedance basis. In the manipulation of the factor $\mathbf{Z}_1/4\mathbf{Z}_2$ in equation (39), care should be exercised in determining the correct sign of the associated angle if the correct sign of β is desired.

Example 6. Let it be required to determine the attenuation and phase shift of a filter section whose full series arm is $565.6\underline{/60^\circ}$ ohms (at a particular frequency) and whose full shunt arm is $200\underline{/-90^\circ}$ ohms. *Note:* Characteristic impedance termination is implied in a case of this kind unless otherwise stated.

$$\mathbf{Z}_1 = 565.6\underline{/60^\circ} \quad \text{and} \quad \mathbf{Z}_2 = 200\underline{/-90^\circ} \text{ ohms}$$

$$\sqrt{\frac{\mathbf{Z}_1}{4\mathbf{Z}_2}} = \sqrt{\frac{565.6\underline{/60^\circ}}{800\underline{/-90^\circ}}} = \sqrt{0.707\underline{/150^\circ}} = 0.841\underline{/75^\circ} = (0.2175 + j0.812)$$

$$\sqrt{1 + \frac{\mathbf{Z}_1}{4\mathbf{Z}_2}} = \sqrt{1\underline{/0^\circ} + 0.707\underline{/150^\circ}} = \sqrt{0.525\underline{/42.4^\circ}}$$

$$= 0.725\underline{/21.2^\circ} = (0.676 + j0.262)$$

$$\alpha + j\beta = 2\log_\epsilon[(0.676 + j0.262) + (0.2175 + j0.812)]$$

$$= 2\log_\epsilon(0.893 + j1.074)$$

$$= 2\log_\epsilon(1.396\underline{/50.25^\circ})$$

$$= (2\log_\epsilon 1.396) + j\frac{100.5}{57.3} = (0.668 + j1.76)$$

The attenuation of the filter section is 0.668 neper or 5.80 decibels. The vector input current is 1.76 radians or 100.5° ahead of the vector output current since $\alpha = 0.668$ neper and $\beta = 1.76$ radians.

In this example the resistance of the series arm is relatively high (565.6/2 ohms) and yet the attenuation is relatively low because the filter section is operating in its pass band.

Example 7. Let it be required to find the attenuation and phase shift of the π-section shown in Fig. 8, page 445, by means of equation (39). The resistances of the circuit elements are to be neglected and the frequency is assumed to be 200 cycles. At 200 cycles, $\omega = 1257$ radians per second and

$$\mathbf{Z}_1 = 0 + j\omega L_1 = 25.14\underline{/90^\circ} \text{ ohms}$$

$$2\mathbf{Z}_2 = 0 - j\frac{1}{\frac{\omega C_2}{2}} = 397.5\underline{/-90^\circ} \text{ ohms}$$

$$4\mathbf{Z}_2 = 795\,\underline{/-90^\circ}\text{ ohms}$$

$$\frac{\mathbf{Z}_1}{4\mathbf{Z}_2} = \frac{25.14\,\underline{/90^\circ}}{795\,\underline{/-90^\circ}} = 0.0316\,\underline{/+180^\circ}$$

$$\alpha + j\beta = 2\log_\epsilon\left[\sqrt{1\,\underline{/0^\circ} + 0.0316\,\underline{/+180^\circ}} + \sqrt{0.0316\,\underline{/+180^\circ}}\right]$$

$$= 2\log_\epsilon(1.0\,\underline{/10.25^\circ}) = (2\log_\epsilon 1.0) + \left(2j\,\frac{10.25}{57.3}\right)$$

$$= 0 + j0.358$$

Therefore $\alpha = 0$ and $\beta = 0.358$ radian or 20.5°. It will be noted that, as a result of neglecting the resistances of the circuit elements, the theoretical attenuation is zero.

Problem 9. A high-pass filter section is composed of two 7.96-μf condensers and a coil having an inductance of 0.0159 henry in the form of a T. The resistance of the inductance coil is assumed to be 4 ohms. (A condenser occupies each of the $\mathbf{Z}_1/2$ positions in Fig. 4*a*, page 440, and the inductance coil occupies the $\mathbf{Z}_2$ position in this T-section.) Find the attenuation and phase shift of this filter section at 200 cycles employing equation (39). At 200 cycles:

$$\omega = 1257 \text{ radians per second} \quad \frac{\mathbf{Z}_1}{2} = 100\,\underline{/-90^\circ} \quad \mathbf{Z}_2 = 20.4\,\underline{/78.7^\circ}\text{ ohms}$$

Ans.: $\alpha = 17.8$ db; $\beta = -165^\circ$.

Problem 10. Evaluate α and β in equation (39) if $\mathbf{Z}_1 = 200\,\underline{/90^\circ}$ ohms and $\mathbf{Z}_2 = 50\,\underline{/-90^\circ}$ ohms. *Ans.:* $\alpha = 0$; $\beta = \pi$ radians.

Filter Section Analysis Assuming Zero Resistance. It is quite customary to neglect the resistive components of $\mathbf{Z}_1$ and $\mathbf{Z}_2$ in filter section analysis because the attenuation produced by these resistive components is incidental to the predominant filtering action that takes place. The discrepancy between theoretical results based on zero resistance and actual results will not be great if the resistances are relatively small compared with the reactances. Also the algebraic manipulations involved in filter design are greatly simplified by neglecting the resistive components of $\mathbf{Z}_1$ and $\mathbf{Z}_2$.

If the above resistances are neglected and if the filter sections are properly terminated, the pass bands are transmitted with zero attenuation while the stop bands experience certain varying degrees of attenuation. It will also be shown that the phase shift is 180° throughout the stop band under the conditions stated above. Before elaborating upon these customary generalizations, two examples based entirely upon equation (39) will be presented.

Example 8. Consider a symmetrical T-section in which $\mathbf{Z}_1 = j\omega L_1$ and in which $\mathbf{Z}_2 = -j\dfrac{1}{\omega C_2}\cdot$ Let it be required to predict the behavior of the filter section wholly in terms of the relationship stated in equation (39).

$$\frac{\mathbf{Z}_1}{4\mathbf{Z}_2} = \frac{-\omega^2 L_1 C_2}{4} = \frac{\omega^2 L_1 C_2}{4} \underline{/+180^\circ}$$

Since $\mathbf{Z}_1/4\mathbf{Z}_2$ possesses the general form given above, it will be convenient to reckon ω in $1/\sqrt{L_1C_2}$ units, thereby giving $\mathbf{Z}_1/4\mathbf{Z}_2$ definite numerical values for various different frequency units. The evaluation of the right-hand member of equation (39) for various frequencies is shown in tabular form in Table I.

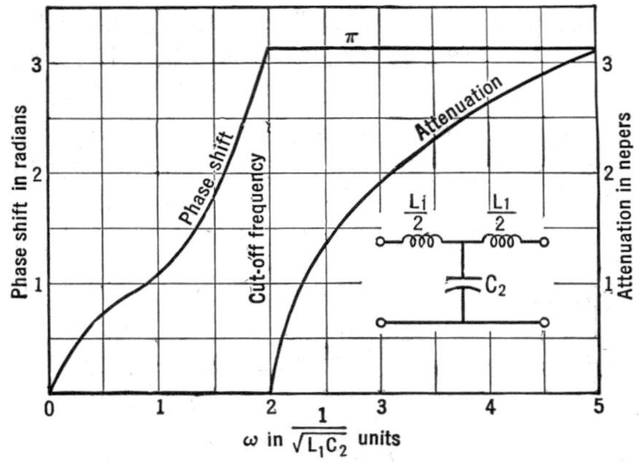

FIG. 12. Variations of phase shift and attenuation in a prototype low-pass filter section. (See Table I, page 459.)

The variations of attenuation and phase shift can readily be determined from an examination of columns (8) and (9) of the table. It will be observed that the filter section which is under discussion has theoretical zero attenuation between the limits of $\omega = 0$ and $\omega = 2/\sqrt{L_1C_2}$ radians per second. The section obviously operates as a low-pass filter. The arrangement of the series and shunt arms of this low-pass filter together with the general trends in the variations of attenuation and phase shift are shown in Fig. 12. The fact that the cut-off point occurs at $\omega = 2/\sqrt{L_1C_2}$ radians per second will be given more attention in a later article. The present example concerns itself primarily with the development of equation (39) in a particular case.

Example 9. Consider a symmetrical T-section in which $\mathbf{Z}_1 = -j\dfrac{1}{\omega C_1}$ and $\mathbf{Z}_2 = j\omega L_2$. Let it be required to predict the behavior of the filter section wholly in terms of equation (39). In the present case:

$$\frac{\mathbf{Z}_1}{4\mathbf{Z}_2} = -\frac{1}{4\omega^2 L_2 C_1} = \frac{1}{4\omega^2 L_2 C_1} \underline{/-180^\circ}$$

The same units of angular velocity as employed in example 8 are convenient units to employ in the present analysis. Also the evaluation of the right-hand member of equation (39) can be conveniently presented in tabular form. The calculations are indicated in Table II, and results are shown graphically in Fig. 13. T-sections

TABLE I

$$\left[\mathbf{Z}_1 = j\omega L_1 \quad \text{and} \quad \mathbf{Z}_2 = -j\frac{1}{\omega C_2}\right] \qquad \frac{\mathbf{Z}_1}{4\mathbf{Z}_2} = \frac{\omega^2 L_1 C_2}{4}\underline{/+180^\circ}$$

(1)	(2)	(3)	(4)	(5)	(6)	(7)	(8)	(9)
ω	$\frac{\mathbf{Z}_1}{4\mathbf{Z}_2}$	$\sqrt{\frac{\mathbf{Z}_1}{4\mathbf{Z}_2}}$	$\sqrt{\frac{\mathbf{Z}_1}{4\mathbf{Z}_2}+1}$	(3) + (4) Cartesian Form	(3) + (4) Polar Form	2 $\log_\epsilon$ (6)	α nepers	β radians
0	0	0	1	$1 + j0$	$1\underline{/0^\circ}$	$0 + j0$	0	0
$1/\sqrt{L_1C_2}$	−0.25	$j0.50$	0.866	$0.866 + j0.5$	$1\underline{/30^\circ}$	$0 + j1.05$	0	1.05
$1.5/\sqrt{L_1C_2}$	−0.563	$j0.75$	0.662	$0.662 + j0.75$	$1\underline{/48.6^\circ}$	$0 + j1.70$	0	1.70
$2/\sqrt{L_1C_2}$	−1.0	$j1.00$	0.000	$0 + j1.0$	$1\underline{/90^\circ}$	$0 + j3.14$	0	3.14
$2.5/\sqrt{L_1C_2}$	−1.562	$j1.25$	$j0.75$	$0 + j2.0$	$2\underline{/90^\circ}$	$1.38 + j3.14$	1.38	3.14
$3/\sqrt{L_1C_2}$	−2.25	$j1.50$	$j1.13$	$0 + j2.63$	$2.63\underline{/90^\circ}$	$1.93 + j3.14$	1.93	3.14
$4/\sqrt{L_1C_2}$	−4.0	$j2.00$	$j1.73$	$0 + j3.73$	$3.73\underline{/90^\circ}$	$2.63 + j3.14$	2.63	3.14
$6/\sqrt{L_1C_2}$	−9.0	$j3.00$	$j2.83$	$0 + j5.83$	$5.83\underline{/90^\circ}$	$3.52 + j3.14$	3.52	3.14
$8/\sqrt{L_1C_2}$	−16.0	$j4.00$	$j3.87$	$0 + j7.87$	$7.87\underline{/90^\circ}$	$4.12 + j3.14$	4.12	3.14
∞	$-\infty$	$j\infty$	$j\infty$	$0 + j\infty$	$\infty\underline{/90^\circ}$	$\infty + j3.14$	∞	3.14

TABLE II

$$\left[\mathbf{Z}_1 = -j\frac{1}{\omega C_1} \quad \text{and} \quad \mathbf{Z}_2 = j\omega L_2\right] \qquad \frac{\mathbf{Z}_1}{4\mathbf{Z}_2} = \frac{1}{4\omega^2 L_2 C_1}\angle{-180°}$$

(1)	(2)	(3)	(4)	(5)	(6)	(7)	(8)	(9)
ω	$\frac{\mathbf{Z}_1}{4\mathbf{Z}_2}$	$\sqrt{\frac{\mathbf{Z}_1}{4\mathbf{Z}_2}}$	$\sqrt{\frac{\mathbf{Z}_1}{4\mathbf{Z}_2}+1}$	(3) + (4) Cartesian Form	(3) + (4) Polar Form	2 log$_\epsilon$ (6)	α nepers	β radians
0	$-\infty$	$-j\infty$	$-j\infty$	$0 - j\infty$	$\infty \angle{-90°}$	$\infty - j3.14$	∞	−3.14
$\frac{0.1}{\sqrt{C_1L_2}}$	−25	$-j5.0$	$-j4.9$	$0 - j9.9$	$9.9\angle{-90°}$	$4.58 - j3.14$	4.58	−3.14
$\frac{0.25}{\sqrt{C_1L_2}}$	−4.0	$-j2.0$	$-j1.73$	$0 - j3.73$	$3.73\angle{-90°}$	$2.63 - j3.14$	2.63	−3.14
$\frac{0.40}{\sqrt{C_1L_2}}$	−1.563	$-j1.25$	$-j0.75$	$0 - j2.00$	$2.0\angle{-90°}$	$1.38 - j3.14$	1.38	−3.14
$\frac{0.50}{\sqrt{C_1L_2}}$	−1.00	$-j1.0$	0.00	$0 - j1.00$	$1.0\angle{-90°}$	$0 - j3.14$	0	−3.14
$\frac{0.60}{\sqrt{C_1L_2}}$	−0.694	$-j0.833$	0.554	$0.554 - j0.833$	$1.0\angle{-56.4°}$	$0 - j1.97$	0	−1.97
$\frac{1.0}{\sqrt{C_1L_2}}$	−0.250	$-j0.500$	0.866	$0.866 - j0.500$	$1.0\angle{-30°}$	$0 - j1.05$	0	−1.05
$\frac{2.0}{\sqrt{C_1L_2}}$	−0.0625	$-j0.250$	0.968	$0.968 - j0.250$	$1.0\angle{-14.5°}$	$0 - j0.506$	0	−0.506
$\frac{4.0}{\sqrt{C_1L_2}}$	−0.0156	$-j0.125$	0.992	$0.992 - j0.125$	$1.0\angle{-7.2°}$	$0 - j0.246$	0	−0.246
∞	0	0	1.00	$1.00 - j0$	$1.0\angle{0°}$	$0 - j0$	0	0

consisting of series-arm condensers and shunt-arm inductances are thus shown to operate effectively as high-pass filters.

The phase shift constant, β, in Table I represents a lag of section output voltage and current with respect to section input voltage and current. In Table II, β represents a lead of section output voltage and current with respect to section input voltage.

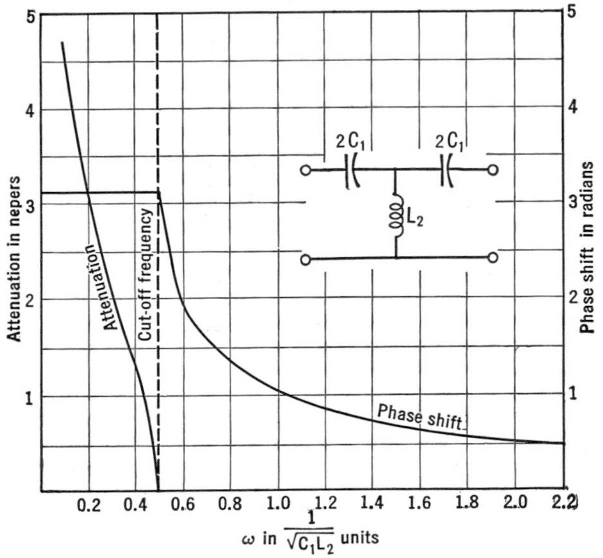

FIG. 13. Variations of phase shift and attenuation in a prototype high-pass filter section. (See Table II, page 460.)

Problem 11. Refer to Table I, page 459. Check all the values listed at $\omega = 1.5/\sqrt{L_1C_2}$ and at $\omega = 3/\sqrt{L_1C_2}$. Compare the results obtained for α and β with those plotted in Fig. 12, page 458.

Problem 12. Refer to Table II, page 460. Check all the values listed at $\omega = 0.25/\sqrt{C_1L_2}$ and at $\omega = 2.0/\sqrt{C_1L_2}$. Compare the results obtained for α and β with those plotted in Fig. 13, page 461.

The chief facts to be gained from the foregoing analyses are:

(1) α is equal to zero within the pass-band region.
(2) β is equal to $\pm\pi$ within the stop-band region.

A study of Tables I and II will show that the pass bands are limited to those regions where $\mathbf{Z}_1/4\mathbf{Z}_2$ possesses values between 0 and -1. These results might have been anticipated mathematically by investigating the possible values of α and β when $\mathbf{Z}_1$ and $\mathbf{Z}_2$ are reactances of opposite types. Let

$$\frac{\mathbf{Z}_1}{4\mathbf{Z}_2} = \mathbf{A}$$

It is plain that $\mathbf{A} = A\underline{/\pm\pi}$ since

$$\frac{X_L\underline{/90^\circ}}{4X_C\underline{/-90^\circ}} \quad \text{or} \quad \frac{X_C\underline{/-90^\circ}}{4X_L\underline{/90^\circ}}$$

are complex numbers which have associated angles of $+\pi$ or $-\pi$ radians, respectively.

If

$$-1 \leqq A \leqq 0$$

$$\begin{aligned} \alpha + j\beta &= 2 \log_\epsilon (\sqrt{1 - A} + \sqrt{-A}) \\ &= 2 \log_\epsilon (\sqrt{1 - A} + j\sqrt{A}) \\ &= 2\left(\log_\epsilon \sqrt{1 - A + A} + j \tan^{-1} \frac{\sqrt{A}}{\sqrt{1 - A}}\right) \end{aligned}$$

Hence $\alpha = 0$ and $\beta = 2 \tan^{-1} (\sqrt{A}/\sqrt{1 - A})$ when $\mathbf{A} = \mathbf{Z}_1/4\mathbf{Z}_2$ lies between 0 and -1.

When $\mathbf{Z}_1/4\mathbf{Z}_2$ lies between -1 and $-\infty$ a similar analysis will show that for $\mathbf{Z}_1/4\mathbf{Z}_2 = A'\underline{/\pm\pi}$, A' being greater in magnitude than unity.

$$\begin{aligned} \alpha + j\beta &= 2 \log_\epsilon (\sqrt{1 - A'} + \sqrt{-A'}) \\ &= 2 \log_\epsilon (j\sqrt{A' - 1} + j\sqrt{A'}) \\ &= 2 \log_\epsilon (\sqrt{A' - 1} + \sqrt{A'}) + j(\pm\pi) \end{aligned}$$

Hence $\alpha = 2 \log_\epsilon (\sqrt{A' - 1} + \sqrt{A'})$ and $\beta = \pm\pi$ when $\mathbf{A}' = \mathbf{Z}_1/4\mathbf{Z}_2$ lies between -1 and $-\infty$.

The above analysis shows that the pass bands are limited to those regions where $\mathbf{Z}_1/4\mathbf{Z}_2$ takes on values between and including 0 and -1. Hence:

$$-1 \leqq \frac{\mathbf{Z}_1}{4\mathbf{Z}_2} \leqq 0 \tag{40}$$

defines the pass-band regions in terms of $\mathbf{Z}_1$ and $\mathbf{Z}_2$. The boundaries of a pass band in a particular case may be obtained by setting:

$$\frac{\mathbf{Z}_1}{4\mathbf{Z}_2} = 0 \quad \text{and} \quad \frac{\mathbf{Z}_1}{4\mathbf{Z}_2} = -1 \tag{41}$$

or by setting

$$\frac{\mathbf{Z}_1}{\mathbf{Z}_2} = 0 \quad \text{and} \quad \frac{\mathbf{Z}_1}{\mathbf{Z}_2} = -4 \tag{42}$$

Reference to equation (39) will show that $\alpha = 0$ when $\mathbf{Z}_1/4\mathbf{Z}_2 = 0$ and when $\mathbf{Z}_1/4\mathbf{Z}_2 = -1$.

Example 10. Refer to the symmetrical π-section shown in Fig. 8, page 445. Let it be required to predict the pass-band boundaries in terms of the relationships stated in (42). The full series arm of Fig. 8 is $L_1 = 0.02$ henry and $\mathbf{Z}_1 = 0.02\omega\underline{/90°}$ ohms. The full shunt arm is $C_2 = 4.0\ \mu$f and $\mathbf{Z}_2 = (10^6/4\omega)\underline{/-90°}$ ohms.

Setting $\mathbf{Z}_1/\mathbf{Z}_2 = 0$ yields

$$\frac{0.02\omega\underline{/90°}}{\frac{10^6}{4\omega}\underline{/-90°}} = 0 \quad \text{or} \quad \omega = 0 \quad \text{(one boundary)}$$

Setting $\mathbf{Z}_1/\mathbf{Z}_2 = -4$ yields

$$\frac{0.02\omega\underline{/90°}}{\frac{10^6}{4\omega}\underline{/-90°}} = \frac{-0.08\omega^2}{10^6} = -4$$

from which

$$\omega^2 = \sqrt{50 \times 10^6}$$

$$\omega = 7070 \text{ radians per second} \quad \text{(one boundary)}$$

The value of ω given above represents the cut-off angular velocity of this particular low-pass filter section and corresponds to a frequency of $7070/2\pi$ or 1125 cycles.

Cut-Off Frequencies of Elementary Low- and High-Pass Sections. The frequency limits of the pass band for an elementary low-pass filter without resistance may be obtained from equation (38). For a low-pass filter $\mathbf{Z}_1 = j\omega L_1$ and $\mathbf{Z}_2 = -j\dfrac{1}{\omega C_2}\cdot$ If these values are substituted in equation (38), the result, after a little algebraic simplification, is:

$$\epsilon^{\alpha+j\beta} = \epsilon^{\alpha}\epsilon^{j\beta} = 1 - \frac{2\omega^2 L_1 C_2}{4} + 2\sqrt{\frac{\omega^4 L_1{}^2 C_2{}^2}{16} - \frac{\omega^2 L_1 C_2}{4}} \tag{43}$$

For no attenuation $\alpha = 0$, and

$$\epsilon^{j\beta} = \cos\beta + j\sin\beta = 1 - \frac{2\omega^2 L_1 C_2}{4} + 2\sqrt{\frac{\omega^4 L_1{}^2 C_2{}^2}{16} - \frac{\omega^2 L_1 C_2}{4}} \tag{44}$$

Since the last term of equation (44) is the only one that may become imaginary, it follows that the real part must be $\cos\beta$. Therefore

$$\cos\beta = 1 - \frac{2\omega^2 L_1 C_2}{4} \tag{45}$$

Since $\cos\beta$ can vary from 1 to -1, the limits for ω may be obtained. Hence

$$\pm 1 = 1 - \frac{2\omega^2 L_1 C_2}{4} \tag{46}$$

and

$$\omega = 0 \quad \text{or} \quad \frac{2}{\sqrt{L_1C_2}} \tag{47}$$

or

$$f_c = \frac{1}{\pi\sqrt{L_1C_2}} \quad \text{(for low-pass)} \tag{48}$$

Equation (48) gives the upper or cut-off frequency for an elementary low-pass filter. In other words, any wave of frequency between zero and f_c is passed without attenuation provided that the filter section is terminated in the characteristic impedance for that frequency.

For a high-pass filter, $\mathbf{Z}_1 = -j\dfrac{1}{\omega C_1}$ and $\mathbf{Z}_2 = j\omega L_2$. If these values are substituted in equation (38), a similar method of analysis as used in obtaining equation (45) gives

$$\cos\beta = 1 - \frac{2}{4\omega^2 C_1 L_2} \tag{49}$$

Substituting the limits of ± 1 for $\cos\beta$, the upper limit of frequency is found to be ∞ while the lower limit or cut-off frequency is:

$$f_c = \frac{1}{4\pi\sqrt{C_1L_2}} \quad \text{for high-pass} \tag{50}$$

Equation (50) gives the cut-off frequency for an elementary high-pass filter. This means that any frequency above the cut-off frequency f_c is passed with no attenuation if the filter section is terminated in the characteristic impedance for the particular frequency.

Constant-*k* Low-Pass Filter. Filter sections in which the series and shunt arms are inverse impedance functions possess a peculiar property. The product of $\mathbf{Z}_1$ and $\mathbf{Z}_2$ is independent of frequency. Reference to either the T- or π-section of Fig. 14 will show that

$$\mathbf{Z}_{1k}\mathbf{Z}_{2k} = (j\omega L_{1k})\left(-j\frac{1}{\omega C_{2k}}\right) = \frac{L_{1k}}{C_{2k}} = R_k^2 \tag{51}$$

$\sqrt{L_{1k}/C_{2k}}$ is an important characteristic of the filter section, and inasmuch as

$$\sqrt{\frac{L_{1k}}{C_{2k}}} = R_k = \text{a constant}$$

filter sections of this type are called constant-k sections. There are many other types of filter sections, several of which are derived in one way or another from constant-k sections. For this reason the parameters of constant-k sections usually carry the subscript k in order to designate properly the type of filter section that is under discussion. The parameters of some of the more elaborate filter sections are specified directly in terms of L_k and C_k.

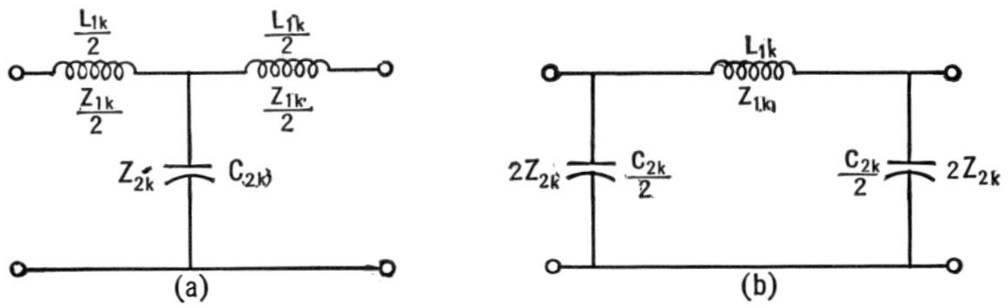

FIG. 14. Prototype or constant-k low-pass filter sections.

The general theory of the constant-k low-pass filter has already been presented. It remains only to develop the design equations for this type of filter.

$$\frac{\mathbf{Z}_{1k}}{\mathbf{Z}_{2k}} = \frac{j\omega L_{1k}}{-j\dfrac{1}{\omega C_{2k}}} = -\omega^2 L_{1k}C_{2k} \tag{52}$$

The boundaries of the pass band are determined by setting $\mathbf{Z}_{1k}/\mathbf{Z}_{2k}$ equal to -4 and equal to zero. [See equation (42), page 462.]

$$-\omega^2 L_{1k}C_{2k} = 0 \quad \text{yields} \quad \omega = 0 \tag{53}$$

$$-\omega^2 L_{1k}C_{2k} = -4 \quad \text{yields} \quad \omega_c = \frac{2}{\sqrt{L_{1k}C_{2k}}} \tag{54}$$

ω_c is the angular velocity at which cut-off takes place and as such forms the upper boundary of the pass band. The *cut-off frequency of a low-pass, constant-k-type* filter is:

$$f_c = \frac{\omega_c}{2\pi} = \frac{1}{\pi\sqrt{L_{1k}C_{2k}}} \tag{55}$$

It will be observed that f_c is governed wholly by the magnitude of the $L_{1k}C_{2k}$ product. The lower the cut-off frequency, the higher is the $L_{1k}C_{2k}$ product, and vice versa.

Another important consideration in either the theory or design of a filter section is the matter of correct terminating impedances. A single section can be properly matched to its sending and receiving ends if terminated on an image basis, as explained on page 439. If more than one filter section is to be employed between sending and receiving ends, it is desirable to design each section to have the same characteristic impedance. Under these conditions minimum reflection loss results when the various sections are arranged as shown in Fig. 10 or Fig. 11. A detailed analysis of these losses will not be given here since they are similar in nature to reflection losses on long lines. (See Chapter X.)

For a constant-k, low-pass T-section:

$$\mathbf{Z}_{oTk} = \sqrt{\frac{L_{1k}}{C_{2k}}\left(1 - \frac{\omega^2 L_{1k}C_{2k}}{4}\right)} \tag{56}$$

$$L_{1k}C_{2k} = \frac{4}{\omega_c^2} \quad \text{[See equation (54).]}$$

Therefore, for a constant-k, low-pass T-section:

$$\mathbf{Z}_{oTk} = \sqrt{\frac{L_{1k}}{C_{2k}}}\sqrt{1 - \frac{f^2}{f_c^2}}$$

$$= R_k\sqrt{1 - \frac{f^2}{f_c^2}} \tag{57}$$

For a constant-k, low-pass π-section:

$$\mathbf{Z}_{o\pi k} = \frac{\sqrt{L_{1k}/C_{2k}}}{\sqrt{1 - \dfrac{f^2}{f_c^2}}} = \frac{R_k}{\sqrt{1 - \dfrac{f^2}{f_c^2}}} \tag{58}$$

The variations of Z_{oTk} and $Z_{o\pi k}$ from $f = 0$ to $f = f_c$ are illustrated in Fig. 15. The fact that the correct terminating impedance of a constant-k section varies over such wide limits is a very serious limitation in certain communication circuits. For a fixed receiving impedance it is plain that either the T- or π-section is correctly terminated at only one frequency. The opposite trends in Z_{oTk} and $Z_{o\pi k}$ are combined in one form of filter section to obtain a characteristic impedance which is reasonably constant over the frequency range of the pass band. (See m-derived filter sections, pages 480–484.)

The zero-frequency value of either Z_{oTk} or $Z_{o\pi k}$ is:

$$R_k = \sqrt{\frac{L_{1k}}{C_{2k}}} \quad \text{[See equations (57) and (58).]} \tag{59}$$

L_{1k} and C_{2k} can be related to one another through the value of R_k^2. [See equation (51).]

$$L_{1k} = R_k^2 C_{2k} \tag{60}$$

$$C_{2k} = \frac{L_{1k}}{R_k^2} \tag{61}$$

The design values of L_{1k} and C_{2k} are usually specified in terms of cut-off frequency, f_c, and the zero-frequency value of the characteristic

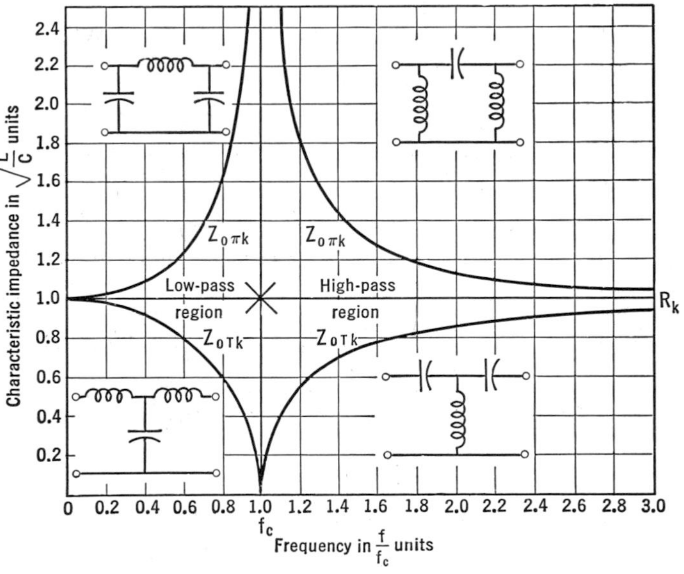

FIG. 15. Variations of the characteristic impedances of low-pass and high-pass constant-k filter sections.

impedance, R_k. It has been shown that:

$$f_c = \frac{1}{\pi\sqrt{L_{1k}C_{2k}}} \qquad \text{[See equation (55).]}$$

Eliminating C_{2k} as given in equation (61) from the above equation yields:

$$f_c = \frac{1}{\pi\sqrt{L_{1k}^2/R_k^2}}$$

or

$$L_{1k} = \frac{R_k}{\pi f_c} \quad \text{(for low-pass filter)} \tag{62}$$

From equations (61) and (62) it is plain that:

$$C_{2k} = \frac{L_{1k}}{R_k^2} = \frac{1}{\pi R_k f_c} \quad \text{(for low-pass filter)} \tag{63}$$

Equations (62) and (63) specify the values of L and C to employ in a constant-k, low-pass filter section in terms of f_c and R_k.

Problem 13. Design both T- and π-section, low-pass filters of the constant-k type which will have a zero-frequency characteristic impedance of 600 ohms and a cut-off frequency of 940 cycles. Draw the circuit arrangement in each case, indicating the particular values (in henrys or microfarads) of each circuit element. *Ans.:* The *full* series arm $L_{1k} = 0.203$ henry; and the *full* shunt arm $C_{2k} = 0.565\ \mu$f.

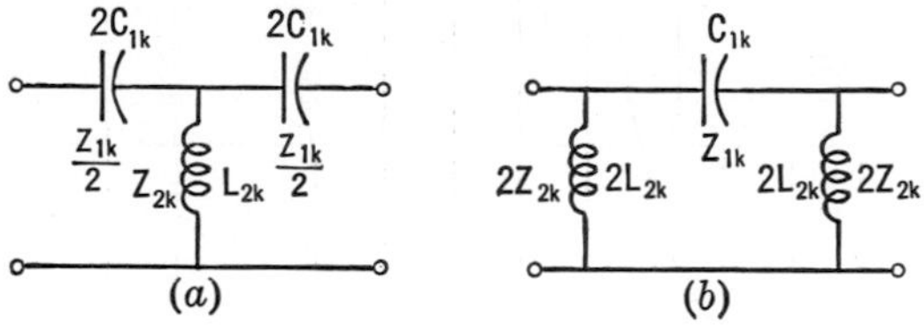

FIG. 16. Prototype or constant-k high-pass filter sections.

Constant-*k* High-Pass Filter. Prototype or constant-k, high-pass filter sections are illustrated in Fig. 16. In the present case:

$$\mathbf{Z}_{1k}\mathbf{Z}_{2k} = \left(-j\frac{1}{\omega C_{1k}}\right)(j\omega L_{2k}) = \frac{L_{2k}}{C_{1k}} = R_k^2 \tag{64}$$

and

$$\frac{\mathbf{Z}_{1k}}{\mathbf{Z}_{2k}} = \frac{-j\dfrac{1}{\omega C_{1k}}}{j\omega L_{2k}} = -\frac{1}{\omega^2 C_{1k}L_{2k}} \tag{65}$$

The boundaries of the pass band are again determined by setting $\mathbf{Z}_{1k}/\mathbf{Z}_{2k}$ equal to -4 and equal to zero. [See equation (42), page 462.]

$$-\frac{1}{\omega^2 C_{1k}L_{2k}} = 0 \quad \text{yields} \quad \omega = \infty \tag{66}$$

$$-\frac{1}{\omega^2 C_{1k}L_{2k}} = -4 \quad \text{yields} \quad \omega_c = \frac{1}{2\sqrt{C_{1k}L_{2k}}} \tag{67}$$

The cut-off frequency of a high-pass, constant-k filter is

$$f_c = \frac{\omega_c}{2\pi} = \frac{1}{4\pi\sqrt{C_{1k}L_{2k}}} \tag{68}$$

$\mathbf{Z}_{oT}$ and $\mathbf{Z}_{o\pi}$ may be expressed in terms of f_c, f, and $\sqrt{L_{2k}/C_{1k}}$ For a constant-k, high-pass T-section:

$$\mathbf{Z}_{oTk} = \sqrt{\frac{L_{2k}}{C_{1k}}} \times \sqrt{1 - \frac{f_c^2}{f^2}} \tag{69}$$

For a constant-k, high-pass π-section:

$$\mathbf{Z}_{o\pi k} = \sqrt{\frac{L_{2k}}{C_{1k}}} \div \sqrt{1 - \frac{f_c^2}{f^2}} \tag{70}$$

General trends in Z_{oTk} and $Z_{o\pi k}$ in constant-k, high-pass filter sections are illustrated in Fig. 15. Both Z_{oTk} and $Z_{o\pi k}$ approach the common value $\sqrt{L_{2k}/C_{1k}}$ at $f = \infty$. Because it is a useful common base from which to work, $\sqrt{L_{2k}/C_{1k}}$ is given special designation, namely R_k. R_k is known as the infinite-frequency characteristic impedance. Since

$$\sqrt{\frac{L_{2k}}{C_{1k}}} = R_k \tag{71}$$

$$L_{2k} = R_k^{\,2} C_{1k} \quad \text{and} \quad C_{1k} = \frac{L_{2k}}{R_k^{\,2}} \tag{72}$$

If the above values are substituted separately in equation (68), the following relationships are obtained:

$$C_{1k} = \frac{1}{4\pi R_k f_c} \quad \text{(for high-pass filter)} \tag{73}$$

$$L_{2k} = \frac{R_k}{4\pi f_c} \quad \text{(for high-pass filter)} \tag{74}$$

Equations (73) and (74) may be employed in the design of constant-k, high-pass filter sections which are to have a particular cut-off frequency and which are to have infinite-frequency characteristic impedances equal to R_k.

Problem 14. What are the cut-off frequency and infinite-frequency characteristic impedance of the high-pass filter section that can be constructed from two 1-μf condensers and one 15-millihenry inductance coil?

Ans.: $f_c = 919$ cycles; $R_k = 173$ ohms.

Tabulation and Review of Constant-*k* Filter Theory. The important features contained in equations (51) to (74) inclusive are summarized concisely in Table III, pages 471–472. The attenuation and phase shift in Table III are expressed in forms which derive directly from " Campbell's " equation. (See footnote 3 on page 455.) It has been shown in examples 8 and 9, pages 457–458, how the attenuation and phase shift may be calculated from equation (39), page 455, without the aid of hyperbolic functions. For the reader who is familiar with complex hyperbolic functions the following derivation and application of " Campbell's " equation may be of interest.

Derivation and Application of Campbell's Equation. The application of Kirchhoff's emf law to the *wxyz* loop of the filter sections shown in Fig. 10, page 452, yields

$$\mathbf{Z}_1\mathbf{I}_2 + \mathbf{Z}_2(\mathbf{I}_2 - \mathbf{I}_3) - \mathbf{Z}_2(\mathbf{I}_1 - \mathbf{I}_2) = 0 \tag{75}$$

or

$$\mathbf{Z}_1\mathbf{I}_2 + 2\mathbf{Z}_2\mathbf{I}_2 - \mathbf{Z}_2\mathbf{I}_3 - \mathbf{Z}_2\mathbf{I}_1 = 0 \tag{76}$$

Dividing the above equation through by $\mathbf{Z}_2\mathbf{I}_2$ and transposing results in

$$\frac{\mathbf{I}_1}{\mathbf{I}_2} + \frac{\mathbf{I}_3}{\mathbf{I}_2} = 2 + \frac{\mathbf{Z}_1}{\mathbf{Z}_2} \tag{77}$$

Since

$$\frac{\mathbf{I}_1}{\mathbf{I}_2} = \epsilon^{\gamma} = \frac{\mathbf{I}_2}{\mathbf{I}_3}$$

it follows that

$$\frac{\mathbf{I}_3}{\mathbf{I}_2} = \epsilon^{-\gamma}$$

$$\epsilon^{\gamma} + \epsilon^{-\gamma} = 2 + \frac{\mathbf{Z}_1}{\mathbf{Z}_2} \tag{78}$$

$$\frac{\epsilon^{\gamma} + \epsilon^{-\gamma}}{2} = \cosh \boldsymbol{\gamma} = 1 + \frac{\mathbf{Z}_1}{2\mathbf{Z}_2} \quad \text{(Campbell's equation)} \tag{79}$$

A more useful form for the purposes at hand may be derived as follows:

$$\cosh \boldsymbol{\gamma} = \cosh (\alpha + j\beta) = \frac{\epsilon^{(\alpha+j\beta)} + \epsilon^{-(\alpha+j\beta)}}{2}$$

$$= \frac{\epsilon^{\alpha}\epsilon^{j\beta} + \epsilon^{-\alpha}\epsilon^{-j\beta}}{2} \tag{80}$$

Converting the $\epsilon^{j\beta}$ terms into their rectangular forms results in:

$$\cosh (\alpha + j\beta) = \frac{\epsilon^{\alpha} (\cos \beta + j \sin \beta) + \epsilon^{-\alpha} (\cos \beta - j \sin \beta)}{2}$$

$$= \frac{(\epsilon^{\alpha} + \epsilon^{-\alpha})}{2} \cos \beta + j \frac{(\epsilon^{\alpha} - \epsilon^{-\alpha})}{2} \sin \beta$$

From the analytical definitions of hyperbolic cosine and hyperbolic sine, it follows that

$$\cosh (\alpha + j\beta) = \cosh \alpha \cos \beta + j \sinh \alpha \sin \beta$$

Therefore

$$\cosh \alpha \cos \beta + j \sinh \alpha \sin \beta = 1 + \frac{\mathbf{Z}_1}{2\mathbf{Z}_2} \tag{81}$$

The above form may be used directly to derive the attenuation and phase-shift expressions given in Table III, page 472.

In the stop band, $\beta = \pi$. Since $\cos \beta$ then becomes -1 in equation

TABLE III

	Constant-k Low Pass		Constant-k High Pass	
	T-Section	π-Section	T-Section	π-Section
Circuit Configuration	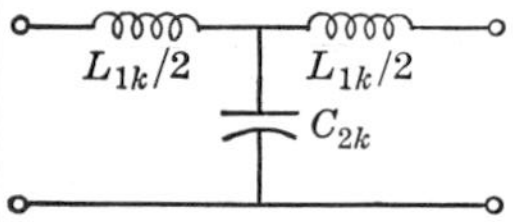	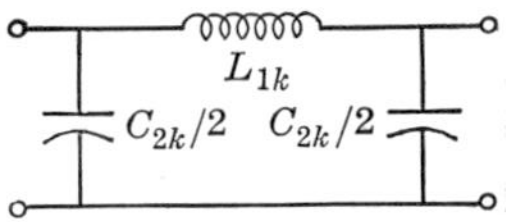	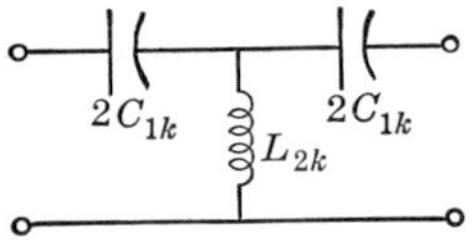	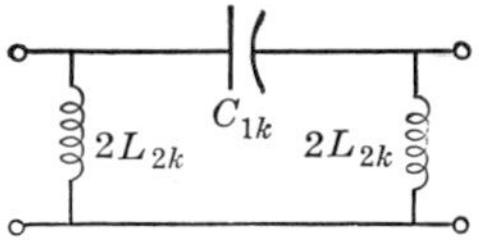
Cut-Off Frequency	$f_c = \dfrac{1}{\pi\sqrt{L_{1k}C_{2k}}}$		$f_c = \dfrac{1}{4\pi\sqrt{C_{1k}L_{2k}}}$	
Z_1Z_2 Base Characteristic Impedance	Zero-Frequency Characteristic Z $R_k = \sqrt{L_{1k}/C_{2k}}$		Infinite-Frequency Characteristic Z $R_k = \sqrt{L_{2k}/C_{1k}}$	
Z_0 With Respect To f	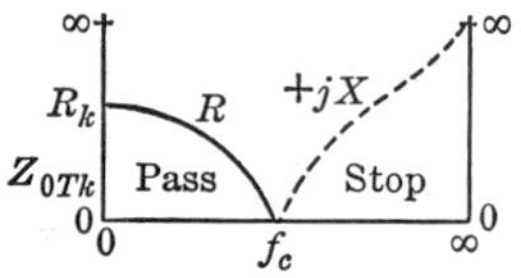	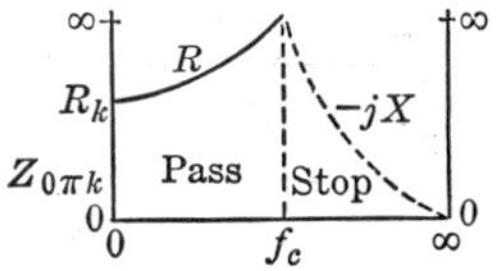	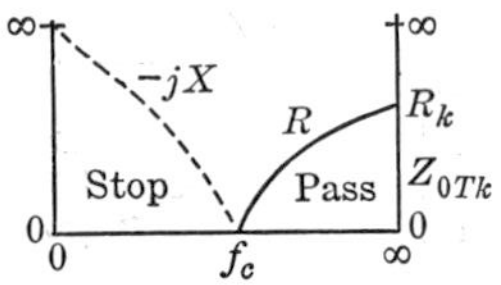	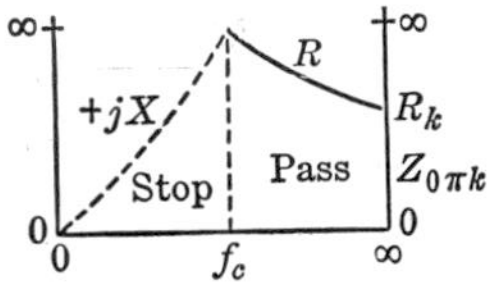
	$Z_{0Tk} = R_k \times \sqrt{1 - f^2/f_c^2}$	$Z_{0\pi k} = R_k/\sqrt{1 - f^2/f_c^2}$	$Z_{0Tk} = R_k \times \sqrt{1 - f_c^2/f^2}$	$Z_{0\pi k} = R_k/\sqrt{1 - f_c^2/f^2}$

TABLE III (*Continued*)

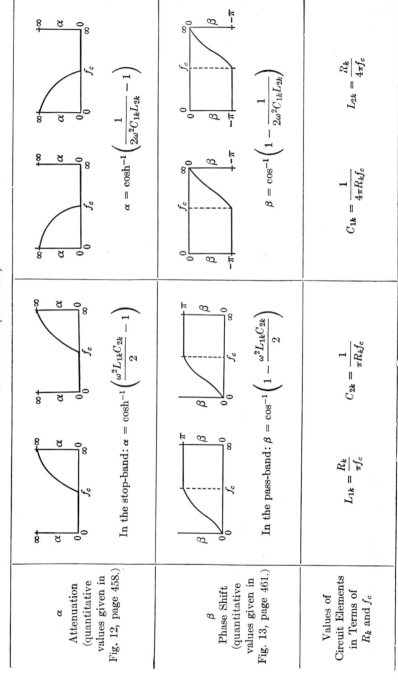

α Attenuation (quantitative values given in Fig. 12, page 458.)	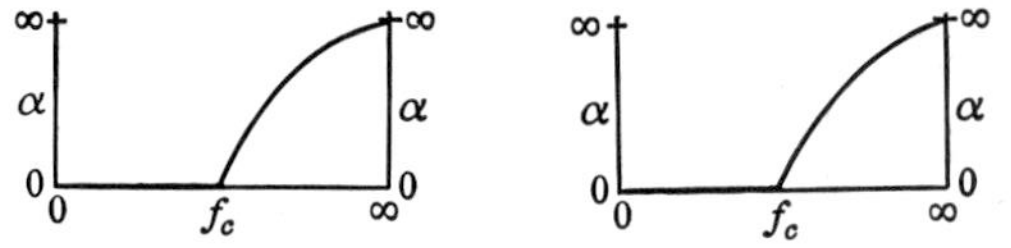 In the stop-band: $\alpha = \cosh^{-1}\left(\frac{\omega^2 L_{1k} C_{2k}}{2} - 1\right)$	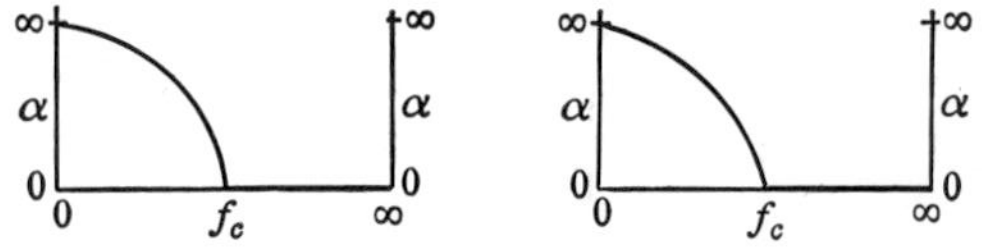 $\alpha = \cosh^{-1}\left(\frac{1}{2\omega^2 C_{1k} L_{2k}} - 1\right)$
β Phase Shift (quantitative values given in Fig. 13, page 461.)	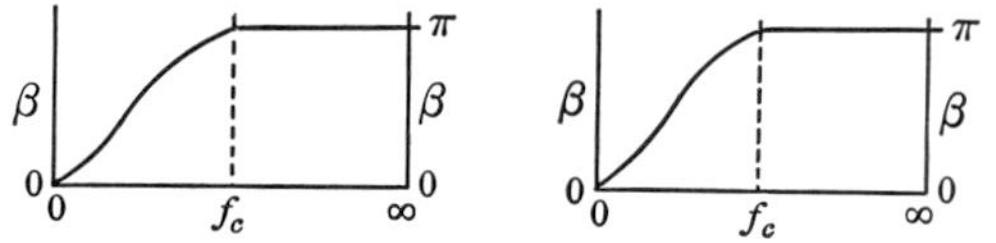 In the pass-band: $\beta = \cos^{-1}\left(1 - \frac{\omega^2 L_{1k} C_{2k}}{2}\right)$	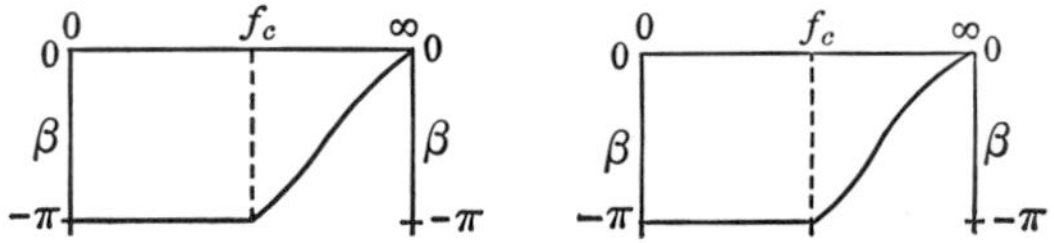 $\beta = \cos^{-1}\left(1 - \frac{1}{2\omega^2 C_{1k} L_{2k}}\right)$
Values of Circuit Elements in Terms of R_k and f_c	$L_{1k} = \frac{R_k}{\pi f_c}$ $C_{2k} = \frac{1}{\pi R_k f_c}$	$C_{1k} = \frac{1}{4\pi R_k f_c}$ $L_{2k} = \frac{R_k}{4\pi f_c}$

(81) and $\sin \beta = 0$:

$$-\cosh \alpha = 1 + \frac{\mathbf{Z}_1}{2\mathbf{Z}_2}$$

$$\alpha = \cosh^{-1}\left(-\frac{\mathbf{Z}_1}{2\mathbf{Z}_2} - 1\right) \quad \text{(in stop band)} \qquad (82)$$

In the pass band, $\alpha = 0$. Since $\cosh 0 = 1$ and $\sinh 0 = 0$, equation (81) becomes:

$$\cos \beta = \left(1 + \frac{\mathbf{Z}_1}{2\mathbf{Z}_2}\right)$$

$$\beta = \cos^{-1}\left(1 + \frac{\mathbf{Z}_1}{2\mathbf{Z}_2}\right) \quad \text{(in pass band)} \qquad (83)$$

As applied to a constant-k low-pass filter section:

$$\mathbf{Z}_1 = \omega L_{1k}\underline{/90^\circ} \quad \mathbf{Z}_2 = \frac{1}{\omega C_{2k}}\underline{/-90^\circ} \quad \frac{\mathbf{Z}_1}{\mathbf{Z}_2} = -\omega^2 L_{1k}C_{2k}$$

Equation (82) then takes the form:

$$\alpha = \cosh^{-1}\left(\frac{\omega^2 L_{1k}C_{2k}}{2} - 1\right)$$

as shown in Table III. Equation (83) takes the form:

$$\beta = \cos^{-1}\left(1 - \frac{\omega^2 L_{1k}C_{2k}}{2}\right)$$

as shown in Table III. Corresponding expressions for α and β may be derived for the constant-k high-pass filter section. The results are shown in Table III.

Band-Pass and Band-Elimination Filters. Band-pass filters are networks which are designed to attenuate all frequencies except those in a specified band. A band-pass filter may be formed by placing a low-pass filter section (having a cut-off frequency of f_{cl}) in series with a high-pass filter section (having a cut-off frequency of f_{ch}). Then f_{cl} is made higher than f_{ch} by the specified band width, which is $f_{cl} - f_{ch}$. A study of the attenuation graphs shown in Table III will show how f_{cl} and f_{ch} should be adjusted to give a zero-attenuation band.

A band-pass filter may take the form of a single section as shown in Fig. 17. The section shown in Fig. 17 is called a constant-k band-pass filter when $L_2C_2 = L_1C_1$ because under these conditions:

$$\mathbf{Z}_1\mathbf{Z}_2 = \frac{L_2}{C_1} = \frac{L_1}{C_2} = \text{a constant}$$

An analysis of the band-pass filter will not be given here, although such an analysis may be carried through in a manner similar to those given for the low-pass and high-pass sections.

Band-elimination filters are networks which are designed to pass all frequencies except those in a specified band. A band-elimination filter may be formed by placing a low-pass section (having a cut-off frequency of f_{cl}) in parallel with a high-pass section (having a cut-off frequency of f_{ch}). Then f_{cl} is made lower than f_{ch} by the specified band width, which is $f_{ch} - f_{cl}$. All frequencies have a pass band (through one of the parallel sections) except where the two attenuation graphs overlap. (See attenuation graphs in Table III.)

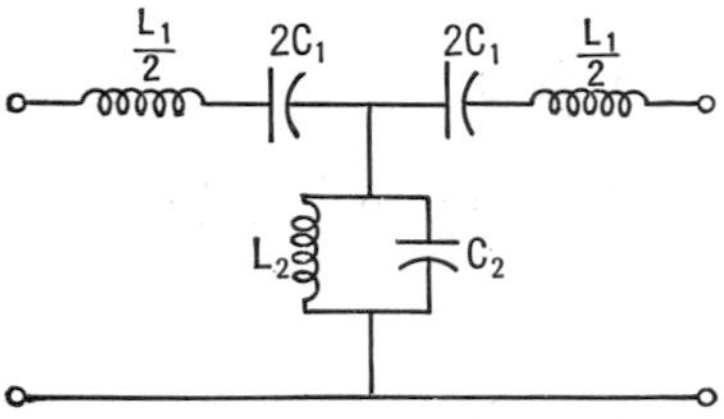

FIG. 17. Band-pass filter contained in a single section.

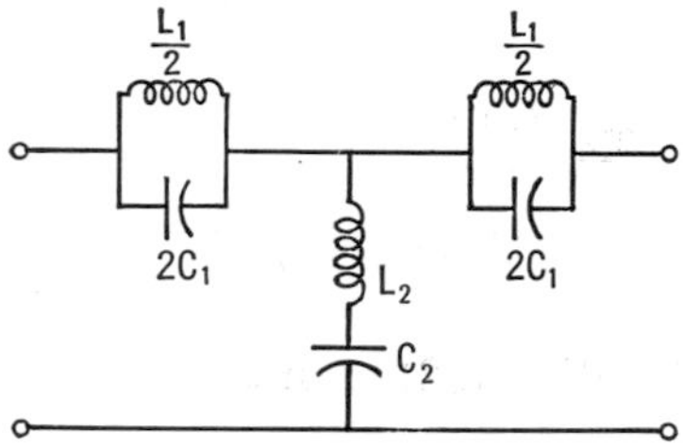

FIG. 18. Band-elimination filter contained in a single section.

A band-elimination filter may take the form of a single section as shown in Fig. 18. The section shown in Fig. 18 is called a constant-k band-elimination filter when $L_2C_2 = L_1C_1$ because under these conditions $\mathbf{Z}_1\mathbf{Z}_2$ is a constant. It will be observed that the arms of Fig. 18 are the reverse of those in Fig. 17.

Two Limitations of Constant-*k* Sections. The constant-k type of filter section has two rather serious shortcomings. First, its characteristic impedance is not sufficiently constant over the transmission band for certain classes of work. (See Fig. 15.) Second, the attenuation does not rise very abruptly at the boundary of the transmission band. (See Figs. 12 and 13.)

In order to overcome the inherent limitations of the constant-k type, Zobel[4] devised a filter section which he called the m-derived type. The m-derived half section may be employed to give practically uniform characteristic impedance over a large part of the pass band and at the same time increase the abruptness with which cut-off occurs. Full m-derived sections may be employed to give further increased attenuation near the cut-off point, and by proper adjustment of the parameter

[4] "Theory and Design of Uniform and Composite Electric Wave Filters," by O. J. Zobel, *Bell System Technical Journal*, January, 1923.

m they can be made to meet any practical attenuation requirement in this region. When worked in conjunction with constant-k sections, the m-derived sections overcome both the aforementioned shortcomings of the constant-k sections. However, m-derived sections by them-

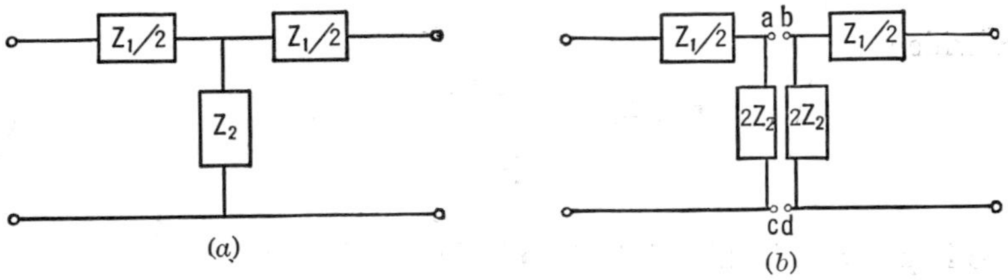

FIG. 19. Illustrating the circuit configuration of half sections formed by longitudinal bisection of shunt arm of a prototype T-section.

selves have certain limitations which will become apparent after the attenuation characteristics of these sections have been studied.

m-Derived Half Sections. If the full shunt arm of Fig. 19a is separated into two parallel paths of $2\mathbf{Z}_2$ ohms each, the original T-section may

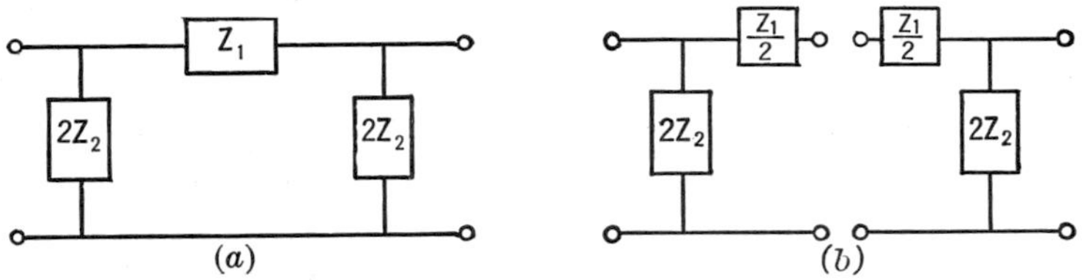

FIG. 20. Illustrating the circuit configuration of half sections formed by longitudinal bisection of the series arm of a prototype π-section.

be separated into two similar parts as shown in Fig. 19b. Each of these parts is known as a half section or as an L-type section. If the full series arm of the π-section shown in Fig. 20a is separated into two series elements of $\mathbf{Z}_1/2$ ohms each, the original π-section can be separated into two half sections as shown in Fig. 20b. A comparison of Fig. 20b with Fig. 19b will show the equivalence of half sections formed by "halving" π-sections and those formed by "halving" T-sections.

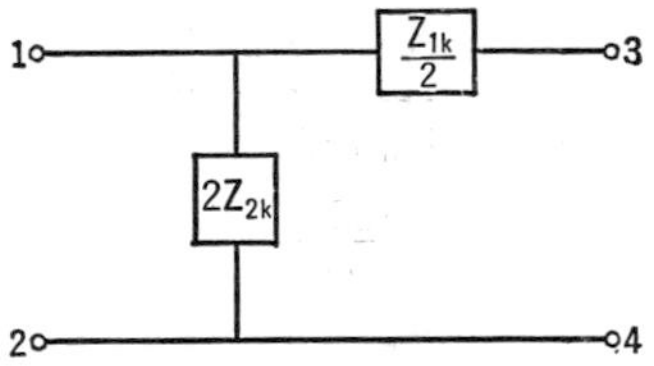

FIG. 21. Constant-k terminating half section.

The image impedances of the half section shown in Fig. 21 may be found from open-circuit and short-circuit conditions. Let the open-circuit and short-circuit impedances be known as $\mathbf{Z}_{o\text{-}c}$ and $\mathbf{Z}_{s\text{-}c}$, respectively.

The impedance looking into terminals 1 and 2 is:

$$\mathbf{Z}_{12} = \sqrt{\mathbf{Z}_{o\text{-}c}\mathbf{Z}_{s\text{-}c}} = \sqrt{\frac{2\mathbf{Z}_{1k}\mathbf{Z}_{2k}^{2}}{\frac{\mathbf{Z}_{1k}}{2} + 2\mathbf{Z}_{2k}}}$$

from which

$$\mathbf{Z}_{12} = \sqrt{\frac{\mathbf{Z}_{1k}\mathbf{Z}_{2k}}{1 + \frac{\mathbf{Z}_{1k}}{4\mathbf{Z}_{2k}}}} = \mathbf{Z}_{o\pi k} \tag{84}$$

The impedance looking into terminals 3 and 4 is:

$$\mathbf{Z}_{34} = \sqrt{\mathbf{Z}_{o\text{-}c}\mathbf{Z}_{s\text{-}c}} = \sqrt{\left(\frac{\mathbf{Z}_{1k}}{2} + 2\mathbf{Z}_{2k}\right)\frac{\mathbf{Z}_{1k}}{2}}$$

or

$$\mathbf{Z}_{34} = \sqrt{\mathbf{Z}_{1k}\mathbf{Z}_{2k}\left(1 + \frac{\mathbf{Z}_{1k}}{4\mathbf{Z}_{2k}}\right)} = \mathbf{Z}_{oTk} \tag{85}$$

The half section shown in Fig. 21 has the impedance characteristics of a π-section between terminals 1 and 2 and the impedance characteristics of a T-section between terminals 3 and 4. It may, therefore, be used to match a π-section to a T-section. Also it may be used to match a filter section to a terminating impedance which differs from the characteristic impedance of the filter section or to change the impedance level at any point in a two-wire line. The proper values of $\mathbf{Z}_{1k}/2$ and $2\mathbf{Z}_{2k}$ to be employed in effecting any desired impedance transformation may be determined by solving equations (84) and (85) simultaneously for $\mathbf{Z}_{1k}$ and $\mathbf{Z}_{2k}$ in terms of $\mathbf{Z}_{12}$ and $\mathbf{Z}_{34}$.

Some little difficulty is usually encountered in presenting m-derived filter theory to beginning students because certain anticipations have to be made at the outset of the investigation. Inasmuch as anticipations must be indulged in in any event, the actual circuit configuration of the m-derived half section will be accepted and its operating characteristics studied.

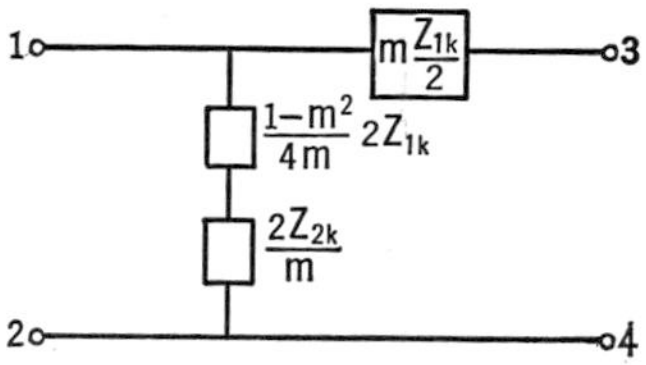

FIG. 22. m-derived terminating half section.

It will now be assumed that the half section shown in Fig. 21 takes the particular form shown in Fig. 22. A new parameter, m, has been arbitrarily introduced. It is simply a numeric which may, for the purposes at hand, range in value from zero to unity. The change in circuit configuration from Fig. 21 to Fig. 22

may be interpreted as follows:

(*a*) $\frac{\mathbf{Z}_{1k}}{2}$ of the constant-*k* half section is changed to some fractional part of $\frac{\mathbf{Z}_{1k}}{2}$ in Fig. 22.

(*b*) $2\mathbf{Z}_{2k}$ of Fig. 21 is changed to $\frac{2\mathbf{Z}_{2k}}{m}$ in Fig. 22.

(*c*) In series with $\frac{2\mathbf{Z}_{2k}}{m}$ in Fig. 22 is placed an impedance $\frac{1-m^2}{4m}\,2\mathbf{Z}_{1k}$.

It may be shown that, if the change in (*a*) is made, the changes in (*b*) and (*c*) must be made if the two half sections shown in Figs. 21 and 22 are to have the same characteristic impedance looking into the 3–4 terminals.

The half section shown in Fig. 22 has some very desirable characteristics. Its characteristic impedance looking into terminals 3 and 4 is:

$$\mathbf{Z}_{34m} = \sqrt{\mathbf{Z}_{o\text{-}c}\mathbf{Z}_{s\text{-}c}} = \sqrt{\left(m\frac{\mathbf{Z}_{1k}}{2} + \frac{1-m^2}{2m}\mathbf{Z}_{1k} + \frac{2\mathbf{Z}_{2k}}{m}\right)m\frac{\mathbf{Z}_{1k}}{2}}$$

$$= \sqrt{\frac{m^2\mathbf{Z}_{1k}^2}{4} + \frac{m\mathbf{Z}_{1k}^2}{4m} - \frac{m^2\mathbf{Z}_{1k}^2}{4} + \frac{2m\mathbf{Z}_{1k}\mathbf{Z}_{2k}}{2m}}$$

$$= \sqrt{\mathbf{Z}_{1k}\mathbf{Z}_{2k} + \frac{\mathbf{Z}_{1k}^2}{4}} = \mathbf{Z}_{oTk} \tag{86}$$

The equation above shows that terminals 3 and 4 of the *m*-derived half section can be used to match the impedance of a constant-*k* T-section or any other equivalent impedance including the 3–4 terminal characteristic impedance of Fig. 21.

The characteristic impedance of the *m*-derived terminating half section looking into terminals 1 and 2 is:

$$\mathbf{Z}_{12m} = \sqrt{\mathbf{Z}_{o\text{-}c}\mathbf{Z}_{s\text{-}c}}$$

where

$$\mathbf{Z}_{o\text{-}c} = \left[\frac{(1-m^2)}{2m}\mathbf{Z}_{1k} + 2\frac{\mathbf{Z}_{2k}}{m}\right]$$

$$\mathbf{Z}_{s\text{-}c} = \frac{\left[\frac{(1-m^2)}{2m}\mathbf{Z}_{1k} + 2\frac{\mathbf{Z}_{2k}}{m}\right]\left[m\frac{\mathbf{Z}_{1k}}{2}\right]}{\left[\frac{(1-m^2)}{2m}\mathbf{Z}_{1k} + 2\frac{\mathbf{Z}_{2k}}{m} + m\frac{\mathbf{Z}_{1k}}{2}\right]}$$

$$\mathbf{Z}_{12m} = \sqrt{\frac{\left(\dfrac{1-m^2}{2m}\,\mathbf{Z}_{1k} + 2\,\dfrac{\mathbf{Z}_{2k}}{m}\right)^2 \left(\dfrac{m^2\mathbf{Z}_{1k}^{\;2}}{4}\right)}{\left(\dfrac{1-m^2}{2m}\,\mathbf{Z}_{1k} + 2\,\dfrac{\mathbf{Z}_{2k}}{m} + m\,\dfrac{\mathbf{Z}_{1k}}{2}\right)\left(\dfrac{m\mathbf{Z}_{1k}}{2}\right)}}$$

$$= \sqrt{\frac{\left(\dfrac{1-m^2}{4}\,\mathbf{Z}_{1k}^{\;2} + \mathbf{Z}_{1k}\mathbf{Z}_{2k}\right)^2}{\dfrac{\mathbf{Z}_{1k}^{\;2}}{4} - \dfrac{m^2\mathbf{Z}_{1k}^{\;2}}{4} + \mathbf{Z}_{1k}\mathbf{Z}_{2k} + \dfrac{m^2\mathbf{Z}_{1k}^{\;2}}{4}}}$$

$$= \frac{\mathbf{Z}_{1k}\mathbf{Z}_{2k} + \dfrac{\mathbf{Z}_{1k}^{\;2}}{4}\,(1-m^2)}{\sqrt{\mathbf{Z}_{1k}\mathbf{Z}_{2k} + \dfrac{\mathbf{Z}_{1k}^{\;2}}{4}}}$$

$$= \frac{\mathbf{Z}_{1k}\mathbf{Z}_{2k}}{\mathbf{Z}_{oTk}}\left[1 + \frac{\mathbf{Z}_{1k}}{4\mathbf{Z}_{2k}}\,(1-m^2)\right] \tag{87}$$

or remembering (9):

$$\mathbf{Z}_{12m} = \mathbf{Z}_{o\pi k}\left[1 + \frac{\mathbf{Z}_{1k}}{4\mathbf{Z}_{2k}}\,(1-m^2)\right] \tag{88}$$

In addition to being a function of $\mathbf{Z}_{1k}$ and $\mathbf{Z}_{2k}$, $\mathbf{Z}_{12m}$ is a function of m. With the proper choice of m, $\mathbf{Z}_{12m}$ can be made reasonably constant over about 90 per cent of the transmission band. The changes of $\mathbf{Z}_{o\pi k}$ and the modifying factor $\left[1 + \dfrac{\mathbf{Z}_{1k}}{4\mathbf{Z}_{2k}}\,(1-m^2)\right]$ with respect to frequency combine in such a manner as to make $\mathbf{Z}_{12m}$ approximately constant over wide ranges of frequency.

Example 11. Consider the general trend of $\mathbf{Z}_{o\pi}$ for the constant-k, low-pass section shown in Fig. 15. Instead of this rapidly rising curve, the change in the output characteristic impedance of a low-pass, m-derived half section at the 1–2 terminals is:

$$\mathbf{Z}_{12m} = \mathbf{Z}_{o\pi k}\left[1 + \frac{j\omega L_{1k}}{-j4\,\dfrac{1}{\omega C_{2k}}}\,(1-m^2)\right]$$

or

$$\mathbf{Z}_{12m} = \mathbf{Z}_{o\pi k}\left[1 - \frac{\omega^2 L_{1k} C_{2k}}{4}\,(1-m^2)\right]$$

Physically, m may be equal to any value between zero and unity. Mathematical experimentation shows that good results are obtained when $m = 0.60$. The calculated values of $\mathbf{Z}_{o\pi k}$ and the modifying factor are shown in Table IV, and a graph of $\mathbf{Z}_{12m}$ for $m = 0.6$ is contained in Fig. 23. It will be remembered that f_c for a

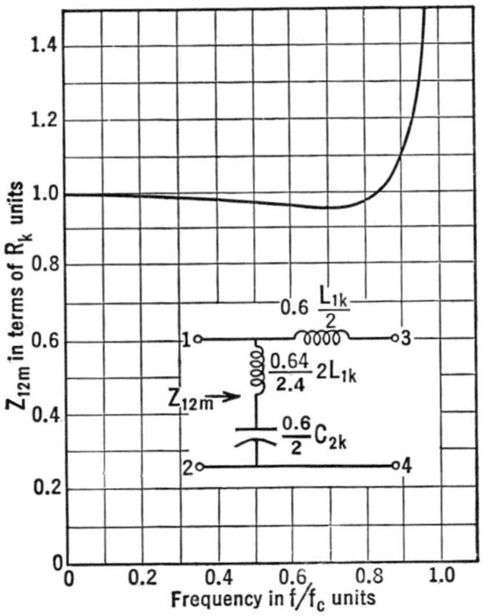

FIG. 23. Variation of Z_{12m} for $m = 0.6$.

TABLE IV

$$\mathbf{Z}_{12m} = \mathbf{Z}_{o\pi k}\left[1 - \frac{f^2}{f_c^2}(1 - m^2)\right] \text{ for } m = 0.6$$

$$R_k = \sqrt{L_{1k}/C_{2k}}$$

$\frac{f}{f_c}$	$\left[1 - \frac{f^2}{f_c^2}(0.64)\right]$	$\mathbf{Z}_{o\pi k}$	$\mathbf{Z}_{12m}$
0	1.000	R_k	R_k
0.10	0.994	1.005 R_k	0.999 R_k
0.20	0.974	1.02 R_k	0.993 R_k
0.40	0.898	1.09 R_k	0.979 R_k
0.60	0.770	1.25 R_k	0.963 R_k
0.80	0.590	1.67 R_k	0.963 R_k
0.90	0.482	2.30 R_k	1.108 R_k
0.95	0.424	3.16 R_k	1.34 R_k
1.00	0.360	∞	∞

low-pass filter section is $1/\pi\sqrt{L_{1k}C_{2k}}$ and that $\mathbf{Z}_{o\pi k} = R_k/\sqrt{1-(f^2/f_c^2)}$. The expression for $\mathbf{Z}_{12m}$ in this particular case is, therefore, reducible to

$$\mathbf{Z}_{12m} = \frac{R_k}{\sqrt{1-\dfrac{f^2}{f_c^2}}}\left[1 - \frac{f^2}{f_c^2}(1-m^2)\right]$$

If it is necessary to work closer to the cut-off frequency than a value of $m = 0.6$ will permit, m may be made somewhat less than 0.60. However, these slightly lower values of m cause the $\mathbf{Z}_{12m}$ variation to be more irregular throughout the first 90 per cent of the transmission band. Numerical experimentation will show the effects caused by different values of m.

Problem 15. Plot, with respect to frequency, the variation of the characteristic output impedance of a low-pass, m-derived terminating half section ($\mathbf{Z}_{12m}$) for $m = 0.55$. Reckon frequency in f/f_c units. (See Table IV and Fig. 23.)

Full *m*-Derived Sections. Full m-derived T-sections are shown in Fig. 24. As in the m-derived half section, the series and shunt arms are specified in terms of the constant-k impedances $\mathbf{Z}_{1k}$ and $\mathbf{Z}_{2k}$. Any constant-k-type section may be altered to yield what is known as an m-derived section. Only the low-pass and high-pass, m-derived T-sections will be considered in detail. These are shown in Fig. 24*b* and 24*c*.

The variations of the characteristic impedance of full m-derived low-pass π-sections are generally similar to the curve shown in Fig. 23. A comparison of the characteristic impedance curves of different m-derived filter sections is shown in Fig. 25.

In establishing an m-derived T-section the parameters are so readjusted from the constant-k values that the m-derived section characteristic impedance is identical with the constant-k section characteristic impedance. This requires that

$$\mathbf{Z}_{2m} = \left[\frac{1-m^2}{4m}\mathbf{Z}_{1k} + \frac{\mathbf{Z}_{2k}}{m}\right] \quad \text{if} \quad \mathbf{Z}_{1m} = m\mathbf{Z}_{1k}$$

as may be seen from the following algebraic steps:

$$\mathbf{Z}_{oTm} = \mathbf{Z}_{oTk} \quad \text{(imposed condition)} \tag{89}$$

Reference to equation (5) will show that, if $\mathbf{Z}_{1m} = m\mathbf{Z}_{1k}$:

$$\sqrt{(m\mathbf{Z}_{1k})\mathbf{Z}_{2m} + \frac{(m\mathbf{Z}_{1k})^2}{4}} = \sqrt{\mathbf{Z}_{1k}\mathbf{Z}_{2k} + \frac{\mathbf{Z}_{1k}^2}{4}} \tag{90}$$

Squaring both sides of the above equation and solving for $\mathbf{Z}_{2m}$:

$$\mathbf{Z}_{2m} = \frac{1-m^2}{4m}\mathbf{Z}_{1k} + \frac{\mathbf{Z}_{2k}}{m} \tag{91}$$

One of the most important characteristics of a full m-derived section is its theoretical infinite attenuation near the point of cut-off.

Frequencies of Infinite Attenuation. Since $\mathbf{Z}_{1k}$ and $\mathbf{Z}_{2k}$ are different types of reactances, the shunt arm of Fig. 24*a* will, at some frequency, become resonant. If the shunt arm is in resonance, its impedance is theoretically equal to zero and the attenuation becomes infinitely large. The frequency at which these phenomena occur is know as f_∞,

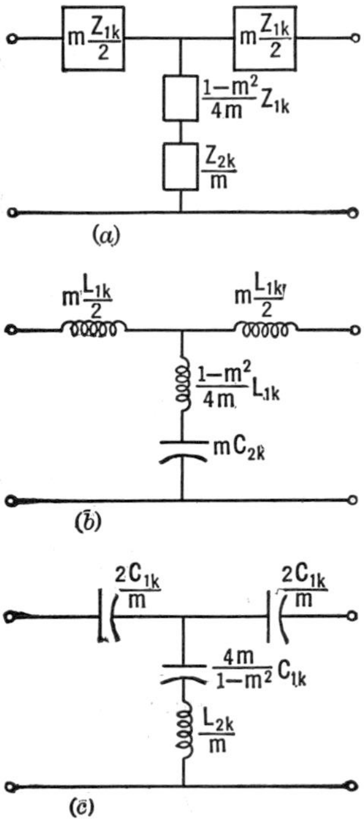

FIG. 24. m-Derived filter sections, with parameters specified in terms of constant-k filter-section parameters.

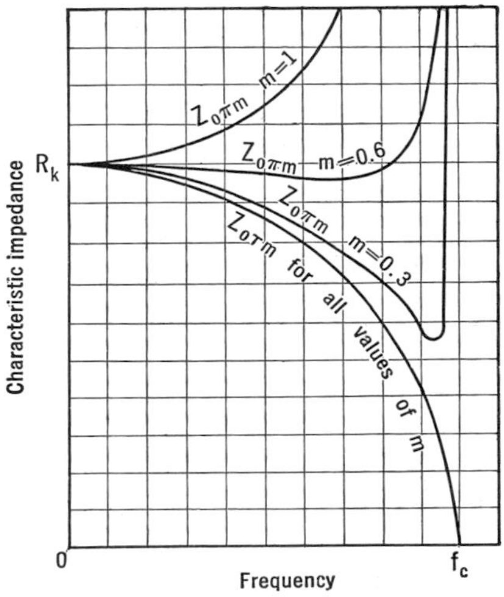

FIG. 25. Characteristic impedance curves for various low-pass m-derived filter sections.

and it may be calculated in any particular case by first setting the left-hand member of equation (91) equal to zero and then solving for f. In a low-pass, m-derived filter section:

$$f_\infty = \frac{1}{2\pi\sqrt{\dfrac{(1-m^2)}{4}L_{1k}C_{2k}}} = \frac{1}{\pi\sqrt{L_{1k}C_{2k}}\sqrt{1-m^2}} \tag{92}$$

The cut-off frequency of the m-derived section is equal to the cut-off frequency of the constant-k section from which it is derived. (See

Table V, page 485.) In the constant-k, low-pass section:

$$f_c = \frac{1}{\pi\sqrt{L_{1k}C_{2k}}} \quad \text{[See equation (55).]}$$

Therefore

$$f_\infty = \frac{f_c}{\sqrt{1 - m^2}} \tag{93}$$

from which

$$m = \sqrt{1 - \frac{f_c^{\,2}}{f_\infty^{\,2}}} \quad \text{(for low-pass section)} \tag{94}$$

In a similar manner it may be shown that for a high-pass, m-derived filter section:

$$f_\infty = f_c\sqrt{1 - m^2} \tag{95}$$

and

$$m = \sqrt{1 - \frac{f_\infty^{\,2}}{f_c^{\,2}}} \quad \text{(for high-pass section)} \tag{96}$$

Equations (94) and (96) illustrate the manner in which f_c and f_∞ determine the value of m that should be employed if theoretical infinite attenuation is to obtain at a specified f_∞. If, for example, a 1000-cycle cut-off frequency, low-pass filter is to have infinite attenuation at 1050 cycles, m is evaluated in accordance with equation (94). Thus:

$$m = \sqrt{1 - \frac{(1000)^2}{(1050)^2}} = 0.307 \quad \text{approximately}$$

The nearer f_∞ is to f_c, the lower will be the value of m. The reverse order of reasoning indicates that the lower the value of m, the sharper will be the cut-off. These facts are illustrated graphically in Fig. 26.

General Method of Analyzing m-Derived Filter Section Operation. Certain aspects of m-derived filter section operation may not be apparent from the cursory treatment that has been presented. The exact manner in which the phase shift and attenuation vary with respect to frequency can be obtained by subjecting the filter section to the "general" method of analysis. This method is summed up in equation (39), which, for convenience, is restated below.

$$\alpha + j\beta = 2\log_\epsilon\left[\sqrt{\frac{\mathbf{Z}_1}{4\mathbf{Z}_2}} + \sqrt{\frac{\mathbf{Z}_1}{4\mathbf{Z}_2} + 1}\right] \tag{39}$$

For the sake of illustration a low-pass, m-derived, T-section will be analyzed. From Fig. 24*b* it is evident that

$$\mathbf{Z}_{1m} = j\omega m L_{1k} = \mathbf{Z}_1$$

and

$$\mathbf{Z}_{2m} = j\left[\omega\,\frac{(1 - m^2)}{4m}\,L_{1k} - \frac{1}{\omega m C_{2k}}\right] = \mathbf{Z}_2$$

Therefore, in the present case,

$$\frac{\mathbf{Z}_1}{4\mathbf{Z}_2} = \frac{\omega m L_{1k}}{4\left[\omega\,\dfrac{(1 - m^2)}{4m}\,L_{1k} - \dfrac{1}{\omega m C_{2k}}\right]}$$

$$= \frac{\omega^2 m^2 L_{1k} C_{2k}}{\omega^2 (1 - m^2) L_{1k} C_{2k} - 4} \qquad (97)$$

The above expression is actually a complex number, the associated angle of which is 180° or 0°, depending upon whether $[\omega^2(1 - m^2)L_{1k}C_{2k}]$ is less than or greater than 4. The foregoing statement follows directly

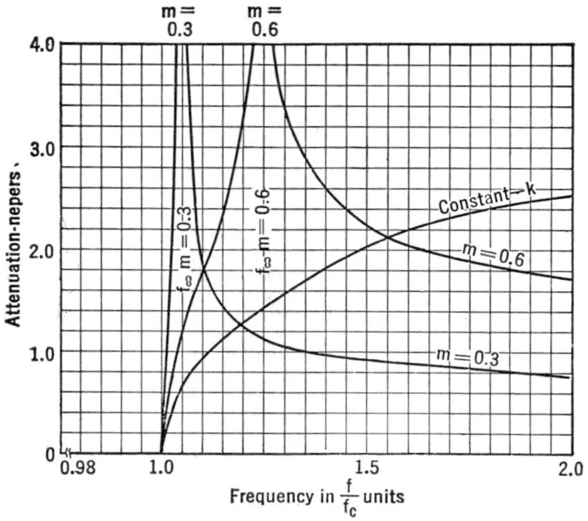

FIG. 26. Attenuation characteristics of two *m*-derived low-pass filter sections compared with those of a constant-*k* low-pass filter section.

from an inspection of $\mathbf{Z}_1/4\mathbf{Z}_2$ wherein all the factors are expressed in polar form. Let ω be arbitrarily reckoned in $1/\sqrt{L_{1k}C_{2k}}$ units. It should be observed that in this method of analysis the cut-off angular velocity or frequency is not necessarily anticipated by the choice of this convenient unit. Thus, for $\omega = 1/\sqrt{L_{1k}C_{2k}}$ radians per second, equation (39) reduces to

$$\alpha + j\beta = 2\log_\epsilon\left[\sqrt{\frac{m^2}{(1 - m^2) - 4}} + \sqrt{\frac{m^2}{(1 - m^2) - 4} + 1}\right]$$

For a particular value of m it becomes a simple matter to evaluate α and β at any desired frequency. The calculations for $m = 0.6$ at various frequencies are shown in Table V. The variations of attenuation are represented graphically in Fig. 26 together with certain other attenuation curves. An inspection of column (9), Table V, will reveal the irregular manner in which the phase shift varies with frequency.

Problem 16. Graph the variation of attenuation with respect to frequency of a low-pass, m-derived T-section in which $m = 0.40$. The frequency may be indicated in terms of $1/\sqrt{L_{1k}C_{2k}}$ units of angular velocity. (See Table V, page 485.)

Comparison of Attenuation Characteristics. Constant-k and m-derived filter sections are sometimes worked in cascade because of the complementary nature of their respective attenuation characteristics. It has been shown that the attenuation of a constant-k, low-pass section is zero at cut-off frequency and that it increases gradually with increases of frequency above cut-off frequency. (See Fig. 12.) A similar situation holds for the constant-k, high-pass section except, of course, for the fact that the attenuation increases as the frequency decreases from the cut-off frequency. The attenuation characteristics of m-derived sections are radically different in character from those of constant-k sections. The differences are shown graphically in Fig. 26 for low-pass sections. Similar curves can be determined for high-pass sections.

It is plain from an inspection of Fig. 26 that a constant-k section can be combined with one or more m-derived sections to give high attenuation near cut-off as well as high attenuation in other regions of the stop band. In general, an m-derived section by itself will not give high attenuation in regions which are too widely removed from the point of theoretical infinite attenuation. (See Fig. 26.)

General Design Procedure. Filter sections are usually designed for a particular characteristic impedance and a particular cut-off frequency (or frequencies). Theoretically, at least, these conditions can be met accurately and straightforwardly. Usually certain attenuation requirements must also be met. These attenuation requirements are generally met by a method of successive approximations.

The *first step* in elementary filter design is the determination of the inductances and capacitances to be employed in a constant-k section. These values are found from the basic design equations.

The *second step* is the evaluation of the m-derived, terminating half-section inductances and capacitances. These values follow directly from the parameters of the constant-k section and the selected value of m. It is assumed here that the terminating half sections are required primarily for impedance-matching purposes, in which case the value of m will generally be 0.6.

TABLE V

Evaluation of $\left[\alpha + j\beta = 2\log_\epsilon\left(\sqrt{\frac{\mathbf{Z}_1}{4\mathbf{Z}_2}} + \sqrt{\frac{\mathbf{Z}_1}{4\mathbf{Z}_2} + 1}\right)\right]$ where $\frac{\mathbf{Z}_1}{4\mathbf{Z}_2} = \frac{\omega^2 m^2 L_{1k}C_{2k}}{\omega^2(1 - m^2)L_{1k}C_{2k} - 4}$

$m = 0.6$ and ω is reckoned in $\left[\frac{1}{\sqrt{L_{1k}C_{2k}}}\right]$ units which are called U. Under these conditions $\frac{Z_1}{4Z_2} = \frac{0.36U^2}{0.64U^2 - 4}$

(1)	(2)	(3)	(4)	(5)	(6)	(7)	(8)	(9)
ω U units	$\frac{\mathbf{Z}_1}{4\mathbf{Z}_2}$	$\sqrt{\frac{\mathbf{Z}_1}{4\mathbf{Z}_2}}$	$\sqrt{\frac{\mathbf{Z}_1}{4\mathbf{Z}_2} + 1}$	(3) + (4) Cartesian Form	(3) + (4) Polar Form	$2\log_\epsilon$ (6)	α nepers	β radians
0	0	0	1	$1 + j0$	$1\,\angle 0^\circ$	$0 + j0$	0	0
1.0	$+0.107\,\angle 180^\circ$	$j0.327$	0.945	$0.945 + j0.327$	$1\,\angle 19.2^\circ$	$0 + j0.67$	0	0.67
1.5	$+0.316\,\angle 180^\circ$	$j0.564$	0.826	$0.826 + j0.564$	$1\,\angle 34.3^\circ$	$0 + j1.197$	0	1.20
2.0	$+1.00\,\angle 180^\circ$	$j1.0$	0	$0 + j1.0$	$1\,\angle 90^\circ$	$0 + j3.14$	0	3.14
2.1	$+1.35\,\angle 180^\circ$	$j1.16$	$j0.59$	$0 + j1.75$	$1.75\,\angle 90^\circ$	$1.12 + j3.14$	1.12	3.14
2.25	$+2.40\,\angle 180^\circ$	$j1.55$	$j1.18$	$0 + j2.73$	$2.73\,\angle 90^\circ$	$2.01 + j3.14$	2.01	3.14
2.50	∞	∞	∞	∞	∞	∞	∞	3.14 0.00
2.75	$+3.24\,\angle 0^\circ$	1.80	2.06	$3.86 + j0$	$3.86\,\angle 0^\circ$	$2.70 + j0$	2.70	0
3.0	$+1.84\,\angle 0^\circ$	1.36	1.68	$3.04 + j0$	$3.04\,\angle 0^\circ$	$2.22 + j0$	2.22	0
4.0	$+0.923\,\angle 0^\circ$	0.961	1.39	$2.35 + j0$	$2.35\,\angle 0^\circ$	$1.71 + j0$	1.71	0
6.0	$+0.683\,\angle 0^\circ$	0.826	1.30	$2.13 + j0$	$2.13\,\angle 0^\circ$	$1.51 + j0$	1.51	0

If a sharp cut-off section is required, a full m-derived section, wherein m is about 0.2 or 0.3, can be employed. The evaluation of the inductances and capacitances to use in the full m-derived section constitutes the *third step* in the general design procedure.

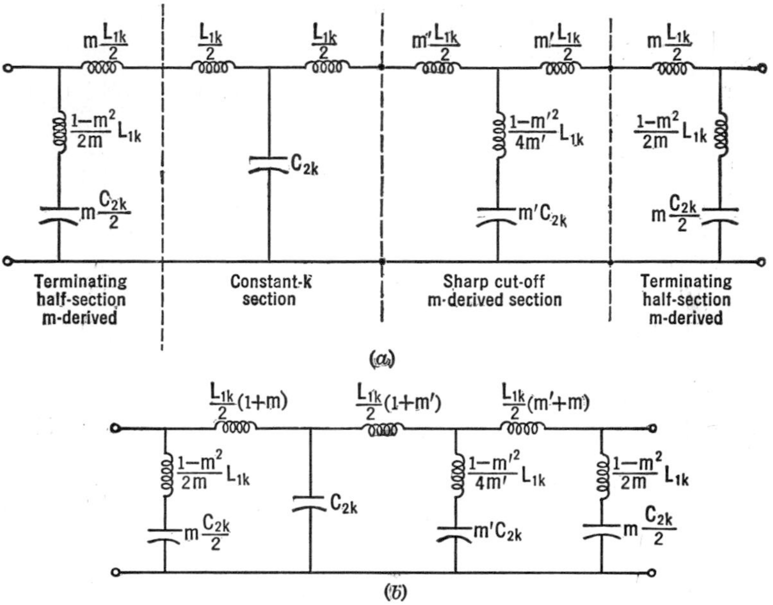

FIG. 27. A composite low-pass filter together with its equivalent circuit.

The *fourth step* is the predetermination of the attenuation characteristic of the composite filter and checking this against the actual attenuation requirements. Adjustments may then be made in the number or in the type of sections in order to meet the attenuation requirements in the most economical manner.

The method of combining a constant-k section, a full m-derived section, and m-derived terminating half sections to form a low-pass filter is illustrated in Fig. 27a. It will be noted that the assembly shown in Fig. 27a is reducible to that shown in Fig. 27b.

PROBLEMS

17. Consider a π-type filter section in which the full series arm, Z_1, consists of a 100-millihenry inductance coil the resistance of which is 50 ohms. Each of the two shunt arms consists of a 0.3-μf condenser the resistance of which is negligibly small.

(a) Find the open-circuit impedance, $Z_{o\text{-}c}$, and the short-circuit impedance, $Z_{s\text{-}c}$, of the section at 500 cycles.

(*b*) Find the characteristic impedance at 500 cycles, at 1300 cycles, and at 2000 cycles.

18. Each of the series arms ($Z_1/2$) of a symmetrical T-section consists of a condenser the capacitance of which is 0.6 μf and the resistance of which is negligibly small. The shunt arm (Z_2) is a 200-millihenry inductance coil the resistance of which is 60 ohms.

(*a*) Find the characteristic impedance and the propagation constant of the section at 200 cycles.

(*b*) Find the characteristic impedance and the propagation constant of the section at 600 cycles.

19. The characteristic impedance of a filter section is to be measured. The measuring device is a 1-B Western Electric impedance bridge which indicates the R component of the impedance directly and the X component in terms of $+L$ or $-L$. Plus L readings indicate that $X = X_L = 2\pi fL$, and negative L readings indicate that $X = X_C = 2\pi f(-L)$. With the output terminals of the section open-circuited the bridge readings are: $R = 10$ ohms and $L = -190$ millihenrys at 400 cycles. With the output terminals of the section short-circuited the bridge readings are: $R = 20$ ohms and $L = +250$ millihenrys at 400 cycles. Find the characteristic impedance of the filter section at 400 cycles.

20. The series arms of a T-section are each of 100 ohms capacitance. The shunt arm is a 100-ohm inductive reactance. (*a*) Determine the characteristic impedance of this section for the constants given. (*b*) Also calculate Z_{oT} for half the frequency at which the constants are given. (*c*) Is the frequency for the reactances given within the pass or stop band? (*d*) Answer for one-half the frequency at which the reactances are given. (*e*) Calculate the attenuation in nepers for the two frequencies. (*f*) What can you say about the characteristic impedance in the pass band as compared with the attenuation band for an ideal prototype section? (*g*) Is this also true of ideal prototype π-sections?

21. A resistanceless, constant-k, low-pass T-section has a cut-off frequency of 10,000 cycles and a zero-frequency characteristic impedance of 800 ohms. Evaluate the phase shift at 1000, 4000, 7000, and 10,000 cycles. Evaluate the attenuation at 11,000, 15,000, 20,000, and 25,000 cycles. Plot phase shift in degrees and attenuation in decibels against cycles per second.

22. Consider a symmetrical π-type section in which the inductance of the full series arm is 0.10 henry and the capacitance of each of the two condensers which go to form the π-section is 0.3 μf.

(*a*) Neglecting the resistive components of the circuit elements, find the propagation constant at 500 cycles, at 1300 cycles, and at 2000 cycles.

(*b*) What is the attenuation in decibels at each of the three frequencies referred to above?

23. (*a*) What is the decibel level of 0.00001 watt with respect to a 1-milliwatt reference power level?

(*b*) What is the decibel level of 6 watts with respect to a 1-milliwatt reference power level?

24. What is the cut-off frequency of a low-pass, constant-k, π-type filter section in which the inductance of the full series arm is 20 henrys and the capacitance of each condenser is 8.0 μf? What is the characteristic impedance of the section at 200 cycles?

25. A T-section filter has series arms $Z_1/2 = j100$ ohms and its shunt arm $Z_2 = -j1000$ ohms.

(*a*) Calculate the characteristic impedance.

(b) Calculate the attenuation in decibels and the phase shift in degrees.

(c) Are the reactances of the section for a frequency within the pass or stop band?

(d) Calculate the characteristic impedance of the section for 5 times the frequency for which the constants are given.

(e) Calculate the attenuation in decibels and phase shift for part (d).

26. A π-section filter has its series arm $Z_1 = -j100$ ohms and its shunt arms $2Z_2 = j500$ ohms.

(a) Calculate the characteristic impedance.

(b) Calculate the attenuation in decibels and the phase shift in degrees.

(c) Are the reactances given for a frequency within the pass band or stop band?

(d) Repeat parts (a), (b), and (c) for a frequency of one-fifth of that for which the impedances are given.

27. Nine T-sections each having series arms of $Z_1/2 = j500$ ohms and shunt arms $Z_2 = -j200$ ohms are connected in series or cascade. If the input voltage is 100, find the output voltage of the ninth section and the output current, assuming characteristic termination.

28. Find the circuit element values of a high-pass, constant-k, T-type filter section which is to have a cut-off frequency of 5000 cycles and an infinite-frequency characteristic impedance of 600 ohms. Repeat for a π-type section. Draw circuit diagrams showing the configurations of the circuit elements and the values of each in millihenrys and microfarads.

29. A generator having an impedance of $800\underline{/0°}$ ohms is to be connected to a load impedance of $100\underline{/0°}$ through a half-section of the kind shown in Fig. 21, page 475. Find the value of $Z_{1k}/2$ (the series arm impedance) and of $2Z_{2k}$ (the shunt arm impedance) which will properly match the generator to the load. $Z_{1k}/2$ is arbitrarily taken as inductive.

30. Design a high-pass, m-derived, T-type filter section which will have a cut-off frequency of 5000 cycles, an infinite-frequency characteristic impedance of 600 ohms, and an infinite-attenuation frequency of 4500 cycles.

31. Design m-derived half sections which will properly match, at 800 cycles, a low-pass, constant-k, T-type section the full series arm of which is 0.30 henry and the full shunt arm of which is 0.03 μf. The value of m is to be taken as 0.60.

32. Consider an m-derived, low-pass, T-section in which Z_{1m} is mL_{1k} and Z_{2m} consists of $(1 - m^2/4m)L_{1k}$ in series with mC_{2k}. Let mL_{1k} be known as L_{1m}, $(1 - m^2/4m)L_{1k}$ be known as L_{2m}, and mC_{2k} be known as C_{2m}. Show that the cut-off frequency, namely, $1/\pi\sqrt{L_{1k}C_{2k}}$, can be written as $1/[\pi\sqrt{(L_{1m} + 4L_{2m})(C_{2m})}]$.

33. Refer to the composite low-pass filter shown in Fig. 27. The requirements to be met are: (1) zero-frequency characteristic impedance of 600 ohms, (2) cut-off frequency of 5000 cycles, (3) variation in characteristic impedance of not more than 30 ohms over the lower 80 per cent of the pass band, (4) attenuation of 40 decibels between the limits of 5242 and 10,000 cycles.

(a) Calculate the values of L_{1k} and C_{2k}.

(b) Design terminating half sections on the basis of $m = 0.60$.

(c) Design the full m-derived section to have theoretical infinite attenuation at 5242 cycles.

(d) Make a graph of the attenuation of the composite filter between the limits of 5242 and 10,000 cycles and compare the results with the attenuation requirements. Use the three attenuation graphs shown in Fig. 26, page 483, at $f/f_c = 1.05$, 1.10, 1.15, 1.20, 1.25, 1.30, 1.35, 1.40, 1.45, 1.50, 1.75, and 2 to obtain the composite attenuation graph.

chapter XII Symmetrical Components

Symmetrical components furnish a tool of great power for analytically determining the performance of certain types of unbalanced electrical circuits involving rotating electrical machines. It is particularly useful in analyzing the performance of polyphase electrical machinery when operated from systems of unbalanced voltages. Although it can be used to solve unbalanced static networks like those in Chapter IX, such application will in general be more cumbersome and laborious than the methods already considered. For unbalanced networks containing rotating machines, however, the method of symmetrical components provides the only practicable method of accounting for the unbalanced effects of these machines and is widely used in practice. It is also convenient for analyzing some types of polyphase transformer problems.

The method of "symmetrical components," in its most useful form, is founded upon Fortescue's[1] theorem regarding the resolution of unbalanced systems into symmetrical components. Although the present discussion will confine itself to three-phase systems, any unbalanced polyphase system of vectors can be resolved into balanced systems of vectors called "symmetrical components."

Fortescue's theorem, applied to a general three-phase system of vectors, is that any unbalanced three-phase system of vectors can be resolved into three balanced systems of vectors, namely:

1. A balanced system of three-phase vectors having the same phase sequence as the original unbalanced system of vectors. This balanced system is called the "positive-sequence system."

2. A balanced system of three-phase vectors having a phase sequence which is opposite to that of the original unbalanced system of vectors. This balanced system is called the "negative-sequence system."

3. A system of three single-phase vectors which are equal in magnitude and which have exactly the same time-phase position with respect to any given reference axis. This system of single-phase vectors is known as the zero-sequence or uniphase system.

A general proof of the resolution theorem will not be given because a little experience with the method will soon convince the reader that

[1] Fortescue, "Method of Symmetrical Co-ordinates Applied to the Solution of Polyphase Networks," *Transactions, A.I.E.E.*, Vol. 37, 1918.

the theorem as stated is correct. In this respect Fortescue's theorem is similar to Fourier's theorem regarding complex waves. In Chapter VI it is shown that any complex wave may be resolved into definite harmonic components by the Fourier method. The ultimate proof of the theorem rests upon the fact that the components thus determined can be synthesized to form the original complex wave. In a similar manner it will be shown that any given unbalanced three-phase system of vectors may be resolved into the three balanced systems outlined above and that the composition of these balanced systems yields the original unbalanced system of vectors.

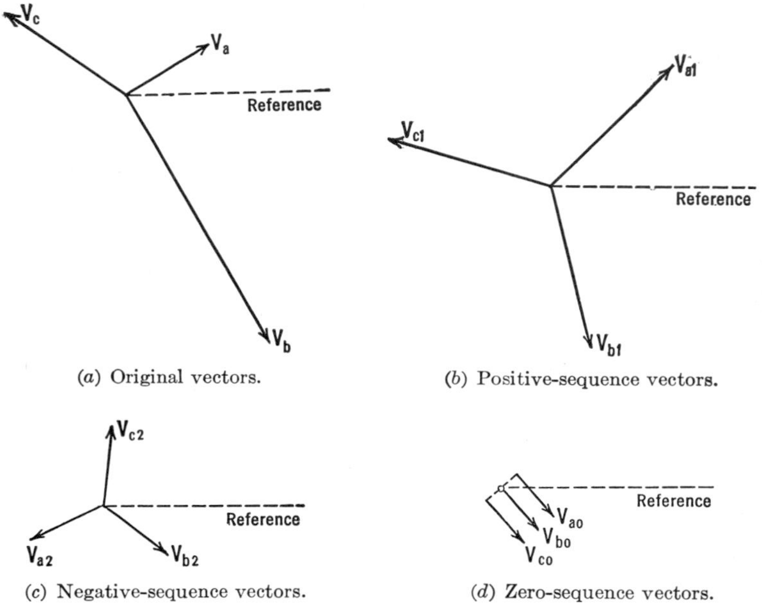

FIG. 1. Original set of three-phase vectors together with their symmetrical components.

The Original Unbalanced System of Vectors. Any number of vectors up to and including three may be considered as an unbalanced system of three-phase vectors. The vectors that form the unbalanced system may have any specified magnitude (including zero) and may possess any specified phase positions with respect to one another. In Fig. 1*a* is shown a set of three unbalanced vectors that will later be resolved into their symmetrical components. If the vectors that form the original unbalanced set come to us merely as three specified vectors, they can arbitrarily be assigned subscripts *a*, *b*, and *c* in the order shown in Fig. 1*a*. Thus the original vectors $\mathbf{V}_a$, $\mathbf{V}_b$, and $\mathbf{V}_c$ are arbitrarily assigned the *abc* phase sequence. (See Chapter IX, pages

383–384.) Although the vectors shown in Fig. 1*a* are labeled as voltages, the proposed resolution applies equally well to a system of current vectors.

Owing to the fact that the symmetrical components will have to carry an additional subscript to designate the system to which they belong, single-subscript notation will be employed in connection with the original vectors wherever this can be done without loss of clarity. For complete specification, the positive circuit directions of the original three-phase voltages or currents must be indicated on a separate circuit diagram. The importance of complete specification will become apparent when numerical problems are considered.

The Positive-Phase Sequence System. As previously stated, the original unbalanced system of vectors is to be resolved into two balanced three-phase systems and one uniphase system. It will be shown presently that the balanced three-phase systems must be of opposite phase sequence. Therefore one balanced system has the same phase sequence as the original three-phase system and the other has a phase sequence opposite to that of the original system.

The balanced system of three-phase vectors that has the same phase sequence as the original system is called the positive-sequence system. If the original vectors are assigned the phase sequence of *abc*, then the phase sequence of the positive-sequence vectors is *abc* as shown in Fig. 1*b*. The positive-sequence vectors are completely determined when the magnitude and phase position of any one of them is known. A method of evaluating any one of the positive-sequence vectors in terms of the original vector values will be given presently. The positive-sequence vectors are designated as

$$\mathbf{V}_{a1}, \quad \mathbf{V}_{b1}, \quad \text{and} \quad \mathbf{V}_{c1}$$

The subscript 1 indicates that the vector thus labeled belongs to the positive-sequence system. The letters refer to the original vector of which the positive-sequence vector is a component part.

The vectors of any balanced three-phase system may be conveniently related to one another with the aid of the operator **a**. The general properties of this operator are considered in Chapter IV, page 121–122.

a1 is a unit vector 120° ahead of the reference axis. $\mathbf{a}^2 1$ is a unit vector 240° ahead of the reference axis. Thus:

$$\left.\begin{aligned} \mathbf{a}1 &= \epsilon^{j120^\circ} = -0.5 + j0.866 \\ \mathbf{a}^2 1 &= \epsilon^{j240^\circ} = -0.5 - j0.866 \end{aligned}\right\} \qquad (1)$$

The operator **a** applied to any vector rotates that vector through 120° in the positive or counterclockwise direction. The operator $\mathbf{a}^2$ applied to any vector rotates that vector through 240° in the positive direction, which is, of course, equivalent to a rotation of 120° in the negative direction.

If, for example, $\mathbf{V}_{a1}$ has been determined, the positive-sequence system may be written simply as

$$\left.\begin{aligned} \mathbf{V}_{a1} &= \mathbf{V}_{a1} \\ \mathbf{V}_{b1} &= \mathbf{a}^2\mathbf{V}_{a1} = \mathbf{V}_{a1}\underline{/-120^\circ} \\ \mathbf{V}_{c1} &= \mathbf{a}\mathbf{V}_{a1} = \mathbf{V}_{a1}\underline{/-240^\circ} \end{aligned}\right\} \text{the positive-sequence system of vectors} \quad (2)$$

The Negative-Phase Sequence System. The balanced system of three-phase vectors which is opposite in phase sequence to that of the original vectors is called the negative-sequence system. If the original vectors have a phase sequence of *abc* the negative-sequence vectors have a phase sequence of *acb* as shown in Fig. 1*c*. Since the negative-sequence system is balanced, it is completely determined when one of the voltages is known. The negative-sequence vectors are designated as

$$\mathbf{V}_{a2}, \quad \mathbf{V}_{b2}, \quad \text{and} \quad \mathbf{V}_{c2}$$

Subscript 2 indicates that the vectors belong to the negative-sequence system. The *a*, *b*, and *c* subscripts indicate components of $\mathbf{V}_a$, $\mathbf{V}_b$, and $\mathbf{V}_c$ respectively. If $\mathbf{V}_{a2}$ is known, the negative-sequence system can be written in the following form:

$$\left.\begin{aligned} \mathbf{V}_{a2} &= \mathbf{V}_{a2} \\ \mathbf{V}_{b2} &= \mathbf{a}\mathbf{V}_{a2} = \mathbf{V}_{a2}\underline{/-240^\circ} \\ \mathbf{V}_{c2} &= \mathbf{a}^2\mathbf{V}_{a2} = \mathbf{V}_{a2}\underline{/-120^\circ} \end{aligned}\right\} \text{the negative-sequence system of vectors} \quad (3)$$

$\mathbf{V}_{a2}$, $\mathbf{V}_{b2}$, and $\mathbf{V}_{c2}$ are shown graphically in Fig. 1*c*.

The Zero-Phase Sequence System. The remaining system consists of three vectors, identical in magnitude and in time phase, as shown in Fig. 1*d*. These vectors form what is known as the uniphase or the zero-sequence system, and have special significance in certain physical problems. For the present it will be sufficient to think of the zero-sequence vectors as components of the original vectors $\mathbf{V}_a$, $\mathbf{V}_b$, and $\mathbf{V}_c$. The zero-sequence vectors are designated as

$$\mathbf{V}_{a0}, \quad \mathbf{V}_{b0}, \quad \text{and} \quad \mathbf{V}_{c0}$$

Since the above voltages are equal:

$$\left.\begin{aligned} \mathbf{V}_{a0} &= \mathbf{V}_{a0} \\ \mathbf{V}_{b0} &= \mathbf{V}_{a0} \\ \mathbf{V}_{c0} &= \mathbf{V}_{a0} \end{aligned}\right\} \text{the zero-sequence system of vectors} \quad (4)$$

Graphical Composition of Sequence Vectors. It is evident that

$$(\mathbf{V}_{a1} + \mathbf{V}_{a2} + \mathbf{V}_{a0})$$
$$(\mathbf{V}_{b1} + \mathbf{V}_{b2} + \mathbf{V}_{b0})$$

and

$$(\mathbf{V}_{c1} + \mathbf{V}_{c2} + \mathbf{V}_{c0})$$

form a three-phase system of voltages which, in general, is unbalanced. The above-indicated compositions are carried out graphically in Fig. 2, employing the individual voltages contained in Figs. 1*b*, 1*c*, and 1*d*.

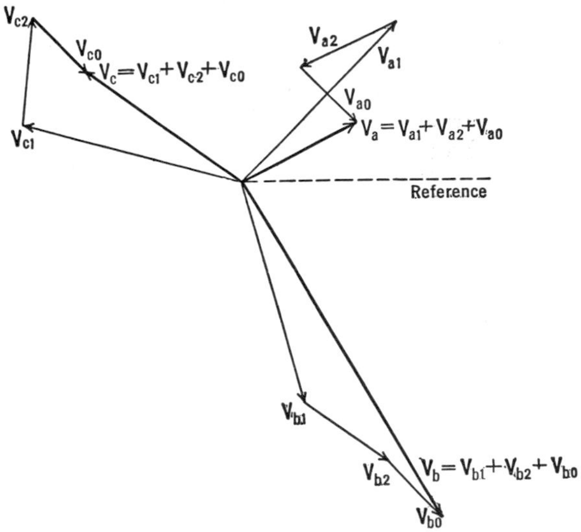

FIG. 2. Illustrating the manner in which the sequence components combine to form $\mathbf{V}_a$, $\mathbf{V}_b$, and $\mathbf{V}_c$.

The resultant system shown in Fig. 2 is identical with the unbalanced system shown in Fig. 1*a*. For the particular case considered it is plain that

$$\mathbf{V}_a = \mathbf{V}_{a1} + \mathbf{V}_{a2} + \mathbf{V}_{a0} \quad (5)$$

$$\mathbf{V}_b = \mathbf{V}_{b1} + \mathbf{V}_{b2} + \mathbf{V}_{b0} \quad (6)$$

$$\mathbf{V}_c = \mathbf{V}_{c1} + \mathbf{V}_{c2} + \mathbf{V}_{c0} \quad (7)$$

In terms of the operator **a**, the above relations may be stated as

$$\mathbf{V}_a = \mathbf{V}_{a1} + \mathbf{V}_{a2} + \mathbf{V}_{a0} \quad (8)$$

$$\mathbf{V}_b = \mathbf{a}^2\mathbf{V}_{a1} + \mathbf{a}\mathbf{V}_{a2} + \mathbf{V}_{a0} \quad (9)$$

$$\mathbf{V}_c = \mathbf{a}\mathbf{V}_{a1} + \mathbf{a}^2\mathbf{V}_{a2} + \mathbf{V}_{a0} \quad (10)$$

An inspection of equations (8), (9), and (10) will show that the original system of vectors can be completely specified in terms of $\mathbf{V}_{a1}$, $\mathbf{V}_{a2}$, $\mathbf{V}_{a0}$, and the operator **a**. The next step in the study of symmetrical components is the evaluation of $\mathbf{V}_{a1}$, $\mathbf{V}_{a2}$, and $\mathbf{V}_{a0}$ in terms of the original vectors $\mathbf{V}_a$, $\mathbf{V}_b$, and $\mathbf{V}_c$.

Evaluation of $\mathbf{V}_{a1}$. The resolution of an unbalanced system of vectors into its symmetrical components is essentially a geometric process, and different geometric methods have been devised whereby the resolution can be effected. However, none of the geometric methods thus far devised possesses the neat simplicity of the complex algebra method given below.

Before proceeding with the algebraic method it is well to understand that certain operations are performed solely for the purpose of obtaining the combination $(1 + \mathbf{a} + \mathbf{a}^2)$ which is equal to zero. Various simplifications may thus be made when quantities can be so collected as to possess the coefficient $(1 + \mathbf{a} + \mathbf{a}^2)$.

If equation (9) is multiplied by **a** the result is:

$$\mathbf{a}\mathbf{V}_b = \mathbf{a}^3\mathbf{V}_{a1} + \mathbf{a}^2\mathbf{V}_{a2} + \mathbf{a}\mathbf{V}_{a0}$$

or, since $\mathbf{a}^3 = 1$,

$$\mathbf{a}\mathbf{V}_b = \mathbf{V}_{a1} + \mathbf{a}^2\mathbf{V}_{a2} + \mathbf{a}\mathbf{V}_{a0} \tag{11}$$

If equation (10) is multiplied by $\mathbf{a}^2$, the result is:

$$\mathbf{a}^2\mathbf{V}_c = \mathbf{a}^3\mathbf{V}_{a1} + \mathbf{a}^4\mathbf{V}_{a2} + \mathbf{a}^2\mathbf{V}_{a0}$$

or, since $\mathbf{a}^4 = \mathbf{a}$,

$$\mathbf{a}^2\mathbf{V}_c = \mathbf{V}_{a1} + \mathbf{a}\mathbf{V}_{a2} + \mathbf{a}^2\mathbf{V}_{a0} \tag{12}$$

Adding equations (8), (11), and (12) yields

$$\mathbf{V}_a + \mathbf{a}\mathbf{V}_b + \mathbf{a}^2\mathbf{V}_c = 3\mathbf{V}_{a1} + (1 + \mathbf{a} + \mathbf{a}^2)(\mathbf{V}_{a2} + \mathbf{V}_{a0})$$

whence:

$$\mathbf{V}_{a1} = \tfrac{1}{3}(\mathbf{V}_a + \mathbf{a}\mathbf{V}_b + \mathbf{a}^2\mathbf{V}_c) = \tfrac{1}{3}(\mathbf{V}_a + \mathbf{V}_b\,\underline{/120°} + \mathbf{V}_c\underline{/240°}) \tag{13}$$

Geometrically speaking, the above equation means that $\mathbf{V}_{a1}$ is a vector one-third as large as the vector which results from the addition of the three vectors $\mathbf{V}_a$, $\mathbf{V}_b\,\underline{/120°}$, and $\mathbf{V}_c\,\underline{/240°}$.

Example 1. If the vectors shown in Fig. 1*a* are:

$$\mathbf{V}_a = 10\,\underline{/30°},\quad \mathbf{V}_b = 30\,\underline{/-60°},\quad \text{and}\quad \mathbf{V}_c = 15\,\underline{/145°}\text{ units}$$

$$\mathbf{V}_{a1} = \tfrac{1}{3}(10\,\underline{/30°} + \mathbf{a}30\,\underline{/-60°} + \mathbf{a}^2 15\,\underline{/145°})$$

$$= \tfrac{1}{3}(10\,\underline{/30°} + 30\,\underline{/60°} + 15\,\underline{/25°})$$

$$= 12.42 + j12.45 = 17.6\,\underline{/45°.0}\text{ units}$$

Since $\mathbf{V}_{b1} = \mathbf{V}_{a1} \underline{/-120°}$ and $\mathbf{V}_{c1} = \mathbf{V}_{a1} \underline{/+120°}$, the positive-sequence system of vectors becomes:

$$\mathbf{V}_{a1} = 17.6 \underline{/45°}, \quad \mathbf{V}_{b1} = 17.6 \underline{/-75°}, \quad \text{and} \quad \mathbf{V}_{c1} = 17.6 \underline{/165°} \text{ units}$$

The above results are indicated graphically in Fig. 1*b*.

Evaluation of $\mathbf{V}_{a2}$. The negative-sequence component of $\mathbf{V}_{a2}$ can be evaluated in a manner almost identical with that given above for the evaluation of $\mathbf{V}_{a1}$. It is simply necessary to study equations (8), (9), and (10) with a view toward eliminating the $\mathbf{V}_{a1}$ and $\mathbf{V}_{a0}$ terms and at the same time retain the $\mathbf{V}_{a2}$ terms. The desired results can be obtained by multiplying equation (9) through by $\mathbf{a}^2$ and equation (10) through by $\mathbf{a}$. Equation (9) multiplied by $\mathbf{a}^2$ reduces to

$$\mathbf{a}^2\mathbf{V}_b = \mathbf{a}\mathbf{V}_{a1} + \mathbf{V}_{a2} + \mathbf{a}^2\mathbf{V}_{a0} \tag{14}$$

Equation (10) multiplied by $\mathbf{a}$ reduces to

$$\mathbf{a}\mathbf{V}_c = \mathbf{a}^2\mathbf{V}_{a1} + \mathbf{V}_{a2} + \mathbf{a}\mathbf{V}_{a0} \tag{15}$$

Adding equations (8), (14), and (15) yields

$$\mathbf{V}_a + \mathbf{a}^2\mathbf{V}_b + \mathbf{a}\mathbf{V}_c = 3\mathbf{V}_{a2} + (1 + \mathbf{a} + \mathbf{a}^2)\,(\mathbf{V}_{a1} + \mathbf{V}_{a0})$$

Since $(1 + \mathbf{a} + \mathbf{a}^2) = 0$,

$$\mathbf{V}_{a2} = \tfrac{1}{3}(\mathbf{V}_a + \mathbf{a}^2\mathbf{V}_b + \mathbf{a}\mathbf{V}_c) = \tfrac{1}{3}(\mathbf{V}_a + \mathbf{V}_b \underline{/240°} + \mathbf{V}_c \underline{/120°}) \tag{16}$$

$\mathbf{V}_{a2}$ is therefore a vector one-third the magnitude of $[\mathbf{V}_a + (\mathbf{V}_b$ rotated through $+240°) + (\mathbf{V}_c$ rotated through $+120°)]$.

Example 2. If $\mathbf{V}_a = 10 \underline{/30°}$, $\mathbf{V}_b = 30 \underline{/-60°}$, and $\mathbf{V}_c = 15 \underline{/145°}$ units:

$$\begin{aligned}\mathbf{V}_{a2} &= \tfrac{1}{3}(10 \underline{/30°} + \mathbf{a}^2 30 \underline{/-60°} + \mathbf{a}15 \underline{/145°}) \\ &= \tfrac{1}{3}(10 \underline{/30°} + 30 \underline{/180°} + 15 \underline{/265°}) \\ &= -7.55 - j3.32 = 8.25 \underline{/-156.2°} \text{ units}\end{aligned}$$

$\mathbf{V}_{a2}$ for this particular case is shown in Fig. 1*c* together with $\mathbf{V}_{b2}$ and $\mathbf{V}_{c2}$. $\mathbf{V}_{b2} = \mathbf{V}_{a2} \underline{/120°}$ and $\mathbf{V}_{c2} = \mathbf{V}_{a2} \underline{/-120°}$.

Evaluation of $\mathbf{V}_{a0}$. The direct addition of equations (8), (9), and (10) will show that:

$$\mathbf{V}_a + \mathbf{V}_b + \mathbf{V}_c = \mathbf{V}_{a1}(1 + \mathbf{a}^2 + \mathbf{a}) + \mathbf{V}_{a2}(1 + \mathbf{a} + \mathbf{a}^2) + 3\mathbf{V}_{a0}$$

or

$$\mathbf{V}_{a0} = \tfrac{1}{3}(\mathbf{V}_a + \mathbf{V}_b + \mathbf{V}_c) \tag{17}$$

The zero-sequence component is simply a vector one-third as large as the vector obtained by adding $\mathbf{V}_a$, $\mathbf{V}_b$, and $\mathbf{V}_c$.

Example 3. If $\mathbf{V}_a = 10\,\underline{/30^\circ}$, $\mathbf{V}_b = 30\,\underline{/-60^\circ}$, and $\mathbf{V}_c = 15\,\underline{/145^\circ}$ units:

$$\mathbf{V}_{a0} = \tfrac{1}{3}(10\,\underline{/30^\circ} + 30\,\underline{/-60^\circ} + 15\,\underline{/145^\circ})$$
$$= 3.79 - j4.13 = 5.60\,\underline{/-47.4^\circ} \text{ units}$$

The above value of $\mathbf{V}_{a0}$ together with corresponding values of $\mathbf{V}_{b0}$ and $\mathbf{V}_{c0}$ are shown in Fig. 1*d*.

Example 4. (*a*) The results obtained in the foregoing examples can be checked by comparing the complex expression for $(\mathbf{V}_{a1} + \mathbf{V}_{a2} + \mathbf{V}_{a0})$ with the complex expression of the original vector $\mathbf{V}_a$. The results of the foregoing examples are tabulated below.

$$\mathbf{V}_{a1} = 12.42 + j12.45 = 17.6\,\underline{/45^\circ} \text{ units}$$
$$\mathbf{V}_{a2} = -7.55 - j3.32 = 8.25\,\underline{/-156.2^\circ} \text{ units}$$
$$\mathbf{V}_{a0} = 3.79 - j4.13 = 5.60\,\underline{/-47.4^\circ} \text{ units}$$
$$(\mathbf{V}_{a1} + \mathbf{V}_{a2} + \mathbf{V}_{a0}) = 8.66 + j5.00 = 10\,\underline{/30^\circ} = \mathbf{V}_a$$

(*b*)
$$\mathbf{V}_{b1} = \mathbf{a}^2 17.6\,\underline{/45^\circ} = 17.6\,\underline{/-75^\circ} = 4.56 - j17.0 \text{ units}$$
$$\mathbf{V}_{b2} = \mathbf{a}8.25\,\underline{/-156.2^\circ} = 8.25\,\underline{/-36.2^\circ} = 6.66 - j4.87 \text{ units}$$
$$\mathbf{V}_{b0} = 5.60\,\underline{/-47.4^\circ} = 3.79 - j4.13 \text{ units}$$
$$(\mathbf{V}_{b1} + \mathbf{V}_{b2} + \mathbf{V}_{b0}) = 15.0 - j26.0 = 30.0\,\underline{/-60^\circ} = \mathbf{V}_b$$

(*c*)
$$\mathbf{V}_{c1} = \mathbf{a}17.6\,\underline{/45^\circ} = 17.6\,\underline{/165^\circ} = -17.0 + j4.56 \text{ units}$$
$$\mathbf{V}_{c2} = \mathbf{a}^2 8.25\,\underline{/-156.2^\circ} = 8.25\,\underline{/83.8^\circ} = 0.89 + j8.20 \text{ units}$$
$$\mathbf{V}_{c0} = 5.60\,\underline{/-47.4^\circ} = 3.79 - j4.13 \text{ units}$$
$$(\mathbf{V}_{c1} + \mathbf{V}_{c2} + \mathbf{V}_{c0}) = -12.32 + j8.63 = 15\,\underline{/145^\circ} = \mathbf{V}_c$$

Problem 1. Given the following three vector voltages: $\mathbf{V}_a = 150\,\underline{/0^\circ}$, $\mathbf{V}_b = 86.6\,\underline{/-90^\circ}$, and $\mathbf{V}_c = 86.6\,\underline{/90^\circ}$ volts.

(*a*) Find the symmetrical components of $\mathbf{V}_a$ and check the results by adding $\mathbf{V}_{a1}$, $\mathbf{V}_{a2}$, and $\mathbf{V}_{a0}$.

(*b*) Evaluate $\mathbf{V}_b$ and $\mathbf{V}_c$ in terms of the symmetrical components of $\mathbf{V}_a$ found in part (*a*).

(*c*) Draw a vector diagram illustrating all symmetrical components.

Ans.: (*a*) $\mathbf{V}_{a1} = 100\,\underline{/0^\circ}$, $\mathbf{V}_{a2} = 0$, $\mathbf{V}_{a0} = 50\,\underline{/0^\circ}$ volts.

Absence of Zero-Sequence Components. The zero-sequence components are non-existent in any system of voltages (or currents) if the vector sum of the original vectors is equal to zero. [See equation (17).] This fact may often be used advantageously in making numerical calculations because the original system of vectors is then directly reducible to two balanced three-phase systems of opposite phase sequence. An absence of zero-sequence components may have important physical significance in the analysis of practical problems. Some of the practical problems in which symmetrical-component analyses are used successfully will be referred to briefly in the following paragraphs and one of these problems will be treated in detail in the next chapter.

Three-Phase, Line-to-Line Voltages. The line-to-line voltages shown in Fig. 3 for either the wye or delta are:

$$\mathbf{V}_{ab} = (\mathbf{V}_{an} - \mathbf{V}_{bn}) \tag{18}$$

$$\mathbf{V}_{bc} = (\mathbf{V}_{bn} - \mathbf{V}_{cn}) \tag{19}$$

$$\mathbf{V}_{ca} = (\mathbf{V}_{cn} - \mathbf{V}_{an}) \tag{20}$$

For the delta the voltages to neutral are those of an equivalent wye. Regardless of the degree of unbalance in the line-to-line voltages

$$\mathbf{V}_{ab} + \mathbf{V}_{bc} + \mathbf{V}_{ca} = (\mathbf{V}_{an} - \mathbf{V}_{bn}) + (\mathbf{V}_{bn} - \mathbf{V}_{cn}) + (\mathbf{V}_{cn} - \mathbf{V}_{an}) = 0 \tag{21}$$

The zero-sequence components of the line-to-line voltages are non-existent because

$$\mathbf{V}_{ab0} = \mathbf{V}_{bc0} = \mathbf{V}_{ca0} = \tfrac{1}{3}(\mathbf{V}_{ab} + \mathbf{V}_{bc} + \mathbf{V}_{ca}) = 0 \tag{22}$$

Therefore three-phase, line-to-line voltages may be represented by a positive-sequence system and a negative-sequence system of voltages as represented by the voltage vector diagrams of Fig. 3. It should be realized that Fig. 3 shows a specific case. As has been previously stated, the relative magnitude of the positive: and negative-sequence voltages and the angle between $\mathbf{V}_{an1}$ and $\mathbf{V}_{an2}$ may take on an infinite number of different values in the most general case. The fact that unbalanced line-to-line voltages may be resolved into two balanced systems of opposite sequence is of considerable importance in the analyses of three-phase rotating machinery. When unbalanced voltages are applied to a three-phase induction motor, for example, the operation of the motor may be analyzed on the basis of balanced systems of voltages of opposite phase sequence.

The positive-sequence voltages and negative-sequence voltages shown in Fig. 3 are obtained in any particular case in terms of the vector values of $\mathbf{V}_{ab}$, $\mathbf{V}_{bc}$, and $\mathbf{V}_{ca}$ as outlined in equations (13) and (16). In terms of the present notation

$$\mathbf{V}_{ab1} = \tfrac{1}{3}(\mathbf{V}_{ab} + \mathbf{V}_{bc}\underline{/120^\circ} + \mathbf{V}_{ca}\underline{/-120^\circ}) \tag{23}$$

$$\mathbf{V}_{ab2} = \tfrac{1}{3}(\mathbf{V}_{ab} + \mathbf{V}_{bc}\underline{/-120^\circ} + \mathbf{V}_{ca}\underline{/120^\circ}) \tag{24}$$

It will be observed from equation (23) that the positive-sequence component of the base vector ($\mathbf{V}_{ab}$ in this case) is obtained by advancing (through 120°) the vector which lags the base vector and retarding (through 120°) the vector which leads the base vector. Reversed operations are employed to secure the negative-sequence components as

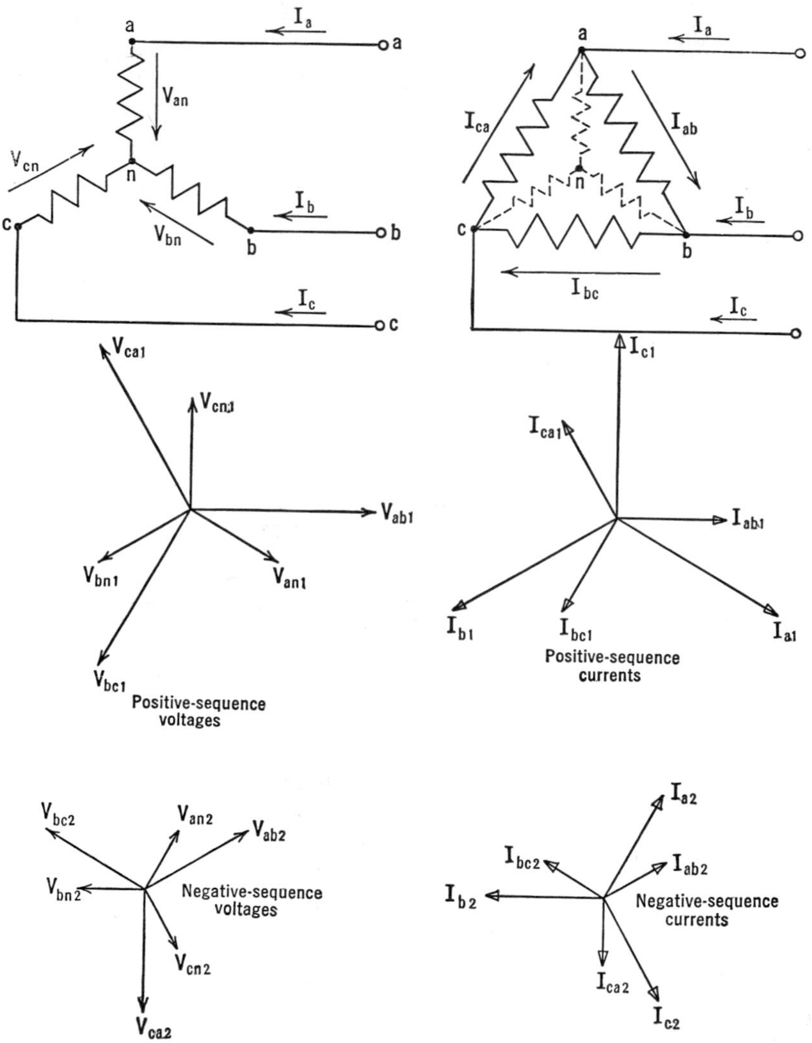

FIG. 3. Positive and negative systems of voltages and currents for a specific three-phase system.

shown in equation (24). If the general scheme is understood, neither changes in notation nor reversals of phase sequence (of the original vectors) can cause confusion.

The statement following equations (23) and (24) and the equations themselves are based upon a line-voltage sequence of *ab–bc–ca* where $\mathbf{V}_{bc}$ actually lags the base vector $\mathbf{V}_{ab}$. Occasions arise where the formulas as given by equations (13), (16) and (17) should be applied as labeled even though the vector of phase *b* does not lag but actually leads the base vector. An illustration involving currents follows. Assume the impedances for the wye load shown in Fig. 3 are $\mathbf{Z}_{na} = 5.77\underline{/0^\circ}$, $\mathbf{Z}_{nb} = 10\underline{/90^\circ}$, and $\mathbf{Z}_{nc} = 10\underline{/-90^\circ}$. If the applied line voltages are $\mathbf{V}_{ba} = 100\underline{/30^\circ}$, $\mathbf{V}_{cb} = 100\underline{/-90^\circ}$, and $\mathbf{V}_{ac} = 100\underline{/150^\circ}$ solution will yield voltages and currents as follows:

$$\mathbf{V}_{na} = 57.7\underline{/0^\circ} \qquad \mathbf{V}_{nb} = 57.7\underline{/-120^\circ} \qquad \mathbf{V}_{nc} = 57.7\underline{/120^\circ}$$

$$\mathbf{I}_{na} = 10\underline{/0^\circ} \qquad \mathbf{I}_{nb} = 5.77\underline{/150^\circ} \qquad \mathbf{I}_{nc} = 5.77\underline{/-150^\circ}$$

Inspection of these results shows the voltage sequence to be *a–b–c*, and this might be the starting point and called the positive sequence system. The actual current sequence is *a–c–b*. If the currents in this case are resolved into their symmetrical components, that in phase *b* should be advanced 120° as equation (13) would indicate even though $\mathbf{I}_{nb}$ actually leads $\mathbf{I}_{na}$ which might be taken as the base vector. Otherwise the system of positive sequence currents would not correspond to the positive sequence system of voltages. In general it is customary at the start to assume a positive sequence of *a–b–c* and initially label the vector which lags the reference vector so the sequence is *a–b–c*. Then the positive sequence voltage or current in any subsequent calculations will be obtained by advancing, that is, rotating counterclockwise 120°, the *b* phase voltage or current regardless of whether it actually lags or leads the base vector. This is necessary to make all positive sequence systems of voltages and currents correspond. Otherwise a negative sequence system of currents may be the one to correspond to a positive sequence system of voltages, and this would lead to confusion.

Problem 2. A three-phase system of line voltages, $\mathbf{V}_{ab}$, $\mathbf{V}_{bc}$, and $\mathbf{V}_{ca}$, are unbalanced to the extent that $\mathbf{V}_{ab1} = 4000\underline{/-60^\circ}$ and $\mathbf{V}_{ab2} = 2000\underline{/180^\circ}$ volts. ($\mathbf{V}_{ab0}$ is, of course, equal to zero.)

(*a*) Draw a common-origin vector diagram illustrating the positive-sequence voltages and the negative-sequence voltages of $\mathbf{V}_{ab}$, $\mathbf{V}_{bc}$, and $\mathbf{V}_{ca}$.

(*b*) Find the magnitudes of the three voltages $\mathbf{V}_{ab}$, $\mathbf{V}_{bc}$, and $\mathbf{V}_{ca}$.

Ans.: (*b*) $V_{ab} = 3464$, $V_{bc} = 3464$, $V_{ca} = 6000$ volts.

Phase Voltages of Wye-Connected Loads. Reference to equation (21) will show that the phase voltages, $\mathbf{V}_{an}$, $\mathbf{V}_{bn}$, and $\mathbf{V}_{cn}$, may possess any vector values whatsoever and yet the vector sum of the line-to-line voltages is zero. In general, however,

$$\mathbf{V}_{an} + \mathbf{V}_{bn} + \mathbf{V}_{cn} \neq 0$$

The individual phase voltages will, therefore, generally possess zero-sequence components even though these components are absent in the line-to-line voltages. Under balanced conditions the phase voltages will, of course, possess no zero-sequence components.

Example 5. In Fig. 3, let

$$\mathbf{V}_{an} = 10\underline{/0^\circ} \quad \mathbf{V}_{bn} = 20\underline{/-90^\circ} \quad \mathbf{V}_{cn} = 10\underline{/135^\circ} \text{ volts}$$

Under these conditions

$$\mathbf{V}_{ab} = (10 + j0) - (0 - j20) = 10 + j20$$

$$\mathbf{V}_{bc} = (0 - j20) - (-7.07 + j7.07) = 7.07 - j27.07$$

$$\mathbf{V}_{ca} = (-7.07 + j7.07) - (10 + j0) = -17.07 + j7.07$$

$$\mathbf{V}_{ab0} = \tfrac{1}{3}[(10 + j20) + (7.07 - j27.07) + (-17.07 + j7.07)] = 0$$

$$\mathbf{V}_{an0} = \tfrac{1}{3}[(10 + j0) + (0 - j20) + (-7.07 + j7.07)]$$
$$= \tfrac{1}{3}(2.93 - j12.93) = 0.98 - j4.31 \text{ volts}$$

It will be noted that triple subscripts have been used in the above example in connection with the component voltages $\mathbf{V}_{ab0}$ and $\mathbf{V}_{an0}$. Where both line-to-line and phase voltages are involved in the same discussion, triple subscripts of this kind may be used advantageously. These subscripts tell whether line-to-line voltages or phase voltages are being considered, they specify the positive circuit direction of the voltages, and they designate the order of the system to which the component voltage belongs.

Delta-Wye Voltage Transformations. In symmetrical-component analyses it is very often particularly advantageous to consider delta-connected systems on an equivalent wye basis. If the delta-connected load shown in Fig. 3 is to be analyzed on an equivalent wye basis, the load impedances are first converted to their equivalent wye values in the conventional manner and then the line-to-line voltages are resolved into their symmetrical components as shown in equations (23) and (24). The remaining problem is that of finding the equivalent wye voltages in terms of the line-to-line voltages.

For *a–b–c* sequence

$$\mathbf{V}_{bn1} = \mathbf{V}_{an1}\underline{/-120^\circ} \quad \text{and} \quad \mathbf{V}_{an1} - \mathbf{V}_{bn1} = \mathbf{V}_{ab1}$$

It follows that

$$\mathbf{V}_{an1} - \mathbf{V}_{an1}\underline{/-120^\circ} = \mathbf{V}_{ab1}$$

$$\mathbf{V}_{an1}[1 - (-0.5 - j0.866)] = \mathbf{V}_{ab1}$$

Hence

$$\mathbf{V}_{an1} = \frac{\mathbf{V}_{ab1}}{\sqrt{3}\underline{/30^\circ}} = \frac{\mathbf{V}_{ab1}}{\sqrt{3}}\underline{/-30^\circ} \tag{25}$$

The complete positive-sequence system of voltages is shown in Fig. 3.

In a corresponding manner it may be shown that

$$\mathbf{V}_{an2} = \frac{\mathbf{V}_{ab2}}{\sqrt{3}\underline{/-30^\circ}} = \frac{\mathbf{V}_{ab2}}{\sqrt{3}}\underline{/30^\circ} \tag{26}$$

The complete negative-sequence system of voltages is shown in Fig. 3.

Equations (25) and (26) are useful in the analysis of either wye- or delta-connected loads where the line-to-line voltages are specified. They are also important in the analysis of delta-wye transformer banks like that shown in Fig. 4.

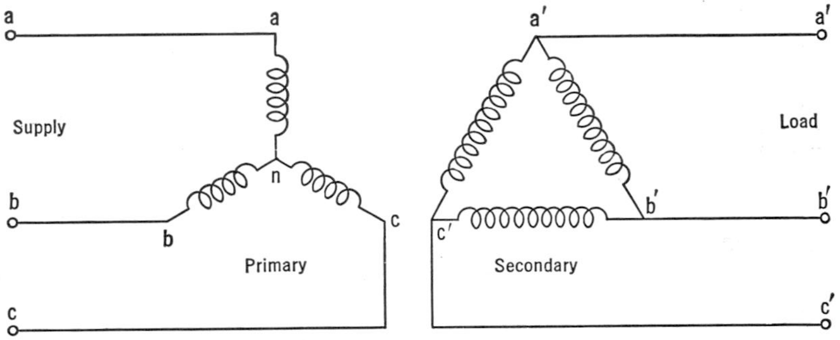

FIG. 4. Wye-delta transformer bank. The windings of transformer a are $a'b'$ and an, transformer b, $b'c'$ and bn, and transformer c, $c'a'$ and cn.

It should be noted in passing that $\mathbf{V}_{an0}$ may possess a finite value even though the zero-sequence components of the line-to-line voltages are of zero value. The fact that $\mathbf{V}_{an0}$ cannot be evaluated in terms of the line-to-line voltages presents no serious handicap as will be shown later, but it does preclude the possibility of immediately evaluating the voltage to neutral ($\mathbf{V}_{an} = \mathbf{V}_{an1} + \mathbf{V}_{an2} + \mathbf{V}_{an0}$).

Problem 3. In the wye-delta transformer bank shown in Fig. 4, the operation of the three transformers, and the polarities of the windings are such that

$$\mathbf{V}_{a'b'} = n\mathbf{V}_{an} \qquad \text{(transformer } a\text{)}$$

$$\mathbf{V}_{b'c'} = n\mathbf{V}_{bn} \qquad \text{(transformer } b\text{)}$$

$$\mathbf{V}_{c'a'} = n\mathbf{V}_{cn} \qquad \text{(transformer } c\text{)}$$

where n is the voltage transformation ratio of the transformers. The primary line-to-line voltages are unbalanced in magnitude to the extent that $\mathbf{V}_{ab1} = 4000\underline{/-60^\circ}$ and $\mathbf{V}_{ab2} = 1000\underline{/-90^\circ}$ volts. ($\mathbf{V}_{ab1}$ and $\mathbf{V}_{ab2}$ are, of course, written with respect to a common reference axis.) The sequence of the primary line-to-line voltages is assumed to be ab–bc–ca, and $\mathbf{V}_{an0}$ is to be taken as zero.

(a) Find the magnitude and vector position of $\mathbf{V}_{ab}$ and of $\mathbf{V}_{bc}$.

(*b*) If the transformation ratio of the transformers is 10, find the magnitude and vector position of $\mathbf{V}_{a'b'}$ and of $\mathbf{V}_{b'c'}$.

Ans.: $\mathbf{V}_{ab} = 4890\underline{/-65.85°}$, $\mathbf{V}_{bc} = 3173\underline{/170.94°}$ volts.
$\mathbf{V}_{a'b'} = 28{,}230\underline{/-84.14°}$, $\mathbf{V}_{b'c'} = 23{,}800\underline{/135.95°}$ volts.

Problem 4. Find the relative vector positions of $\mathbf{V}_{ab}$ and $\mathbf{V}_{a'b'}$ of the wye-delta transformer bank of Fig. 4 if $\mathbf{V}_{ab2} = 0$ and $\mathbf{V}_{an0} = 0$. Find the relative vector positions of $\mathbf{V}_{bc}$ and $\mathbf{V}_{b'c'}$ under the same conditions. (The sequence of the supply voltages $\mathbf{V}_{ab}$, $\mathbf{V}_{bc}$, and $\mathbf{V}_{ca}$ is assumed to be *ab–bc–ca*.)

Ans.: $\mathbf{V}_{a'b'}$ lags $\mathbf{V}_{ab}$ by 30°; $\mathbf{V}_{b'c'}$ lags $\mathbf{V}_{bc}$ by 30°.
The supply voltages are balanced and the positive-sequence voltage vector diagram of Fig. 3 applies directly since $\mathbf{V}_{a'b'} = n\mathbf{V}_{an}$, and $\mathbf{V}_{b'c'} = n\mathbf{V}_{bn}$.

Three-Phase, Three-Wire Line Currents and Associated Delta-Phase Currents. The line currents of a three-phase, three-wire system can contain no zero-sequence components regardless of whether the system is wye- or delta-connected. Reference to the wye-connected load given in Fig. 3 will show that at the junction n

$$\mathbf{I}_a + \mathbf{I}_b + \mathbf{I}_c = 0$$

Therefore,

$$\mathbf{I}_{a0} = \tfrac{1}{3}(\mathbf{I}_a + \mathbf{I}_b + \mathbf{I}_c) = 0 \tag{27}$$

Reference to the delta-connected load given in Fig. 3 will show that

$$\mathbf{I}_a = \mathbf{I}_{ab} - \mathbf{I}_{ca} \tag{28}$$

$$\mathbf{I}_b = \mathbf{I}_{bc} - \mathbf{I}_{ab} \tag{29}$$

$$\mathbf{I}_c = \mathbf{I}_{ca} - \mathbf{I}_{bc} \tag{30}$$

Hence

$$\mathbf{I}_a + \mathbf{I}_b + \mathbf{I}_c = (\mathbf{I}_{ab} - \mathbf{I}_{ca}) + (\mathbf{I}_{bc} - \mathbf{I}_{ab}) + (\mathbf{I}_{ca} - \mathbf{I}_{bc}) = 0 \tag{31}$$

Regardless of the degree of unbalance of the individual phase currents, $\mathbf{I}_{ab}$, $\mathbf{I}_{bc}$, and $\mathbf{I}_{ca}$, the vector sum of the line currents, $\mathbf{I}_a$, $\mathbf{I}_b$, and $\mathbf{I}_c$, is equal to zero and therefore no zero-sequence components are present in the line currents.

The individual delta-phase currents will, in general, possess zero-sequence components since $(\mathbf{I}_{ab} + \mathbf{I}_{bc} + \mathbf{I}_{ca})$ is, in general, not equal to zero. The zero-sequence components of the phase currents in a delta-connected system cannot be evaluated in terms of the line currents.

For *a–b–c* sequence of line currents,

$$\mathbf{I}_{ab1} - \mathbf{I}_{ca1} = \mathbf{I}_{a1} \quad \text{and} \quad \mathbf{I}_{ca1} = \mathbf{I}_{ab1}\underline{/120°}$$

Employing the same type of derivation as that employed in the derivation of equation (25), it is easy to show that

$$\mathbf{I}_{ab1}[1 - (-0.5 + j0.866)] = \mathbf{I}_{a1}$$

$$\mathbf{I}_{ab1} = \frac{\mathbf{I}_{a1}}{\sqrt{3}} \underline{/30^\circ} \qquad (32)$$

A complete positive-sequence system of currents is shown in Fig. 3. The vector diagram of the positive-sequence currents shows that $\mathbf{I}_{ab1}$ is $1/\sqrt{3}$ as large as $\mathbf{I}_{a1}$ and 30° in advance of $\mathbf{I}_{a1}$.

In a corresponding manner it may be shown that

$$\mathbf{I}_{ab2} = \frac{\mathbf{I}_{a2}}{\sqrt{3}} \underline{/-30^\circ} \qquad (33)$$

In a wye-delta transformer bank like that shown in Fig. 4 where no zero-sequence components of current can exist in the wye primary windings, no zero-sequence currents will be present in the delta secondary windings since $N_pI_p = N_sI_s$. In this connection, N_p represents the primary turns and N_s the secondary turns of one transformer. (The magnetizing current is neglected in the statement $N_pI_p = N_sI_s$ or else I_p represents simply the load component of the primary current.) The fact that a transformer bank like that shown in Fig. 4 eliminates zero-sequence currents is of importance in power network short-circuit studies.

Problem 5. Find the line current, $\mathbf{I}_a$, in the delta-connected system shown in Fig. 3 if

$$\mathbf{I}_{ab1} = 10\underline{/0^\circ}, \quad \mathbf{I}_{ab2} = 5\underline{/60^\circ}, \quad \text{and} \quad \mathbf{I}_{ab0} = 7\underline{/19.5^\circ} \text{ amperes}$$

Ans.: $\mathbf{I}_a = 15\underline{/0^\circ}$ amperes.

Three-Phase Line Currents Associated with a Neutral Return. If a wye-wye system operates with grounded neutrals or with a connecting wire between neutrals, the vector sum of the line currents will not, in general, be equal to zero. In this case:

$$\mathbf{I}_{a0} = \mathbf{I}_{b0} = \mathbf{I}_{c0} = \tfrac{1}{3}(\mathbf{I}_a + \mathbf{I}_b + \mathbf{I}_c) \qquad (34)$$

It will be noted that the ground or neutral return current, namely, $(\mathbf{I}_a + \mathbf{I}_b + \mathbf{I}_c)$, is three times as large as the individual zero-sequence components of the line currents. Each line wire carries a component of current which is equal in magnitude and in time phase with similar components in the other two lines. These zero-sequence components are sometimes called *uniphase* components and have important physical significance in connection with the inductive interference between three-phase power lines and paralleling telephone lines.

Where the line currents possess uniphase components, no manner of transposition of the power system line wires will prevent these components from establishing inductive interference in paralleling telephone lines, the reason being that the uniphase components in the three line wires establish similarly directed magnetic interference. In a case of this kind, transposition of the telephone wires themselves is required to balance out the undesirable emf's that are induced by the power system currents. Inductive interference studies usually refer to the uniphase or zero-sequence currents as *residuals* since they represent the component currents that remain after the positive- and negative-sequence components have been taken from the original unbalanced system of currents. The fact that the *residuals* can be separated from the two balanced systems of currents is an important feature in interference problems.

The zero-sequence components of the line currents of grounded or four-wire wye systems are also of importance in the evaluation of the short-circuit currents in power systems.

Example 6. A line-to-ground short circuit on a grounded wye-connected alternator is shown in Fig. 5. Let it be required to find the three-phase symmetrical

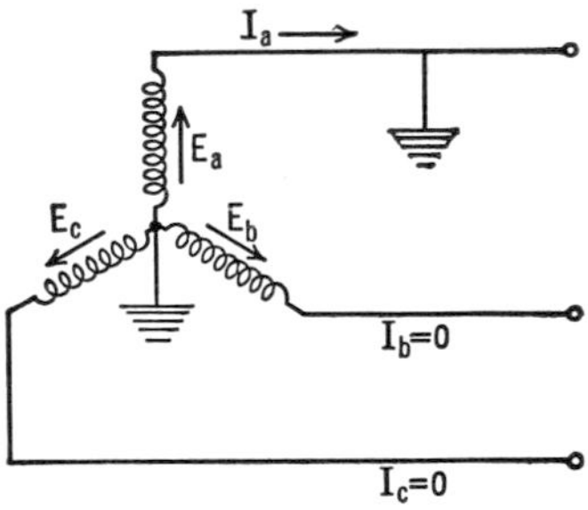

FIG. 5. A particular case of unbalanced three-phase line currents.

components of the line currents $\mathbf{I}_a$, $\mathbf{I}_b$, and $\mathbf{I}_c$, where $\mathbf{I}_a = I\underline{/\alpha}$, $I_b = 0$, and $I_c = 0$. I is the magnitude of the short-circuit current, $\mathbf{I}_a$, and α is the angular displacement of this current from any arbitrary reference axis. The three line currents may be considered as an unbalanced three-phase system of currents even though two of the currents are equal to zero.

The original system of currents is represented by

$$\mathbf{I}_a = I\underline{/\alpha} \quad \mathbf{I}_b = 0 \quad \mathbf{I}_c = 0$$

The positive-sequence components of the above currents are

$$\mathbf{I}_{a1} = \tfrac{1}{3}I\underline{/\alpha} \quad \mathbf{I}_{b1} = \tfrac{1}{3}I\underline{/\alpha - 120^\circ} \quad \mathbf{I}_{c1} = \tfrac{1}{3}I\underline{/\alpha + 120^\circ}$$

The negative-sequence components are

$$\mathbf{I}_{a2} = \tfrac{1}{3}I\underline{/\alpha} \quad \mathbf{I}_{b2} = \tfrac{1}{3}I\underline{/\alpha + 120°} \quad \mathbf{I}_{c2} = \tfrac{1}{3}I\underline{/\alpha - 120°}$$

The zero-sequence components are

$$\mathbf{I}_{a0} = \mathbf{I}_{b0} = \mathbf{I}_{c0} = \tfrac{1}{3}I\underline{/\alpha}$$

Graphical representations of the above results are shown in Fig. 6. It will be observed that

$$\mathbf{I}_{a1} + \mathbf{I}_{a2} + \mathbf{I}_{a0} = \mathbf{I}_a = I\underline{/\alpha}$$

$$\mathbf{I}_{b1} + \mathbf{I}_{b2} + \mathbf{I}_{b0} = \mathbf{I}_b = 0$$

$$\mathbf{I}_{c1} + \mathbf{I}_{c2} + \mathbf{I}_{c0} = \mathbf{I}_c = 0$$

Symmetrical components of the kind given above are used in single line-to-ground

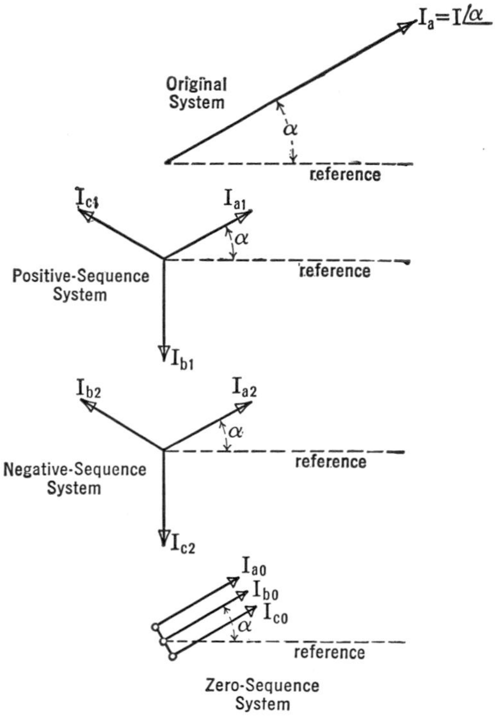

FIG. 6. The resolution of a single current $I\underline{/\alpha}$ into its three-phase symmetrical components.

short-circuit current analyses, and although this type of problem is not considered in the present chapter a study of Fig. 6 at this stage will prove to be instructive.

Problem 6. The three line currents in a four-wire wye system like that shown in Fig. 7, are:

$\mathbf{I}_{a'a} = \mathbf{I}_a = 20\underline{/-60°}$, $\mathbf{I}_{b'b} = \mathbf{I}_b = 12\underline{/-100°}$, and $\mathbf{I}_{c'c} = \mathbf{I}_c = 10\underline{/75°}$ amperes

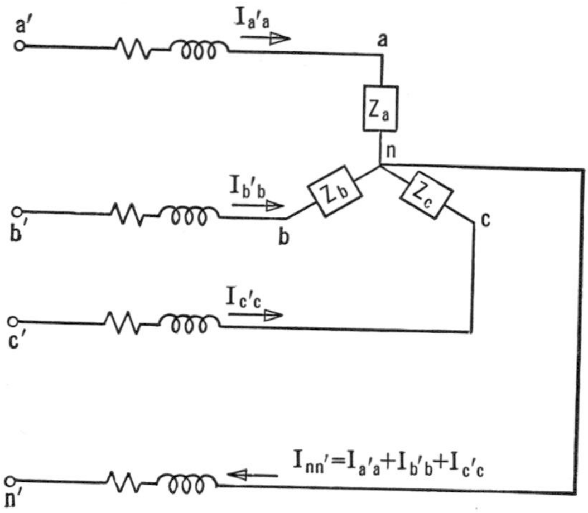

FIG. 7. Three-phase four-wire system for Problem 6.

Find the positive-, negative-, and zero-sequence components of the above line currents and check the results either graphically or by the vector addition of the symmetrical components.

Ans.: $\mathbf{I}_{a1} = 9.45 - j6.76 = 11.62\underline{/-35.6°}$ amperes

$\mathbf{I}_{b1} = -10.58 - j4.80 = 11.62\underline{/-155.6°}$ amperes

$\mathbf{I}_{c1} = 1.136 + j11.58 = 11.62\underline{/84.4°}$ amperes

$\mathbf{I}_{a2} = -2.95 - j4.07 = 5.03\underline{/-125.9°}$ amperes

$\mathbf{I}_{b2} = 5.0 - j0.517 = 5.03\underline{/-5.9°}$ amperes

$\mathbf{I}_{c2} = -2.05 + j4.59 = 5.03\underline{/114.1°}$ amperes

$\mathbf{I}_{a0} = 3.503 - j6.49 = 7.375\underline{/-61.65°}$ amperes

Power from Symmetrical Components. For any unbalanced three-phase system the total power consumed is the sum of the powers absorbed in each phase. Thus

$$P = P_a + P_b + P_c = V_a I_a \cos \theta_{\mathbf{V}_a}^{\mathbf{I}_a} + V_b I_b \cos \theta_{\mathbf{V}_b}^{\mathbf{I}_b} + V_c I_c \cos \theta_{\mathbf{V}_c}^{\mathbf{I}_c}$$

If the voltage of a given phase, say $\mathbf{V}_a$, is resolved into several components, the power for that phase may be obtained by adding the products of each component of voltage by the current times the cosine of the angle between the particular voltage component and the current. Reference to Fig. 8 will make this evident. Here

$$P_a = I_a(V_a \cos\theta) = I_a(V_1 \cos\theta_1 + V_2 \cos\theta_2 + V_0 \cos\theta_0)$$
$$= I_a V_1 \cos\theta_{\mathbf{I}_a}^{\mathbf{V}_1} + I_a V_2 \cos\theta_{\mathbf{I}_a}^{\mathbf{V}_2} + I_a V_0 \cos\theta_{\mathbf{I}_a}^{\mathbf{V}_0}$$

Similarly, if the current is divided into components, the power is the sum of the products of voltage by the current times the cosine of the phase angle between the respective components of current and the voltage. From these facts it should be apparent that if both voltage and current are resolved into components, the power will be the sum of the products of each component of voltage by each component of current times the cosine of the angle between the particular component of voltage and current appearing in each of the products.

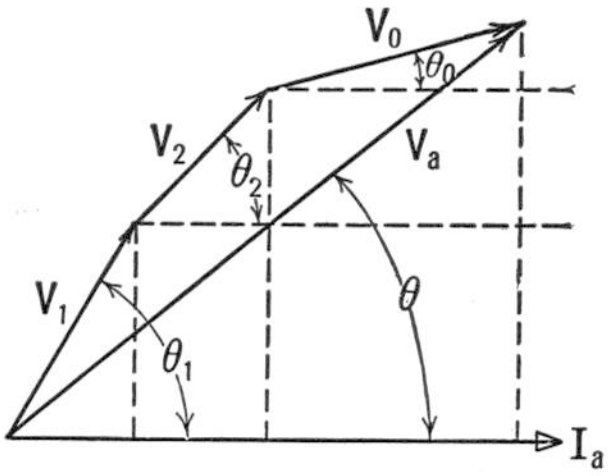

FIG. 8. In-phase component of $\mathbf{V}_a$ with respect to $\mathbf{I}_a$ is the sum of the in-phase components of each of the component voltages of $\mathbf{V}_a$.

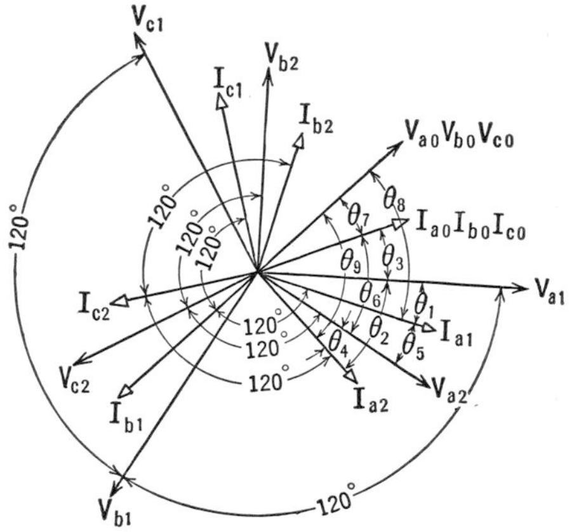

FIG. 9. Symmetrical components of voltages and currents of a general three-phase system.

Figure 9 shows the symmetrical components of currents and voltages for any three-phase system. The subscripts a, b, and c denote the phase while 0, 1, and 2 are the usual symbols denoting the sequence components. In terms of the components shown for phase a, the power is

$$P_a = V_{a1}I_{a1}\cos\theta_1 + V_{a1}I_{a2}\cos\theta_2 + V_{a1}I_{a0}\cos\theta_3 + V_{a2}I_{a2}\cos\theta_4$$
$$+ V_{a2}I_{a1}\cos\theta_5 + V_{a2}I_{a0}\cos\theta_6 + V_{a0}I_{a0}\cos\theta_7 + V_{a0}I_{a1}\cos\theta_8$$
$$+ V_{a0}I_{a2}\cos\theta_9 \qquad (35)$$

For phase b

$$P_b = V_{b1}I_{b1}\cos\theta_1 + V_{b1}I_{b2}\cos(120° + \theta_2) + V_{b1}I_{b0}\cos(120° + \theta_3)$$
$$+ V_{b2}I_{b2}\cos\theta_4 + V_{b2}I_{b1}\cos(120° + \theta_5) + V_{b2}I_{b0}\cos(120° - \theta_6)$$
$$+ V_{b0}I_{b0}\cos\theta_7 + V_{b0}I_{b1}\cos(120° + \theta_8)$$
$$+ V_{b0}I_{b2}\cos(120° - \theta_9) \qquad (36)$$

For phase *c*

$$
\begin{aligned}
P_c = {} & V_{c1}I_{c1}\cos\theta_1 + V_{c1}I_{c2}\cos(240^\circ + \theta_2) + V_{c1}I_{c0}\cos(240^\circ + \theta_3) \\
& + V_{c2}I_{c2}\cos\theta_4 + V_{c2}I_{c1}\cos(240^\circ + \theta_5) + V_{c2}I_{c0}\cos(240^\circ - \theta_6) \\
& + V_{c0}I_{c0}\cos\theta_7 + V_{c0}I_{c1}\cos(240^\circ + \theta_8) \\
& + V_{c0}I_{c2}\cos(240^\circ - \theta_9)
\end{aligned}
\quad (37)
$$

It should be remembered that only magnitudes of voltages and currents appear in equations (35), (36), and (37), and that $V_{a1} = V_{b1} = V_{c1}$, $V_{a2} = V_{b2} = V_{c2}$, $V_{a0} = V_{b0} = V_{c0}$, $I_{a1} = I_{b1} = I_{c1}$, $I_{a2} = I_{b2} = I_{c2}$, and $I_{a0} = I_{b0} = I_{c0}$. Under these conditions if equations (35), (36), and (37) are added, the terms containing θ_2 add to zero because they represent three equal quantities at 120-degree angles. Similarly, the terms containing θ_3, θ_5, θ_6, θ_8, and θ_9 add to zero. Dropping reference to particular phases, this leaves

$$P = P_a + P_b + P_c = 3V_1I_1\cos\theta_1 + 3V_2I_2\cos\theta_4 + 3V_0I_0\cos\theta_7 \quad (38)$$

It will be noted that $\cos\theta_1 = \cos\theta_{\mathbf{V}_1}^{\mathbf{I}_1}$, $\cos\theta_4 = \cos\theta_{\mathbf{V}_2}^{\mathbf{I}_2}$, and $\cos\theta_7 = \cos\theta_{\mathbf{V}_0}^{\mathbf{I}_0}$. Hence

$$P = 3V_1I_1\cos\theta_{\mathbf{V}_1}^{\mathbf{I}_1} + 3V_2I_2\cos\theta_{\mathbf{V}_2}^{\mathbf{I}_2} + 3V_0I_0\cos\theta_{\mathbf{V}_0}^{\mathbf{I}_0} \quad (39)$$

Equation (39) shows that the total power consumed by an unbalanced three-phase system is the sum of the powers represented by each of the symmetrical component systems. Hence, to obtain total power the algebraic sum of the total positive-, total negative-, and total zero-sequence powers may be calculated.

Copper Losses in Terms of Symmetrical Components. The copper loss for any unbalanced three-phase system is

$$P = I_a^2R_a + I_b^2R_b + I_c^2R_c \quad (40)$$

where phase currents and the corresponding phase resistances are used.

By referring to Fig. 10 and by remembering that

$$\mathbf{I}_a = \mathbf{I}_{a1} + \mathbf{I}_{a2} + \mathbf{I}_{a0}$$

it follows that

$$I_a^2 = (I_{a1} + I_{a2}\cos\beta + I_{a0}\cos\alpha)^2 + (I_{a2}\sin\beta + I_{a0}\sin\alpha)^2 \quad (41)$$

Similarly,

$$
\begin{aligned}
I_b^2 = {} & [I_{b1}\cos 240^\circ + I_{b2}\cos(120^\circ - \beta) + I_{b0}\cos\alpha]^2 \\
& + [I_{b1}\sin 240^\circ + I_{b2}\sin(120^\circ - \beta) + I_{b0}\sin\alpha]^2
\end{aligned}
\quad (42)
$$

$$
\begin{aligned}
I_c^2 = {} & [I_{c1}\cos 120^\circ + I_{c2}\cos(240^\circ - \beta) + I_{c0}\cos\alpha]^2 \\
& + [I_{c1}\sin 120^\circ + I_{c2}\sin(240^\circ - \beta) + I_{c0}\sin\alpha]^2
\end{aligned}
\quad (43)
$$

When R_a, R_b, and R_c are different the sequence components of current should be combined to obtain I_a, I_b, and I_c, and equation (40) used to calculate the copper loss. If, however, $R_a = R_b = R_c = R$, substitution of equations (41), (42), and (43) in equation (40), dropping reference to phase, and expanding and combining terms algebraically give

$$P = 3I_1{}^2R + 3I_2{}^2R + 3I_0{}^2R$$
$$= 3(I_1{}^2 + I_2{}^2 + I_0{}^2)R \qquad (44)$$

Equation (44) shows that the total copper loss due to the resultant currents is the same as the sum of the copper losses due to the sequence components calculated separately.

If the resistances to the positive-, negative-, and zero-sequence currents are different, the copper loss may be determined from

$$P = 3I_1{}^2R_1 + 3I_2{}^2R_2 + 3I_0{}^2R_0 \qquad (45)$$

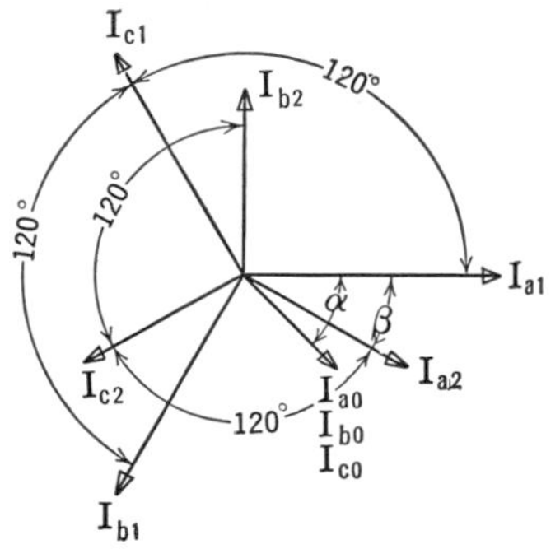

FIG. 10. Symmetrical components of currents in a general three-phase system.

where R_1, R_2, and R_0 are respectively the *resistance to* the positive-, negative-, and zero-sequence components of current. In using equation (45) it must be remembered that each of the sequence resistances must be the same for all three phases, since equality of phase resistances was assumed in obtaining equation (44), of which (45) is a modification.

Positive-, Negative-, and Zero-Sequence Impedance Components. For purposes of some analyses, three self-impedances may be separated or resolved into their symmetrical components exactly like three voltages or currents. If the voltages or currents which are to be associated with these component impedances are resolved in the order *a–b–c*, then the impedances should be resolved in the same order. [See equations (13), (16), and (17).] The term self-impedance implies that no mutual coupling exists between the individual impedances. In order to distinguish the components of self-impedance from the components of mutual impedance which are considered later, double subscripts of the kind given below will be used.

The symmetrical components of three self-impedances, $\mathbf{Z}_{aa}$, $\mathbf{Z}_{bb}$, and $\mathbf{Z}_{cc}$ are

$$\mathbf{Z}_{aa1} = \tfrac{1}{3}(\mathbf{Z}_{aa} + \mathbf{Z}_{bb}\underline{/120°} + \mathbf{Z}_{cc}\underline{/-120°}) \qquad (46)$$

$$\mathbf{Z}_{aa2} = \tfrac{1}{3}(\mathbf{Z}_{aa} + \mathbf{Z}_{bb}\underline{/-120°} + \mathbf{Z}_{cc}\underline{/120°}) \qquad (47)$$

$$\mathbf{Z}_{aa0} = \tfrac{1}{3}(\mathbf{Z}_{aa} + \mathbf{Z}_{bb} + \mathbf{Z}_{cc}) \qquad (48)$$

As above defined $\mathbf{Z}_{aa1}$, $\mathbf{Z}_{aa2}$, and $\mathbf{Z}_{aa0}$ are called positive-sequence impedance, negative-sequence impedance, and zero-sequence impedance respectively. These component impedances have little physical significance but they are useful in a general mathematical formulation of symmetrical-component theory. It should be pointed out at this stage that the resistance (or in-phase) parts of the component impedances may possess negative signs even though the real parts of $\mathbf{Z}_{aa}$, $\mathbf{Z}_{bb}$, and $\mathbf{Z}_{cc}$ are all positive.

The above symmetrical components of an unbalanced *set of impedances* should not be confused with impedance to positive-, negative-, and zero-sequence currents which are defined as follows:

$$\text{Impedance to positive-sequence,} \quad \mathbf{Z}_{a1} = \frac{\mathbf{V}_{a1}}{\mathbf{I}_{a1}}$$

$$\text{Impedance to negative-sequence,} \quad \mathbf{Z}_{a2} = \frac{\mathbf{V}_{a2}}{\mathbf{I}_{a2}}$$

$$\text{Impedance to zero-sequence,} \quad \mathbf{Z}_{a0} = \frac{\mathbf{V}_{a0}}{\mathbf{I}_{a0}}$$

These impedances to sequence component currents are usually applied to systems where the impedances of all phases are the same or balanced. In order to avoid confusion a *double-letter subscript* will be used on positive-, negative-, and zero-sequence *components of impedance.* For *impedance* to positive-, negative-, and zero-sequence currents a *single-letter subscript* will be used. In both cases the figure subscripts 1, 2, and 0 will denote positive, negative, and zero sequence, respectively.

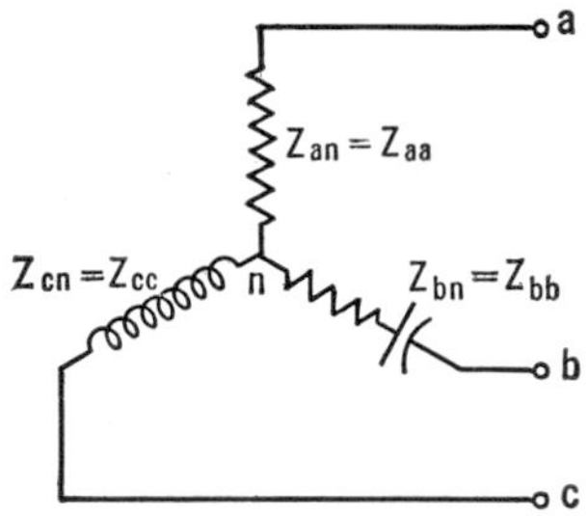

FIG. 11. See example 7.

Example 7. Let the wye-connected impedances of Fig. 11 be

$$\mathbf{Z}_{aa} = (6 + j0) \quad \mathbf{Z}_{bb} = (5.2 - j3) \quad \mathbf{Z}_{cc} = (0 + j12) \text{ ohms}$$

Employing equations (46), (47), and (48), the component impedances are

$$\begin{aligned}\mathbf{Z}_{aa1} &= \tfrac{1}{3}[(6 + j0) + (5.2 - j3)(-0.5 + j0.866) + (0 + j12)(-0.5 - j0.866)] \\ &= \tfrac{1}{3}[(6 + j0) + (0 + j6) + (10.4 - j6)] \\ &= \tfrac{1}{3}(16.4 + j0) = 5.47 + j0 \text{ ohms}\end{aligned}$$

$$\begin{aligned}\mathbf{Z}_{aa2} &= \tfrac{1}{3}[(6 + j0) + (5.2 - j3)(-0.5 - j0.866) + (0 + j12)(-0.5 + j0.866)] \\ &= \tfrac{1}{3}[(6 + j0) + (-5.2 - j3) + (-10.4 - j6)] \\ &= \tfrac{1}{3}(-9.6 - j9) = -3.2 - j3 \text{ ohms}\end{aligned}$$

$$\begin{aligned}\mathbf{Z}_{aa0} &= \tfrac{1}{3}[(6 + j0) + (5.2 - j3) + (0 + j12)] \\ &= \tfrac{1}{3}(11.2 + j9) = 3.73 + j3 \text{ ohms}\end{aligned}$$

In accordance with previous considerations, it follows that

$$\mathbf{Z}_{bb1} = \mathbf{Z}_{aa1}\underline{/-120°} \qquad \mathbf{Z}_{cc1} = \mathbf{Z}_{aa1}\underline{/120°}$$

$$\mathbf{Z}_{bb2} = \mathbf{Z}_{aa2}\underline{/120°} \qquad \mathbf{Z}_{cc2} = \mathbf{Z}_{aa2}\underline{/-120°}$$

$$\mathbf{Z}_{bb0} = \mathbf{Z}_{aa0} \qquad \mathbf{Z}_{cc0} = \mathbf{Z}_{aa0}$$

The sum of the impedance components of one phase equals the actual impedance of that phase. For example,

$$\mathbf{Z}_{aa} = (5.47 + j0) + (-3.2 - j3) + (3.73 + j3) = 6 + j0 \text{ ohms}$$

Problem 7. Find $\mathbf{Z}_{bb1}$, $\mathbf{Z}_{bb2}$, and $\mathbf{Z}_{bb0}$ in the above example, employing the values of $\mathbf{Z}_{aa1}$, $\mathbf{Z}_{aa2}$, and $\mathbf{Z}_{aa0}$ which have been evaluated. Repeat for $\mathbf{Z}_{cc1}$, $\mathbf{Z}_{cc2}$, and $\mathbf{Z}_{cc0}$.

Ans.: $\mathbf{Z}_{bb} = \mathbf{Z}_{bb1} + \mathbf{Z}_{bb2} + \mathbf{Z}_{bb0}$
$= (-2.73 - j4.73) + (4.20 - j1.27) + (3.73 + j3.0)$
$= (5.2 - j3.0)$ ohms.

Problem 8. Given three wye-connected impedances:

$$\mathbf{Z}_{an} = (15 + j0) \quad \mathbf{Z}_{bn} = (6 - j3.464) \quad \mathbf{Z}_{cn} = (6 + j3.464) \text{ ohms}$$

(*a*) Find the symmetrical components of $\mathbf{Z}_{an}$ in accordance with the resolutions given in equations (46), (47), and (48).

(*b*) Find $\mathbf{Z}_{bn1}$, $\mathbf{Z}_{bn2}$, and $\mathbf{Z}_{bn0}$ in terms of the symmetrical components of $\mathbf{Z}_{an}$ and check $(\mathbf{Z}_{bn1} + \mathbf{Z}_{bn2} + \mathbf{Z}_{bn0})$ with the given value of $(6 - j3.464)$ ohms.

Ans.: (*a*) $\mathbf{Z}_{an1} = 5\underline{/0°}$; $\mathbf{Z}_{an2} = 1\underline{/0°}$; $\mathbf{Z}_{an0} = 9\underline{/0°}$ ohms.

Sequence Rule as Applied to Component Voltages. If the voltage drop across one phase, say phase a, is written in terms of the symmetrical components of both current and impedance, nine component voltages appear. That is,

$$\begin{aligned}\mathbf{V}_a &= \mathbf{I}_a\mathbf{Z}_a = (\mathbf{I}_{a1} + \mathbf{I}_{a2} + \mathbf{I}_{a0})(\mathbf{Z}_{aa1} + \mathbf{Z}_{aa2} + \mathbf{Z}_{aa0}) \\ &= \mathbf{I}_{a1}\mathbf{Z}_{aa1} + \mathbf{I}_{a1}\mathbf{Z}_{aa2} + \mathbf{I}_{a1}\mathbf{Z}_{aa0} + \mathbf{I}_{a2}\mathbf{Z}_{aa1} + \mathbf{I}_{a2}\mathbf{Z}_{aa2} + \mathbf{I}_{a2}\mathbf{Z}_{aa0} \\ &\quad + \mathbf{I}_{a0}\mathbf{Z}_{aa1} + \mathbf{I}_{a0}\mathbf{Z}_{aa2} + \mathbf{I}_{a0}\mathbf{Z}_{aa0}\end{aligned} \tag{49}$$

These nine component voltages may be grouped in such a manner as to form the positive-, negative-, and zero-sequence components of $\mathbf{V}_a$, and this grouping may be made in accordance with an easily remembered rule.

The Sequence Rule

The order of the voltage system to which an **IZ** ***drop belongs is equal to the sum of the orders of the systems to which*** **I** ***and*** **Z** ***belong individually.***

In the application of the sequence rule, positive-sequence terms are of first order, negative-sequence terms are of second order, and zero-sequence terms are of zero or third order. In summing the orders both $(1 + 0)$ and $(2 + 2)$ are considered as belonging to the first order, since order 4 is considered as order 1, there being only three orders. In this connection, the zero in $(1 + 0)$ may be reckoned either as zero or three. Also $(1 + 2)$ is of order 3, or a zero-sequence term. As applied to the component voltages of equation (49), the sequence rule states

$$\mathbf{V}_{a1} = \mathbf{I}_{a1}\mathbf{Z}_{aa0} + \mathbf{I}_{a2}\mathbf{Z}_{aa2} + \mathbf{I}_{a0}\mathbf{Z}_{aa1} \tag{50}$$

$$\mathbf{V}_{a2} = \mathbf{I}_{a1}\mathbf{Z}_{aa1} + \mathbf{I}_{a2}\mathbf{Z}_{aa0} + \mathbf{I}_{a0}\mathbf{Z}_{aa2} \tag{51}$$

$$\mathbf{V}_{a0} = \mathbf{I}_{a1}\mathbf{Z}_{aa2} + \mathbf{I}_{a2}\mathbf{Z}_{aa1} + \mathbf{I}_{a0}\mathbf{Z}_{aa0} \tag{52}$$

Obviously the real basis upon which the above equations are written is that, as written, they satisfy the definitions which were originally attached to $\mathbf{V}_{a1}$, $\mathbf{V}_{a2}$, and $\mathbf{V}_{a0}$. To satisfy these definitions, $\mathbf{V}_{a1}$ must be the positive-sequence component of the base vector $\mathbf{V}_a$, $\mathbf{V}_{a2}$ must be the negative-sequence component of the base vector $\mathbf{V}_a$, and $\mathbf{V}_{a0}$ must be the zero-sequence component. The proof that $\mathbf{V}_{a1}$, as written in equation (50), satisfies the definition of a positive-sequence voltage is outlined below.

Applying equation (50) to the b phase and making appropriate substitutions,

$$\begin{aligned}\mathbf{V}_{b1} &= \mathbf{I}_{b1}\mathbf{Z}_{bb0} + \mathbf{I}_{b2}\mathbf{Z}_{bb2} + \mathbf{I}_{b0}\mathbf{Z}_{bb1} \\ &= (\mathbf{I}_{a1}\underline{/-120^\circ})\mathbf{Z}_{aa0} + (\mathbf{I}_{a2}\underline{/120^\circ})\mathbf{Z}_{aa2}\underline{/120^\circ} + \mathbf{I}_{a0}\mathbf{Z}_{aa1}\underline{/-120^\circ} \\ &= \mathbf{I}_{a1}\mathbf{Z}_{aa0}\underline{/-120^\circ} + \mathbf{I}_{a2}\mathbf{Z}_{aa2}\underline{/-120^\circ} + \mathbf{I}_{a0}\mathbf{Z}_{aa1}\underline{/-120^\circ}\end{aligned} \tag{50a}$$

Comparison of equations (50a) and (50) will show that $\mathbf{V}_{b1}$ is equal in magnitude to $\mathbf{V}_{a1}$ and 120° behind $\mathbf{V}_{a1}$, as, of course, it should be if $\mathbf{V}_{a1}$, $\mathbf{V}_{b1}$, and $\mathbf{V}_{c1}$ are to form a positive-sequence system.

Applying equation (50) to the c phase and making appropriate substitutions,

$$\begin{aligned}\mathbf{V}_{c1} &= \mathbf{I}_{c1}\mathbf{Z}_{cc0} + \mathbf{I}_{c2}\mathbf{Z}_{cc2} + \mathbf{I}_{c0}\mathbf{Z}_{cc1} \\ &= (\mathbf{I}_{a1}\underline{/120^\circ})\mathbf{Z}_{aa0} + (\mathbf{I}_{a2}\underline{/-120^\circ})\mathbf{Z}_{aa2}\underline{/-120^\circ} + \mathbf{I}_{a0}\mathbf{Z}_{aa1}\underline{/120^\circ} \\ &= \mathbf{I}_{a1}\mathbf{Z}_{aa0}\underline{/120^\circ} + \mathbf{I}_{a2}\mathbf{Z}_{aa2}\underline{/120^\circ} + \mathbf{I}_{a0}\mathbf{Z}_{aa1}\underline{/120^\circ} \qquad (50b)\end{aligned}$$

Comparison of equations (50b) and (50) will show that $\mathbf{V}_{c1}$ is equal in magnitude to $\mathbf{V}_{a1}$ and 120° ahead of $\mathbf{V}_{a1}$, which is the necessary requirement that $\mathbf{V}_{a1}$, $\mathbf{V}_{b1}$, and $\mathbf{V}_{c1}$ form a positive-sequence system of voltages.

In a manner similar to that outlined above, $\mathbf{V}_{a2}$ of equation (51) may be shown to be a member of a balanced negative-sequence system of voltages $\mathbf{V}_{a2}$, $\mathbf{V}_{b2}$, and $\mathbf{V}_{c2}$.

In the following problem the reader is asked to analyze equation (52) with a view toward showing that the **IZ** components of that equation are correctly chosen to form a zero-sequence system of voltages.

Problem 9. Prove that $\mathbf{V}_{a0}$ (equal to $\mathbf{I}_{a1}\mathbf{Z}_{aa2} + \mathbf{I}_{a2}\mathbf{Z}_{aa1} + \mathbf{I}_{a0}\mathbf{Z}_{aa0}$) is equal in magnitude and in time phase, with

$$\mathbf{V}_{b0} = \mathbf{I}_{b1}\mathbf{Z}_{bb2} + \mathbf{I}_{b2}\mathbf{Z}_{bb1} + \mathbf{I}_{b0}\mathbf{Z}_{bb0}$$

and with

$$\mathbf{V}_{c0} = \mathbf{I}_{c1}\mathbf{Z}_{cc2} + \mathbf{I}_{c2}\mathbf{Z}_{cc1} + \mathbf{I}_{c0}\mathbf{Z}_{cc0}$$

Application of the Sequence Rule to Unbalanced Three-Wire Loads. The foregoing theory may be applied to any three-wire load which consists of individual or non-coupled phase impedances. Since the individual phases of three-phase rotating equipment are closely coupled magnetically, the present method of analysis does not apply directly to rotating equipment. (A method of accounting for the mutual impedances of rotating equipment is given in Chapter XIII, and a general method of accounting for mutual impedance effects is given later in the present chapter.)

In applying equations (50), (51), and (52) to the a phase of a wye-connected load like that shown in Fig. 11, it is noted that, since $\mathbf{I}_{a0} = 0$,

$$\mathbf{V}_{an1} = \mathbf{I}_{a1}\mathbf{Z}_{an0} + \mathbf{I}_{a2}\mathbf{Z}_{an2} \qquad (53)$$

$$\mathbf{V}_{an2} = \mathbf{I}_{a1}\mathbf{Z}_{an1} + \mathbf{I}_{a2}\mathbf{Z}_{an0} \qquad (54)$$

$$\mathbf{V}_{an0} = \mathbf{I}_{a1}\mathbf{Z}_{an2} + \mathbf{I}_{a2}\mathbf{Z}_{an1} \qquad (55)$$

If the line-to-line voltages, namely, $\mathbf{V}_{ab}$, $\mathbf{V}_{bc}$, and $\mathbf{V}_{ca}$, are known, $\mathbf{V}_{an1}$ and $\mathbf{V}_{an2}$ may be evaluated directly from equations (25) and (26). (See page 500.) If $\mathbf{V}_{an1}$ and $\mathbf{V}_{an2}$ are known, $\mathbf{I}_{a1}$ and $\mathbf{I}_{a2}$ may be determined directly from equations (53) and (54), provided that $\mathbf{Z}_{an1}$, $\mathbf{Z}_{an2}$, and $\mathbf{Z}_{an0}$ are known.

Since $\mathbf{I}_{a0} = 0$,

$$\mathbf{I}_{an} = \mathbf{I}_a = \mathbf{I}_{a1} + \mathbf{I}_{a2} \tag{56}$$

$$\mathbf{I}_{bn} = \mathbf{I}_b = \mathbf{I}_{a1}\underline{/-120^\circ} + \mathbf{I}_{a2}\underline{/120^\circ} \tag{57}$$

$$\mathbf{I}_{cn} = \mathbf{I}_c = \mathbf{I}_{a1}\underline{/120^\circ} + \mathbf{I}_{a2}\underline{/-120^\circ} \tag{58}$$

Even though $\mathbf{I}_{a0} = 0$, $\mathbf{V}_{an0}$ will, in general, possess a finite value since by equation (55) $\mathbf{V}_{an0} = \mathbf{I}_{a1}\mathbf{Z}_{an2} + \mathbf{I}_{a2}\mathbf{Z}_{an1}$.

Example 8. Let the line-to-line voltages and the phase impedances of the wye-connected load shown in Fig. 11 be as follows:

$$V_{ab} = 200 \quad V_{bc} = 141.4 \quad V_{ca} = 141.4 \text{ volts}$$

$$\mathbf{Z}_{an} = (6 + j0) \quad \mathbf{Z}_{bn} = (5.2 - j3) \quad \mathbf{Z}_{cn} = (0 + j12) \text{ ohms}$$

If the voltage sequence is *ab–bc–ca* and if $\mathbf{V}_{ab}$ is taken as reference,

$$\mathbf{V}_{ab} = 200\underline{/0^\circ} \quad \mathbf{V}_{bc} = 141.4\underline{/-135^\circ} \quad \mathbf{V}_{ca} = 141.4\underline{/135^\circ} \text{ volts}$$

Resolution of the above line-to-line voltages into symmetrical components yields

$$\mathbf{V}_{ab1} = \tfrac{1}{3}[200\underline{/0^\circ} + 141.4\underline{/-15^\circ} + 141.4\underline{/15^\circ}] = 157.8\underline{/0^\circ} \text{ volts}$$

$$\mathbf{V}_{ab2} = \tfrac{1}{3}[200\underline{/0^\circ} + 141.4\underline{/105^\circ} + 141.4\underline{/-105^\circ}] = 42.3\underline{/0^\circ} \text{ volts}$$

$$\mathbf{V}_{ab0} = \tfrac{1}{3}[200\underline{/0^\circ} + 141.4\underline{/-135^\circ} + 141.4\underline{/135^\circ}] = 0$$

From equations (25) and (26)

$$\mathbf{V}_{an1} = \frac{157.8\underline{/0^\circ}}{\sqrt{3}}\underline{/-30^\circ} = 91\underline{/-30^\circ} \text{ volts}$$

$$\mathbf{V}_{an2} = \frac{42.3\underline{/0^\circ}}{\sqrt{3}}\underline{/30^\circ} = 24.4\underline{/30^\circ} \text{ volts}$$

The symmetrical components of the phase impedances are

$$\mathbf{Z}_{an1} = 5.47\underline{/0^\circ}, \quad \mathbf{Z}_{an2} = (-3.2 - j3) = 4.38\underline{/-136.8^\circ}$$

and

$$\mathbf{Z}_{an0} = (3.73 + j3) = 4.78\underline{/38.8^\circ} \text{ ohms}$$ (See example 7, page 510.)

From equations (53) and (54)

$$\mathbf{I}_{a1} = \frac{\begin{vmatrix} \mathbf{V}_{an1} & \mathbf{Z}_{an2} \\ \mathbf{V}_{an2} & \mathbf{Z}_{an0} \end{vmatrix}}{\begin{vmatrix} \mathbf{Z}_{an0} & \mathbf{Z}_{an2} \\ \mathbf{Z}_{an1} & \mathbf{Z}_{an0} \end{vmatrix}} = \frac{\begin{vmatrix} 91\angle{-30^\circ} & 4.38\angle{-136.8^\circ} \\ 24.4\angle{30^\circ} & 4.78\angle{38.8^\circ} \end{vmatrix}}{\begin{vmatrix} 4.78\angle{38.8^\circ} & 4.38\angle{-136.8^\circ} \\ 5.47\angle{0^\circ} & 4.78\angle{38.8^\circ} \end{vmatrix}} = \frac{491\angle{20.15^\circ}}{44.8\angle{59.95^\circ}}$$

$$\mathbf{I}_{a1} = 10.95\angle{-39.8^\circ} = 8.42 - j7.02 \text{ amperes}$$

$$\mathbf{I}_{a2} = \frac{\begin{vmatrix} \mathbf{Z}_{an0} & \mathbf{V}_{an1} \\ \mathbf{Z}_{an1} & \mathbf{V}_{an2} \end{vmatrix}}{\begin{vmatrix} \mathbf{Z}_{an0} & \mathbf{Z}_{an2} \\ \mathbf{Z}_{an1} & \mathbf{Z}_{an0} \end{vmatrix}} = \frac{\begin{vmatrix} 4.78\angle{38.8^\circ} & 91\angle{-30^\circ} \\ 5.47\angle{0^\circ} & 24.4\angle{30^\circ} \end{vmatrix}}{44.8\angle{59.95^\circ}} = \frac{528\angle{137.5^\circ}}{44.8\angle{59.95^\circ}}$$

$$\mathbf{I}_{a2} = 11.8\angle{77.45^\circ} = 2.56 + j11.5 \text{ amperes}$$

$$\mathbf{I}_{an} = \mathbf{I}_a = \mathbf{I}_{a1} + \mathbf{I}_{a2} = (8.42 - j7.02) + (2.56 + j11.5)$$
$$= 10.98 + j4.48 \text{ amperes}$$

In polar form

$$\mathbf{I}_a = 11.83\angle{22.2^\circ} \text{ amperes}$$

After $\mathbf{I}_{a1}$ and $\mathbf{I}_{a2}$ have been evaluated, $\mathbf{I}_{b1}$, $\mathbf{I}_{b2}$, $\mathbf{I}_{c1}$, and $\mathbf{I}_{c2}$ follow directly, and hence $\mathbf{I}_{bn}$ and $\mathbf{I}_{cn}$ may be determined from the values of $\mathbf{I}_{a1}$ and $\mathbf{I}_{a2}$.

If the value of $\mathbf{V}_{an}$ is to be determined by the method of symmetrical components,

$$\mathbf{V}_{an} = \mathbf{V}_{an1} + \mathbf{V}_{an2} + \mathbf{V}_{an0}$$

where, from equation (55), $\mathbf{V}_{an0} = \mathbf{I}_{a1}\mathbf{Z}_{an2} + \mathbf{I}_{a2}\mathbf{Z}_{an1}$. In this case

$$\mathbf{V}_{an0} = (10.95\angle{-39.8^\circ})\,(4.38\angle{-136.8^\circ}) + (11.8\angle{77.45^\circ})\,(5.47\angle{0^\circ})$$
$$= -34 + j60.2 \text{ volts}$$

$$\mathbf{V}_{an} = (78.85 - j45.5) + (21.15 + j12.2) + (-34 + j60.2)$$
$$= 66 + j26.9 \text{ volts}$$

Problem 10. Study through the details of the above example and evaluate $\mathbf{I}_b$, $\mathbf{I}_c$, $\mathbf{V}_{bn}$, and $\mathbf{V}_{cn}$ by the method of symmetrical components. Check $\mathbf{V}_{an} - \mathbf{V}_{bn}$ against the given value of $\mathbf{V}_{ab} = 200\angle{0^\circ}$ volts, recognizing that slide-rule calculations were employed in the evaluations of $\mathbf{I}_{a1}$, $\mathbf{I}_{a2}$, and $\mathbf{V}_{an}$.

Ans.: $\mathbf{I}_b = -21.53 - j7.31 = 22.7\angle{-161.2^\circ}$ amperes.

Magnetic Coupling between Phases. If the three phases (including the line wires) possess mutual coupling of the kind shown in Fig. 12, the voltage drop in phase *an* due to its mutual coupling with phases *bn* and *cn* is:

$$\mathbf{V}_{am} = \mathbf{I}_b\mathbf{Z}_{ab} + \mathbf{I}_c\mathbf{Z}_{ac} \tag{59}$$

where subscript m designates the fact that this voltage drop excludes the self-impedance voltage drop, namely, $\mathbf{I}_a\mathbf{Z}_{aa}$. If simple magnetic coupling is involved,

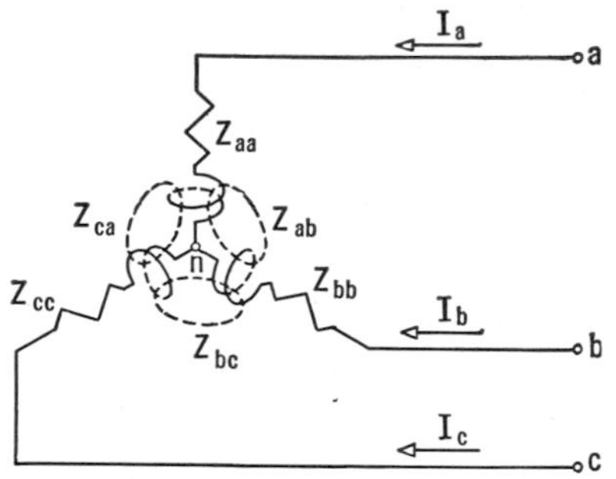

FIG. 12. Impedance in wye with mutual coupling between phases.

$$\mathbf{Z}_{ab} = jX_{ab} = \pm j\omega M_{ab} \quad (60)$$

$$\mathbf{Z}_{ac} = jX_{ac} = \pm j\omega M_{ac} \quad (61)$$

(See Chapter VII.)

The signs of the mutual reactances are defined by the assigned directions of current flow and the modes of winding the mutually coupled coils.

The impedance drop in phase an due to the self-impedance of that phase will be called $\mathbf{V}_{aa}$, and the total voltage drop in phase an then becomes:

$$\mathbf{V}_{an} = \mathbf{V}_{aa} + \mathbf{V}_{am} = \mathbf{I}_a\mathbf{Z}_{aa} + \mathbf{I}_b\mathbf{Z}_{ab} + \mathbf{I}_c\mathbf{Z}_{ac} \quad (62)$$

The problem of expressing the impedance drops of equation (62) in terms of symmetrical components will now be undertaken. Obviously $\mathbf{I}_a$, $\mathbf{I}_b$, and $\mathbf{I}_c$ may be expressed in terms of the symmetrical components of any one of these currents and $\mathbf{Z}_{aa}$ may be resolved into symmetrical components if the other self-impedances $\mathbf{Z}_{bb}$ and $\mathbf{Z}_{cc}$ are known. In this connection:

$$\mathbf{Z}_{aa1} = \tfrac{1}{3}(\mathbf{Z}_{aa} + \mathbf{Z}_{bb}\underline{/120^\circ} + \mathbf{Z}_{cc}\underline{/-120^\circ}), \quad \text{etc.}$$

if the other resolutions are effected in the a–b–c order.

The self-impedance voltage drop in phase an may be written in terms of symmetrical components in accordance with the sequence rule.

$$\mathbf{V}_{aa} = \mathbf{V}_{aa1} + \mathbf{V}_{aa2} + \mathbf{V}_{aa0} \quad (63)$$

where

$$\mathbf{V}_{aa1} = \mathbf{I}_{a1}\mathbf{Z}_{aa0} + \mathbf{I}_{a2}\mathbf{Z}_{aa2} + \mathbf{I}_{a0}\mathbf{Z}_{aa1} \quad (64)$$

$$\mathbf{V}_{aa2} = \mathbf{I}_{a1}\mathbf{Z}_{aa1} + \mathbf{I}_{a2}\mathbf{Z}_{aa0} + \mathbf{I}_{a0}\mathbf{Z}_{aa2} \quad (65)$$

$$\mathbf{V}_{aa0} = \mathbf{I}_{a1}\mathbf{Z}_{aa2} + \mathbf{I}_{a2}\mathbf{Z}_{aa1} + \mathbf{I}_{a0}\mathbf{Z}_{aa0} \quad (66)$$

There remains the problem of resolving the mutual impedances $\mathbf{Z}_{ab} = \mathbf{Z}_{ba}$, $\mathbf{Z}_{bc} = \mathbf{Z}_{cb}$, and $\mathbf{Z}_{ca} = \mathbf{Z}_{ac}$ into symmetrical components that can be advantageously associated with $\mathbf{I}_{a1}$, $\mathbf{I}_{a2}$, and $\mathbf{I}_{a0}$ to account for the presence of $\mathbf{I}_b\mathbf{Z}_{ab}$ and $\mathbf{I}_c\mathbf{Z}_{ac}$ in equation (62). At this stage of the development it is rather difficult to say which of the three mutual impedances should be considered as the base mutual impedance. It turns out that the symmetrical components of $\mathbf{Z}_{bc}$ can best be associated with $\mathbf{I}_{a1}$, $\mathbf{I}_{a2}$, and $\mathbf{I}_{a0}$. See equation (72).

Resolving the mutual impedances into symmetrical components with $\mathbf{Z}_{bc}$ as base yields

$$\mathbf{Z}_{bc1} = \tfrac{1}{3}(\mathbf{Z}_{bc} + \mathbf{Z}_{ca}\underline{/120^\circ} + \mathbf{Z}_{ab}\underline{/-120^\circ}) \tag{67}$$

$$\mathbf{Z}_{bc2} = \tfrac{1}{3}(\mathbf{Z}_{bc} + \mathbf{Z}_{ca}\underline{/-120^\circ} + \mathbf{Z}_{ab}\underline{/120^\circ}) \tag{68}$$

$$\mathbf{Z}_{bc0} = \tfrac{1}{3}(\mathbf{Z}_{bc} + \mathbf{Z}_{ca} + \mathbf{Z}_{ab}) = \mathbf{Z}_{ca0} = \mathbf{Z}_{ab0} \tag{69}$$

$$\mathbf{Z}_{ab1} = \mathbf{Z}_{bc1}\underline{/120^\circ} \quad \mathbf{Z}_{ca1} = \mathbf{Z}_{bc1}\underline{/-120^\circ} \tag{70}$$

$$\mathbf{Z}_{ab2} = \mathbf{Z}_{bc2}\underline{/-120^\circ} \quad \mathbf{Z}_{ca2} = \mathbf{Z}_{bc2}\underline{/120^\circ} \tag{71}$$

In terms of symmetrical components,

$$\begin{aligned}\mathbf{V}_{am} &= \mathbf{I}_b\mathbf{Z}_{ab} + \mathbf{I}_c\mathbf{Z}_{ac} \\ &= (\mathbf{I}_{a1}\underline{/-120^\circ} + \mathbf{I}_{a2}\underline{/120^\circ} + \mathbf{I}_{a0})(\mathbf{Z}_{bc1}\underline{/120^\circ} + \mathbf{Z}_{bc2}\underline{/-120^\circ} \\ &\quad + \mathbf{Z}_{bc0}) + (\mathbf{I}_{a1}\underline{/120^\circ} + \mathbf{I}_{a2}\underline{/-120^\circ} + \mathbf{I}_{a0})(\mathbf{Z}_{bc1}\underline{/-120^\circ} \\ &\quad + \mathbf{Z}_{bc2}\underline{/120^\circ} + \mathbf{Z}_{bc0})\end{aligned} \tag{72}$$

Eighteen component voltages appear if the multiplications indicated in equation (72) are carried out. These components may be grouped into positive-, negative-, and zero-sequence terms in accordance with the sequence rule. For example, the component voltages of the first order are

$$\begin{aligned}\mathbf{I}_{a1}\mathbf{Z}_{bc0}\underline{/-120^\circ} + \mathbf{I}_{a2}\mathbf{Z}_{bc2} + \mathbf{I}_{a0}\mathbf{Z}_{bc1}\underline{/120^\circ} + \mathbf{I}_{a1}\mathbf{Z}_{bc0}\underline{/120^\circ} + \mathbf{I}_{a2}\mathbf{Z}_{bc2} \\ + \mathbf{I}_{a0}\mathbf{Z}_{bc1}\underline{/-120^\circ} = \mathbf{V}_{am1}\end{aligned} \tag{73}$$

If the like terms in the above equations are further grouped, the following form results:

$$\mathbf{V}_{am1} = -\mathbf{I}_{a1}\mathbf{Z}_{bc0} + 2\mathbf{I}_{a2}\mathbf{Z}_{bc2} - \mathbf{I}_{a0}\mathbf{Z}_{bc1} \tag{74}$$

The negative-sequence or second-order terms of equation (72) may be combined to form

$$\mathbf{V}_{am2} = 2\mathbf{I}_{a1}\mathbf{Z}_{bc1} - \mathbf{I}_{a2}\mathbf{Z}_{bc0} - \mathbf{I}_{a0}\mathbf{Z}_{bc2} \tag{75}$$

The zero-sequence terms of equation (72) may be combined to form

$$\mathbf{V}_{am0} = -\mathbf{I}_{a1}\mathbf{Z}_{bc2} - \mathbf{I}_{a2}\mathbf{Z}_{bc1} + 2\mathbf{I}_{a0}\mathbf{Z}_{bc0} \tag{76}$$

Equations (74), (75), and (76) contain all eighteen component voltages represented in equation (72), and these equations may be combined systematically with equations (64), (65), and (66) to yield the positive-, negative-, and zero-sequence components of the complete phase voltage, namely, $\mathbf{V}_{an} = \mathbf{V}_{aa} + \mathbf{V}_{am}$.

Adding equations (64) and (74), equations (65) and (75), and equations (66) and (76) results in

$$\mathbf{V}_{an1} = \mathbf{I}_{a1}(\mathbf{Z}_{aa0} - \mathbf{Z}_{bc0}) + \mathbf{I}_{a2}(\mathbf{Z}_{aa2} + 2\mathbf{Z}_{bc2}) + \mathbf{I}_{a0}(\mathbf{Z}_{aa1} - \mathbf{Z}_{bc1}) \quad (77)$$

$$\mathbf{V}_{an2} = \mathbf{I}_{a1}(\mathbf{Z}_{aa1} + 2\mathbf{Z}_{bc1}) + \mathbf{I}_{a2}(\mathbf{Z}_{aa0} - \mathbf{Z}_{bc0}) + \mathbf{I}_{a0}(\mathbf{Z}_{aa2} - \mathbf{Z}_{bc2}) \quad (78)$$

$$\mathbf{V}_{an0} = \mathbf{I}_{a1}(\mathbf{Z}_{aa2} - \mathbf{Z}_{bc2}) + \mathbf{I}_{a2}(\mathbf{Z}_{aa1} - \mathbf{Z}_{bc1}) + \mathbf{I}_{a0}(\mathbf{Z}_{aa0} + 2\mathbf{Z}_{bc0}) \quad (79)$$

The above set of equations represents a powerful tool in the field of circuit analysis because with the aid of this set of equations any degree of unbalance and any degree of magnetic or capacitive coupling may be handled on a symmetrical-component basis. Equations (77), (78), and (79) are particularly useful in accounting for transmission line reactance voltage drops because these voltage drops result from mutual coupling between the line wires. These equations are also useful in accounting for the mutual impedance of the fourth wire of a four-wire, three-phase system.

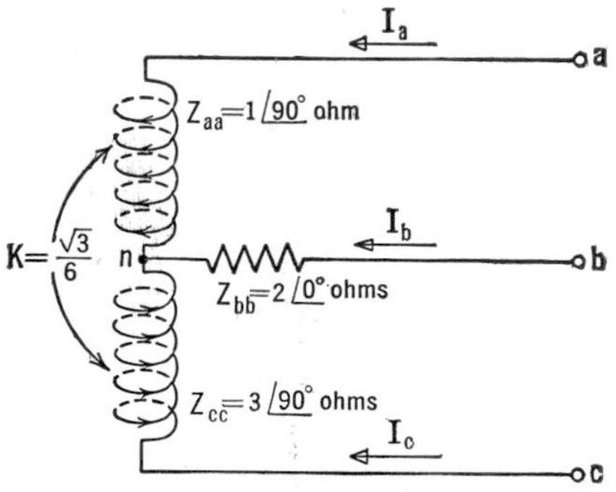

FIG. 13. See example 9.

Example 9. Let it be required to find the current $\mathbf{I}_a$ in Fig. 13 by the method of symmetrical components, if $\mathbf{V}_{ab} = \mathbf{V}_{bc} = \mathbf{V}_{ca} = 100$ volts and the sequence of these voltages is *ab–bc–ca*. From previous considerations, it is plain that

$$\mathbf{V}_{an1} = \frac{\mathbf{V}_{ab1}}{\sqrt{3}} \underline{/-30^\circ} \quad \text{and} \quad \mathbf{V}_{an2} = 0$$

If $\mathbf{V}_{ab}$ is chosen as the reference vector,

$$\mathbf{V}_{an1} = \frac{100}{\sqrt{3}} \underline{/-30^\circ} = (50 - j28.9) \text{ volts}$$

The self-impedances [$\mathbf{Z}_{aa} = (0 + j1)$, $\mathbf{Z}_{bb} = (2 + j0)$, and $\mathbf{Z}_{cc} = (0 + j3)$] may be resolved into symmetrical components in the usual manner.

$$Z_{aa1} = \tfrac{1}{3}(Z_{aa} + Z_{bb}\underline{/120^\circ} + Z_{cc}\underline{/-120^\circ}) = (0.533 + j0.411) \text{ ohms}$$

$$Z_{aa2} = \tfrac{1}{3}(Z_{aa} + Z_{bb}\underline{/-120^\circ} + Z_{cc}\underline{/120^\circ}) = (-1.199 - j0.744) \text{ ohms}$$

$$Z_{aa0} = \tfrac{1}{3}(Z_{aa} + Z_{bb} + Z_{cc}) = (0.667 + j1.33) \text{ ohms}$$

As indicated on the circuit diagram (Fig. 13), the coefficient of coupling between the two inductance coils is $\sqrt{3}/6$. This coefficient is interpreted to mean that

$$\omega M_{ca} = \omega M_{ac} = \frac{\sqrt{3}}{6}\sqrt{\omega L_{aa} \times \omega L_{cc}} = \frac{\sqrt{3}}{6}\sqrt{1 \times 3} = 0.5 \text{ ohm}$$

If the modes of winding and the space positions of the coils are as represented in Fig. 13,

$$Z_{ca} = (0 - j\omega M_{ca}) = (0 - j0.5) \text{ ohm}$$

Z_{ab} and Z_{bc} are both zero because no coupling exists between phases a and b or between phases b and c under the specified conditions.

In accordance with equations (67), (68), and (69),

$$Z_{bc1} = \tfrac{1}{3}(0.5\underline{/-90^\circ + 120^\circ}) = 0.144 + j0.083 \text{ ohm}$$

$$Z_{bc2} = \tfrac{1}{3}(0.5\underline{/-90^\circ - 120^\circ}) = -0.144 + j0.083 \text{ ohm}$$

$$Z_{bc0} = \tfrac{1}{3}(0.5\underline{/-90^\circ}) = 0 - j0.167 \text{ ohm}$$

Since I_{a0} is equal to zero, it follows from equations (77) and (78) that

$$V_{an1} = 50 - j28.9 = I_{a1}(0.667 + j1.50) + I_{a2}(-1.487 - j0.578)$$

$$V_{an2} = 0 \qquad\qquad = I_{a1}(0.821 + j0.578) + I_{a2}(0.667 + j1.50)$$

The above equations may be solved simultaneously for I_{a1} and I_{a2}

$$I_{a1} = \frac{\begin{vmatrix} (50 - j28.9) & (-1.487 - j0.578) \\ 0 & (0.667 + j1.50) \end{vmatrix}}{\begin{vmatrix} (0.667 + j1.50) & (-1.487 - j0.578) \\ (0.821 + j0.578) & (0.667 + j1.50) \end{vmatrix}} = \frac{76.6 + j55.7}{-0.918 + j3.33}$$

$$= (9.63 - j25.6) \text{ amperes}$$

$$I_{a2} = \frac{\begin{vmatrix} (0.667 + j1.50) & (50 - j28.9) \\ (0.821 + j0.578) & 0 \end{vmatrix}}{(-0.918 + j3.33)} = \frac{-57.7 - j5.1}{-0.918 + j3.33}$$

$$= (3.01 + j16.46) \text{ amperes}$$

$$I_a = I_{a1} + I_{a2} = (9.63 - j25.6) + (3.01 + j16.46)$$

$$= (12.64 - j9.14) = 15.6\underline{/-35.85^\circ} \text{ amperes}$$

PROBLEMS

11. The line-to-neutral voltages of a four-wire, three-phase system are represented by the following vector expressions: $V_a = 200\underline{/0^\circ}$, $V_b = 100\underline{/-75^\circ}$, $V_c = 150\underline{/-150^\circ}$.

Find the positive-, negative-, and zero-sequence components of the above voltages, and check the results obtained by graphical additions of the symmetrical components.

12. The three line currents of a four-wire wye load (like that shown in Fig. 7, page 506) directed to the common junction are $\mathbf{I}_{an} = 15 - j20$, $\mathbf{I}_{bn} = -8 + j15$, and $\mathbf{I}_{cn} = 8 - j25$ amperes. Find $\mathbf{I}_{an1}$, $\mathbf{I}_{an2}$, and $\mathbf{I}_{an0}$ assuming these currents were calculated from a voltage system where the actual voltage sequence was *a–b–c*.

13. Voltages to neutral on a four-wire Y-load are maintained at $\mathbf{V}_{na} = 100\underline{/0^\circ}$, $\mathbf{V}_{nb} = 100\underline{/-120^\circ}$, and $\mathbf{V}_{nc} = 100\underline{/120^\circ}$ volts. Impedances are $\mathbf{Z}_{na} = 10\underline{/0^\circ}$, $\mathbf{Z}_{nb} = 10\underline{/90^\circ}$, and $\mathbf{Z}_{nc} = 10\underline{/-90^\circ}$.

(*a*) Find the positive-, negative-, and zero-sequence line currents, if the positive-sequence voltage system is *a–b–c*.

(*b*) Find the power due to each of the sequences, positive, negative, and zero.

(*c*) Should the phasor which lags the base phasor be rotated forward 120° to obtain the positive-sequence current? Why?

14. (*a*) Three-phase voltages are supplied by lines *a*, *b*, and *c*. If a short circuit is placed from line *a* to line *b*, find positive-, negative-, and zero-sequence components of the line voltages at the short circuit in terms of a line voltage of *V*.

(*b*) If the short-circuit current is *I* find the symmetrical components of the current at the short circuit.

15. The three wye-connected impedances through which the currents of Problem 12 flow are, respectively,

$$\mathbf{Z}_{an} = 20 - j20 \text{ ohms}$$

$$\mathbf{Z}_{bn} = 30 + j10 \text{ ohms}$$

$$\mathbf{Z}_{cn} = 10 - j20 \text{ ohms}$$

Find $\mathbf{Z}_{an1}$, $\mathbf{Z}_{an2}$, and $\mathbf{Z}_{an0}$.

16. Employing the symmetrical components $\mathbf{I}_{an1}$, $\mathbf{I}_{an2}$, $\mathbf{I}_{an0}$, $\mathbf{Z}_{an1}$, $\mathbf{Z}_{an2}$, and $\mathbf{Z}_{an0}$ determined in Problems 12 and 15, evaluate $\mathbf{V}_{an} = \mathbf{I}_{an}\mathbf{Z}_{an}$ in terms of symmetrical components and check the result against the known value of $\mathbf{I}_{an}\mathbf{Z}_{an}$.

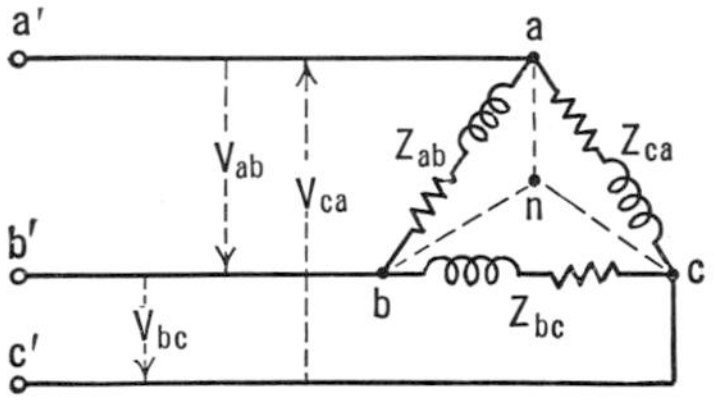

FIG. 14. See Problem 17.

17. Assume that the three-phase line voltages shown in Fig. 14 are

$$V_{bc} = 200\underline{/0^\circ}, \quad V_{ca} = 100\underline{/120^\circ}, \quad V_{ab} = 173.2\underline{/210^\circ}$$

(*a*) Find $\mathbf{V}_{bc1}$, $\mathbf{V}_{bc2}$, and $\mathbf{V}_{bc0}$.

(*b*) Find $\mathbf{V}_{nc1}$, $\mathbf{V}_{nc2}$, and $\mathbf{V}_{nc0}$. Employ phase sequence *bc*, *ab*, *ca*.

18. The three line-to-line voltages shown in Fig. 14 are

$$V_{ab} = 100, \quad V_{bc} = 150, \quad V_{ca} = 175 \text{ volts}$$

Sequence *ab–bc–ca*.

(*a*) Find $\mathbf{V}_{ab1}$, $\mathbf{V}_{ab2}$, and $\mathbf{V}_{ab0}$.

(*b*) Find $\mathbf{V}_{an1}$ and $\mathbf{V}_{an2}$, the equivalent wye voltages of the delta load shown in Fig. 14.

(*c*) Explain how the line currents may be determined from $\mathbf{V}_{an1}$, $\mathbf{V}_{an2}$, and the delta load impedances.

19. The line-to-line voltages of a three-wire, three-phase system are $V_{ab} = 200$ volts, $V_{bc} = 141.4$ volts, and $V_{ca} = 141.4$ volts. The sequence of the voltages is *ab–ca–bc*. A wye-connected set of static impedances ($\mathbf{Z}_{an} = 20\underline{/0°}$ ohms, $\mathbf{Z}_{bn} = 30\underline{/60°}$ ohms, and $\mathbf{Z}_{cn} = 20\underline{/0°}$ ohms) is connected to the three lines *a*, *b*, and *c* in the order indicated by the subscripts. Find the line currents $\mathbf{I}_{an}$, $\mathbf{I}_{bn}$, and $\mathbf{I}_{cn}$ by the method of symmetrical components.

20. Solve for $\mathbf{I}_a$ in Fig. 13 by the method of symmetrical components if $V_{ab} = 200$, $V_{bc} = 173.2$, and $V_{ca} = 100$ volts. The sequence of the line-to-line voltages is *ab–bc–ca*.

chapter XIII Power System Short-Circuit Calculations

Power systems are subject to three kinds of short circuits. First, all three lines of a three-phase system may become electrically connected. This is known as a three-phase short circuit. Second, only two lines may be electrically connected, which constitutes a line-to-line short circuit. Third, a single wire may be electrically connected to ground. This is called a line-to-ground short circuit. Although the electrical connections referred to may be of varying impedance, short-circuit calculations are based upon zero impedance at the point of short circuit. In other words, a perfect short circuit is assumed. Short circuits on systems are usually called faults.

A distribution system should be protected in such a way that a faulty or short-circuited section will be isolated from the rest of the system. This is accomplished through the use of relays which operate circuit breakers. To protect a system, relays are set to trip in a certain length of time after the fault occurs. By varying the amount of time required for a relay to operate, certain selective operation of circuit breakers may be obtained. After proper adjustments are made, this selective operation causes only the faulty section of the line to be isolated. In order to determine the proper time settings of these relays and in order to determine the sizes of circuit breakers necessary, the magnitudes of the short-circuit currents that these devices are to handle must be known. In general, different values of short-circuit current occur for the three-phase symmetrical, line-to-line, and line-to-ground short circuits. Usually the three-phase symmetrical short circuit yields the lowest value of short-circuit current (except when the system has practically no grounds). Hence relay settings are usually based upon three-phase symmetrical faults because it is desirable to protect a system for the minimum fault current. If the relay trips a circuit breaker for minimum fault current, it will obviously open the breaker for the highest fault current, but the converse is not true. Since a breaker must interrupt the largest short-circuit current that can possibly exist, the size of a circuit breaker is determined by the largest possible fault current. The greatest current usually occurs for either the line-to-line or line-to-ground fault. Obviously, the determination of short-circuit currents in power systems is required if the proper settings of relays and proper selection of circuit-breaker sizes are to be made.

Bases for Short-Circuit Calculations. A distribution network consists of many lines which may be connected by transformers and which, in general, operate at different nominal voltages. To establish a simple network for purposes of calculation, the impedances of all lines and transformers are expressed in ohms referred to a common voltage base or in percentage referred to a common kilovolt-ampere base. The former generally appears simpler to the beginner, but the latter method is actually the better and is to be preferred. The two methods yield identical results.

Method Using Ohms on a Kilovolt Base. In general, various branches of an electrical distribution system operate at different potentials. In representing such a system by a system of impedances, it is desirable to employ a scheme which permits the combination of the different impedances so that the network can be represented by a single impedance between the source and the fault. This requires the determination of an impedance, Z_2, which may be used with an arbitrarily selected voltage, V_2, such that the same kva will be taken as when the actual impedance, Z_1, is used with the actual voltage V_1. Stated algebraically,

$$\left(\frac{V_2}{Z_2}\right) V_2 = \frac{V_1}{Z_1} V_1$$

or

$$Z_2 = Z_1 \left(\frac{V_2}{V_1}\right)^2 \tag{1}$$

Equation (1) shows that the original impedance must be multiplied by the square of the ratio of voltage to be used to the nominal operating voltage for the impedance. To illustrate, suppose that 1000 volts are impressed on an impedance of 100 ohms and that it is desired to find the current and kva taken.

$$I_1 = \frac{1000}{100} = 10 \text{ amperes}$$

$$va = 1000 \times 10 = 10{,}000$$

Now assume that it is desired to work the same problem when all values are referred to a 2000-volt base. Then

$$Z_2 = \left(\frac{2000}{1000}\right)^2 \times 100 = 400 \text{ ohms}$$

$$I_2 = \frac{2000}{400} = 5 \text{ amperes}$$

$$va = 2000 \times 5 = 10{,}000$$

The foregoing example shows that there is no difference between calculating the volt-amperes for the actual voltage and impedance and for some other selected voltage and an equivalent impedance found by multiplying the original impedance by the square of the ratio of the selected voltage to the original. The current on the actual voltage base is then found by multiplying the result calculated on the selected voltage base by the ratio of the voltages. Thus the actual current at 1000 volts is:

$$I_1 = 5 \times \frac{2000}{1000} = 10 \text{ amperes}$$

This procedure is evident from the following relationship.

$$V_1 I_1 = V_2 I_2$$

or

$$I_1 = \frac{V_2}{V_1} I_2$$

Example 1. Calculate the short-circuit current for the system shown in Fig. 1. A 10 to 1 ratio wye-wye connected transformer bank is represented at A. A transformer has resistance and leakage reactance which may be referred to either side as

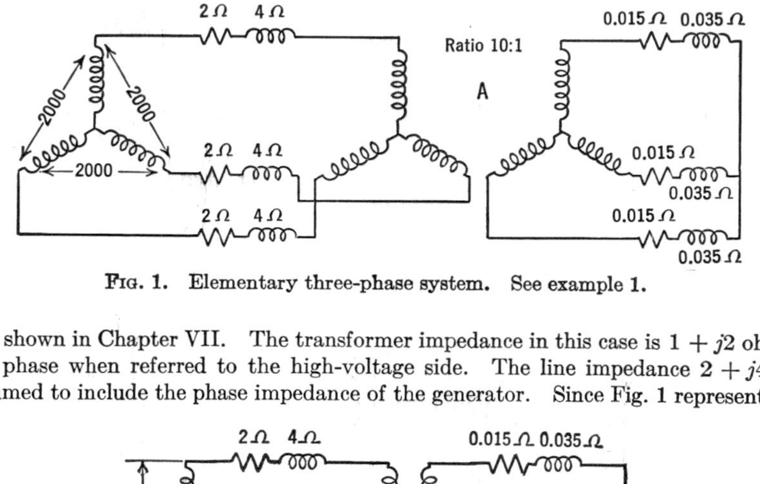

FIG. 1. Elementary three-phase system. See example 1.

was shown in Chapter VII. The transformer impedance in this case is $1 + j2$ ohms per phase when referred to the high-voltage side. The line impedance $2 + j4$ is assumed to include the phase impedance of the generator. Since Fig. 1 represents a

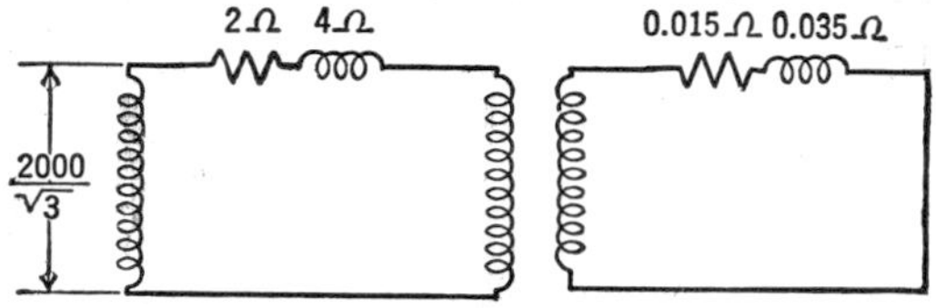

FIG. 2. Equivalent circuit per phase of Fig. 1.

balanced circuit, all calculations will be made per phase. The equivalent circuit for one phase to neutral is shown in Fig. 2, and the corresponding one-line diagram is shown in Fig. 3. A short line at the generator neutral is used to represent the neutral bus, and a cross at the end of the line denotes the point of short circuit. The per phase voltage is impressed between the neutral bus and the point X. The trans-

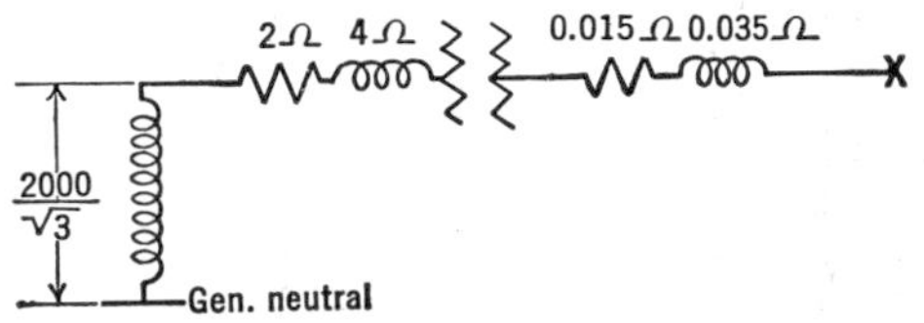

FIG. 3. One-line diagram of Fig. 2 and Fig. 1.

former impedance causes a drop in voltage from its primary to its secondary side and therefore acts like a series impedance. Transferring the impedance of the secondary line to its equivalent value on a 2000-volt base (the primary line-to-line voltage), or

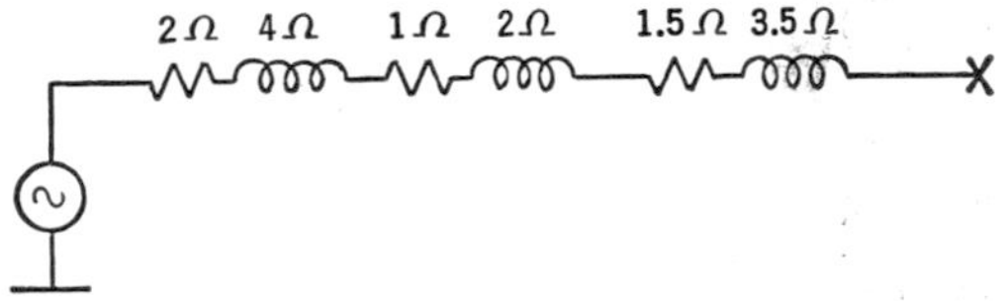

FIG. 4. Reduction of Fig. 3 to a series of impedances.

to a $2000/\sqrt{3}$ volts to neutral base which is the same, and inserting the transformer equivalent impedance, reduces the one-line diagram to the equivalent circuit shown in Fig. 4. Then

$$\mathbf{I} = \frac{2000/\sqrt{3}}{(2 + j4) + (1 + j2) + (1.5 + j3.5)}$$
$$= 47 - j99.2 \quad \text{or} \quad 109.8 \text{ amperes}$$

The actual current at the fault is found by referring the current to the voltage of the faulty line.

$$\text{Fault current} = 109.8 \times 10 = 1098 \text{ amperes}$$

Problem 1. A wye-connected generator rated at 2200 terminal volts has 0.2 ohm resistance and 2 ohms reactance per phase. The generator is connected by lines each having an impedance of $2.06 \underline{/29.05^\circ}$ ohms to a wye-wye transformer bank. Each transformer has a total equivalent impedance referred to the high side of $100 \underline{/60^\circ}$ ohms, and the transformer bank is connected to a load through lines each of which has a resistance of 50 ohms and an inductive reactance of 100 ohms. If the ratio of transformation is 6 and the low-voltage side is connected to the generator lines, calculate the actual fault current for a three-phase symmetrical short circuit at the load.

Ans.: 22.3 amperes.

Percentage Method. In general, short-circuit calculations are made through the use of percentage resistances and reactances. Percentage reactance is defined as the percentage of the rated voltage which is consumed in the reactance drop when rated current flows. Expressed algebraically,

$$\% \text{ reactance} = \frac{I_{\text{rated}} \times \text{ohms}}{V_{\text{rated}}} \times 100 \tag{2}$$

Percentage resistance is similarly defined. Percentage values are manipulated like ohmic values. When percentage values are employed, a common kva base is used instead of a common voltage base as employed in the ohmic method. The derivation of the method for determining the percentage reactance on different kva bases follows. Three-phase will be assumed since it is the most common.

Let p be the percentage reactance based on a particular 3-phase kva.

kv = the voltage between the three-phase lines in kilovolts.
X = the reactance in ohms.

Then
$$IX = \frac{X \text{ kva } 10^{-3}}{\sqrt{3} \text{ kv}} \text{ kilovolts}$$

$$p = \frac{100IX}{\text{kv}/\sqrt{3}} = \frac{\dfrac{100X \text{ kva } 10^{-3}}{\sqrt{3} \text{ kv}}}{\text{kv}/\sqrt{3}} = \frac{X \text{ kva}}{\overline{\text{kv}}^2\, 10} \tag{3}$$

Equation (3) shows that percentage reactance varies directly with the kva when the rest of the factors remain constant. A similar relation holds true for percentage resistance. Although equation (3) was derived on the assumption of three-phase it is equally applicable to single-phase.

Example 2. By way of illustrating the use of percentage resistance and reactance, example 1, which was worked on the ohmic basis, will be reworked employing the percentage method. Ordinarily, much of the data on a system is expressed in percentage and no transformation from ohmic to percentage impedance is necessary. Since the parameters in the previous example are given in ohms, the transformation to percentage will be shown. Also, to illustrate changing to a common base, the percentage impedance of the lines on the generator side of the transformer and the transformer will be found on a 10,000-kva base, while that on the secondary side will be found on a 100-kva base.

For the lines on generator side of transformer:

$$\text{Base current } I = \frac{10{,}000{,}000}{\sqrt{3}\, 2000} = 2885 \text{ amperes}$$

$$\% \, IX \text{ drop due to base current} = 100 \times \frac{2885 \times 4}{2000/\sqrt{3}} = 1000, \text{ or } 1000\% \text{ reactance}$$

$$\% \, IR \text{ drop due to base current} = 100 \times \frac{2885 \times 2}{2000/\sqrt{3}} = 500, \text{ or } 500\% \text{ resistance}$$

Transformer impedance on 10,000-kva base:

$$\% \, IR \text{ drop} = \frac{100 \times 2885 \times 1}{2000/\sqrt{3}} = 250$$

$$\% \, IX \text{ drop} = \frac{100 \times 2885 \times 2}{2000/\sqrt{3}} = 500$$

The line impedance on the secondary side of the transformer based on 100 kva is determined as follows:

$$\text{Nominal rated voltage on secondary} \frac{2000}{10} = 200 \text{ volts}$$

$$\text{Base current } I = \frac{100{,}000}{\sqrt{3}\,200} = 288.5 \text{ amperes}$$

$$\% \, IX \text{ drop} = \frac{100 \times 288.5 \times 0.035}{200/\sqrt{3}} = 8.75$$

$$\% \, IR \text{ drop} = \frac{100 \times 288.5 \times 0.015}{200/\sqrt{3}} = 3.75$$

The circuit of Fig. 1 with parameters expressed in percentage is shown in Fig. 5. It is common to receive data on distribution networks expressed like those in Fig. 5.

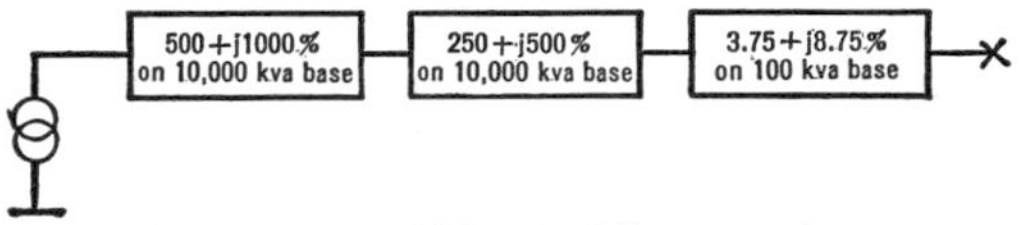

FIG. 5. One-line diagram of Fig. 1 with parameters expressed on a percentage basis.

Before simplifying, a common kva base is chosen to which all constants are referred. This base may be any arbitrarily selected. A 1000-kva base is chosen for this example because it yields convenient numerical quantities.

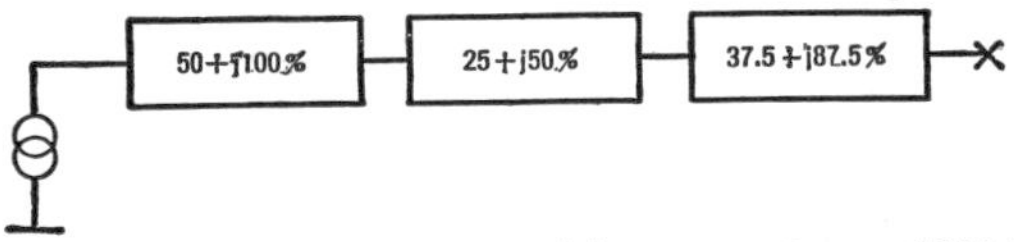

FIG. 6. Impedances of Fig. 5 expressed in per cent on a 1000-kva base.

It was shown that percentage reactance and resistance, and hence impedance, vary directly with the kva base. Employing this principle yields the circuit shown in Fig. 6. The combined impedance to the fault is

$$50 + j100 + 25 + j50 + 37.5 + j87.5 = 112.5 + j237.5\%$$

or

$$\sqrt{112.5^2 + 237.5^2} = 263\%$$

This result indicates that 263 per cent of the rated voltage is necessary to cause 1000 kva to be delivered by the generator. Since only rated voltage, or 100 per cent voltage, is available, the total short-circuit kva must be $\frac{100}{263} \times 1000 = 380.5$ kva. If the fault current is desired at the actual voltage of the faulty line, namely, 200 volts, it is found as follows:

$$I_{\text{fault}} = \frac{380.5 \times 1000}{\sqrt{3} \times 200} = 1098 \text{ amperes}$$

Problem 2. Rework Problem 1, page 525, employing percentage values.

Per Unit Method. A study of the percentage method will show that problems could be worked by using percentage values expressed in hundredths, which would be equivalent to moving the decimal point two places to the left in the calculations shown in example 2. In other words, quantities could be expressed on a per unit basis instead of on a per hundred basis as in the percentage method. Thus instead of a reactance of 15 per cent a value of 0.15 would be used. A little experience with both schemes shows relatively little difference in the methods. Both methods are used according to personal preferences.

Accuracy of Short-Circuit Calculations. In general, extreme accuracy in the determination of short-circuit currents in distribution systems is not required. Because the resistance of most synchronous apparatus is low compared to the reactance, the final impedance to the fault in many cases is about the same as the reactance. For this reason, and because of the resulting simplification of the calculations, only reactances are generally used. An exception to these statements occurs when stability studies of systems are made. It then becomes necessary to consider phase angles, and then both resistance and reactance must be considered.

When several sources of current are in parallel, it is customary to assume that all the generated voltages are in phase and equal in magnitude at the time of short circuit. Load currents on the system are neglected. All synchronous apparatus like generators, synchronous motors, and rotary converters are considered as sources of short-circuit current. The kinetic energy of these rotating machines causes them to act like generators during the first few cycles of short circuit. In spite of all these approximations, tests have shown that calculations based upon these assumptions are usually within about 5 per cent of the correct values. From 5 to 10 per cent error in the values of short-circuit currents is usually tolerable in the determination of circuit-breaker sizes and relay settings.

Three-Phase Short Circuits. Three-phase short-circuit currents are determined by means of the same principles employed in the analysis of balanced three-phase systems. The method is best shown by an example.

Example 3. It is desired to find the short-circuit current for the system shown in Fig. 7. The data for the system are shown in Table I. A symmetrical three-phase

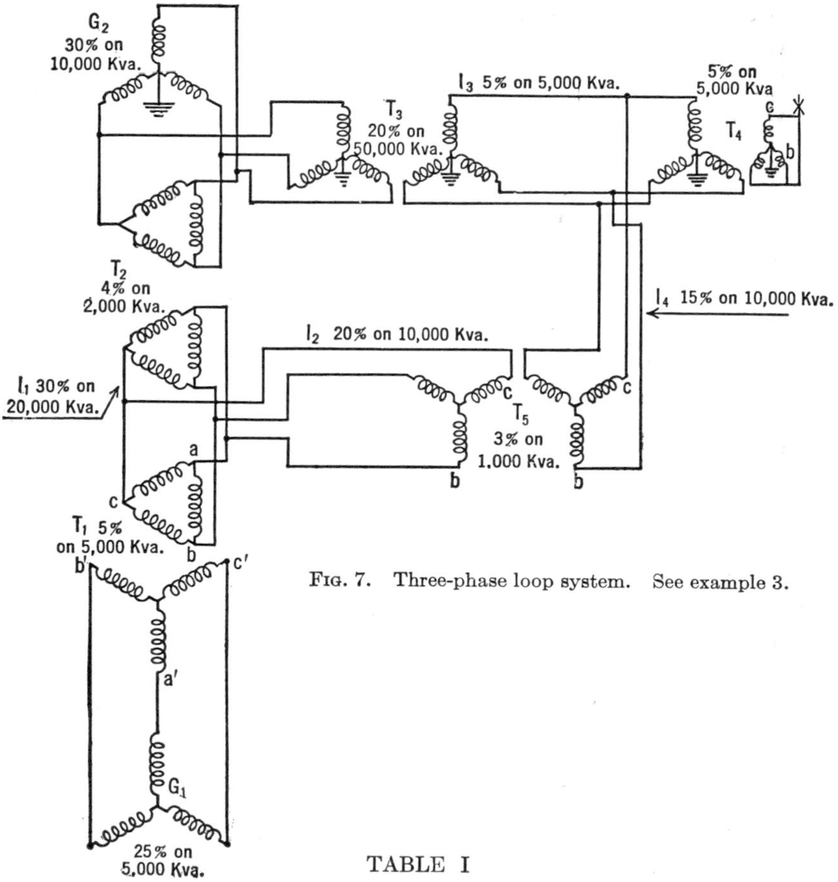

FIG. 7. Three-phase loop system. See example 3.

TABLE I

Apparatus	Rating kva	% Reactance	% Reactance based on kva
Generator 1	5,000	25	5,000
Generator 2	10,000	30	10,000
Transformer 1	4,000	5	5,000
Transformer 2	2,000	4	2,000
Transformer 3	5,000	20	50,000
Transformer 4	5,000	5	5,000
Transformer 5	1,000	3	1,000
Line 1		30	20,000
Line 2		20	10,000
Line 3		5	5,000
Line 4		15	10,000

short circuit is assumed at the point denoted by the cross in the upper right-hand corner of the circuit diagram.

The following represents a satisfactory procedure.

1. A one-line diagram of the system as shown in Fig. 8 is drawn.

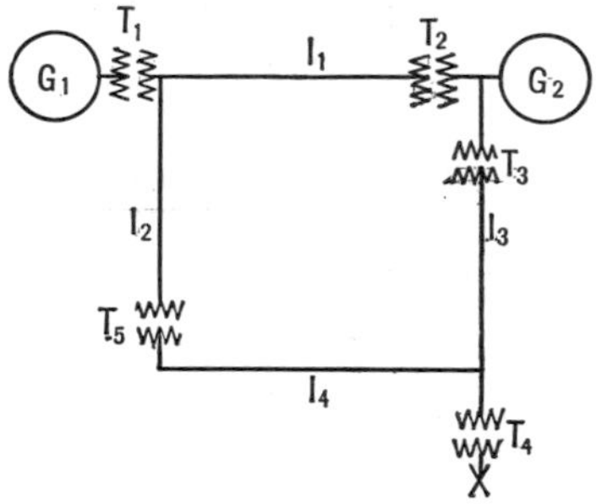

FIG. 8. One-line diagram of Fig. 7.

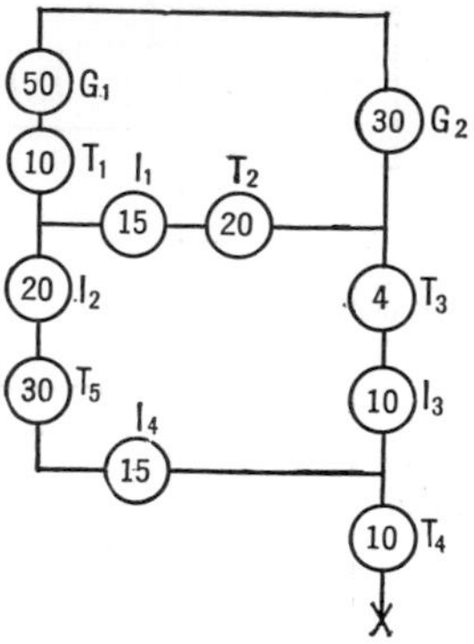

FIG. 9. One-line diagram of Fig. 8 where G_1 and G_2 are connected to a common neutral bus and all reactances are shown on a 10,000-kva base.

2. A common kva base upon which all reactances are based is chosen. Any convenient base may be used; here a 10,000-kva base is selected.

3. A one-line diagram is drawn in which all sources of current are connected to a so-called neutral bus. Circles represent reactances, and the value of the various re-

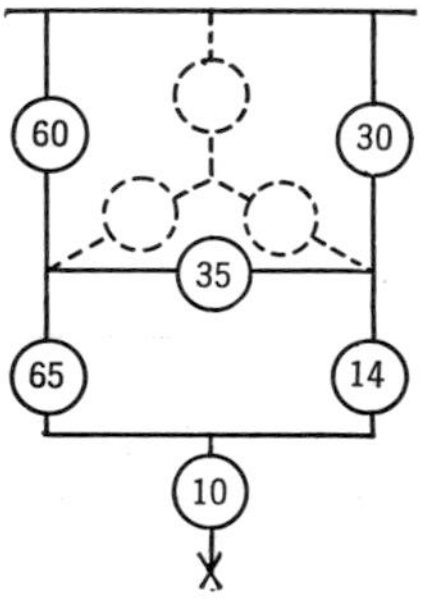

FIG. 10.

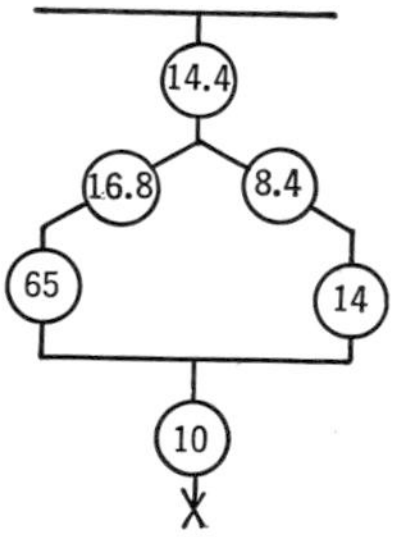

FIG. 11.

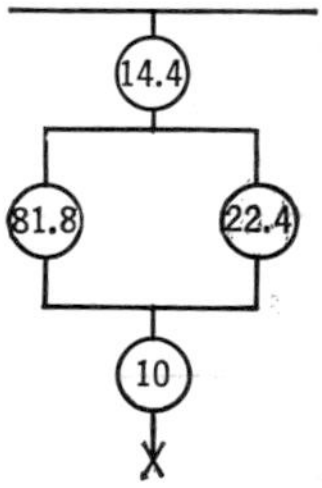

FIG. 12.

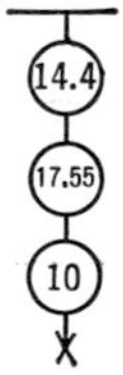

FIG. 13.

actances referred to the selected common kva base is placed in the circle as shown in Fig. 9.

4. Reactances are combined according to laws of series or parallel circuits, and substitution of wyes for deltas or the reverse are made so as to obtain a single reactance between the neutral bus and the point of short circuit. These steps are illustrated in the successive Figs. 10, 11, 12, 13, and 14. The dotted lines and circles indicate the circuit arrangement to be employed in replacing an existing circuit arrangement. The resultant reactance to the fault based on

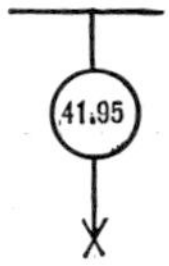

FIG. 14. Resultant percentage of reactance on a 10,000-kva base of Fig. 7 to the point of short circuit.

10,000 kva is 41.95 per cent.

$$\text{Short-circuit kva} = \frac{100}{41.95} \times 10{,}000 = 23{,}800$$

If the nominal voltage of the line at the short circuit is 12,000 volts, the current at the fault is

$$\frac{23{,}800 \times 1000}{\sqrt{3}\ 12{,}000} = 1144 \text{ amperes}$$

The distribution of currents throughout the network may be determined by retracing the steps and using the percentage values just exactly as though they were ohmic quantities. For example, the currents in the divided circuit of Fig. 12 may be determined as follows. To indicate the branch under consideration, a subscript which is the same as the branch impedance is used.

$$V_{17.55} = 17.55 \times 1144 \text{ volts}^1$$

$$I_{81.8} = \frac{17.55 \times 1144}{81.8} = 246 \text{ amperes}$$

$$I_{22.4} = \frac{17.55 \times 1144}{22.4} = 898 \text{ amperes}$$

If the nominal voltage of any line differs from the 12,000-volt base used above, the actual current is determined by multiplying the current calculated on the 12,000-volt base by the ratio of 12,000 to the nominal voltage for the line in question.

Problem 3. Find the actual currents delivered by generators G_1 and G_2.
Ans.: $I_{G1} = 344$ amperes, $I_{G2} = 800$ amperes.

Line-to-Line Short Circuits. Line-to-line short-circuit currents may be determined in accordance with the principles set forth in Chapter IX, or they may be calculated by the method of symmetrical components. The method of symmetrical components possesses the advantage of accounting in a measure for the change in the impedance of synchronous machines when the loading is changed from balanced three-phase to single-phase line-to-line loading. Furthermore the method of symmetrical components reduces the calculations to the solution of balanced three-phase systems. Certain modifications of the network parameters are necessary in employing the method of symmetrical components, and in addition the combination of the balanced systems solutions must be properly made to obtain the final result.

The method of symmetrical components for effecting a solution of the line-to-line short-circuit problem will be developed with reference to Fig. 15. The fundamental objective is to determine the positive- and negative-sequence components of current in terms of (the known quanti-

[1] This number of volts is only proportional to the actual voltage and is used merely as a convenient means to determine the distribution of currents.

ties) the induced voltage and impedance. The following symbols are used:

E, generated voltage per phase
n', electrical neutral at the point of short circuit
V_1, positive-sequence voltage to neutral at the short circuit
V_2, negative-sequence voltage to neutral at the short circuit
V_0, zero-sequence voltage to neutral at the short circuit
Z_1, impedance to positive sequence
Z_2, impedance to negative sequence

According to Kirchhoff's voltage law, the positive-sequence voltage to neutral at the short circuit must be the positive-sequence generated voltage minus the positive-sequence drop. A similar relation obtains

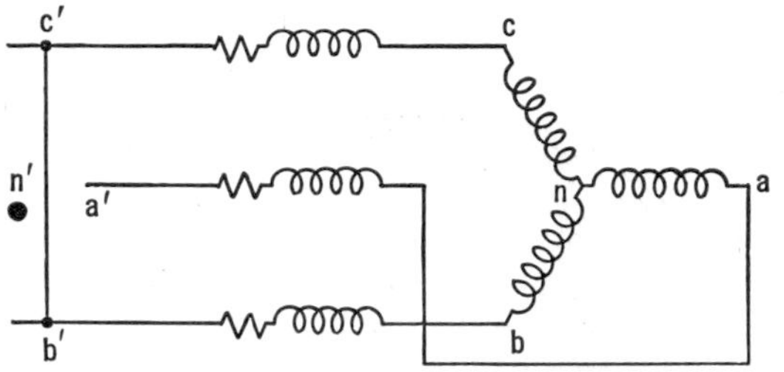

FIG. 15. Line-to-line short circuit on a three-phase system.

for the negative sequence. Since all generated voltages at the generator are assumed to be balanced, the positive-sequence generated voltage is E. The negative-sequence generated voltage is zero. Hence for any particular phase

$$\mathbf{V}_1 = \mathbf{E} - \mathbf{I}_1\mathbf{Z}_1 \tag{4}$$

$$\mathbf{V}_2 = 0 - \mathbf{I}_2\mathbf{Z}_2 \tag{5}$$

Since there is no ground return or fourth wire in Fig. 15, there can be no zero-sequence current in this system. At the short circuit

$$\mathbf{V}_{b'c'} = \mathbf{V}_{b'n'} + \mathbf{V}_{n'c'} = 0 \tag{6}$$

or

$$\mathbf{V}_{n'b'} = \mathbf{V}_{n'c'} \tag{7}$$

The three voltages to neutral at the short circuit in terms of their symmetrical components are (assuming *ab-bc-ca* sequence)

$$\mathbf{V}_{n'a'} = \mathbf{V}_1 + \mathbf{V}_2 + \mathbf{V}_0 \tag{8}$$

$$\mathbf{V}_{n'b'} = \mathbf{V}_1\underline{/-120°} + \mathbf{V}_2\underline{/120°} + \mathbf{V}_0 \tag{9}$$

$$\mathbf{V}_{n'c'} = \mathbf{V}_1\underline{/120°} + \mathbf{V}_2\underline{/-120°} + \mathbf{V}_0 \tag{10}$$

Substituting equations (9) and (10) in equation (7),

$$\mathbf{V}_1\angle{-120°} + \mathbf{V}_2\angle{120°} + \mathbf{V}_0 = \mathbf{V}_1\angle{120°} + \mathbf{V}_2\angle{-120°} + \mathbf{V}_0$$

$$\mathbf{V}_1(\angle{-120°} - \angle{120°}) = \mathbf{V}_2(\angle{-120°} - \angle{120°})$$

or

$$\mathbf{V}_1 = \mathbf{V}_2 \tag{11}$$

Equation (11) shows that equations (4) and (5) are equal. Therefore

$$\mathbf{E} - \mathbf{I}_1\mathbf{Z}_1 = -\mathbf{I}_2\mathbf{Z}_2 \tag{12}$$

If $\mathbf{I}_2$ can be expressed in terms of $\mathbf{I}_1$, the sequence components of currents can be found. Since no zero-sequence current can exist in the circuit of Fig. 15, $\mathbf{I}_1$ and $\mathbf{I}_2$ are found as shown below.

$$\mathbf{I}_{na} = \mathbf{I}_1 + \mathbf{I}_2 = 0 \quad \text{(Line } na \text{ is open.)} \tag{13}$$

$$\mathbf{I}_{nb} = \mathbf{I}_1\angle{-120°} + \mathbf{I}_2\angle{120°} \tag{14}$$

$$\mathbf{I}_{nc} = \mathbf{I}_1\angle{120°} + \mathbf{I}_2\angle{-120°} \tag{15}$$

Because of the short circuit,

$$\mathbf{I}_{nb} = \mathbf{I}_{cn} = -\mathbf{I}_{nc} \tag{16}$$

Substituting equations (14) and (15) in equation (16),

$$\mathbf{I}_1\angle{-120°} + \mathbf{I}_2\angle{120°} = -\mathbf{I}_1\angle{120°} - \mathbf{I}_2\angle{-120°}$$

$$\mathbf{I}_1(\angle{-120°} + \angle{120°}) + \mathbf{I}_2(\angle{-120°} + \angle{120°}) = 0$$

$$\mathbf{I}_1 = -\mathbf{I}_2 \tag{17}$$

Substituting equation (17) in equation (12) yields

$$\mathbf{E} - \mathbf{I}_1\mathbf{Z}_1 - \mathbf{I}_1\mathbf{Z}_2 = 0$$

$$\mathbf{I}_1 = \frac{\mathbf{E}}{\mathbf{Z}_1 + \mathbf{Z}_2} \tag{18}$$

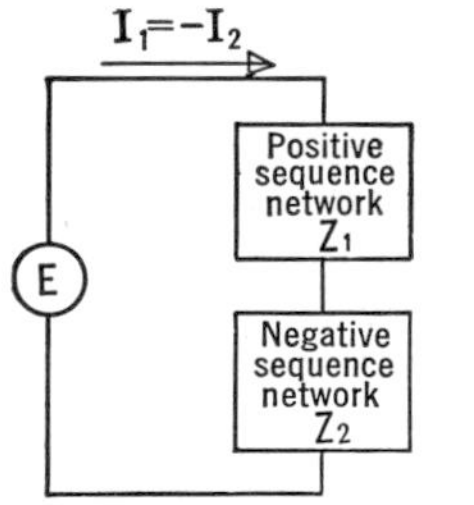

FIG. 16. Arrangement of sequence networks for determination of positive- and negative-sequence currents for a line-to-line short circuit.

Equations 17 and 18 show that the arrangement illustrated in Fig. 16 may be used to calculate the positive- and negative-sequence currents at the fault for a line-to-line short circuit.

Impedances to Positive and Negative Sequence. Before equation (18) can be applied, the values of the impedances to positive and negative sequence must be known. The impedance to positive sequence is the impedance offered to a system whose voltages *a*, *b*, and *c*, respectively, lag the one preceding it by 120°. The impedance to negative sequence is the impedance offered to a system whose voltages a, b, and c, respectively, lead the one preceding it by 120°. It should be apparent, and it can be demonstrated by test, that the impedances of lines and transformers are no different for a polyphase system of voltages when two lines are interchanged (opposite sequence). Hence impedances to positive and negative sequence for all lines and static machinery like transformers are the same. For a synchronous generator it would seem that these impedances are different since one system causes a reaction from the armature that rotates in the same direction as the rotating field structure, whereas the other causes an armature reaction that rotates in a direction opposite to the field structure. The values of Z_1 and Z_2 may be obtained from a three-phase and a line-to-line short-circuit test. The relation between the line-to-line short-circuit current designated by I' and the three-phase short-circuit current represented by I''' is established for an alternator of voltage E_n to neutral as follows:

$$I''' = \frac{E_n}{Z_1} \tag{19}$$

For a line-to-line short circuit between terminals b and c at the generator, Fig. 15, a combination of equations (15), (17), and (18) gives the current:

$$\begin{aligned}\mathbf{I}' = \mathbf{I}_{nc} &= \frac{\mathbf{E}_n}{\mathbf{Z}_1 + \mathbf{Z}_2}\underline{/120^\circ} - \frac{\mathbf{E}_n}{\mathbf{Z}_1 + \mathbf{Z}_2}\underline{/-120^\circ} \\ &= \frac{\mathbf{E}_n}{\mathbf{Z}_1 + \mathbf{Z}_2}(\cos 120^\circ + j \sin 120^\circ - \cos 120^\circ + j \sin 120^\circ) \\ &= +j\sqrt{3}\,\frac{\mathbf{E}_n}{\mathbf{Z}_1 + \mathbf{Z}_2} \end{aligned} \tag{20}$$

Since $\mathbf{Z}_1 + \mathbf{Z}_2$ is practically $Z_1 + Z_2$ owing to the resistances in both cases being small compared to the reactance,[2] the magnitude of $\mathbf{I}'$ is:

$$I' = \frac{\sqrt{3}E_n}{Z_1 + Z_2} \tag{21}$$

Let $k = I'/I'''$. Then

$$k\frac{E_n}{Z_1} = \frac{\sqrt{3}E_n}{Z_1 + Z_2}$$

[2] In general the resistances of generators and transformers are sufficiently low in comparison with the corresponding reactances that it is customary to neglect resistances in making short-circuit calculations. For this reason reactances only are used in many of the subsequent computations even though the formulas are written in terms of impedances. If these facts are not kept in mind the rather loose use of the terms reactance and impedance may become confusing.

or

$$Z_2 = \frac{\sqrt{3}Z_1}{k} - Z_1 \tag{22}$$

Equation (22) shows that Z_2 depends upon the ratio, k, of the line-to-line and three-phase short-circuit currents. When this ratio is known and the impedance to positive sequence is determined by the ordinary methods, Z_2 can be determined. One salient-pole machine with an amortisseur winding tested by one of the authors gave a value of 1.44 for k, while another non-salient pole machine without an amortisseur winding yielded a value of 1.46.[3]

TABLE II

IMPEDANCES AND REACTANCES TO DIFFERENT SEQUENCES OF SALIENT-POLE SYNCHRONOUS GENERATORS WITH DAMPER WINDINGS

Name of Reactance	Synchronous X_s	Positive-Sequence X_1	Negative-Sequence X_2	Zero-Sequence X_0
Per Cent Reactances	100	100	Approximate Range 25–50	Approximate Range 2–20
Name of Impedance	Synchronous Z_s	Positive-Sequence Z_1	Negative-Sequence Z_2	Zero-Sequence Z_0
Approximate Per Cent Impedances	100	100	Approximate Range 25–50	Approximate Range 3–20

Table II shows approximate ranges of impedances to positive-, negative-, and zero-sequence currents of one class of generators with reference to the synchronous impedance taken as 100.

Example 4. Each of the line reactances in Fig. 15 is 10 per cent based on 1000 kva, and the positive-sequence impedance of the alternator is 25 per cent based on 1000 kva. A value of 1.45 is assumed for k. The short-circuit currents in the three lines for a short circuit between lines b and c are to be determined. The nominal rated

[3] The values of reactances to negative sequence depend upon the size and the design of the machines and vary over rather wide limits for special cases. The reader is referred to Wagner and Evans, "Symmetrical Components," p. 99, McGraw-Hill Book Company, for extensive data on synchronous generator reactances to the different sequences.

line voltage of the system is 2200 volts. For the generator

$$Z_2 = \frac{\sqrt{3}}{1.45} Z_1 - Z_1 = 1.2Z_1 - Z_1 = 0.2Z_1$$
$$= 0.2 \times 25 = 5\%$$

The positive- and negative-sequence circuits are shown in Figs. 17 and 18, respectively. The resultant impedances to positive and negative sequence are 35 per cent and 15 per cent, respectively. From equation (18) and Fig. 16,

$$\mathbf{I}_1 = \frac{1{,}000{,}000}{\sqrt{3} \times 2200} \times \frac{100}{(35 + 15)} = 525 \text{ amperes}$$

$$\mathbf{I}_2 = -\mathbf{I}_1 = -525\underline{/0^\circ} \text{ amperes}$$

$$\mathbf{I}_{na} = \mathbf{I}_1 + \mathbf{I}_2 = 525\underline{/0^\circ} - 525\underline{/0^\circ} = 0$$

$$\mathbf{I}_{nb} = \mathbf{I}_1\underline{/-120^\circ} + \mathbf{I}_2\underline{/120^\circ} = 525\underline{/-120^\circ} - 525\underline{/120^\circ} = -j910 \text{ amperes}$$

$$\mathbf{I}_{nc} = \mathbf{I}_1\underline{/120^\circ} + \mathbf{I}_2\underline{/-120^\circ} = 525\underline{/120^\circ} - 525\underline{/-120^\circ} = +j910 \text{ amperes}$$

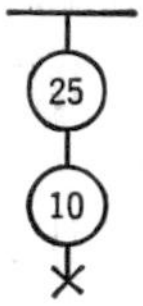

FIG. 17. Positive-sequence system of Fig. 15. See example 4.

Example 5. The short-circuit current for the system shown in Fig. 7 for a line-to-line short circuit is to be determined. The ratio k will be used as 1.45. Nominal line voltage at short circuit is 12,000 volts. The lines shorted are designated as b and c, and the fault is again assumed at the upper right-hand corner of the diagram.

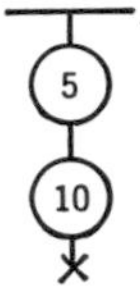

FIG. 18. Negative-sequence system of Fig. 15. See example 4.

Solution. A 10,000-kva base will be used. The positive-sequence network is the same as that shown in Fig. 9. The negative-sequence network shown in Fig. 19 is similar to the positive-sequence system except for the values of the generator reactances. For the generators

$$Z_2 = \frac{\sqrt{3}Z_1}{1.45} - Z_1 = 0.2Z_1$$

The resultant Z_1 (Fig. 14) is 41.95 per cent.

The resultant Z_2 (Fig. 23) is 26.17 per cent as obtained from the reductions indicated by Figs. 20, 21, 22, and 23.

$$\mathbf{I}_1 = -\mathbf{I}_2 = \frac{10{,}000{,}000}{\sqrt{3}\ 12{,}000} \times \frac{100}{41.95 + 26.17} + 706 \text{ amperes}$$

At the short circuit where currents in all three lines are considered in the same direction, that is, either to or from the short circuit,

$$\mathbf{I}_a = \mathbf{I}_1 + \mathbf{I}_2 = 706\underline{/0^\circ} - 706\underline{/0^\circ} = 0$$

$$\mathbf{I}_b = 706\underline{/-120^\circ} - 706\underline{/120^\circ} = -j1223 \text{ amperes}$$

$$\mathbf{I}_c = 706\underline{/120^\circ} - 706\underline{/-120^\circ} = +j1223 \text{ amperes}$$

To obtain the currents in the other lines, the positive- and negative-sequence currents should first be found by retracing the steps in each system as outlined for the three-phase short circuit. The current in the lines from the secondaries of transformer T_1 will be found in order to illustrate the procedure. The distribution of positive-

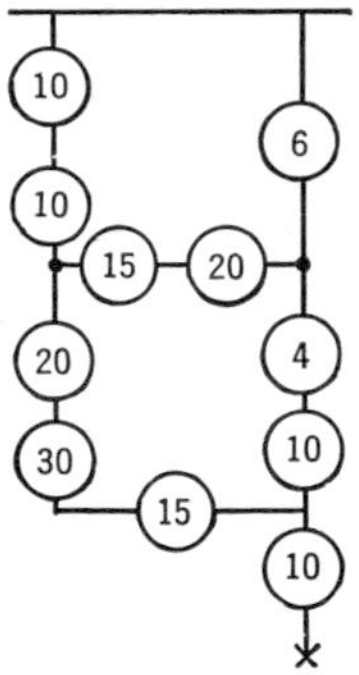

FIG. 19. Negative-sequence network of FIG. 7 for a line-to-line short circuit at the point indicated by the cross.

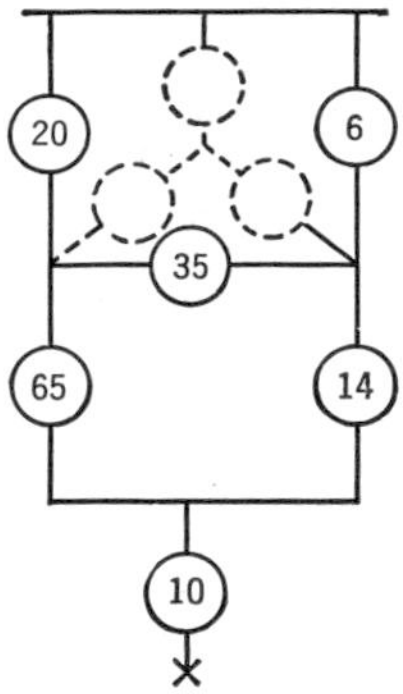

FIG. 20.

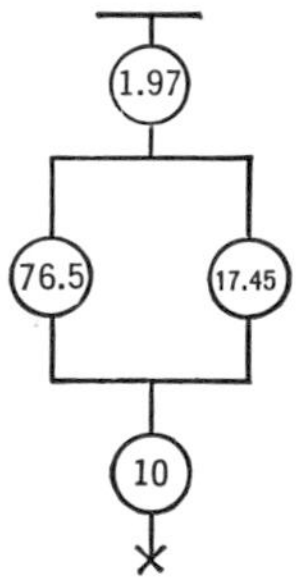

FIG. 21.

and negative-sequence components of current as shown in Figs. 24 and 25 are first found by retracing previous steps. If, when retracing the network from the short circuit, only transformers with both primary and secondary windings similarly connected are encountered, the actual current may be found by combining the sequence components as determined for Figs. 24 and 25. When a transformer like T_1 which is connected differently on primary and secondary is encountered, the symmetrical components in the lines on the primary side are no longer the same as those in the secondary lines. Failure to recognize this fact will introduce large errors in the short-circuit calculations. The short-circuit currents in the secondary lines from transformer T_1 are found from the sequence components shown in Figs. 24 and 25, as follows:

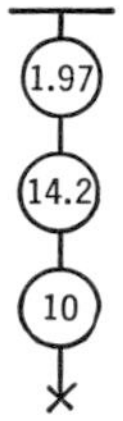

FIG. 22.

FIG. 23. Resultant percentage of reactance to negative sequence for a line-to-line short circuit at point indicated on Fig. 7.

$$\mathbf{I}_a = \mathbf{I}_1 + \mathbf{I}_2 = 212\underline{/0^\circ} - 144.7\underline{/0^\circ} = 67.3 \text{ amperes}$$

$$\mathbf{I}_b = 212\underline{/-120^\circ} - 144.7\underline{/120^\circ} = -33.65 - j308.8 \text{ amperes}$$

$$\mathbf{I}_c = 212\underline{/120^\circ} - 144.7\underline{/-120^\circ} = -33.65 + j308.8 \text{ amperes}$$

The currents in the lines on the primary of T_1, Fig. 7, are determined from the phase currents in the delta and are obviously equal to them if the ratio of each transformer is 1 to 1 and the magnetizing currents are neglected. If the impedances of all phases of a delta-connected bank of transformers like that shown in Fig. 26 are equal, and if the sum of the generated voltages of the three phases is zero, application of Kirchhoff's laws will yield the following equations:

$$\mathbf{I}_{aa'} + \mathbf{I}_{bb'} + \mathbf{I}_{cc'} = 0 \tag{23}$$

$$\mathbf{I}_{ba}\mathbf{Z}_{ba} + \mathbf{I}_{ac}\mathbf{Z}_{ac} + \mathbf{I}_{cb}\mathbf{Z}_{cb} = \mathbf{E}_{ba} + \mathbf{E}_{ac} + \mathbf{E}_{cb} = 0 \tag{24}$$

Since $\mathbf{Z}_{ba} = \mathbf{Z}_{ac} = \mathbf{Z}_{cb}$, equation (24) becomes

$$\mathbf{I}_{ba} + \mathbf{I}_{ac} + \mathbf{I}_{cb} = 0 \tag{25}$$

Further application of Kirchhoff's current law gives

$$\mathbf{I}_{aa'} = \mathbf{I}_{ba} - \mathbf{I}_{ac} \tag{26}$$

$$\mathbf{I}_{bb'} = \mathbf{I}_{cb} - \mathbf{I}_{ba} \tag{27}$$

$$\mathbf{I}_{cc'} = \mathbf{I}_{ac} - \mathbf{I}_{cb} \tag{28}$$

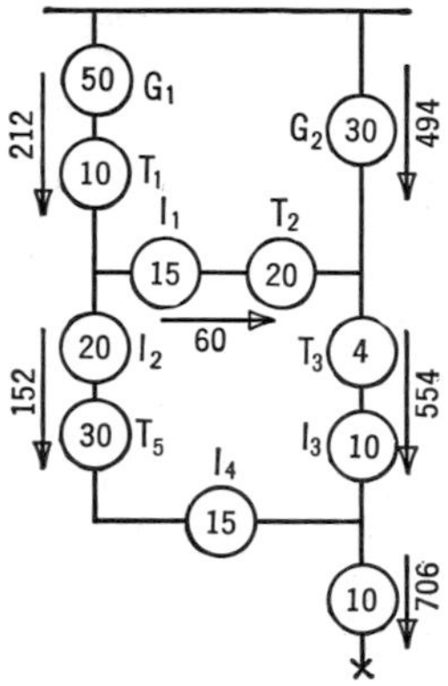

FIG. 24. Distribution of positive-sequence component currents for example 5.

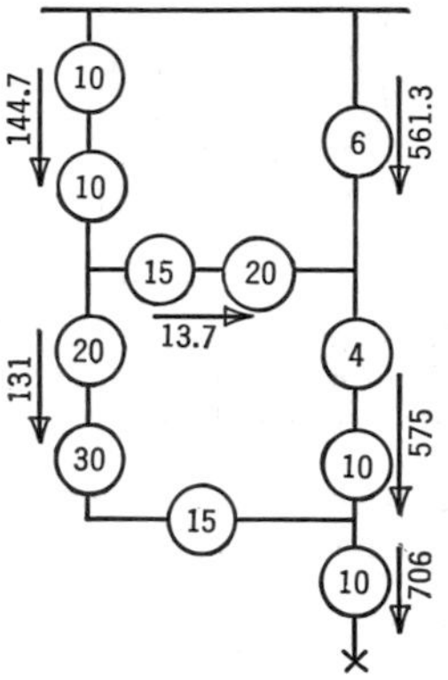

FIG. 25. Distribution of negative-sequence component currents for example 5.

Substituting $\mathbf{I}_{ac}$ from equation (25) in equation (26), then eliminating $\mathbf{I}_{cb}$ between this result and equation (27), and finally substituting the value of $\mathbf{I}_{bb'}$ from equation (23), the following expression for $\mathbf{I}_{ba}$ results:

$$\mathbf{I}_{ba} = \tfrac{2}{3}\mathbf{I}_{aa'} + \tfrac{1}{3}\mathbf{I}_{cc'} \tag{29}$$

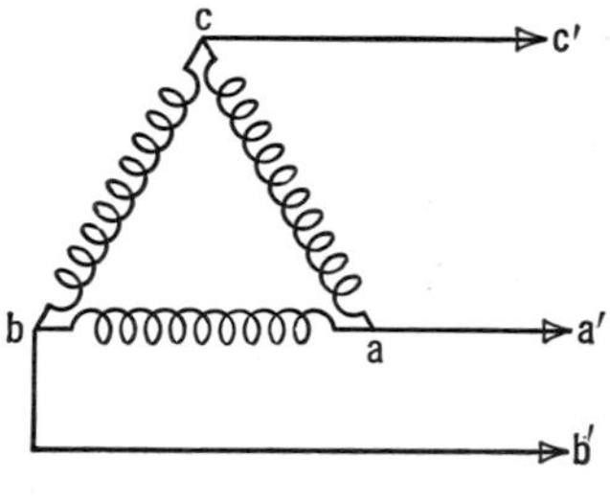

FIG. 26.

Similarly $\mathbf{I}_{ac}$ and $\mathbf{I}_{cb}$ are found to be, respectively,

$$\mathbf{I}_{ac} = \tfrac{2}{3}\mathbf{I}_{cc'} + \tfrac{1}{3}\mathbf{I}_{bb'} \tag{30}$$

$$\mathbf{I}_{cb} = \tfrac{2}{3}\mathbf{I}_{bb'} + \tfrac{1}{3}\mathbf{I}_{aa'} \tag{31}$$

The currents $\mathbf{I}_a$, $\mathbf{I}_b$, and $\mathbf{I}_c$ in the secondary lines of T_1 of Fig. 7 correspond to $\mathbf{I}_{aa'}$,

$\mathbf{I}_{bb'}$, and $\mathbf{I}_{cc'}$, respectively, in equations (29), (30), and (31).[4] Hence

$$\mathbf{I}_{ba} = \tfrac{2}{3}(67.3) + \tfrac{1}{3}(-33.65 + j308.8)$$
$$= 33.7 + j102.9 = 108.2\angle 71.8^\circ \text{ amperes}$$
$$\mathbf{I}_{ac} = \tfrac{2}{3}(-33.65 + j308.8) + \tfrac{1}{3}(-33.65 - j308.8)$$
$$= -33.7 + j102.9 = 108.2\angle 108.2^\circ \text{ amperes}$$
$$\mathbf{I}_{cb} = \tfrac{2}{3}(-33.65 - j308.8) + \tfrac{1}{3}(67.3)$$
$$= -j205.8 = 205.8\angle -90^\circ \text{ amperes}$$

On a 1 to 1 ratio, $\mathbf{I}_{ba}$, $\mathbf{I}_{ca}$, and $\mathbf{I}_{cb}$ above are the line currents from generator G_1, Fig. 7, or, in other words, the above currents are on a $\sqrt{3}$ 12,000-volt base. If the nominal voltage of the generator is 6600 volts, the currents in the three lines from the generator are

$$108.2 \times \frac{\sqrt{3}\ 12{,}000}{6600} = 341 \text{ amperes}$$

$$108.2 \times \frac{\sqrt{3}\ 12{,}000}{6600} = 341 \text{ amperes}$$

$$205.8 \times \frac{\sqrt{3}\ 12{,}000}{6600} = 648 \text{ amperes}$$

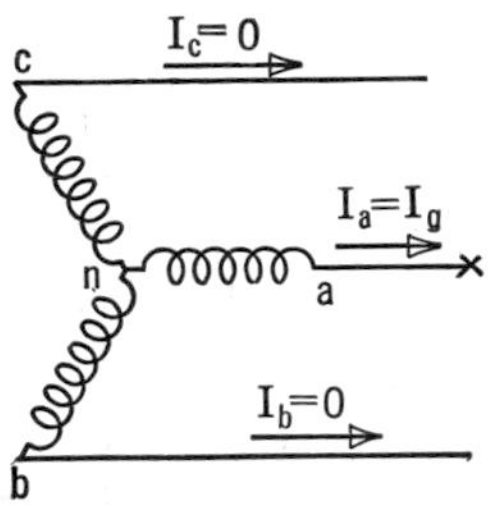

Fig. 27. Line-to-ground fault. Neutral n of the three-phase generator is assumed grounded.

Line-to-Ground Short Circuits. If a system has a number of wye-connected generators and transformers with grounded neutrals, there is a possibility of having a large short-circuit current for a line-to-ground fault. Such fault currents are most conveniently calculated with the aid of symmetrical components. An elementary circuit illustrating a line-to-ground fault is shown in Fig. 27. Application of equations (13), (16), and (17) of Chapter XII gives the symmetrical components of the currents as

$$\mathbf{I}_0 = \tfrac{1}{3}(\mathbf{I}_a + \mathbf{I}_b + \mathbf{I}_c) = \frac{\mathbf{I}_a}{3} \tag{32}$$

$$\mathbf{I}_1 = \tfrac{1}{3}(\mathbf{I}_a + \mathbf{I}_b\angle 120^\circ + \mathbf{I}_c\angle -120^\circ) = \frac{\mathbf{I}_a}{3} \tag{33}$$

$$\mathbf{I}_2 = \tfrac{1}{3}(\mathbf{I}_a + \mathbf{I}_b\angle -120^\circ + \mathbf{I}_c\angle 120^\circ) = \frac{\mathbf{I}_a}{3} \tag{34}$$

Therefore

$$\mathbf{I}_0 = \mathbf{I}_1 = \mathbf{I}_2 = \frac{\mathbf{I}_a}{3} \tag{35}$$

[4] Equations other than (29), (30), and (31) for the currents in the transformer windings can be derived from the basic equations given.

Let **E** be the induced voltage in phase a of the generator. According to Kirchhoff's emf law, the sum of all the drops must be equal to the sum of the emf's around a closed loop. Then

$$\mathbf{E} = \mathbf{I}_0\mathbf{Z}_0 + \mathbf{I}_1\mathbf{Z}_1 + \mathbf{I}_2\mathbf{Z}_2$$

Substituting equation (35) gives

$$\mathbf{E} = \mathbf{I}_0\,(\mathbf{Z}_0 + \mathbf{Z}_1 + \mathbf{Z}_2) \tag{36}$$

Combining equations (35) and (36),

$$\mathbf{I}_0 = \frac{\mathbf{I}_a}{3} = \frac{\mathbf{E}}{\mathbf{Z}_0 + \mathbf{Z}_1 + \mathbf{Z}_2} \tag{37}$$

Equation (37) is the working equation for the line-to-ground fault.

Equations 35 and 37 show that the arrangement illustrated in Fig. 28 may be used to calculate the positive-, negative-, and zero-sequence currents at the fault for a line-to-ground short circuit.

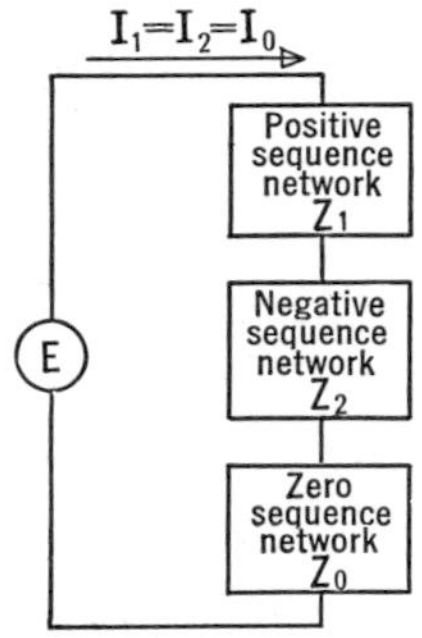

FIG. 28. Arrangement of sequence networks for calculating positive-, negative-, and zero-sequence currents for a line-to-ground short circuit.

The impedances to positive and negative sequence $\mathbf{Z}_1$ and $\mathbf{Z}_2$ are exactly the same as those used for the line-to-line fault. The impedance to zero sequence, however, is different. Whereas the positive- and negative-sequence networks were alike in the number and arrangement of circuit elements, the zero-sequence network is radically different and usually much simpler.

Impedance to Zero Sequence for Generators. The determination of the impedance to zero sequence for generators is analogous to the determination of the impedance to negative sequence.

Let I_n represent the line-to-ground short-circuit current for a generator.

Let I''' represent the short-circuit current for a three-phase symmetrical short circuit.

Also let

$$\frac{I_n}{I'''} = k_n \tag{38}$$

From equation (37), if the ratio of X/R for all impedances is the same or if R is negligible compared to X, as is usual,

$$I_n = 3I_0 = \frac{3E}{Z_1 + Z_2 + Z_0} \tag{39}$$

Also

$$I''' = \frac{E}{Z_1} \quad \text{and} \quad k_n I''' = I_n = k_n \frac{E}{Z_1}$$

Therefore

$$k_n \frac{E}{Z_1} = \frac{3E}{Z_1 + Z_2 + Z_0} \tag{40}$$

Solving equation (40) for Z_0 gives

$$Z_0 = Z_1 \left(\frac{3}{k_n} - 1 \right) - Z_2 \tag{41}$$

The value of Z_0 thus depends upon the values of the impedances to positive and negative sequence and also upon the ratio of the line-to-ground and three-phase short-circuit currents. For example, k_n for the nonsalient-pole machine used in the previous example was shown by test to be about 2.4. For this machine

$$Z_0 = Z_1 \left(\frac{3}{2.4} - 1 \right) - 0.2Z_1 = 0.05Z_1$$

The approximate range of impedance to zero sequence for one class of generators is shown in Table II on page 535. The values are given relative to the synchronous impedance taken as 100.

Impedance to Zero Sequence for Transformers. The impedance to zero sequence for transformers is either infinite or the ordinary leakage impedance,[5] depending upon the connection. Where the connection permits zero-sequence currents to flow, the impedance to zero sequence is the ordinary impedance of the transformer; otherwise it is infinite. Since the zero-sequence currents in the three lines of a three-phase system are all in phase, a fourth wire or ground connection on the neutral of transformers connected in wye is required to furnish a complete circuit for the return of the zero-sequence line currents. In addition, there must be another winding on the transformer to permit current to flow so that the resultant magnetomotive force acting upon the transformer core due to the zero-sequence current is zero (exciting current neglected). If these compensating currents are not permitted to exist, the inductive reactance of a single winding to the zero-sequence current is so high that the amount of this current which can flow is entirely negligible. The corresponding impedance may then be considered

[5] If the transformers have more than two windings which carry zero-sequence current, reactance due to certain mutual-inductance effects of the several windings should be included. For a discussion of the reactance of multiwinding transformers, see O. G. C. Dahl, "Electric Circuits," McGraw-Hill Book Company.

infinite. A few examples as shown in Fig. 29 will illustrate these principles.

Transformer Bank A. No zero-sequence currents can flow since there is no return path. Therefore the impedance to zero sequence is infinite.

Transformer Bank B. Zero-sequence currents can flow. Winding p furnishes a path for the compensating currents of those in winding S. Hence the impedance to zero sequence is the ordinary leakage impedance.

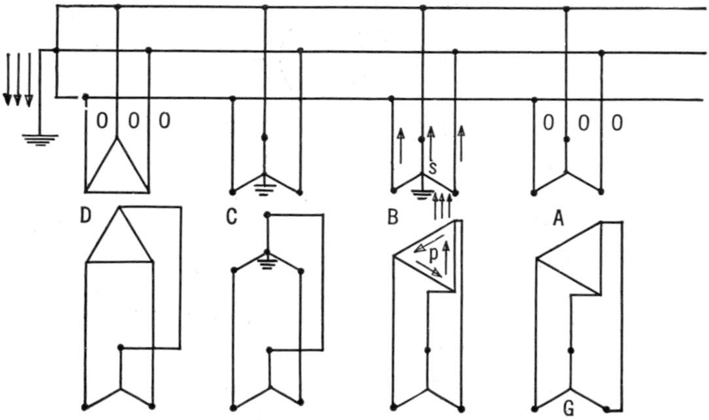

FIG. 29. Zero-sequence currents can flow in B but not in any of the other transformers.

Transformer Banks C and D. No zero-sequence currents can flow. The impedances to zero sequence are infinite. If the neutral of the wye-connected generator supplying transformer bank C were grounded, zero-sequence currents could flow in both primary and secondary of C. Under these conditions the impedance to zero sequence of transformer bank C would be the ordinary leakage impedance.

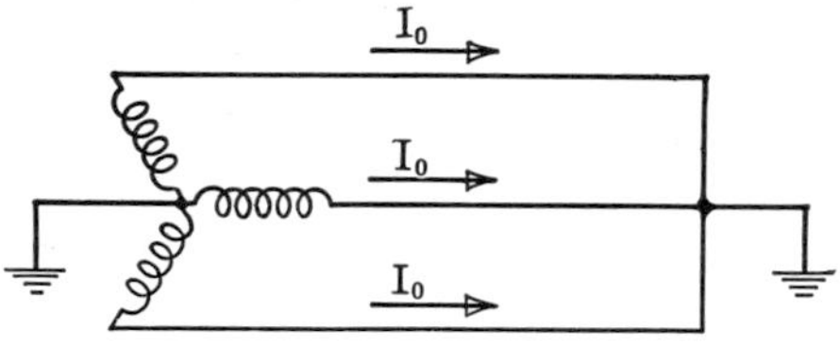

FIG. 30. Zero-sequence impedance of a transmission line is the impedance of the three conductors in parallel in series with a ground return.

Impedance to Zero Sequence of Transmission Lines. The impedance to zero sequence of a transmission line, Fig. 30, is the impedance of the three conductors in parallel with a ground return. The reactance depends upon the depth at which the return current appears to flow. A discussion sufficiently adequate to yield a working knowledge of the determination of reactance to zero sequence of transmission lines is somewhat involved and beyond the scope of this book. Those interested are referred to other works on the subject.[6] For purposes of illustration of the method of calculating line-to-ground fault currents in this book, certain values of reactance to zero sequence of a line are assumed.

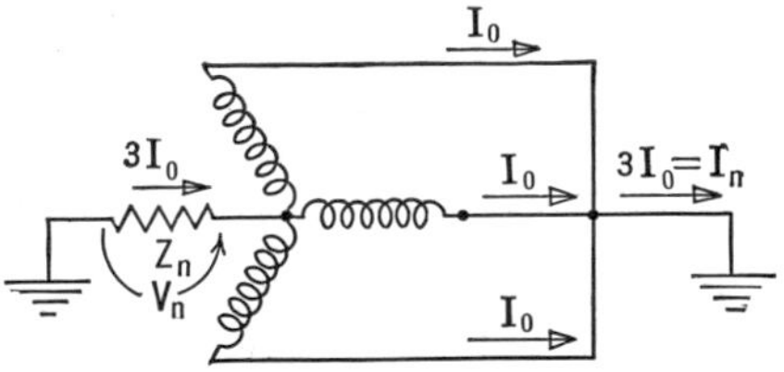

FIG. 31. Flow of zero-sequence currents through an impedance in the neutral.

If an impedance Z_n as shown in the neutral of the generator of Fig. 31 is encountered, it should be entered into the zero-sequence networks as $3\mathbf{Z}_n$. This may be shown as follows. The ordinary impedance $\mathbf{Z}_n$ is defined as the drop $\mathbf{V}_n$ across the impedance divided by the current through it. Hence

$$\mathbf{Z}_n = \frac{\mathbf{V}_n}{\mathbf{I}_n} \tag{42}$$

Since

$$\mathbf{I}_n = 3\mathbf{I}_0$$

$$\mathbf{Z}_n = \frac{\mathbf{V}_n}{3\mathbf{I}_0} \tag{43}$$

Since there are no positive- or negative-sequence currents in the neutral, $\mathbf{V}_n$ for this case is considered the zero-sequence voltage which is due to the zero-sequence current $\mathbf{I}_0$. Hence

$$\mathbf{Z}_0 = \frac{\mathbf{V}_0}{\mathbf{I}_0} = \frac{\mathbf{V}_n}{\mathbf{I}_0} \tag{44}$$

Substitution of $\mathbf{V}_n/\mathbf{I}_0$ from equation (43) in equation (44) gives

$$\mathbf{Z}_0 = 3\mathbf{Z}_n \tag{45}$$

Thus the impedance to zero sequence as defined in equation (45) is three times as large as the actual impedance in the conductor. Since the only zero-sequence current flowing in the zero-sequence network is $\mathbf{I}_0$, the

[6] See " Symmetrical Components " by Wagner and Evans and " Applications of the Method of Symmetrical Components " by Lyon, McGraw-Hill Book Company.

value $\mathbf{Z}_0 = 3\mathbf{Z}_n$ should be entered into the zero-sequence network to yield the correct voltage drop.

Calculation of Line-to-Ground Fault Current. The system shown in Fig. 7, which was previously employed for three-phase and line-to-line short circuits, will be calculated for a line-to-ground fault on one of the secondary lines of transformer T_4. A determination of the reactance to zero-sequence of line l_3 is assumed to yield 20 per cent reactance on a 5000-kva base. The problem will be worked on a 10,000-kva base as before.

Solution. The positive- and negative-sequence networks are the same as those previously employed. They are shown in Figs. 24 and 25. The impedances to positive and negative sequence are the same for the line-to-ground fault solution and the general distribution of the positive- and negative-sequence currents is the same, but the actual magnitudes of the positive- and negative-sequence currents will be different because of the effect of the impedance to zero sequence in reducing the magnitude of the resultant positive- and negative-sequence currents. The resultant impedances to positive and negative sequence of 41.95 and 26.17 per cent, respectively, are still valid. An inspection of Fig. 7 shows that no zero-sequence current can exist in transformers T_5, T_2, T_1, or generator G_1. Therefore the zero-sequence network consists of G_2, T_3, and T_4 along with line l_3. The zero-sequence network is shown in Fig. 32. If $k_n = 2.4$ and $k_1 = 1.45$, substitution in equation (41) gives $Z_0 = 0.05Z_1$. For generator G_2

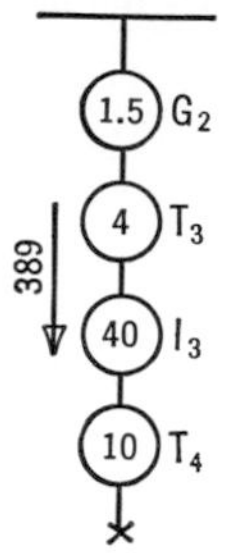

FIG. 32. Zero-sequence network for a line-to-ground fault on Fig. 7 at the point indicated by the cross.

$$Z_0 = 0.05 \times 30 = 1.5 \text{ per cent}$$

Resultant Z_0 for the zero-sequence network $= 1.5 + 4 + 40 + 10 = 55.5$ per cent.

$$\mathbf{I}_0 = \mathbf{I}_1 = \mathbf{I}_2 = \frac{\mathbf{I}_a}{3} = \frac{E}{Z_0 + Z_1 + Z_2}$$

In terms of percentage impedances,

$$\mathbf{I}_0 = \mathbf{I}_1 = \mathbf{I}_2 = \frac{\mathbf{I}_a}{3} = \frac{10{,}000{,}000}{\sqrt{3}\,12{,}000} \times \frac{100}{55.5 + 41.95 + 26.17}$$
$$= 389\underline{/0^\circ} \text{ amperes}$$

For a positive-sequence current of 389 amperes the distribution is shown in Fig. 33. These values are determined by multiplying the currents in Fig. 24 by 389/706. Similarly the negative-sequence current distribution is determined and shown in Fig. 34.

The currents on a 12,000-volt base are now found by combining the symmetrical components.

Fault current:

$$\mathbf{I}_a = \mathbf{I}_1 + \mathbf{I}_2 + \mathbf{I}_0 = 3 \times 389\underline{/0^\circ} = 1167\underline{/0^\circ} \text{ amperes}$$
$$\mathbf{I}_b = 389\underline{/-120^\circ} + 389\underline{/120^\circ} + 389 = 0$$
$$\mathbf{I}_c = 389\underline{/120^\circ} + 389\underline{/-120^\circ} + 389 = 0$$

Transformer T_3 and line l_3:

$\mathbf{I}_a = 305.2 + 316.8 + 389 = 1011$ $\qquad I_a = 1011$ amperes

$\mathbf{I}_b = 305.2\underline{/-120^\circ} + 316.8\underline{/120^\circ} + 389 = 78 + j10.5$ $\qquad I_b = 78.7$ amperes

$\mathbf{I}_c = 305.2\underline{/120^\circ} + 316.8\underline{/-120^\circ} + 389 = 78 - j10.5$ $\qquad I_c = 78.7$ amperes

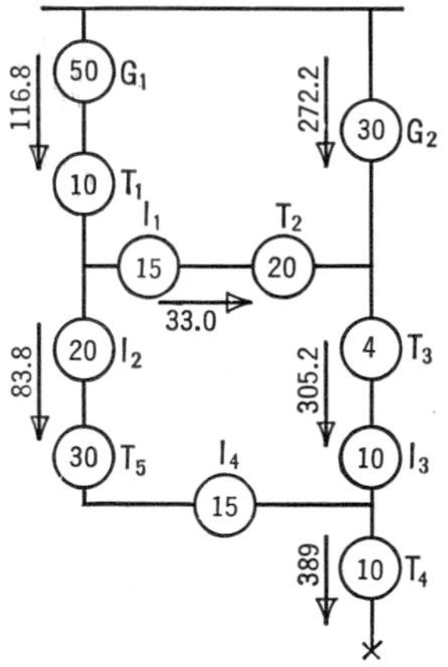

FIG. 33. Positive-sequence current distribution for line-to-ground fault on Fig. 7.

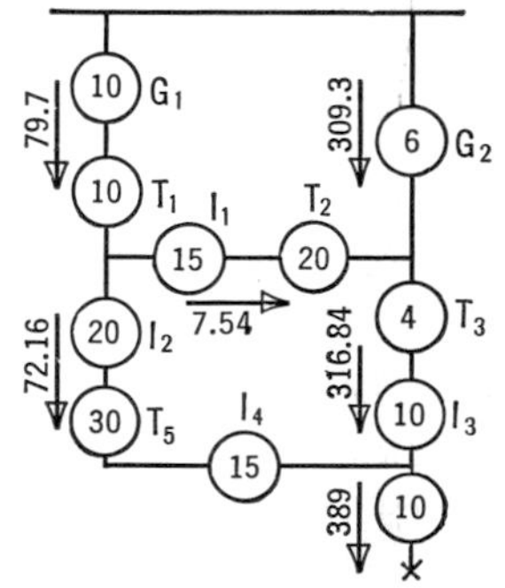

FIG. 34. Negative-sequence current distribution for line-to-ground fault on Fig. 7.

Line l_2, transformer T_5, and l_4:

$\mathbf{I}_a = 83.8 + 72.16 = 155.9$ $\qquad I_a = 155.9$ amperes

$\mathbf{I}_b = 83.8\underline{/-120^\circ} + 72.16\underline{/120^\circ} = -77.95 - j10$ $\qquad I_b = 78.6$ amperes

$\mathbf{I}_c = 83.8\underline{/120^\circ} + 72.16\underline{/-120^\circ} = -77.95 + j10$ $\qquad I_c = 78.6$ amperes

Line l_1 and transformer T_2:

$\mathbf{I}_a = 33.0 + 7.54 = 40.54$ $\qquad I_a = 40.5$ amperes

$\mathbf{I}_b = 33.0\underline{/-120^\circ} + 7.54\underline{/120^\circ} = -20.3 - j22.0$ $\qquad I_b = 30.0$ amperes

$\mathbf{I}_c = 33.0\underline{/120^\circ} + 7.54\underline{/-120^\circ} = -20.3 + j22.0$ $\qquad I_c = 30.0$ amperes

Secondary side of transformer T_1:

$\mathbf{I}_a = 116.8 + 79.7 = 196.5$ $\qquad I_a = 196.5$ amperes

$\mathbf{I}_b = 116.8\underline{/-120^\circ} + 79.7\underline{/120^\circ} = -98.2 - j32$ $\qquad I_b = 103.3$ amperes

$\mathbf{I}_c = 116.8\underline{/120^\circ} + 79.7\underline{/-120^\circ} = -98.2 + j32$ $\qquad I_c = 103.3$ amperes

Current in windings of transformer T_1 (see Fig. 7):

$\mathbf{I}_{ba} = \frac{2}{3}(196.5) + \frac{1}{3}(-98.25 + j32) = 98.3 + j10.7$ $\qquad I_{ba} = 98.9$ amperes

$\mathbf{I}_{ac} = \frac{2}{3}(-98.25 + j32) + \frac{1}{3}(-98.25 - j32)$

$= -98.3 + j10.7$ $\qquad I_{ac} = 98.9$ amperes

$\mathbf{I}_{cb} = \frac{2}{3}(-98.25 - j32) + \frac{1}{3}(196.5) = -j21.4$ $\qquad I_{cb} = 21.4$ amperes

Since these are the delta transformer currents, on a 1 to 1 ratio they are also the currents in the phases of the wye primary, and therefore the currents in the lines from generator G_1 on a $\sqrt{3}$ 12,000 line voltage base.

Current in G_2:

$$\mathbf{I}_a = 272.2 + 309.3 + 389 = 970.5 \qquad I_a = 970.5 \text{ amperes}$$

$$\mathbf{I}_b = 272.2\underline{/-120^\circ} + 309.3\underline{/120^\circ} + 389 = 98.25 + j32 \qquad I_b = 103.3 \text{ amperes}$$

$$\mathbf{I}_c = 272.2\underline{/120^\circ} + 309.3\underline{/-120^\circ} + 389 = 98.25 - j32 \qquad I_c = 103.3 \text{ amperes}$$

PROBLEMS

4. Refer to Fig. 35. All circuit elements are assumed to have zero resistance. The reactances to positive sequence are the numbers preceded by j on the diagram. Generator A is a 3000-kva machine having a rated terminal voltage of 6600-volts. Generator B is a 6600-volt, 5000-kva machine.

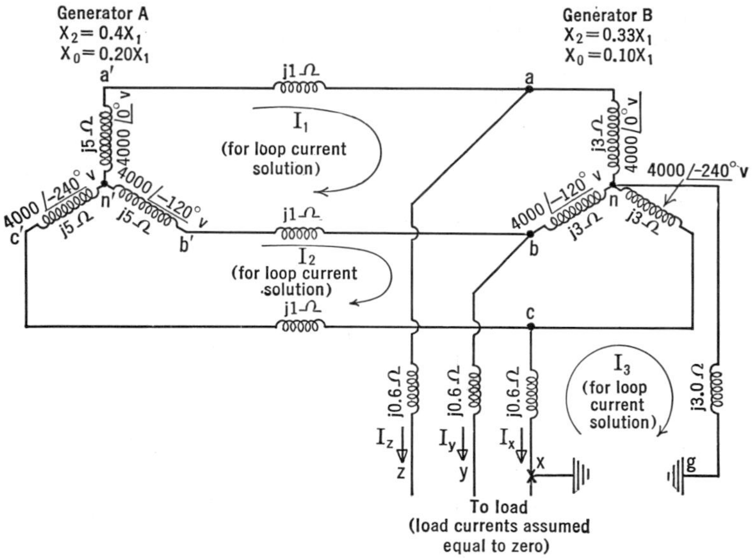

FIG. 35. See Problem 4.

(*a*) Solve for the currents in all branches by one of the methods considered in Chapter IX, assuming that the impedances shown on the diagram hold for any kind of unbalance.

(*b*) Solve for the currents in all branches by the method of symmetrical components, taking into account the difference in impedance to the positive, negative, and zero sequences. Impedances to positive sequence for the generators are those shown on the diagram.

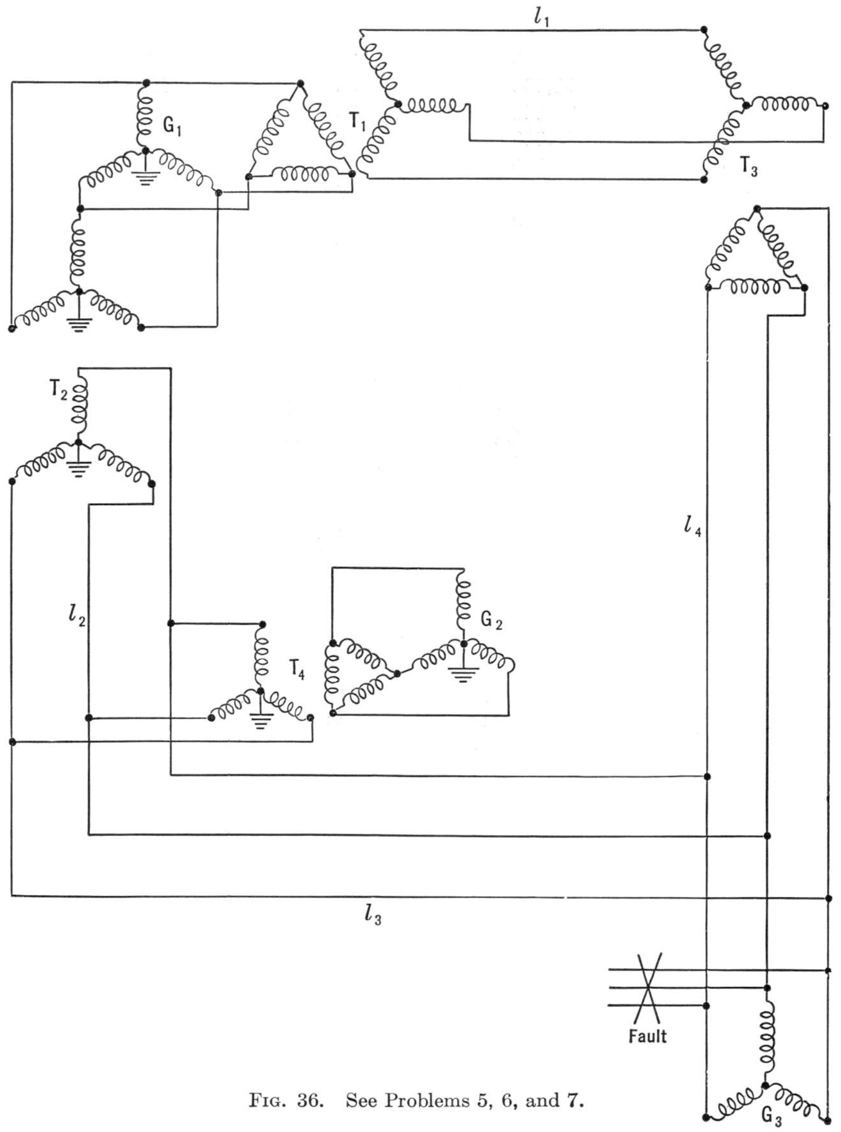

FIG. 36. See Problems 5, 6, and 7.

5. The following data refer to Fig. 36.

Apparatus	Kva Rating	% Reactance	Kva Base for % Reactance
G_1	20,000	30	10,000
G_2	10,000	50	10,000
G_3	20,000	20	10,000
T_1	10,000	2	2,500
T_2	10,000	20	30,000
T_3	10,000	6	10,000
T_4	10,000	7	10,000
l_1		30	20,000
l_2		20	10,000
l_3		10	4,000
l_4		40	30,000

Generator	k	k_n
G_1	1.4	2.1
G_2	1.5	2.3
G_3	1.3	

All resistances are assumed negligible.

Calculate currents in all lines, transformers, and generators for a 3-phase symmetrical short circuit at the point marked fault. Express currents on a 33-kv base.

6. Calculate currents in all lines, transformers, and generators for a line-to-line fault at the point marked fault. Express currents on a 33-kv base.

7. Calculate currents in all lines, transformers, and generators for a line-to-ground fault at the point marked fault. Use 25 per cent based on 10,000 kva as the zero-sequence reactance of l_2 including lines and ground return. The zero-sequence reactance of l_3 including lines and ground return is 12 per cent based on 4,000 kva. Assume negligible resistance, and express currents on a 33-kv base.

chapter XIV Transient Conditions

The expressions which have thus far been derived for currents and voltages have carried with them certain tacit assumptions. All the alternating currents and voltages in any particular circuit have been assumed to be recurring, periodic functions of time; in other words, the circuit in question has been assumed to be in a steady-state condition.

Before a circuit (or machine) can arrive at a steady-state condition of operation which is different from some previous state, the circuit (or machine) passes through a transition period in which the currents and voltages are not recurring periodic functions of time. For example, immediately after the establishment of a circuit the currents and voltages have not, in general, settled into their steady-state conditions. The period required for the currents and voltages to adjust themselves to their steady-state modes of variation is called the transient period. During transient periods the mathematical expressions for the currents and voltages contain certain terms other than the steady-state terms. These additional terms are called transient terms, and they are usually of short duration, being damped out by certain damping factors which depend for their values upon the circuit parameters.

In general, any switching operation within the circuit itself or any voltage which is suddenly induced from an outside source will cause transient conditions to exist in the circuit. Although transient periods are generally of short duration, it is during these periods that some of the most serious and involved operating problems are encountered.

It should not be inferred that transient variations are always violent or that they always represent undesirable circuit conditions. Various devices actually operate by virtue of recurring transient phenomena. Notable among these devices are: (1) certain classes of sweep circuits, and (2) certain types of tube inverters. Sweep circuits are employed extensively to produce linear time axes in cathode-ray oscillographs and cathode-ray television tubes. Inverters are employed to convert direct to alternating current.

Examples of Elementary Transient Conditions. Example 1. In Fig. 1 it is assumed that the *RL* branch is suddenly energized with a constant potential difference by closing the switch S at $t = 0$. The general equation for voltage equilibrium in the resulting series circuit is:

$$L\frac{di}{dt} + Ri = E \tag{1}$$

If L, R, and E are constant the above equation may be solved explicitly for i in any one of several different ways. One of the most direct methods of solution in a simple case of this kind is to separate variables and integrate. Thus:

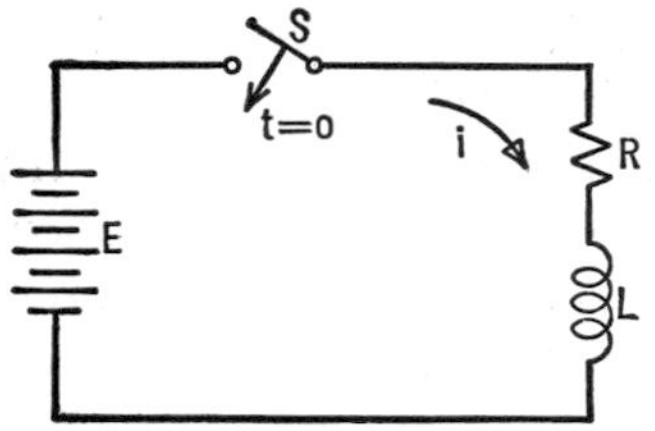

FIG. 1. A series RL branch which is suddenly energized by a constant potential difference E at $t = 0$.

$$L\frac{di}{(E - Ri)} = dt$$

or

$$L\int\frac{di}{(E - Ri)} = \int dt \tag{2}$$

Whence:

$$-\frac{L}{R}\log_\epsilon (E - Ri) = t + c$$

or

$$\log_\epsilon (E - Ri) = -\frac{Rt}{L} + c_1 \tag{3}$$

where ϵ is the base of the natural logarithms, namely, 2.71828 · · ·, and c_1 is a constant of integration. From the definition of a logarithm it follows that:

$$E - Ri = \epsilon^{(-Rt/L)+c_1}$$

Therefore:

$$E - Ri = c_2\epsilon^{-Rt/L} \tag{4}$$

Solving the above equation for i yields:

$$i = \frac{E}{R} - c_3\epsilon^{-Rt/L} \tag{5}$$

The constant of integration c_3 must be evaluated in terms of the boundary conditions that surround the switching operation. Boundary conditions are usually specified in terms of the circuit currents and the condenser voltages that exist at the instant a given switching operation is performed. In general, the specification and incorporation of boundary conditions require an understanding of the natural characteristics of the circuit parameters involved. For example, if a circuit possesses inductance the current cannot change abruptly, that is, cannot become discontinuous with respect to time. Therefore the current in an inductive branch at the instant a given switching operation is performed is equal to the current that exists in the branch just prior to switching operation. In the present case: $i = 0$ at $t = 0$, and this physical fact can be employed to determine the value of c_3 in equation (5). Imposing the boundary condition on equation (5) results in:

$$0 = \frac{E}{R} - c_3 \quad \text{or} \quad c_3 = \frac{E}{R} \tag{6}$$

The general expression for current becomes:

$$i = \underbrace{\frac{E}{R}}_{\text{steady-state term}} - \underbrace{\frac{E}{R}\epsilon^{-Rt/L}}_{\text{transient term}} \tag{7}$$

It will be noted that the complete expression for i consists of two terms: a steady-state term and a transient term. In general this distinct division of terms is present in complete current solutions. Under cer-

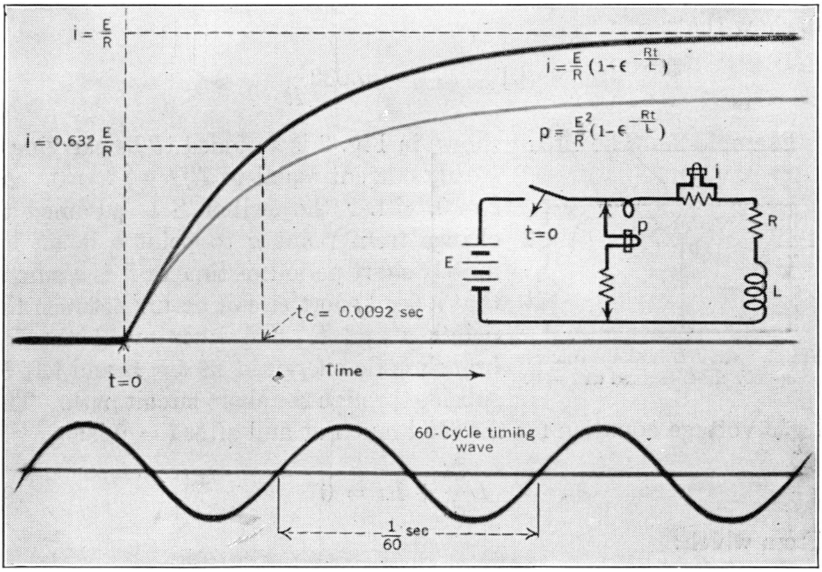

OSCILLOGRAM 1. Growth of current in an *RL* circuit which is suddenly energized with a constant potential difference, *E*. The instantaneous power delivered to the circuit is also shown.

tain conditions one or the other of the terms may be zero. The fact that the complete expression for current can be divided distinctly into a steady-state term and a transient term is of considerable importance. Under ordinary conditions the steady-state term can be evaluated in terms of elementary circuit concepts rather than by involved processes of integration. The transient term can usually be found in terms of simple exponential components if the circuit parameters are constant.

The time variations of the two terms of the current solution given in equation (7) can easily be visualized. The steady-state term, E/R, is independent of time; the transient term has a value of $(-E/R)$ at $t = 0$ and approaches zero exponentially as time increases. The two terms combine to form the current that actually flows in the RL circuit during the transient period. Oscillogram 1 illustrates the actual growth of current in an RL circuit when it is suddenly energized with a constant potential difference. It will be noted that the transition in current in this case is from zero to a steady d-c value equal to E/R.

In certain elementary types of circuits the length of time required for the current to make 63.2 per cent of its total transition is called the time constant of the circuit. The time constant of the RL circuit is L/R, as may be shown by direct substitution in equation (7). Thus if t is set equal to L/R in equation (7) it is simply a matter of algebra to show that:

$$[i]_{\text{at } t = L/R} = 0.632 \frac{E}{R}$$

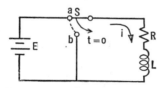

Example 2. The circuit shown in Fig. 2 is assumed to be carrying a steady current equal to E/R at $t = 0$. At $t = 0$, either the switch S is assumed to change from point a to point b in an infinitely short period of time or it is assumed that a dead short circuit occurs between the points a and b. In either event the RL branch is de-energized at $t = 0$ and left to subside through the short-circuit path. The basic voltage equation for the RL branch at and after $t = 0$ is:

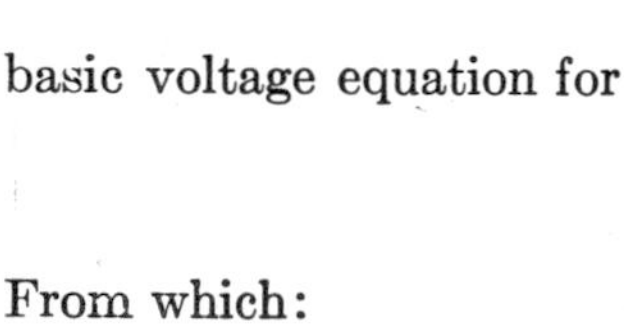

FIG. 2. An RL branch which is suddenly de-energized at $t = 0$.

$$L\frac{di}{dt} + Ri = 0 \tag{8}$$

From which:

$$i = \underset{\text{steady-state term}}{0} + \underset{\text{transient term}}{c_1 \epsilon^{-Rt/L}} \tag{9}$$

As previously mentioned, a current flowing through a circuit which has an appreciable amount of inductance cannot change its value instantaneously. Since $i = E/R$ just prior to $t = 0$, i is also equal to E/R at $t = 0$. Therefore:

$$\frac{E}{R} = c_1 \tag{10}$$

and

$$i = \underset{\text{steady-state term}}{0} + \underset{\text{transient term}}{\frac{E}{R}\epsilon^{-Rt/L}} \quad (11)$$

It will be observed that the transition in current is from (E/R) at $t = 0$ to zero current at $t = \infty$ and that the rate of subsidence is governed by the ratio of R to L. The current actually comes to zero in a relatively short period of time because the driving voltage, $L\,di/dt$ or $N\,d\phi/dt$, becomes so small that it can no longer maintain a net movement of electrons in one direction. Thus when the energy of the collapsing magnetic field becomes so small that it cannot overcome the internal atomic forces that tend to prevent net drifts of electrons, the current actually becomes zero. The failure of theoretical equations to account for exceedingly minute effects of this kind is of no practical importance.

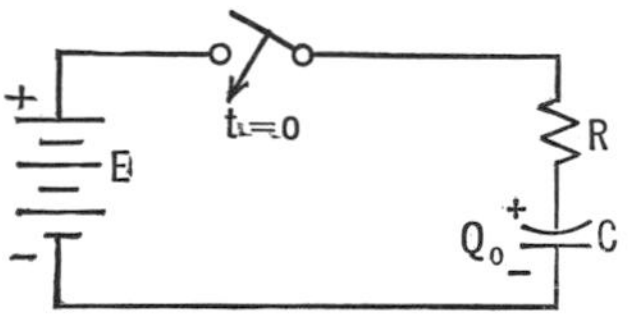

FIG. 3. A series RC circuit suddenly energized with a constant potential difference of E volts.

Example 3. If the condenser shown in Fig. 3 has a charge of Q_0 units of electrical charge at $t = 0$, the basic voltage equation at and after $t = 0$ is:

$$Ri + \frac{q}{C} = E \quad (12)$$

where

$$q = \int_0^t i\,dt + Q_0 \quad (13)$$

Differentiating equation (12) with respect to t and substituting i for dq/dt yields:

$$R\frac{di}{dt} + \frac{i}{C} = 0 \quad (14)$$

From which:

$$i = c_1\epsilon^{-t/RC} \quad (15)$$

The resultant voltage causing current to flow in the circuit at the instant of closing the switch is $(E - Q_0/C)$. Therefore the current instantly acquires a value $\frac{(E - Q_0/C)}{R}$ at $t = 0$ since the self-inductance is assumed to be negligibly small. In this connection it should be noted that the initial Q_0/C voltage of the condenser may possess either polarity with respect to the applied voltage E. For the case shown in Fig. 3

the polarity of Q_0/C is opposite to that of the applied voltage E. Since

$$i = \frac{(E - Q_0/C)}{R} \quad \text{at} \quad t = 0$$

it follows that

$$c_1 = \frac{(E - Q_0/C)}{R} \tag{16}$$

and

$$i = \frac{(E - Q_0/C)}{R} \epsilon^{-t/RC} \tag{17}$$

Equation (17) is the mathematical expression for the direct charging current taken by a condenser when the self-inductance of the circuit is negligibly small.

The variation of charge can be found by solving equation (12) for q and then substituting for i its value from equation (17). Thus

$$\begin{aligned} q &= CE - CRi \\ &= CE - (CE - Q_0)\epsilon^{-t/RC} \end{aligned} \tag{18}$$

If the initial charge $Q_0 = 0$, the variations of current and charge as given by equations (17) and (18) are shown in Fig. 4.

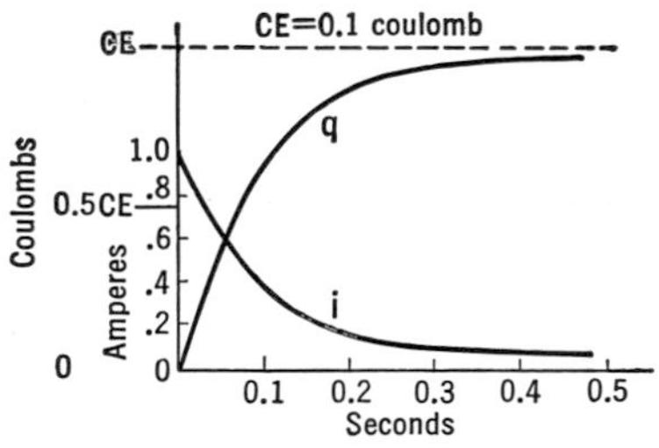

FIG. 4. Charging a condenser $C = 100\mu f$ through a resistance $R = 1000$ ohms from a d-c source of 1000 volts.

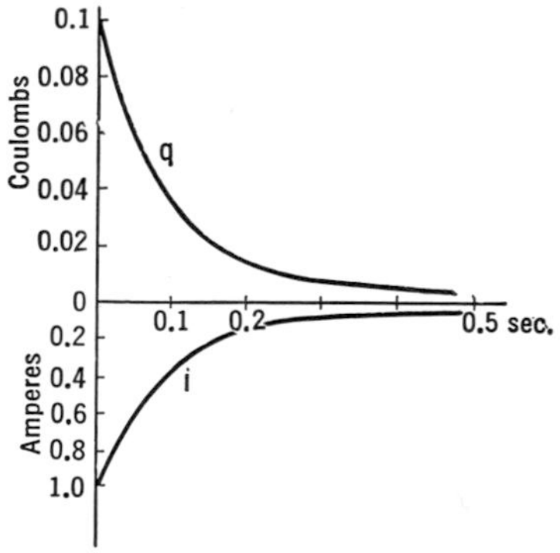

FIG. 5. Discharge of a condenser $C = 100\mu f$ through a resistance $R = 1000$ ohms. Initial charge at a potential of 1000 volts.

If a condenser of C units capacitance replaces the inductance L of Fig. 2, it is a simple matter to show that:

$$i = -\frac{E}{R}\epsilon^{-t/RC} \tag{19}$$

and

$$q = CE\epsilon^{-t/RC} \tag{20}$$

Equation (19) is the expression for the discharge current in an RC circuit which contains a condenser initially charged to a potential difference of E volts. Equation (20) is the expression for the decay of charge under the same conditions. The variations of current and charge as given by equations (19) and (20) are shown in Fig. 5. Condenser charge and discharge currents are similar except for sign and are simple exponential variations. The steady-state current in either of the two cases is obviously equal to zero.

The time constants of the above RC circuits are both equal to RC since it is at this value of time that the current has made 63.2 per cent of its total change.

Sawtooth Wave Form Produced by Simple Transient Effects. Various forms of circuits have been devised to produce sawtooth wave forms or approximations thereto. One of the most elementary is

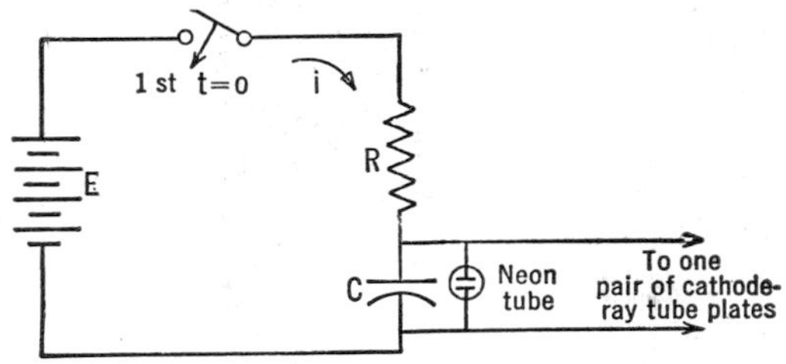

FIG. 6. An elementary form of sweep circuit the operation of which depends upon recurring transient phenomena.

shown in Fig. 6.[1] The operation of the device depends upon the natural behavior of the circuit elements, the details of which are listed below.

1. A transient voltage appears across the condenser due to the transient inrush of current to the main RC series circuit. Until a certain critical voltage is established across the condenser, the neon discharge tube remains un-ionized and acts practically as an open circuit.

2. When the condenser voltage has built up to a certain critical value, say E_1, the neon tube ionizes and suddenly places a low-resistance path across the condenser. The ionized tube thus provides a means of discharging the condenser because the time constant of the discharge path is relatively very small as compared with the time constant of the main RC series circuit. The voltage across the condenser drops from the value E_1 to some lower value, say E_2, in a very small fraction of the time required for the establishment of E_1.

[1] In practice the neon tube of Fig. 6 would probably be replaced by a gas triode which has an extremely low de-ionization time, for example, a type 885 tube. In this case the anode-cathode path of the triode replaces the neon tube of Fig. 6 and the grid of the triode can be used to control the starting of the discharge current.

3. After the condenser has been discharged to the voltage E_2, the neon tube ceases to be a conducting path (becomes de-ionized) and permits the applied potential difference to recharge the condenser. The cycle of transient phenomena thus repeats itself, and the voltage e_c takes on an approximate sawtooth wave form.

During the charging period the condenser voltage is:

$$e_{c1} = \frac{q}{C} = \frac{\int_0^t i\,dt + Q_0}{C} \tag{21}$$

or

$$e_{c1} = \frac{\int_0^t i\,dt}{C} + E_2 \tag{22}$$

E_2 is the voltage left on the condenser from the previous cycle due to the discharge tube de-ionizing before zero condenser voltage is reached.

From equation (17) it is evident that

$$i = \frac{E - E_2}{R} \epsilon^{-t/RC} \tag{23}$$

Therefore,

$$e_{c1} = \frac{E - E_2}{RC} \int_0^t \epsilon^{-t/RC}\,dt + E_2 \tag{24}$$

or

$$e_{c1} = E - (E - E_2)\epsilon^{-t/RC} \tag{25}$$

The rising condenser voltage is in this case exponential in character rather than linear. However, when the actual change in voltage, $(E_1 - E_2)$, is small as compared with $(E - E_2)$ fairly satisfactory results can be obtained.

The condenser voltage continues to build up in accordance with equation (25) until the voltage E_1 is attained, at which time the neon tube discharges the condenser in the manner previously described. Obviously E must be greater than E_1.

A mathematical analysis of the conditions during the discharge period is complicated by the variability of the resistance of the discharge path. The exact behavior of the circuit during the discharge period is usually unimportant because the discharge period is of relatively short duration and does not represent the "working" part of the cycle. It should be recognized that the series resistance, R, is generally of the order of 10,000 times the value of the tube resistance when the tube is ionized. Therefore during the discharge period the tube cannot receive any appreciable percentage of the applied voltage. It is plain that the device would cease to function as a sawtooth-wave-form generator, if, during an ionized period, the tube received a voltage sufficient to sustain ionization.

The general nature of the approximate sawtooth wave form produced is shown in Fig. 7. An obvious place for improvement is in the rising or building-up portion of the curve. The rising part of the curve can be made practically linear by replacing the constant resistance, R,

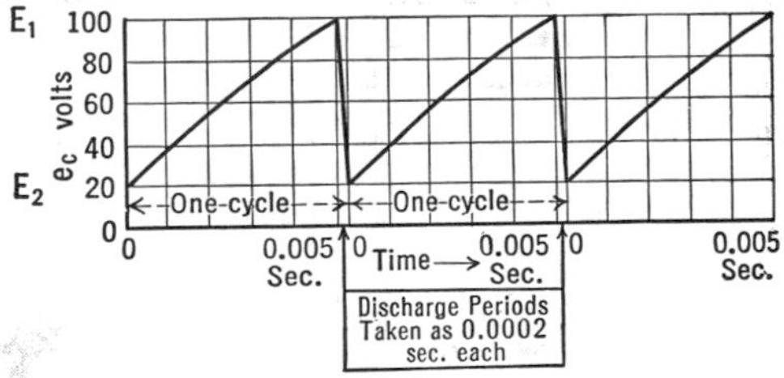

FIG. 7. Approximate sawtooth wave form as determined from equation (25) for the particular case of $E = 220$ volts, $E_1 = 100$ volts, $E_2 = 20$ volts, $R = 100{,}000$ ohms, and $C = 0.1\ \mu f$. The overall time of one cycle under these conditions is approximately 0.0052 second.

with a resistance that varies inversely as the amount of current passing through it. Many of the modern vacuum tubes, particularly the pentodes, possess this resistance characteristic from plate to cathode, provided they are worked between certain limits as regards plate-to-cathode voltage.

If the transient current inrush is maintained constant at I amperes by means of a variable resistance, then

$$e_{c1} = K \int_0^t I\, dt + E_2$$

$$= KIt + E_2$$

Under the conditions stated above, the rising part of the voltage curve shown in Fig. 7 would become linear with respect to time.

In addition to the use of a pentode type tube for maintaining constant charging or discharging current, some sweep circuits employ a grid-controlled mercury-vapor discharge tube as a starting and stopping valve. Various other combinations of electron tubes are also employed to produce sawtooth wave forms.

Oscillogram 2 is a photographic record of the wave form produced by a modern sweep circuit which employs a series of transient conditions to effect the desired result. In obtaining the photographic record one pair of plates of a cathode-ray tube are energized with one sweep-circuit potential difference and another pair of plates are energized with the potential difference developed by an identical sweep circuit. The linearity of the sweep-circuit voltage is clearly shown.

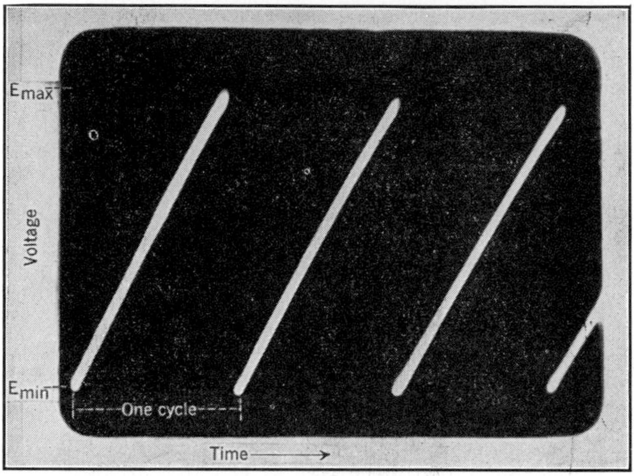

OSCILLOGRAM 2. Illustrating the linearity of the potential difference developed by a modern sweep circuit. In this particular case the return time, that is, the time required for the voltage to return from E_{max} to E_{min}, is so short that the trace is not discernible on the photographic record.

The *RL* Circuit Energized with an Alternating Potential Difference. If an alternating potential difference replaces the battery shown in Fig. 1, the expression for dynamic equilibrium is:

$$L\frac{di}{dt} + Ri = E_m \sin(\omega t + \lambda) \tag{26}$$

or

$$\frac{di}{dt} + \frac{R}{L}i = \frac{E_m}{L}\sin(\omega t + \lambda) \tag{27}$$

The symbol λ represents the phase of the voltage wave at which the switch of Fig. 1 is closed. Reference to Fig. 8 will show more clearly the exact meaning of λ. It is the angular displacement expressed in degrees or radians between the point $e = 0$ and the point $t = 0$ measured positively from the point where $e = 0$ and de/dt is positive.

The factor λ provides a convenient means of examining a-c transient conditions. In general, the magnitude of an a-c transient depends upon the time of the cycle at which the switching operation is performed. Most switching operations are performed with no regard for, or rather no knowledge of, the point on the voltage wave at which the transient period begins. Under these circumstances the investigator analyzes the effect of starting the transient disturbance at different points along the voltage wave. This is done by assigning different values to λ. In the case of surges or inrushes most attention is paid to those values of λ that produce the greatest currents or voltages.

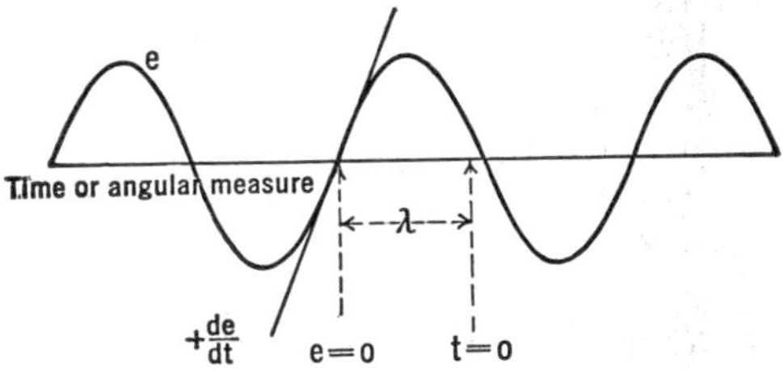

FIG. 8. Illustrating the physical significance of the symbol λ.

Equation (27) is representative of a general class of differential equations. The derivative of the dependent variable, (i), with respect to the independent variable, (t), added to the dependent variable, times some coefficient, equals some function of time. This form of equation defines the basic relationships involved in many physical problems, being particularly prevalent among the problems of electric circuit theory. The equation admits of relatively simple solution if all coefficients are constant and the right member is an exponential or sinusoidal function of time.

Let equation (27) be written as

$$\frac{di}{dt} + ai = h \sin (\omega t + \lambda) \tag{28}$$

where $a = R/L$ and $h = E_m/L$.

The solution of equation (28) takes the following form:

$$i = h\epsilon^{-at} \int \epsilon^{at} \sin (\omega t + \lambda)\, dt + c_1\epsilon^{-at} \tag{29}$$

The proof of the solution stated above rests in its ability to satisfy the original equation, namely, equation (28). In terms of the above solution:

$$\frac{di}{dt} = h\epsilon^{-at}\epsilon^{at} \sin (\omega t + \lambda) - ah\epsilon^{-at} \int \epsilon^{at} \sin (\omega t + \lambda)\, dt - ac_1\epsilon^{-at} \tag{30}$$

and

$$ai = ah\epsilon^{-at} \int \epsilon^{at} \sin (\omega t + \lambda)\, dt + ac_1\epsilon^{-at} \tag{31}$$

Adding equations (30) and (31) will show that equation (29) is a general solution of equation (28). The solution stated in equation (29) is limited to those cases where a and h are constant. For the particular problem at hand this means that R, L, and E_m must be constant before equation (29) can be employed as a solution of (28).

The solution for current in an RL circuit with sinusoidal voltage applied is:

$$i = \underbrace{\frac{E_m}{L}\epsilon^{-Rt/L}\int \epsilon^{Rt/L}\sin(\omega t + \lambda)\,dt}_{\text{steady-state term}} + \underbrace{c_1\epsilon^{-Rt/L}}_{\text{transient term}} \tag{32}$$

The relative complexities of the two terms in the above solution should be noted. Mathematically, the steady-state term is known as the "particular integral," and the transient term as the "complementary function." The integration involved in the evaluation of the steady-state term can be carried out by the method of successive parts, but the algebraic simplification of the results is a tedious process.

With sinusoidal applied voltages, familiar algebraic methods may be employed to find the steady-state terms of general current solutions. Many of the disagreeable details connected with the evaluation of complete current solutions are thus avoided. For example, several lengthy mathematical relations are involved in the integration method of finding the steady-state term of equation (32) which is simply:

$$i_s = \frac{E_m}{Z}\sin(\omega t + \lambda - \theta) \tag{33}$$

where

$$Z = \sqrt{R^2 + \omega^2 L^2} \quad \text{and} \quad \theta = \tan^{-1}\omega L/R$$

Actually equation (33) can be thought of as following from two physical facts. The maximum value of the steady-state current is E_m/Z where $Z = \sqrt{R^2 + \omega^2 L^2}$, and the steady-state current wave lags the applied voltage wave by the angle whose tangent is $\omega L/R$. The complete expression for current becomes:

$$i = \frac{E_m}{Z}\sin(\omega t + \lambda - \theta) + c_1\epsilon^{-Rt/L} \tag{34}$$

The constant of integration c_1 must be found from the initial conditions — those existing at the time of closing the switch. If the circuit current is zero just prior to closing the switch, then,

$$i = 0 \quad \text{at} \quad t = 0$$ (See page 550.)

Imposing the above condition on equation (34) yields

$$0 = \frac{E_m}{Z} \sin (\lambda - \theta) + c_1$$

From which:

$$c_1 = \frac{-E_m}{Z} \sin (\lambda - \theta) \tag{35}$$

and

$$i = \underbrace{\frac{E_m}{Z} \sin (\omega t + \lambda - \theta)}_{\text{steady-state term}} - \underbrace{\frac{E_m}{Z} \sin (\lambda - \theta) \epsilon^{-Rt/L}}_{\text{transient term}} \tag{36}$$

It will be noted from the above equation that the transient term is equal to zero when $(\lambda - \theta) = 0, \pi, 2\pi$, etc. If the RL branch is highly inductive the ratio of ωL to R is large, thereby causing θ to approach $\pi/2$ as an upper limit. In cases of this kind the transient term is zero when λ is approximately equal to $\pi/2, 3\pi/2, 5\pi/2$, etc. Physically this means that zero transient effects take place in highly inductive circuits when the circuit is energized at points of approximately maximum voltage on the voltage wave.

The transient term of equation (36) is maximum (for given values of R, L, ω, and E_m) when $(\lambda - \theta) = \pi/2, 3\pi/2, 5\pi/2$, etc. When θ is approximately equal to $\pi/2$ it is plain that the transient term is a maximum when λ is approximately equal to $0, \pi, 2\pi$, etc. Therefore in a highly inductive circuit the transient term is maximum when the switch is closed at points of approximately zero voltage on the voltage wave. A detailed study of equation (36) will show that conditions which make for the maximum possible transient terms do not necessarily make for the maximum possible values of i. In highly inductive circuits the difference between the two sets of conditions is not large and maximum transient disturbance is usually assumed to be the result of those conditions that make $\sin (\lambda - \theta) = 1$ or $\sin (\lambda - \theta) = -1$.

The steady-state term and the transient term, together with the resultant current, are illustrated in Fig. 9 for the case of $\theta = 85°$ and for $(\lambda - \theta) = 3\pi/2$. Under these conditions:

$$\lambda = 270° + 85° = 355° = -5°$$

It will be noted that the switch is closed when the steady-state term is at a maximum (negative) value and that the transient term is at its maximum (positive) value. The transient term and the steady-state term combine at $t = 0$ to make the resultant current equal to zero, which of course must be the case in an inductive circuit which is at rest just prior to the application of a potential difference.

Under the condition of constant R and L, the maximum value of the resultant current i is less than $2I_m$, where $I_m = E_m/Z$, the maximum value of the steady-state term. This fact may be easily substantiated

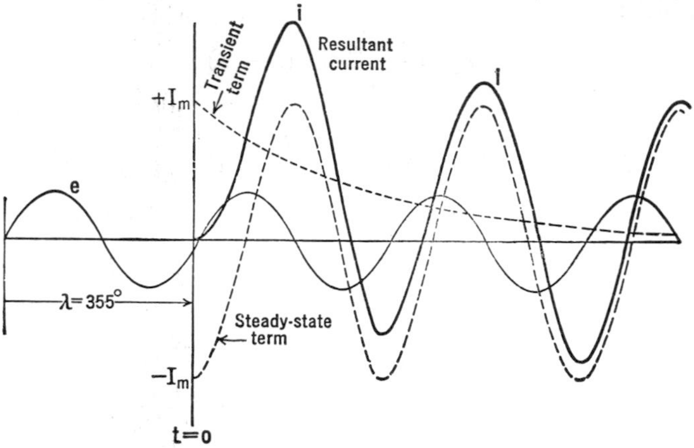

FIG. 9. Illustrating the manner in which the steady-state term and the transient term of equation (36) combine to form the resultant current. For the case shown, $\theta = 85°$ and $\sin(\lambda - \theta) = -1$.

from the graphs shown in Fig. 9. The effective value of the current during the early transient period is somewhat less than

$$\sqrt{I_{dc}^2 + I^2} = \sqrt{2I^2 + I^2} = \sqrt{3}I \quad \text{[See equation (28), page 252.]}$$

where $I_{dc} = I_m = \sqrt{2}I$ and I is the effective value of the steady-state term.

The transient term in an RL circuit is often referred to as the d-c component since it is unidirectional. This subsiding unidirectional component of current is of theoretical interest because it is partly responsible for the radical changes that take place in synchronous generator impedances during transient periods.

Oscillogram 3 illustrates the resultant current in a highly inductive circuit when $\lambda = 0$ and $\lambda = \pi/2$. The two current records are placed on the same oscillogram by means of superimposed exposures. In taking oscillograms of this kind it is necessary to employ some device for closing the circuit at the desired point on the voltage wave.

Problem 1. Plot the steady-state term and the transient term of equation (36) for two cycles of the steady-state variation under the following conditions:

(*a*) The applied voltage is a 60-cycle sinusoidal variation, the maximum value of which is 311 volts.

(*b*) $R = \omega L = 4$ ohms.

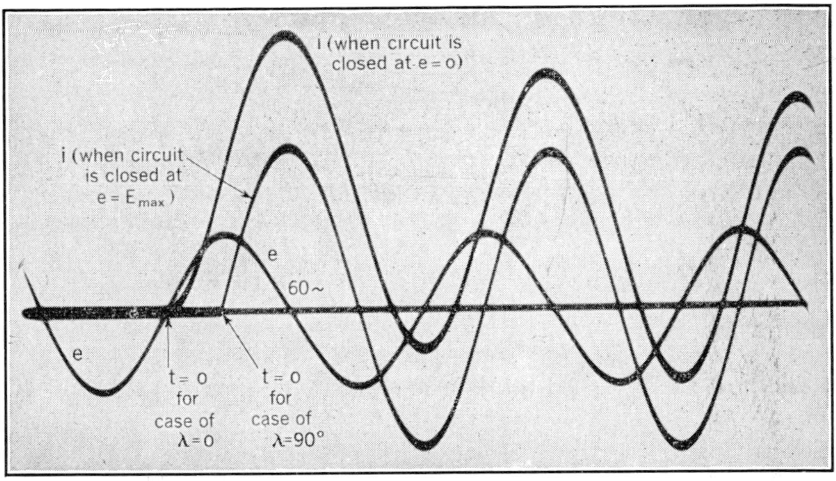

OSCILLOGRAM 3. Illustrating the current variations in an RL circuit which is suddenly energized with a p.d. of sinusoidal wave form. R and L, in this particular case, are sensibly constant. Two cases, namely, $\lambda = 0$ and $\lambda = 90°$, are shown.

(c) The switch is closed at such a time as to make the transient term acquire a negative maximum value.

Graph the resultant current i on the same plot.

Ans.: $i = 55 \sin (377t + 90°) - 55\epsilon^{-377t}$ amperes.

Problem 2. Analyze equation (36) for the case in which L is negligibly small.

Ans.: $i = \frac{E_m}{R} \sin (\omega t + \lambda)$.

The *RC* Circuit Energized with an Alternating Potential Difference. If an alternating potential difference replaces the battery shown in Fig. 3, the expression for dynamic equilibrium is:

$$Ri + \frac{q}{C} = E_m \sin (\omega t + \lambda) \tag{37}$$

Since $i = \frac{dq}{dt}$

$$R\frac{dq}{dt} + \frac{q}{C} = E_m \sin (\omega t + \lambda) \tag{38}$$

or

$$\frac{dq}{dt} + \frac{q}{RC} = \frac{E_m}{R} \sin (\omega t + \lambda) \tag{39}$$

Since equation (39) is a linear differential equation of the first order and first degree, the integrating factor[2] which makes the left-hand side

[2] Consult any standard book on differential equations.

..n exact derivative is:

$$\epsilon^{\int \frac{dt}{RC}} = \epsilon^{t/RC} \tag{40}$$

Multiplying equation (39) by $\epsilon^{t/RC}$ gives

$$\epsilon^{t/RC}\frac{dq}{dt} + \epsilon^{t/RC}\frac{q}{CR} = \epsilon^{t/RC}\frac{E_m}{R}\sin(\omega t + \lambda) \tag{41}$$

or

$$\epsilon^{t/RC}\,dq + \epsilon^{t/RC}\frac{q}{CR}\,dt = \epsilon^{t/RC}\frac{E_m}{R}\sin(\omega t + \lambda)\,dt \tag{42}$$

Integrating gives

$$q\epsilon^{t/RC} = \int \epsilon^{t/RC}\frac{E_m}{R}\sin(\omega t + \lambda)\,dt + K$$

or

$$q\epsilon^{t/RC} = \frac{E_m}{R}\left\{\frac{\epsilon^{t/RC}\left[\frac{1}{RC}\sin(\omega t + \lambda) - \omega\cos(\omega t + \lambda)\right]}{\frac{1}{R^2C^2} + \omega^2}\right\} + K \tag{43}$$

Dividing equation (43) through by $\epsilon^{t/RC}$, expressing the difference of the sine and cosine terms as a single cosine function, and making a few algebraic transformations give

$$q = -\frac{E_m}{\omega\sqrt{R^2 + \frac{1}{\omega^2C^2}}}\cos(\omega t + \lambda + \theta) + K\epsilon^{-t/RC} \tag{44}$$

where $\theta = \tan^{-1}\dfrac{1}{\omega CR} = \tan^{-1}\dfrac{X_c}{R}$.

Imposing the initial condition, namely, $q = Q_0$ when $t = 0$, and solving for K give

$$K = Q_0 + \frac{E_m}{\omega\sqrt{R^2 + \frac{1}{\omega^2C^2}}}\cos(\lambda + \theta) \tag{45}$$

Substituting (45) in (44) and replacing $\dfrac{1}{\omega C}$ by X_c

$$q = -\frac{E_m}{\omega\sqrt{R^2 + X_c^2}}\cos(\omega t + \lambda + \theta) + \left[Q_0 + \frac{E_m}{\omega\sqrt{R^2 + X_c^2}}\cos(\lambda + \theta)\right]\epsilon^{-t/RC} \tag{46}$$

Equation (46) is the general equation for the charge on the condenser. If the initial charge is zero,

$$q = -\frac{E_m}{\omega\sqrt{R^2 + X_c^2}}\cos(\omega t + \lambda + \theta) + \frac{E_m \epsilon^{-t/RC}}{\omega\sqrt{R^2 + X_c^2}}\cos(\lambda + \theta) \tag{47}$$

The first term of the right-hand member of equation (47) is the steady-state term whereas the last term is the transient. It should be noted that at the time $t = 0$, the transient is always exactly equal and opposite

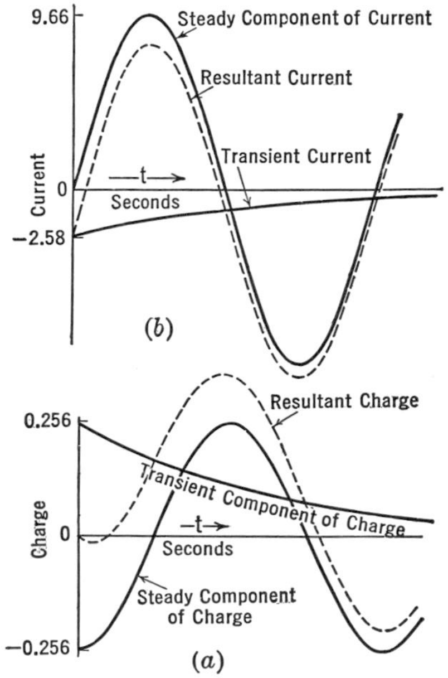

FIG. 10. Circuit containing $R = 100$ ohms, $C = 100\ \mu$f when $e = 1000 \sin(377t - 14.95°)$ volts is impressed. Initial charge on condenser = 0.

to the steady-state component. These results are shown in Fig. 10*a*. This is the same relation that exists between the steady-state term and transient of *current* in the *RL* circuit.

The current in the *RC* circuit is obtained by differentiation of equation (47). Thus

$$i = \frac{dq}{dt} = \frac{E_m}{\sqrt{R^2 + X_c^2}}\sin(\omega t + \lambda + \theta) - \frac{E_m \epsilon^{-t/RC}}{RC\omega\sqrt{R^2 + X_c^2}}\cos(\lambda + \theta) \tag{48}$$

A study of equation (48) and the corresponding graph, Fig. 10*b*, reveals that there is no fixed relation between the transient and the steady-state component of current at the time $t = 0$. The relative magnitudes are dependent upon the ratio of $\frac{X_c}{R} = \frac{1}{RC\omega}$ and the time angle λ at which the switch is closed.

The *RLC* Series Circuit with a Constant Direct Voltage Suddenly Applied. Since the emf applied to the circuit must equal the sum of all the drops at every instant, the condition for dynamic equilibrium is:

$$L\frac{di}{dt} + Ri + \frac{1}{C}\int i\,dt = E \tag{49}$$

Differentiating equation (49),

$$L\frac{d^2i}{dt^2} + R\frac{di}{dt} + \frac{i}{C} = 0 \tag{50}$$

Employing the usual method of solving a second-order, first-degree linear differential equation,[3] the auxiliary equation is:

$$L\alpha^2 + R\alpha + \frac{1}{C} = 0$$

Hence,

$$\alpha = \frac{-R \pm \sqrt{R^2 - \frac{4L}{C}}}{2L} = -\frac{R}{2L} \pm \sqrt{\frac{R^2}{4L^2} - \frac{1}{LC}}$$

Let

$$a = \frac{R}{2L} \quad \text{and} \quad b = \sqrt{\frac{R^2}{4L^2} - \frac{1}{LC}}$$

The complementary function is then

$$i = k_1\epsilon^{(-a+b)t} + k_2\epsilon^{(-a-b)t}$$

The complete solution is the sum of the complementary function and the particular integral, the latter being the steady-state current. Since this case involves a constant direct voltage on a condenser, the steady-state current is 0.

Hence the complete solution is:

$$i = k_1\epsilon^{(-a+b)t} + k_2\epsilon^{(-a-b)t} + 0 \tag{51}$$

The constants k_1 and k_2 must be evaluated by imposing certain known conditions. In this case when $t = 0$, $i = 0$, and $q = Q_0$, the latter being the initial charge on the condenser before closing the switch.

[3] See any standard book on differential equations.

For $i = 0$ and $t = 0$ in equation (51)

$$0 = k_1 + k_2 \quad \text{or} \quad k_2 = -k_1 \tag{52}$$

From equation (49)

$$\frac{1}{C}\int i\,dt = \frac{q}{C} = E - L\frac{di}{dt} - Ri$$

and

$$q = CE - CL\frac{di}{dt} - CRi \tag{53}$$

Substituting (51) in (53) gives

$$q = CE - CL[k_1(-a+b)\epsilon^{(-a+b)t} + k_2(-a-b)\epsilon^{(-a-b)t}] \\ -CR\,k_1\epsilon^{(-a+b)t} - CR\,k_2\epsilon^{(-a-b)t} \tag{54}$$

Imposing[4] the condition that $q = Q_0$ when $t = 0$ on equation (54), substituting equation (52), and solving for k_1 give

$$k_1 = \frac{CE - Q_0}{2CLb} \tag{55}$$

From equation (52)

$$k_2 = -k_1 = -\frac{CE - Q_0}{2CLb} \tag{56}$$

The final equation for current is now obtained by substituting equations (55) and (56) in equation (51) and replacing b by its equal. Hence,

Since $b = \sqrt{\dfrac{R^2}{4L^2} - \dfrac{1}{LC}}$ [in equations (57) and (58)] may be real, imaginary or zero, there are three cases to be considered.

[4] It is important that initial conditions be imposed on the original equation rather than on one of the differentiated forms. Note that equation (54) comes from equation (49) without any differentiation of the original voltage equation (49).

$$i = \frac{CE - Q_0}{\sqrt{R^2C^2 - 4LC}}[\epsilon^{(-a+b)t} - \epsilon^{(-a-b)t}] \tag{57}$$

If the values of k_1, k_2, a and b are substituted in equation (54), the expression for charge becomes

$$q = CE - (CE - Q_0)\left[\frac{RC + \sqrt{R^2C^2 - 4LC}}{2\sqrt{R^2C^2 - 4LC}}\epsilon^{(-a+b)t} - \frac{RC - \sqrt{R^2C^2 - 4LC}}{2\sqrt{R^2C^2 - 4LC}}\epsilon^{(-a-b)t}\right] \tag{58}$$

Case I. When $\frac{R^2}{4L^2} > \frac{1}{LC}$, the exponents of ε in equations (57) and (58) are real. When $t = 0$, the current is zero, and the quantity of electricity on the condenser is the initial charge before the switch was closed. Since $a = \frac{R}{2L}$ while $b = \sqrt{\left(\frac{R}{2L}\right)^2 - \frac{1}{LC}}$, $-a + b$ will be negative as long as $\left(\frac{R}{2L}\right)^2 > \frac{1}{LC}$. Hence as t becomes infinite, the exponential terms become zero. The current therefore becomes zero and the charge on the condenser becomes CE. A graphical representation of the variation of current and charge is shown in Fig. 11. Both the current and charge are unidirectional and the phenomena are non-oscillatory.

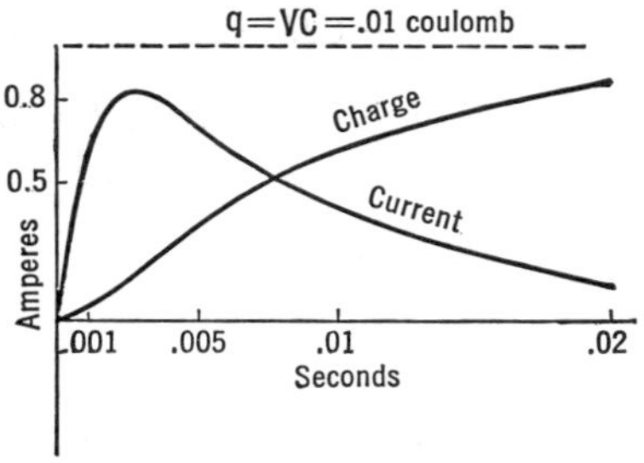

FIG. 11. Circuit containing $R = 100$ ohms, $C = 100\ \mu f$, $L = 0.1$ henry when a d-c voltage $V = 100$ volts is impressed. Initial charge $= 0$.

Case II. When $\frac{R^2}{4L^2} < \frac{1}{LC}$, b becomes imaginary. To evaluate the expression for b it may be written as

$$\sqrt{(-1)\left(\frac{1}{LC} - \frac{R^2}{4L^2}\right)} = \sqrt{-1}\sqrt{\frac{1}{LC} - \frac{R^2}{4L^2}} = j\beta$$

where

$$\beta = \sqrt{\frac{1}{LC} - \frac{R^2}{4L^2}}$$

Equation (57) then becomes:

$$\begin{aligned} i &= \frac{CE - Q_0}{\sqrt{R^2C^2 - 4LC}}[\epsilon^{(-a+j\beta)t} - \epsilon^{(-a-j\beta)t}] \\ &= \frac{CE - Q_0}{\sqrt{R^2C^2 - 4LC}}[\epsilon^{-at}\epsilon^{j\beta t} - \epsilon^{-at}\epsilon^{-j\beta t}] \\ &= \frac{(CE - Q_0)\epsilon^{-at}}{\sqrt{R^2C^2 - 4LC}}[\cos \beta t + j \sin \beta t - \cos \beta t + j \sin \beta t] \\ &= \frac{(CE - Q_0)\epsilon^{-at}}{\sqrt{R^2C^2 - 4LC}}[2j \sin \beta t] \end{aligned} \tag{59}$$

For $\frac{R^2}{4L^2} < \frac{1}{LC}$, $R^2C^2 < 4LC$ and the denominator of equation (59) may be written as $j\sqrt{4LC - R^2C^2}$. Substituting $j\sqrt{4LC - R^2C^2}$ for $\sqrt{R^2C^2 - 4LC}$ in equation (59) gives the final expression for current in terms of all real quantities, as

$$i = \frac{2(CE - Q_0)\epsilon^{-at}}{\sqrt{4LC - R^2C^2}} \sin \beta t \qquad (60)$$

Through a similar series of substitutions in and algebraic transformations of equation (58), the charge is found to be

$$q = CE - \frac{2(CE - Q_0)\sqrt{LC}\,\epsilon^{-at}}{\sqrt{4LC - R^2C^2}} \sin (\beta t + \theta) \qquad (61)$$

where

$$\theta = \tan^{-1} \frac{\sqrt{4LC - R^2C^2}}{RC}$$

If the initial charge on the condenser is zero, the expressions for current and charge respectively are:

$$i = \frac{2CE\epsilon^{-at}}{\sqrt{4LC - R^2C^2}} \sin \beta t \qquad (62)$$

$$q = CE - \frac{2CE\sqrt{LC}\,\epsilon^{-at}}{\sqrt{4LC - R^2C^2}} \sin (\beta t + \theta) \qquad (63)$$

A graphical representation of equations (62) and (63) is shown in Fig. 12. Oscillogram 4 also shows the variation of current with time in another *RLC* circuit. It should be noted that the current is proportional to the slope dq/dt of the curve of charge variation at every instant. An examination of equation (62) shows that after an infinite time the current becomes zero which is the steady state. Also equation (63) reveals that the charge becomes *CE* after an infinite time has elapsed. For all practical purposes, however, these final or steady states are sensibly reached after a few seconds; in some cases in a few microseconds. (See page 553 for explanation.) From the time of closing the switch to the time of reaching the final state the current and quantity oscillate about their final values. Case II is therefore called the oscilla-

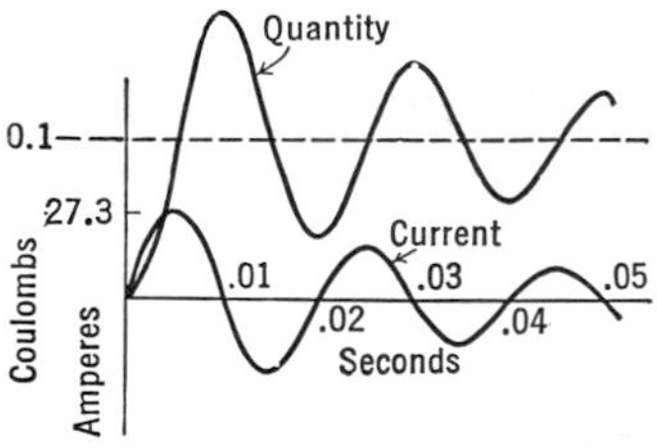

FIG. 12. Circuit containing $R = 5$ ohms, $C = 100$ μf, $L = 0.1$ henry, when a d-c voltage $V = 1000$ volts is impressed. Initial condenser charge $= 0$.

tory case. It is sometimes called the trigonometric case. Physically the current starts to flow and charges the condenser. Because of the low resistance compared with the inductance, the current continues to flow into the condenser when the magnetic field of the inductance collapses. The condenser charge thus overruns its final value and the potential drop across the condenser becomes higher than the impressed

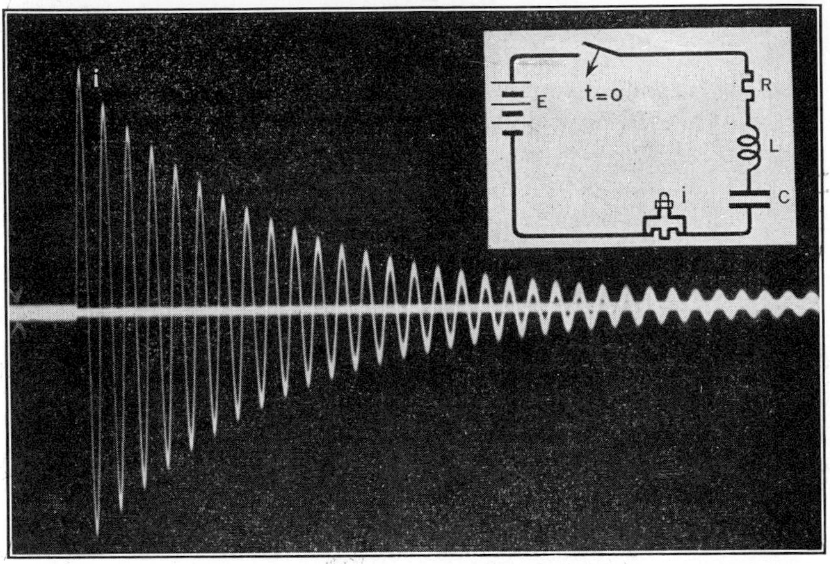

OSCILLOGRAM 4. Photographic record of the current variation in a particular *RLC* series circuit which is suddenly energized with a constant potential difference.

voltage. The condenser then begins to discharge. These oscillations continue until the excess energy is dissipated in the resistance. The phenomenon is analogous to the case of a weight suspended from a spring with a low value of mechanical damping.

The frequency of the oscillation f_0 is obtained from equation (62) or (63). For a complete cycle βt must be 2π radians and since the time for a complete cycle is defined as the period T, we may write

$$\beta T = 2\pi$$

or

$$T = \frac{1}{f_0} = \frac{2\pi}{\beta} = \frac{2\pi}{\sqrt{\frac{1}{LC} - \frac{R^2}{4L^2}}} \tag{64}$$

Hence

$$f_0 = \frac{1}{2\pi}\sqrt{\frac{1}{LC} - \frac{R^2}{4L^2}} \tag{65}$$

A comparison of the above equation with equation (10) on page 145 shows that the oscillatory frequency of the series RLC circuit when the resistance is zero is the same as the resonant frequency. Practically, they become the same when $R^2/4L^2$ is negligibly small compared with $1/LC$.

Case III. When $R^2/4L^2 = 1/LC$, $b = 0$ and the exponents of ε in equations (57) and (58) are real and negative as in case I. Hence the variations of current and charge are similar to those in case I. Case III is called the critical or limiting case and like case I is non-oscillatory.

Decay of Current and Charge in an *RLC* Circuit. The basic equation for this condition is:

$$L\frac{di}{dt} + Ri + \frac{1}{C}\int i\,dt = 0 \tag{66}$$

Equation (66) is obviously a special case of equation (49) where $E = 0$. Since equation (49) was solved in detail, the results of equation (66) will be found as special cases of equations (57), (58), (60), and (61) by making $E = 0$. It is plain that there will be three cases for the condition of zero voltage on (or short circuit of) the RLC circuit. These, as before, are the non-oscillatory case I where $R^2/4L^2 > 1/LC$, the oscillatory case 2 where $R^2/4L^2 < 1/LC$, and the critical case III, also non-oscillatory, where $R^2/4L^2 = 1/LC$.

Non-Oscillatory Case. The equations for current and charge for the non-oscillatory case are obtained from equations (57) and (58) respectively by setting $E = 0$. Thus

$$i = \frac{-Q_0}{\sqrt{R^2C^2 - 4LC}}[\epsilon^{(-a+b)t} - \epsilon^{(-a-b)t}] \tag{67}$$

and

$$q = Q_0\left[\frac{RC + \sqrt{R^2C^2 - 4LC}}{2\sqrt{R^2C^2 - 4LC}}\epsilon^{(-a+b)t} - \frac{RC - \sqrt{R^2C^2 - 4LC}}{2\sqrt{R^2C^2 - 4LC}}\epsilon^{(-a-b)t}\right] \tag{68}$$

A graphical representation of equations (67) and (68) is shown in Fig. 13. If desired, Q_0 can be replaced in the above equations by CV where V is the voltage drop across the condenser for the charge Q_0.

Oscillatory Case. If E is made equal to zero in equations (60) and (61), the equations for the decay of current and charge respectively are obtained as follows:

$$i = \frac{-2Q_0\epsilon^{-at}}{\sqrt{4LC - R^2C^2}} \sin \beta t \tag{69}$$

$$q = \frac{2Q_0\sqrt{LC}\epsilon^{-at}}{\sqrt{4LC - R^2C^2}} \sin (\beta t + \theta) \tag{70}$$

The variation of i and q as given by these equations is shown in Fig. 14. A comparison of equations (69) and (70) with equations (62) and (63) will show that the frequencies of oscillation for all of them are identical and are therefore given by equation (65).

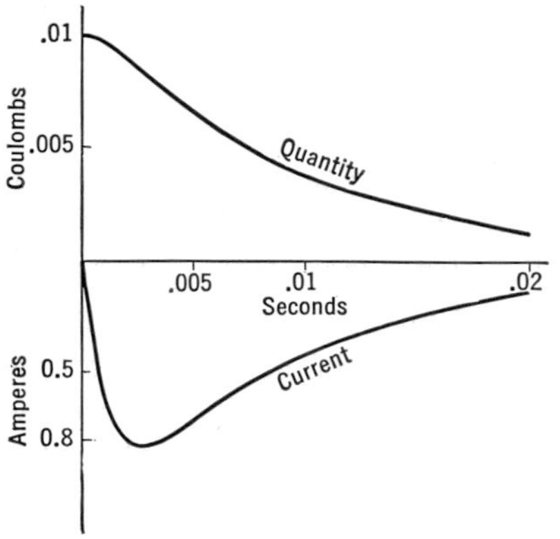

FIG. 13. Decay of current and charge or quantity in a circuit containing $R = 100$ ohms, $C = 100$ μf, and $L = 0.1$ henry when the initial charge on the condenser is 0.01 coulomb at a potential of 100 volts.

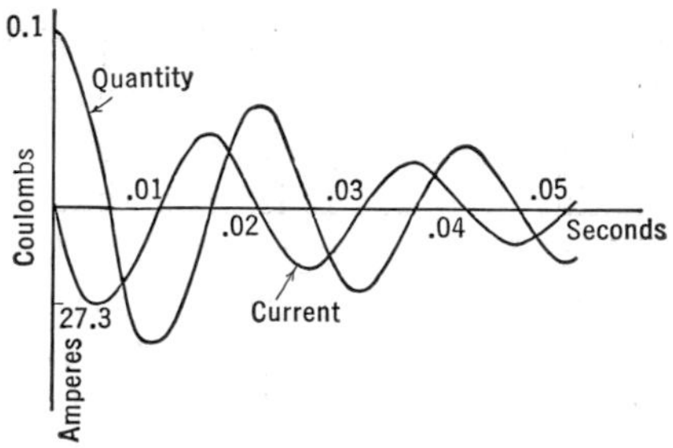

FIG. 14. Decay of current and charge or quantity in a circuit containing $R = 5$ ohms, $C = 100$ μf, and $L = 0.1$ henry when the initial charge on the condenser is 0.1 coulomb at a potential of 1000 volts.

Critical Case. Qualitatively this case is no different from the non-oscillatory case previously discussed. If b in equations (67) and (68) is made zero, the equations for the critical case result. Obviously Fig. 13 represents the general type of variation of current and charge for this condition.

Natural Circuit Behavior in Terms of Poles and Zeros. The concept of complex frequency was introduced in Chapter V in order to illustrate how steady-state circuit behavior could be obtained from the s-plane poles and zeros which characterized the network function which was under discussion. In actual practice, complex frequency probably finds a greater field of usefulness in transient analysis than it does in the analysis of the steady state. If, for example, the LRC series circuit is energized at $t = 0$ with the voltage having an angular frequency of ω_d

radians/second

$$e = E_m \sin(\omega_d t + 90°) = E_m \cos \omega_d t$$

the analysis may be carried forward with the aid of a complex exponential voltage excitation of the form

$$\mathsf{e} = \mathbf{E}\epsilon^{\mathrm{s}_d t} = \mathbf{E}\epsilon^{\alpha_d t}\epsilon^{j\omega_d t} \tag{71}$$

For this case we recognize that $\mathbf{E} = E_m\underline{/0°}$ and $\alpha_d = 0$. Since

$$\epsilon^{j\omega_d t} = \cos \omega_d t + j \sin \omega_d t \tag{72}$$

it is apparent that the *real* part of e corresponds to the desired excitation. We may carry through the solution for $\mathbf{i}$ and at the end retain only the real part of $\mathbf{i}$ as the real $i(t)$. In other words, $\epsilon^{j\omega_d t} = \cos \omega_d t + j \sin \omega_d t$ corresponds to two voltage excitations, only one of which is actually used to energize the circuit. As long as the circuit is linear, each exciting voltage develops its own current, and in the present instance we are interested in the current associated with the real part of e. If $e = E_m \sin \omega_d t$ had been the specified driving voltage, it might have been more convenient to employ the imaginary part of e. The fact that the $\mathbf{E}$ of $\mathsf{e} = \mathbf{E}\epsilon^{\mathrm{s}_d t}$ is a complex number actually allows us to use either the real or the imaginary part of the final solution depending largely upon the manner in which the actual driving voltage $e(t)$ is specified.

In solving for $i(t)$ by way of the complex exponential $\mathbf{i}$, we let

$$\mathbf{i} = \mathbf{i}_s + \mathbf{i}_t \tag{73}$$

in

$$L\frac{d\mathbf{i}}{dt} + R\mathbf{i} + \frac{1}{C}\int \mathbf{i}\, dt = \mathsf{e} = \mathbf{E}\epsilon^{\mathrm{s}_d t} \tag{74}$$

where $\mathbf{i}_s$ is the steady-state component of the current

$\mathbf{i}_t$ is the transient component of the current

The fact that

$$\mathbf{i}_s = \mathbf{I}_s\epsilon^{\mathrm{s}_d t} \tag{75}$$

may be verified by direct substitution in equation (74). This substitution will also show that

$$\mathbf{I}_s = \frac{\mathbf{E}}{L\mathrm{s}_d + R + \dfrac{1}{C\mathrm{s}_d}} = \frac{\mathbf{E}}{L}\left(\frac{\mathrm{s}_d}{\mathrm{s}_d^{\,2} + \dfrac{R}{L}\mathrm{s}_d + \dfrac{1}{LC}}\right) \tag{76}$$

It follows that

$$L\frac{d\mathbf{i}_t}{dt} + R\mathbf{i}_t + \frac{1}{C}\int \mathbf{i}_t\, dt = 0 \tag{77}$$

This homogeneous equation is evidently satisfied by

$$\mathbf{i}_t = \mathbf{A}\epsilon^{\mathbf{s}t} \tag{78}$$

provided that

$$\left(L\mathbf{s} + R + \frac{1}{C\mathbf{s}}\right) = 0 \tag{79}$$

Solving this equation for $\mathbf{s}$ yields

$$\mathbf{s} = \mathbf{s}_1 = -\frac{R}{2L} + j\sqrt{\frac{1}{LC} - \frac{R^2}{4L^2}} = \alpha_n + j\omega_n \tag{80}$$

$$\mathbf{s} = \mathbf{s}_2 = -\frac{R}{2L} - j\sqrt{\frac{1}{LC} - \frac{R^2}{4L^2}} = \alpha_n - j\omega_n \tag{81}$$

ω_n is the natural angular frequency of the circuit, and $\alpha_n = -R/2L$ is the natural damping factor. Since two values of $\mathbf{s}$ satisfy equation (79), we have

$$\mathbf{i}_t = \mathbf{A}_1\epsilon^{\mathbf{s}_1 t} + \mathbf{A}_2\epsilon^{\mathbf{s}_2 t} \tag{82}$$

In complex exponential form, the complete circuit current is found by substituting equation (82) in equation (73). Thus

$$\mathbf{i} = \mathbf{I}_s\epsilon^{\mathbf{s}_d t} + \mathbf{A}_1\epsilon^{\mathbf{s}_1 t} + \mathbf{A}_2\epsilon^{\mathbf{s}_2 t} \tag{83}$$

and the corresponding capacitor charge is

$$\mathbf{q} = \int \mathbf{i}\,dt = \frac{\mathbf{I}_s}{\mathbf{s}_d}\epsilon^{\mathbf{s}_d t} + \frac{\mathbf{A}_1}{\mathbf{s}_1}\epsilon^{\mathbf{s}_1 t} + \frac{\mathbf{A}_2}{\mathbf{s}_2}\epsilon^{\mathbf{s}_2 t} \tag{84}$$

The $\mathbf{A}$'s depend for their values upon the initial circuit conditions, for example, the values of $\mathbf{i}$ and $\mathbf{q}$ at $t = 0$. If $\mathbf{i} = 0$ and $\mathbf{q} = 0$ at $t = 0$, substitution in equation (83) gives

$$\mathbf{A}_1 + \mathbf{A}_2 = -\mathbf{I}_s = -\frac{\mathbf{E}}{L}\frac{\mathbf{s}_d}{(\mathbf{s}_d - \mathbf{s}_1)(\mathbf{s}_d - \mathbf{s}_2)} \quad \text{[See equation (76)]} \tag{85}$$

Similarly, substitution in equation (84) yields

$$\frac{\mathbf{A}_1}{\mathbf{s}_1} + \frac{\mathbf{A}_2}{\mathbf{s}_2} = -\frac{\mathbf{I}_s}{\mathbf{s}_d} = -\frac{\mathbf{E}}{L}\frac{1}{(\mathbf{s}_d - \mathbf{s}_1)(\mathbf{s}_d - \mathbf{s}_2)} \tag{86}$$

Solving equations (85) and (86) for $\mathbf{A}_1$ and $\mathbf{A}_2$ yields

$$\mathbf{A}_1 = \frac{\mathbf{E}}{L}\frac{\mathbf{s}_1}{(\mathbf{s}_d - \mathbf{s}_1)(\mathbf{s}_2 - \mathbf{s}_1)} \tag{87}$$

$$\mathbf{A}_2 = -\frac{\mathbf{E}}{L}\frac{\mathbf{s}_2}{(\mathbf{s}_d - \mathbf{s}_2)(\mathbf{s}_2 - \mathbf{s}_1)} \tag{88}$$

If these values of $\mathbf{A}_1$ and $\mathbf{A}_2$ along with $\mathbf{I}_s$ from equation (76) are substituted in equation (83), the expression for i is obtained. The actual circuit current is the real part of i. It may be expressed as

$$i(t) = \mathcal{R}\left[\frac{\mathbf{E}}{L}\left(\frac{\mathbf{s}_d\epsilon^{\mathbf{s}_d t}}{(\mathbf{s}_d - \mathbf{s}_1)(\mathbf{s}_d - \mathbf{s}_2)} + \frac{\mathbf{s}_1\epsilon^{\mathbf{s}_1 t}}{(\mathbf{s}_d - \mathbf{s}_1)(\mathbf{s}_2 - \mathbf{s}_1)} - \frac{\mathbf{s}_2\epsilon^{\mathbf{s}_2 t}}{(\mathbf{s}_d - \mathbf{s}_2)(\mathbf{s}_2 - \mathbf{s}_1)}\right)\right] \quad (89)$$

The price paid for using complex exponential forms of current and voltage is the transformation back to real current or voltage at the close of the solution. If, for example, we want the actual *steady-state component* of current in equation (89), we evaluate the real part of the steady-state component of this current. This is

$$\mathcal{R}\left[\frac{\mathbf{E}}{L}\,\frac{\mathbf{s}_d\epsilon^{\mathbf{s}_d t}}{(\mathbf{s}_d - \mathbf{s}_1)(\mathbf{s}_d - \mathbf{s}_2)}\right] = \mathcal{R}\left[\frac{\mathbf{E}}{L}\,\frac{\mathbf{s}_d\epsilon^{\mathbf{s}_d t}}{\mathbf{s}_d^{\,2} + \dfrac{R}{L}\mathbf{s}_d + \dfrac{1}{LC}}\right]$$

For $\mathbf{s}_d = j\omega_d$ and $\mathbf{E} = E_m\underline{/0°}$ the expression within the bracket becomes

$$\frac{E_m}{(L/j\omega_d)}\,\frac{\epsilon^{j\omega_d t}}{\left(\dfrac{1}{LC} - \omega_d^{\,2}\right) + j\dfrac{R}{L}\omega_d} = \frac{E_m(\cos\omega_d t + j\sin\omega_d t)}{R + j\left(\omega_d L - \dfrac{1}{\omega_d C}\right)}$$

The real part of the above expression is

$$\mathcal{R}\left[\frac{E_m}{(L/j\omega_d)}\,\frac{\epsilon^{j\omega_d t}}{\left(\dfrac{1}{LC} - \omega_d^{\,2}\right) + j\dfrac{R}{L}\omega_d}\right]$$

$$= \frac{E_m\left[R\cos\omega_d t + \left(\omega_d L - \dfrac{1}{\omega_d C}\right)\sin\omega_d t\right]}{R^2 + \left(\omega_d L - \dfrac{1}{\omega_d C}\right)^2}$$

$$= [E_m\cos(\omega_d t - \theta)]/Z \quad (90)$$

where $Z = \sqrt{R^2 + \left(\omega_d L - \dfrac{1}{\omega_d C}\right)^2}$ and $\theta = \tan^{-1}\dfrac{\left(\omega_d L - \dfrac{1}{\omega_d C}\right)}{R}$

Transformations from the s plane to the t plane are often accomplished by means of Laplace transforms, a technique which the reader will encounter repeatedly in later courses.

The *RLC* Series Circuit with Alternating Voltage Suddenly Applied. The basic voltage equation of the *RLC* circuit shown in Fig. 15 is

$$L\frac{di}{dt} + Ri + \frac{q}{C} = E_m \sin(\omega t + \lambda) \tag{91}$$

The above equation can be put in terms of one dependent variable by differentiating the entire equation with respect to the independent variable, t. Differentiating as indicated above,

$$L\frac{d^2i}{dt^2} + R\frac{di}{dt} + \frac{1}{C}\frac{dq}{dt} = E_m\omega \cos(\omega t + \lambda) \tag{92}$$

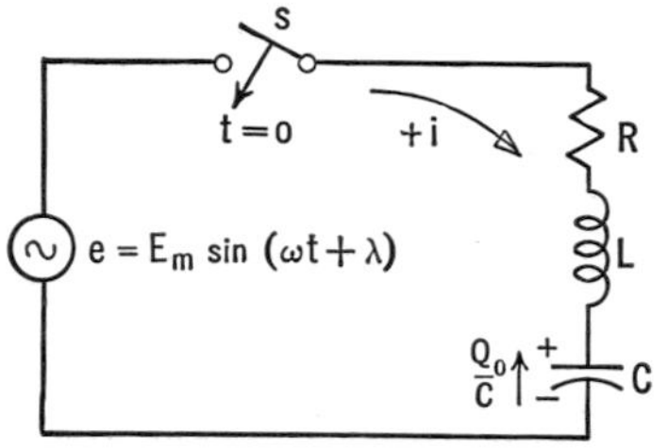

FIG. 15. An *RLC* series circuit energized with an alternating voltage at $t = 0$.

Dividing through by L and substituting i for dq/dt results in

$$\frac{d^2i}{dt^2} + \frac{R}{L}\frac{di}{dt} + \frac{i}{LC} = \frac{E_m\omega}{L}\cos(\omega t + \lambda) \tag{93}$$

Equation (93) is a linear differential equation of the second order, first degree, the solution of which consists of the sum of a complementary function or transient term and the particular integral or steady-state term. The former is obtained as indicated previously. The auxiliary equation is

$$\alpha^2 + \frac{R}{L}\alpha + \frac{1}{LC} = 0 \tag{94}$$

and

$$\alpha = \frac{-\frac{R}{L} \pm \sqrt{\frac{R^2}{L^2} - \frac{4}{LC}}}{2} = -\frac{R}{2L} \pm \sqrt{\frac{R^2}{4L^2} - \frac{1}{LC}} \tag{95}$$

Let

$$a = \frac{R}{2L} \quad \text{and} \quad b = \sqrt{\frac{R^2}{4L^2} - \frac{1}{LC}} \tag{96}$$

By definition

$$\alpha_1 = -a + b \quad \text{and} \quad \alpha_2 = -a - b \tag{97}$$

The transient term of the complete solution is

$$i_t = c_1\epsilon^{(-a+b)t} + c_2\epsilon^{(-a-b)t} \tag{98}$$

The steady-state term of the complete solution is

$$i_s = \frac{E_m}{Z}\sin(\omega t + \lambda - \theta) \tag{99}$$

where

$$Z = \sqrt{R^2 + \left(\omega L - \frac{1}{\omega C}\right)^2} \quad \text{and} \quad \theta = \tan^{-1}\frac{\left(\omega L - \frac{1}{\omega C}\right)}{R}$$

The complete expression for current becomes

$$i = \frac{E_m}{Z}\sin(\omega t + \lambda - \theta) + c_1\epsilon^{(-a+b)t} + c_2\epsilon^{(-a-b)t} \tag{100}$$

The two physical facts from which c_1 and c_2 can be evaluated are the state of current and the state of charge that exist in the circuit at the instant of closing the switch. Let it be assumed that

$$\left.\begin{array}{l} i = 0 \\ q = Q_0 \end{array}\right\} \quad \text{at} \quad t = 0 \tag{101}$$

If the original voltage equation has been differentiated it is important that the initial conditions be imposed upon the original voltage equation rather than upon one of the differentiated forms. In the present case the initial conditions can be imposed upon equations (91) and (100).

Imposing the initial conditions upon equation (91) yields

$$L\left[\frac{di}{dt}\right]_{t=0} + \frac{Q_0}{C} = E_m \sin\lambda$$

or

$$L\left[\frac{E_m\omega}{Z}\cos(\lambda - \theta) + c_1\alpha_1 + c_2\alpha_2\right] + \frac{Q_0}{C} = E_m \sin\lambda$$

From which

$$c_1\alpha_1 + c_2\alpha_2 = \frac{E_m}{L}\sin\lambda - \frac{Q_0}{LC} - \frac{E_m\omega}{Z}\cos(\lambda - \theta) \tag{102}$$

Imposing the initial conditions on equation (100) results in

$$0 = \frac{E_m}{Z}\sin(\lambda - \theta) + c_1 + c_2$$

or

$$c_1 + c_2 = -\frac{E_m}{Z}\sin(\lambda - \theta) \tag{103}$$

Equations (102) and (103) may be solved simultaneously for c_1 and c_2. From equation (103)

$$c_2 = -\frac{E_m}{Z}\sin(\lambda - \theta) - c_1 \tag{104}$$

Substituting the above value of c_2 into equation (102) yields

$$c_1\alpha_1 - \left[\frac{E_m}{Z}\sin(\lambda - \theta)\right]\alpha_2 - c_1\alpha_2 = \frac{E_m}{L}\sin\lambda - \frac{Q_0}{LC} - \frac{E_m\omega}{Z}\cos(\lambda - \theta)$$

Whence

$$c_1(\alpha_1 - \alpha_2) = \frac{1}{L}\left[E_m \sin\lambda - \frac{Q_0}{C} - \frac{E_m\omega L}{Z}\cos(\lambda - \theta)\right] + \alpha_2\frac{E_m}{Z}\sin(\lambda - \theta) \tag{105}$$

It will be remembered that

$$\alpha_1 = (-a + b) \quad \text{and} \quad \alpha_2 = (-a - b)$$

Therefore

$$\alpha_1 - \alpha_2 = 2b$$

and

$$\frac{\alpha_2}{\alpha_1 - \alpha_2} = -\frac{a}{2b} - \frac{b}{2b} = -\frac{R}{4Lb} - \frac{1}{2}$$

Dividing equation (105) through by $(\alpha_1 - \alpha_2)$ and making substitutions for $(\alpha_1 - \alpha_2)$ and α_2,

$$c_1 = \frac{1}{2bL}\left[E_m \sin\lambda - \frac{Q_0}{C} - \frac{E_m\omega L}{Z}\cos(\lambda - \theta)\right] - \frac{R}{4bL}\frac{E_m}{Z}\sin(\lambda - \theta) - \frac{E_m}{2Z}\sin(\lambda - \theta)$$

Collecting the b terms in the above equation,

$$c_1 = \frac{1}{2bL}\left[E_m \sin\lambda - \frac{Q_0}{C} - \frac{E_m\omega L}{Z}\cos(\lambda - \theta) - \frac{E_m R}{2Z}\sin(\lambda - \theta)\right] - \frac{E_m}{2Z}\sin(\lambda - \theta) \tag{106}$$

From equation (103) it is evident that

$$c_2 = -c_1 - \frac{E_m}{Z}\sin(\lambda - \theta) \tag{107}$$

Therefore,

$$c_2 = -\frac{1}{2bL}\left[E_m \sin\lambda - \frac{Q_0}{C} - \frac{E_m\omega L}{Z}\cos(\lambda-\theta) - \frac{E_m R}{2Z}\sin(\lambda-\theta)\right] - \frac{E_m}{2Z}\sin(\lambda-\theta) \quad (108)$$

For the sake of simplicity in writing, the following abbreviation will be adopted:

$$\left[E_m \sin\lambda - \frac{Q_0}{C} - \frac{E_m\omega L}{Z}\cos(\lambda-\theta) - \frac{E_m R}{2Z}\sin(\lambda-\theta)\right] = E_d \quad (109)$$

It will be observed that E_d is a voltage which is governed in magnitude by E_m, λ, Q_0, and the circuit parameters. The complete expression for current can now be written in terms of the applied voltage, the initial condenser charge, and the circuit parameters.

$$i = \frac{E_m}{Z}\sin(\omega t + \lambda - \theta) + \frac{E_d\epsilon^{-at}}{bL}\left[\frac{\epsilon^{bt} - \epsilon^{-bt}}{2}\right] - \frac{E_m}{Z}\sin(\lambda-\theta)\,\epsilon^{-at}\left[\frac{\epsilon^{bt} + \epsilon^{-bt}}{2}\right] \quad (110)$$

The transient component of the current consists of two terms, each of which is damped out with the damping factor ϵ^{-at} or $\epsilon^{-Rt/2L}$. The transient terms may be given different mathematical forms depending upon the nature of the symbol b. Since b is equal to $\sqrt{\dfrac{R^2}{4L^2} - \dfrac{1}{LC}}$ it is evident that b may be either real or imaginary. A singular condition exists when b is equal to zero.

Case I. If $R^2/4L^2$ is greater than $1/LC$, b is a real number and the complete expression for current in the RLC series circuit may be written as

$$i = \underbrace{\frac{E_m}{Z}\sin(\omega t + \lambda - \theta)}_{\text{steady-state term}} + \underbrace{\frac{E_d}{bL}\epsilon^{-at}\sinh bt - \frac{E_m}{Z}\sin(\lambda-\theta)\epsilon^{-at}\cosh bt}_{\text{transient terms}} \quad (111)$$

The above expression follows directly from equation (110) since, if b is real,

$$\frac{\epsilon^{bt} - \epsilon^{-bt}}{2} = \sinh bt \quad \text{and} \quad \frac{\epsilon^{bt} + \epsilon^{-bt}}{2} = \cosh bt$$

Both transient terms are damped out by $\epsilon^{-Rt/2L}$. The damping factor

$Rt/2L$ is relatively large when $\dfrac{R^2}{4L^2} > \dfrac{1}{LC}$ because of the relatively large value of $R/2L$. In general, the transient terms in this case are not predominantly large as compared with the steady-state term.

Case II. If $R^2/4L^2$ is less than $1/LC$, b takes the form of an imaginary number and a change in notation becomes desirable. Let

$$b = j\beta \quad \text{where} \quad \beta = \sqrt{\frac{1}{LC} - \frac{R^2}{4L^2}}$$

If $\dfrac{R^2}{4L^2} < \dfrac{1}{LC}$, β is a real number and b in equation (110) can be replaced by its equivalent, $j\beta$. In this connection j has its customary significance, namely, $\sqrt{-1}$.

$$i = \underbrace{\frac{E_m}{Z}\sin(\omega t + \lambda - \theta)}_{\text{steady-state term}} + \underbrace{\frac{E_d}{\beta L}\epsilon^{-at}\sin\beta t - \frac{E_m}{Z}\sin(\lambda - \theta)\epsilon^{-at}\cos\beta t}_{\text{transient terms}} \quad (112)$$

The above equation comes directly from equation (110) if it is recognized that the analytical expressions for sin βt and cos βt are

$$\frac{\epsilon^{j\beta t} - \epsilon^{-j\beta t}}{2j} = \sin\beta t \quad \text{and} \quad \frac{\epsilon^{j\beta t} + \epsilon^{-j\beta t}}{2} = \cos\beta t$$

The two transient terms of equation (112) are exponentially damped sine and cosine terms of like frequency. Since the damping factors are identical, the sine and cosine terms can be combined by the method outlined on page 241. If the two transient terms are combined, equation (112) takes the following form:

$$i = \underbrace{\frac{E_m}{Z}\sin(\omega t + \lambda - \theta)}_{\text{steady-state term}} + \underbrace{I_t\epsilon^{-at}\sin(\beta t - \sigma)}_{\text{transient term}} \quad (113)$$

where

$$I_t = \sqrt{\left[\frac{E_d}{\beta L}\right]^2 + \left[\frac{E_m}{Z}\sin(\lambda - \theta)\right]^2}$$

and

$$\sigma = \tan^{-1}\frac{E_m\beta L\sin(\lambda - \theta)}{E_d Z}$$

In the present case the complete expression for current consists of two sinusoidal terms. The frequency of the steady-state term, $\omega/2\pi$, is determined solely by the frequency of the applied voltage; that of the transient term, $\beta/2\pi$, is governed entirely by the circuit parameters, R, L, and C. The frequency of the transient term may be less than, equal to, or greater than that of the applied voltage. In any event the transient oscillation disappears as soon as the damping factor, $\epsilon^{-Rt/2L}$, causes the transient term to become sensibly equal to zero.

Oscillograms 5 and 6 illustrate the current variations in a particular RLC series circuit during transient periods. For the conditions shown, $\frac{R^2}{4L^2} < \frac{1}{LC}$ and $\beta > \omega$. The exponentially damped transient component can easily be discerned as the higher frequency variation which is superimposed on the 60-cycle steady-state variation. Also the effect of closing the circuit at different points on the voltage wave can be observed by comparing Oscillograms 5 and 6. The transient term is shown to be several times as large in Oscillogram 5 as it is in Oscillogram 6.

The Iron-Clad *RL* Circuit Energized by an Alternating Potential Difference. The mathematical analysis given in the article on page 558 for the case of constant R and L cannot, in general, be applied to an iron-clad circuit because of the wide variations of L that occur. For the iron-clad circuit, L in equation (26) is a function of i which in turn is an intricate function of time. The fact that L is variable makes both the coefficients of equation (27) or (28) variable. In general, the solution of differential equations with variable coefficients is a difficult task. It is plain that no general solution can be obtained because the variation of L in any particular case must necessarily be defined in terms of particular constants rather than in terms of arbitrary constants. Although the variation of L can sometimes be approximated with the aid of simple functions, the actual variation in many cases of importance cannot be expressed in terms of practical mathematical functions.

It is well known that L, being equal to $N\, d\phi/di$, depends upon the ϕ–i characteristic of the magnetic material that surrounds the L coil. The inductance that is operative in establishing an $L\, di/dt$ voltage drop depends for its value upon the exact degree of magnetic saturation of the surrounding magnetic material. Under any a–c condition the degree of saturation varies considerably with time and under transient conditions these variations are very often exaggerated. Reference to any typical B–H or ϕ–i curve will show that

$$L = N\frac{d\phi}{di}$$

is much greater over the straight portion of the curve than it is after the upper bend is reached. This fact plays an important role in determining the current inrush to iron-clad circuits, because, in general, circuits of this character are highly inductive and the variable L becomes an extremely influential parameter.

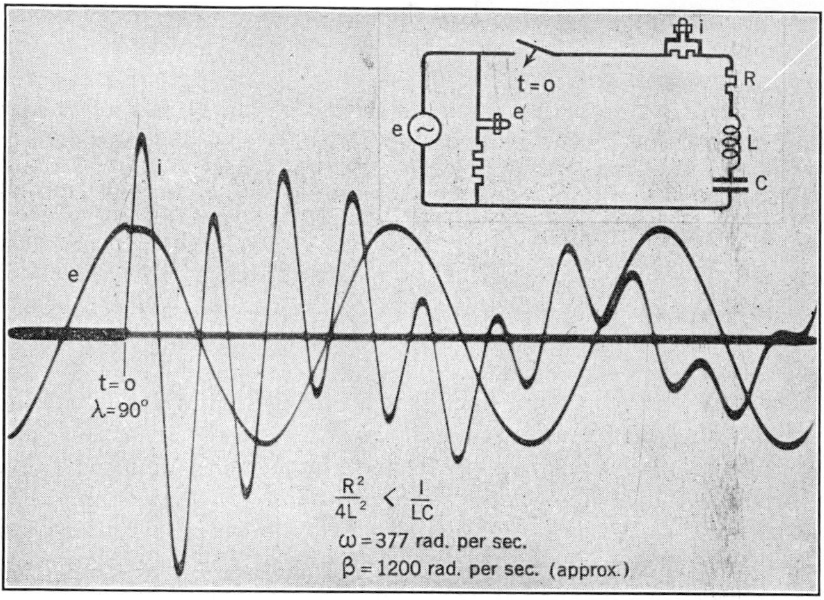

OSCILLOGRAM 5. Photographic record of the current variation in a particular *RLC* series circuit which is suddenly energized with an alternating potential difference. *R*, *L*, and *C* are sensibly constant.

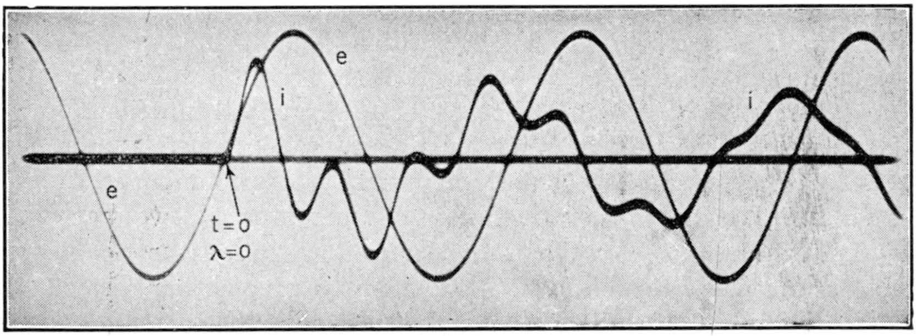

OSCILLOGRAM 6. Circuit arrangement and circuit parameters similar in every respect to those shown in connection with Oscillogram 5 except for the point on the voltage wave at which the circuit is energized. In the present case $\lambda = 0°$.

Circuit problems involving variable parameters can be solved by step-by-step methods provided the exact variation of the parameters is known. In the present case the variation of L is known if the $N\phi/i$ characteristic of the surrounding magnetic material is known. The data usually take the form of either the ϕ–i characteristic and the number of turns or the B–H characteristic, the dimensions of the magnetic circuit, and the number of turns. In any event it is somewhat more direct to substitute for $L\ di/dt$ [in equation (26)] its equivalent $N\ d\phi/dt$ value. The basic equation then becomes

$$N\frac{d\phi}{dt} + Ri = E_m \sin(\omega t + \lambda) \tag{114}$$

where ϕ is expressed in webers if the other quantities are expressed in practical units.

In many iron-clad circuits the maximum magnitude of the Ri term is of the order of 1 per cent of the maximum magnitude of the applied voltage. Under these conditions the $N\ d\phi/dt$ component of equation (114) is very nearly equal to the applied voltage and in approximate steady-state solutions the Ri drop can be neglected. The Ri drop cannot be entirely neglected in the transient solution of the problem because it is instrumental in helping to govern the maximum value of the initial current inrush. The resistance is also an important factor in governing the length of time required for the iron-clad circuit to adjust itself to steady-state operating conditions.

If the Ri drop is neglected and if it is assumed that $\lambda = 0$, equation (114) reduces to

$$N\frac{d\phi}{dt} = E_m \sin \omega t \tag{115}$$

from which

$$\phi = \frac{E_m}{N}\int \sin \omega t\, dt = -\frac{E_m}{\omega N}\cos \omega t + c_1 \tag{116}$$

The constant of integration c_1 may be evaluated in terms of the residual magnetism. ϕ may be at either positive or negative residual values at $t = 0$, and in general the exact state of residual magnetism is unknown. A compromise may be made by assuming that $\phi = 0$ at $t = 0$ unless the maximum possible current inrush is to be determined. In this case a maximum value of positive residual magnetism is assumed if the applied voltage is taken as $E_m \sin \omega t$. The manner in which residual magnetism helps to determine the initial current inrush will soon be apparent.

Assuming that $\phi = 0$ at $t = 0$, c_1 of equation (116) becomes

$$c_1 = \frac{E_m}{\omega N} \tag{117}$$

Under these conditions

$$\phi = \frac{E_m}{\omega N}(1 - \cos \omega t) \tag{118}$$

or

$$\phi = \phi_m (1 - \cos \omega t) \qquad (119)$$

where $\phi_m = E_m/\omega N$, the approximate maximum value of the magnetic flux under steady-state operating conditions. Since $(\cos \omega t)$ varies between $+1$ and -1, it is plain that the flux variation as defined by

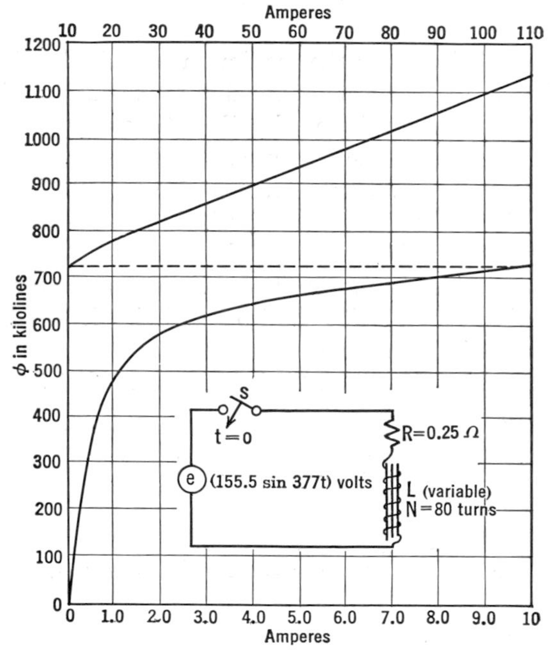

FIG. 16. Magnetization curve of a particular iron-clad RL circuit.

equation (119) varies from zero at $t = 0$ to $2\phi_m$ at $t = T/2$. In order to produce a flux equal to $2\phi_m$, the iron-clad inductance coil must draw a particular value of magnetizing current as defined by the ϕ–i characteristic of the magnetic circuit. For example, in the circuit shown in Fig. 16

$$\phi_m = \frac{155.5}{377 \times 80} = 0.00516 \text{ weber}$$

or

$$\phi_m = 0.00516 \times 10^5 = 516 \text{ kilolines}$$

Reference to the magnetization curve will show that the current required to establish ϕ_m is approximately 1.2 amperes, whereas current required to establish $2\phi_m$ is approximately 84 amperes. This great change in current is due primarily to the flattening out of the magnetization curve.

If the magnetic core referred to above had possessed a residual magnetism of, say, $+0.5\phi_m$, it is evident that a much larger current than the 84 amperes would finally be required to produce the $2\phi_m$ change in flux during the first half cycle. Actually the initial current inrush to an iron-clad circuit is somewhat less than that required to produce a $2\phi_m$ flux change.

It will be remembered that equation (119) carries with it the assumption that the Ri drop is negligibly small. This assumption may be perfectly justified if the flux is worked between its normal steady-state values of $+\phi_m$ and $-\phi_m$. But in attempting to produce a $2\phi_m$ change in flux starting with zero flux, the circuit draws such a large current that the Ri drop becomes significantly large and must be taken into consideration. Under the above conditions the Ri drop consumes an appreciable portion of the applied voltage during the second quarter cycle after the switch is closed, thereby reducing the magnitude of the $N\,d\phi/dt$ component in this region. As a result, ϕ reaches a maximum value of something less than $2\phi_m$ shortly before $t = T/2$, and it is at this point that the maximum instantaneous current occurs.

The ordinary iron-core transformer with open secondary operates as a simple iron-core RL circuit. Oscillogram 7 illustrates the nature of the starting current taken by the primary winding of an iron-core transformer when the secondary is open-circuited. In this particular case the initial peak current is considerably more than 100 times the steady-state maximum value of primary current when the secondary is open-circuited. However, the initial current inrush reaches a peak value which is only about 4.5 times the value of the maximum full-load current of the transformer. For the case shown in Oscillogram 7 the actual transient period is of approximately 0.5-second duration. Only the early part of the transient period is shown in the oscillogram.

The Method of Finite Differences. Although it involves step-by-step calculations, the " method of finite differences " is very often employed in circuit analysis when variable parameters are encountered. The step-by-step calculations are based upon the assumption that the parameters remain sensibly constant over small finite intervals of time. Usually the basic voltage equation is rewritten so that all differentials take the form of finite increments. The circuit voltage and current are then assumed to remain constant over an arbitrarily assigned increment of time, Δt. As a first approximation the applied voltage and current are assumed to be constant at their " start-of-period " values. If, then, after assigning a particular value to Δt, only a single unknown incre-

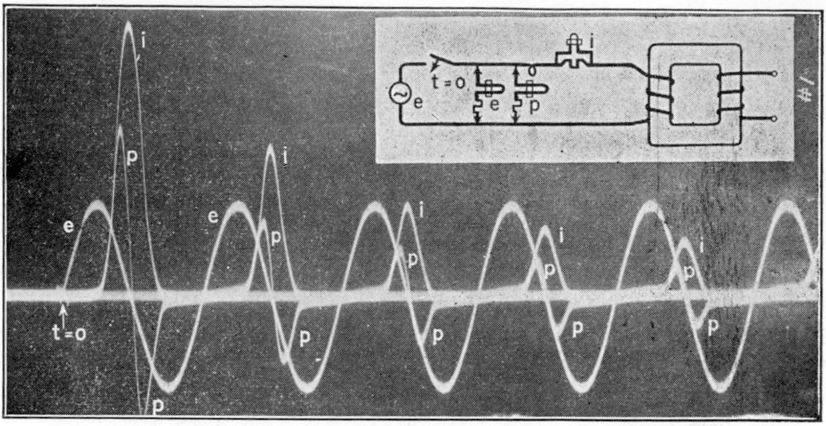

OSCILLOGRAM 7. Iron-core transformer current and power inrushes when the primary is energized at the $e = 0$ point on the voltage wave.

e = 60-cycle applied emf	E (eff.) = 117 volts
i = instantaneous current	Peak i = 174 amperes
p = instantaneous power	Peak p = 10.5 kw

Steady-state conditions: $P_{av} = 30$ watts, $I_{eff} = 0.825$ ampere.
Transformer rating: 115 volts, 3 kva, 26.1 amperes, 60 cycles.

mental quantity remains in the equation, it can be solved for by methods of elementary algebra. The process can best be illustrated by means of an example.

The predetermination of the initial current inrush to an iron-clad circuit will serve to illustrate the details of the method of finite differences. If finite differences of ϕ and t are employed, equation (114) takes the following form:

$$N \frac{\Delta\phi}{\Delta t} + Ri = E_m \sin\left(\sum \Delta\rho + \lambda\right) \tag{120}$$

where $\sum \Delta\rho = \sum\omega\,\Delta t$, the angular displacement along the voltage wave of the point under investigation from the point of $t = 0$.

Judgment must be exercised in the choice of Δt in any particular case. The selection of the size of Δt in a–c circuits is governed largely by the magnitude of ω. If points every 10° along the voltage wave are desired, then each Δt is taken as $\frac{1}{18}$ of π/ω second. The choice of smaller increments will, of course, make for more accurate solutions. Δt should never be chosen so large that significant changes in the parameters take place within the time interval represented by Δt.

At the beginning of a period i and $E_m \sin\left(\sum \Delta\rho + \lambda\right)$ have particular values. Letting $E_m \sin\left(\sum \Delta\rho + \lambda\right)$ be written as e and solving equation (120) for $\Delta\phi$ results in

$$\Delta\phi = \frac{(e - Ri)\,\Delta t}{N} \tag{121}$$

If practical units of e, R, i, and t are employed in the above equation, $\Delta\phi$ is given in webers.

Various refinements can be employed to improve the accuracy of the method of finite differences as outlined above. Very often, however, the improved accuracy is not warranted because of the uncertainties that surround the initial conditions and other experimental data.

Numerical Example. (1) The emf applied to the iron-clad RL circuit shown in Fig. 16 is

$$e = \sqrt{2} \times 110 \sin 377t \text{ volts}$$

This signifies that a 60-cycle voltage, the effective value of which is 110 volts, is applied to the circuit at the point of zero voltage where de/dt is positive. A simpler way of expressing the same thing is to say that a 110-volt 60-cycle voltage is applied at $\lambda = 0$.

(2) $N = 80$ turns and $R = 0.25$ ohm as indicated in the circuit diagram of Fig. 16.

(3) The residual magnetism is zero, and the flux varies in accordance with the ϕ–i curve given in Fig. 16 for the first half cycle of the applied emf.

(4) Only the first maximum instantaneous value of current is to be determined. Therefore the hysteresis effects which occur after the first half cycle and which complicate the determination of succeeding maxima can be neglected. Let the numerical coefficients enumerated above be inserted into equation (120).

$$80\,\frac{\Delta\phi}{\Delta t} + 0.25i = 155.5 \sin \sum \Delta\rho$$

or

$$\Delta\phi = \frac{(155.5 \sin \sum \Delta\rho - 0.25i)}{80}\,\Delta t \text{ webers}$$

It will be somewhat more convenient in the present example if $\Delta\phi$ is reckoned in kilolines.

$$\Delta\phi = \frac{(e - 0.25i)\,\Delta t}{80} \times 10^5 \text{ kilolines}$$

where $e = 155.5 \sin \sum \Delta\rho$.

Each time increment will be taken as 0.0005 second, a value which corresponds to an angular displacement along a 60-cycle wave of 10.8°.

The initial conditions are such as to make both e and i zero at $t = 0$. Assuming that both e and i maintain zero value throughout the first time interval, the change in flux during this period, $\Delta\phi_1$, is equal to zero.

At the beginning of the second period, $\sum \Delta t = 0.0005$ second and $e = 155.5 \sin 10.8°$ volts. For each interval i is assumed to have its "start-of-period" value, which in this case is zero.

$$\Delta\phi_2 = \frac{(29.1 - 0)\,0.0005}{80} \times 10^5$$

$$= 18.2 \text{ kilolines}$$

At the close of the second or the beginning of the third period the current is assumed to have acquired the value required for the establishment of $\Delta\phi_2$. Reference to the magnetization curve will show that the establishment of 18.2 kilolines requires approximately 0.03 ampere.

At the beginning of the third period, $\sum \Delta t = 0.001$ second and $e = 155.5 \sin 21.6°$ volts.

$$\Delta\phi_3 = \frac{(57.2 - 0.25 \times 0.03)\ 0.0005}{80} \times 10^5$$

$$= 35.7 \text{ kilolines}$$

The current required to establish $\sum \Delta\phi$ [(18.2 + 35.7) kilolines] is approximately 0.09 ampere. Other $\Delta\phi$'s can be added by the step-by-step method outlined above. The results of a series of such calculations are shown in Table I.

TABLE I

Period	$\Sigma\ \Delta t$ seconds	$\Sigma\ \Delta\rho$ degrees	$E_m \sin \Sigma\ \Delta\rho$ volts	Ri volts	$\Delta\phi$ kilolines	$\Sigma\ \Delta\phi$ kilolines	i amperes
1	0	0	0	0	0	0	0
2	0.0005	10.8	29.1	0	18.2	18.2	0.03
3	0.0010	21.6	55.7	Negligible	35.7	53.9	0.09
4	0.0015	32.4	83.3	Negligible	52.1	106.0	0.18
5	0.0020	43.2	106.0	Negligible	66.0	172.0	0.29
6	0.0025	54.0	126.0	Negligible	79.0	251.0	0.43
7	0.0030	64.8	141.0	Negligible	88.0	339.0	0.58
8	0.0035	75.6	151.0	Negligible	94.0	433.0	0.75
9	0.0040	86.4	155.0	Negligible	97.0	530.0	1.4
10	0.0045	97.2	154.0	Negligible	96.0	626.0	3.1
11	0.0050	108.0	148.0	0.78	92.0	718.0	9.0
12	0.0055	118.8	136.0	2.25	84.0	802.0	25.0
13	0.0060	129.6	120.0	6.25	71.0	873.0	44.5
14	0.0065	140.4	99.2	11.1	55.0	928.0	58.0
15	0.0070	151.2	74.9	14.5	38.0	966.0	66.5
16	0.0075	162.0	48.1	16.6	20.0	986.0	72.0
17	0.0080	172.8	19.5	18.0	1.0	987.0	72.0
18	0.0085	183.6	−9.8	18.0	−17.0	970.0	67.0
19	0.0090	194.4	−38.7	16.7	−35.0	935.0	59.0
20	0.0095	205.2	−66.2	14.7	−51.0	884.0	47.0

It will be noted that the current reaches a maximum value of approximately 72 amperes at $t = 0.008$ second. This corresponds to a point approximately 173° out along the voltage wave from the point at which the switch is closed, namely, the $e = 0$ point.

The general trend of the current variation is similar to that shown in Oscillogram 7. It will be observed that the current values are relatively very small during the first quarter cycle after the switch is closed. It is during this period that the Ri drop is negligibly small.

The change of flux that occurs during the period of negligible Ri drop can be calculated straightforwardly, and it may be of interest to compare the step-by-step results with a result which is very nearly accurate from a theoretical point of view. From equation (118)

$$\phi = \frac{155.5}{377 \times 80}(1 - \cos 377t) \text{ webers}$$

If t is taken as 0.0045 second, $(377t)$ is equal to approximately 1.7 radians or 97.2°. At $t = 0.0045$ second,

$$\phi = \frac{155.5}{377 \times 80}(1 - \cos 97.2°) \times 10^5 \text{ kilolines}$$

or

$$\phi = 579 \text{ kilolines} \quad \text{at} \quad t = 0.0045 \text{ second}$$

The value ϕ at $t = 0.0045$ second as determined by the step-by-step method is 626 kilolines. (See Table I.)

PROBLEMS

3. (*a*) Find the current in a coil containing $L = 1$ henry and $R = 0.4$ ohm one second after applying a d-c voltage of 10 volts.

(*b*) What will the current be after 2.5 seconds?

(*c*) What is the value of the voltage accelerating the current after 1 second? after 2.5 seconds?

4. A coil has 0.1 henry and 1 ohm resistance and carries 10 amperes. If its terminals are suddenly short-circuited, what will be the value of current 0.1 second later? How long will it take the current to fall to 0.1 ampere?

5. Find the number of ohms resistance which may be placed in series with an inductance of 0.1 henry so as to permit the current in the circuit to reach 63.2 per cent of its final value in 2 seconds after the voltage is applied.

6. Ten volts direct current are applied to a 0.1-ohm resistance in series with a 1-henry inductance.

(*a*) Calculate the energy stored in the inductance 10 seconds after the voltage is applied. State units.

(*b*) Derive the expression for the energy dissipated in the resistance in the time t after the voltage is applied.

7. A 50-μf condenser with no initial charge is in series with a 1-megohm resistor. How long will it take to attain 63.2 per cent of its final charge?

8. A 50-μf condenser has stored 0.1 coulomb.

(*a*) If it is discharged through a 1000-ohm resistor, how long will it take until it has 0.001 coulomb remaining?

(*b*) What will be the initial value of current?

(*c*) What will be the value of current when 0.001 coulomb remains on the condenser?

9. A 100-μf condenser has a charge of 0.1 coulomb. If it is discharged through a 10,000-ohm resistance, what will be the amount of energy in joules remaining in the condenser 1 second after the discharge is started?

10. A d-c voltage was applied to a resistance of 10,000 ohms in series with a 100-μf condenser. After 1 second there were 19.98 joules stored in the condenser which had no initial charge. How many volts were applied to the circuit?

11. A 1-megohm resistance is in series with a 1-μf condenser. A d-c voltage of 100 volts is suddenly applied to the circuit.

(*a*) Calculate the energy stored in the condenser 1 second after the voltage is applied.

(*b*) Derive the expression for the energy dissipated in the resistance during the first second after the voltage is applied.

(*c*) How much energy will be dissipated in the resistance in charging the condenser to full charge?

12. What fraction of total charge will the condenser in Problem 11 have after 2 seconds?

13. A voltage $e = 100 \sin [377t + (\pi/4)]$ is impressed on a 1-henry inductance coil containing 1 ohm resistance. What are the values of the steady and the transient components of current at $t = 0$?

14. A voltage $e = 100 \sin (377t + 30°)$ is impressed on a 100-μf condenser having no initial charge and containing 1 ohm resistance.

(*a*) What are the values of the steady and transient components of charge at $t = 0$?

(*b*) What are the corresponding values of current?

15. A circuit contains $R = 100$ ohms, $C = 200$ μf, and $L = 0.1$ henry in series. If a d-c voltage of 50 volts is impressed, calculate the current and charge after 0.01 second, assuming no initial charge on the condenser.

16. A circuit contains $R = 5$ ohms, $L = 0.1$ henry, and $C = 200$ μf in series.

(*a*) Calculate the current and charge 0.01 second after 1000 volts are impressed if there was no initial charge on the condenser.

(*b*) Is the circuit oscillatory?

(*c*) If so, what is its frequency?

17. The condenser in the circuit of Problem 16 is charged to a potential of 1000 volts. If the circuit is connected upon itself, what will be the value of current and charge after 0.0125 second has elapsed?

18. Given an *RLC* series circuit which is suddenly energized with an alternating potential difference which is equal to

$$e = 141 \sin (377t - 45°) \text{ volts}$$

$R = 1.0$ ohm $L = 0.041$ henry $C = 18.7$ μf $Q_0 = 0$

(*a*) Write equation (113) for this particular case, employing numerical coefficients. The result is to be in the form:

$$i = k_1 \sin (k_2t + k_3) + k_4\epsilon^{-k_5t} \sin (k_6t - k_7) \text{ amperes}$$

where all k's are expressed numerically.

(*b*) Make sketches of the steady-state term, the transient term, and the resultant current for the first three or four cycles of steady-state phenomena on the same plot. Show also the e variation.

Index

Accuracy of short-circuit calculations, 528
Addition, of admittances, 158, 159
  of complex waves, 261
  of currents, 128
  of impedances, 142, 143, 158
  of vectors, 68
  of voltages, 68, 128
  of volt-amperes, 347, 395
Admittance, addition of, 158, 159
  definition, 158
  surge, 418
Air-core transformer, 291, 314, 317
  vector diagram, 295, 315, 316
Algebra of phasors, 107
Alternating current, amount used in United States, 45
  ampere value, 85
  average value, 86, 88
  beginning of systems, 45
  components of, 99
  definition, 47, 48
  effective value, 87
  equation of, 51
  four-phase systems, 328
  generation of, 45, 46
  lagging, 52, 53
  sine-wave representation, 51, 91
  three-phase, 331, 334
  two-phase systems, 328
Alternating volt, definition, 86
Alternating voltage, components of, 99
  definition, 47, 48
  see also Alternating current
Amplitude factor, 89
Analysis, methods of, loop-current, 7, 274, 377
    nodal, 198
    node-pair, 15–22
Analysis of non-sinusoidal waves, 225
  analytical method, 228
  analyzing tables, 237–240
  graphical method, 233, 242
  rectangular wave, 231, 232
  triangular wave, 231, 232, 233
Analytical method for determining whether two waves are of the same form, 248–250
Angular frequency, 50
Angular velocity, 50
Attenuation, 136
  band, 435
  constant or factor of a filter section, 449
  constant or factor of a long transmission line, 417
  decibels of, 136, 451
  frequency of infinite, 481
  general, 136
  method of expressing for filter, 449–453
  nepers of, 136, 450, 451
  see also Filters, high- and low-pass
Auto-transformer, air-core, 317
Average value of a wave, 86, 88

Balanced delta load, 339
Balanced delta system of currents, 334, 335
Balanced systems, power in, 343, 344, 349
Balanced wye load, 337
Balanced wye system of currents, 333
Band, side, 266
Band-eliminator filter, 473, 474
Band-pass filter, definition, 473
Bands, pass or transmission, 435
  stop or attenuation, 435
Bases for expressing impedances, 523
Boundary conditions, 550

Branch, 5
link, 23
tree, 23

Capacitance, effect of in a circuit, 62–66
energy stored in, 65
impedance due to, 63
phasor diagram, branch of, 94
tables of, for transmission lines, 430
transmission line, 425
vector diagram, branch of, 94
Capacitive coupling, 276
Capacitive reactance, 63
Capacitive susceptance, 159–163
Carrier frequency, 264, 266
Cartesian form, of impedance, 125
of operator, 108, 109
Characteristic impedance, 439
determination from open- and short-circuit impedances, 443
low-pass constant-k, π-section, 466
T-section, 466
π-section, 440
T-section, 440
variation of for constant-k sections, 467
Circle diagram of series circuit, 155
Circuit, capacitive only, 62–66
coupled capacitively, 276
coupled conductively, 273
coupled mutual inductively, 278
definition, 273
direction, 7, 46, 95, 129, 379
inductive only, 59, 94
parallel, 158
polyphase, 325
resistive, inductive, and capacitive, 75
resistive and capacitive, 74
resistive and inductive, 66
resistive only, 57, 93
series, 142
series-parallel, 174
sweep, 557
Coefficient, of coupling, 277, 283
of mutual inductance, 279
of self-inductance, 279–280
Coil, iron-core magnetizing current of, 224
Complex frequency, 179, 572
Complex notation, 107
Complex waves, 223
addition of, 261
components of, 225
definition, 225
subtraction of, 261
Conditions, boundary, 550
Conductance, 15, 160
matrix, 20, 21
Conductive coupling, types of, 273–276
Conductively coupled circuit, 273
Conjugates of voltage and current, 132, 133
Connection checks, for wattmeters, 350, 352
Constant-k filter, *see* Filters, constant-k type
Copper, comparison of requirements for transmission, 358–360
Coupled circuits, 273
design, 309
equations of voltage for, 282
impedance of, 299
loose, 283
maximum current in, 306
partial resonance of, 303
resonance of, 301–314
Coupling, capacitive, 276
coefficient of, 277, 283
conductive, 273, 276
critical, 306
inductive, 278
loose, 283
mutual inductance, 278
range of, 283
resistance, 276
Crest factor, 89
Critical coupling, 306
Current, alternating, definition, 46, 47, 48
average value, 86, 87, 88
components of, 99
effective value, 85, 88
fault, 522
instantaneous, 51, 78, 91, 261
in parallel branches, 158
loop, or mesh, 7, 274, 377
resonance, 162–168
rms value, 85, 88
in series branches, 142
for non-sinusoidal voltages, 256–262

Current, in series-parallel branches, 174–176
for series resonance, 145, 146
source, 1, 3, 199, 200
virtual value of, 85
Current loci, for parallel branches, 164, 165
for series branches, 155–158
Currents, addition of, 128
subtraction of, 128
Cut-off frequency, 454, 463, 465, 481
Cycle, 48

Decibel, definition of, 451
Degrees of symmetry of waves, 246
Delta connection, balanced load, 339
current for, 334, 335
equivalent for wye, 206–211
harmonics in, 365
symmetrical components of phase currents, 502, 503
unbalanced, current relations, 400
solution of, 373, 381
voltage, 334
Delta-wye conversion, 207, 382
Delta and wye loads combined, solution of, 376
Deviation factor, definition of, 256
determination of, 256
use, 256
Directions, circuit, 7, 46, 95, 129, 379
Direct wave of a transmission line, 417
Displaced a-c wave, effective value of, 562
Distorted waves, 223
Distributed parameters, 413
Division of phasors or vectors, 119
Dot-marked terminal, 286
Double-subscript notation, 327
Drain, high-frequency line, 435
low-frequency line, 436
Dual networks, 31
Duality, 29, 32, 400

Effective value, 85, 88
current, 85, 86, 88
displaced a-c wave, 562
non-sinusoidal wave, 250
sinusoid, 88
voltage, 86, 88

Electric wave filters, 435
Energy, stored in capacitance, 65
stored in inductance, 62
Equivalent current source, 3, 4, 199, 200
Equivalent delta for wye, 206, 207, 210
Equivalent equilateral spacing for transmission lines, 428
Equivalent plate circuit of vacuum tube, 203
Equivalent sine waves, 255
phase difference of, 255
Equivalent wye, for delta conversion, 206
formula for, 207
Euler's equation, 110
Even harmonics, effect of, 246–248
Evolution of a phasor or vector, 121
Experimental determination, of currents in polyphase loads, 400
of voltages in polyphase loads, 400
Exponential, complex, 179, 573–575
Exponential operator, 110

Factor, amplitude, 89
crest, 89
deviation, 256
form, 88
peak, 89
power, definition, 99
see also Power factor
reactive, 99, 345
transfer, 300
Fault, defined, 522
Fault currents, solving for, 528, 531, 539
Faults, kind of, 522
Filters, attenuation constant, 449–453
band-eliminator, 473, 474
definition, 474
band-pass, definition, 473
comparison of characteristics of constant-k and m-derived types, 484
constant-k type, definition, 464
high-pass, cut-off frequency, 468
design equations, 468–469
summary of characteristics, 471, 472
limitations, 474
low-pass, characteristic impedance, 466
cut-off frequency, 465

Filters, constant-k type, low-pass, design equations, 466, 467
summary of characteristics, 471, 472
zero-frequency value of impedance, 466
definition, 435
electric wave, 435
full m-derived, 480
attenuation and phase shift, 483
effect of cut-off and infinite attenuation frequencies on value of m, 438
frequencies of infinite attenuation, 481
high-pass, 482
low-pass, 481, 482
fundamental equation of, 454–456
general design procedure, 484
half section, 475–479
high-pass, attenuation, 461
definition, 454
low-pass, attenuation, 458
definition, 454
m-derived half sections, 475
characteristic impedance, 477
general equations of, 477, 478
open-circuit impedance, 439, 443
phase constant β, 449, 450
phase shift, 455, 458, 461
π-section, 440
propagation constant, 449
short-circuit impedance, 439, 443
T-section, 440
without resistance, 457
Finite differences, method of solving equations by, 585
Flux, in iron-core transformer, 581–585
leakage, 279, 314
mutual, 279, 314
Form factor, 88
Foster's reactance theorem, 188
Fourier analysis, general, 225
analytical method, 228
analyzing tables, 237–240
graphical method, 233–242
rectangular wave, 231–233
triangular wave, 228–232
Fourier series, 225
coefficients of, 227
Four-phase systems, 328
Four-terminal network, 438
Four-wire, three-phase system, 331
Frequency, 48, 49
angular, 50
carrier, 264, 265
common for power use, 49
complex, 179, 572
components of modulated waves, 264, 265
cut-off, 454, 463, 465, 468, 481
infinite attenuation for filters, 481
oscillatory, 570
range of pass band for RLC circuit, 152
resonant, for parallel branches, 166
for series circuit, 145

Generation of alternating current, 45, 46, 325
Geometric mean spacing of transmission conductors, 428
Graphical composition of symmetrical components, 493
Graphical method, for rms value determination, 86
for wave analysis, 233, 242

Half-power points, 152
Half-wave resonance, 418
Half-wave symmetry, 246, 247
Harmonics, caused by variation of circuit parameters, 262
components of a complex wave, 225
in a delta system, 365
effect of even on a wave, 246, 248
in a wye system, 361
High-pass filter, *see* Filters

Image basis of termination of filter section, 442
Image impedance, 438
Impedance, base, 523
capacitive, 63
cartesian form of, 125
characteristic, for filters, 439
for T- and π-sections, 440
see also Characteristic impedance
coupled circuit, 299
diagram for series RLC branch, variable capacitance, 149

Impedance, variable frequency, 150
variable inductance, 147
function, defined, 56
image, 438
inductive, 60
matching, 192
mutual, 273, 281
negative-sequence, 510–511, 533, 535
negative-sequence component of, 509
open circuit of a filter, 439, 443
percentage of, 525
polar form of, 124
positive-sequence, 510, 533, 535
positive-sequence component of, 509
rectangular form of, *see* Impedance, cartesian form of
referred to a common base, 523
reflected, 299, 300
resistive, 57
resistive, inductive, and capacitive, 75
resistive and capacitive, 75
resistive and inductive, 69
short-circuit, of filter, 439
surge, 418
transfer, 197
transfer factor, 300
transferred, 298
zero-sequence, 535, 540
of generators, 535, 540
of transformers, 541
Impedance, zero-sequence, of transmission lines, 542
zero-sequence component of, 509
Impedances, addition of, 142, 143, 158
parallel, 158
series, 142, 143
series-parallel, 174
Inductance, coefficient of mutual, 279
coefficient of self-, 279, 280
effect of, 60
energy stored in, 62
leakage, 316
mutual, 279
definition, 280
phasor diagram of branch, 94
transmission line, formula, 425
general, 423
transmission line table, 429
vector diagram of branch, 94
Inductive coupling, 278
Inductive reactance, 60
Inductive susceptance, 158–162
Infinite-frequency characteristic impedance, 469
Instantaneous currents, combination of, 78, 91, 92
Instantaneous power, 57, 61, 63–65, 70, 71, 348
Instantaneous value of current and voltage, 51, 52
Involution of a phasor, 122
Iron-clad *RL* circuit, transients in, 581
Iron-core coil, current in, 224

j, operator, 107

Kilovolt-amperes, 99
Kirchhoff's laws, application of, 30, 377
Kirchhoff's law, application to alternating current, 377

Ladder structures, 453
Lagging current, 53–55
Leakage flux, 279, 314
inductance, 316
Line calculations, approximate methods, 410–413
exact method, 413
Line constants, formulas for, 425–428
tables of, 429, 430
Line drain, high-frequency, 435
low-frequency, 436
Line-to-ground short circuit, 539
Line-to-line short circuit, 531
Links, 23
Logarithm of a phasor, 123
Loop current solution, 7, 274, 377
see also Mesh, current solution
Loose coupling, 283
Lower side-band, 266
Low-pass constant-*k* filter, *see* Filters, constant-*k* type
Low-pass filter, *see* Filters

Magnetic coupling or mutual inductive coupling, 278
Magnetic coupling between phases, 515–518
Magnetizing current of iron-core coil, 224
Matching of impedances, 192

Matrix, 10, 12
  conductance, 20
  determinant of, 11, 12
  resistance, 11, 13–15
Maximum power transfer, 192–193
m-derived filter section, full, 480
m-derived half section, 475
Measurement, of power in balanced systems, 349
  of reactive volt-amperes, 344, 396–398
  of three-phase power by three wattmeters, 387, 388
  of three-phase power by two wattmeters, 349, 389
Mesh, 23
  connection, general, 334, 335
  current solution, 274
  four-phase, 330
  n-phase, 336
  three-phase, *see* Delta connection
Mho, 15, 159
Modulated waves, composition of, 264, 265
Modulation, definition of percentage, 265
Multiplication of phasors, 116
Mutual flux, 279, 314
Mutual inductance or induction, 279
  between parallel branches, 289
  between series branches, 286
  coefficient of, 279
  definition, 279
  impedance, 273, 281
  reactance due to, 281
  sign of, 284
Mutual induction voltage, 281
  direction of, 284
Mutual inductive coupling, 278, 279

Napier, definition, 451
Negative-sequence components, 490, 492
  evaluation, 495
  impedance component, 510
Negative-sequence impedances of rotating machines, 533–536
Neper, definition, 136, 450, 451
Network, image impedance, 438
  smoothing, 436, 438
  theorems, 194, 196, 197, 205
  topology, 22
  variables, 6
Networks, 194
  dual, 31
  π, 211
  T, 211
  theorems, 194, 196, 197, 205
Nodal method of circuit solution, 15–22, 198
Node, 7, 199
Node-pair voltages, 15
Non-linear parameters, step-by-step solutions, 585–589
Non-sinusoidal waves, 223
  circuit analysis for, 225, 256, 258
  effective value of, 250
  expressing, 225
  parallel circuit analysis for, 258
  power calculations for, 252
  power factor for, 254
  series circuit analysis for, 256
  shifting the phase of, 249
  volt-amperes of, 254
Norton's theorem, 205
Notation, double-subscript, 327
n-phase mesh, 336
n-phase star, 336

Ohmic method of short-circuit calculations, 523
Open-circuit impedance of a filter, 439, 443
Open-line check, 352
Operator, cartesian form, 108, 109
  exponential, 110
  j, 108
  polar form, 111
  rectangular form, 110
Oscillatory term of RLC circuit, 568, 569, 580
  frequency of, 570

Parallel, impedances in, 158
Parallel branch analysis, 158
  for non-sinusoidal waves, 258
Parallel branch current loci, 164–166
Parallel branches, resonance in, 162
Parallel branch resonance for all frequencies, 170
Parallel resonance, 162–168
  by varying C, 165
  by varying f, 166

Parallel resonance, by varying L, 163
by varying R_c, 167
by varying R_L, 167
Parameters, distributed, 413
effect of variation on wave form, 262
non-linear, step-by-step solution, 585–589
transmission line, 423
Partial resonance of coupled circuits, 303
Pass band, boundary of, for filters, 458–465, 473, 481
definition, for filters, 435
for series RLC circuit, 151
width of, for series RLC circuit, 152
Peak factor, 89
Percentage method of expressing parameters, 525
Percentage of modulation, 265
Percentage reactance, 526
Percentage resistance, 526
Period, definition, 48
Per unit method of expressing parameters, 528
Phase, 52
angle, 52
constant, of a filter, 449
of a long line, 418, 421
of current and voltage, 57, 60, 63, 67, 69, 75
difference, 53
for equivalent sine waves, 255
magnetic coupling between phases, 515–518
n-phase mesh, 336
n-phase star, 336
sequence, 326, 327, 339
effects, 383
impedances, 509, 510, 533, 540
methods of checking, 383, 384
shift, general, 137
of high-pass filter section, 461
of low-pass filter section, 458
shifting of a non-sinusoidal wave, 249
Phasor, 90
Phasors, addition of, 112
algebra of, 107
cartesian form of notation for, 108
division of, 119
evolution of, 121
involution of, 122
Phasors, logarithm of, 123
multiplication of, 116
raising to powers, 121
rectangular form of notation for, 108
representing sine waves, 90
root of, 122
subtraction of, 114
π-network, 211
π-section filter, 440
attenuation of, 455
characteristic impedance, 440, 443
phase shift, 455
Polar form, of impedance, 123
of operator, 111
Polarity marks, 286
Poles, 182, 572
Polyphase, generation of voltages, 325
see also Mesh, Star connection, Delta connection, Wye, n-phase mesh
Polyphase power, balanced systems, 343
comparison with single-phase power, 348
unbalanced systems, 387–390
see also Power
Polyphase unbalanced, general, 373, 377
Positive directions of voltages and currents, 95, 128, 284
Positive-phase sequence system, 489, 491
evaluation of, 494, 533
impedance of rotating machines, 534, 535
impedance of static elements, 509
Power, half-power points, 152
instantaneous, 57, 61, 63–65, 70, 71, 348
maximum from circle diagram, 157
maximum transfer in a series circuit, 192
measurement, of balanced polyphase, 349
in an n-wire system, 357, 392
by three-wattmeter method, 387
by two-wattmeter method, 349, 387–390
in a purely capacitive branch, 64
in a purely inductive branch, 61
in a purely resistive branch, 58
reactive, in general, 96
real, in general, 96
in a resistive and inductive branch, 70

Power, in an *RLC* branch, 76
system short-circuit calculations, 522
three-phase, 343, 387–390
of a phasor, 121
Power calculation, of balanced polyphase, 343
of balanced three-phase, 343
from complex forms, 131
from conjugate of *V* and *I*, 133
for non-sinusoidal waves, 252
of single and three-phase, 348
Power factor, balanced three-phase, 345
definition, 99, 345
for non-sinusoidal waves, 254
of series branch, 143
in unbalanced polyphase systems, 394
Power formula, for balanced three-phase, 343, 345
for single-phase, 96
Propagation, velocity of, 419
of a wave, 417
Propagation constant, of a filter, 449
of a long line, 417

Q, of a coil, 153
of a parallel circuit, 171
of a series circuit, 153
Quarter-phase, *see* Four-phase systems
Quarter-wave resonance of a long line, 418
Quarter-wave symmetry, 247

Range of coupling, 283
RC branch, transients, 553
Reactance, capacitive, 63
inductive, 60
mutual, 281
percentage, 526
per unit, 525, 528
Reactive factor, 100, 345
Reactive power, *see* Reactive volt-amperes
Reactive volt-amperes, 71, 96, 344
balanced three-phase, 344
calculated from complex expressions, 131
determination from conjugates of *V* and *I*, 133
formula, for balanced three-phase, 344, 345
Reactive volt-amperes, formula, for single-phase, 97
measurement, of balanced three-phase, 353
in unbalanced four-wire, three-phase, 392
sign of, 76, 97
Reciprocity theorem, 196
Rectangular form, of impedance, 125
of operator, 109, 110
Rectangular wave, 231, 233
Rectifier, constants for smoothing network of, 437, 438
smoothing network for, 436, 438
Reflected impedance, 299, 300
Reflected wave, 417, 418
Reflections, terminal of a line, 419
Resistance, effect of, 57
impedance due to, 57
percentage of, defined, 526
in series, with capacitance, 75
with inductance, 69
with inductance and capacitance, 75
vector diagram of branch, 93
Resistance coupling, 276
Resonance, in coupled circuits, 301–314
of a long transmission line, half-wave, 418
quarter-wave, 418
three-quarter-wave, 418
in parallel circuits, 162
see also Parallel resonance
series circuits, 144
see also Series resonance
RL branch transients and steady current in, for alternating current, 558
for direct current, 551
RLC branch, selective properties, *see* Selective *RLC* circuit
vector diagram, 95
RLC series branch, equation of current, 579
oscillatory term of, 580
transients in, 566, 571, 576
for $R^2/4L^2 > 1/LC$, 568, 571, 579
for $R^2/4L^2 < 1/LC$, 568, 571, 580
RL iron-clad circuit, transients in, 581–585
rms value, 85, 88
of a displaced sinusoidal wave, 562

rms value, graphical determination of, 86
of a sinusoidal wave, 88
Root of a phasor, 122

Sawtooth wave form, 555
Selective properties of circuit elements, 435
high-frequency line drain, 435
low-frequency line drain, 436
Selective *RLC* circuit, 151
pass band, definition, 151
width of, 152
Selectivity of *RLC* series branch, 152, 153
Self-inductance, 279
voltage of, 282
Sequence, phase, 326, 327, 339
checking, 383
effects of, 383
negative-phase sequence system, 490, 492, 495
impedance, 509, 533–536
positive-phase sequence system, 489, 491, 494
impedance, 509, 534, 535
rule, 512, 513
zero-phase sequence system, 490, 492, 495
impedance, 509, 535, 540, 541, 542
Series, impedances in, 142
resonance, 144
Series branch, 142
circle diagram, 155
efficiency of for transmission, 157
Series circuit, 142
analysis for non-sinusoidal waves, 256
circle diagram of, 155
current loci, 155, 156
maximum power transfer of, 192
Series-parallel branches, 174
Series-parallel tuning, 176
Series resonance, 144
frequency for, 145
by varying capacitance, 148
by varying frequency, 149
by varying inductance, 146
voltage drops, 145
Shifting the reference point of a non-sinusoidal wave, 249
Short circuit, accuracy of calculations, 528
calculation, by ohmic method, 523
by percentage method, 525
by per unit method, 528
in power systems, 522
impedance of a filter, 443
definition, 439, 443
line-to-ground, 539
calculation of, 539, 544
line-to-line, 531
calculation of, 536
Side bands, 266
Sign of readings of wattmeters, 350–353
Sine wave, representation of alternating current, 50
Sine waves, equivalent, 255
Sinusoidal wave, average value of, 88
crest factor of, 89
effective value, 85, 88
form factor, 88
vector representation of, 90
Smoothing network, 436, 438
constants for, 437
Sources, current, 2, 3
ideal voltage, 4
voltage, 1, 3
S-plane, 181, 184, 187
Star connection, general, 336
four-phase, 329
n-phase, 336
three-phase, 331, 332
Steady-state term, 551, 553, 560, 561, 565, 580
Step-by-step method solution for non-linear parameters, 585–589
Stop band, 435
Subtraction, of currents, 128
of phasors, 114
Superposition, principle, 5, 20
theorem, 194
Surge admittance, 418
Surge impedance, 418
Susceptance, 159–162
Sweep circuit, 557
Symbolic notation, *see* Phasors, algebra of
Symmetrical components, 489
copper losses from, 508
delta-wye voltage transformations, 500
graphical composition of, 493

Symmetrical components, line-to-ground current representation, 504, 505
negative-sequence system, 490, 492
evaluation, 495, 533
impedance, for rotating machines, 535
for static elements, 509
of phase currents in delta-connected loads, 502
positive-sequence system, 489, 491
evaluation, 494, 533
impedance, for rotating machines, 535
for static elements, 509
power from, 506–508
solution for fault currents, 522–546
unbalanced current representation, 502–506
unbalanced line voltage representation, 497, 500–501
use of, 489
zero-sequence system, 490, 492, 495
evaluation, 494–496, 533, 539
impedance, for rotating machines, 533–535, 540–541
zero-sequence system, impedance, for static elements, 509
Symmetry, of complex waves, 246
degrees of, 246
half-wave, 246
non-sine waves, 246
positive and negative loops, 246
quarter-wave, 247
of wave about its 90° ordinate, 247
Systems, four-phase, 328
three-phase, 331–336
two-phase, 328
see also Alternating current

Tables, of capacitance for transmission lines, 430
of inductance for transmission lines, 429
Terminal reflections, 419
Termination of filter section on image basis, 442
Thévenin's theorem, 197
Three-origin vector diagram, 341
Three-phase, four-wire system, 331
Three-phase, three-wire system, 334
Three-phase power measurement, 387–390
Three-quarter-wave resonance of a long line, 418
Three-wire, two-phase system, 331
Time constant, of *RC* branch, 555
of *RL* branch, 552
T-network, 211
Topological warping, 23
Topology, 22
Transfer factor, 300
Transfer impedance, 135, 197
Transferred impedance, 298
Transformer, air-core, 291–298, 314–317
vector diagram of, 315, 316
air-core auto-, 317
Transient, application of, 549
defined, 549
sawtooth wave, 555–558
Transients, of *RC* branch, 553
of *RL* branch, 549, 581
of *RLC* series circuit, 566–581, 582
oscillatory frequency of, 570, 572, 580
$R^2/4L^2 > 1/LC$, 568, 571, 579
$R^2/4L^2 < 1/LC$, 568, 571, 580
of *RL* iron-clad circuit, 581–585
Transmission, 134
Transmission band, 435
Transmission line, general, 409
approximate solution, by Steinmetz method, 412
exact solution, 413
geometric mean spacing of conductor, 428
by π-line, 411
representation of, 409
by T-line, 410
Transmission line parameters, 423
capacitance, formula, 428
table, 430
derivation of formulas, 423, 425
inductance, formula, 425
table, 429
Transmission of power, comparison of copper requirements, 358–360
Tree, topological, 23
Triangular waves, analysis of, 231–233
equation of, 229, 232, 233

T-section, filter, 440
 attenuation of, 455, 458, 461
 characteristic impedance of, 439–441, 443
 phase shift, 449, 455, 458, 461
 series arm, 456
 shunt arm, 456
Tuning, series-parallel, 176
Two-phase systems, 328
Two-wattmeter method of measuring 3-phase power, 349, 387–390

Unbalanced currents, representation by symmetrical components, 502–506
Unbalanced polyphase circuits, general, 373, 377
 delta, solution of, 382
 power factor of, 394–396
 solution by Kirchhoff's laws, 377
 wye-wye with neutral solution, 381
 wye-wye without neutral solution, 377, 379
Unbalanced voltage, representation by symmetrical components, 497–502
Upper side band, 266

Var, 72, 98
Varmeter, 72
 see also Reactive volt-amperes, meter
Vector, 90
Vector algebra, *see* Phasors, algebra of
Vector diagrams or phasor diagrams, general, 94, 97
 C-branch, 94
 L-branch, 94
 R-branch, 93
 RC-branch, 95
 RL-branch, 94
 RLC-branch, 95
 three-origin, 341
Vector volt-amperes, 394, 395
Velocity, angular, 50
 of wave propagation, 419
Virtual value of current or voltage, 85
Volt, alternating defined, 86
Voltage, alternating, components of, 99
 definition, 45, 46
Voltage, drop, 95
 drops, across series-parallel branches, 174
  at series resonance, 145
 equations of coupled circuits, 282
 instantaneous, 51
 mutual, direction of, 284
 mutual induction, 279
 node-pair, 7, 15
 resonance, 144
 rise, 95
 self-induced, 282
 series branch for non-sinusoidal waves, 256
 source, 1, 3
Voltages, addition of, 102, 103, 127
 delta, 334
 generation of polyphase, 325
 vector addition of, 127, 128
 vector combination of, 102, 103, 127
 vector subtraction of, 102, 103, 127
 wye, 332
Volt-amperes, 99, 344
 addition of, 394, 395
 balanced three-phase, 344
 non-sinusoidal waves, for, 254
 reactive, 71, 96, 132, 133
  in three-phase, 344, 392
 vector, 394, 395

Warping, topological, 23
Wattmeters, checking signs of, 352, 353
Watt-ratio curve, 352
Wave, sawtooth, 555
Wave analysis, 225
 analytical method, 228
 graphical method, 233, 242
Wave form, 47, 246, 248, 251
 of current in an iron-core coil, 224
Wave-length constant, of a filter, *see* Phase constant, of a filter
 of a long line, 418, 421
Wave propagation, velocity of, 419
Waves, addition of complex, 261
 attenuation of, 417
 complex or non-sinusoidal, 223, 225
 composite, 223, 225
 direct, 417, 418
 modulated, 263
 propagation of, 417, 419

Waves, rectangular, 231, 233
reflected, 417, 418
of same shape or form analytical method of determining, 248
sawtooth, 555
subtraction of, 91, 92, 261
triangular, 231, 233
Wave shape, 47, 50, 246–251
effect of shifting an harmonic on, 248, 250, 251
Wave trap, 169
Weber-turns, 281
Wye, general, 332, 336
and delta loads combined, solution of, 376
balanced load, 337
connection, voltages and currents in, 332, 333
magnetic coupling between phases of, 515–518
Wye-delta, conversion, 206–210, 374, 375
Wye-delta, unbalanced, solution of, 382
Wye system, currents in, 333
harmonics in, 361
Wye-wye system, unbalanced, with neutral, 381
without neutral, 377–380

Y, *see* Wye

Zeros, 182, 572
Zero-frequency characteristic impedance, 466
Zero-sequence component of impedance, 509
Zero-sequence impedance, of rotating machines, 535, 540
of transformers, 541
of transmission lines, 542
Zero-sequence system, 490, 492, 495
evaluation of, 495, 496